2017/18

THE GUIDE TO

UK COMPANY GIVING

11th edition

Jennifer Reynolds,
Jodie Huyton
& Carly Hobson

Additional research by:
Rachel Cain, Ian Pembridge,
Judith Turner & Anne Cutress

Published by the Directory of Social Change (Registered Charity no. 800517 in England and Wales)

Head office: Resource for London, 352 Holloway Rd, London N7 6PA

Northern office: Suite 103, 1 Old Hall Street, Liverpool L3 9HG

Tel: 0207 697 4200

Visit www.dsc.org.uk to find out more about our books, subscription funding websites and training events. You can also sign up for e-newsletters so that you're always the first to hear about what's new.

The publisher welcomes suggestions and comments that will help to inform and improve future versions of this and all of our titles. Please give us your feedback by emailing publications@dsc.org.uk.

First published 1998
Second edition 1999
Third edition 2000
Fourth edition 2002
Fifth edition 2004
Sixth edition 2007
Seventh edition 2009
Eighth edition 2011
Ninth edition 2013
Tenth edition 2015
Eleventh edition 2017

ISBN 978 1 78482 025 1

British Library Cataloguing in Publication Data
A catalogue record for this book is available from the British Library

Cover and text design by Kate Griffith
Typeset by Marlinzo Services, Frome
Printed and bound by Page Bros, Norwich

Contents

Foreword

Community investment is integral to Provident Financial's overarching business strategy. We recognise the value and contribution that we can make to the communities where we operate. So harnessing our corporate resource to effectively channel funding and other support is a responsibility we take extremely seriously. And we've realised the best way for us to make the greatest difference and social impact is to be fixed and focused, applying a single-minded approach to the way we invest in our communities.

We're clear that our programme must generate measurable impacts for society. There have been increasing calls for businesses to ensure that their community programmes focus on delivering activities that support their core mission statement and which deliver impacts that result in clear, measureable and auditable business and societal benefits.

Our own approach to community investment is closely aligned to our core business strategy and addresses issues that are material to us, focusing on two main areas. Firstly, helping to address the social inclusion needs of people who live in some of the most deprived communities in the UK and Ireland. And, secondly, supporting the money advice sector to address financial education issues, and carrying out research into broader, social matters that relate to our customers.

Today's fundraising environment is challenging to say the least, with ever-increasing demands on traditional funding streams – something that's unlikely to change any time soon. So innovation is needed in the quest to contribute to the continuance of our hugely valued voluntary sector. This is evident in the way that corporate community investment programmes are evolving to reflect the changing nature of the companies' own businesses, their communities and our wider society.

The Guide to UK Company Giving is a unique reference tool for businesses, charities, community groups and other voluntary organisations. The guide contains a plethora of information; indeed, such is the value of this publication, that we recently gave each of our community partners a copy of the guide to support their own fundraising activities as part of a programme of specialist support we offer to help with the development of their long-term organisational sustainability. We also delivered an accompanying workshop which provided them with advice on how to approach companies when seeking funding.

One of the key elements that we picked up on when engaging with our community partners is the need for them to undertake thorough research when identifying potential corporate partners. This enables them to understand what it is that the company does and how they approach community investment. What's their strategy? What might they be looking for in a potential partner? Who do they already support? What's their volunteering proposition? How do they use that for employee development? How much do they invest? What impacts do they measure? It's about understanding how a potential corporate funder approaches community investment and then tailoring a funding proposal to maximise the chances of getting a positive response.

The Guide to UK Company Giving is so comprehensive that it means a lot of the desk research – which would otherwise put an even greater drain on scarce resources – is already at your fingertips. At a time when effective partnerships are the key to lasting sustainability, this guide offers a powerful lens through which to identify strategic corporate/voluntary partnership opportunities in a dynamic and changing corporate community investment landscape.

Sharon Orr
Community Affairs Manager, Provident Financial Group

Introduction

Welcome to the eleventh edition of *The Guide to UK Company Giving* which continues to provide relevant, updated policy information and commentary on the current state of corporate community involvement in the UK.

This edition features 406 companies, which gave at least £420 million in community support, mostly in the financial years 2014/15, 2015 or 2015/16. The edition also includes full details of 132 associated corporate charities which gave in total £321 million. This figure was derived from the combined grant totals of each of the corporate charities listed and does not represent what was given by the companies themselves.

In the last edition of this guide we explained how reforms to the Companies Act 2006, brought in by the Department for Business Innovation and Skills (which came into force for financial periods ending on or after 30 September 2013), mean that companies no longer have a legal obligation to declare charitable donations. Although government legislation has changed and it is no longer possible to make cash giving our focus, we had already begun, over a period of years, to recognise the very substantial contribution many companies are now making to their communities both in cash and in kind. Many of these companies are also aligning their giving with their own type of business and we see the very positive effect this can have on both those receiving the support and the givers themselves.

We are endeavouring to cover the many and very different ways in which companies structure their community contribution and also to provide an insight into what each company prioritises for its business practices. For example, does the company acknowledge the recent provisions of anti-slavery legislation? What is the ratio of women to men on its board? Does it pay a living wage?

The corporate charities section on page 337 is a review of information on 132 corporate charities established by and/or closely associated with a company listed in the guide, often acting as a channel for its charitable giving. (For more detail about this section see page xiii.) We hope that this will be of real use to our readers when looking for charitable funding given by companies.

This edition of the guide also includes for the first time a chapter dedicated to football clubs. Focusing on the 20 football clubs competing in the Premier League in the 2016/17 season, we shine a light on the community involvement of some of the most widely known football clubs in the world, in what is perhaps the highest-profile corporate sector.

Each of the 406 company entries provides essential information for accessing funding and other resources. Throughout our research we look at thousands of pages of annual reports, accounts and corporate social responsibility (CSR) reports as well as the companies' own websites, with the aim of providing a comprehensive overview of the community-related activities by a particular business. The entries focus on a company's contributions to its local community and/or society as a whole which include both cash donations (where figures are available) and all forms of in-kind support from pro bono work to equipment. We also make a note of commercially led, yet community-related initiatives, or other community-orientated contributions by the company.

Most of the guide consists of individual company entries, but it also contains additional sections offering advice and information for fundraisers, voluntary organisations, community groups, companies and individuals.

The companies in this guide

In previous editions of this guide, cash donations have been the primary, albeit not the sole, way in which DSC has measured companies' community involvement. While DSC maintains that it is good practice for companies to declare charitable donations, and applauds those companies that continue to do so, the shift in focus away from cash donations and towards corporate community contributions has presented us with the opportunity to draw attention to the other, sometimes very innovative, ways in which companies contribute to communities – the value of such contributions cannot always be properly translated into monetary terms.

Methodology

As it was no longer possible to use a threshold for financial contributions as we had done in previous years (in the tenth edition, for example, we omitted companies that had been known to give less than £5,000 in charitable donations annually), we opened up our basic criteria and have included companies whose CSR activities benefit communities in the UK directly. Generally, this would

Charity partners and/or Charity of the Year

Where applicable, we specify details of any existing or previous charity partnerships. Quite often these will be in a form of a Charity of the Year programme, whereby the company will support and/or staff members will fundraise/volunteer for (usually) employee-chosen causes, although we are increasingly seeing more innovative partnerships between companies and charities. See an overview of Charity of the Year partnerships on page xviii.

Company gives to smaller charities

This shows that we found evidence to suggest that the company's community activities specifically benefit smaller-sized charities. However, even if a company does not have this ticked, it does not necessarily mean that it will not support smaller charities; rather it means that we did not find evidence to suggest that it is an area of particular priority.

Corporate charity

This shows that the company has an associated registered charity which is featured in the corporate charities chapter of this guide.

Employee-led support

Employees are often a valuable asset to companies' CSR activities. Staff members lend their fundraising and volunteering efforts to a wide range of local, national and international causes. Fundraising activities can include anything from sponsored runs to bake sales or employee lotteries, and volunteering can range from individually organised regular commitments to one-off team efforts.

For more information on employee volunteering see page xxvii.

FTSE 100

This shows that a company was in the FTSE 100 Index at a date towards the end of the research process (8 December 2016).

Gifts in kind

Gifts in kind originally referred solely to goods, pieces of furniture or items of equipment (nearly always second-hand). Now, with CSR high on the agenda for many companies, corporates are increasingly offering staff time and skills as gifts in kind, which can be a very valuable asset for a charity and equally provide useful new skills and experience for staff development. The term is often used in relation to physical items alone without reference to professional or support services, and this can cause confusion.

Humanitarian aid (overseas)

Some of the companies in this guide lend support to assist with aid efforts in the aftermath of natural disasters and man-made crises. Examples of support include financial donations to humanitarian organisations during the Ebola outbreak in West Africa, donations of pharmaceutical products to international charity partners, and customer and employee donations for relief efforts in the aftermath of the Nepal earthquake.

Humanitarian aid (UK, including food banks)

Examples of humanitarian aid provided in the UK include the response to the 2015 floods in northern England, following which some of the companies in this guide set up help centres and provided food, clothing and fuel for people affected. This category also takes into account the work some companies are doing to support the work of food banks, at both local and national levels. Examples of support include donations of unwanted supermarket food and the provision of hosting space for local food bank representatives.

Market-led giving

We include examples of any cause-related marketing initiatives that a company may have undertaken; however, we do not include this in the total community contributions figure for the year because the motivation and priority of such giving is the company's profits and it is not driven by philanthropy.

Notably, many of the companies featured in this edition and specialising in retail, particularly supermarkets, have started to redistribute funds raised from the statutory single-use carrier bag charge to charities. This legislation came in force in England in October 2015 following similar legislation in Wales (2011), Northern Ireland (2013) and Scotland (2014).

Matched funding

Matched-funding schemes provide a way for companies to encourage and support their employees' charitable fundraising efforts. Typically, companies will match funding up to a certain amount per employee per year. Some companies match funds on a pound-for-pound basis, whereas others match up to a certain percentage of funds raised.

Payroll giving

Payroll giving allows employees to make donations from their wages in a tax-efficient way. There are a number of schemes on offer, perhaps the best known being the Charities Aid Foundation's Give As You Earn (GAYE) scheme. The majority of schemes work by taking a monthly donation from the salary of participating employees, although there are some which operate slightly differently. Pennies from Heaven, for example, works by taking odd pennies from individual employees' monthly wage packets.

Pro bono

Pro bono work can provide a way for charities to access invaluable professional skills and knowledge from companies free of charge. Many people think of pro bono work as being the domain of law and accountancy firms; however, companies in this guide from across the corporate sector provide charities with various specialisms, sometimes with remarkably innovative outcomes.

Sponsorship

Sponsorship is vastly different from charitable donations: it is a business arrangement that provides the charity with an opportunity to raise funds and the company with the chance to improve its image and to promote and sell its products or services. Sponsorship is typically given in the form of money, although it can also be in products, services or space. For more information on sponsorship see page xxvii.

STEM-focused

STEM subjects (science, technology, engineering and mathematics) are considered by many to be vital to future economic growth and sustainability. Some companies have prioritised the promotion of STEM subjects as part of their CSR strategy. This could be in the form of special classes or on-site visits for school pupils, or mentoring for university students. A particular focus of companies in this area is the promotion of STEM subjects and careers to young women. This is a direct response to the fact that still only a small proportion of the STEM sector's workforce is made up of women.

Unpopular causes

Companies usually prefer to support causes which relate to their business. Unfortunately, this means that some causes are less commonly supported than others – these causes include work with people with addictions, women's causes and work with young people in care.

Unregistered charities/NFP

Many companies will only give to registered charities; however, there is a handful prepared to support unregistered not-for-profit (NFP) organisations such as CICs and social enterprises.

Gender diversity on company boards

For the last two editions of this guide we have recorded the ratio of women to men on corporate boards and made simple comparisons and observations of general trends. Throughout our research for this edition, we also noted instances of a company's commitment to supporting women into education, training and leadership.

This time around we were able to determine the gender ratio of 399 companies in the UK and saw that the overall percentage of women on boards was around 22%. Almost 44% of the 406 companies had 25% or more female members on their boards and 4% of all boards had either equal numbers of women and men or were female-led. Of all boards, 16% had no female board members at all, a significant decrease from the 33% we found when we first started recording this information.

Our previous research indicated that female-led companies were extremely rare, and this has not changed significantly. The six companies that we did find included a co-operative, a pharmaceutical group, a manufacturing company, an electronics company, an engineering firm, and an information technology service provider.

The 2015 review of the Lord Davies recommendations indicates that having more women on boards is an asset. This was reflected in case studies elsewhere: 'having a mix of male and female traits and views allows for considered decision-making that drives change and delivers with impact' (Hampton and Alexander 2016a). 'There is equally no doubt that whilst one woman makes a difference it is only when there is more than one that the gender issue evaporates and a more productive and constructive decision making environment evolves' (Hampton and Alexander, 2016b).

CSR reports continued to neglect other barriers faced by women, such as the gender pay gap, although this could change significantly later in 2017 as newly passed legislation specifically targets this issue. An amendment to The Equality Act 2010 ((Gender Pay Gap Information) Regulations 2017) was passed in January 2017 and requires companies to report on both the mean and median gender pay gaps as well as differences between bonus payments and the percentage of men and women who received them. This will apply to employers in the private and voluntary sectors who employ over 250 people and so the companies featured in this book will be affected. It will be interesting to continue to monitor the ways in which the corporate world rises to the challenge of diversifying its culture.

Modern slavery and CSR

In March 2015 the government passed the Modern Slavery Act in an effort to punish perpetrators more effectively and to support and protect victims of modern slavery and human trafficking. The term 'modern slavery' is used to encompass the various situations where ownership is exercised over a person, for example through forced labour or human trafficking. The government added a clause for companies with an annual turnover in excess of £36 million instructing them to provide an annual statement detailing what action they have taken to ensure there is no modern slavery in their business or supply chains.

The CSR reports used in our research were largely from 2015, so many included an initial perfunctory statement expressing commitment to eradicating slavery from their business and supply chains. Some examples of Modern Slavery Act reporting that we found during our research demonstrate an encouraging start that we hope will show the way for other businesses.

Vodafone (2016) has a detailed Modern Slavery Act statement that identifies points in the supply chain where raw materials or manufacturing outsourcing may involve slaves and the actions it will take to eliminate these points. The company works with social enterprises to enable employees to anonymously feedback on their working conditions and is a member of several committees aiming to address the issues across all tiers of the supply chain. Similarly, Marks and Spencer (2016) has examined several supply tiers and produced a detailed analysis of the areas that affect human rights in its production chains. It has begun to work with experts in other countries to address these areas and ensure it complies with the standards laid out by UK laws.

We applaud this kind of analysis, especially as the Act only focuses on trafficking and slavery in the UK, yet the majority of the companies rely on overseas workers. Future editions of this guide will continue to monitor companies' Modern Slavery Act statements and highlight successful actions that have been implemented to end modern slavery.

Membership organisations

As in previous editions, during our research for this guide we recorded companies which are members of CSR membership organisations, specifically Business in the Community (BITC) and the London Benchmarking Group (LBG). We include this information to demonstrate that there are large organisations encouraging transparency and openness in order to assist voluntary sector and community organisations looking for corporate support.

Within our sample of corporates in the guide there were 71 companies signed up to the membership of LBG; however, we cannot say how many of these are truly compliant with the LBG reporting standard. For more information on LBG, including a full list of members, see page 419.

Our research found that there are 157 companies within our sample that hold the membership of BITC, with 19 achieving the CommunityMark status. For more information on BITC, including a full list of members, see page 413.

The corporate charities section

The corporate charities chapter focuses on grant-making charities associated with the companies in this guide. The 132 charities listed have an association, either historically or currently, with a company and each entry includes full details of the charity, its purposes and contact details. Information is provided on how much the charities donate, to which organisations they give and the areas in which they focus their giving.

To be deemed a corporate charity in line with DSC's criteria and consequently to have a place in this guide, charities, generally speaking, must be run by directors or employees of the company, or have them as members on the trustee body, and usually have their support costs and overheads covered by the associated company. These charities should also receive all, or a substantial amount of their income from a connected company through an annual donation from the company's profits or in the form of income derived from an initial endowment of the company's shares.

As well as the traditional method of receiving donations directly from the yearly profits of the company, corporate charities can also receive income from other sources, for example from staff/customer fundraising. All income streams contribute towards grant-making unless they have a predetermined restriction which prevents this. Many corporate charities also receive in-kind support from the company, such as staff time and expertise, and facilities and office space on the premises of the company.

We have only included corporate charities that are linked to the companies in the main section of this guide; furthermore, we have focused solely on those that make grants to organisations. Some companies have corporate charities which do not make grants, instead delivering their own activities directly or offering support in other forms. Where applicable, these are detailed in the main section of the guide under the relevant company.

Corporate charities can be an excellent vehicle for corporate giving. They:

- Provide a professional, structured and effective channel for charitable donations with trustees acting in the best interest of the charity (and not the company)
- Often employ skilled, motivated staff
- Apply the Charities SORP, which provides openness and transparency often lacking in companies' reporting
- Are often a way for companies to focus their charitable giving while demonstrating long-term support for their communities through the voluntary sector

Corporate organisations can contribute to the communities in which they operate through the charity's activities while also seeing an indirect benefit to their business. For example, a finance company might want to fund debt advice agencies and can do so through its corporate charity, provided this falls within the charity's objects.

Most corporate charities form part of a company's wider CSR programme and often focus on the same causes. Some are used as a vehicle to deliver other aspects of the company's CSR activities – for example, providing matched funding for employee-led fundraising initiatives or supporting a nominated Charity of the Year. In some cases there may be multiple corporate charities associated with one company, each delivering different aspects of the company's community involvement.

The ways in which corporate charities offer support may vary as much as their relationship with the company. In this edition there are corporate charities listed that give nationally and internationally as well as those that give only in the areas in which they have a local presence. Some charities focusing on local communities might also offer in-kind support, such as employee volunteering, to complement a financial grant. Application procedures can vary too; some may favour charities or causes with which employees of the company are already involved or may allow customers to nominate charities for support. Others may welcome applications from any charity working in a particular area or for any cause. As when applying to any grant-maker, we advise that you consider the eligibility criteria and exclusions of each funder carefully, and tailor your approach appropriately.

From our research for this edition of the guide, the total amount given in grants through corporate charities came to almost £321 million. This figure was derived from the combined grant totals of each of the corporate charities listed and does not represent what was given by the companies themselves in that financial year.

The corporate charities section of this guide is a valuable component of DSC's examination of UK companies' charitable giving. It is a traditional and straightforward way of giving but, nevertheless, an important and worthwhile avenue for charities to consider when searching for funding. These grant-makers have the advantage of being familiar to fundraisers who will understand their protocols and processes.

Corporate social responsibility

Corporate social responsibility (CSR), also known as corporate responsibility, corporate citizenship or sustainable responsible business (SRB), is a much-used term which seeks to define what an increasing number of people and groups believe the wider role of business in society should be.

Ideally, a CSR model should provide for the self-regulation of a company's impact on society and how to address that with measurable targets where possible. It should include the monitoring and review of its ethical policies and procedures, environmental policy, health and safety procedures, employees' welfare, and the effect the company's business has on its customers, suppliers, communities and stakeholders.

Many companies, depending on the nature of their business, quite naturally focus on the environmental impact they are having and what measures they are taking to try to redress the negative aspect of their activities. These programmes are often under the heading of sustainability as opposed to CSR.

For the benefit of our readers, we focus our research on companies' contributions to UK voluntary organisations. Where a company gives abroad and provides information, we will record this but it is the small and medium-sized charity working with beneficiaries in the UK that we hope to assist most.

From our research we know that companies which establish partnerships or close links with the charities they support appreciate those organisations, their staff and the needs which they meet. This is probably more so for those that have a link to the nature of the company's business; for example, a sports clothing retailer has a very direct link with the beneficiaries of a voluntary group supporting young people. In this way, the beneficiaries of the voluntary organisation are often the company's customers or potential customers – 'a win–win situation', as one CSR spokesperson said.

Companies are also realising that there are substantial benefits to be gained in supporting such voluntary groups. These benefits include:

- Getting good publicity and building brand awareness through association with an organisation or cause
- Gaining a deeper understanding of their own customer base
- Receiving the advantages of staff development opportunities where employees are involved in volunteering such as mentoring or pro bono work

Clearly, working in partnership can be of mutual benefit: companies bring their core business skills, including financial or logistical expertise, and access to supply chains and high-level contacts; charities can provide their own professional skills and a real knowledge of what is needed on the ground and what approaches will be most effective. We know that companies continue to set up corporate charities through which to channel their community/ charitable contributions, realising that the skills present in the voluntary sector are exactly those required to carry out the company's CSR-related charitable objectives.

Caution – please note

We are told that companies continue to receive many unsolicited or inappropriate appeals for support. While many bring this upon themselves due to a lack of clear guidelines for potential applicants, this should not be seen as an excuse to conduct blanket mailings. It is vitally important for success to do your research thoroughly and only apply to those companies which are likely to consider your application or request.

Further information on how to approach businesses for support successfully is given in the 'Applying to companies' section on page xxiv. In general, however, before approaching any company in this guide, its entry should be read carefully. As we have stated previously, unless there is some clear link with a company, or your project is clearly within its defined areas of support, you are unlikely to be successful.

We also recommend that you download a copy of *Charities Working with Business Code of Fundraising Practice*, published by the Institute of Fundraising. This gives a good overview of the issues involved in undertaking a relationship with a company and is available at: www.institute-of-fundraising.org.uk.

Conclusion

At this point in previous editions we would normally comment on whether the companies listed in this guide have given more or less than in our last edition, providing narrative on any change in the companies' funding landscape. In light of decreasing transparency in company reporting we are no longer able to make a meaningful comparison of purely financial contributions by corporates. However, what we have seen during our research for this edition of the guide is how companies' charitable cash donations are only one part of the multi-faceted approach companies now take to their corporate social responsibilities. While declaring cash donations can provide a categorical and measurable way to evaluate companies' input, they are not necessarily the best way to measure *impact*.

Over the course of our research, we have seen the direct benefits of non-cash contributions, particularly of pro bono time and skills, gifts in kind, and unique and productive charity partnerships. In many ways, this sort of involvement demonstrates a commitment that a straightforward signing of a cheque does not.

What is apparent is that many companies in this guide appear to be increasingly willing to facilitate and support their employees' community involvement – whether this is in the form of a volunteering policy, a payroll giving scheme, or by matching funds or time. Furthermore, it is particularly encouraging that there are a high number of companies willing to work in partnerships with charities. The success of many of the charity partnerships we looked at in this guide is testament to the unique creativity and innovation that can be produced when two very different sectors come together to exchange their professional knowledge and values.

As we have already noted in the previous edition of this guide, companies are becoming increasingly aware of the advantages of CSR reporting, with more and more taking steps to present their reporting in new and exciting ways – from microsites to CSR 'live tracker' tools. We take this is as a positive sign that companies are taking their CSR monitoring and reporting commitments seriously.

As always, however, there remains a long way to go for companies in terms of transparency in their CSR reporting and in publicising their social responsibility policies.

In this guide, as in previous editions, some companies continue to use their marketing expertise to promulgate an image of their community involvement that is not a truthful depiction of what they actually do.

What is more, during our research we regularly came across companies for which it was impossible to find community giving guidelines, criteria or relevant contacts. Transparency in these areas saves time, effort and resources of both the companies involved and those seeking funding or assistance. Those companies that do provide clear guidelines and criteria will no doubt attract applications from charities that fit within their priorities and will receive fewer ineligible applications. Charities, in turn, can apply their resources to target those companies most likely to support their cause.

The aim of this guide is to provide the knowledge necessary to obtain corporate support through the provision of profile information on individual companies, identifying the kind of support available and how to access it effectively. We hope that this guide will continue to be an invaluable and comprehensive source of information for all of those with an interest in corporate giving in the UK.

DSC campaigns and the current environment

DSC campaigns to achieve better funding relationships between charities and their funders. We want to support and help develop good funding practice among those organisations which give to charities and other voluntary organisations. DSC calls on companies to give more, for more companies to give, and for more companies to be better givers.

We use research to develop recommendations and practical tools for funders and fundraisers to positively change behaviour and practice. For example, our first *UK Company Giving Almanac*, which came out in 2013, mapped and analysed company giving to UK charitable causes.

Companies provide less than 5% of the UK voluntary sector's income (NCVO 2016). Understanding what is given by companies has become even more difficult, as we have previously outlined, following the recent changes to company reporting requirements which make company giving less transparent.

The lack of transparency apparent when a company chooses not to make available any information about its giving strategy neither benefits the company nor the charity seeking support. It results in fundraisers and others who are looking for assistance having no information available to them of that particular company's giving and, as a consequence, not knowing whether they should invest resources in making an approach for support. It also affects the conclusions of research carried out to map company giving geographically, by cause or by any other criterion.

Good communication between charities and companies is mutually beneficial. It means that companies can find like-minded organisations to work with to fulfil their CSR objectives, and that charities can access valuable support. Some very simple information, published on a company's website, can make a big difference. Does the company make donations to charities or provide in-kind support? Who is the best person to contact about the company's community contributions? It is equally helpful if companies state clearly that they do not support unsolicited requests from charities – this prevents charities using valuable time and resources on an ineligible application and avoids the company having to field queries from ineligible applicants.

The difficult economic climate in recent years has simultaneously made it harder for many charities to raise funds and increased demand for charities' services. The economy has been difficult for business too, but we believe there is still huge potential for companies to give more, for more companies to give, and for companies to be better givers.

Acknowledgements

We would like to thank all the companies that have helped to compile this guide: both those which we have contacted directly and those which have made their annual reports and accounts and/or their websites informative and accessible.

We would also like to thank Sharon Orr for writing the foreword for this edition. Sharon Orr is a senior community investment manager with extensive experience in corporate social responsibility, marketing and communication. Currently the Community Affairs Manager at Provident Financial Group, Sharon is committed to promoting the support of communities through corporate giving.

We would like to thank Del Redvers for once again allowing us to feature his article 'Charity of the Year and smaller organisations', and also Andy Melia and Louise Barrett for taking the time to provide us with new articles – 'Corporate volunteering' and 'A fundraiser's perspective', respectively.

References

Accenture (2016), *A 2020 Vision for Employer Supported Volunteering* [PDF], available on www.accenture.com

BBC (2015), 'Rise of Premier League TV income' figure in 'Premier League TV rights: Sky and BT pay £5.1bn for live games' [news release], available on www.bbc.com/sport/football/31357409, dated 10 February 2015

Brooks, Katya and Schlenkhoff-Hus, Angela on behalf of CSV (2013), *Employee Volunteering: Who is Benefitting Now?* [PDF], Volunteering Matters, available on volunteeringmatters.org.uk

Business in the Community (2013), The Gender Business Case. The benefits of increasing agility, balancing boards and eliminating the pay gap [PDF], available on www.gender.bitc.org.uk

Conservative Manifesto (2015), *The Conservative Party Manifesto 2015* [online report], available on www.conservatives.com/manifesto, accessed 20 February 2017

Davies, Evan Mervyn (2011), *Women on Boards* [PDF], Department for Business, Innovation & Skills, available on www.gov.uk

Davies, Evan Mervyn (2015), *Women on Boards Davies Review Five Year Summary* [PDF], Department for Business, Innovation & Skills, available on www.gov.uk

Geared for Giving (2016), 'Transforming Payroll Giving in the UK' [web page], www.gearedforgiving.org, accessed 27 February 2017

GlaxoSmithKline (2017), 'Responsibility, Our People, Our Commitment' [web page], www.gsk.com, accessed 14 February 2017

Hampton, Philip and Alexander, Helen (2016a), Steve Rowe, CEO of Marks and Spencer quoted in *Hampton-Alexander Review. FTSE Women Leaders. Improving gender balance in FTSE leadership* [PDF], available on www.ftsewomenleaders.com

Hampton, Philip and Alexander, Helen (2016b), Sir Roger Carr, Chair of BAE Systems PLC quoted in *Hampton-Alexander Review. FTSE Women Leaders. Improving gender balance in FTSE leadership* [PDF], available on www.ftsewomenleaders.com

IBM (2017), 'On Demand Community' [web page], www.ibm.com/ibm/ondemandcommunity, accessed 19 March 2017

Living Wage Foundation (2017), 'What is the real Living Wage?' [web page], www.livingwage.org.uk, accessed 20 March 2017

Marks and Spencer (2016), *Human Rights Report 2016* [PDF], available on www.corporate.marksandspencer.com

McMurtry, David Roberts (2015), *The engineering skills gap – no quick fix* [PDF press release], Renishaw, available on www.renishaw.com

NCVO (2016), *UK Civil Society Almanac*, available on data.ncvo.org.uk

Premier League (2015), 'League awards UK live broadcast rights for 2016/17 to 2018/19' [news release], available on www.premierleague.com/news/60495, dated 10 February 2015

Sealy, Ruth; Doldor, Elena; and Vinnicombe, Susan (2016), *The Female FTSE Board Report 2016* [PDF], Cranfield University, available on www.cranfield.ac.uk

Shop Direct (2016), 'Shop Direct kickstarts development of Alder Hey app with £210,000 fundraising' [news release], available on www.shopdirect.com, dated 11 October 2016

Standard Life (2016), *UK Community Impact Report 2013–2016* [PDF], available on www.standardlife.com

the7stars Foundation (2017), 'Our Story' [web page], the7starsfoundation.co.uk, accessed 21 March 2017

TONI&GUY (2017), 'Strength in Style' [web page], toniandguy.com/charity/strength-in-style, accessed 19 March 2017

Vodafone (2016), 'Slavery and Human Trafficking Statement 2016', *Sustainable Business Report 2015–16* [PDF], available on www.vodafone.com

Various examples of charitable activities and initiatives discussed above come from our research and were gathered from either the annual reports and accounts or the information stated on the websites of the relevant companies.

And finally . . .

If you have any comments about the guide, positive or negative, please get in touch with us at the Research Department, DSC, Suite 103, 1 Old Hall Street, Liverpool L3 9HG; tel: 0151 708 0136; email: research@dsc.org.uk.

About the Directory of Social Change

DSC has a vision of an independent voluntary sector at the heart of social change. The activities of independent charities, voluntary organisations and community groups are fundamental to achieve social change. We exist to help these organisations and the people who support them to achieve their goals.

We do this by:

- Providing practical tools that organisations and activists need, including online and printed publications, training courses, and conferences on a huge range of topics
- Acting as a 'concerned citizen' in public policy debates, often on behalf of smaller charities, voluntary organisations and community groups
- Leading campaigns and stimulating debate on key policy issues that affect those groups
- Carrying out research and providing information to influence policymakers

DSC is the leading provider of information and training for the voluntary sector and publishes an extensive range of guides and handbooks covering subjects such as fundraising, management, communication, finance and law. We have a range of subscription-based websites containing a wealth of information on funding from grant-making charities, companies and government sources. We run more than 300 training courses each year, including bespoke in-house training provided at the client's location. DSC conferences, many of which run on an annual basis, include the Charity Management Conference, the Charity Accountants' Conference and the Charity Law Conference. DSC's major annual event is Charityfair, which provides low-cost training on a wide variety of subjects.

For details of all our activities, and to order publications and book courses, go to www.dsc.org.uk, call 0207 697 4200 or email publications@dsc.org.uk.

Charity of the Year and smaller organisations

Del Redvers

This article has been included in previous editions of this guide; subsequently Business Community Connections has ceased operating. Nevertheless, we think the content of the article will still be of interest and use to many of our readers.

Del Redvers writes:

Charity of the Year is a label increasingly applied to all manner of partnerships, but what does it really mean? Business Community Connections (BCConnections) researched how different charities and businesses use the Charity of the Year concept and in doing so identified several critical factors for success.

There are many forms of Charity of the Year partnership but with certain common themes. Most obviously and significantly they are time limited relationships although certainly not always one year in duration. The most widespread understanding of the term is a partnership in which the staff from a business undertake a range of activities to raise money for the identified charity. At the end of the year businesses often feel the need to replace the charity they support in order to prevent fundraising fatigue, and to ensure wider appeal to staff and customers, as no one charity will be relevant to all stakeholders. This also gives the business the opportunity to support another charity.

Increasingly, however, other elements are added to the staff fundraising concept, such as cash donations, employee volunteering or other in-kind donations, sponsorship, cause related marketing or lobbying and campaigning. Sometimes these partnerships involve very little or no staff fundraising at all. Many businesses involved in these other types of Charity of the Year relationship would not be able to support a staff fundraising partnership, perhaps because they have smaller numbers of higher paid staff with less free time. Similarly, it makes sense for companies with relevant goods or services to donate them in kind to the charity as part of their contribution. The term Charity of the Year is used to brand a relationship, because although it can be misleading, it is a widely understood and accepted term.

For smaller organisations

Traditionally Charity of the Year relationships have been the preserve of large charities, frequently those able to offer national exposure to large corporate partners. There is, however, evidence to suggest a growing trend in the number of smaller charities seeking and successfully establishing Charity of the Year partnerships. The BCConnections research shows no reason why Charity of the Year should be out of bounds to small or medium sized charities and by the same token to Small and Medium Enterprises (SMEs). There are however a number of risks which can offset the many benefits available to both charities and businesses and which need to be weighed very carefully irrespective of the size of the organisation.

The advantages . . .

The research suggests that in general Charity of the Year partnerships do work for both partners. On the whole charities tend to put a financial value on the relationship of six or seven times the cost of establishing and managing the partnership. Whilst larger charities frequently net income in excess of £100,000 through these relationships, smaller charities also tend to consider them worthwhile activities even if they are very unlikely to achieve a six-figure financial contribution. A Charity of the Year partnership can . . .

1 Provide a reasonably predictable and often large income stream over a fixed period of time.

2 Provide an excellent opportunity to significantly increase the profile and reputation of the charity.

3 Create a track record of working with the corporate sector.
4 Lever support from other businesses and customers.
5 Increase fundraising activity from existing supporters.
6 Educate the workforce and customers of the business about the charity or its cause.
7 Offer access to employees as a new market of potential supporters.
8 Last longer than one year. There is a growing trend towards the 'Charity of 2 or 3 years' giving the security of a longer-term income stream.
9 Generate unrestricted income, although there is a developing trend towards restricted funds in these relationships.
10 Increase the morale at the charity, especially amongst the fundraising team.

And pitfalls . . .

There are many issues for a charity to consider before deciding whether or not to pursue a Charity of the Year relationship.

These partnerships can be resource intensive to manage, most significantly in terms of staff time. The cost benefit analysis section of the BCConnections research reveals that managing a small Charity of the Year partnership often takes at least 10% of one person's time. A large partnership can occupy from one to three employees on a full-time basis. There may also be costs associated with legal agreements for joint promotions, licencing and sponsorship arrangements.

Pitching for major Charity of the Year partnerships can be a significant undertaking in itself, requiring the investment of resources at an early stage, with no promise of a return. Once a partnership is agreed there is often a lengthy planning period before it is launched. Consequently, there exists a time lag between investing resources to develop the partnership and receiving the support. This can create a cashflow problem, particularly for smaller charities but also where a charity is expected to cover early costs such as producing badges and promotional material. Despite what can amount to considerable set-up costs, these partnerships will always be time limited and therefore, for most charities, cannot be considered a sustainable source of income.

Frequently, businesses use voting schemes to engage staff in selecting the Charity of the Year. This often results in the exclusion of many types of charities from the selection process as in an unrestricted ballot, staff have a tendency to vote for charities such as children, cancer and other health related charities with poignant issues.

There is always an element of risk on both sides in any corporate community relationship as a link is forged between the reputations of the two partners. With Charity of the Year this link is likely to be well publicised and consequently the relationship can backfire if it is considered to be unethical.

Getting a Charity of the Year partnership

If your organisation is seeking a Charity of the Year partnership, there are some things you should bear in mind . . .

1 Be strategic in your approach. Focus on the good fit between your charity and your target companies. Start building relationships with these businesses and try to grow the company contacts you already have. Think ahead and plan which business may adopt you next year or the year after that.
2 Decide on the cost benefit ratio you are prepared to accept. This is usually not just a financial exercise as it may involve judgements about intangible benefits and the potential worth of a partnership with the company in the longer term.
3 Be prepared to walk away. One of the most important messages to come out of the research is that charities need to assess at an early stage the potential value of the partnership, and then negotiate and decide whether or not it is worthwhile pursuing.
4 Consider approaching new businesses not previously involved in Charity of the Year partnerships.
5 Consider the benefits and drawbacks of a Charity of the Year partnership from the business point of view. Try to gain an understanding of why your target business might want a Charity of the Year partnership and more specifically with your organisation. This can help you to value your charity's worth and feel more confident about negotiating with the business.
6 If possible seek advice from a previous Charity of the Year of your target business. This should increase your understanding of the company, how they work and what they may want out of the partnership. This should be supplemented by in-depth research on the company from published sources.
7 Ask the business for a meeting at an early stage. This will give you more guidance about what they want from the partnership, before you invest significant resources. It will also help start to develop a relationship.
8 Be flexible about including other types of involvement for the partnership, apart from staff fundraising.
9 Consider at the outset how you could monitor the impact of your proposed Charity of the Year partnership on the wider community.

The pitch

When pitching for a Charity of the Year partnership, a key consideration is how the charity will be selected. If it is a management decision, there needs to be a focus on benefits to the business whilst for a staff ballot the proposal should be more emotive.

Where possible engage the beneficiaries of the charity in the process.

Proposals should be tailored specifically to the business you are approaching and stick to any brief given. Should the pitch fail, always ask for feedback and if appropriate a contribution; it is worth asking if the business can compensate you in any way for the time and resources invested. However, always be mindful of possible future relationships with that business.

For smaller Charity of the Year partnerships there is often no formal pitch process. Businesses that already engage in small scale Charity of the Year partnerships are more likely to use existing contacts or staff recommendations to identify future partners. Smaller businesses that have never had a Charity of the Year may need some guidance from the charity to help them appreciate the potential of the relationship.

Setting up the partnership

Planning

The importance of development time prior to publicising the partnership cannot be underestimated. In the BCConnections research over a quarter of the organisations did not plan the partnerships. Many larger businesses now select their Charity of the Year six months to one year before the publicised partnership year begins. For smaller partnerships, however, one or two months can provide ample planning time.

Agreement

A written agreement outlining the parameters of the relationships (objectives, targets, timeframes and budgets) plays an important role in managing the expectations of your partner. Clearly allocate responsibility for tasks and costs.

Seek to maximise the mutual benefit of the partnership. The greater the benefit for your business partner, the more seriously they will take the relationship and the greater the likelihood they will invest in Charity of the Year partnerships in the future.

Develop a plan of events, and a process for regular communication and review. Use the expertise of charity fundraisers to generate ideas for activities. Most charities find it easier to have a phased programme of fundraising events rather than doing everything at once.

Financial return

Consider whether there should be a minimum guaranteed return to the charity from the partnership. Some charities recommended including minimum guarantees in any documentation to protect against risk such as a minimum amount of cash to be raised. In addition agree what percentage of money raised will be restricted. Some charities will ask for a percentage of funding to be unrestricted to cover the costs of running the partnership. Also establish the timings of payments to the charity throughout the year and consider the impact on cashflow.

Whilst a single large cheque handed over at the end of the year may look impressive, it is often not a practical option, particularly for smaller charities.

Communications

Establish who will be responsible for the overall publicity of the partnership. If a logo is to be designed for the new partnership who will pay for it? Ensure that use of logos is agreed in advance.

There is also the issue of internal communication with the company's employees. Several charities have commented that it takes time to motivate and inspire staff to get involved in a programme of fundraising or other activities and the timetable should allow for this. The appointment of charity champions amongst the staff of the business can help to co-ordinate activity and provides a communication channel, particularly for multi-site operations.

Thinking ahead

Discuss the sustainability of the partnership and develop an exit strategy early on in the relationship. During review meetings consider whether it is beneficial to both partners to keep the relationship going beyond the year. Even if the charity is not designated Charity of the Year going forward, it may be possible to maintain and develop specific elements of the relationship, such as relationships with suppliers and payroll giving.

Measuring and monitoring

There has been an increasing emphasis on measuring the impact and benefits of Charity of the Year partnerships as with all other aspects of corporate community involvement. Like other types of relationship, there need to be mechanisms for measuring the social impact, benefits to the business and benefits to the charity. Significantly, Charity of the Year partnerships require careful measurement of the relationship itself as it is often more involved than other types of corporate community partnership.

Critically both parties need to know if there was a positive benefit compared with the cost of their involvement. Effective measurement of the partnership enables both parties to decide whether to undertake similar ventures in the future and identifies areas for improvement. Knowing what you want to measure at the outset allows for the correct accounting procedures to be put in place. For instance, without prior planning it may be easy for a company to breakdown staff fundraising by office or team but not by individual activities. This would make it impossible to measure the effectiveness of each activity.

The following represent some of the measures used by the businesses and charities we interviewed during the course of the research to assess the success of the partnership.

- Targets met or exceeded in planning and preparation
- Financial target met or exceeded
- % of company branches involved
- Outcome of the partnership for charity beneficiaries; e.g. number of individuals helped as a result, or number

of pieces of equipment purchased, amount of research time enabled, etc.

- Positive PR; e.g. the number of articles/column cms or amount of television time
- Number of contacts the charity has developed
- Staff and customer surveys; e.g. awareness and perceptions of business and charity
- Feel good factor; e.g. for business – number of letters, comments received in chat room, etc.
- Number of charity champions that come forward in the business

Conclusions

Charity of the Year relationships are a popular and highly visible way for charities and businesses to work together for mutual benefit and to target the social impact of corporate support for the voluntary sector. Whilst there are no hard and fast rules about establishing and managing Charity of the Year partnerships, a considered and strategic approach will help to maximise the many advantages offered by this type of relationship while minimising the risk.

Smaller charities should be encouraged to consider how they can adapt the models developed by larger organisations. Although there is definitely the opportunity for charities of all sizes to benefit from Charity of the Year relationships, they are not necessarily appropriate for all organisations and represent just one of several types of relationship that can form between the voluntary and corporate sector.

Del Redvers, Head of Sustainability for BMT Group Ltd. Del's role involves advising BMT's companies and customers on sustainability issues and co-ordinating the group's corporate sustainability strategy. He is also responsible for BMT Giveback, the group-wide philanthropic initiative.

Corporate volunteering *Andy Melia*

Corporate volunteering is a powerful way for charities and business to connect and understand their roles in the community. Approaches to volunteering through work have changed over the years and businesses are increasingly sharing professional skills so that charity groups benefit more from volunteering which has a sustainable and long-term impact.

Corporate volunteering can mean anything from staff going into local schools to support children with their reading, to volunteering that uses skills such as business planning or legal expertise (known as pro bono work). Corporate volunteering is most effective when based on a partnership rather than ad hoc, one-off donations of time, and most successful when both sides follow some core principles. At Business in the Community, we recommend that:

- Charities should assess the skills they need for themselves or their beneficiaries and think about the corporates who could provide these skills and are the best fit
- Once a partnership is created, both sides need to agree common objectives, supported by both senior teams
- Partners need to be clear on who is responsible for what, and ensure management and progress is reviewed regularly
- Partnerships have a clear end, and both sides communicate regularly and, crucially, are open and honest about what is working well and what needs improving.

We work with many businesses who have developed long-term and high-impact partnerships that focus on skills-based volunteering. Investec, for example, won the Experian Building Stronger Communities Award in 2016 for its partnership with the Bromley by Bow Centre. The company's Beyond Business programme incubates social enterprises with Investec employees providing intensive support and mentoring in business planning. Over 140 entrepreneurs have benefited from the programme helping them to scale and create over 300 jobs, and Investec staff have had the chance to grow and develop their management and leadership skills.

When business knows its communities (local places, employees, customers and suppliers) and understands the issues affecting them, corporate volunteering can move from a 'nice to do' to an invaluable asset for both voluntary sector organisations and the business.

Andy Melia
Head of Community Investment, Business in the Community

A fundraiser's perspective *Louise Barrett*

Corporate fundraising is one of the areas where there is real potential for growth. At a time when charities have to think even harder about a sustainable, diverse income portfolio, as corporate fundraisers we have a real opportunity to think outside the box. Focus on looking for opportunities where corporates can help achieve the charity's vision and address its challenges by gifting their expertise. Corporate fundraisers should not underestimate the value this can have on the bottom line.

My passion is to make a difference to the lives of others, I am currently doing that at the most amazing children's hospital, Alder Hey. Over the past ten years I have had varied fundraising experience; I have picked out some key learning as a practical guide to help you be the best you can be.

Passion – get this right and the rest will fall into place.

Passion is the key to success; when asking for help the person/organisation should be able to feel the problem through how you tell the story. An example of that: when I talk about research into childhood diseases I recall a conversation and more importantly the feeling I got from a surgeon when he talked about fighting monsters (diseases) who attack children at will. I could see a mix of emotions displayed in his body language and his eyes were telling their own story. I believe with passion I can also help the team fight these monsters. I recall this story and the feeling I got every time I ask for support into research.

You can't get enough passion; a practical tip: Who do you know in your organisation and do you really know what they do and the impact it has on your beneficiaries? What are their stories/experiences/challenges? Start a book of stories/problems so you don't forget any of them, remember to note how they made you feel.

To enable Alder Hey to achieve its goals I need to know everything – its vision and challenges. How well do you really know your organisation? Continuously explore it, find out what its biggest costs are, what are the challenges it is facing? You have to become the expert.

Now that you have established this you can explore how a corporate body can support you. It is not always obvious; at first you have to get to know the company, the nature of its business and its challenges too. *The Guide to UK Company Giving* is a fantastic resource that has done most of the work for you; all that is left for you to do is start building relationships and connecting the dots.

Another practical piece of advice: create a stakeholder map of your organisation and the company you're interested in using *The Guide to UK Company Giving* as an aide. Then start to link up people from both organisations and using your expert knowledge start to create chances for them to interact, this is when opportunities will start to appear.

Finally, be patient – opportunities don't always present themselves immediately and 80% of success is being present. Continuously be the expert, repeat the above cycle and you can't fail.

Louise Barrett
Head of SuperFun and Head of Corporate and Major Giving, Alder Hey Children's Charity

Applying to companies

This section gives basic information on identifying potential companies to approach, how to establish contact with them and how to put together a proposal for them to consider.

Corporate social responsibility

This guide deals with one aspect of CSR which, broadly speaking, is the philanthropic activities, usually referred to as the company's 'charitable or community investment'. Despite the increasing use of CSR policies and programmes adopted by companies, it should be remembered that company giving is way below that of the general public and, to a lesser extent, grant-making charities. Nevertheless, companies remain an important target for local, regional and national charities seeking funding.

Why apply to companies?

Company boards are ultimately responsible to their shareholders and answer to them as to how they use their profits. They will not be motivated primarily by philanthropy or by a desire to see new and pioneering voluntary activity. In many cases, companies will be looking to improve their image and their economic position in relation to their competitors, whether at a local, regional or national level.

There is, however, among some businesses, a desire to be seen to be giving something back to their community or society in general, and it is important for charities to have a strategy for applying to such companies. It must be kept in mind that they are a different animal to grant-making charities and require a different approach.

An increasing number of companies have now set up their own charities which, while having close ties to and receiving assets from the company, are separate legal entities. Whether they are truly independent of the company in their giving is not always clear, but they are nominally self-governing and set up for charitable purposes for the benefit of the public. In this respect, they should be applied to in the same way you would make an application to any other grant-making charity.

The relationship you have with any company which donates to your cause, whether by cash, gifts in kind, staff time or other resources, is a two-way association. While you will be pleased to receive funding, the company will also benefit from the good publicity, awareness of local issues which they may not have previously had and a boost in morale for their staff. As with any relationship, your organisation needs to be selective about who it approaches: you need to be comfortable with the association you are about to establish. Research the company's website, or any other information, with this in mind and be sure there is no clear or potential ethical conflict.

Why companies give

To make an effective appeal to corporates you must have a basic understanding of why companies give. This will enable you to put forward good reasons why they should support your work. Many companies, especially the larger, higher-profile ones, receive hundreds, if not thousands, of requests for support from charities, voluntary sector organisations and local community groups each year. For your appeal/application to be successful it needs to be more than a general plea to for them to 'put something back into the community'.

You can help a company justify its charitable support to its shareholders by telling them not just why you want the money, but why giving you support will be of interest to them. You can also tell them about any benefits they will receive in return for their investment and about the impact their donation will have on your work. At the very least you should be able to demonstrate a clear link with the company through a geographical, product, or employee contact or some other relevant connection.

Most companies give out of enlightened self-interest rather than for pure altruistic or philanthropic reasons, and see their giving in terms of 'community involvement' or 'community investment'. The main reasons why companies give are:

- To create goodwill. Companies like to be seen as good citizens in the communities in which they operate and as caring companies by their employees and society at large.
- To be associated with causes that relate to their business. Financial companies often like to support debt advice charities, for example.
- To build good relations with employees. Support for employee volunteering is a growing area of company giving, creating a 'feel-good factor' among employees and a sense of loyalty to their socially responsible employer. Increasingly some preference is given to those charities for which staff are raising money or doing volunteer work. Funds raised may be matched (usually up to a set limit) and/or employees can be given time off work in which to volunteer.
- To use the opportunity of secondments, volunteering and pro bono work as an excellent staff-development resource.
- To discover more about their customers.
- Because now more than ever, society expects it of them.
- They do not want to be seen as unaware or not sufficiently caring in relation to other rival companies in their particular business sector. They are concerned that the quantity and quality of their giving is appropriate to their status as a company.
- Because the chair/senior directors are interested in a particular cause (and perhaps support it personally).
- Because they have always given. Some companies never review their contributions policy. They see giving more as an annual subscription to a list of charities they wish to support each year. Your aim should be to get your charity's name onto such a list, where it exists.
- Because the charity persists in its approach to the company and the company does not want to keep refusing a worthwhile cause. Persistence can pay, although if you are turned down you should consider whether you can improve your application, ask through another method, or ask for something else.
- For tax reasons. Giving to a charity can be done tax-effectively. This will be an added benefit for the company (but seldom a determining factor).

It is worth pointing out that there is relatively little consistency in company giving. For privately owned or family-controlled companies their giving is often little different from personal giving. For public companies, where it is the shareholders' funds that are being given away, there is more likely to be a structure in place and some well-defined criteria. Where the company publishes its guidelines and criteria, please respect them. Dealing with a mass of clearly inappropriate applications is time-wasting for the corporate giver, and has caused some to consider winding up their charitable support programme altogether.

What companies give

There are a variety of ways in which companies can support charities:

- A cash donation (usually a one-off grant)
- Pro bono (without charge) professional or technical work
- Sponsorship of an event or activity
- Sponsorship of promotional and educational materials
- Sponsorship of an award scheme
- Running a cause-related marketing campaign where the company contributes a donation to the charity in return for each product sold (in order to encourage sales)
- Donating physical items such as company products or surplus office equipment; making company facilities available, including meeting rooms, printing or design facilities; help with mailings
- Secondment of a member of staff to work with the charity, where a member of the company's staff helps on an agreed basis while remaining employed (and paid) by the company
- Offering internships or work experience to a charity's beneficiary or student at an educational establishment
- Offering a senior member of staff to the charity's management board/trustee body
- Providing expertise and advice or training
- Encouraging and making it easy for employees to volunteer
- Organising a fundraising campaign among employees, including encouraging employees to give through payroll giving
- Advertising in charity brochures and publications

Companies will always receive more applications than they will have the budget to meet. Community involvement budgets have not expanded in line with demands for support, and many companies now focus their grant-making quite narrowly and/or proactively.

Some larger companies set up small grants schemes in regions or towns where they have a major factory or business presence. Others have matching schemes, where they match money collected or donated by employees. Some develop special grants programmes, while others have a Charity of the Year for their major donation and as a focus for encouraging staff involvement and a mutually beneficial investment.

Cash donations

This is the most obvious way that a company can be asked to support your organisation and is probably the help you would most like to receive. Many cash donations from companies are small, although some companies will match their employees' fundraising which results in much larger total sums. You are more likely to be successful if you offer a 'shopping list' detailing the cost of specific items, rather than a vague request for general support.

In the individual company entries section further on in the guide we try to give an idea of the range of grants available from the large companies and what they like to support. This varies greatly from company to company. Some will have well-defined policies which work in a similar way to grant-making charities and will be clear about the causes they want to assist.

Some companies – especially the smaller ones – will have an informal approach. Here, any applications will be looked at by anyone from the personnel officer to the managing director, or their PA. They will not necessarily have any special insight into the voluntary sector and they will be doing the community support task on top of their work, and so often may have to fit it into the odd Friday afternoon once a month. It is most unlikely that they have the time to work through piles of paper or attend lengthy meetings to get to know the issues you are facing and the work you are doing. As with all applications, tailor your request to these companies accordingly.

A good number of companies will operate on the basis of the chair's six favourite charities and if you are not on the list you will have to find a way in, as the company's giving policy will already be fixed. If you are successful with this sort of company, you may be successful with others, as part of company giving works on recommendation.

You might stand more chance of success if you can tie your application in with an event or celebration. For example, anniversaries are useful and you may be able to find a company to tie in with your or the company's 50th year, or your 500th member. It will be particularly attractive if you have a time limit to your fundraising – this gives those working in the supporting company a definite target to work towards.

Gifts in kind

Giving items or services rather than money can often be easier for a company. The value of the gift to the charity may be much more than the cost to the company. Companies might give:

- Products for use by the charity
- Pro bono professional and technical advice
- Staff time
- Products as prizes or as lots to be auctioned
- Old stock and end-of-line products for resale in charity shops
- Facilities such as meeting rooms, conference facilities or training

If a company donates items that it makes or sells in the course of its trade, or that it has used in its trade (such as computers and furniture), then this can be treated as a tax-deductible business expense. The 'book value' of donated items (value as given in the accounts) is written off before the donation is made (unsaleable or damaged stock, end-of-line products, etc.) and attracts full tax relief. There are organisations which act as clearing houses for gifts in kind, such as In Kind Direct.

What kind of gift is a gift in kind?

Gifts in kind are donations of items or services, rather than the money to buy them. You might consider approaching specific companies for one of the following gifts, preferably establishing a link between the gift required and the company's business, making it less expensive for the company and more easily obtained:

- Secondment of staff with key skills to train or mentor your trustees, employees or volunteers
- Donation of coach, train, airline or ferry tickets
- Advertising on company websites
- Use of surplus storage or sports facilities
- Donation of hotel accommodation
- Use of telephones for helplines
- Design and printing of leaflets or posters
- Donation of surplus food or drinks
- Access to information on customer demography, attitudes or preferences
- Vacant sites for recreation projects
- Free loan of equipment, scaffolding, marquees, Portaloos, etc.
- Free advertising space on temporarily unused sites
- Insertion of a charity leaflet or appeal in a regular business or customer mailshot
- Free servicing of vehicles

Here are some practical tips on how to set about getting support in kind:

1. Make a list of everything you need – a 'wish list'. This can include services as well as products (such as the design for a leaflet you plan to produce).
2. Go through the list and using the indexes contained in this guide (see pages 429 and 446) try to identify companies that might have what you require. Personal knowledge can also be useful and you might want to use business directories as well to widen your choice.
3. Make contact. Writing a letter can act as an introduction but you will probably need to follow it up with a phone call or personal visit. Try not to write reams; state your request, saying that it is for a charity, indicating how well used it will be or what impact it will make and how important it is to your organisation's future. If the company does not want to donate, it might be able to give you a discount.
4. Be positive and enthusiastic but always professional. It can be very difficult for the company to refuse if it knows what you want and how important it is for you and the local community. It will always cost the company far less to donate the item than it would cost you to purchase it and you can subtly point this out.
5. Say thank you. Report back subsequently on the difference the donation has made. Send them your annual report and later, perhaps, try to recruit the company as a cash donor.

Employee volunteering/secondments/pro bono work

A major resource that companies can offer is their staff time and this can be provided in a number of ways:

Employee volunteering: many of the large companies encourage their staff to volunteer, within or outside office hours, on the basis that this enhances the skills of their employees and promotes good community relations. Some companies match the amount an employee has raised for a chosen project.

Professional skills: banks, law firms, accountants, advertising and PR companies can all encourage staff to give their professional skills free of charge or to become trustees.

Secondment: this is where the company loans you a member of staff full time for an extended period. There needs to be a good reason why the company would do this, as it is an expensive form of support.

Employee volunteering is not only valuable in itself, it is also strategically important since you will be building a relationship with a member of staff who can then act as an intermediary in asking the company for other forms of support at a later date, including cash donations.

Advertising

Companies will sometimes pay for an advertisement in a publication. Possibilities include:

- Your annual report
- Programmes produced specifically for fundraising events
- Conference folders, pads and pens (bearing the company's name/logo)
- Leaflets aimed at your service users and others
- Posters, including educational wall charts

However, you do need to think through whether you actually want an advertisement or company logo to appear prominently on your materials.

Advertising can be broken down into two categories:

Goodwill advertising: where the primary purpose of the advertiser is to support a charity and to be seen supporting a good cause; this creates goodwill for the company rather than selling its products

Commercial advertising: where the advertiser wishes to reach the audience that the charity's publication goes to, and the decision is made for purely financial considerations

What are you offering to advertisers?

Before trying to sell the advertising, you need to recognise what you are offering. If it is goodwill advertising, then the prestige of the event, the nature of the audience, the location and any celebrities who will be present will be major incentives. Price is less of an issue than the work of the charity, although the advertiser will want to know the circulation and readership of the publication, any special characteristics of that readership and any particular connection between it and the company's product. If it is commercial advertising, these details become much more significant.

Pricing the advertising

The first consideration when pricing the advertising is the format of the publication. A lavish souvenir brochure is different from an annual report, and this in turn is very different from a single-colour newsletter produced on your computer. There are two factors to consider when deciding the cost of the advertising.

1. How much do you want to raise? Divide this target by the number of pages of advertising to get a page rate.
2. How much are advertisers prepared to pay? For commercial advertising this is especially important. Try to define the value of your audience to them.

Once you have decided a page rate, then you can set prices for smaller spaces that are slightly higher than pro rata. For example, if the page rate is £250, then a half page might be priced at £150, a quarter page at £85, and an eighth page at £50. You can ask for higher sums for special positions, such as the back cover, the inside front cover and facing the contents page. For a regular publication, you could offer a series discount for taking space in several issues.

You might consider producing a rate card which contains all the information that the advertiser needs to know, including:

- A deadline for agreeing to take space
- A deadline for receipt of artwork and an address where it is to be sent
- Publication size
- Print run
- Use of colour on cover and inside pages
- Page rates, including special positions, size of advertising space, and whether VAT is chargeable
- Payment details

A simple brochure or covering letter which sets out the reasons for advertising is useful, but posting copies out ad hoc will generate little response. The way to sell advertising is on the telephone, where you make a call to follow up a letter you have sent. For larger advertisers, you might try to arrange a personal visit. The majority of people you approach might say 'no' but your job is to persuade a significant proportion to buy a space.

Business sponsorship

Sponsorship needs to be carefully defined. It is not a donation and the fact that your organisation is a charity is largely irrelevant: it is a business arrangement. The charity is looking to raise funds for its work and the company wants to improve its image, promote and sell its products or entertain its customers.

The sponsor's contribution is usually money, although it could be a gift of goods such as football kits, services such as free transport, professional expertise such as promotion or marketing consultancy, the use of buildings such as an exhibition centre, or free promotion such as media coverage in a newspaper.

Many companies will provide much more in sponsorship than they would as a donation, but only so long as the commercial benefits warrant it. Developing links with major national and local corporate sponsors could be an investment in your future that is well worth making now, although it requires a significant amount of work and care.

Most sponsors are commercial companies. There are four main options for sponsorship:

1 Businesses wanting to promote themselves, to create a better image or generate awareness in the local communities where they operate. This includes those companies with an 'image problem' – for example, mining and extraction companies associated with damaging the environment that want to project a cleaner image by being associated with a conservationist cause.

2 Businesses wanting to introduce or promote a product or service. This could include a new brand of trainers or shampoo, or a supermarket opening in the area. Public awareness is important if a product or service is to get accepted, so companies may be open to proposals that give a product or service more exposure.

3 Companies looking for entertainment opportunities to influence customers, suppliers, regulators, the media and other opinion formers. They may be interested in sponsoring a concert, a theatrical event, an art exhibition or a sporting event which would provide them with an appropriate entertainment opportunity and the chance to meet and mingle.

4 Companies that are committed supporters of your organisation. You may be able to offer them a particular project or event that they feel an affinity with and would like to sponsor, even if it is not strictly for business but partly for philanthropic reasons.

What are companies looking for?

Voluntary organisations looking for sponsorship should be able to offer at least some of the following things:

- A respectable partner (with the right image).
- A real partnership. What involvement is the sponsor looking for and how well does this opportunity meet its needs?
- A proven track record (preferably in securing and delivering sponsorships) and a professional approach. Has the applicant approached the process of getting sponsorship in a professional way, and can they demonstrate a similar level of professionalism in the running of their organisation?
- An interesting project (at least to the company's management team and possibly also its staff) and a new initiative. Does the sponsorship represent something that would not happen without the company's support? Is it interesting and lively?
- Continuity. Is there scope for a continuing relationship (over the next few years), or is the activity or event just a one-off?
- Genuine value for money. What are the benefits and how much money is the voluntary organisation asking for? How does this compare with other possible sponsorships that the company might consider? The relationship of cost to return and the importance of the return to the company are the dominant factors affecting the decision to sponsor.
- Visibility. How 'visible' will the event be, and what specific publicity and PR benefits will accrue to the sponsor? Will the company name be given a high profile?
- Appropriateness. Is the activity or event appropriate to the sponsor? (Are you approaching the right company that has an interest in what you are doing?)
- A targeted audience. (Could the activity or event lead to a direct marketing opportunity, such as providing the company's fair trade coffee at a reception for young entrepreneurs?)
- Other tangible benefits; for example, could the activity or event offer good publicity, media coverage, a link with brand advertising, entertainment opportunities for the company's directors and staff, access to VIPs, involvement of the company's employees or retirees, training or experience for members of staff, etc.?

Why companies like sponsorship

- It helps them get their message across
- It can enhance or change their image
- It can reach a target audience very precisely
- It can be a very cost-effective form of advertising or product promotion
- Further marketing opportunities may develop from the sponsorship
- It generates good publicity for the sponsor, often of a kind that money can't buy
- It generates an awareness of the company within the community in which the company operates and from where it draws its workforce and customers
- Sponsors can entertain important clients at the events they sponsor

What can be sponsored?

There is an extremely wide range of things that can be sponsored, including:

- Cultural and sporting events
- Mass-participation fundraising events, such as a marathon or fun run
- The publication of a report or a book, with an attendant launch
- The production of fundraising materials, leaflets and posters, or the sponsorship of a complete fundraising campaign
- Conferences and seminars, especially to specialist audiences (such as GPs) where promotional material can be displayed
- Vehicles, where the acknowledgement can be painted on the side

- Equipment such as cars or computers produced by the company
- Competitions, awards and prizes
- Scholarships, bursaries and travel grants

The bulk of corporate sponsorship money goes to sport, with motor racing, golf, tennis, athletics, football and cricket all receiving huge amounts. These offer extensive media coverage, good opportunities for corporate entertainment and an association with a popular activity. The arts is another big recipient of company sponsorship when corporates can publicise their more cultural leanings or reach a new audience. Social sponsorship is much smaller by comparison, however; the 'market' is less crowded and there are all sorts of imaginative ways in which companies can sponsor events and activities run by charities.

Getting sponsorship: 10 practical tips

1. Before you begin, think about an ethical code. Are there some companies you would not wish to be associated with? Have a written policy agreed by your trustees and/or senior management.
2. Identify the right person in the company to contact. You need their name and job title. This will often be the marketing manager.
3. Stress the benefits of the sponsorship to the potential sponsor. This should be done often and as clearly as possible, and backed up with statistics or other supporting information.
4. The size of the payment will be dependent upon the value of the sponsorship to the sponsor, not the cost of the work for you.
5. Help companies use their own resources to make the sponsorship work. Suggest, for instance, that they might like a picture story in their house magazine or in the trade press. Most are very keen to impress their colleagues and their rivals, but may not think of this without prompting.
6. Sponsorship, especially long-term deals, is all about working together. Promise only what you know you can deliver, and always try to deliver a little bit more than you promised.
7. Remember that most sponsorship money for small and medium-sized charities comes in sums of under £10,000 and that it is a local event you are planning, not Live Aid.
8. Get into the habit of reading adverts. Look particularly at local papers and trade press. Who has got money to spend on promotion? What kind of image are they trying to promote? Who are they trying to reach? How can you help them?
9. Mention another company that supports you. One satisfied sponsor can help you to get another.
10. Keep trying. It is hard work but sponsorships can be really valuable.

There may be an advertising agency or marketing consultant that can introduce sponsorship opportunities to sponsors. They will sometimes charge you a fee; more usually they will receive a commission from the sponsor. It depends who retains them, and in whose interests they are acting. You need to be fully aware of the costs here and any terms and conditions attached before you go ahead.

Your sponsorship package

It is not enough to offer a company a potential target audience if, for example, it sponsors your event. You need to say who that target audience will be and how the company might benefit from their attendance at the event.

Think of each group that you reach in one way or another, say young people. Estimate an annual number for each group. The more you can define your different groups and find a link between them and the sponsor, the more likely the corporate is to support your event.

Contractual issues

Sponsorship involves giving something in return for the money you are receiving, so you need to agree terms through a contract. This can be set out in a legal agreement (for larger sponsorships) or in the form of a letter. You need to be clear about the following:

- How long the arrangement will run. Is it for one year, which would require you to find a new sponsor next year, or can you get a commitment for several years? What happens at the end of this period – does the sponsor have a first refusal on the following year's event? Most successful sponsorships last for several years, and the benefit builds up over the sponsorship period. However, some companies do not like being tied to sponsoring something indefinitely – their sponsorship programme might begin to look stale.
- The fee to be paid, and when the instalments are due. What benefits are to be delivered in return for the fee? These should be specified as clearly as possible, so that you know precisely what you are contracted to deliver.
- Whether VAT is chargeable. This will depend on whether your organisation is registered for VAT and the extent of the benefits offered to the sponsor. If VAT is chargeable, this should be discussed at the outset, and the fee agreed should be exclusive of VAT.
- Who will pay for what costs? Who pays for insurance (there may be more than one type needed) and the additional publicity the sponsor requires? Such items can be forgotten but are important and need to be agreed in writing. There needs to be a clear agreement as to who is responsible for what, so you can ensure that everything is covered and there are no misunderstandings later on.
- Who is responsible for doing what? You will need to clarify who will be responsible for the public relations, who will handle the bookings, who will invite the guests, whose staff will receive the guests, and so on.
- Any termination arrangements in the event of the activity having to be cancelled.
- Who is responsible for managing the sponsorship? You will need a named person on both sides.

- Whether the sponsor is a 'commercial participator', as defined by the Charities Act 1992, where legal requirements will apply.

If everything is written down and agreed, there will be fewer problems later and it ensures that everything has been properly thought through at the outset.

Note: The above list is not exhaustive and you should contact the Charity Commission for further information or advice: see www.charitycommission.gov.uk.

Joint promotions and cause-related marketing

Many larger charities are involved in promotional activity to help market a commercial product – this is often known as cause-related marketing. This can bring in large amounts of money and expose the name of the charity (and sponsor) to literally millions of people. The same idea on a smaller scale can also be adapted for use by local charities through local promotions.

Commercial promotions can include on-pack and licensing promotional deals, affinity credit cards, competitions and awards, the use of phone lines, etc. What they have in common is that they present an opportunity to raise money for your cause and to project your charity to new audiences, but they require that you work with the company and on its terms to achieve this.

This arrangement benefits both the charity and the commercial partner. It differs from sponsorship in that you are promoting the company's product or service (in return for a payment) as the primary purpose of the arrangement. But as with sponsorship, you will need to make a business case for it.

Getting started with promotions

Joint promotions are quite difficult to arrange and you must first talk about the possibility of your developing promotional links with companies with someone who has experience of this or with a marketing or advertising agency (but these can be costly).

You need to decide whether your charity is the type which can expect a commercial link of this sort. It has been generally accepted that national household-name charities and those addressing popular causes (such as helping children) are more likely to benefit from this area of fundraising than the less well-known charities or those addressing 'less popular' causes.

You should take the initiative yourself by contacting companies that might be interested in your work. You can also contact promotional agencies to make them aware of the opportunities you are offering which they could include when appropriate in their sales pitch to companies.

If you are approached by a promotional agency pitching for business, this does not mean that anything is certain. It may be working independently, hoping that a good idea that involves your charity can then be sold to a company. Often these ideas come to nothing, and you may find you have put in considerable effort without getting any return.

Issues with sponsorships and joint promotions

Sponsorship involves a close working relationship with a company. Therefore you will need to be sure when you enter into any sponsorship agreement that this relationship will benefit your organisation and will not damage your charity's reputation. With commercial promotions the relationship is even closer. The charity is actively promoting the products of the company, so it is important that the product you are associated with is good value and good quality. With both arrangements it is important that you have no ethical problems in associating with that company. You should develop an ethical donations policy before you apply for any sponsorship or suggest a joint promotion – agreeing in advance which types of company you are happy to work with and which you are not. (See 'Ethical issues' on page xxxiii)

There is also the question of who will benefit most from the arrangement. How much you should expect to receive from a sponsorship or commercial promotion is also a difficult question. It may be worth a great deal to the company to be linked with you. Any negotiation should start from what you think the association is worth to the potential corporate partner. Your need for money should not dim the value of your commercial worth.

Finally, there are important legal issues arising from current charity legislation which need to be addressed when engaging in commercial ventures (for more information, see the Institute of Fundraising Code of Fundraising Practice L9.0 Commercial Participators.)

In its guidance to charity trustees (see guidance CC20), the Charity Commission suggests that trustees should consider the following points before allowing the charity's name to be associated with a particular business or product:

- The relationship is appropriate and will not damage the particular charity or the good name of charity as a whole
- The proposed fundraising venture is a more effective way of raising money than others that might be considered, and that the terms of the arrangement are generally advantageous to the charity
- The arrangement is set out in some detail and kept under review, such that the charity's name is not misused or improperly exploited, and the charity has the right to prevent future use of its name if the arrangement proves unsatisfactory; it may be worth taking legal advice in drawing up the terms of the arrangement

The types of companies that give

Multinational companies

Most multinational companies have global giving programmes, generally tied to areas where they have or are developing business interests. Some multinational companies have an international structure for managing their giving, with budgets set for each area and a common policy regarding what they wish to support. With others, community investment remains at the discretion of local company management in the country concerned.

Geographically speaking, the further out from the centre (i.e. the company's headquarters or operational sites) you are, the less support you can expect to receive. In general, most money is spent in the home country of the giving company and often in the headquarters' town or region or areas where it operates.

Leading national companies

These are most likely to support large national charities, have their own sponsorship schemes and make smaller donations to local charities in the area in which they are headquartered or have a major business presence. Numerous national companies make grants through regional offices, while retail stores such as B&Q might use the local store manager to give advice on a local application. Such stores may also provide the manager with a small budget to spend at their discretion.

Larger local companies

In any city or region there are large companies which are important to the local economy. They will often feel a responsibility to support voluntary action and community initiatives in areas where they have operations, and value the good publicity this provides.

There are also companies with a regional remit. The water, electricity and independent television companies all have a specific geographical area within which they operate, even if they are part of a multinational company/group.

Smaller local companies

There are a myriad of companies that make up the local business community. Referred to as small and medium enterprises (SMEs), they are often overlooked in the rush to target the large companies on which plenty of information is generally available. However, from manufacturers on trading estates to accountants and solicitors in the high street, the majority of SMEs will say they have some involvement with their local community. Many of these companies are privately owned, so the best approach will often be through the managing director or a senior partner.

The best sources of information on what companies exist in your area are:

- The local Chamber of Commerce, where most of the more prominent local companies will be members
- The Kompass directory of companies, which is regionally organised and can be searched online (gb.kompass.com)
- The local council: the business department might produce a list of major business ratepayers; the economic development section may have a list of major employers
- The local newspaper, which will carry stories from time to time that mention local companies, and may provide information on new companies planning to set up in the area
- You – by keeping your eyes open you can often identify local companies that it could just be worth approaching

It is likely that most of the smaller companies you approach will not have a donations policy in place (if they give at all), and may well make their decisions on the basis of the personal interests of their managing director or senior partners. Some may never have made a charitable donation before and may not know about the related tax advantages available to them, so be prepared to tell them about these opportunities.

Some of these companies may prefer to give in kind – for example, a prize for a raffle or advertising in a souvenir brochure for a fundraising event. It might be easier to approach these companies for this sort of support in the first instance, and later on, once they have given something, see if they would like to make a cash donation.

Small and medium-sized businesses will react quickly to economic conditions. When business is falling, their concerns will be for their staff and not giving money to charities.

Staff time is also at a premium as numbers are small and people are usually stretched with their workload. Staff volunteering schemes are therefore unlikely to be entered into.

Charitable giving is often led by the enthusiasms of the partners or directors, but employees might also be responsive to your good cause. One local business has suggested to us the following advice:

- Match your request to what the business can afford. If a project is too large and the business can only give a small donation they will see their contribution as being swallowed up and not making any difference at all.
- Lengthy letters take up too much time to consider. It is much better if they are simple, succinct and concise.
- Letters should be typed rather than hand-written.
- A good track record gives the appeal credence.
- Corporate giving is not just about money – partners tend to give their time and skills through involvement, more so than cash.
- Telephone to make things happen. If you have someone on your management committee who already has links with business people, they might be better placed to make the call.

Who to approach

Key factors in approaching companies

Research

Research is very important, not only into companies but also into personal contacts. When planning an appeal, an important first step is to find which of the people associated with your charity have influence or know people who have. If you can find a link between one of your supporters/volunteers/staff/trustees and a particular company – use it.

You should try to find out as much as you can about the companies you have identified as potential donors. But, remember:

- Companies, generally, have less well-defined policies than grant-making charities, although you can often determine a pattern in their giving.
- The chance of an application made 'out of the blue' getting substantial support is low.
- Appeals made towards the end of a company's financial year are less likely to succeed.
- Companies are more conservative in their giving and are less likely to support innovative projects (at least until they are established) or anything that is risky or controversial.
- Companies' policies change more frequently than those of grant-makers, because of mergers, takeovers, or a fall/rise in profits, so ensure your research is up to date. Consulting a copy of the company's latest annual report and accounts is not necessarily enough; they may have been taken over since then. Check the company's website and the financial press on a regular basis, or make a quick telephone call to see if anything has changed, for example the company's name, address or your contact person.

The company

Which companies to approach will depend on the nature of your organisation. If you are a national organisation then an appeal to the country's leading companies is appropriate. Local groups should approach local firms and local branches of national companies which have a presence in their area. Organisations can approach companies in allied fields: for example, theatres can appeal to fabric companies. Be imaginative when looking for a connection.

As outlined in the 'Smaller local companies' section on page xxxi, most local companies have no donations policy and you may have to explain the advantages of giving and approach them for in-kind support in the first instance.

Larger companies might have a manager who is responsible for dealing with charitable appeals, although a donations committee (which often includes senior management) may have the final say. The largest companies might also employ specialist staff to assess the applications and make recommendations.

You need to be selective when you decide on which companies to approach and then find out who you should contact within the company. The choice of company will depend upon what connection you have with them.

First, identify and match possible companies with various aspects of your work. In particular, try to find any local companies that are known for their generosity or might want to support your particular beneficiary group.

Second, contact BITC to find out about its membership or to help you identify local companies through its regional network.

Next, consider the following questions:

- Has the company supported you before?
- Does it have a stated interest in your project such as the environmental initiative that you are promoting?
- Is the company local to your community?
- Are you consumers of its service or product?
- Does the company need better publicity in the community and could you offer that with a link?
- Do your activities contribute to improving the business environment?
- Is the company a large employer in the area with an interest in the current and future workforce?

Lastly, one big problem you may face involves the ownership of seemingly independent companies. Many companies are in fact part of much larger concerns. There are frequent mergers and takeovers, plus the buying and selling of business between corporations. A useful, although expensive, source of information is the directory *Who Owns Whom* (published by GAP Books), which has an index listing most subsidiaries of companies included in this guide. Check your local library to see if they have a copy.

You can also use companies' annual reports, which (for most companies) can be obtained from their website or on request. These reports provide good background information on the company concerned, and occasionally information on its charitable support programme. Some private (and occasionally public) companies will not send out annual reports except to shareholders; in such cases you can go to the Companies House to get hold of a copy. Offices are situated in Cardiff, Edinburgh, Belfast and London and the website address is: www.companieshouse.gov.uk.

The person

Once you have decided on the company, you will need to find out how it is organised and who makes any decisions about charitable giving. Where a company has a number of branches or operating units throughout the country these may have some autonomy in providing grants. There is usually a maximum amount that they can decide, over which the application will be passed to the next level: regional or national. If you can find this out beforehand it will save time in the long run.

You need to tailor your request to the level at which you are asking and to which budget it might come from; it may not necessarily be from the company's charitable giving budget but possibly marketing or personnel. Once you have established the budget source and level, you will then need to find the right person to talk and write to. Here are a few tips:

1. Find out what, if any, previous contact you or your organisation has had with companies: any previous fundraising approaches that have been made, and with what success.
2. Find out whether any of your management committee, volunteers or supporters have any personal contact with the companies you plan to approach – and whether they know people who have credibility in the

business world who can help you do the asking. It may be appropriate for one of these contacts to sign the appeal letter.

3 Look into whether one of your volunteers or supporters is an employee of the company.
4 Find out if any of your clients or users work for the company.
5 Alternatively, you might be able to tie your appeal in to a known personal interest of a director.
6 Enlist a senior business leader to assist you with your fundraising. This can be someone to serve as a chair of a development or fundraising committee, or just to contact a few colleagues and sign a few letters.

Generally, an appeal through a personal contact will work best. But if you don't have a contact and can see no way of developing one, then you will have to come up with another link.

As a first step you might contact the company to find out:

- Who is responsible for dealing with charitable appeals and their name and job title.
- What information they can send regarding their company.
- Any procedure or timetable for submitting applications.
- Whether they might be interested in coming to see your organisation at work; visits are useful when discussing bigger donations with the larger companies, but are difficult to arrange for anything small.

Unfortunately, there is no short cut if you have no inside knowledge of the company. Be prepared to spend time on the company's website or the telephone, particularly if the company has no decided policy on giving.

Almost certainly your appeal will be in the form of a letter. Make this as personal as you can. Circular letters are likely to end up in the bin and many companies will not consider them as a point of policy. Make the letter professional but motivating, and short and to the point.

Be specific in your approach

Rather than sending out a circular appeal to 100 or 1,000 companies, you will be more successful if you select a few companies you believe will be particularly interested in your project, and target your application to them and their policy.

Find a good reason why you believe the company should support you and include this prominently in your letter. You may be able to relate what you are doing as a charity to companies which have some relevance to your work: for example, a children's charity might appeal to companies making children's products; a housing charity to construction companies, building societies, etc. Any relationship, however tenuous, creates a point of contact on which you can build a good case for obtaining the company's support. If you can find no relationship, should you be approaching that company at all?

There may be occasions when a charity will not want to accept money from a company in a related industry (see the environmental/youth group examples in 'Ethical issues' below). Similarly, a local charity might not want money from a company that has made people in the area redundant. Each charity has to judge where it draws the line and ultimately what is in the best interests of the charity.

Be clear about why you need the money

You must be clear about the objectives of the work for which you are raising money, particularly its timescale and how it relates to your overall programme of work. Try to think in project terms rather than seeking money to cover basic administration costs. You need to develop projects out of your current activities to present to potential donors. You can build a percentage of administration costs into the costs of a project. If you relate what you are doing to a specific timescale, this again makes what you are applying for a project rather than a contribution to your year-on-year core costs.

Be persistent

Do not underestimate the persistence factor. If you do not receive a donation in the first year, do not assume that the company will never support you. Go back a second and even a third time.

If you are going back, mention the fact that you have applied to the company previously, perhaps saying that you are now presenting something different which may be (you hope) of more interest.

If the company gives you reasons for refusing support, use these to help you put in more appropriate applications in the future. If the response is that the company does not give to your particular type of activity, then you know that it is no use you going back. If the company said its funds were fully committed, you can try to find out when would be a better time in the year to apply.

Note the response to your appeal and use any information you can glean to improve your chances the next time.

Ethical issues

Receiving support from companies can be problematic if the business values or practice of the company conflict with what your organisation stands for. There are two approaches:

1 Some organisations will accept money from anyone, on the basis that the money can be used to do good.
2 Others define certain types of company that they will not accept support from. Tobacco, alcohol, gambling, armaments, mining/oil industries, polluters and companies operating overseas or at home that underpay their workforce are all areas of business activity that can cause problems.

An ethical stance is of particular importance where the work of the charity is directly connected with the issue.

Decide your ethical policy before approaching companies. It should be agreed by the trustees, perhaps in consultation with staff if they think that is necessary, and recorded.

Sometimes the issues are clear cut. It is relatively easy, for example, for an environmental group to decide whether to accept money from a nuclear power company, or a youth charity from a tobacco or alcohol company. The product relationship with the cause is clear, and all the charity has to do is agree a position on the issue in its ethical policy.

Three organisations that chart the ethical behaviour of companies and which can provide you with the information you need to formulate an ethical donations policy:

1. EIRIS (Ethical Investment Research Services) researches companies on the FTSE All-Share Index. Its main aim is to advise on socially responsible investment. A charge is made for its services.
2. Ethical Consumer Research Association produces *Corporate Critic*, which rates more than 25,000 companies on their ethical performance at: www.corporatecritic.org.
3. Ethical Corporation provides 'business intelligence for sustainability', mainly aimed at big businesses but it also provides information which charities may find useful. It is a subscription service, although some free information is also available; see: www.ethicalcorp.com.

Writing an appeal letter

Put yourself in the position of the company. Why should it want to give its shareholders' funds to you? Why should it choose your charity's appeal ahead of any others it might receive? Think about the benefits it will get from supporting you and mention these in your letter (for sponsorship proposals these benefits will be central to your success or failure). Then consider the following important points:

- Think of a project or aspect of your work that the business sector might like to support. Generally, do not appeal for administration costs or a contribution to an endowment fund. Recognise that companies are likely to be interested in some ideas and not others. For example, a charity supporting people with drug misuse problems might be more likely to get money for education rather than rehabilitation. An appreciation of the kind of projects that a particular company would like to support will be very helpful to you.
- Your letter should be clear and concise. Try to get it all on one side of A4. You can always supply other information as attachments. It should be written clearly and be free from jargon. Someone not familiar with what you are doing should be able to read and understand it and be persuaded to act on it. Give your letter in draft to someone outside your charity to read and comment on before finalising it and sending it out.
- State why you need the money and exactly how it will be spent. The letter itself should be straightforward. It should include the following information: why you think the company might be interested in supporting you – show the connection between your organisation and the company; what your organisation does and some brief background on how it was set up; who the organisation serves; why the organisation needs funds; and how the donation would be spent if received.
- Attempt to communicate the urgency of your appeal. Fundraising is an intensively competitive business; there is a limited amount of money to give away, and you have to ensure that some of it comes your way. If it appears that although you would like the money now it would not matter terribly much if you got it next year, this might encourage the company to consider more pressing applications. But do not give the impression you are fundraising at the last minute. Show that you are professional and have carefully planned your fundraising appeal. You should also try to show that your charity is well-run, efficient and cost-effective in how it operates.
- You should mention why you think the company should support your cause. This could range from specific advantages such as improved customer relations and the good publicity the company will get from supporting your cause to more generalised notions of corporate responsibility and the creation of goodwill in the local community. If the company's generosity is to be made public, for example through advertising or any publicity arising from the gift, then emphasise the goodwill which will accrue to the company.
- Ask for something specific. Many companies, having been persuaded to give, are not sure how much to give. You can ask a corporate funder to give a donation of a specific amount (matched to what you believe its ability to contribute is), or to contribute the cost of a particular item. You can suggest a figure by mentioning what other companies are giving. You can mention a total and say how many donations you will need to achieve this. Do not be unreasonable in your expectations. Just because a company is large and rich, this doesn't mean that it makes large contributions.
- If you can demonstrate some form of 'leverage' this will be an added attraction. Corporate donations on the whole are quite modest, but companies like to feel they are having a substantial impact with the money they spend. If you can show that a small amount of money will enable a much larger project to go ahead, or will release further funds, say, on a matching basis from another source, this will definitely be an advantage.
- Having written a short appeal letter, you can append some background support literature. This should not be a 50-page treatise outlining your latest policies but, like your letter, should be concise and to the point: a record of your achievements, your latest annual report, press cuttings, or even a specially produced leaflet to accompany your appeal.

- Make sure that the letter is addressed to the correct person at the correct address. It pays to do this background research. Keep all the information on file as it will make your job much easier next time.
- Do not assume that every company will give. Make parallel approaches to a number of companies.
- Consider who might be the best person to make the approach or sign the letter. It may not be you but could be a senior business executive from another company which has already supported your organisation. Their endorsement of your work can provide reassurance to other companies.

After the application

If you are unsuccessful in obtaining funding, check if the company is registered for payroll giving and, if it is, ask if you can promote your cause to its employees. In addition, you could try asking again next year (unless the company says that it is not its policy to support your type of organisation or to give to charity at all).

If you are successful, remember to say thank you; this is an elementary courtesy which is too often forgotten. If the company gives you any substantial amount of money, then you should try to keep it in touch with the achievements related to its donation (such as a brief progress report or copies of your annual report or latest publications).

If you have already received a donation, go back again next year. The company has demonstrated that it is interested in what you are doing and in supporting you. It may well do it again next year, especially if you have thanked it for the donation and kept it in touch with how the project developed.

How companies reply to you

Sadly, many companies will not even reply to your appeal. A few may acknowledge receipt of your letter, and occasionally you will get thanked for your request and be told that it is being considered and you will only hear the outcome if you are successful. Larger companies have a system for dealing with charity mail, and most will see it as good PR to send a reply.

Smaller companies which do not give much charitable support will not have the time or the resources to do anything but scan the mail and only consider those requests which stand out.

What sort of reply should you expect? If you do an extensive appeal, you will inevitably get a lot of refusals. These will normally be generic letters apologising and saying that the company cannot support you; occasionally you may get a letter sent to you personally. If your letter is a run-of-the-mill pro forma, you will be lucky to get any response at all. On the other hand, if all goes as you have planned, you could receive a cheque.

Good luck!

How to use this guide

Alphabetical listing of companies

This section gives information on 406 companies from all sectors of industry, gathered from a combination of annual reports and company websites, and supplemented by our further research.

Types of company

A company may be: a public limited company (designated PLC), normally a company with shares quoted on the stock exchange; a privately owned company; or a subsidiary company. If it is a subsidiary it may have retained its own identity for charitable donations and we would include an entry in this guide. Other subsidiaries included are UK-based subsidiaries of an overseas-based company.

Where a company has been recently acquired it may not yet have decided whether it will continue to manage its own charitable donations budget.

Through acquisitions and mergers, companies may now be owned by a holding company, a conglomerate, or a transnational company. You may have to do your own research to link local companies and plants with the head office that may have ultimate control over their donations. The company's annual report, usually available free online or on request, lists subsidiary and associate (less than 50% owned) companies and reports on the activity of the company during the year. We have included a selection of subsidiaries of each company within the entry. However, for many companies this is taken from the latest annual report, which can be several months out of date by the time you decide to approach the company. The *Who Owns Whom* directory (published by GAP Books) also lists subsidiaries of UK companies, and more up-to-date information can often be found on companies' websites.

Interpreting charitable giving information

Where information was available – either from an annual report and accounts, a CSR report or from a website – we have included a figure for total UK community contributions. This includes cash donations as well as the value of employee time and skills and gifts in kind, given in the UK. Where a separate figure for cash donations was available – albeit for the minority of companies in this guide – we have specified it.

A company's present level of donations does not necessarily indicate future commitments. Sending an appeal to comparatively less generous companies may actually persuade them to increase their donations. Certainly if they never receive appeals there will be no outside pressure on them to change their policy, although, in general, if a company is only giving a little your chances of success are reduced.

Normally, a co-ordinated corporate donor will budget a certain sum for its charitable contributions and stick to this amount. Some allocate their entire budget at an annual meeting; others spread contributions throughout the year. Some give to causes they wish to support until the budget is used up and then stop; others continue to give even after the budget is spent if an appeal takes their fancy. If companies reply to your appeal, many will write and say that their budget is fully committed.

The year end is important in that if you get your appeal in soon afterwards, the company may not have spent its charitable budget for the coming year. However, if a company allocates its budget evenly throughout the year and receives a flood of applications at the start of its new financial year, some, which would have been supported later in the year, now miss out. There is no fail-safe answer to this problem. Nevertheless, your chances of success are usually improved by sending the application earlier rather than later in the company's financial year.

How to interpret the donations policy

There are certain standard phrases that are used in the company entries, some of which may need further clarification:

No response to circular appeals

This means that 'Dear Sir/Madam' letters, whether they are hand-signed or use photocopied signatures, are probably not even read, let alone replied to.

Preference for local charities in areas of the company's presence/Preference for appeals relevant to the company's business/Preference for charities where a member of staff is involved

These are more or less self-explanatory. Local charities should check whether appeals can be made locally or must be sent to head office. Any link with the company should be highlighted.

Preferred areas of support are . . .

This information is taken from our most recent research and is subject to change.

Exclusions (no grants are given for . . .)

As above.

Entry layout

The layout used for the entries in this guide is described in the breakdown of the fictional company entry, Fictitious Productions PLC, on page xxxviii. We hope that this example will help users in accessing the information they require on the various types of support that each company offers.

Indexes and activity listings

Most companies state that a link between the company and the charity must exist for any appeal to be considered. To help you prepare a preliminary list of companies to look at further, we have included a listing of the companies in this guide according to their business activity (see page 424).

As a new feature to this edition of the guide, we have also included two indexes: the first listing companies according to the causes they support, and the second according to the types of support they provide (see pages 429 and 446).

Comprehensive search facilities are available at DSC's subscription-based website: www.companygiving.org.uk.

Company memberships

There are companies which, by virtue of membership of one or more specific organisations, have declared an interest in supporting the community. So, even though the companies concerned do not necessarily have an entry in this guide (because they do not meet our criteria), we have listed all current corporate members of Business in the Community (BITC), and London Benchmarking Group (LBG). We have also listed those companies which have achieved BITC's CommunityMark status which recognises companies that take an active and more holistic approach to community investment.

Fictional company entry

Below is a typical company entry, showing the format we have used to present the information obtained from each of the companies. Remember to always check the company's website for information before making an application. You should submit your request in writing, but may wish to ask for details of the grants procedure, check the contact for charitable donations or request a copy of the latest annual report. The latter, along with community support information, may also be obtained via the quoted website address.

Fictitious Productions PLC

The full name of the company is given with the companies listed in alphabetical order.

Spin

Correspondent: A. Grant, CSR Manager, 68 Nowhere Street, Anytown AN6 2LM (tel: 01510 000000; fax: 01511 000000; website: www.fictprod.co.uk)

Some companies in the guide have specialist staff to deal with appeals (in these cases, where available, we have included direct contact details). However, in other companies appeals are dealt with by the company secretary, or public relations or marketing departments. The address refers to the most relevant address; whether this is the company's head office, the office where the CSR department is located, or the company's corporate charity.

Directors: Terence Story, Chair; Shelley Yarn, Chief Executive; Luther Tale (women: 1; men: 2)

We give all available names of the directors and include the ratio of women to men on the board, where known.

Year end	31/12/2015
Turnover	£837,300,000
Pre-tax profit	£292,000,000

Financial statistics: the year end, turnover and pre-tax profit (a figure in brackets denotes a loss). Most relate to 2014/15 or 2015. The figures give an indication of the scale of the company's giving relative to its size.

Nature of business: The company is involved in the production of fictitious information.

The main area of the company's activity. This can be useful if you are looking for a product link.

Company registration number: 116565

The registration number at the Companies House. In the case of a financial institution, such as a Building Society, its FSA number is also included.

Subsidiaries include: Cashflow Industries; False Publications; Sundry Matters; Wage Packet Co.

A sample of the company's subsidiaries is listed here. Full details are usually given within the company's annual accounts.

Brands include: Storytime; Truth Ltd; Dizzy Media; Blank Page.

A sample of the company's brands is given here. Full details are available on the company's website.

UK employees: 3,872

Total employees: 7,689

The number of total employees and UK employees, where information is available.

Focus of giving: general charitable purposes.

We list the company's charitable preferences.

Membership: BITC, LBG

Indicates whether the company is a member of Business in the Community and LBG.

Community involvement	✓
Community contributions	✓
CSR report	✓
CSR or charity committee	✓
Cash donations declared	✓
Charity of the Year	✓
Employee-led support	✓
Gifts in kind	✓
Matched funding	✓
Overseas giving	✓
Payroll giving	✓
Pro bono	✓
Sponsorship	✓

These tick boxes provide an overview of the company's CSR activities.

Charitable donations

Cash UK (latest available):	2015	£420,000
Total UK (cash and in kind):	2015	£575,000
Cash worldwide:	2015	£1,234,000
Total worldwide (cash and in kind):	2015	£7,868,000

Where available, figures for total UK and total worldwide contributions are given and these include the value of in-kind giving, good-cause sponsorship, secondments and so on.

Community involvement

The company supports local enterprise agencies and considers secondment of employees to local economic development initiatives.

This provides an overview of the company's community support, detailing preferred causes and any geographical areas that are favoured.

Main locations

Bristol (head office), Grimsby, Liverpool, Perth.

We indicate where the company's main areas of activity are.

Corporate giving

The company's community contributions totalled £575,000 in 2015. This included in-kind giving, the cost of secondments and charitable donations totalling £420,000.

Beneficiaries included: Any Town LGBT Network (for information leaflets), Perth Parent & Toddler Association (towards play equipment) and the local wildlife trust.

Quotes total cash donations or community contributions made.

Examples of grants and their size, where known, are listed. Large grants are often a good indicator of the company's strategic priorities.

In-kind support

The company donates surplus or used furniture/equipment to local causes.

Some companies give gifts in kind, which can be anything from used stock to valuable pro bono work.

Employee-led support

A charity is selected each year to benefit from employee fundraising, with the company making a contribution by way of matched funding.

Payroll giving

A scheme is operated by the company.

Many company employees give time and money to local causes, including fundraising and volunteering. If a payroll giving scheme is operated, we state so.

Commercially led support

Sponsorship

The arts: The typical sponsorship range is from £1,000 to £25,000. The company sponsors Southport Sinfonietta and supported music festivals in Grimsby and Perth.

Covers good-cause sponsorship, if undertaken, and will include a contact, if different from the main correspondent. Provides information on commercially led promotions, if applicable.

Exclusions

No response is given to circular appeals. No grants are given for fundraising events, purely denominational religious appeals, local appeals not in areas of the company's presence, large national appeals, overseas projects, political activities or individuals. Non-commercial advertising is not supported. The company does not sponsor individuals or travel.

Lists any areas, subjects or types of grants the company will not consider.

Applications

Apply in writing to the correspondent. Applications are considered by a donations committee which meets three times a year.

Includes how to apply and when to submit an application. We also state whether there is further information available from the company.

3i Group PLC

Financial services

Correspondent: See 'Applications' for contacts, 16 Palace Street, London SW1E 5JD (tel: 020 7975 3131; website: www.3i.com)

Directors: Caroline Banszky; David Hutchison; Jonathan Asquith; Julia Wilson, Group Finance Director; Martine Verluyten; Peter Grosch; Simon Borrows, Chief Executive; Simon Thompson, Chair; Stephen Daintith (women: 3; men: 6)

Year end	31/03/2016
Pre-tax profit	£819,000,000

Nature of business: 3i is an investment company with three complementary businesses (private equity, infrastructure and debt management), specialising in core investment markets in Northern Europe and North America.

Company registration number: 1142830

Subsidiary undertakings include: Action; Element Materials Technology; Inspecta.

UK employees: 281

Total employees: 281

Focus of giving: Education, heritage, housing, homelessness, arts, culture, poverty and social exclusion, children, young people, community/social welfare.

Accredited Living Wage Employer	✓
Community involvement	✓
Community contributions	✓
Company reports on anti-slavery	✓
CSR report	✓
Cash donations declared	✓
Charity partner(s)	✓
Employee-led support	✓
FTSE 100	✓
Matched funding	✓
Payroll giving	✓

Charitable donations

Cash UK (latest available):	2016	£324,000
Total UK (cash and in kind):	2016	£324,000
Cash worldwide:	2016	£324,000
Total worldwide (cash and in kind):	2016	£324,000

Community involvement

From June 2016, 3i will be supporting the Snowdon Trust, a charity that provides grants to people with physical disabilities and students with sensory impairments studying in the UK, in further or higher education, or those training towards employment. The grants will help cover additional costs that students incur as a result of their disability and which available statutory funding does not cover.

Case study

Taken from the 2016 CSR report:

> ***Community Links***
> Community Links is based in Newham, one of the most deprived boroughs in London. It provides 'early action' work, which includes running youth clubs and safe play areas through to providing advice on debt, welfare benefits, form filling etc. It also carries out specialist intervention work when people are experiencing severe problems such as exclusion from school and prolonged periods of unemployment. In addition to our regular contribution to this charity, 3i's London-based employees have been contributing to the Community Links Christmas toy appeal for a number of years and donated 85 presents to the charity's 2015 appeal.

Main locations

Main UK location: London.

Worldwide: Amsterdam; Frankfurt; Madrid; Mumbai; New York; Paris; Singapore; Stockholm.

Community contributions

The group focuses its charitable activities on individuals who are disadvantaged, young people and education. Charities are supported on the basis of their effectiveness and impact. According to the 2016 CSR report, charitable giving for the year to 31 March 2016 totalled £324,000.

Beneficiaries included: Community Links; Historic Royal Palaces; National Youth Orchestra; and The Passage.

Employee-led support

Staff contribute via the Give As You Earn scheme in the UK, administered by the Charities Aid Foundation. 3i employees donated £37,000 through this scheme in the year to 31 March 2016 (taken from the Corporate Responsibility Report 2016).

Matched funding

3i has a policy of matching the amount raised by UK staff through sponsorship by family and friends of their fundraising efforts for UK-registered charities. 3i contributed £14,000 in matching donations in the year to 31 March 2016. It is not clear if this amount has been included in the total contribution figure of £324,000.

Exclusions

No support is given for political appeals or individuals.

Applications

Apply in writing to the correspondent/s below, referenced 'Community support'.

Toby Bates, Interim Communications Director, tel: 020 7975 3032, email: toby.bates@3i.com, or: Kathryn van der Kroft, Communications Director, tel: 020 7975 3021, kathryn.vanderkroft@3i.com.

3M United Kingdom PLC

Chemicals and plastics

Correspondent: Communities Team, 3M Community, 3M United Kingdom PLC, 3M Centre, Cain Road, Bracknell RG12 8HT (tel: 0870 536 0036; website: www.3M.com/uk)

Directors: Donald Gray, General Manager, Finance; Paul Keel, Managing Director; Paul Williams; Stella Heggarty (women: 2; men: 2)

Year end	31/12/2015
Turnover	£516,039,000
Pre-tax profit	£21,096,000

Nature of business: 3M is fundamentally a science-based company. Products manufactured in the UK include coated abrasives, personal safety equipment, adhesive tapes, industrial microbiology products, drug delivery systems, high performance coatings, secure documents, passport readers and imaging systems.

Company registration number: 1123045

Subsidiary undertakings include: 3M United Kingdom PLC is a wholly owned subsidiary of 3M Company, a company incorporated in the United States, as the ultimate parent company and controlling party.

Brands include: Post-it; Scotch; Scotch-Brite; Scotchgard.

Focus of giving: Education, environment, poverty and social exclusion, community/social welfare.

Membership: BITC, LBG

Community involvement	✓
Community contributions	✓
Company reports on anti-slavery	✓
Cash donations declared	✓
Employee-led support	✓

Charitable donations

Cash UK (latest available):	2015	£261,000
Total UK (cash and in kind):	2015	£261,000
Cash worldwide:	2015	£261,000
Total worldwide (cash and in kind):	2015	£261,000

Community involvement

The company believes that commercial success and corporate responsibility are inextricably linked and, therefore, its contribution is towards communities in which it has operations. It should be noted that the community programme is structured and not about responding to general requests. The website states that the company will 'support organisations that help communities help themselves'.

National programme

As 3M is a technology company, a large number of its employees hold qualifications in STEM (science, technology, engineering and maths) subjects. It is recognised that too few pupils – in particular female students – are staying with these subjects beyond GCSE. 3M hopes to redress that in some way by working with educational specialists in order to provide free online educational resources that help make these subjects real and relevant to pupils.

This programme involves partnering with schools local to 3M's major sites; the donation of in-kind gifts of 3M products and services; visits to (and the use of) 3M facilities; encouragement of employee volunteering – particularly STEM Ambassadors; matching employees' fundraising achievements, and creating free online teaching resources that can be used by schools throughout the UK and Ireland.

STEM Ambassadors go into school to show that a wide range of interesting careers are open to people with STEM qualifications.

3M Careerwise

The 3M Careerwise programme provides resources for children to help them think about what careers they would like to pursue and what skills and qualifications they will need to get them there.

Main locations

Aberdeen; Atherstone; Aycliffe; Bangor; Bedford; Bridgend; Clitheroe; Daventry; Dublin; Gorseinon; London; Loughborough; Manchester; North Allerton; Manchester.

Community contributions

In 2015 the amount contributed in charitable donations by the UK company was £261,000. Donations were broken down as follows:

Education	£217,500
Other	£29,500
Relief of suffering	£13,500
Environment	£660

Employee-led support

Employee volunteering

3M holds an annual Global Volunteer Day. Employees in the UK helped local schools, a hospice, a food bank and a wildlife trust.

Applications

For more information, use the online facility at 'Contact Us' and reference 'Community'.

AA PLC

Insurance, motors and accessories

Correspondent: Catherine Hammond, Fanum House, Basing View, Basingstoke RG21 4EA (email: publicaffairs@theaa.com; website: www.theaa.com/public_affairs/aa-charitable-trust-for-road-safety-and-the-environment.html)

Directors: Andrew Blowers; Andrew Miller; Bob McKenzie, Executive Chair; John Leach; Mark Millar; Martin Clarke, Chief Financial Officer; Simon Breakwell; Suzi Williams (women: 1; men: 7)

Year end	31/01/2016
Turnover	£973,000,000
Pre-tax profit	£17,000,000

Nature of business: The AA is a motoring association which provides services including roadside assistance, motor and home insurance, and home services. The AA operates in the UK and in Ireland.

Subsidiary undertakings include: AA The Driving School Agency Ltd; AA Corporation Ltd; Automobile Association Insurance Services Ltd.

Total employees: 7,862

Focus of giving: Armed forces; education; environment; health; road safety.

Community involvement	✓
Community contributions	✓
CSR report	✓
Directors have other relevant posts	✓
AF Covenant	✓
Armed forces personnel	✓
Employee-led support	✓
Gifts in kind	✓

Community involvement

The AA's community and charitable work is carried out by The AA Charitable Trust for Road Safety and the Environment (Charity Commission no. 1125119). AA employees fundraise for a range of national charities.

The AA Charitable Trust for Road Safety and the Environment

The trust was set up in 2008 and is primarily funded by donations from the group. According to the trust's website, its objectives are:

> The preservation and protection of human life and health by the prevention of personal injury to, and death of, individuals on roads and in motor vehicles in the United Kingdom in particular but not exclusively through:
>
> - Educating road users in road safety
> - Campaigning on issues of road safety
> - Promoting understanding and awareness of road safety and eco-driving to reduce environmental impact of motoring and to protect the environment

The trust is not a grant-making charity but rather runs a number of programmes which support its objects. The trust's page on the AA website describes its recent initiatives:

- **Improving road safety**: The trust has created a range of training initiatives, with the aim of improving drivers' skills and confidence. These include free courses such as Drive Motorway, Drive Confident and Drive Smart. It also supports events, including Thames Valley Police's Safe Drive Stay Alive roadshow
- **Driving lessons for young people in care:** In collaboration with the University of Bristol and Bristol Council, the trust provided four young people from within the care system the opportunity to take driving lessons, with the aim of analysing the effect on their confidence and self-esteem. The AA website describes that the scheme is being 'rolled-out in Newcastle, Medway and Westminster and a further pilot is planned in Bristol'
- **Campaigning**: Current AA campaigns include 'Think Bikes', which has been adopted in 24 countries. During 2016 the AA also worked on and supported campaigns in areas such as motorway hard-shoulder safety, drink-driving, and the UN Decade of Action on Road Safety

Possible future plans for the trust's work are briefly detailed on the website and include motorcycle safety and drug-driving. However, the website also states: 'The AA Charitable Trust for Road Safety and the Environment would be pleased to receive ideas/proposals from AA Members for possible future schemes aligned with its charitable objectives.'

Directors with other relevant posts

Andrew Blowers: trustee at CVQO.

Main locations

The group operates across the UK, but has eight office sites: Basingstoke (head office); Cardiff; Cheadle; Leicestershire; London; Newcastle; Oldbury; Preston.

Community contributions

A figure for charitable donations was not included in the group's annual report and accounts for 2016.

Employee-led support

Employee fundraising

In the 2015/16 financial year, AA employees raised more than £150,000 for national charities such as the Children's Heart Unit Fund and the Royal National Institute of Blind People. Funds and blankets were also collected for the Nepal earthquake appeal. At a local level, employees also raised funds and took part with events for smaller charities. The Corporate Responsibility report also explains that many AA employees support the automotive industry charity, BEN. Activities during the year included litter clean-ups, charity bike rides and, for some patrols, taking part in the Help for Heroes 4x4 European Rally.

Commercially led support

Armed Forces

The AA works with armed forces charity The Poppy Factory to help ex-service people who have been wounded, injured or ill back into work by matching their skills and qualities with positions within the business. According to the group's annual report and accounts for 2016, more than 60 armed forces veterans were employed within the preceding year alone. As a signatory of the UK Government's Armed Forces Covenant, the AA received a Gold Award in the Armed Forces Covenant Employer Recognition Scheme.

Applications

Ideas and proposals for possible future schemes within the objectives of the AA Charitable Trust for Road Safety and the Environment can be sent by email to publicaffairs@theaa.com.

Abbott Mead Vickers – BBDO Ltd

Advertising/marketing

Correspondent: Company Secretary, 151 Marylebone Road, London NW1 5QE (tel: 020 7616 3500; website: www.amvbbdo.com)

Directors: Colin Fleming; Ian Pearman; Priscilla Snowball (women: 1; men: 2)

Year end	31/12/2015
Turnover	£118,000,000
Pre-tax profit	£19,300,000

Nature of business: Abbott Mead Vickers BBDO is an advertising agency that works with over 85 brands.

Company registration number: 1935786

Subsidiary undertakings include: The company is a subsidiary undertaking of Omnicom Group Inc., incorporated in the USA.

Focus of giving: General charitable purposes.

Community involvement	✓
Community contributions	✓
Cash donations declared	✓
Payroll giving	✓

Charitable donations

Cash UK (latest available):	2015	£98,000
Total UK (cash and in kind):	2015	£98,000
Cash worldwide:	2015	£98,000
Total worldwide (cash and in kind):	2015	£98,000

Community involvement

Unfortunately we could not find any useful, relevant information regarding this company's charitable giving apart from its payroll giving scheme.

Main locations

The Abbott Mead Vickers – BBDO UK office is in London.

Community contributions

In 2015 the company made charitable donations of £98,000.

Employee-led support

The company have received a platinum award for its payroll giving scheme which is administered by the Charities Aid Foundation.

Applications

Apply in writing to the correspondent.

Aberdeen Asset Management PLC

Financial services

Correspondent: Aberdeen Asset Management Charitable Foundation, 10 Queen's Terrace, Aberdeen AB10 1YG (tel: 01224 631999; fax: 01224 647010; email: foundation.uk@aberdeen-asset.com; website: www.aberdeen-asset.co.uk)

Directors: Akira Suzuki; Andrew Laing; Bill Rattray; Gerhard Fusenig; Hugh Young; Julie Chakraverty; Jutta af Rosenborg; Martin Gilbert; Richard Mully; Rod MacRae; Simon Troughton, Chair; Val Rahmani (women: 3; men: 9)

Year end	27/11/2015
Turnover	£1,169,000,000
Pre-tax profit	£491,600,000

Nature of business: Aberdeen Asset Management PLC is a global investment management group, managing assets for both institutional and retail clients from some 38 offices in 25 countries.

Company registration number: 82015

Subsidiary undertakings include: Aberdeen Asset Management Asia Ltd; Aberdeen Asset Managers Ltd; Aberdeen Asset Management Inc.

Total employees: 2,800

Focus of giving: General charitable purposes, health, ill health, older people, overseas projects, children, young people, community/social welfare.

Membership: BITC

Accredited Living Wage Employer	✓
Community involvement	✓
Community contributions	✓
CSR report	✓
CSR or charity committee	✓
Directors have other relevant posts	✓
Corporate charity	✓
Gifts in kind	✓
Humanitarian aid: overseas	✓
Matched funding	✓
Overseas giving	✓
Payroll giving	✓
Sponsorship	✓

Charitable donations

Total worldwide (cash and in kind):	2015	£1,600,000

Community involvement

The company's website gives the following details:

> Each regional office nominates and administrates its own charity committee with new members joining on an annual basis. The committee consists of a group of individuals across the business who manage volunteering and fundraising activities and are responsible for selecting local charities to support with the funding allocated for each office by the Charitable Foundation.
>
> Each regional charity committee manages the local funding applications for the Charitable Foundation along with the organisation of office based fundraising events. This includes cakes sales, wine auctions, pub quizzes and challenge events such as 10k runs. All employees are also entitled to match funding for personal fundraising activities which is administered by the local charity committee.

Aberdeen Asset Management Charitable Foundation

Most of the company's charitable cash giving appears to be delivered through its corporate charity Aberdeen Asset Management Charitable Foundation (OSCR no. SC042597).

The company's website states:

> The Foundation seeks to develop partnerships with charities tackling the educational needs of disadvantaged young people in emerging market countries.
>
> The Foundation will invest in a different emerging market each year typically over a three year period and partner with charities that deliver real change on the ground through long-term investments. As part of the partnerships, a group of Aberdeen employees are able to volunteer at each of the projects.

Previous partners of the foundation have included: Action for Brazil's Children; SeeBeyondBorders; Afrikids; Childhope.

Case study – local community project

This example of Hellebro project in Copenhagen was taken from the Corporate Responsibility Report 2015:

> The Hellebro association was established in April 2015 by Aberdeen, in close partnership with a number of local homeless charities. It has been built on in-kind contributions from Aberdeen's business partners and a tremendous effort from local volunteers. Hellebro provides the only shelter in Greater Copenhagen for young homeless people and is open in the evenings on every week day. With the number of young homeless people between 18 and 29 years of age doubling every year in Denmark, around 3,500 young people in Greater Copenhagen are currently not able to focus on obtaining a job or their education

> while they do not have a permanent home.
>
> At Hellebro, these young people are welcomed into a safe, friendly environment to cook and prepare meals; take a shower; wash their clothes or use the internet café to seek employment and apply for an apartment. The Aberdeen Charitable Foundation's donation covers the operating costs throughout the year. In addition, Aberdeen employees are also actively involved in the daily operation of Hellebro, contributing their time, skills and warm clothes to help homeless young people endure the cold Danish winters.

Directors with other relevant posts

Julie Chakraverty (Senior Independent Director) is a trustee of The Girls Day School Trust (Charity Commission no. 306983). The trust aims to extend excellence and innovation in dynamic educational settings and maintain leadership in the education of young people, principally women.

Main locations

Main UK locations: Aberdeen; Edinburgh; London.

There are also a number of locations worldwide.

Community contributions

In 2015 the company's charitable contribution was declared as £1.6 million with the qualification that 'this includes donations made by the foundation (Aberdeen Asset Management Charitable Foundation), Aberdeen PLC and GAYE employer contributions, but excludes unspent contributions made by the PLC to the foundation'.

In-kind support

Support is given by the company to charities and good causes by the provision of volunteers, staff receiving time off work for this purpose.

The company also provides overseas volunteering opportunities to the global workforce at Aberdeen. This allows employees to see the impact that the corporate charity is having. Employees so far have volunteered in Brazil, Cambodia and Ghana.

Employee-led support

Volunteering

At a local level, committees in the group's global offices supported a wide range of charities, all of which were selected for the positive impact they have on the areas where employees live and work. In 2015 the group participated in Global Give and Gain Day with over 200 employees from 20 cities taking part in a range of local community projects. In 2016 over 400 employees volunteered from 24 of the company's global offices. The company encourages all employees to volunteer and fundraise for charitable projects and all permanent employees are provided with two days of leave for volunteering per annum.

Commercially led support

Aberdeen's sponsorship

The company sponsors a variety of activities from sporting fixtures to cultural events to demonstrate it supports the community and encourages excellence. Sponsorship includes that for: Golf Ambassadors and Swiss Ski Schools.

Corporate charity

Aberdeen Asset Management Charitable Foundation (OSCR no. SC042597).

Exclusions

The foundation does not support political causes, parties or organisations or charities with a religious focus.

Applications

It appears that the majority of the company's giving is delivered through its foundation, the Aberdeen Asset Management Charitable Foundation (OSCR no. SC042597).

Aberdeen Asset Management Charitable Foundation

The funding criteria and application forms are available from the company's website and once completed should be emailed to: foundation.uk@aberdeen-asset.com.

Note:

- Successful applicants will be notified within a three-month period following application
- Due to the volume of requests received, the foundation will not be able to respond to all unsuccessful applicants
- If a grant is awarded, an annual impact assessment form will be required to be completed

Ensure you attach a PDF copy of your latest annual review and do not send DVDs or CDs.

The company's website also states:

> As a business we value the communities in which we operate and invest, recognising the benefits we gain from them as well as the potential impact we can have. The Foundation therefore allocates a proportion of its funding to the local communities in with Aberdeen employees live and work.

Addleshaw Goddard LLP

Legal

Correspondent: Rachel Williams, CSR Manger, Milton Gate, 60 Chiswell Street, London EC1Y 4AG (tel: 020 7606 8855/ 0113 209 7659; email: rachel.williams@ addleshawgoddard.com; website: www. addleshawgoddard.com)

Directors: Adrian Collins; Andrew Smith; John Joyce; Michael Leftley; Monica Burch; Paul Salsbury; Susan Garrett; William Wastie (women: 2; men: 6)

Year end	30/04/2015
Turnover	£186,946,000
Pre-tax profit	£60,079,000

Nature of business: The provision of legal services.

Company registration number: OC318149

Focus of giving: Education, poverty and social exclusion, community/social welfare.

Membership: BITC

Community involvement	✓
Community contributions	✓
Company reports on anti-slavery	✓
CSR report	✓
CSR or charity committee	✓
Charity of the Year	✓
Corporate charity	✓
Employee-led support	✓
Gifts in kind	✓
Overseas giving	✓
Pro bono	✓

Charitable donations

Cash UK (latest available):	2015	£50,000
Total UK (cash and in kind):	2015	£50,000
Cash worldwide:	2015	£50,000
Total worldwide (cash and in kind):	2015	£50,000

Community involvement

The Addleshaw Goddard Charitable Trust (Charity Commission no. 286887)

The trust was established in 2003 and receives most of its funding from the company. Support is given to good causes and local CSR-related projects.

Community initiatives

Community initiatives are focused on furthering social inclusion through education. Projects have included primary school reading projects and senior school mentoring programmes.

Charity of the Year

Each office nominates and fundraises for its own Charity of the Year.

Main locations

London, Leeds and Manchester.

Community contributions

In 2014/15 the company donated £50,000 to its corporate charity.

In-kind support

Pro bono work is provided in partnership with Law Works.

Employee-led support

Employee volunteering

Trainees have the opportunity to volunteer on a project before they start work. Recently employees have been volunteering for Habitat for Humanity, a charity that builds homes in financially developing countries.

Corporate charity

The Addleshaw Goddard Charitable Trust (Charity Commission no. 286887).

Applications

Apply in writing to the correspondent.

Admiral Group PLC

Insurance

Correspondent: Mark Waters, Company Secretary, Admiral Group PLC, Ty Admiral, David Street, Cardiff CF10 2EH (tel: 0871 882 8282; website: www.admiralgroup.co.uk)

Directors: Alistair Lyons, Chair; Annette Court; Colin Holmes; David Stevens; Geraint Jones, Chief Financial Officer; Jean Park; Justine Roberts; Manning Rountree; Owen Clarke; Penny James (women: 4; men: 6)

Year end	31/12/2015
Turnover	£2,104,600,000
Pre-tax profit	£376,800,000

Nature of business: The group's core business is selling and underwriting private car insurance in the UK through four brands – Admiral, Bell, Diamond and elephant.co.uk.

Company registration number: 3849958

Subsidiary undertakings include: Admiral Insurance Company Ltd; Admiral Insurance (Gibraltar) Ltd; Able Insurance Services Ltd.

Brands include: Diamond; elephant.co.uk; Confused.com.

Focus of giving: General charitable purposes, animal welfare, arts, culture, sport, recreation.

Community involvement	✓
Community contributions	✓
CSR report	✓
Directors have other relevant posts	✓
Cash donations declared	✓
Employee-led support	✓
FTSE 100	✓
Matched funding	✓
Payroll giving	✓
Sponsorship	✓

Charitable donations

Cash UK (latest available):	2015	£196,000
Cash worldwide:	2015	£196,000

Community involvement

This group would appear to have a very practical approach to giving. It draws its selection of beneficiary organisations by consulting with its staff members and taking the initiative for their and their families' fundraising efforts. Its sponsorship deals benefit staff in a very personal way (see 'Commercially led support') as well as marketing the company. Admiral Group states that it sponsors many different events in South Wales for a number of reasons:

- To support the community of South Wales of which it is a part
- To support events that staff might have an interest in
- To reflect Admiral's vibrancy and fun culture
- To raise its profile as a good employer with the community

Directors with other relevant posts

David Stevens (Chief Operating Officer) is currently a trustee of the Waterloo Foundation (Charity Commission no. 1117535), the charity which supports world development in the poorest countries.

Case study

The following case study has been taken from the company's 2015 CSR report:

> Admiral Community Chest is a fund set up to provide funding for charities and local organisations which our people and their families are involved with. The Chest has been running for over ten years and in that time we have been able to contribute to over 700 charities and organisations. In 2015 we donated £100,000 to over 180 charities and organisations through the Chest. This year we helped Home-Start Cardiff by purchasing vital baby safety equipment and helped fund a summer production of West Side Story by Superstars in the Making (Barry) by donating money towards printing flyers, posters, banners and hospitality.

Main locations

UK locations: Cardiff; Newport; Swansea.

Worldwide: Canada; France; India; Italy; Spain; USA.

Community contributions

In 2015 Admiral Group donated £196,000 to local and national charities and provided £948,000 to sponsor events and organisations. We have taken the figure of £196,000 as the company's overall charitable giving figure.

Employee-led support

According to the group's website: 'Our employees also do a lot of fundraising in work for charities close to their hearts, as well as volunteering for local organisations. Through Community Chest the company will match the money our staff raise for charities.'

Matched funding

In 1998, CEO Henry Engelhardt set up Admiral Community Chest to help staff and their families who are involved with local charities, clubs and organisations. Employees' fundraising endeavours are matched by the group from this community fund.

The 2015 CSR report explains that the group plays a positive role in the community through charitable giving and sponsorship of local community partnerships, promotes payroll giving and provides matched funding.

Commercially led support

Sponsorship

The group's sponsorship includes that for the Welsh Rugby Union who display the Admiral logo on their national team jersey. The group is able to secure some staff benefits through this sponsorship such as free rugby tickets and opportunities to attend training sessions and meet players.

The group also sponsors Chapter Arts Centre and NoFit State Circus both based in Cardiff. Again, staff members can benefit from discounts and visits.

The group have teamed with the Road Safety Team to raise awareness of road safety in the Swansea area, helping to keep children in the area safe when going to and from school.

Exclusions

No support is given for local appeals not in areas of the company's presence or political appeals.

Applications

Apply in writing to the correspondent referenced 'CR/Community'. Note, however, that local support tends to be directed towards organisations involved with Admiral employees or their immediate family.

Adnams PLC

Hotels, brewers/distillers

Correspondent: Rebecca Abrahall, Charity Administrator, Sole Bay Brewery, Southwold, Suffolk IP18 6JW (tel: 01502 727200; fax: 01502 727201; email: charity@adnams.co.uk; website: www.adnams.co.uk)

Directors: Dr Andy Woods, Chief Executive; Stephen Pugh, Finance Director; Dr Karen Hester; Nicky Dulieu; Bridget McIntyre; Steven Sharp; Guy Heald; Jonathan Adnams, Chair (women: 3; men: 5)

Year end	31/12/2015
Turnover	£65,698,000
Pre-tax profit	£4,093,000

Nature of business: The principal activities of the company are brewing, retailing and wholesaling beer, wines, spirits and minerals; and property ownership and hotel management.

Company registration number: 31114

Subsidiary undertakings include: Adnams Bio Energy Ltd.

Focus of giving: Education, environment, health, ill health, arts, culture, sport, recreation, bricks and mortar appeals.

Membership: BITC

Community involvement	✓
Community contributions	✓
CSR report	✓
Corporate charity	✓
Market-led giving	✓

Charitable donations

Cash UK (latest available):	2015	£42,000
Total UK (cash and in kind):	2015	£42,000
Cash worldwide:	2015	£42,000
Total worldwide (cash and in kind):	2015	£42,000

Community involvement

The Adnams Community Trust (Charity Commission no. 1000203)
The company's charitable giving is channelled through this, its associated charity.

The company has electronic Pennies charity boxes in all its stores and raised £40,000 from these in 2015.

Main locations
Southwold, Suffolk.

Community contributions

Adnams gives a percentage of its annual profits to charitable causes through The Adnams Community Trust. Donations to the trust during the year amounted to £42,000.

Commercially led support

During the year a limited-edition beer Prop Hop was brewed to support the Matt Hampson Foundation. Its release was timed to coincide with the 2015 Rugby World Cup.

Corporate charity

The Adnams Community Trust (Charity Commission no. 1000203).

Exclusions

The Adnams Community Trust does not normally make grants to religious organisations or private clubs unless these can demonstrate that the purpose of the grant is for something of clear public benefit, accessible to all. No grants are made to individuals, although public bodies and charities may apply on behalf of individuals.

Applications

An application form is available from the Charity Administrator via details given at 'Correspondent'.

Aggregate Industries Ltd

Building materials, quarrying

Correspondent: Local Community Liaison Group, Bardon Hall, Copt Oak Road, Markfield, Leicestershire LE67 9PJ (tel: 01530 816600; website: www.aggregate.com)

Directors: Francois Petry, Chief Executive Officer; John Bowater, Chief Financial Officer; Roland Köhler (women: 0; men: 3)

Year end	31/12/2015
Pre-tax profit	£32,638

Nature of business: Aggregate Industries and its subsidiaries are engaged in the exploitation of land and mineral reserves principally for the supply of heavy building materials for construction activities. Operating at locations across the UK, Channel Islands, Norway and Northern Europe it employs over 3,500 people.

Aggregate Industries Ltd itself is a holding company with no employees. In 2005 it became part of the Holcim Group which is incorporated in Switzerland.

Company registration number: 5655952

Subsidiary undertakings include: Aggregate Industries UK Ltd; Evered Ltd; International Aggregates Ltd.

Focus of giving: Education, environment, community/social welfare.

Community involvement	✓
Community contributions	✓
Company reports on anti-slavery	✓
CSR report	✓
CSR or charity committee	✓
Employee-led support	✓
Gifts in kind	✓

Charitable donations

Total UK (cash and in kind):	2015	£140,500
Total worldwide (cash and in kind):	2015	£140,500

Community involvement

Community initiatives
The company carries out a number of community engagement initiatives at its quarries. During the year there were 20 visits from schools to Callow Rock quarry covering topics such as local industrial history and safety. Work experience students were taken from local schools. A new 5km nature trail was also opened at Croft quarry in Leicestershire.

Main locations
The group has sites throughout the UK. Community giving seems to be focused around the group's headquarters in Leicestershire.

Community contributions

In 2015 the group donated over £140,000 to local groups through labour, materials, skills and funding.

In-kind support

Over £30,000 worth of materials and labour were donated towards a new national standard BMX track in Leicestershire.

Employee-led support

There is an agreement with all UK colleagues that every year they can spend a day volunteering in the company's time.

Applications

Apply in writing to your local site addressed 'Community Liaison Group' and referenced 'Community Giving'.

Allen & Overy LLP

Legal

Correspondent: See 'Applications', Bishops Square, One Bishops Square, London E1 6AD (tel: 020 3088 0000; website: www.allenovery.com)

Directors: Andrew Brammer; David Morley; Genevieve Tennant; Jason Haines; Richard Grove; Wim Dejonghe (women: 1; men: 5)

Year end	30/04/2015
Turnover	£1,280,000,000
Pre-tax profit	£570,000,000

Nature of business: International law firm.

Company registration number: OC306763

Total employees: 4,949

Focus of giving: Human rights, education.

Membership: BITC

Community involvement	✓
Community contributions	✓
Company reports on anti-slavery	✓
CSR report	✓
Charity partner(s)	✓
Corporate charity	✓
Employee-led support	✓
Gifts in kind	✓
Pro bono	✓

Charitable donations

Cash UK (latest available):	2015	£269,000
Cash worldwide:	2015	£269,000
Total worldwide (cash and in kind):	2015	£10,869,000

Community involvement

The company's pro bono work is focused on two major themes – access to justice and access to education and employment.

Access to justice
Rule of Law – Allen & Overy work with emerging economies to develop the rule of law.

Free legal advice – free legal advice is provided to vulnerable people in a number of countries.

Human Rights Working Group – pro bono support is provided to human rights charities such as Liberty, Amicus and Fair Trials International

Microfinance and Social Investment Group – advice is provided to microfinance institutions and social enterprises in developing economies around the world.

Access to education and employment

Artbeat – students in London and New York are given the opportunity to work with professional artists to create a range of art to be displayed at Allen & Overy's offices and their schools.

Smart Start – a work experience scheme that gives year 12 students from non-privileged backgrounds the opportunity to work at Allen & Overy's offices for a week.

The Allen & Overy Foundation (Charity Commission no. 1153738)
The foundation is funded by contributions from all Allen & Overy partners around the world. Around 75% of funds are allocated to support local projects with the remaining 25% being donated to international causes.

UK locations
London

Community contributions

In 2014/15 pro bono support equivalent to £10.6 million was given by the company. Donations totalling £269,000 were also given to The Allen & Overy Foundation.

In-kind support

In 2014/15 Allen & Overy provided £10.6 million in pro bono legal support.

Corporate charity

The Allen & Overy Foundation (Charity Commission no. 1153738).

Applications

Pro bono, Artbeat and Smart Start
Apply in writing to the relevant contact:

Emma Turnbull, Artbeat contact, 020 3088 3820, Emma.Turnbull@allenovery.com

Kate Cavelle, Head of Pro Bono and Community Involvement, 020 3088 2198, kate.cavelle@allenovery.com

Sue Wisbey, Smart Start contact, Sue.Wisbey@AllenOvery.com

The Allen & Overy Foundation (Charity Commission no. 1153738)
Details of how to apply can be found on the foundation's website: www.allenovery.com/corporate-responsibility/charitable-giving/Pages/default.aspx.

Alliance Boots Holdings Ltd

Healthcare, pharmaceuticals

Correspondent: Julie Lawrence, Trust Administrator, 1 Thane Road West, Nottingham NG2 3AA (tel: 0345 070 8090; email: Julie.Lawrence@boots.co.uk; website: www.boots-uk.com/csr)

Directors: Aidan Clare; Frank Standish; Martin Delve (women: 0; men: 3)

Year end	31/08/2015
Pre-tax profit	£1,481,000,000

Nature of business: Alliance Boots Holdings Ltd is a holding company. Boots UK is part of the Retail Pharmacy International Division of Walgreens Boots Alliance, Inc. (Nasdaq: WBA), the first global pharmacy-led, health and well-being enterprise. Boots became a subsidiary of the new company, Walgreens Boots Alliance, on 31 December 2014.

Company registration number: 4452715

Subsidiary undertakings include: Boots UK Ltd; Boots Opticians; Aroma Actives Ltd.

Focus of giving: Education, health, ill health, local groups, armed forces, community/social welfare.

Community involvement	✓
Community contributions	✓
Armed forces personnel	✓
Charity partner(s)	✓
Community Mark	✓
Corporate charity	✓
Employee-led support	✓
Matched funding	✓
Payroll giving	✓

Charitable donations

Cash UK (latest available):	2015	£354,000
Total UK (cash and in kind):	2015	£354,000
Cash worldwide:	2015	£354,000
Total worldwide (cash and in kind):	2015	£354,000

Community involvement

Note: All of the information contained herein refers to Boots UK.

Charity partners
In the UK Boots is working with two key charity partners – Macmillan Cancer Support and BBC Children in Need (which it has supported for a number of years).

Employability
Boots runs several employability schemes to support people into work. These include work experience, apprentice and graduate schemes and a military work placement scheme.

The Boots Charitable Trust (Charity Commission no. 1045927)
The trust is an independent grant-maker established in the 1970's and wholly funded by the company. Currently the trust's giving is focused in the county of Nottinghamshire, in recognition of Boots' long history with the area.

The trust gives to charities and voluntary organisations that benefit Nottingham and Nottinghamshire. The trust's website states that grants are given in the areas of health, lifelong learning, community development and social care.

Boots Benevolent Fund (Charity Commission no. 1046559)
The Boots Benevolent Fund is a registered charity which provides financial help and support to serving and retired colleagues who are unexpectedly experiencing financial hardship. The fund is open to all Boots' colleagues in the UK. It aims to help when unexpected events happen and staff are faced with homelessness, debts involving bailiffs, large utility bill arrears or essential living requirements where they are facing financial hardship. It annually supports about 600–800 people with grants and loans.

Main locations
The group has offices across the UK. Its head office is in Nottingham.

Community contributions

We were not able to find details of the company's charitable giving for 2014/15. However, The Boots Charitable Trust's accounts state that it received £354,000 from Boots UK during this period.

Employee-led support

Fundraising for charity partners
Employees, customers and suppliers fundraise for the two core charities, Children in Need and Macmillan Cancer Support. Since support for these partners began almost £12 million has been raised.

Macmillan in Every Community
A volunteer-led scheme that offers practical support to people affected by cancer, Macmillan in Every Community helps those affected by cancer get access to the services they need and to maintain independence and control over their lives.

Payroll giving
The company offers the Give As You Earn payroll giving facility. There are currently 3,000 employees giving regularly to a charity of their choice in this way.

Matched funding
Employees are encouraged to share their expertise to help people lead healthier lifestyles and are provided with opportunities to devote their time and

energy to supporting causes that matter. Employees' fundraising efforts are also supported and the company provides a matched giving scheme to staff, enabling them to claim up to £500 to match their own funds raised.

Commercially led support

The Boots Learning Store

The Boots Learning Store website provides educational support for children, teachers and parents. This is an interactive educational resource for all ages addressing issues of health, science and well-being. It includes a comprehensive set of teachers' notes which are available to download. The site also has a dedicated parents' section providing health advice and links to other health-related sites. See www.bootslearningstore.com.

Corporate charity

Boots Charitable Trust (Charity Commission no. 1045927).

Applications

Boots Charitable Trust

Applications to the trust are only accepted on the official application form which must be accompanied by your latest annual report and detailed accounts.

The application form can be downloaded as a Word document, or it can be posted to you by the correspondent, to whom it should be returned once completed.

Grants range in size from £100 to £10,000, although applications for larger amounts will be considered.

The trustees' meetings are held bimonthly in January, March, May, July, September and November. The deadline for receipt of applications is the 7th of the month preceding the meeting (i.e. 7 February for the March meeting, 7 April for the May meeting and so on). The decision period is two to four months.

Contact: Julie Lawrence, Boots Charitable Trust; email: Julie.Lawrence@boots.co.uk.

Boots Benevolent Fund

Applications are processed under delegated powers which permit donations and interest-free loans to be made of up to £1,500.

Email: bbf@boots.co.uk; tel: 0115 959 1285.

Alliance Trust PLC

Financial services

Correspondent: Surrani Kali, Secretary of the Committee, 8 West Marketgait, Dundee DD1 1QN (tel: 01382 321000/ 01382 321071; fax: 01382 321185; email: ATFoundation@alliancetrust.co.uk; website: www.alliancetrust.co.uk)

Directors: Anthony Brooke; Chris Samuel; Clare Dobie; Gregor Stewart; Karl Sternberg; Lord Smith of Kelvin, Chair; Rory Macnamara (women: 1; men: 6)

Year end	31/12/2015
Turnover	£114,386,000
Pre-tax profit	£145,036,000

Nature of business: Alliance Trust is an investment and savings business. The company's products and services include a renowned investment trust and a range of investment strategies and funds.

Company registration number: SC1731

Focus of giving: General charitable purposes, humanitarian help.

Community involvement	✓
Community contributions	✓
CSR report	✓
Directors have other relevant posts	✓
Armed forces personnel	✓
Company gives to smaller charities	✓
Corporate charity	✓
Employee-led support	✓
Gifts in kind	✓
Humanitarian aid: UK including food banks	✓
Matched funding	✓
Sponsorship	✓

Charitable donations

Cash worldwide:	2015	£10,000

Community involvement

The Alliance Trust Foundation
(OSCR no. SC044113)

The Alliance Trust Foundation, formerly known as the Alliance Trust Staff Foundation, is a charity registered in Scotland and was formed with the purpose of building partnerships between the Alliance Trust and its local communities in Dundee, Edinburgh and London. The foundation is run by a committee of Alliance Trust employees from across the business. It aims to engage staff through various initiatives such as dress-down days and bake sales to raise money for local charities. With funds raised from larger events, such as the Cateran Yomp, it donates to a select number of charities during the year.

Food bank

The group has continued the initiative with the Dundee Food bank, donating thousands of pounds worth of food in 2015 to help feed those in need in the Dundee area.

There was no separate CSR report; however, there is a corporate responsibility section in the annual report and also an Alliance Trust Foundation Newsletter which contains details of charitable giving.

Directors with other relevant posts

Anthony Brooke (non-executive director) sits on the Investment Committee of the National Portrait Gallery and is a trustee of The Portrait Trust (Charity Commission no. 1148994), which has a particular focus on education, the arts and culture.

Main locations

Dundee; Edinburgh; London.

Community contributions

In 2014/15 The Alliance Trust Foundation, which raises money through the Alliance Trust Cateran Yomp and fundraising activities by staff, distributed £27,000 to six charities nominated by staff as part of the annual grant process. In addition the group made smaller donations to local charities and in the year this amounted to £10,000. We have taken the figure of £10,000 as the company's worldwide cash contribution. In December the foundation donated over £2,000 to support food banks and other charities seeking to alleviate poverty at Christmas in Dundee, Edinburgh and London. However, we were unable to determine a figure for the company's overall contribution for the reporting year.

Beneficiaries included: Linlithgow Rose Community Football Club; Melanoma Focus; Mindroom; Kick it Kick off; Tayside Mountain Rescue; Tayside Children with Cancer and Leukaemia; the Syrian Refugee Appeal; The Yomp; The Young Mothers Unit at Menzieshill High School; Unite Against Cancer.

Employee-led support

Staff fundraising through various events is what sustains the Alliance Trust Foundation, together with matched funding from the company. The foundation has supported numerous local charities operating within Dundee, Edinburgh and London.

Volunteering

Two volunteering days per staff member are allocated each year in order to encourage participation with local projects and communities. The company's Annual Newsletter for 2015 states: 'Staff from across the entire business have been supporting our local communities through various organisations such as Action for Children, Tomorrow's Talent and the Brae.'

Commercially led support

Sponsorship

2015 marked the 5th Alliance Trust Cateran Yomp with over 600 registered participants.

In 2015 a total of £154,000 went to support ABF Soldiers' Charity and £77,000 to support the company's Alliance Trust Staff Foundation which will enable the foundation to make donations to a number of local charitable organisations next year.

Corporate charity

Alliance Trust Foundation (OSCR no. SC044113).

Exclusions

None known.

Applications

Apply in writing to the correspondent. Most of the group's charitable giving is directed through its associated foundation – see 'Community involvement' section.

Allianz Insurance PLC

Insurance

Correspondent: Richard Foulerton, CSR Manager, 57 Ladymead, Guildford, Surrey GU1 1DB (email: richard.foulerton@allianz.co.uk; website: www.allianz.co.uk/about-allianz-insurance/social-responsibility.html)

Directors: Axel Theis; Brigitte Bovermann; Christian Dinesen; David Torrance; Jonathan Dye; Mark Churchlow; Richard Hudson; Rosanne Murison (women: 2; men: 6)

Year end	31/12/2016
Turnover	£1,859,000,000
Pre-tax profit	£67,000,000

Nature of business: The group undertakes all classes of insurance business.

Company registration number: 84638

Subsidiary undertakings include: Allianz Properties Ltd; British Reserve Insurance Company Ltd; Pet Plan Ltd; Trafalgar Insurance Public Ltd Company.

Focus of giving: General charitable purposes, education, enterprise/training, animal welfare.

Membership: BITC, LBG

Community involvement	✓
Community contributions	✓
CSR report	✓
Cash donations declared	✓
Charity partner(s)	✓
Corporate charity	✓
Employee-led support	✓
Gifts in kind	✓
Humanitarian aid: overseas	✓
Payroll giving	✓
Sponsorship	✓

Charitable donations

Cash UK (latest available):	2016	£250,000
Cash worldwide:	2016	£250,000

Community involvement

Community Programme

The company aims to:

- Support charities and voluntary initiatives in the community that are relevant to its business objectives and brand values
- Increase financial contributions through company donations, employee fundraising and payroll giving
- Maximise contribution delivered through non-financial means, such as employee volunteering
- Create lasting value for community partners and employees through training and skills development
- Maximise the value of partnerships by measuring key performance indicators

Petplan Charitable Trust (Charity Commission no. 1032907)

There is an international network of 14 Allianz-affiliated corporate foundations. Petplan is a subsidiary of Allianz Insurance PLC and raises funds by requesting a donation with the premiums paid by policyholders. The trust aims to promote the welfare of dogs, cats, horses and rabbits by funding animal research and welfare projects. Capital grants are also available to veterinary institutions.

The Prince's Trust

The Prince's Trust gives practical and financial support to 14- to 30-year-olds who have struggled at school, have been in care, are long-term unemployed or have been in trouble with the law and helps them to develop key workplace skills.

The company has supported The Prince's Trust since 2005 and aims to utilise the skills of its employees through volunteering with the trust to help young people enjoy a better future. The company's employees are offered volunteering opportunities to deliver workshops as part of the trust's Team programme, including on work-placements, and CV and interview skills. By delivering the workshops, employees will not only help the young people on the programmes, but also develop their own skills – including communication, leadership and management, presenting, adaptability, problem-solving, team work, and project management.

Association of Air Ambulances Charity

The Association of Air Ambulances Charity works with all 20 regional air ambulance charities in the UK. Allianz offices are paired with their nearest air ambulance meaning that employee fundraising will be supporting life-saving services in their local area.

Main UK locations

Allianz has 26 offices throughout the UK.

Community contributions

In 2015 community investment totalled £250,000.

In-kind support

Employees are encouraged to give their time and skills to their local community and are supported with ten hours paid volunteering leave each year.

Employee-led support

In the event of a natural disaster that prompts an appeal by the Disaster Emergency Committee (DEC), Allianz responds by offering an immediate one-off payroll giving facility through which employees can make a tax-efficient donation to the disaster appeal.

Corporate charity

Petplan Charitable Trust (Charity Commission no. 1032907).

Applications

For further details contact the correspondent.

Petplan Charitable Trust

Application forms are available from the trust's website: www.petplantrust.org/index.php.

Amec Foster Wheeler PLC (formerly Amec PLC)

Building/construction, consulting engineers, engineering, oil and gas/fuel, property

Correspondent: Frances Fay, Global Director of Sustainability, Old Change House, 128 Queen Victoria Street, London EC4V 4BJ (tel: 020 7429 7500; email: frances.fay@amecfw.com; website: www.amecfw.com)

Directors: Colin Day; Ian McHoul, Chief Financial Officer; John Connolly, Chair; Jonathan Lewis, Chief Executive Officer; Kent Masters; Linda Adamany; Neil Carson; Roy Franklin; Stephanie Newby (women: 2; men: 7)

Year end	31/12/2015
Turnover	£5,455,000,000
Pre-tax profit	(£235,000,000)

Nature of business: Amec Foster Wheeler designs, delivers and maintains strategic and complex infrastructure assets across a range of markets. It has a strong presence across the onshore and offshore oil and gas value chain – from production through to processing, gas monetisation, midstream, oil refining and chemicals. Amec Foster Wheeler is also in the mining, clean-energy, power-generation, environment and infrastructure markets. In addition, the company is a leading designer, fabricator and supplier of advanced boiler systems for the power generation and industrial markets. It has operations in over 55 countries.

Company registration number: 1675285

Subsidiary undertakings include: AMEC Civil Engineering Ltd; Amec Foster Wheeler Energy Ltd; Foster Wheeler (London) Ltd.

Total employees: 40,000

Focus of giving: General charitable purposes, economic generation, education, enterprise/training, environment, health, ill health, medical research, local groups, arts, culture, overseas projects, poverty and social exclusion, science technology, children, young people, community/social welfare, disasters.

Membership: BITC

Community involvement	✓
Community contributions	✓
Company reports on anti-slavery	✓
CSR report	✓
CSR or charity committee	✓
Directors have other relevant posts	✓
AF Covenant	✓
Cash donations declared	✓
Charity partner(s)	✓
Employee-led support	✓
Gifts in kind	✓
Humanitarian aid: overseas	✓
Matched funding	✓
Overseas giving	✓
Shared-value alliances	✓
STEM-focused	✓

Charitable donations

Cash worldwide:	2015	£461,000

Community involvement

The group supports its global charity partner, as well as local charities for a wide range of causes, with a focus on providing matched funding for employee fundraising. It also supports STEM activities for young people.

SOS Children's Villages

The group has had a long-standing partnership with SOS Children's Villages (Charity Commission no. 1069204), offering support through donations from the group and employee fundraising. Since 2007, the group has supported 24 projects and donated £662,000. Particular efforts are made for emergency relief appeals, such as the Nepal earthquake, for which employees raised £49,000.

In 2015 a total of £144,000 was raised through employee fundraising and matched funding from the group, which supported three educational projects run by the charity in Azerbaijan, Canada and China. Activities planned in 2017 include continued support of these three projects, as well as a celebration of the role of mothers in the SOS Villages. Further details of the partnership are outlined in a dedicated report, available on the website.

Other partnerships

The group is a member of the World Economic Forum's Disaster Resource Partnership, providing technical and engineering expertise for humanitarian assistance. The group is also committed to the UN Global Compact, supporting the UN Sustainable Development Goals.

STEM activities

The group promotes STEM education among young people through working with schools and colleges, supported by employee volunteering. Examples of activities in 2015 include: an employee-led Young Engineering Scheme bringing together young people from local schools in Reading; a school go-kart building competition led by employees on the group's graduate scheme; a zombie apocalypse-themed event for young people in partnership with the Institution of Civil Engineers. The group also has a partnership with Dalziel High School in Motherwell, Scotland, encouraging students to engage with STEM subjects and engineering courses, and the group is working with Education Scotland to develop further partnerships between schools and industry in Scotland.

Community engagement

The group also contributes to various initiatives in the communities where it has operations, such as taking part in community clean-up activities and supporting local schools.

Directors with other relevant posts

John Connolly is also Chair of Trustees of Great Ormond Street Hospital Charity (Charity Commission no. 1160024).

Main locations

The group operates in more than 55 countries, including offices across the UK.

Community contributions

According to the Community Investment report, the group donated a total of £461,000 in 2015, including matched funding for employee fundraising. In addition, employees raised £425,000 and contributed £19,900 through in-kind support.

The group provided the following breakdown of how the cash donations were distributed among different causes:

Cause	Cash donations
Social welfare	44%
Health	41%
Education and young people	8%
Emergency relief	5%
Environment	1%

The following breakdown of volunteering hours was also provided:

Cause	Volunteering hours
Education and young people	72%
Social welfare	14%
Economic development	7%
Health	5%
Emergency relief	1%
Arts/science	1%

In-kind support

The group offers in-kind support through donations such as office equipment, unused supplies and obsolete branded items.

Employee-led support

Employee volunteering

The Community Investment report states that in 2015 a total of 5,133 employees were engaged in volunteering, contributing a total of 8,294 hours, amounting to £19,900 worth of the company's time.

Employee fundraising

The group provides matched funding for employee fundraising efforts. Much of employee fundraising activity focuses on supporting the group's partner, SOS Children's Villages. In 2015 employees took part in a number of fundraising activities for the charity, including the Steptember Challenge, with 500 employees committing to walk the number of steps amounting to the distance between the villages supported in 2015.

Examples of other initiatives during the year included: participating in Movember; fundraising for charities local to the group's operations in America; supporting children in local schools in the Philippines.

Applications

The company assists, through matched funding, charity and community events that its employees/local offices support. For this reason, applications for support should be made to the company's local offices. See www.amecfw.com/aboutus/offices to find a local office.

Other queries regarding information on the group's policies in this area, or for information about its global strategic charity partner, SOS Children, or the company's overseas and humanitarian aid, write to the Head of Sustainability, Frances Fay, at the Old Change House address given, or email frances.fay@amecfw.com.

Amey UK PLC

Miscellaneous

Correspondent: Social Responsibility Department, Sherard Building, Edmund Halley Road, Oxford OX4 4DQ (website: www.amey.co.uk)

Directors: Alfredo García; Andres Camacho; Andrew Nelson, Chief Financial Officer; Andy Milner; Santiago Olivares, Chief Executive Officer; Sir Richard Mottram, Chair; Wayne Robertson (women: 0; men: 7)

Year end	31/12/2015
Turnover	£2,230,551,000
Pre-tax profit	£23,641,000

Nature of business: A leading provider of support services in the UK, ranging from transportation and education, to defence and health.

Company registration number: 4736639

Subsidiary undertakings include: AHL Holdings (Manchester) Ltd; ALC (FMC) Ltd; Amey Birmingham Highways Holdings Ltd; Amey FMP Belfast; Amey Hallam Highways Holdings Ltd; AmeyCespa (MK) Holding Co. Ltd; Carillion Enterprise Ltd; EduAction (Waltham Forest) Ltd; GEO Amey PECS Ltd; Integrated Bradford PSP Ltd; Modern Housing Solutions (Prime) Ltd; RSP (Holdings) Ltd; Services Support (Avon and Somerset) Holdings.

Focus of giving: Enterprise/training, overseas projects, safety and crime prevention, sport, recreation, children, young people, community/social welfare.

Membership: BITC

Community involvement	✓
Community contributions	✓
Company reports on anti-slavery	✓
CSR report	✓
Armed forces personnel	✓
Charity partner(s)	✓
Employee-led support	✓

Charitable donations

Total UK (cash and in kind):	2015	£174,000
Total worldwide (cash and in kind):	2015	£4,500,000

Community involvement

In supporting employment, education and skills, the company conducts targeted employment, skills and training programmes aimed at disadvantaged people, including those who are unemployed, young people, ex-offenders and ex-military personnel.

Partnerships

Amey has supported youth charity The Duke of Edinburgh's Award (DofE) for over ten years and in 2014 the company began a new initiative to help young people from disadvantaged backgrounds across the UK take part in the scheme. The programme identifies underserved communities and expands local DofE provision to help improve the life chances and employability of young people.

Through local community partnerships, Amey works with over 300 ex-offenders, homeless and disadvantaged young people to provide them with skills and support to find employment. The company's partnership with the Ministry of Justice enables it to recruit ex-offenders in highway maintenance as part of a scheme designed specifically to reduce reoffending rates.

Main locations

Oxford; Glasgow; Liverpool.

Community contributions

In the parent company's 2015 Integrated Annual Report the company lists its 'voluntary contributions' in the UK as £174,000 and the total worldwide as £4.5 million.

Employee-led support

The Amey Foundation (not a registered charity, it appears to be a fund held by the company) supports employee charity fundraising activities in their local communities. Any employee taking part in an event to raise money for charity can apply for additional fundraising from the foundation which will match their efforts up to a total of £500.

The company provides one paid day a year for employees to participate in charitable and community projects of their choice. With 21,000 employees, this is the equivalent of over 160,000 hours of community volunteering.

Exclusions

There is no funding or other support to political organisations of any sort, and only exceptionally help can be provided through funding or support to religious organisations as part of an initiative to the general benefit of a community. No funding or support will be given to individuals outside the business.

Applications

Apply in writing to the correspondent referenced 'Community Engagement'.

MS Amlin PLC (formerly Amlin PLC)

Insurance

Correspondent: Community & Charities Panel, 122 Leadenhall St, London EC3V 4AG (tel: 020 7746 1000; fax: 020 7746 1696; website: www.amlin.com/about-amlin/responsibility.aspx)

Directors: Charles Philipps, Chief Executive; Hironori Morimoto; James Illingworth; Kenichi Fukuhara; Kiyotaka Shuto; Oliver Peterken; Philip Calnan; Richard Davey, Chair; Richard Hextall, Chief Finance and Operations Officer; Robin Adam; Shonaid Jemmett-Page; Simon Beale (women: 1; men: 11)

Year end	31/12/2015
Pre-tax profit	£252,300,000

Nature of business: Amlin is an independent insurer specialising in providing insurance cover to commercial enterprises and reinsurance protection to other insurance companies around the world.

In late 2015 it was announced that Amlin PLC had been acquired by the Mitsui Sumitomo Insurance Company, Ltd, which is a wholly owned subsidiary of MS and AD Insurance Group Holdings, Inc. The group's name was then changed from Amlin PLC to MS Amlin PLC.

Company registration number: 2854310

Subsidiary undertakings include: Allied Underwriting Agencies Ltd; Amlin UK Ltd; Amlin Underwriting Ltd.

Total employees: 1,888

Focus of giving: General charitable purposes, health, ill health, arts, culture, overseas projects, children, young people, community/social welfare.

Community involvement	✓
Community contributions	✓
CSR report	✓
CSR or charity committee	✓
Directors have other relevant posts	✓
Cash donations declared	✓
Charity partner(s)	✓
Employee-led support	✓
Matched funding	✓
Overseas giving	✓
Sponsorship	✓

Charitable donations

Cash UK (latest available):	2015	£150,000
Total UK (cash and in kind):	2015	£150,000
Cash worldwide:	2015	£150,000
Total worldwide (cash and in kind):	2015	£150,000

Community involvement

Support is given in the communities in which Amlin does business and for the education and development of young people, as well as to charities which are relevant to employees. In the UK, charitable giving is co-ordinated through a Community and Charities Panel which is chaired by a senior underwriter. Outside the UK, community and charities budgets are managed by local boards.

Partner charities

During 2015 partners included Macmillan Cancer Support and The Outward Bound Trust.

Directors with other relevant posts
Charles Philipps: trustee of the Outward Bound Trust and director of Outward Bound Oman UK.

Main UK locations
The group's UK offices are located in the City of London, Chelmsford in Essex, and West Malling in Kent.

The group also has a presence in Europe, the Middle East, Asia and the United States.

Community contributions

The 'Community' section of the annual report states that 'in 2015 Amlin supported more than 40 UK charities with a total budget of £150,000'. We have taken this figure as the group's cash donations for the year.

We were not able to determine the value of the in-kind support given by the group.

Employee-led support

Employee fundraising
Employees raise funds for a wide range of charities. In 2015 Amlin also entered a team in The City Three Peaks Challenge. The charity abseil down three landmarks of the City of London – The Leadenhall Building, 20 Fenchurch Street and 30 St Mary Axe – raised £100,000 for the Outward Bound Trust.

Matched funding
The annual report for 2015 notes how 'in many cases' Amlin will make a further donation to a charity supported by an employee.

Commercially led support

Sponsorship
Amlin has a dedicated website, Amlin World (www.amlinworld.com) which shares 'in-depth stories' about the activities sponsored and supported by the group and 'showcases everything from sport and the arts, to research and philanthropy'.

Applications

More information about Amlin's community, charitable and sponsorship activities can be obtained by contacting Amlin Communications (communications@amlin.com).

Anglian Water

Water

Correspondent: Sustainable Development Department, Lancaster House, Lancaster Way, Ermine Business Park, Huntingdon, Cambridgeshire PE29 6XU (tel: 0345 791 9155; website: www.awg.com)

Directors: Chris Newsome; Duncan Symonds; James Bryce; Jean Spencer; John Hirst; Niall Mills; Paul Whittaker; Peter Simpson; Polly Courtice; Scott Longhurst; Stephen Billingham, Chair; Steve Good (women: 2; men: 10)

Year end	31/03/2016
Turnover	£260,800,000
Pre-tax profit	£89,100,000

Nature of business: Water supply and distribution, waste water collection and treatment, providing social housing repairs and property development. The group is registered under the Companies (Jersey) Law 1991.

Company registration number: 2366656

Subsidiary undertakings include: Alpheus Environmental Ltd; Anglian Water (Osprey) Financing PLC; AWG Parent Co. Ltd; AWG Group Ltd; AWG Holdings Ltd; AWG UK Holdings Ltd; Osprey Acquisitions Ltd; Osprey Holdco Ltd; Rutland Insurance Ltd. A full list of subsidiaries is lodged with the Companies House.

Focus of giving: Education, environment, heritage, overseas projects, children, young people, community/ social welfare.

Membership: BITC, LBG

Community involvement	✓
Community contributions	✓
Company reports on anti-slavery	✓
CSR report	✓
Directors have other relevant posts	✓
AF Covenant	✓
Cash donations declared	✓
Charity partner(s)	✓
Gifts in kind	✓
Humanitarian aid: overseas	✓
Market-led giving	✓
Overseas giving	✓
Payroll giving	✓
Sponsorship	✓

Charitable donations

Cash UK (latest available):	2016	£40,000
Total UK (cash and in kind):	2016	£40,000
Cash worldwide:	2016	£40,000
Total worldwide (cash and in kind):	2016	£40,000

Community involvement

Many employees give active support to a lot of good causes in the community. Community activities can range from volunteering with local scouts, through to being a school governor. However, the Anglian website points out: 'Due to the high numbers of requests, we are unable to give sponsorship to local events/ charities. However, support can be given through volunteering under Love to Help.'

Directors with other relevant posts
John Hirst (senior independent non-executive director) is a trustee of Epilepsy Research UK (Charity Commission no. 1100394) and SUDEP Action (Charity Commission no. 1164250) this charity exists to support those bereaved by sudden unexpected death in epilepsy and works towards prevention of deaths from epilepsy.

Main locations
Main UK location – Cambridgeshire.

However, there are a number of locations worldwide.

Community contributions

According to the Anglian Water website, in 2015–16, Anglian Water staff, partners and customers raised £754,900 for WaterAid. Through the WaterAid lottery, staff donated £46,500 to the charity. According to the 2015/6 annual report and accounts, during the year, the company also donated £40,000 to WaterAid. We take this figure as the company's overall worldwide charitable contribution. We have no breakdown of the company's UK charitable giving.

Employee-led support

Give As You Earn
Employees are able to donate to their chosen charity through a scheme facilitated through the Charities Aid Foundation. There is also an employee volunteering scheme – Love to Help. It is a way of contributing to local communities whereby employees can choose one of three ways to volunteer through the programme and the company pledges to match up to thirty hours per year of work time to help staff do more volunteering.

Exclusions

No support can be given for advertising in charity brochures, appeals from individuals, political appeals, sports (unless at educational level), animal welfare, medical research or religious appeals.

Applications

According the 2016 annual report: 'We continue to provide support to WaterAid – our nominated charity – and do not offer charitable donations or sponsorships to other charities. Part of the funds raised in 2015/16 directly supported the work of WaterAid in two countries, Nepal and Liberia.'

Anglo American PLC

Mining

Correspondent: Laura Dunne, Manager, Anglo American Group Foundation, 20 Carlton House Terrace, London SW1Y 5AN (tel: 020 7968 8888; email: aagf@angloamerican.com; website: www.angloamerican.co.uk)

Directors: Anne Stevens; Byron Grote; Jack Thompson; Jim Rutherford; Judy Diamini; Mark Cutifani, Chief Executive;

Mphu Ramatlapeng; Rene Medori, Finance Director; Roy O'Rourke; Sir John Parker, Chair; Sir Philip Hampton; Tony O'Neill (women: 3; men: 9)

Year end	31/12/2015
Turnover	£16,483,000,000
Pre-tax profit	(£4,395,000,000)

Nature of business: Anglo American is a global mining business.

Company registration number: 3564138

Subsidiary undertakings include: Anglo American REACH Ltd; De Beers UK Ltd; Reunion Mining Ltd.

Total employees: 91,000

Focus of giving: Economic generation, education, enterprise/training, environment, health, ill health, local groups, arts, culture, overseas projects, poverty and social exclusion, sport, recreation, community/social welfare.

Membership: BITC

Accredited Living Wage Employer	✓
Community involvement	✓
Community contributions	✓
CSR report	✓
CSR or charity committee	✓
Directors have other relevant posts	✓
AF Covenant	✓
Charity partner(s)	✓
Corporate charity	✓
Employee-led support	✓
FTSE 100	✓
Gifts in kind	✓
Humanitarian aid: overseas	✓
Matched funding	✓
Overseas giving	✓
Pro bono	✓
Sponsorship	✓

Charitable donations

Total UK (cash and in kind):	2015	£387,000

Community involvement

The group focuses mainly on supporting community development, education and health, through its corporate charity.

Globally, much of the group's community investment is focused on supporting community and health programmes in the areas where it operates, particularly in South Africa and South America.

Anglo American Group Foundation
The group's corporate charity, the Anglo American Group Foundation (Charity Commission no. 1111719) supports projects in: the UK; Brazil; Chile; China; Colombia; India; Peru; Zimbabwe. The foundation supports registered charities associated with the following causes: education; international development; health/HIV; environment; community development in London.

The foundation also provides matched funding for employee fundraising in London and Luxembourg.

Beneficiaries have previously included: Engineers Without Borders (£461,000); Save the Children (£300,000); Prince's Trust (£213,000); Right to Play (£205,000); Body and Soul (£135,000); SOS Children's Villages of India (£22,000); St Andrew's Club (£15,000).

Partnerships
The group works with a number of organisations to deliver its sustainability goals, including CARE International UK, to support community development activities, and Fauna and Flora International, to manage biodiversity in its operations.

The group is also a supporter of the UN Sustainable Development Goals and the Global Vaccine Alliance.

Directors with other relevant posts
Judy Diamini is founder and trustee of the Mkhiwa Trust, an education and health charity in South Africa. Mphu Ramatlapeng is the Executive Vice President for the HIV/AIDs, Tuberculosis and Health Financing programmes at the Clinton Health Access Initiative.

Main locations
The company's only office in the UK is its headquarters, based in London. It also has offices and operations in Luxembourg; Canada; South America; South Africa; East Asia; and Australia.

Community contributions

The 2015 sustainability report states that in that year, the group's total Corporate Social Investment (including cash and in-kind contributions from the Anglo American Chair's Fund, the Anglo American Group Foundation, and the group's enterprise development programmes) amounted to $124.1 million (around £100 million), around 6% of pre-tax profit. Corporate Social Investment in the UK totalled $480,000 (around £387,000). There was no breakdown of charitable giving in the UK; however, the following breakdown of global spending was provided:

Community development	41%
Education and training	18%
Other	12%
Health and welfare	11%
Sports, arts, culture and heritage	5%
Institutional capacity development	4%
Water and sanitation	4%
Environment	2%
Disaster and emergency relief	2%
Energy and climate change	1%
Employee matched giving and fundraising	

Employee-led support

Employee volunteering
Employee volunteering is generally organised by each individual business within the group, but the 2015 sustainability report states that these initiatives are 'informing the development of a group-wide approach'. The group has a particular focus on: education, skills and youth development; the environment; sustainable community development.

The group is using its 'Ambassadors' volunteering programme in Chile as a model for a group-wide approach. The scheme involves employee teams partnering with local community groups to run projects which can receive up to $5,000 in funding, as well as capacity-building training for community development.

The Anglo American Group Foundation also provides matched funding for funds raised by employees in London and Luxembourg.

Corporate charity

Anglo American Group Foundation (Charity Commission no. 1111719).

Exclusions

The Anglo American Group Foundation does not support: animal welfare; armed forces charities; community interest companies; educational fees; expeditions overseas; general health charities; hospital trusts; individuals; music festivals and choirs; political or quasi-political bodies; religious organisations (except for community outreach); trade unions.

Applications

Anglo American Group Foundation
Apply in writing to the correspondent.

AO World PLC

Retail – electrical

Correspondent: Karen Hunter, Unit 5A, The Parklands, Lostock, Bolton BL6 4SD (tel: 07713 312014/07713 312014; email: Karen@AOSmileFoundation.org; website: ao.com/corporate/responsibility/our-approach)

Directors: Brian McBride; Charles Holroyd; Christopher Hopkinson; John Roberts, Chief Executive Officer; Marissa Cassoni; Richard Rose, Chair; Rudolf Lamprecht; Stephen Caunce (women: 1; men: 7)

Year end	31/03/2016
Turnover	£599,000,000
Pre-tax profit	(£6,700,000)

Nature of business: AO World is an online retailer of electrical products and household appliances.

Company registration number: 5525751

Total employees: 2,101

Focus of giving: Children, young people.

Community involvement	✓
Community contributions	✓
Corporate charity	✓
Gifts in kind	✓
Matched funding	✓
Payroll giving	✓

Community involvement

AO actively encourages all employees to support and give back to their local community and the AO Smile Foundation (Charity Commission no. 1157111) continues to facilitate this.

The AO Smile Foundation

The foundation helps children be the best they can be and creates opportunities for those who would otherwise be deprived of such chances. According to the group's website, it 'has supported AO Smile with a number of community projects, including a DIY SOS challenge that saw employees volunteer to help transform the home of a local family in need'.

Comic Relief

AO also supported Comic Relief's Red Nose Day, according to the 2015 annual report:

> All of our trucks were dressed with the infamous red noses and we transformed our customer service centre to be an official Red Nose Day call centre. Almost 150 employees gave up their time on a Friday night for Comic Relief and over £57,000 was raised for the cause.

Main location

Bolton and other various locations throughout the UK.

Community contributions

According to the 2015 annual report, AO actively encourages all employees to get involved with their local community and the AO Smile Foundation was launched during the year to help with this. The foundation holds a Gold Award from the Institute of Fundraising, and the group supports the charity by providing, free of charge, a charity manager and other services such as financial, payroll and legal support. We were unable to determine a figure for the company's contribution.

In-kind support

Volunteering

The group encourages colleagues to have a positive impact within their local communities and gives each employee two 'make a difference' days per year to work with a charity.

Employee-led support

Matched funding

52% of UK employees make a regular monthly gift to the charity, and during the year over £75,000 was raised through payroll giving (taken from the company's website 2016).

During 2015 the group has supported AO Smile with a number of community projects.

Corporate charity

AO Smile Foundation (Charity Commission no. 1157111).

Applications

Apply in writing to the correspondent.

Apax Partners LLP

Financial services

Correspondent: Kate Albert, Manager, The Apax Foundation, 33 Jermyn Street, London SW1Y 6DN (tel: 020 7872 6300; fax: 020 7666 6441; email: Apax.Foundation@apax.com; website: www.apax.com)

Directors: Andrew Sillitoe, Co-Chief Executive; Mitch Truwit, Co-Chief Executive

Year end	31/03/2015
Turnover	£138,646,000
Pre-tax profit	£66,848,000

Nature of business: Apax Partners is an independent global private equity advisory firm.

Company registration number: OC303117

Subsidiary undertakings include: Apax Partners Worldwide Holdings Ltd; Apax Partners International Ltd;

Total employees: 232

Focus of giving: General charitable purposes, economic generation, education, enterprise/training, overseas projects, poverty and social exclusion.

Community involvement	✓
Community contributions	✓
Company reports on anti-slavery	✓
CSR or charity committee	✓
Corporate charity	✓
Employee-led support	✓
Gifts in kind	✓
Matched funding	✓
Overseas giving	✓

Charitable donations

Total UK (cash and in kind):	2015	£802,500
Total worldwide (cash and in kind):	2015	£802,500

Community involvement

The group focuses its community involvement through its corporate charity, the Apax Foundation, which mainly supports social entrepreneurship.

The Apax Foundation (Charity Commission no. 1112845)

The foundation's current focus is on social entrepreneurship, particularly in the areas of education and relief of poverty. It tends to make a small number of larger donations, and a larger number of grants under £10,000. The foundation is also used to make donations through the matched funding scheme for employees.

The Apax Foundation has a proportion of its assets in social investment, including: East London Bond; Emmaus UK; Finance in Motion.

Beneficiaries included: Impetus – The Private Equity Foundation (£393,000); Dasra (£258,000); The Prince's Trust (£166,000); Elton John AIDS Foundation (£17,500); Crisis UK (£13,500).

Main locations

The group's UK office is located in London. There are also seven offices worldwide: Hong Kong; Mumbai; Munich; New York; Sao Paulo; Shanghai; Tel Aviv.

Community contributions

No figure was given for the group's charitable contributions.

The Apax Foundation receives a percentage of the firm's profits and carried interest through the foundation's subsidiary undertaking, Apax E Member Ltd. In 2015 this donation totalled £802,500, with a further £7,700 donated for staff costs from the employees of Apax Partners UK Ltd and Apax Worldwide Holdings Ltd.

Employee-led support

Matched funding

Through the Apax Foundation, the group makes donations of at least £5,000 to any charity with which an Apax employee is involved.

Corporate charity

The Apax Foundation (Charity Commission no. 1112845).

Applications

The Apax Foundation

Apply in writing to the correspondent. The group's charitable giving is channelled through the Apax Foundation.

Arla Foods Ltd

Food manufacture

Correspondent: See 'Applications', Arla House, 4 Savannah Way, Leeds Valley Park, Leeds LS10 1AB (tel: 0113 382 7000; fax: 0113 382 7030; website: www.arlafoods.co.uk/overview/arla-in-the-uk/community-involvement)

Directors: Afshin Amirahmadi; Anders Haegg; Dan Kolding; Peter Giørtz-Carlsen; Simon Stevens; Tanjot Soar; Vania Jussara da Silva Almeida

Year end	31/12/2015
Turnover	£2,575,087,000
Pre-tax profit	(£63,782,000)

Nature of business: This company is a subsidiary of Arla Foods UK PLC, which is a leading supplier of milk and dairy products in the UK market. The group supplies liquid milk, cream, butter, spreads, cheeses, fresh dairy products, yoghurts and desserts to the major supermarkets.

Company registration number: 2143253

Subsidiary undertakings include: Arla Foods (Westbury) Ltd; Arla Foods Cheese Company Ltd; Arla Foods Ingredients UK Ltd.

UK employees: 3,489

Total employees: 3,489

Focus of giving: General charitable purposes, health, ill health, local groups, community/social welfare.

Community involvement	✓
Community contributions	✓
Cash donations declared	✓
Charity partner(s)	✓
Employee-led support	✓
Matched funding	✓
Sponsorship	✓

Charitable donations

Cash UK (latest available):	2015	£86,000
Total UK (cash and in kind):	2015	£86,000
Cash worldwide:	2015	£86,000
Total worldwide (cash and in kind):	2015	£86,000

Community involvement

Arla has developed the Community Challenge initiative which allows colleagues to have an input on how the company's community involvement budget is used. Community Challenge supports employees' communities in two ways: firstly, funds raised by Arla employees for causes important to them are matched; and secondly, funding is given to causes with which employees volunteer.

Charity partner

In the UK, Arla is a corporate partner to Marie Curie Cancer Care, which sees support to branches of the charity local to Arla's sites.

Main locations

The group's head office is in Leeds. It also has sites in: Aylesbury; Cheshire; Cornwall; Devon; Hatfield; Leeds; Leicester; Llandyrnog; Lockerbie; London; Oswestry; Settle; Wiltshire.

Community contributions

In 2015 the company declared donations to UK charities of £86,000. A list of beneficiaries was not available.

Commercially led support

Sponsorship

In 2016 Arla sponsored a number of events including the International Cheese Awards and Open Farm Sunday.

Arla Farmers Milk

In 2016 Arla launched Arla Farmers Milk. An extra 25p from the sale of each bottle goes back to its co-operative dairy farmers.

Applications

Through the Community Challenge, support is given either in the form of matched funding or to causes where Arla employees volunteer.

Arup Group Ltd

Consulting engineers

Correspondent: Alison Ball, Associate, Environment and Sustainability, 13 Fitzroy Street, London W1T 4BQ (tel: 020 7636 1531/0151 227 9397; fax: 020 7580 3924; email: alison.ball@arup.com; website: www.arup.com)

Directors: Alan Belfield; David Whittleton, Deputy Chair; Dervilla Mitchell; Gregory Hodkinson, Chair; L. M. Lui; Mahadev Raman; Michael Bear; Michael Kwok; Ngaire Woods; Peter Bailey; Peter Chamley; Tristram Carfrae, Deputy Chair

Year end	31/03/2015
Turnover	£1,125,510,000
Pre-tax profit	£32,713,000

Nature of business: Arup is an independent firm of planners, designers, engineers and consultants working across the built environment. It is a wholly independent organisation, which is owned in trust for the benefit of its employees and their dependants, and has no shareholders or external investors. Each of Arup's employees receives a share of the firm's operating profit each year.

Company registration number: 1312454

Subsidiary undertakings include: Arup Americas Inc.; Arup Ireland Ltd; Ove Arup Partnership Ltd.

Total employees: 12,143

Focus of giving: General charitable purposes, education, environment, health, ill health, heritage, non-registered charities, local groups, humanitarian help, overseas projects, poverty and social exclusion, children, young people, community/social welfare, disasters.

Membership: BITC

Accredited Living Wage Employer	✓
Community involvement	✓
Community contributions	✓
Company reports on anti-slavery	✓
CSR report	✓
Directors have other relevant posts	✓
Cash donations declared	✓
Charity partner(s)	✓
Corporate charity	✓
Employee-led support	✓
Gifts in kind	✓
Humanitarian aid: overseas	✓
Humanitarian aid: UK including food banks	✓
Overseas giving	✓
Pro bono	✓
STEM-focused	✓
Unregistered charities/NFP	✓

Charitable donations

Cash UK (latest available):	2015	£357,500
Cash worldwide:	2015	£796,000
Total worldwide (cash and in kind):	2015	£1,436,000

Community involvement

The annual report for 2014/15 notes that one of the company's core values is social usefulness, which the company expresses in its commitment to various charitable causes. Donations are made by the company itself and also through its various charities. Employees around the world also volunteer their time, offer pro bono work and fundraise for various causes that share the same values as the group.

The Ove Arup Partnership Charitable Trust (Charity Commission no. 1038737)

The trust was established in 1978 by a Deed of Settlement. Income is received through gifts from Arup Group Ltd and the trust's objects are making grants for general charitable purposes, with preference for: education; social care; health and welfare; disaster relief and alleviation of poverty; local community development; sustainability and the environment; and technology. The beneficiaries would appear to be UK-registered charities. In 2014/15 grants were made totalling £356,500.

The Ove Arup Foundation (Charity Commission no. 328138)

Established to commemorate the life of the late Sir Ove Arup, The Ove Arup Foundation is an educational charity supporting initiatives related to the built environment. It supports academic research and any charitable activities with similar purposes. Grants are made to organisations worldwide, with some preference for the UK. In 2014/15 the charity made grants totalling £201,000.

Arup Education Trust, South Africa

The Arup Education Trust (AET) provides financial assistance to eligible beneficiaries in tertiary and secondary education. AET places qualified students into the corporate environment, eliminating the gap between study and employment.

Charity partners

The company's founder, Ove Arup, was also a founding member of RedR, a UK-based international charity that deploys skilled professionals in emergency situations around the world. The company has a long-standing partnership with this charity, with its own engineers providing support during disasters such as earthquakes and hurricanes. Employees also regularly fundraise for the charity.

The company also partners with numerous other organisations, see the 'Employee-led support' section for further information.

Climate change

In 2015 the company announced a partnership with the C40 Cities Climate Leadership Group, committing US$1 million of consultancy support over three years. The C40 is a global network of cities working to tackle climate change, reduce emissions and risks, and increase the health, well-being and economic opportunities of urban citizens.

Directors with other relevant posts

Gregory Hodkinson is a trustee of The Ove Arup Foundation (Charity Commission no. 328138) and fellow of the Royal Society of Arts. He was also formerly a trustee of WaterAid (Charity Commission no. 288701) but left this position in 2014.

Main locations

The group's head office is in London and it has various offices around England, plus an office in Belfast, Cardiff and Glasgow. The group also operates in a further 32 countries around the world.

Community contributions

According to the annual report, in 2014/15 the company donated £796,000 to charitable causes worldwide. At least £357,500 of this went to one UK organisation, The Ove Arup Partnership Charitable Trust.

The company has also calculated the equivalent cost of employees' volunteering with the pro bono programme at over £640,000 worldwide. There was no breakdown available regarding total support in the UK alone during the year.

Beneficiaries included: The Ove Arup Partnership Charitable Trust (£357,500).

Employee-led support

Arup community engagement

Employees are encouraged to participate across a broad range of activities in the local communities where the company operates by donating their skills and expertise. The company has set up a partnering fund to facilitate this, for further information visit www.arupcommunity.org

During 2014/15 employees in the UK:

- Volunteered for Habitat for Humanity for two days to restore a children's playground in London
- Hosted World of Work Days to support The Prince's Trust, helping young people develop employability skills all over the UK
- Volunteered with Year 8 and 9 students through a ten-week STEM (science, technology, engineering and mathematics) experience with the Engineering Development Trust

Community partners include commercial, humanitarian and charitable organisations that share the same values as the company. In the UK, the company's current partners include: Class of Your Own; Engineering Development Trust; Engineers Without Borders; Frank Water; RedR; The Prince's Trust.

The Arup Cause

This is a global initiative to encourage community and educational activities. The company funds and provides structured opportunities for its employees to develop, both personally and professionally, and contribute to development projects around the world. The cause runs a different theme each year, such as water or shelter. Employees contribute through fundraising activities, volunteering and pro bono work.

Pro bono programme

Employees undertake pro bono work, which is sponsored by Arup who makes a contribution towards costs of approved projects. In 2014/15 employees volunteered 7,000 hours of company time to this programme.

Corporate charity

Ove Arup Partnership Charitable Trust (Charity Commission no. 1038737) and The Ove Arup Foundation (Charity Commission no. 328138).

Applications

The Ove Arup Partnership Charitable Trust

Applications can be directed to Stephanie Wilde (PA to Group Company Secretary) at the group's head office, or by email: stephanie.wilde@arup.com.

The Ove Arup Foundation

Application forms can be downloaded from the charity's website www.ovearupfoundation.org and sent to John Ward at the group's head office, or by email: ovarfound@arup.com.

Community engagement

Applications regarding Arup community engagement projects and causes can be directed to the correspondent. All other enquiries can be directed to the group's head office.

ASDA Stores Ltd

Retail – supermarkets

Correspondent: Julie Ward, The ASDA Foundation Administrator, ASDA House, Southbank, Great Wilson Street, Leeds LS11 5AD (tel: 0113 243 5435; fax: 0113 241 8666; website: www.asda.com)

Directors: A. Russo; A. Simpson; R. Burnley; S. Clarke (women: 0; men: 4)

Year end	31/12/2015
Turnover	£22,100,000,000
Pre-tax profit	£633,300,000

Nature of business: The retail of food, clothing, general merchandise and services throughout the UK and online. In 1999 ASDA became part of Wal-Mart Stores Inc., based in Arkansas.

Company registration number: 464777

Subsidiary undertakings include: ASDA Storage Ltd; ASDA Supermarkets Ltd; Ever 1295 Ltd; Netto Foodstores Ltd.

Brands include: George; Smart Price; Extra Special; Good for You!; ASDA Brand; ASDA Organics; ASDA Great Stuff.

UK employees: 163,514

Focus of giving: General charitable purposes, economic generation, education, health, ill health, sport, recreation, women's issues, children, young people, community/social welfare.

Membership: BITC

Community involvement	✓
Community contributions	✓
CSR report	✓
AF Covenant	✓
Charity partner(s)	✓
Company gives to smaller charities	✓
Corporate charity	✓
Employee-led support	✓
Gifts in kind	✓
Humanitarian aid: UK including food banks	✓
Market-led giving	✓
Unregistered charities/NFP	✓

Community involvement

ASDA's charitable giving appears to be made mainly through its charity, The ASDA Foundation (Charity Commission no. 1124268), where the trustees will distribute the funds to charities nominated by store colleagues. The foundation supplements the good causes that colleagues support locally, as well as a number of bigger ad hoc projects. In addition ASDA provides space in its stores for charities and community groups to use free of charge.

You can find information for your local area on community initiatives, your local community champion and the opportunity to nominate an organisation by visiting the 'Find your nearest ASDA' facility on the community web page.

Main locations

ASDA has locations throughout the UK

Community contributions

In 2015 the company's total cash donation including monies raised through store collections and product sales, totalled £13.9 million. This includes donations to the ASDA Foundation totalling £6.2 million. Unfortunately, there is no breakdown between cash raised by customers and staff and cash donated by the company from its profits.

ASDA Foundation also supported a range of local charities and sustainable local projects. These projects are cause-related activities, contributing to local charities or causes that ASDA's colleagues wish to support. The aim of the ASDA Foundation is to transform communities and improve the lives of people in the UK, now and in the future. It funds ASDA Community programme, which aims to make a difference in communities by focusing on four key areas: Working Life – better prospects for young people; Local Life – families are better connected to their communities; Healthier Life – improved health and well-being for everyone; and Greener Life – families living in cleaner, safer environments. The foundation will also support UK disaster appeals.

In-kind support

ASDA stores are FareShare partners but the authors have not been able to ascertain the extent of this support.

Employee-led support

ASDA's charitable giving appears to be made mainly through its charity, The ASDA Foundation (Charity Commission no. 1124268), beneficiaries of which are selected by ASDA's employees.

The foundation helps a variety of good causes and community activities. It also administers funds raised by staff and customers for:

- British Heart Foundation
- Children in Need
- Orchid
- Sporting Chance
- Tickled Pink
- Tommy's
- Whizz-Kidz

In 2015 the ASDA Foundation and Tickled Pink donated 11.5 million to charitable organisations and other community projects. In 2016 donations included: Peterhead – Dial a Community Bus (£27,500); Deen City Farm (£25,000); Wolverhampton and District MS Therapy Centre Ltd (£11,000).

Details of all ASDA's national charities and examples of staff's fundraising activities and achievements can be found at: www.asdafoundation.org.

Commercially led support

Carrier Bag Sales

In Wales the net proceeds of carrier bag charges amounted to £269,519 which was donated to Social Investment Cymru to support the social enterprise sector in Wales.

In Scotland support is made to Social Investment Scotland and Foundation Scotland, each receiving half of the net proceeds from the carrier bag charge.

At the time of writing (December 2016) ASDA have not publicised where the proceeds of carrier bag charges which are now being collected in England will go.

Corporate charity

The ASDA Foundation (Charity Commission no. 1124268).

Exclusions

Political and military groups; single religious or ethnic groups; sponsorship; advertising or overseas charities. In addition ASDA does not top up funds raised by local groups collecting or bag packing in store or makes contributions to money being raised for ASDA's National charities as it prefers to focus on money being raised by colleagues locally. Applications will also not be accepted where they are for the benefit of only one user group, where there are existing similar facilities in the local area, for revenue funding only, and where the applicant does not have a current three- to five-year project plan in place.

Applications

The ASDA Foundation funds significant local community projects, provides top-up funding grants, and runs the Community Life Programme 'chosen by you...given by us' which helps local charities and good causes nominated by ASDA customers and colleagues. In addition, there is a hardship fund for current and past colleagues. ASDA recommends prospective applicants to use the eligibility checker on its website (www.asdafoundation.org/applying-forfunding#what-we-fund) to determine if you are eligible to apply. Applicants should then approach the Community Champion at their local store.

Ashmore Group PLC

Business services

Correspondent: The Secretary to the Trustees, 61 Aldwych, London WC2B 4AE (tel: 020 3077 6000/020 3077 6153; email: foundation@ashmoregroup.com; website: www.ashmoregroup.com)

Directors: Clive Adamson; Dame Anne Pringle; David Bennett; Mark Coombs, Chief Executive Officer; Nick Land; Peter Gibbs; Simon Fraser; Tom Shippey, Group Finance Director (women: 1; men: 7)

Year end	30/06/2015
Turnover	£211,600,000
Pre-tax profit	£181,300,000

Nature of business: Ashmore Group is a specialist emerging markets fund manager across six core investment themes: external debt, local currency, special situations, equity, corporate high yield and multi-strategy.

Company registration number: 3675683

Subsidiary undertakings include: Ashmore Investments (UK) Ltd.

Total employees: 300

Focus of giving: General charitable purposes, education, health, ill health, overseas projects, disability.

Community involvement	✓
Community contributions	✓
CSR report	✓
CSR or charity committee	✓
Directors have other relevant posts	✓
Cash donations declared	✓
Corporate charity	✓
Employee-led support	✓
Gifts in kind	✓
Humanitarian aid: overseas	✓
Matched funding	✓
Pro bono	✓

Charitable donations

Cash UK (latest available):	2015	£100,000
Total UK (cash and in kind):	2015	£100,000
Cash worldwide:	2015	£100,000
Total worldwide (cash and in kind):	2015	£100,000

Community involvement

The Ashmore Foundation

The Ashmore Foundation (Charity Commission no. 1122351) currently has seven priority countries (Brazil, Colombia, Mexico, India, Indonesia, Philippines and Turkey) based on the location of Ashmore offices and significant investments, as well as the existence of a strong civil sector and clear social needs on which the Ashmore Foundation can focus.

Directors with other relevant posts

Nick Land, non-executive director, is a trustee of the Vodafone Group Foundation (Charity Commission no. 1089625).

Main locations

UK location: London.

Ashmore also has a number of worldwide locations.

Community contributions

In 2014/15 the group made charitable donations of £100,000 through its corporate charity, the Ashmore Foundation.

In-kind support

Ashmore also supports the foundation's charitable activities through the provision of pro bono office space, administrative support and a matched funding commitment for employee donations to the Ashmore Foundation.

Employee-led support

The Ashmore Foundation is supported solely by Ashmore and its employees globally. Crucially, this support from employees extends beyond financial aid to include active engagement in fundraising – such as the Ashmore Three Peaks Challenge which raised over £53,000 for two grantees – and a network of support which includes mentoring and helping NGOs expand their network of contacts.

Corporate charity

The Ashmore Foundation (Charity Commission no. 1122351).

Applications

The Ashmore Foundation does not accept unsolicited applications. It sources new partners through recommendations from experts, existing partners, suggestions from Ashmore staff and detailed research by the foundation's team.

Ashtead Group PLC

Industrial products/services

Correspondent: Eric Watkins, Company Secretary, Ashtead Group PLC, 100 Cheapside, London EC2V 6DT (tel: 020 7726 9700; fax: 020 7726 9705; website: www.ashtead-group.com)

Directors: Brendan Horgan; Chris Cole, Chair; Geoff Drabble; Ian Sutcliffe; Lucinda Riches; Sat Dhaiwal; Suzanne Wood; Tanya Fratto; Wayne Edmunds (women: 3; men: 6)

Year end	30/04/2016
Turnover	£25,457,000,000
Pre-tax profit	£645,000,000

Nature of business: Ashtead is an international equipment rental company with national networks in the US and the UK and a small presence in Canada. The group rents a full range of construction and industrial equipment across a wide variety of applications to a diverse customer base.

Company registration number: 1807982

Subsidiary undertakings include: Ashtead Holdings PLC; Sunbelt Rentals, Inc.; Ashtead Plant Hire Company Ltd; Ashtead Capital.

Total employees: 13,112

Focus of giving: Housing, homelessness, armed forces, overseas projects.

Community involvement	✓
Community contributions	✓
CSR report	✓
Directors have other relevant posts	✓
Armed forces personnel	✓
Cash donations declared	✓
Charity partner(s)	✓
Employee-led support	✓
FTSE 100	✓
Gifts in kind	✓
Humanitarian aid: overseas	✓
Matched funding	✓
Overseas giving	✓
Payroll giving	✓
Sponsorship	✓

Charitable donations

Total worldwide (cash and in kind):	2016	£225,000

Community involvement

Directors with other relevant posts

Lucinda Riches (independent non-executive director) is a trustee of Sue Ryder (Charity Commission no. 1052076), a charity that provides specialist palliative care both at hospital and at the patient's home.

Main locations

London and the USA.

Community contributions

As part of the group's commitment to The Prince's Trust, in 2015/16 Ashtead made a donation of £15,000 which helped young people gain access to jobs in construction, civil engineering and other sectors associated with the built environment. The 2015/16 annual report and accounts state that charitable donations in the year totalled £225,000. It is unclear how much of the donations came from employee contributions and we have taken this as the overall figure for the total worldwide contribution, we have no UK figure available.

In-kind support

In the UK the group supports CRASH, the construction and property industry's charity for homeless people. In 2015 the group was also involved in setting up Emmaus Salford, a new community recently opened in Greater Manchester which comprises a shop and accommodation for homeless people. The group supplied a range of equipment during the refurbishment.

In the US the group works closely with the American Red Cross and its affiliates such as the Second Harvest Food Bank for which the group has a food drive every November. The group allows employees to make payroll deductions to contribute to the American Red Cross or the Sunbelt Rentals Employee Relief Fund.

Employee-led support

The group's stores regularly support and participate in local charity events and community service. The London to Brighton Bike Ride took place in June and an Ashtead and A-Plant contingent rode the gruelling 54 miles from capital to coast to raise money for the British Heart Foundation. A total of 23 cyclists took part, including work colleagues, friends and customers and raised over £3,000 for the British Heart Foundation.

Commercially led support

In the US, the group sponsors a local softball team in Dallas and various charity golf tournaments. It also supports the Gary Sinse Foundation with the R.I.S.E. (Restoring Independence Supporting Empowerment) programme which provides severely wounded veterans and their families with resources to overcome the challenges of life after their injuries. A major area of focus for R.I.S.E. is the building of custom smart homes. The group's partnership with R.I.S.E. gives contractors access to tools and equipment at no cost.

Applications

Apply in writing to the correspondent.

Associated British Foods PLC

Food manufacture, retail – miscellaneous

Correspondent: Assistant Company Secretary, Weston Centre, 10 Grosvenor Street, London W1K 4QY (tel: 020 7399 6500; website: www.abfoods.com)

Directors: Charles Sinclair, Chair; Emma Adamo; George Weston, Chief Executive; Javier Ferrán; John Bason; Ruth Cairnie; Timothy Clarke; Wolfhart Hauser

Year end	17/09/2016
Turnover	£13,400,000,000
Pre-tax profit	£1,071,000,000

Nature of business: The activities of the group principally concern the processing and manufacture of food worldwide and textile retailing in the UK and continental Europe. Associated British Foods has five key business areas: Sugar, Agriculture, Retail, Grocery and Ingredients. The ultimate holding company is Wittington Investments Ltd.

Company registration number: 293262

Brands include: AB Agri; Billingtons; Blue Dragon; Jordans; Mazola; Ovaltine; Patak's; Primark; Ryvita; Silver Spoon; Twinings.

Focus of giving: General charitable purposes.

Community involvement	✓
Community contributions	✓
Company reports on anti-slavery	✓
Corporate charity	✓
FTSE 100	✓

Community involvement

Garfield Weston Foundation (Charity Commission no. 230260)
The Garfield Weston Foundation was set up in 1958 by the founder of Associated British Foods, W. Garfield Weston. The foundation owns a majority stake in a privately owned holding company, Wittington Investments Ltd. Wittington holds a diverse portfolio of investments including a 54.5% share in Associated British Foods. Due to the success of the foundation's investments it is now one of the UK's largest grant-makers and during 2015/16 awarded £58.7 million to over 1,600 charities.

Grants are made in most fields apart from animal welfare. Project funding, capital costs and core costs are all considered. The foundation favours small, local projects and community organisations. In 2016 about 92% of the grants made were for less than £100,000.

Community contributions

A figure for the group's community contributions was not available. Each of the group's brands has its own CSR programme.

Corporate charity

The Garfield Weston Foundation (Charity Commission no. 230260).

Applications

See the entry for The Garfield Weston Foundation on page 407.

AstraZeneca

Pharmaceuticals

Correspondent: Corporate Responsibility Team, 15 Stanhope Gate, London W1K 1LN (tel: 020 7304 5000; website: www.astrazeneca.com)

Directors: Ann Cairns; Baroness Shriti Vadera; Bruce Burlington; Genevieve Berger; Graham Chipchase; Leif Johansson, Chair; Marc Dunoyer, Chief Financial Officer; Marcus Wallenberg; Pascal Soriot, Chief Executive; Rudy Markham (women: 4; men: 9)

Year end	31/12/2015
Turnover	£24,708,000,000
Pre-tax profit	£3,069,000,000

Nature of business: The group's principal activities are the research, development and marketing of medicines for serious health conditions.

Company registration number: 2723534

Subsidiary undertakings include: AlphaCore Pharma Ltd; Astra Pharmaceuticals Ltd; AstraZeneca Investments Ltd.

Brands include: Crestor; Seroquel; Symbicort.

UK employees: 6,700

Focus of giving: Education, health, ill health, housing, homelessness, medical research, science technology, children, young people, community/social welfare.

Membership: LBG

Community involvement	✓
Community contributions	✓
CSR report	✓
Cash donations declared	✓
Charity partner(s)	✓
FTSE 100	✓
Gifts in kind	✓
Humanitarian aid: overseas	✓
Overseas giving	✓
Sponsorship	✓
STEM-focused	✓

Charitable donations

Cash UK (latest available):	2015	£407,000
Total worldwide (cash and in kind):	2015	£519 million

Community involvement

The group's community investment strategy focuses on community healthcare and STEM education. It also supports disaster relief.

Charity partner
The British Red Cross continues to be the group's global disaster relief partner, with the majority of disaster relief donations channelled through it.

Patient organisations
The group works with patient groups and health charities to share knowledge and information. It provides charitable donations and sponsorship to organisations benefitting healthcare, health promotion and the NHS.

Other organisations
The group also works with organisations including the NHS, research institutions and other healthcare organisations.

Main locations
AstraZeneca has various locations throughout the UK and worldwide.

Community contributions

Global contributions
According to AstraZeneca's annual report, in 2015, at a global level, the group spent a total of approximately $680 million (£519 million) on community investment sponsorships, partnerships and charitable donations worldwide, including the product donation and patient assistance programmes which make medicines available free of charge or at reduced prices. We take the figure of $680 million (£519 million) as the company's worldwide contribution. Through the three patient assistance programmes in the US the company donated products valued at an average wholesale price of over $617 million (£468 million). The company also donated products worth over $17 million (£12.9 million), valued at average wholesale price, to charitable organisation AmeriCares.

The British Red Cross continues as the group's global disaster relief partner, through which most of its global disaster relief donations are channelled. In 2015 the following donations were made to the British Red Cross: £50,000 was donated for the Nepal Earthquake appeal; $200,000 (around £162,000) for the refurbishment of the Kuala Lumpur Emergency Response Unit; and £50,000 to the charity's Europe Refugee Crisis Appeal.

Contributions to patient groups in the UK
In 2015 the group made contributions to patient organisations totalling almost £145,000.

Beneficiaries included: Diabetes UK (£93,000); The Roy Castle Lung Cancer Foundation (£14,000); Asthma UK (£12,000); British Lung Foundation (£500).

In-kind support

The group provides in-kind support of product donations to charitable organisations.

Employee-led support

Volunteering
The group has a global volunteering allowance for all employees.

Commercially led support

Partnership
2015 was the fifth year of the partnership with the UK educational charity Career Ready to support increased participation by 16- to 19-year-olds in science, technology, engineering and maths (STEM subjects).

Exclusions

No support is given for circulars, advertising in charity brochures, individuals, older people, fundraising events, political/discriminatory groups, religious appeals, sport, anything contrary to the company's business, capital projects or building appeals.

Applications

Apply in writing to the correspondent.

Autonomous Research LLP

Business services

Correspondent: Martin Pollock, Autonomous Research Charitable Trust, Floor 2, 1 Bartholomew Lane, London EC2N 2AX (tel: 020 7776 3400; fax: 020 7776 3401; email: martinpollock@moorestephens.com; website: www.autonomous-research.com)

Directors: Erickson Davies, Deputy Chief Executive; Lord Myners, Chair; Stuart Graham, Chief Executive

Year end	31/03/2016
Turnover	£27,700,000
Pre-tax profit	£16,200,000

Nature of business: Independent provider of research on banking and insurance companies.

Company registration number: OC343985

UK employees: 28

Total employees: 28

Focus of giving: General charitable purposes, education, health, ill health, financial education, humanitarian help, arts, culture, overseas projects, poverty and social exclusion, community/social welfare, disability.

Community involvement	✓
Community contributions	✓
Cash donations declared	✓
Charity partner(s)	✓
Corporate charity	✓
Humanitarian aid: overseas	✓
Humanitarian aid: UK including food banks	✓
Sponsorship	✓

Charitable donations

Cash UK (latest available):	2016	£174,000
Total UK (cash and in kind):	2016	£174,000
Cash worldwide:	2016	£174,000
Total worldwide (cash and in kind):	2016	£174,000

Community involvement

The company's website states that it partners with a small number of charities, and also allocates a share of its profits to charitable causes through its corporate charities – the Autonomous Research Charitable Trust in the UK; and the Autonomous Research Foundation in the USA.

Autonomous Research Charitable Trust (Charity Commission no. 1137503)

The group's corporate charity, the Autonomous Research Charitable Trust provides grants to charitable organisations, as well as mentoring and business and careers advice. The trust's aims, according to its latest accounts, are 'to help disadvantaged people get a step up in life' and 'to empower people to improve the quality of their lives'. The trust also states that it tends to support 'a small number of key partner charities, both in London and abroad, where we feel we can make a difference and establish long-term relationships'.

Partner charities

The company's website states that its current core charities are: Food Cycle, a UK-registered charity which tackles food waste and food poverty; Five Talents, a UK-registered charity which provides savings schemes, small loans, and business training for those in need in rural Kenya, Tanzania, and Uganda; and W!SE (Working In Support of Education), a USA-based charity which provides financial education. Previous partner charities have included: Find Your Feet; One Degree; Plan International; Smart Works.

Main locations

The company's UK office is in London. There are also offices in Hong Kong and New York.

Community contributions

The company's 2015/16 accounts state that charitable donations during the year totalled £174,000 and were made to UK-registered charities.

The latest accounts available from the Charity Commission at the time of writing (January 2017) for the Autonomous Research Trust were the 2013/14 accounts. In this year, donations from The Partners of Autonomous Research LLP totalled £319,000.

Commercially led support

Sponsorship

Through its partnership with the charity Five Talents, the group is sponsoring the charity's 2017 Tanzanian Marathon.

Corporate charity

Autonomous Research Charitable Trust (Charity Commission no. 1137503).

Applications

Autonomous Research Charitable Trust

The trustees agree a small number of core partner charities to support each year, but they also make ad hoc grants to other charities as appropriate. The 2013/14 accounts state the following information:

> Unsolicited applications are accepted, but the trustees do receive a high number of grant applications which, in line with the trustees' grant making policy, are mostly unsuccessful. The trustees prefer to support donations to charities whose work they have researched and which is in accordance with the aims and objectives of the charity for the year.

Aveva Group PLC

Information Technology

Correspondent: Corporate Responsibility Team, High Cross, Madingley Road, Cambridge CB3 0HB (tel: 01223 556655; fax: 01223 556666; website: www.aveva.com)

Directors: Christopher Humphrey; David Ward; James Kidd, Chief Financial Officer; Jennifer Allerton; Philip Aiken, Chair; Philip Dayer; Richard Longdon, Chief Executive (women: 1; men: 6)

Year end	31/03/2016
Turnover	£201,500,000
Pre-tax profit	£29,400,000

Nature of business: The principal activities of the group are the marketing and development of computer software and services for engineering and related solutions.

Company registration number: 2937296

Subsidiary undertakings include: Aveva Solutions Ltd; Aveva East Asia Ltd; Aveva Pty Ltd; Aveva SA.

Total employees: 1,703

Focus of giving: General charitable purposes, education, health, ill health, overseas projects, children, young people.

Community involvement	✓
Community contributions	✓
CSR report	✓
CSR or charity committee	✓
Cash donations declared	✓
Employee-led support	✓
Humanitarian aid: overseas	✓
Matched funding	✓
Overseas giving	✓

Charitable donations

Cash worldwide:	2016	£59,500

Community involvement

The company appears to support the community largely through employee-led activities.

Case study

Taken from the 2015/16 annual report:

> One of the many fine examples of the fantastic support that our teams have given during the course of the year comes from our team in Japan, who wanted to provide support to the growing number of refugees who find themselves in difficult situations. The team took part in a charity initiative to donate their used clothes to help raise funds through a Japanese clothing retail chain. The chain have been donating clothing to many vulnerable groups in the region: evacuees, victims of disaster, expectant and nursing mothers, as well as others in need across the globe. The team collected a vast amount of clothing and are looking to continue to support this charity in such a simple but effective way to make a difference to people's lives.

Main locations

UK locations: Cambridge.

Aveva also has a number of locations worldwide.

Community contributions

According to the 2015/16 annual report, this year the group matched employees' fundraising with a total of £59,500 to support local communities. We were not able to determine a figure relating to the UK giving.

Employee-led support

Employees continue to support many local, national and international charities.

Matched funding

The group matched funding raised by employees who have participated in various events, such as marathons, charity auctions, events, and fun runs.

Commercially led support

Education Partnerships

The Aveva Academic Initiative is a strategic investment that provides benefits to Aveva, universities, and the broader engineering discipline.

Applications

Apply in writing to the correspondent.

Aviva PLC

Insurance

Correspondent: Corporate Responsibility Team, St Helen's, 1 Undershaft, London EC3P 3DQ (tel: 020 7283 2000; email: cr.team@aviva.com; website: www.aviva.com)

Directors: Andy Briggs; Belen Romana Garcia; Bob Stein; Claudia Arney; Glyn Barker; Mark Wilson, Group Chief Executive Officer; Michael Hawker; Michael Mire; Patricia Cross; Scott Wheway; Sir Adrian Montague, Chair; Sir Malcolm Williamson; Tom Stoddard, Chief Financial Officer (women: 3; men: 10)

Year end	31/12/2015
Turnover	£23,728,000,000
Pre-tax profit	£1,172,000,000

Nature of business: The company transacts life assurance and long-term savings business, fund management, and all classes of general insurance through its subsidiaries, associates and branches in the UK, Europe, Asia and Canada.

Company registration number: 2468686

Subsidiary undertakings include: Aviva Health UK Ltd; AXA Sun Life Private Equity (No. 1) Ltd Partnership; Friends Life Ltd.

Total employees: 29,600

Focus of giving: Environment, health, ill health, heritage, small groups, local groups, humanitarian help, older people, poverty and social exclusion, safety and crime prevention, sport, recreation, children, young people, community/social welfare, disability, disasters.

Membership: BITC, LBG

Accredited Living Wage Employer	✓
Community involvement	✓
Community contributions	✓
Company reports on anti-slavery	✓
CSR report	✓
CSR or charity committee	✓
Directors have other relevant posts	✓
Charity partner(s)	✓
Company gives to smaller charities	✓
Corporate charity	✓
Employee-led support	✓
FTSE 100	✓
Gifts in kind	✓
Humanitarian aid: overseas	✓
Humanitarian aid: UK including food banks	✓
Matched funding	✓
Pro bono	✓
Sponsorship	✓

Charitable donations

Total worldwide (cash and in kind):	2015	£10,800,000

Community involvement

The group refreshed its corporate responsibility strategy in 2015. Most of its support is given through the Aviva Community Fund, which provides grants for organisations to run community projects, focusing on: health; disability; children and young people; older people; sport; environment; and community. The group also has a partnership with the British Red Cross, and offers volunteering leave for employees and matched funding for employee fundraising.

Aviva Community Fund UK

Community projects can be submitted online by a community organisation or charity in the UK. Projects can then be voted for online and the final winners are picked by a judging panel and awarded funding. There are four categories of grants that can be awarded: up to £1,000; up to £5,000; up to £10,000; up to £25,000. There are six categories of projects that can be supported: health, disability and well-being; supporting the younger generation; supporting the older generation; sport in the community; environment; community support. In 2016 a total of 800 projects were supported across the UK.

Projects which are not successful can also be entered into the Helping Hand Prize Draw, which will provide a further 40 awards of £500.

The group has also set up community funds in: Canada; Poland; France; Italy; and Hong Kong.

Partnerships

In early 2016, the group began a three-year partnership with the British Red Cross, working to support community resilience to disasters in the UK and globally. The group is a member of the Disaster Relief Alliance, investing in the Red Cross' work in preparedness, response, recovery and innovation, and has sponsored the British Red Cross emergency app. The group will also offer its expertise in risk management, employee volunteering and matched funding for employee fundraising.

The group is also working in partnership with Premiership Rugby to deliver Aviva Tackling Numbers, an educational programme focused on numeracy through rugby-based games for seven- to nine-year-olds.

Directors with other relevant posts

Sir Adrian Montague is also the Chair of Trustees of The Point of Care Foundation (Charity Commission no. 1151628). Andy Briggs is a member of the fundraising council for NSPCC (Charity Commission no. 216401). Sir Malcolm Williamson is a trustee of Youth Business International (Charity Commission no. 1123946). Glyn Barker is a trustee of English National Opera (Charity Commission no. 257210).

The group is a founding partner in Project Everyone, committed to supporting the UN Global Goals for Sustainable Development. The group's Chief Executive, Mark Wilson, addressed the UN General Assembly at the launch of the goals.

Main locations

The group has offices across the UK, as well as in a number of countries worldwide.

Community contributions

In 2015 the group contributed a total of £10.8 million worldwide, mainly through its community funds. Employee fundraising during the year totalled over £1.5 million.

Beneficiaries of the Aviva Community Fund UK include: 2nd Swanley Scout Group; GoodGym; Honiton Youth Orchestra; Llangennech RFC Juniors; National Osteoporosis Society; New Mills Community Festival; Reading Samaritans; Refugee Action York; St Christopher's Hospice; Surbiton Wildlife Group.

Employee-led support

Employee fundraising and volunteering

The group offers paid volunteering leave to employees, and also provides matched funding for employee fundraising. In 2015 the group provided matched funding for employee donations in response to humanitarian appeals for the Nepal earthquake and the European refugee crisis, bringing the total amount donated to £135,000. In 2015 employees volunteered for a total of almost 41,000 hours and raised over £1.5 million. The group has set an aim of reaching 200,000 hours of volunteering by 2020.

Exclusions

A full list of exclusions from the Aviva Community Fund is provided on the fund's website: community-fund.aviva.co.uk.

Applications

Apply in writing via post or email to the Corporate Responsibility Team.

Avon Cosmetics Ltd

Health/beauty products

Correspondent: Charitable Donations Department, Nunn Mills Road, Northampton NN1 5PA (tel: 01604 232425; website: www.avon.uk.com)

Directors: Samantha Hutchinson; Alastair Judge; Robert Loughran; Andrea Slater (women: 2; men: 2)

Year end	31/12/2015
Turnover	£236,000,000
Pre-tax profit	(£3,200,000)

Nature of business: The principal activities of the company are the distribution and sale of beauty, gift and decorative products.

Company registration number: 592235

Focus of giving: Health, ill health, safety and crime prevention, women's issues.

Community involvement	✓
Community contributions	✓
Cash donations declared	✓
Charity partner(s)	✓
Gifts in kind	✓
Market-led giving	✓

Charitable donations

Cash UK (latest available):	2015	£260,000
Total UK (cash and in kind):	2015	£260,000
Cash worldwide:	2015	£260,000
Total worldwide (cash and in kind):	2015	£260,000

Community involvement

Charity partners

Avon's three main charity partners are Breast Cancer Now, Women's Aid and Refuge. Support is also given to Crazy Hats and Look Good Feel Better.

The Avon Foundation (USA)

In 1955 the company formalised its philanthropic efforts with the creation of the Avon Foundation, which advances the mission to improve the lives of women and their families.

The foundation's main efforts are today focused on the critical issues of breast cancer and domestic violence and Avon global philanthropy is advancing these causes in more than 50 countries.

The latest annual report of the foundation and details on mission programs, grants, educational materials and financial reports can be found on the Avon Foundation website – www.avonfoundation.org

Community contributions

In 2015 the company made charitable donations amounting to £239,000 supporting the battle against breast cancer and the fight to end violence against women. The company spent an additional £21,000 on campaigns and other charitable activities.

Beneficiaries included: Breakthrough; Cransley Hospice; Crazy Hats; Northampton Health Charity; Refuge; Women's Aid.

In-kind support

Avon provides hampers to anyone fundraising for one of their partner charities.

Commercially led support

Representatives around the world sell specially designed 'pink ribbon' products that provide the opportunity for anyone to participate in the fight against breast cancer. Avon and the Avon Foundation award a portion of the proceeds to organisations and institutions to help eradicate breast cancer, with grants made within the country in which the funds are raised.

Applications

Apply writing to the correspondent or contact your nearest Avon representative.

To apply for a product hamper to support your fundraising activities, make contact as follows:

- Breast Cancer Now: avon@breakthrough.org.uk
- WomensAid: fundraising@womensaid.org.uk
- Refuge: fundraising@refuge.org.uk

Make sure you include:

- The name of the charity you are supporting
- The date of your fundraising event
- How you will use the product hamper to raise funds or awareness
- Your delivery address

BAE Systems PLC

Defence, aerospace

Correspondent: Community Investment Team, 6 Carlton Gardens, London SW1Y 5AD (tel: 01252 373232; email: community@baesystems.com; website: www.baesystems.com)

Directors: Charles Woodburn, Chief Operating Officer; Chris Grigg; Elizabeth Corley; Harriet Green; Ian King, Chief Executive; Ian Tyler; Jerry DeMuro; Nick Rose; Paula Rosput Reynolds; Peter Lynas, Group Finance Director; Sir Roger Carr, Chair (women: 3; men: 8)

Year end	31/12/2015
Turnover	£16,787,000,000
Pre-tax profit	£1,090,000,000

Nature of business: The main activity of the group is defence – comprising the design and manufacture of civil and military aircraft, surface ships, submarines, space systems, radar, avionics, communications, electronics and guided weapon systems.

Company registration number: 1470151

Subsidiary undertakings include: BAE Systems Applied Intelligence Ltd; Armor Holdings Inc.; Piper Group PLC.

Total employees: 82,500

Focus of giving: Overseas projects, armed forces, humanitarian help.

Membership: LBG

Community involvement	✓
Community contributions	✓
CSR report	✓
Armed forces personnel	✓
Employee-led support	✓
FTSE 100	✓
Humanitarian aid: overseas	✓
Humanitarian aid: UK including food banks	✓
Market-led giving	✓
Overseas giving	✓
Payroll giving	✓
Sponsorship	✓

Community involvement

Support is mainly focused on issues connected to the group's business such as the armed forces and science, technology, engineering and mathematics education.

The group states that as well as one-off support it undertakes longer projects that help charities plan their work further in advance. This includes BAE's Relationship Charity Awards (in the UK) that fund specific projects for up to five years.

Armed Forces

In the UK the group supports five leading armed forces charities: SAFA, ABF The Soldiers Charity, Combat Stress, RAF Benevolent Fund and the Royal Navy and Royal Marines Charity.

The group funds educational and vocational bursaries through its Relationship Charity Award to ABF the Soldiers Charity. In 2015 this helped over 100 veterans improve their career prospects.

The group has also made a donation of £5 million over five years to the new Defence and National Rehabilitation Centre which will replace the UK's current facility at Headley Court.

Education

The group's UK businesses are involved in programmes that encourage young people to follow careers in engineering. BAE Systems sponsors the Queen Elizabeth Prize for Engineering and the Big Bang Science Fair.

Disaster relief

In 2015 donations were made to charitable organisations working to provide relief for the Nepal Earthquake and the Cumbrian floods.

Directors with other relevant posts

Ian Tyler is President of Construction Industry Relief, Assistance and Support for the Homeless Ltd, the construction and property industry charity for the homeless.

Main locations

BAE Systems has offices throughout the United Kingdom, Australia, India, Saudi Arabia and the United States.

Community contributions

In 2015 the group and its employees contributed more than £11 million through the BAE's Community Investment programme.

Beneficiaries included: ABF, the Soldiers Charity; British Forces Foundation; Combat Stress; the Queen Elizabeth Prize for Engineering; the RAF Benevolent Fund; the Royal Navy and Royal Marines Charity; SSAFA; UK Defence and National Rehabilitation Centre.

Employee-led support

Employee volunteering

Employees contribute their time, knowledge and skills to local schools and charities. Where possible volunteering is integrated into formal career-development programmes.

Payroll giving

Various payroll deduction schemes are operated in some parts of the business.

Commercially led support

Sponsorship

Sponsorship is undertaken by the group including that of the British Forces Foundation.

Exclusions

Funding and support is not provided to individuals or non-charitable organisations involved in fundraising activities.

Applications

Apply in writing to the correspondent. Requests for funding or support should fall within one of the four following areas:

- The armed forces and their families
- Science, technology, engineering and maths education
- Local communities
- Employee fundraising and volunteering

Ted Baker PLC

Retail – clothing and footwear

Correspondent: Ted's Conscience Team, Ugly Brown Building, 6A St Pancras Way, London NW1 0TB (tel: 020 7255 4800; email: ask.ted@tedbaker.com; website: www.tedbakerplc.com)

Directors: Andrew Jennings; Anne Sheinfeld; David Bernstein, Chair; Lindsay Page; Raymond Kelvin, Chief Executive; Ronald Stewart (women: 2; men: 4)

Year end	31/01/2016
Turnover	£456,200,000
Pre-tax profit	£58,700,000

Nature of business: The company is a British fashion design retailer, with stores and concessions worldwide.

Company registration number: 3393836

Subsidiary undertakings include: No Ordinary Designer Label Ltd; Ted Baker Japan KK; Big Lobster Ltd.

Total employees: 2,955

Focus of giving: General charitable purposes, children, young people, community/social welfare.

Community involvement	✓
Community contributions	✓
Company reports on anti-slavery	✓
CSR or charity committee	✓
Charity partner(s)	✓
Employee-led support	✓
Gifts in kind	✓

Community involvement

Social, environmental and ethical matters are co-ordinated by a team of representatives from different departments, known as the Ted's Conscience Team.

The Ted's Conscience Team sends a monthly 'DO SOMETHING' email to all employees in the company's head office to encourage charitable and environmental activities.

Charity

The website states that the company doesn't 'shout about' its work with charities, but that it provides both financial and in-kind support to a variety of organisations.

Sustainability

The company works with the charities Oxfam and Newlife to ensure that faulty or end-of-life garments do not end up in landfill.

The company is also working in partnership with the not-for-profit organisation MADE-BY, and has become one of the first brands to publish a brand scorecard on the MADE-BY website, tracking their progress on sustainability issues (www.made-by.org/modetracker).

Directors with other relevant posts

David Bernstein is Chair of Trustees of the British Red Cross (Charity Commission no. 220949). Ronald Stewart is a trustee of a number of charities including Reed's School (Charity Commission no. 312008) and Jemima Octavia Cooper for the Poor (Charity Commission no. 200187).

Main locations

The group has a head office in London, with retail operations worldwide.

Community contributions

The annual report for 2015/16 states that charitable donations during the year totalled £30,500. It was not specified how much of this was in the UK, in cash or in kind, or how much came from employee fundraising or from the company.

In-kind support

The annual report provides an example of the company's in-kind support: the company donated products as well as raising money for The Tope Project, which provides Christmas dinners for care leavers in London.

Employee-led support

According to the 2015/16 annual report, most of the company's charitable giving appears to be employee-led. Examples of employee contributions during the year include donating unwanted clothes to Oxfam and collecting donations for the charity Magic Breakfast, which provides breakfast clubs to disadvantaged children.

Applications

Apply in writing to the correspondent.

Balfour Beatty PLC

Business services

Correspondent: Bekir Andrews, Sustainability Director, 130 Wilton Road, London SW1V 1LQ (tel: 020 7216 6800; email: sustainability@balfourbeatty.com; website: www.balfourbeatty.com)

Directors: Dr Stephen Billingham; Ian Ferguson; Leo Quinn, Chief Executive Officer; Maureen Kempston Darkes; Philip Aitken; Philip Harrison, Chief Financial Officer; Stuart Doughty (women: 1; men: 6)

Year end	31/12/2015
Turnover	£8,235,000,000
Pre-tax profit	(£44,000,000)

Nature of business: Balfour Beatty is an international infrastructure group that delivers services essential to the development, creation and care of infrastructure assets (from finance and development, through to design and project management, to construction and maintenance) either alone or in partnership and by integrating local supply chains.

Company registration number: 2818602

Total employees: 34,000

Focus of giving: General charitable purposes, education, enterprise/training, overseas projects, sport, recreation, children, young people.

Community involvement	✓
Community contributions	✓
Company reports on anti-slavery	✓
CSR report	✓
Cash donations declared	✓
Charity partner(s)	✓
Corporate charity	✓
Employee-led support	✓
Gifts in kind	✓
Overseas giving	✓
Sponsorship	✓

Charitable donations

Cash UK (latest available):	2015	£82,500
Total UK (cash and in kind):	2015	£234,500
Cash worldwide:	2015	£82,500
Total worldwide (cash and in kind):	2015	£234,500

Community involvement

The company helps local communities by taking part in and supporting organisations and activities that aim to improve social cohesion and inclusion and through contributing to charitable causes.

Balfour Beatty Charitable Trust (Charity Commission no. 1127453)

The company channels much of its giving through its trust which was established in the company's centenary year 2009, to advance in life and relieve the needs of young people suffering from disadvantage by assisting with the provision of advice, training and education and other activities. The trust can also support general charitable purposes. The trust was founded by Balfour Beatty to support the company's corporate and social responsibility provision and to act as a focus for employee fundraising as well as to develop into a significant grant-funder.

Balfour Beatty matches donations which have been raised by employees through fundraising activities for the trust and has indicated that there will be continuing financial support of the trust's aims. However, there is no formal link between the trust and Balfour Beatty PLC.

Through the trust, branded 'Building Better Futures', the company has worked principally in partnership with Action for Children, The Prince's Trust and more recently Corum and Barnardo's, to deliver a series of programmes aimed at helping disadvantaged young people.

Building Better Futures is focused on three themes:

- Young people's employability and employment
- Helping the most disadvantaged young people in society
- Health, sport and well-being

Main locations

The group operates across the UK: www.balfourbeatty.com/contacts/office-locations/uk-ireland. Its head office is in London.

Community contributions

In 2015 the company made charitable contributions totalling £234,500 which included direct donations totalling £57,000, matched funding totalling £25,500 and in-kind contributions totalling £152,000. A further £104,000 was raised through employee fundraising.

In-kind support

The company has provided in-kind support to several projects during the year. In Scotland it worked with the charity Aberlour to refurbish a disused army barracks and turn it into a youth club. In Manchester it helped transform 62 homes and create a support centre for veterans' charity Walking with the Wounded. Employees also spent two weeks building a bridge to connect two isolated communities in Rwanda.

Employee-led support

Employee volunteering

During the year 150 employees volunteered at the London Youth Games.

Commercially led support

Sponsorship

Balfour Beatty is the leading sponsor of the London Youth Games, Europe's largest annual youth sports event.

Corporate charity

The Balfour Beatty Charitable Trust (Charity Commission no. 1127453).

Applications

Apply in writing to the correspondent.

Bank of Ireland UK (PLC)

Financial services

Correspondent: Corporate Responsibility Officer, Head Office GB, Bow Bells House, 1 Bread Street, London EC4M 9BE (email: responsiblebusiness@boi.com; website: www.bank-of-ireland.co.uk)

Directors: Andrew Keating, Group Chief Financial Officer; Archie Kane; Brad Martin; Davida Marston; Fiona Muldoon; Kent Atkinson; Pat Butler; Patrick Haren; Patrick Kennedy; Patrick Mulvihill; Richie Boucher, Group Chief Executive Officer; Tom Considine (women: 2; men: 10)

Year end	31/12/2015
Turnover	£1,232,000

Nature of business: Bank of Ireland UK's principal activities are the provision of an extensive range of banking and other financial services in Great Britain and Northern Ireland.

Company registration number: 7022885

Subsidiary undertakings include: Bank of Ireland International Finance Ltd; New Ireland Assurance Company PLC; Bank of Ireland Mortgage Bank.

Focus of giving: Education, overseas projects, poverty and social exclusion, children, young people.

Community involvement	✓
Community contributions	✓
CSR report	✓
Charity partner(s)	✓
Employee-led support	✓
Gifts in kind	✓
Humanitarian aid: overseas	✓
Matched funding	✓
Payroll giving	✓
Sponsorship	✓

Charitable donations

Cash UK (latest available):	2015	£703,000
Total UK (cash and in kind):	2015	£703,000
Cash worldwide:	2015	£703,000
Total worldwide (cash and in kind):	2015	£703,000

Community involvement

Charity partners

As well as the charities chosen by colleagues the bank also works with five flagship charities: St Vincent De Paul, Barnardo's, The Irish Cancer Charity, Peta House and Co-operation Ireland.

Give Together

The company's main approach has been to channel community investment into encouraging, facilitating and supporting employee volunteer and fundraising activities through an initiative called Give Together. To this end, every Bank of Ireland employee is given a day each year to volunteer for the cause of their choice. As well as facilitating employee volunteering, employees can supplement their fundraising efforts by applying for matched funding when they are involved in fundraising for a community or charitable organisation. There is also funding available for team volunteering to buy materials and equipment to enable their volunteering project.

Main locations

Offices throughout the UK.

Community contributions

The bank's total community giving was £2.5 million in 2015. However, this figure includes employee and customer fundraising. The bank provided £703,000 in matched funding which we have taken to be their cash contributions for the year.

In-kind support

Employees are given one day's paid volunteering leave per year. In 2015 employees volunteered a total of over 1,000 days.

Training for charities

Training was provided to 245 charities through the bank's learning zone.

Education initiatives

The bank runs several educational initiatives for schoolchildren. Bizworld is a skills development and entrepreneurship challenge and Learn to Earn teaches schoolchildren about financial management.

Employee-led support

Payroll giving

Employees participate in payroll giving schemes which provide funding for the bank's Florin Fund and its Third World Fund which supports projects in financially developing countries. During the year €846,000 was given by the fund in support of 43 projects in 26 financially developing countries.

Matched funding

The bank matches employees' fundraising. In 2015 the bank matched £703,000 of employee fundraising.

Employee fundraising

Events included cycling challenges and the Darkness into Light walk.

Applications

Apply in writing to the correspondent.

The Banks Group Ltd

Mining, property

Correspondent: James Eaglesham, Fund Manager, Inkerman House, St John's Road, Meadowfield, Durham DH7 8XL (tel: 0191 378 6100/0191 378 6342; fax: 0191 378 2409; email: james@bankscommunityfund.org.uk; website: www.hjbanks.com)

Directors: Christopher Gill; David Martin; Gavin Styles; Harry Banks, Chief Executive and Chair; Richard Dunkley; Simon Fisher, Finance Director (women: 0; men: 6)

Year end	04/10/2015
Turnover	£101,233,000
Pre-tax profit	£27,558,000

Nature of business: The company is involved in opencast coal mining, renewable energy and the development of interests in land. Respectively, the Banks Group's activities are undertaken under three operational divisions: Banks Mining; Banks Renewables; and Banks Property.

Company registration number: 2267400

Subsidiary undertakings include: Banks Brothers Transport Ltd; Banks Renewables (Penny Hill Wind Farm) Ltd; H. J. Banks and Company Ltd.

UK employees: 397

Focus of giving: General charitable purposes, education, enterprise/training, environment, fundraising events, groups not already known, non-registered charities, small groups, local groups, older people, playgroups, sport, recreation, bricks and mortar appeals, children, young people, community/social welfare, disability.

Membership: BITC

Community involvement	✓
Community contributions	✓
CSR or charity committee	✓
Company gives to smaller charities	✓
Employee-led support	✓
Unregistered charities/NFP	✓

Community involvement

The Banks Group focuses its charitable and community giving around the various sites in which it operates through its community fund. Preference is given to community projects that provide physical benefits (including improvements to community buildings, community renewable-energy projects, biodiversity projects, club or sporting facilities) or social benefits (such as increasing employment opportunities, skills and training).

The Banks Community Fund

The fund was established in 1997 and provides support to community groups, voluntary organisations and environmental projects located near to a current or proposed Banks Group development. It is administered by the County Durham Community Foundation.

The fund gains its income from a variety of sources from within the Banks Group. A funding panel, which includes representatives from the local community, oversees the fund. Grants are normally of up to £5,000 but can, in exceptional circumstances, be more. Examples of previously funded projects are available on the group's website. Projects seeking support must aim to:

- Bring land back into use
- Reduce or prevent pollution
- Provide information on sustainable waste management
- Build, improve or maintain public parks or amenities
- Build, improve or maintain community buildings or amenities
- Improve quality of life in a local environment
- Promote or conserve biological diversity through the provision, conservation, restoration or enhancement of a natural habitat or the maintenance or recovery of a species in its natural habitat

Funding is available to support organisations within a ten-mile radius of a proposed Banks operation where a specific fund is not yet in place. Funding is also available under the following categories:

Wind Farm Community Funds

This fund provides grants to organisations located near, or benefitting the local people in the area of, one of the group's wind farms. Funding can be provided for local training and employment initiatives among other causes.

Surface Coal Mine Community Fund

This fund provides grants to organisations located near the group's mining sites.

Connect2Renewables

Connect2Renewables is an initiative between the local communities, Banks and South Lanarkshire Council which seeks to maximise the social and economic benefit of the development to the local area. The scheme will focus on supporting local people to gain apprenticeships and workplace learning placements and will be administered by South Lanarkshire Council.

Main locations

The group's main office locations are in Durham and Lanarkshire. It also operates in various locations across: Midlands; North East England; North West England; Scotland; and Yorkshire.

Community contributions

The group did not declare its charitable or community contributions in its latest accounts for 2014/15.

Some beneficiaries of the Banks Community Fund were listed in the 'News' section of the company's website and are detailed below.

Beneficiaries included: Hazlerigg Victory Football Club (£8,000); Hawick and Wilton Cricket Club (£6,000); Cramlington Town Council, Dinnington Village Social Club, The Bill McLaren Foundation and The Briardale Community Centre (£5,000 each); Ashington Amateur Boxing Club (£3,900); Hickleton Village Hall (£3,000); Groundwork Cresswell, Ashfield and Mansfield (£2,000); Avondale Community Beekeepers (£1,400); Barnburgh Church (£1,000); Rotherham Brownie Pack (£250).

Employee-led support

Employee fundraising

According to the news section of the company's website, employees regularly hold fundraising events to support local community groups and charities.

Applications

The Banks Community Fund
To apply to the fund first contact the group's Fund Manager by phone or email. Applicants may then be able to make a full application on the County Durham Community Foundation's website, where application guidelines and deadline dates are also available: www.cdcf.org.uk/apply-for-a-grant/grants-for-groups/banks-community-fund.

Barclays PLC

Banking

Correspondent: Barclays Community Affairs, 1 Churchill Place, Canary Wharf, London E14 5HP (tel: 020 7116 4451; email: ukcommunity@barclays.co.uk; website: www.barclays.com)

Directors: Crawford Gillies; Dambisa Moyo; Diane de Saint Victor; Diane Schueneman; Jes Staley, Group Chief Executive Officer; John McFarlane, Chair; Mike Ashley; Reuben Jeffery III; Sir Gerry Grimstone; Stephen Thieke; Tim Breedon; Tushar Morzaria, Group Finance Director (women: 3; men: 9)

Year end	31/12/2015
Turnover	£25,454,000,000
Pre-tax profit	£5,403,000,000

Nature of business: Barclays PLC is a UK-based financial-services group engaged primarily in the banking and investment-banking businesses. In terms of assets employed, Barclays is one of the biggest financial-service groups in the UK. The group also operates in many other countries around the world.

Company registration number: 48839

Subsidiary undertakings include: Barclays Bank Delaware; Barclays Bank of Kenya Ltd; Barclays Capital Securities Ltd; and Barclays Private Clients International Ltd. A full list of subsidiaries can be found in the group's accounts.

Brands include: Barclaycard; FirstPlus; Woolwich

Focus of giving: Education, environment, heritage, small groups, less popular charitable purposes, financial education, armed forces, overseas projects, arts, culture, poverty and social exclusion, sport, recreation, children, young people, disability.

Membership: Arts & Business, BITC, LBG

Accredited Living Wage Employer	✓
Community involvement	✓
Community contributions	✓
CSR report	✓
CSR or charity committee	✓
Directors have other relevant posts	✓
Armed forces personnel	✓
Cash donations declared	✓
Charity partner(s)	✓
Community Mark	✓
Company gives to smaller charities	✓
Employee-led support	✓
FTSE 100	✓
Gifts in kind	✓
Matched funding	✓
Overseas giving	✓
Payroll giving	✓
Pro bono	✓
Sponsorship	✓
Unpopular causes	✓

Charitable donations

Cash worldwide:	2015	£54,900,000
Total worldwide (cash and in kind):	2015	£63,000,000

Community involvement

Barclays is committed to playing a broader role in the communities in which its employees live and work beyond what is delivered through the company's core activities. This is undertaken through the company's community investment programmes and the direct efforts of its employees. It is reported in the Citizenship Data Supplement to the Annual Report and in the 'Citizenship' section of the company's website.

Shared Growth Ambition
The current stage of the company's Citizenship journey is its Shared Growth Ambition. This strategy focuses on three areas: access to employment; access to financial and digital empowerment and access to financing.

Barclays runs a number of community investment programmes globally and in the UK. For example, Barclays Spaces for Sports is a programme where Barclays works with partners who are experts in harnessing the positive values of sport to run programmes which help young people fulfil their potential. There are over 200 community sports sites in the UK and support from Barclays includes its employees sharing their skills and expertise.

The company's website provides up-to-date stories of its latest projects.

The Armed Forces Transition Employment and Resettlement programme (AFTER)
AFTER was launched in partnership with the Ministry of Defence and a number of service charities to support the transition of armed forces personnel to civilian employment. Barclays Military Services Network runs two or three Military Talent Days each year outlining opportunities within the company for veterans. The network also runs CV and interview workshops and there is a Military Internship Programme.

Charity partners also run educational and vocational courses funded by Barclays. Partners include Stoll, RFEA, ABF The Soldiers' Charity, The Royal Navy Benevolent Trust, Support Our Paras and the Royal Air Force Benevolent Fund.

Diversity
Barclays deploys a global diversity and inclusion (D&I) strategy to enable employees to be themselves. Its five global agenda pillars are gender, LGBT, disability, multigenerational and multicultural, thus catering for the entire network of diverse employees at Barclays. The company has achieved a number of awards and recognition for its work and support to diverse community events.

Barclays has partnered the UK Lord Mayors' Appeal 'This is Me in the City' to raise awareness of mental health issues in the workplace. It also partners the UK Women's Business Council launch of the 'Comeback Toolkit' focused on women who may have taken a career break. It is the headline sponsor for Pride London for the 3rd consecutive year. Barclays Bolder Apprenticeship Scheme supports older people aged between 24 and 65 to return to the workplace or start a career.

Directors with other relevant posts
Mike Ashley sits on the board of the Charity Commission.

Reuben Jeffery III is a director of the Financial Services Volunteer Corps.

Main locations
London (head office) with branches across the UK.

Community contributions

In 2015 Barclays group provided £63 million in total through its community investment (£72 million in 2013).

This is used in three ways. Firstly £54.9 million (87%) is direct cash donations to charities and NGOs. A further £5.7 million (9%) is the monetary cost of providing 62,000 colleagues to work with the community projects. They have provided 350,000 hours of their time to use their skills and expertise for the benefit of a range of projects and initiatives. Supporting colleagues through Barclays' community employee programmes, including matched giving and volunteer grants, accounts for the remaining £2.4 million (4%).

Employee-led support

Volunteering
Because of the wide range of organisations (national and local) Barclays employees want to support,

traditionally the group's approach has been not to limit help to a single 'adopted' charity but rather support employees in their choices in a variety of ways.

Barclays has an annual Make a Difference volunteering campaign in October each year which is inspired by its Community Service Volunteers. This encourages employees to give time and their skills. The latest figures on the company's website for the volunteering globally show that in 2014 almost half of employees (65,000) around the world invested their time, skills or money to help their local communities. Employees volunteered nearly 419,000 hours and raised and donated over £32.19 million to the causes they care about.

Additionally, there is a funding programme whereby Barclays matches the amount raised by its employees.

Payroll giving

Barclays also supports employees in the UK who wish to make regular contributions to charities and community organisations in the following ways:

- Payroll giving (Give As You Earn). As well as this being a tax-efficient way for employees to give, Barclays matches each employee's contributions by up to £750 per employee each year
- Pennies from Heaven allows the company's employees to donate from their salary each month to nominated charities

Recognising achievements

Barclays recognises the outstanding achievements of their employees each year through the Barclays Citizenship Awards, details of which can be found on the company's website.

Commercially led support

Sponsorships

Barclays sponsors three areas and is looking for sponsorships which could benefit from positive associations with its brand. The areas are: Arts and Culture, including popular culture and entertainment; Sport (both local and global); and Thought Leadership which is defined as wanting to be associated with like-minded properties and organisations that will help create distinction from Barclays' competitors.

Arts and Culture

- The Barclaycard Arena in Birmingham (formerly known as the National Indoor Arena) is an example of a sponsorship deal which covers both arts and sports events
- Barclays is the principal sponsor of the Donmar Warehouse which is a 250-seat subsidised theatre in the heart of London's West End
- Barclaycard presents the British Summer Time annual event in Hyde Park

Sports

- Barclays sponsors the ATP Tennis World Tour Finals held at the O2 Arena in London which is the largest indoor tennis tournament in the world
- Barclays sponsors a number of other global events such as the first event of the end-of-season FedEx Cup on the PGA Golf Tour in the US

Thought Leadership

Barclays is working with Prelude's Speaker Boutique to help to inspire entrepreneurs who do not necessarily have access to large networks of support. The Speaker Boutique is a series of small events where successful entrepreneurs share their real-life experiences around a particular business topic.

Supporting 10- to 35-year-olds

There is an apprenticeship scheme operating, delivered as part of the citizenship agenda and over the last four years Barclays helped 2,263 young people through this scheme.

Globally, in 2015 Barclays concluded its 5 million Young Futures programme. Through partnerships with NGOs, charities and social enterprises the company delivered global investment through community programmes in line with its Community Investment strategy. The number of young people who benefitted in 2015 was 1.57 million which has led to Barclays surpassing its three-year target as they have reached 5.76 million young people between 2012 and 2015.

Apprenticeships for mature people

Barclays launched its Bolder Apprenticeship Scheme in 2013 to enable people between the age of 24 and 65 to return to the workplace or start a career as they believe that reskilling can be achieved at any age.

Exclusions

According to its website, Barclays cannot fund the following:

- political or religious associations
- sponsorship properties which have already given significant exposure for its competitors in banking
- sponsorship properties which are perceived to have or encompass a dangerous or violent nature (e.g. boxing)
- sponsorship where Barclays or its employees have or are perceived to have a conflict of interest
- the sponsorship of individuals (by exception only)
- the arts (unless the donation provides direct support to a disadvantaged group)
- an event which is due to commence in the next two months

Barclays does not normally give any money for political purposes in the UK or the rest of the EU.

Applications

Barclays Community Affairs

Enquiries for charitable or community sponsorship should be made by email to ukcommunity@barclays.co.uk or by phone to 02071164451.

Event Sponsorship

Barclays sponsors events which will help to provide positive associations with their brand in the following areas: Sports, Thought Leadership and Art and Culture.

Enquiries for event sponsorship should be made by email to sponsorshipenquiries@barclays.co.uk. Check the 'Applying for sponsorship' section on the website for the details required on the email application.

The group states on the website:

> Our aim is to review EVERY proposal received, however, we are only able to reply to those opportunities that we feel fit with existing marketing and business objectives and require further investigation, although we will ensure that all enquiries sent to us are logged and held on file for future consideration should our focus and position change.

A. G. Barr PLC

Drinks manufacture

Correspondent: Marie Holcroft, Charity, Good Cause & Community Team, Westfield House, 4 Mollins Road, Westfield, Cumbernauld G68 9HD (tel: 01236 852400; website: www.agbarr.co.uk)

Directors: Andrew Memmot; David Ritchie; John Nicolson, Chair; Jonathan Kemp; Julie Barr; Martin Griffiths; Pamela Powell; Robin Barr; Roger White, Chief Executive; Stuart Lorimer, Finance Director (women: 2; men: 8)

Year end	31/01/2016
Turnover	£258,600,000
Pre-tax profit	£41,300,000

Nature of business: The group trades principally as a manufacturer, distributor and seller of soft drinks.

Company registration number: SC005653

Subsidiary undertakings include: Findlays Ltd; Rubicon Drinks Ltd.

Brands include: IRN-BRU; Orangina; Rubicon; Strathmore Water; Tizer.

UK employees: 1,000

Focus of giving: Environment, poverty and social exclusion, sport, recreation, community/social welfare.

Community involvement ✓
Community contributions ✓

Company reports on anti-slavery	✓
CSR report	✓
Charity of the Year	✓
Employee-led support	✓
Gifts in kind	✓
Sponsorship	✓

Charitable donations

Cash UK (latest available):	2016	£343,000
Total UK (cash and in kind):	2016	£343,000
Cash worldwide:	2016	£343,000
Total worldwide (cash and in kind):	2016	£343,000

Community involvement

Support for Charities and Community Groups

Local and national charities are helped through financial assistance, in-kind support and sponsorship. According to the company's website, support is focused in three main areas:

- Encouraging health, wellbeing and physical activity
- Protecting the environment and championing sustainability
- Tackling social inequality

Wind turbine

A wind turbine was recently installed at the Cumbernauld site. Over the lifespan of the turbine (20 years), employees will have the opportunity to nominate local charities to receive a share of £6,000 per year.

Charity of the Year

The company will support Macmillan Cancer Care for three years from August 2016 by providing financial, in-kind and practical support as well as employee volunteering.

Main locations

Cumbernauld; Bolton; Forfar; London; Manchester; Milton Keynes; Sheffield; Walthamstow; Wednesbury.

Community contributions

There appears to be no record of the total amount in donations given in 2015/16 to charitable causes. However, in the past the company has stated in its annual report that it gives 1% of after-tax profit to charitable causes. On this basis donations to charitable causes would be £343,000 in 2015/16.

Beneficiaries included: the British Asian Trust; Keep Scotland Beautiful; The Prince and Princess of Wales Hospice; The Prince's Trust.

In-kind support

In-kind support is normally provided through donations of products. In 2015/16 over 500,000 bottles of Strathmore Water were provided to community and charity road races.

Employee-led support

Employee fundraising

Around £74,000 has been raised for The Prince and Princess of Wales Hospice Brick by Brick Appeal through direct and employee fundraising.

Employee support

The Site Community Fund allows employees at each site to support charities which are important to them by nominating causes and engaging in community initiatives.

Commercially led support

The company sponsors The Prince's Trust's Community Impact Award which recognises the contribution young people make to their local communities.

Applications

Requests for support can be made through the 'Community and Charity Enquires' section of the company's website: www.agbarr.co.uk/contact-us/community-charity-enquiries.

Bayer PLC

Chemicals and plastics

Correspondent: CSR Committee, Bayer House, Strawberry Hill, Newbury, Berkshire RG14 1JA (fax: 01635 563513; email: communications.ukireland@bayer.com; website: www.bayer.co.uk)

Directors: Dr Alexander Moscho; Ute Bockstegers; Vera Hahn (women: 2; men: 1)

Year end	31/12/2015
Turnover	£443,547,000
Pre-tax profit	£17,365,000

Nature of business: Bayer in the UK/Ireland region is part of the global concern Bayer AG, based in Leverkusen, Germany. In the UK and Ireland, the business includes: pharmaceuticals; consumer health; crop science; animal health; and material sciences.

Company registration number: 935048

Subsidiary undertakings include: Bayer CropScience Ltd; Medrad UK Ltd; Schering Heath Care Ltd.

Brands include: Alka-Seltzer; Berocca; Canesten.

UK employees: 732

Total employees: 117,000

Focus of giving: Education, enterprise/training, environment, health, ill health, medical research, overseas projects, arts, culture, children, young people, community/social welfare.

Membership: BITC

Community involvement	✓
Community contributions	✓
CSR report	✓
CSR or charity committee	✓
Charity partner(s)	✓
Employee-led support	✓
Gifts in kind	✓
Humanitarian aid: overseas	✓
Shared-value alliances	✓
Sponsorship	✓

Charitable donations

Total UK (cash and in kind):	2015	£737,000
Total worldwide (cash and in kind):	2015	£737,000

Community involvement

Bayer UK and Ireland has been involved in social, community and environmental programmes across the region for a number of years. It supports numerous social responsibility programs, often in partnership with other organisations. The company supports activities that are local to its operations, and are also linked to employees' community activities or connected to the company's products or services.

Charitable giving

The website states clear criteria for what the company will support.

Support is given for activities which enhance local quality of life through:

- The environment
- Community care
- Culture and the arts
- Education
- Projects in line with the company's Mission Statement
- Projects benefiting groups and not individuals

While activities meeting the above criteria will be considered, other factors (such as budget already committed) will also be taken into account.

Grants to patient groups and healthcare organisations

The company also makes grants to patient advocacy and other voluntary health groups to raise awareness and develop interventions.

The company also provides funding and in-kind support for organisations involved with health professionals or research for the purposes of improving patient care.

Manversation

The company is funding the Manversation campaign, developed in partnership with the charities Orchid Male Cancer and Tackle Prostate Cancer, to raise awareness of the symptoms of advanced prostate cancer.

Partners – Science Museum

Bayer has an ongoing partnership with London's Science Museum. This partnership has included support of an exhibition space that focuses on climate science.

Cultivate Young Entrepreneur Challenge

The group worked in partnership with the Greenham Common Trust to deliver the annual Cultivate Young Entrepreneur Challenge 2015, in which teams of young people compete for a £1,000 prize to develop a business idea.

International – Bayer foundations
The group has two corporate foundations, based in Leverkusen, Germany. The Bayer Science and Education Foundation supports science fellowships, science programmes in schools and other science awards. The Bayer Cares Foundation supports volunteering programmes, disaster relief and social innovation in health.

Main locations
The group's locations in the UK and Ireland are: Cambridge; Dublin; Newbury (headquarters). Internationally, the group is based in Germany and has operations across the world.

Community contributions

The 2015 annual report states that the company spent £737,000 on its corporate social responsibility programmes during the year.

In-kind support

In 2016 the group formed a partnership with the charity International Health Partners, providing £320,000 of in-kind support through healthcare product donations for female refugees living in camps and settlements in the Middle East.

Employee-led support

Employee fundraising and volunteering
The company encourages employee volunteering and has previously worked with Volunteer Centre West Berkshire to develop volunteering opportunities. Employees also volunteer to help organise, as well as take part in, the Newbury 10k, which is sponsored by the company and raises money for charities.

Examples of employee-led fundraising activities in 2016 include: teams of UK employees taking part in a 545 cycle ride which raised £34,000 for the charity Together for Short Lives; employees collecting Easter eggs to donate to families through A2Dominion Group, which manages a women's refuge in Berkshire; Bayer's Culture Club, a social group formed by employees, organised a raffle, film night and quiz night to fundraise for West Berkshire Mencap.

Commercially led support

Sponsorship
The group sponsors the Newbury 10k, working in partnerships with a local athletics club to organise the event, with a local charity benefitting from the entrance fees each year.

Exclusions

According to the website, Bayer is unable to support:

- individuals rather than group activities
- religious, political or racially aligned movements
- projects or activities bridging a gap in government or local authority funding
- sporting or recreational activities unless closely associated to Bayer
- entries in log books, year books or support advertising
- projects of a local nature which are outside key locations of Newbury, Cambridge, Norwich and Dublin
- conferences, lectures, trips, respite breaks or holidays

Applications

Applications for support can be made using a form available to download from the website, along with eligibility criteria. Forms can be submitted by post to:

CSR Committee, Bayer PLC, Bayer House, Strawberry Hill, Newbury, Berkshire RG14 1JA

Alternatively, you can send it by email to corporate.communications@bayer.co.uk; or by fax at 01635 563513. Note that Bayer only accepts postal, email or faxed requests and unable to take phone calls to discuss individual requests.

Bayer's committee reviews applications received on a monthly basis throughout the year. Bayer will contact you by email or letter to inform you of the committee's decision.

BBA Aviation PLC

Engineering, transport and communications

Correspondent: Kathryn Zielinski, 105 Wigmore Street, London W1U 1QY (tel: 020 7514 3999; fax: 020 7408 2318; email: kzielinski@bbaaviation.com; website: www.bbaaviation.com)

Directors: Mike Powell, Group Finance Director; Nigel Rudd, Chair; Peter Edwards; Peter Ratcliffe; Peter Ventress; Simon Pryce, Chief Executive; Susan Kilsby; Wayne Edmunds (women: 1; men: 7)

Year end	31/12/2015
Turnover	£1,830,500,000
Pre-tax profit	£137,700,000

Nature of business: An international group of aviation services and materials technology businesses.

Company registration number: 53688

Subsidiary undertakings include: Signature Flight Support Paris SA; APPH Ltd; APPH Aviation Services Ltd; ASIG Ltd.

Focus of giving: Education, overseas projects, children, young people, community/social welfare.

Community involvement	✓
Community contributions	✓
CSR report	✓
CSR or charity committee	✓
Employee-led support	✓
Gifts in kind	✓
Overseas giving	✓

Charitable donations

Cash worldwide:	2015	£502,500

Community involvement

Established in 2010, BBA Aviation's group-wide Community Involvement and Charitable Giving Framework sets out the approach the company's sites should take to projects, volunteering and fundraising in their local communities. Having this framework has led to a more structured way of working and has encouraged businesses and employees to focus on fewer, more ambitious activities, enabling teams to make a bigger contribution to the causes that they care about and fostering longer-term relationships with those organisations.

The CSR report for 2015 states:

> BBA Aviations companies and locations are encouraged to focus their fundraising and volunteering efforts in four key areas:
>
> - Organisations or activities that benefit the communities in which they operate
> - Aviation related organisations
> - Educational programmes
> - Engineering activities

Case study
This case study was taken from BBA Aviation's annual report for 2015:

> In 2015, $10,000 [£7,500] was donated through BBA Aviation's parent company charitable giving programme to FlyQuest, which provides aviation education and career preparation for young people. FlyQuest provides an introduction to the basics of aviation, together with advice on career options in the areas of piloting, aircraft maintenance, and air traffic control and setting goals for the for the future.

Main location
London and various locations throughout the UK.

BBA aviation also has locations worldwide.

Community contributions

In 2014/15 the group's donations to charities worldwide totalled $675,000 (£502,500). Charitable cash donations in the UK were not declared.

Beneficiaries included: Opportunity Village Foundation; Philabundance; The Scottish Burned Children's Club; Southern California Aviation Association; TriStar History and Preservation; Amelia Trust Farm.

Employee-led support

Employees are encouraged to fundraise and get involved with local community and charitable groups. In 2015 a total of 41 employees volunteered for the GRACE (Grapevine Relief and Community Exchange) Feed Our Kids programme at which 1,381 lunches were served to local children over the course of a week.

Applications

Apply in writing to the correspondent. Under the BBA Aviation charitable giving programme employees or sites can, on behalf of a charity or not-for-profit organisation, apply to the BBA Aviation Charitable Giving Committee for a donation. Priority is given to organisations with a strong local connection to sites and/or those connected with aviation, engineering or education.

BC Partners Ltd

Financial services

Correspondent: Secretary, BCP Foundation, 40 Portman Square, London W1H 6DA (tel: 020 7009 4800; fax: 020 7009 4899; email: bcpfoundation@bcpartners.com; website: www.bcpartners.com)

Directors: Graeme Dell; Stefano Curzio (men: 2)

Year end	31/12/2014
Turnover	£95,500,000
Pre-tax profit	£8,000,000

Nature of business: Investment advisers to the managers of offshore funds for investment in principally unquoted companies.

Company registration number: 2020410

Subsidiary undertakings include: BC Partners SARL; BC Partners GmbH.

Focus of giving: General charitable purposes, education, environment, general appeals, overseas projects, arts, culture, community/social welfare.

Community involvement	✓
Community contributions	✓
Cash donations declared	✓
Charity partner(s)	✓
Corporate charity	✓
Employee-led support	✓
Humanitarian aid: overseas	✓
Matched funding	✓

Charitable donations

Cash UK (latest available):	2014	£429,500
Total UK (cash and in kind):	2014	£429,509
Cash worldwide:	2014	£429,509
Total worldwide (cash and in kind):	2014	£429,509

Community involvement

The company's charitable giving is channelled through its corporate charity, the BC Partners Foundation. The foundation supports charities nominated by employees.

BC Partners Foundation

The company's charitable contributions are mainly channelled through its corporate charity, the BC Partners Foundation (Charity Commission no. 1136956). The foundation mainly supports charities nominated by employees, providing matched funding for their own initiatives. There is a focus on the following areas:

- Community development, including infrastructure, overseas aid and healthcare
- Environmental conservation, including pollution abatement, protection of nature and clean technology
- Arts and education

The company also has a sister charity in the US, the BC Partners Foundation (US) Inc.

Main locations

The company has offices in London; Hamburg; New York; and Paris.

Community contributions

The 2014 accounts were the latest available for the company at the time of writing. In 2014 the company donated £429,500 to charities, of which £339,000 went to the BC Partners Foundation.

The 2015 accounts for the BC Partners Foundation were available at the time of writing (November 2016), and state that BC Partners donated £311,000 to the foundation during the year.

The foundation made grants totalling £543,000 in 2015.

Beneficiaries of the foundation included: The Private Equity Foundation (£103,000); American School in London Foundation (£50,000); Over the Wall (£23,000); Wildlife Heritage Trust (£10,000); Fine Cell Works (£5,400); Music as Therapy and The Dolphin Society (£5,000 each); Médecins Sans Frontières (£3,300); 4th Farnham Scout Group (£2,500); Royal Opera House (£1,000).

Employee-led support

Employee fundraising and volunteering

The BC Partners Foundation provides matched funding for employee fundraising initiatives and supports charities proposed by the employees of BC Partners or trustees of the BC Partners Foundation. The foundation's 2015 annual report states that each office nominates two charities per year to support through donations and, where possible, volunteering. The group also holds 'days of engagement', encouraging employees to get involved.

Corporate charity

BC Partners Foundation (Charity Commission no. 1136956).

Applications

The foundation does not accept unsolicited applications.

Beazley PLC

Insurance

Correspondent: UK Charity Committee, Plantation Place South, 60 Great Tower Street, London EC3R 5AD (tel: 020 7667 0623; email: info@beazley.ie; website: www.beazley.com)

Directors: Adrian Cox; Andrew Horton, Chief Executive; Clive Washbourn; Jonathan Gray; Martin Bride, Finance Director; Neil Maidment; Nicholas Furlonge (women: 0; men: 7)

Year end	31/12/2015
Turnover	£1,455,000,000
Pre-tax profit	£231,000,000

Nature of business: Insurance.

Company registration number: 102680

Subsidiary undertakings include: Beazley Group Ltd; Beazley Furlonge Holdings Ltd; Beazley Solutions Ltd.

Focus of giving: Education, humanitarian help.

Community involvement	✓
Community contributions	✓
Company reports on anti-slavery	✓
CSR report	✓
CSR or charity committee	✓
Cash donations declared	✓
Charity partner(s)	✓
Employee-led support	✓
Humanitarian aid: overseas	✓
Matched funding	✓
Sponsorship	✓
STEM-focused	✓

Charitable donations

Cash worldwide:	2015	£293,000
Total worldwide (cash and in kind):	2015	£293,000

Community involvement

The group's charitable work is focused on improving the skills of young people (six years old to graduate level) from disadvantaged backgrounds to help them enter the workforce. The group also supports disaster relief with donations made for relief work after the Vanuatu and Nepal earthquakes and flooding in Texas.

Internships and work experience

The groups takes on interns through its partnership with the charity, The Brokerage CityLink. Internships are also available in the London, New York and San Francisco offices.

Main locations

Manchester, Leeds, Ipswich and London.

Community contributions

In 2014 the group made charitable donations in the UK and the US totalling around £293,000. We were unable to discover how the money was split between the UK and the US. The company also supports staff in fundraising for their chosen charities.

Charity partners: The Conservation Fund; Feeding America; Shelterbox; Feeding America; World Child Cancer.

Employee-led support

In 2015 a third of all employees volunteered on over 30 projects in Australia, Ireland, Singapore, the UK and US. Volunteering projects in the UK included assisting the Teesdale and Hollybush Tenants and Resident Association (TRA) with maintenance projects around estates in East London and taking part in City Giving day in London.

Matched funding

Beazley PLC matched funds raised by employees during the year.

Applications

Apply in writing to the correspondent.

Bellway PLC

Building/construction

Correspondent: Simon Scougall, Company Secretary, Seaton Burn House, Dudley Lane, Seaton Burn, Newcastle upon Tyne NE13 6BE (tel: 0191 217 0717; fax: 0191 236 6230; email: bellway4good@bellway.co.uk; website: www.bellway.co.uk)

Directors: Denise Jagger; Edward Ayres, Chief Executive; John Cuthbert; John Watson; Keith Adey, Finance Director; Mike Toms; Paul Hampden Smith (women: 1; men: 6)

Year end	31/07/2015
Turnover	£1,765,400,000
Pre-tax profit	£354,200,000

Nature of business: The company's main activity is house building.

Company registration number: 1372603

Subsidiary undertakings include: Litrose Investments Ltd; Bellway Financial Services Ltd; Bellway Housing Trust Ltd.

UK employees: 2,000

Total employees: 2,000

Focus of giving: General charitable purposes, children, young people, community/social welfare.

Community involvement	✓
Community contributions	✓
CSR report	✓
CSR or charity committee	✓
Cash donations declared	✓
Employee-led support	✓
Gifts in kind	✓
Matched funding	✓
Pro bono	✓

Charitable donations

Cash UK (latest available):	2015	£146,000
Total UK (cash and in kind):	2015	£146,000
Cash worldwide:	2015	£146,000
Total worldwide (cash and in kind):	2015	£146,000

Community involvement

There is very little information on charitable giving within the communities in which the group operates or society in general.

Case study

This case study has been taken from the 2014/15 CSR report:

> One of Bellways nominated national charity partners is Construction Youth Trust who work with disadvantaged young people to help them to access career opportunities in the construction industry. In July employees across Bellway donned Lycra and took part in a static bike challenge to raise money for the charity. The aim was to cycle a total of 912 miles, the distance of a journey calling at all of Bellways divisional offices. Each division was set a target of 57 miles to cycle in the fastest possible time and the team from Essex won bragging rights and the title of 'Tour de Bellway' Champions, completing the distance in an amazing 1 hour 49 minutes. Across the business we raised £8,463.25 and when matched by Group, almost £100,000 was donated to construction Youth Trust.

Main locations

Newcastle upon Tyne.

Bellway has a number of locations throughout the UK.

Community contributions

In 2014/15 the group gave £146,000 to numerous charities, community groups and good causes, including two nominated national charities. This figure has been taken as the company's overall contribution. In addition, employees raised a further £37,500 through fundraising activities ranging from dress-down days to sponsored challenges. The British Heart Foundation and Construction Youth Trust were selected as national charity partners.

Bellway also makes small donations through the Community Foundation of Tyne and Wear and Northumberland.

Employee-led support

Employees get involved in local charitable projects.

It was reported in the 2014/15 CSR report that employees raised and donated £185,000 to charities, community groups and local good causes.

Exclusions

No support can be given for advertising in charity brochures, appeals from individuals, animal welfare, fundraising events, overseas projects, political appeals, or religious appeals.

Applications

Apply in writing to the correspondent.

Berkeley Group PLC

Building/construction, property

Correspondent: Stuart Cowen, Administrator of the Berkeley Foundation, Berkeley House, 19 Portsmouth Road, Cobham, Surrey KT11 1JG (tel: 020 7720 2600; email: info@berkeleyfoundation.org.uk; website: www.berkeleygroup.com)

Directors: Adrian Li; Alison Nimmo; Andy Myers; David Howell; Diana Brightmore; Glyn Barber; Greg Fry; Karl Whiteman; Nick Simpkin, Group Finance Director; Rob Perrins, Managing Director; Sean Ellis; Sir John Armitt; Tony Pidgley, Chair; Veronica Wadley

Year end	30/04/2016
Turnover	£2,047,500,000
Pre-tax profit	£530,900,000

Nature of business: Berkeley is a developer of residential-led, mixed-use schemes building homes and neighbourhoods in its core markets of London and South England.

Company registration number: 1454064

Subsidiary undertakings include: Berkeley Commercial Developments Ltd; Berkeley First Ltd; Berkeley Homes (Capital) PLC; Berkeley Partnership Homes Ltd.

Focus of giving: General charitable purposes, environment, health, ill health, heritage, housing, homelessness, children, young people, community/social welfare, disability.

Membership: LBG

Community involvement	✓
Community contributions	✓
Company reports on anti-slavery	✓
Charity partner(s)	✓
Corporate charity	✓
Gifts in kind	✓
Payroll giving	✓

Community involvement

The Berkeley Foundation

The group channels its charitable and community giving through its registered charity, The Berkeley Foundation (Charity Commission no. 1152596) which was established by the Berkeley Group in March 2011. The foundation is focused on supporting projects which tackle homelessness, develop skills, create jobs, and help people to live positively with disability or illness. Partnerships range from major national charities, such as Shelter and the Lord's Taverners, to smaller charities.

Anti-slavery

During the year, the group has introduced a Human Rights, Modern Slavery and Child Labour Policy in support of human rights which is implicit in all of its pre-existing corporate policies and procedures.

Main locations

UK locations: Surrey; London; Kent; Berkshire; Buckinghamshire.

Community contributions

The company's charitable contributions are made through The Berkeley Foundation. Since it was established in 2011, the Berkeley Foundation has committed £7.9 million to more than 85 charities, with 2.7 million having been raised by Berkeley staff. It is not clear how much the group contributed in 2015/16.

In-kind support

Staff are encouraged to volunteer both for the foundation and for local charities.

Employee-led support

Payroll giving

In 2015/16 Berkeley received a Platinum Award from the Charities Aid Foundation for its Give As You Earn scheme, with 33% of staff giving to the Berkeley Foundation in this way. Through this, and other activities, Berkeley's staff have raised just under £1 million in the year. During the year, 10% of Berkeley staff took part in Vertical Rush, climbing 200,000 steps and raising £56,000 for Shelter.

Corporate charity

The Berkeley Charitable Foundation (Charity Commission no. 1152596).

Exclusions

No support is given for political appeals.

Applications

The Berkeley Foundation

Apply in writing to the correspondent for an application to the foundation. However, the foundation's website states: 'A lot of people and organisations write to us asking for a grant. We very rarely make unsolicited donations.'

Bestway (Holdings) Ltd

Building materials, Cash 'n' Carry, property, retail – miscellaneous, banking, wholesale

Correspondent: Younus Sheikh, Secretary to the Foundation, 2 Abbey Road, Park Royal, London NW10 7BW (tel: 020 8453 1234; fax: 020 8961 9697; email: zulfikaur.wajid-hasan@bestway.co.uk; website: www.bestway.co.uk)

Directors: Abdul Khalique Bhatti; Adalat Khan Chaudhary; Arshad Chaudhary; Dawood Pervez; Rizwan Pervez; Sir Anwar Pervez, Chair; Younus Sheikh; Zameer Choudrey (women: 0; men: 8)

Year end	30/06/2015
Turnover	£2,515,405,000
Pre-tax profit	£355,377,000

Nature of business: Bestway is a family-owned business with operations in the wholesale, cement, banking, real estate and pharmacy sectors.

Company registration number: 1392861

Subsidiary undertakings include: Bestway Cash and Carry Ltd; Bestway Cement Ltd; Bestway Pharmacy NDC Ltd.

Brands include: Batleys Food Service; Best-one; Well Pharmacy.

Focus of giving: Education, health, ill health, older people, arts, culture, overseas projects, poverty and social exclusion, sport, recreation, community/ social welfare, disability, disasters.

Community involvement	✓
Community contributions	✓
CSR report	✓
Directors have other relevant posts	✓
Cash donations declared	✓
Charity partner(s)	✓
Corporate charity	✓
Humanitarian aid: overseas	✓
Overseas giving	✓
Sponsorship	✓

Charitable donations

Cash UK (latest available):	2015	£1,276,000
Total UK (cash and in kind):	2015	£1,276,000
Cash worldwide:	2015	£1,276,000
Total worldwide (cash and in kind):	2015	£1,276,000

Community involvement

The company donates 2.5% of its yearly profits to charitable causes, almost all of which is channelled through the group's charities, the Bestway Foundation (Charity Commission no. 297178) and the Bestway Foundation Pakistan. Bestway's Corporate Social Responsibility report for 2015 notes that 'the Bestway Group has donated in excess of £14.1 million in the UK alone to fund the Foundation in its charitable activities and in Pakistan Bestway Cement and United Bank have donated over US$10.5 million [approximately £8.4 million]'.

Bestway's website sets out the following mission statement:

- The advancement of education for public benefit in both the UK and overseas by providing assistance through promotion of local schools; provision of scholarships to university students; supporting education initiatives and endowing universities
- The relief of sickness and the preservation of health for public benefit in both the UK and overseas by way of grants and endowments to existing hospitals, clinics, medical research establishments; and by establishing new health facilities
- The provision of financial and material support to victims of natural disasters
- To have a significant impact on poverty reduction in Pakistan through strategic investments in affordable financial and social services catering to the poor
- The development of technical skills within the local communities in which we operate through structured apprenticeship and training programmes

Bestway Foundation UK

Bestway's UK foundation was established in 1987 by Sir Anwar Pervez, Chair of Bestway Group. The foundation's board of trustees is made up of the group's directors.

The foundation's Charity Commission record states that it provides scholarships and grants to university students of South Asian origin (South Asia being India, Pakistan, Bangladesh or Sri Lanka) both in the UK and overseas, and also supports the relief of sickness and preservation of health by making grants to hospitals, clinics or medical-research establishments and by building or endowing new hospitals or clinics.

The foundation regularly supports rehabilitation and relief efforts in the wake of natural disasters and has supported trades charities, such as GroceryAid and the Wines and Spirits Trades Benevolent Society. Bestway Group's annual report for 2014/15 further states that the foundation also supports the relief of suffering of older people, people with disabilities and people who are in need.

In order to further enhance the grant-giving mechanism, a sister organisation was established in Pakistan in 1997 and Zameer Choudrey was appointed Chair of Bestway Foundation Pakistan.

Charity partners

Through its foundation, Bestway has built a number of long-standing partnerships with charities, some of which it has trustees in common with.

The Duke of Edinburgh's Award: Bestway has partnered The Duke of Edinburgh's Award for more than 20 years, during which time it has donated over £380,000. In 2014 Bestway was awarded Gold Partner status by the charity.

GroceryAid: The group has worked with GroceryAid for a number of years; Zameer Choudrey, the group's CEO, is a trustee of the charity.

Crimestoppers: Bestway first began working alongside Crimestoppers, where Zameer Choudrey is also a trustee, in 1999 to help combat increasing numbers of crimes committed against high-street retailers.

Farm Africa: Bestway Wholesale became a sponsor of the charity's Silver Food for Good scheme in 2014.

The Huddersfield Partnership

The group's Batleys depot in Huddersfield has supported numerous charitable causes in the town. The CSR report explains that support has included 'a series of donations, mainly connected with local sports and the arts'. Examples of projects which have received donations include: YMCA to help build a sports centre named after Batleys's founder, Lawrence Batley; The Kirklees Theatre Trust to enable the conversion of an old mission building into the Lawrence Batley Theatre; and The Lawrence Batley Centre for The National Arts Education Archive (Trust) at Bretton Hall. Batleys depot also supported the building of the McAlpine Sports Stadium which is home to Huddersfield Town Football Club and Huddersfield Giants Rugby League team.

Directors with other relevant posts

Sir Anwar Pervez: Chair of Bestway Foundation UK; patron-in-chief of Bestway Foundation Pakistan; trustee of Memorial Gates Trust; and charter member of the Duke of Edinburgh's Award.

Zameer Choudrey: trustee of Bestway Foundation UK; Chair of Bestway Foundation Pakistan; trustee of Crimestoppers UK; trustee of GroceryAid; member of HRH Prince of Wales Pakistan Recovery Fund international leadership team; and member of the advisory council of the British Asian Trust.

Younus Sheikh, Abdul Khalique Bhatti, Adalat Khan Chaudhary and Arshad Chaudhary: trustees of Bestway Foundations in the UK and Pakistan.

Dawood Pervez and Rizwan Pervez: trustees of Bestway Foundation UK.

Main locations

UK and South Asia (particularly Pakistan).

Community contributions

The 2014/15 annual report and accounts state that:

> The Group made charitable donations of £1,276,000 (2014: £705,000) to the Bestway Foundation whose objectives are the advancement of education, the relief of sickness, the preservation and protection of health and the relief of suffering of the old, disabled and needy.

Beneficiaries: The Bestway Foundation (£1.28 million).

Employee-led support

Employee community involvement

The CSR report explains that individual depots are 'urged to get involved locally by regularly donating in terms of money and products to a whole host of charities, worthy causes, churches and mosques'.

Commercially led support

Sponsorship

Royal Ascot Charity Race Day: Bestway stages this annual event, each year selecting a charity to which the proceeds are donated. To date the event has raised more than £1.5 million for a wide variety of worthy causes, including: Barnardo's, Crimestoppers, Great Ormond Street Hospital Charity, Imran Khan Cancer Appeal, National Hospital Development Fund, President of Pakistan Earthquake Relief Fund, Save the Children and Sports Aid. In 2015 the event's chosen charity was GroceryAid, where Bestway Group's CEO, Zameer Choudrey, is a trustee.

Corporate charity

The Bestway Foundation (Charity Commission no. 297178).

Applications

Applications may be made in writing to the correspondent, enclosing an sae. The foundation has previously noted that telephone calls are not invited.

BHP Billiton

Mining

Correspondent: BHP Billiton Sustainable Communities, Neathouse Place, London SW1V 1LH (tel: 020 7802 4000; fax: 020 7802 4111; email: hsec@bhpbilliton.com; website: www.bhpbilliton.com)

Directors: Andrew Mackenzie; Anita Frew; Baroness Shriti Vadera; Carolyn Hewson; Dr John Schubert; Jacques Nasser, Chair; Ken Mackenzie; Lindsay Maxsted; Malcolm Brinded; Malcolm Broomhead; Pat Davies; Wayne Murdy (women: 3; men: 9)

Year end	30/06/2015
Turnover	£44,636,000,000
Pre-tax profit	£8,056,000,000

Nature of business: The principal activities of the group are the discovery, acquisition, development and marketing of natural resources. The company's website states: 'Our strategy is to own and operate large, long-life, low-cost, expandable, upstream assets diversified by commodity, geography and market.'

Company registration number: 3196209

Subsidiary undertakings include: BHP Billiton Aluminium Australia Pty Ltd; BHP Billiton Aluminium (RAA) Pty Ltd; BHP Billiton Aluminium (Worsley) Pty Ltd.

Focus of giving: Education, environment, overseas projects, community/social welfare, disasters.

Accredited Living Wage Employer	✓
Community involvement	✓
Community contributions	✓
CSR report	✓
CSR or charity committee	✓
Cash donations declared	✓
Corporate charity	✓
Employee-led support	✓
FTSE 100	✓
Gifts in kind	✓
Humanitarian aid: overseas	✓
Matched funding	✓
Overseas giving	✓

Charitable donations

Total worldwide (cash and in kind):	2015	£173,300,000

Community involvement

This group gives generously worldwide in areas where it has operational sites. It no longer has this in the UK, since the Liverpool Bay operation was divested in 2014, but the registered office is still in London and in-kind giving may be available from there. It would appear that the UK charity will continue for at least the next five years. It is not clear if UK charities can still benefit from grants during that time but even if that were the case, most grant-giving has in the past been overseas.

The origins of BHP Billiton go back to the mid-19th century when the two original mining companies, Broken Hill Proprietary and Billiton, were established in Australia and Indonesia respectively. Following the merger of these companies in 2001, BHP Billiton is now a major developer and producer of natural resources, including aluminium, coal, copper, iron ore, manganese, nickel, silver and uranium, and also oil and gas. The company is registered in the UK and headquartered in London, although the BHP Billiton Group is based in Melbourne, Australia.

Corporate charities

The group has two corporate charities: BHP Billiton Foundation in the USA and BHP Billiton Sustainable Communities in the UK.

In the 2015 corporate responsibility report, the group states that both charities 'provide grants to organisations, allowing them to deliver long-term social projects that aim to create sustainable outcomes across a footprint that extends beyond the operations of its business'.

The charities do not accept unsolicited proposals, but work proactively to identify significant social issues in the region of interest, and then work collaboratively with non-government organisations that have a strong track record in the issue, to design an appropriate project. According to the company's Sustainability Report for 2015: 'In assessing potential partner organisations, important criteria include the capacity to effectively deliver a large scale project, compliance with due diligence and anti-corruption criteria and experience operating in the country and region of interest.'

The corporate charities aim to complement the local community development work undertaken by BHP Billiton's businesses. When developing projects, care is taken not to duplicate or displace existing agencies and services, but rather to strengthen and support local capacity development.

Projects are generally selected from three broad areas – health, education and governance.

BHP Billiton Sustainable Communities (Charity Commission no. 1131066)

According to the charity's 2014/15 annual report, it focuses on 'enabling people to improve their quality of life, contribute to the conservation of the environment and developing the community's capacity to advocate for and manage effective change'. Grants are given in four categories: flagship programmes aiming to address the Sustainable Development Goals; one-off donations and national projects in the countries where the group operates; natural disaster relief; matched giving for employee donations.

Main locations

London and various locations worldwide.

Community contributions

The company gives annually 1% of pre-tax profits invested in community programmes, including cash, in-kind support and administration, calculated on the average of the previous three years' pre-tax profit. In 2015 community investment totalled US$225 million (£173.3 million) comprising US$142 million (£109.4 million) in cash, in-kind support and administrative costs and a US$83 million (contribution to the BHP Billiton Foundation).

The annual report states:

> The cash component of the 2015 community investment is an aggregate of the total funds invested across the group and includes:
>
> - Direct voluntary funding provided as one-off donations and to support medium to longer-term community projects
> - Contributions made at the local operational level to charitable foundations (excluding the BHP Billiton Foundation and the BHP Billiton Sustainable Communities)
> - Funds used to deliver the Enterprise Development and Socio-economic Development components of Broad-Based Black Economic Empowerment programs in South Africa
>
> Excluding the contribution to the BHP Billiton Foundation, 49 per cent of the cash component of our expenditure was invested in local communities, 28 per cent was invested regionally, and the remaining 23 per cent was invested in national or international programs in countries where we operate.

In-kind support

International relief

The company contributes to relief efforts following natural disasters. Depending on the specific circumstances and nature of the disaster, this may be through a financial contribution to an NGO participating in emergency or recovery activities, in-kind support, such as the provision of equipment or machinery, or through employees' volunteering their time and expertise.

Employee-led support

Matched Giving

BHP Billiton has established a matched-giving programme through which the company will match the community contributions made by employees. Every employee (including full- and part-time colleagues) is entitled each year to have their contributions to not-for-profit organisations that benefit the community matched. These contributions can be employee volunteering, fundraising or cash donations (including pay-roll donations). The company's Sustainability Report for 2015 states:

> In 2015 more than 8,500 of our employees participated in the Matched Giving Program, volunteering approximately 65,000 hours of their personal time to community activities. Employee contributions benefitted more than 1,000 not-for-profit organisations.

Give As You Earn

There is a system in place.

Corporate charity

BHP Billiton Sustainable Communities (Charity Commission no. 1131066).

Applications

Applications to the registered charity BHP Billiton Sustainable Communities (Charity Commission no. 1131066) should be made in writing to the correspondent after checking the website for information regarding grants from the charity.

Big Yellow Group PLC

Services

Correspondent: Paul Donnelly, Corporate Social Responsibility Manager, 2 The Deans, Bridge Road, Bagshot, Surrey GU19 5AT (tel: 01276 470190; fax: 01276 470191; email: pdonnelly@bigyellow.co.uk; website: bigyellow.hemscottir.com)

Directors: Adrian Lee; Georgina Harvey; James Gibson, Chief Executive Officer; John Trotman; Mark Richardson; Nicholas Vetch, Chair; Richard Cotton; Steve Johnson; Tim Clark (women: 1; men: 8)

Year end	31/03/2015
Turnover	£84,276,000
Pre-tax profit	£105,236,000

Nature of business: Provision of self-storage and related services.

Company registration number: 3625199

Subsidiary undertakings include: BYSSCo Ltd, BYRCo Ltd.

Focus of giving: Health, ill health, community/social welfare.

Community involvement	✓
Community contributions	✓
CSR report	✓
Directors have other relevant posts	✓
Cash donations declared	✓

Community involvement

The group provides free storage space and during the year 2015 the space occupied by charities in Big Yellow and Armadillo stores was 37,800 square feet worth approximately £750,000 per annum. Some of the charities that have benefitted from the free storage include the National Childbirth Trust, Cancer Research, British Heart Foundation, and a number of food bank charities.

Directors with other relevant posts

Mark Richardson (non-executive director) is a trustee of WWF-UK, and he is also a trustee and treasurer of the children's communication charity ICAN.

James Gibson is a trustee of the London Children's Ballet.

Main locations

Surrey and various locations throughout the UK.

Community contributions

Throughout the year a total of £37,000 was raised for the company charities selected by employees and a further £24,000 was raised for other charities. It is unclear how much the company contributed to this total of £61,000.

Employee-led support

The company supported fifteen different company charities which were elected by the store and head office teams. Staff undertook variety of activities for the charities, with donations also being made by the company. Examples include one employee who ran the London Marathon raising £1,600 for the charity RP fighting blindness and seven team members who took on the Three Peaks Challenge and raised just under £2,600 for Cystic Fibrosis.

Applications

Apply in writing to the correspondent.

Birmingham International Airport Ltd

Airport operators

Correspondent: Andy Holding, Corporate Responsibility Manager, Diamond House, Birmingham Airport, Birmingham B26 3QJ (tel: 0121 767 7448; fax: 0121 767 7065; email: community@birminghamairport.co.uk or andy.holding@birminghamairport.co.uk; website: www.bhx.co.uk)

Directors: Brett O'Reilly; David Stanton; David Welsh; George Richards; Hilary Bills; John Clancy; John Hudson, Chair; Michael Bird; Michael Toms; Neil Fleming; Paul Calvin; Paul Dransfield; Paul Kehoe, Chief Executive; Robert Piper; Tersaim Singh (women: 1; men: 14)

Year end	31/03/2016
Turnover	£130,546,000
Pre-tax profit	£25,064,000

Nature of business: The principal activity is the operation and management of Birmingham International Airport and the provision of associated facilities and services.

Company registration number: 3312673

Subsidiary undertakings include: BHX Fire and Rescue Ltd; Euro-hub (Birmingham) Ltd; First Castle Developments Ltd.

UK employees: 619

Total employees: 619

Focus of giving: Education, enterprise/training, environment, health, ill health, heritage, local groups, older people, arts, culture, poverty and social exclusion, sport, recreation, children, young people, community/social welfare.

Membership: BITC

Community involvement	✓
Community contributions	✓
Company reports on anti-slavery	✓
CSR report	✓
Charity partner(s)	✓
Corporate charity	✓
Employee-led support	✓
Gifts in kind	✓
Sponsorship	✓

Charitable donations

Cash UK (latest available):	2016	£78,000
Total UK (cash and in kind):	2016	£78,000
Cash worldwide:	2016	£78,000
Total worldwide (cash and in kind):	2016	£78,000

Community involvement

The airport's charitable involvement is focused on disadvantaged communities in the area where it operates, particularly East Birmingham and the north of Solihull. Support is given for causes such as education, community and children and young people. Grants are made through the airport's corporate charity for: heritage; the environment; sport and recreation; and health and well-being.

CSR strategy

According the 2015–16 corporate responsibility report, the company reviewed its CSR strategy during the year. It was decided that 30% of the company's community investment would be targeted at disadvantaged communities in the east of Birmingham, while another 30% would be focused on disadvantaged communities in the north of Solihull. The remaining 40% would be shared among other communities that are impacted by the airport's activities but have lower levels of deprivation and need.

The company has adapted its practices in response to this strategy, including: amending the criteria for the Community Trust Fund; focusing educational initiatives on target communities; working with partners to provide training opportunities in target communities.

Birmingham International Airport Community Trust Fund

The airport's corporate charity, The Birmingham International Airport Community Trust Fund (Charity Commission no. 1071176), receives around £75,000 investment from the company every year, in addition to any fees charged to airlines breaching noise regulations. Grants of up to £3,000 are available for charities and community groups in the areas of benefit (see the website for a list of postcodes), for capital or revenue costs. A broad range of causes are supported under the aim of improving quality of life in the local communities, with the following areas of focus:

- Heritage
- Environment
- Community cohesion through sport, recreation and leisure
- Health, well-being and employment

Beneficiaries included: John Taylor Hospice – Men's Shed and Training Ship Stirling (£3,000 each); Spotlight Stage School (£2,000); Coleshill Parish Church (£1,000).

Nominated charity

The airport has a long-established partnership with Acorns Children's Hospice Trust in Birmingham, which receives most of the proceeds of employee fundraising activities.

Other partnerships

The company also provides support for projects which do not meet the criteria of its corporate charity. For example, in 2015, the airport sponsored two sculptures of owls as part of The Big Hoot, an arts project raising money for Birmingham Children's Hospital Charity's Star Appeal. In 2016 the group began a partnership with a local organisation, Little Bird, to run a children's literacy project at the airport focused on empowering children across the world.

Education and training

In 2016 the airport launched a new educational facility, the Learning Hub, for activities such as workshops with partner schools, school holiday projects and continuing professional development sessions for teachers. The airport also worked with The Prince's Trust to deliver free programmes for young people, to help them develop vocational skills and experience.

Community contributions

In 2015/16, the company donated £78,000 to the Birmingham International Airport Community Trust Fund. A further £2,400 was donated through airport fines.

Employee-led support

Employee fundraising

Most employee fundraising initiatives are focused on supporting the airport's nominated charity, Acorns Children's Hospice. In 2015 more than 50 employees took part in a sponsored abseil, raising £10,000 for the hospice.

Corporate charity

The Birmingham International Airport Community Trust Fund (Charity Commission no. 1071176).

Exclusions

The Birmingham International Airport Community Trust Fund will not support:

- Running costs, such as salaries or expenses
- Individuals
- Medical treatment
- Organisations with statutory responsibilities, unless the project is clearly above their obligations
- Purchase of land and buildings, or general repair and maintenance (adaptions for disability or security may be supported)

- Sports kits or uniforms
- Short-term projects, such as events or trips
- Projects which have already taken place

Branches of national or international organisations are not usually supported.

Applications

Charity support request form
There is a form on the website for charities to request support: birminghamairport.custhelp.com/app/applications/charities/p/51.

There is also a form on the website for arranging educational visits.

Birmingham International Airport Community Trust Fund
Application packs can be requested by filling in the form available on the website: www.birminghamairport.co.uk/about-us/community-and-environment/community-investment/community-trust-fund. Grants are awarded twice a year, in April and October.

Bloomsbury Publishing PLC

Media

Correspondent: Michael Daykin, Company Secretary, 31 Bedford Avenue, London WC1B 3AT (tel: 020 7631 5600; fax: 020 7434 0151; email: contact@bloomsbury.com; website: www.bloomsbury.com)

Directors: Jill Jones; John Warren; Jonathan Glasspool; Nigel Newton, Chief Executive; Richard Charkin; Sir Anthony Salz, Chair; Stephen Page; Wendy Pallot, Finance Director (women: 2; men: 6)

Year end	28/02/2016
Turnover	£123,700,000
Pre-tax profit	£10,400,000

Nature of business: Bloomsbury Publishing PLC is an independent worldwide publisher listed on the London stock exchange with publishing offices in London, New York and Sydney.

Company registration number: 1984336

Subsidiary undertakings include: British Wildlife Publishing Ltd; Berg Fashion Library Ltd; Osprey Publishing Ltd.

Total employees: 585

Focus of giving: General charitable purposes, education, housing, homelessness, local groups, arts, culture, overseas projects, children, young people, community/social welfare.

Community involvement	✓
Community contributions	✓
Company reports on anti-slavery	✓
CSR report	✓
Directors have other relevant posts	✓
Cash donations declared	✓
Charity partner(s)	✓
Employee-led support	✓
Gifts in kind	✓
Market-led giving	✓
Overseas giving	✓
Pro bono	✓
Sponsorship	✓

Charitable donations

Cash worldwide:	2016	£4,000
Total worldwide (cash and in kind):	2016	£4,000

Community involvement

The group has a focus on supporting causes relating to literacy, literature and education. The annual report states that the group makes a small number of cash donations to charitable organisations supporting these purposes and also works with schools, universities, libraries and charities worldwide.

Partnerships
The 2015/16 annual report states that the group worked with the National Literacy Trust on two projects – the New Fiction Prize, which offered the chance to have a novel published, and a children's poetry competition – both of which raised funds for the charity.

The group's Methuen Dram publisher works in partnership with Prison Reading Groups to support the reading of plays in prisons, as well as providing books and arranging drama workshops.

The group also provides work experience opportunities for school students and invites university students to pay a visit to find out about careers in publishing.

Directors with other relevant posts
Nigel Newton is President of Book Aid International (Charity Commission no. 313869), Chair of Trustees of The British Library Trust (Charity Commission no. 114860) and a trustee of the International Institute for Strategic Studies (Charity Commission no. 206504). Wendy Pallot is a trustee of The Central School of Ballet Charitable Trust Ltd (Charity Commission no. 285398). Richard Charkin is a trustee of The Common Purpose Charitable Trust (Charity Commission no. 1023384). Jonathan Glasspool is a trustee of The Publishing Training Centre Foundation (Charity Commission no. 1083081) and Publishing Qualifications Board (Charity Commission no. 1002928). Sir Anthony Salz is a trustee of a number of charities, including Paul Hamlyn Foundation (Charity Commission no. 1102927), Tate Foundation (Charity Commission no. 1085314) and Reprieve (Charity Commission no. 1114900). Stephen Page is a trustee of Creative Skillset – Sector Skills Council Ltd (Charity Commission no. 1015324).

Main locations
The group's UK offices are based in London and Oxford. There are also offices in New Delhi, India; New York, USA; and Sydney, Australia.

Community contributions

In 2015/16 the group's cash donations to charities totalled £4,000.

Beneficiaries have included: Book Aid International; Independent Publishers Guild; The Charleston Trust; Woodland Trust.

In-kind support

In the UK, the US and Australia, the group provides in-kind donations (or at a reduced cost) of books to a range of good causes. This includes schools and libraries, charities such as Book Trust, Barnardo's, Oxfam and Red Cross, and also smaller organisations local to its offices. The group's London office donates books to disadvantaged children in London and the group's nautical publisher, Adlard Coles Nautical, donates relevant books to RNLI for fundraising purposes.

The Bloomsbury Institute, which organises events in the group, has run fundraising events for charitable causes such as Book Aid and International Women's Day.

Employee-led support

Employee volunteering
Staff volunteer in their own time for good causes sometimes either directly or indirectly assisted by the business. For example, over 30 employees, both privately and through a Bloomsbury co-ordinator, are involved in formal volunteer reading schemes in schools in the UK and US. Employees also volunteer to visit schools and colleges to deliver talks on careers and reading skills in the workplace, and to assist with practice interviews and school magazines. Employees also volunteer with initiatives in the communities local to Bloomsbury's offices, such as homelessness charities. In 2015/16 a UK employee visited Nigeria to train teachers in setting up classroom libraries.

The group also hosted a Reading for Pleasure roadshow at its London office, where related charities were invited to talk about their work and how employees could get involved.

Commercially led support

Sponsorship
The group is a sponsor and partner of World Book Day and also sponsors achievement prizes in the UK and US universities.

Applications

Apply in writing to the correspondent.

The Body Shop International PLC

Retail – miscellaneous

Correspondent: See 'Community involvement', Watersmead, Littlehampton, West Sussex BN17 6LS (website: www.thebodyshop.com/en-gb/commitment)

Directors: Christian Mulliez; Geoff Skingsley; Jeremy Schwartz, Chief Executive Officer (women: 0; men: 3)

Year end	31/12/2015
Turnover	£404,100,000
Pre-tax profit	£44,900,000

Nature of business: The Body Shop is a multilocal, values-led, global retailer of personal care products sold through its own shops and franchised outlets.

The Body Shop is a wholly owned subsidiary of the L'Oréal SA, a company incorporated in France.

Company registration number: 1284170

Subsidiary undertakings include: The Body Shop Americas Inc.; The Body Shop On-line (II) Ltd; The Body Shop Worldwide Ltd.

Total employees: 2,638

Membership: BITC

Corporate charity ✓

Charitable donations

Cash UK (latest available):	2015	£680,500
Total UK (cash and in kind):	2015	£707,500
Cash worldwide:	2015	£680,500
Total worldwide (cash and in kind):	2015	£707,500

Community involvement

The majority of The Body Shop International PLC's charitable contributions were channelled through The Body Shop Foundation (Charity Commission no. 802757), which was established as an entirely independent body so that it could lend support in areas the company couldn't. However, on 18 November 2016 the foundation announced that it would be closing down in early 2017.

The announcement stated:

> Over our 27 years, with over £24 million donated and invested, we're incredibly proud to have found & funded some of the world's most progressive organisations working for positive social and environmental change. Our funding focus – deliberately flexible – allowed us to be nimble and quick, funding cutting edge, dynamic and undercover work on issues relevant and current to us all.
>
> We've seen huge success from the impact of our funding but we've also faced challenges, seen the business change hands and lost a beloved mentor.
>
> Over the years, the charity has been primarily funded by The Body Shop International and we worked side by side on a shared set of values to make the world a better place.
>
> Unfortunately, despite our history and impact our lengthy conversations with the current management of The Body Shop have not resulted in a shared vision for the independent future of the Foundation. A committed funding stream has not been agreed, nor has a fundraising product been put in place for us in 2017.
>
> This means that Foundation is now unsustainable as the independent organisation that our founders envisaged. This is why, sadly – and to quote The Body Shop themselves, 'we've been unable to align our future'.

Enrich Not Exploit™

The company has announced it will launch a new foundation under the same name, 'The Body Shop Foundation', which will complement the sustainability aims of its Enrich Not Exploit™ Commitment. It stated:

> Having launched our Enrich Not Exploit™ Commitment in February 2016, we have mobilised The Body Shop global family around a new aim of true sustainability.
>
> Many of us at The Body Shop worked directly with our founder, Anita Roddick, and the Commitment is not only inspired by her fundamental belief that business can be a force for good, but also by the company's thinking around sustainability in the 1990s.
>
> To deliver this ambitious aim of true sustainability we need to think differently and more radically and creatively than before across the full range of our activities, including our philanthropic efforts. To that end, we invited The Body Shop Foundation to work with us in a new way. Unfortunately, the Trustees declined our offer so, sadly, we accepted that decision. To ensure our philanthropic activities remain a fundamental part of the business, we will be launching a new The Body Shop Foundation in 2017.

Through Enrich Not Exploit™, The Body Shop International has set itself 14 goals to achieve by 2020. The company's progress will be measured both internally and through the publication of annual 'Commitment reports'. Examples of the targets set out in the manifesto are to:

- Invest 250,000 hours of our skills and know-how to enrich the biodiversity of our local communities
- Help 40,000 economically vulnerable people access work around the world
- Double our community trade programme from 19 to 40 ingredients and help enrich communities that produce them
- Engage 8 million people in our Enrich Not Exploit™ mission, creating our biggest campaign ever

Main locations

The Body Shop has shops throughout the UK.

Community contributions

A figure for charitable donations was not declared in the company's annual report and accounts for 2015. The Body Shop Foundation's annual report and accounts for the year ending 28 February 2015 show that it received £680,500 from corporate donors, which we have attributed to the company and have taken as the figure for its cash donations. A further £27,000 was received by the foundation in the form of gifts in kind.

Beneficiaries included: The Body Shop Foundation (£707,500 – £680,500 in cash donations and £27,000 in gifts in kind).

Applications

At the time of writing (November 2017) The Body Shop Foundation (Charity Commission no. 802757-R) was due to close down in early 2017. The Body Shop has announced plans to establish a new charity, also to be known as The Body Shop Foundation.

Boodle & Dunthorne Ltd

Retail – miscellaneous

Correspondent: Nicholas Wainwright, Trustee, The Boodle & Dunthorne Charitable Trust, Boodles House, 35 Lord Street, Liverpool L2 9SQ (tel: 0151 224 0580; website: www.boodles.co.uk)

Directors: Elizabeth Wainwright; Frances Wainwright; James Amos; Jonathan Wainwright; Michael Wainwright, Managing Director; Nicholas Wainwright, Chair (women: 2; men: 4)

Year end	28/02/2015
Turnover	£60,700,000
Pre-tax profit	£8,100,000

Nature of business: Boodles is a family-owned luxury jewellers with stores in London, Liverpool, Manchester, Chester and Dublin.

Company registration number: 472968

UK employees: 95

Total employees: 95

Focus of giving: Overseas projects, children, young people.

Community involvement	✓
Community contributions	✓
Directors have other relevant posts	✓
Cash donations declared	✓
Corporate charity	✓
Overseas giving	✓
Sponsorship	✓

Charitable donations

Cash UK (latest available):	2015	£408,000
Total UK (cash and in kind):	2015	£408,000
Cash worldwide:	2015	£408,000
Total worldwide (cash and in kind):	2015	£408,000

Community involvement

Charitable giving is channelled through the company's associated charity, The Boodle & Dunthorne Charitable Trust (Charity Commission no. 1077748). The trust directs its grant-making towards organisations working to help young people.

Boodles Boxing Ball

In 2015 the sixth and final Boodles Boxing Ball charity fundraising event was held, raising £550,000 for The Gordon Ramsay Foundation supporting Cancer Research UK.

Directors with other relevant posts

Nicholas and Michael Wainwright are trustees of the company's associated charity.

Main locations

There are stores in Chester, Liverpool, London, and Manchester; and the head office is in London.

Community contributions

In 2014/15 the company declared charitable donations totalling £408,000, of which £200,000 was given to The Boodle & Dunthorne Charitable Trust.

The beneficiaries of The Boodle & Dunthorne Charitable Trust in 2014/15 were: Shining Faces in India (£55,000); Rainbow Trust (£48,500); The Message Trust (£15,000).

Commercially led support

Sponsorship

Boodles sponsors a number of sporting events, including race days and a tennis tournament.

Corporate charity

The Boodle & Dunthorne Charitable Trust (Charity Commission no. 1077748).

Applications

Apply in writing to the correspondent.

Booker Group PLC

Cash 'n' Carry, wholesale

Correspondent: Mark Chilton, Company Secretary, Equity House, Irthlingborough Road, Wellingborough, Northamptonshire NN8 1LT (tel: 01933 371000; fax: 01933 371010; email: info@bookergroup.com; website: www.bookergroup.com)

Directors: Andrew Cripps; Charles Wilson, Chief Executive; Gary Hughes; Guy Farrant; Helena Andreas; Jonathan Prentis, Group Finance Director; Karen Jones; Stewart Gilliland (women: 2; men: 6)

Year end	25/03/2016
Turnover	£4,991,500,000
Pre-tax profit	£150,800,000

Nature of business: Booker Group is the UK's leading food wholesaler. It supplies caterers, retailers and small businesses via the Internet, delivery and cash and carry.

Company registration number: 5145685

Subsidiary undertakings include: Booker Ltd; Makro Holding Ltd; Makro Self Service Wholesalers Ltd.

Brands include: Makro; Booker Direct; Classic Drinks; Ritter Courivaud.

Focus of giving: General charitable purposes, local groups.

Community involvement	✓
Community contributions	✓
Charity partner(s)	✓
Gifts in kind	✓

Community involvement

The group's CSR focuses mainly on environmental and sustainability issues and states that it 'aims to build sustainable relationships with its customers, who are mainly independent businesses at the heart of their communities, by improving the choice, price and service of products and services supplied'.

According to the ethical code of conduct report, at a corporate level Booker actively supports 'Caravan' and 'Sweet charity'. However, we have no other information supporting this.

Main locations

Northamptonshire and branches throughout the UK.

Community contributions

In the group's 2016 annual report and accounts, no charitable cash donations were declared but it is stated that than over half a million meals were donated to charities. There was also no breakdown of cash and in-kind costings.

In-kind support

Surplus food is distributed to local charities. According to the 2016 annual report, over half a million meals were donated to charities and an additional 14 tonnes of food donated to animal charities (each business centre, distribution centre and support centre has a nominated local charity).

According to the ethical code of conduct report, each business centre has a nominated local charity that it supports. The company may also support local community initiatives; for example, through donations of products for raffles, allowing colleagues time off to support good causes, through local sponsorship or events, etc.

Employee-led support

The 2016 annual report explained that each business centre, distribution centre and support centre has a nominated local charity. During the year ending 25 March 2016, colleagues raised £65,500 for these charities.

Applications

Contact the local outlet or the correspondent.

BP PLC

Oil and gas/fuel

Correspondent: The UK Social & Community Affairs Team, International Headquarters, 1 St James's Square, London SW1Y 4PD (tel: 020 7496 4000; fax: 020 7496 4630; website: www.bp.com)

Directors: Alan Boeckmann; Andrew Shilston; Bob Dudley, Group Chief Executive Officer; Brendan Nelson; Carl-Henric Svanberg, Chair; Cynthia Carroll; Dr Brian Gilvary; Frank Bowman; Ian Davis; Paul Anderson; Paula Rosput Reynolds; Prof. Ann Dowling; Sir John Sawers (women: 3; men: 10)

Year end	31/12/2015

Nature of business: The group's principal activities comprise exploration and production of crude oil and natural gas, including refining, marketing, supply and transportation; and the manufacturing and marketing of petrochemicals. BP has major operations in Europe, North and South America, Asia, Australasia and parts of Africa.

Company registration number: 102498

Subsidiary undertakings include: Atlantic Richfield Company; BP Capital Markets; BP Exploration Operating Company; BP Company North America; BP Oil International; Burmah Castrol; and Standard Oil Company. A full list of subsidiary undertakings can be obtained from the Companies House.

UK employees: 15,000

Focus of giving: Education, enterprise/training, environment, arts, culture, science technology, children, young people.

Membership: BITC

Community involvement	✓
Community contributions	✓
CSR report	✓
Cash donations declared	✓
Employee-led support	✓
FTSE 100	✓
Gifts in kind	✓
Humanitarian aid: overseas	✓
Matched funding	✓
Overseas giving	✓

Sponsorship	✓
STEM-focused	✓

Charitable donations

Cash worldwide:	2015	£7,200,000
Total worldwide (cash and in kind):	2015	£7,200,000

Community involvement

The BP Foundation is a charitable organisation working to benefit communities around the world by prioritising donations to charities that support science, technology, engineering and maths education and humanitarian relief. The BP foundation is based in the USA.

STEM

For over 45 years, BP has been working to address the gap in STEM skills through targeted investment at all levels of education. BP invests £3.25 million each year in STEM-related educational activities in the UK and estimates its resources have reached an estimated 2.8 million UK students over the past five years.

Community contributions

The Sustainability Report for 2015 notes the foundation contributed $370,000 (£279,000) to organisations and schools around the world that aligned with the company's focus areas and $310,000 (£233,000) to locally based relief organisations. The foundation also matches the personal contributions that BP employees make to eligible charities of their choice. In 2015 employees gave around $6.9 million (£520,500), which was matched with grants of approximately $9.6 million (£7.2 million). We have taken £7.2 million to be the overall total donated. We do not have a figure for giving in the UK.

(**Note:** In the annual report and accounts financial figures are given in US dollars. We have used the exchange rates applicable at the time of writing – November 2016.)

In-kind support

Employee time and skills.

BP says that it supports a range of mentoring and coaching programmes to enhance the skills and confidence of people in its local communities.

Employee-led support

Employees get involved in volunteering and fundraising activities.

Matched funding

The foundation also matches the personal contributions that BP employees make to eligible charities of their choice.

Applications

The BP Foundation in the US **does not accept unsolicited proposals**, but rather reviews requests submitted by BP businesses around the world.

Brewin Dolphin Holdings

Financial services

Correspondent: Louise Meads, Company Secretary, 12 Smithfield Street, London EC1A 9BD (email: london@brewin.co.uk; website: www.brewin.co.uk/corporate-responsibility/our-communities)

Directors: Andrew Westenberger, Finance Director; Angela Knight; Caroline Taylor; David Nicol, Chief Executive; Ian Dewar; Michael Williams; Paul Wilson; Simon Miller, Chair; Sir Stephen Lamport; Stephen Ford (women: 2; men: 8)

Year end	01/12/2015
Turnover	£283,691,000
Pre-tax profit	£61,000,000

Nature of business: Brewin Dolphin PLC is a British investment management and financial planning firm with 39 offices throughout the UK, Channel Islands and the Republic of Ireland.

Company registration number: 2135876

Total employees: 1,900

Focus of giving: Overseas projects, children and young people, health, education.

Membership: BITC

Community involvement	✓
Community contributions	✓
CSR report	✓
CSR or charity committee	✓
Charity partner(s)	✓
Employee-led support	✓
Gifts in kind	✓
Humanitarian aid: overseas	✓
Matched funding	✓
Overseas giving	✓
Payroll giving	✓
Sponsorship	✓

Community involvement

The company's website states:

> Each office has a nominated corporate responsibility ambassador who helps to organise a calendar of activities throughout the year and we encourage our people to get involved in a variety of ways including fundraising, sponsorships, volunteering and small grant giving.

In recognition of the company's 250th anniversary in 2012, the Brewin Dolphin Foundation was established. It co-ordinates charitable activities under one umbrella in order to raise funds for worthy causes and generate a greater impact for beneficiaries. Following a review, the foundation was further refined in September 2015 with support from the Charities Aid Foundation (Charity Commission no. 268369) to increase employee engagement and make it easier to take part in charitable activities.

The Brewin Dolphin Foundation

Staff are offered the opportunity to apply to the foundation for grants for small charities that support the local community. During the year the foundation donated grants to organisations including Nottinghamshire Hospice, Children's Hospice South West, MediCinema and West of Scotland Deaf Children's Society. The foundation is administered by the Charities Aid Foundation.

Disaster appeal donations

As well as supporting local communities and causes, the company may be prompted by employees to make donations to communities in immediate need both in the UK and overseas such as the British Red Cross Hurricane Matthew Appeal, Unicef's Ecuador Earthquake Appeal, the Cumbria Community Foundation Flood Appeal and Unicef's Syria Appeal.

Case study

The following case study was taken from the company's annual report and accounts for 2015:

> Brewin Dolphin is a sponsor of Enabling Enterprise. Enabling Enterprise's primary aim is that one day all students will leave school equipped with the skills that make them employable, with workplace experience and an aspiration to succeed. These are aims we wholeheartedly endorse and support and with which we are very proud to be associated. Founded by a group of teachers in 2009, it now works with a growing number of students nationally – currently 45,000 – and with over 2,000 teachers. Enabling Enterprise wants to make enterprise a core part of the school curriculum, with dedicated lessons in class and student work experience with businesses. We have been supporting Enabling Enterprise since 2013 by hosting visits from students to our offices, supported by Brewin Dolphin staff volunteers. These visits have proved enormously successful for everyone involved. We are keen to support Enabling Enterprise as it develops its programme in the Midlands, the South, the North East and the North West. During the year we staged Enabling Enterprise days at our London head office and our Birmingham office for pupils from a number of local schools. Other Group offices are planning to hold similar events in the coming year. Students worked in teams, with a volunteer, to plan a sweet shop business, pitch for funding and make investment decisions, mimicking the financial decision making process in the real world.

Directors with other relevant posts

Paul Wilson (non-executive director) is International Chair of Action Against Hunger (Charity Commission no. 1047501), a global charity addressing the problems of acute malnutrition in children, in 35 countries worldwide.

The company's website states: 'Placing such a premium on personal relationships, we've built a network of 28 offices across the UK, Channel Islands and Ireland, so there is one near to wherever you are.'

Main locations

Main UK location – London. However, there are various offices throughout the UK.

Community contributions

Unfortunately we have no financial information available regarding the company's charitable giving, It appears that the majority of the company's giving is through the Brewin Dolphin Foundation.

In-kind support

The company took part in the Lord Mayor's City Giving Day in London on 30 September 2015 by holding a number of activities to celebrate and encouraging charitable giving including the launch of the volunteering policy which offers every member of staff one paid day off to volunteer every year.

Employee-led support

Payroll giving

According to the 2014/15 annual report, more than £144,000 was raised in charitable donations by employees for more than 120 charities. During the year staff took part in a wide variety of fundraising events, both small and large, local and national, such as Race for Life for Cancer Research UK and staff hosting a Christmas Jumper Day for Age UK and Save the Children.

Commercially led support

In September 2015 the company announced sponsorship of Enabling Enterprise, an organisation the company's employees have been working with for a number of years, which helps equip school pupils with workplace skills.

Applications

Apply in writing to the correspondent.

Brit Ltd (formerly a record for Brit Insurance Holdings PLC)

Insurance

Correspondent: Social Committee, 55 Bishopsgate, London EC2N 3AS (tel: 020 7984 8500; fax: 020 7984 8501; website: www.britinsurance.com)

Directors: Andrew Barnard; Bijan Khosrowshahi; Dr Richard Ward, Chair; Jeremy Ehrlich; Mark Allan, Chief Finance Officer; Mark Cloutier, Chief Executive Officer; Matthew Wilson (women: 0; men: 7)

Year end	31/12/2015
Turnover	£1,621,760,000
Pre-tax profit	£6,246,000

Nature of business: A provider of global specialty insurance and reinsurance.

This record previously contained information regarding Brit Insurance Holdings PLC which in the past reported charitable donations from the group. However, as this is no longer the case, we have taken our CSR information from the annual report and accounts of Brit Ltd, the immediate parent company of Brit Insurance Holdings PLC.

The financial information in this record was originally reported in USD and was converted into GBP at the time of writing (November 2016).

Company registration number: 8821629

Subsidiary undertakings include: Brit Insurance Holdings Ltd; Brit Insurance Services Ltd; Brit Investment Holdings Ltd.

Total employees: 504

Focus of giving: General charitable purposes, health, ill health, overseas projects.

Community involvement	✓
Community contributions	✓
CSR report	✓
CSR or charity committee	✓
Charity partner(s)	✓
Employee-led support	✓
Gifts in kind	✓
Matched funding	✓
Overseas giving	✓
Payroll giving	✓

Charitable donations

Cash worldwide:	2015	£243,500
Total worldwide (cash and in kind):	2015	£243,500

Community involvement

Brit supports the communities in which it operates and charities close to the hearts of its employees. According to the 'Social and community' report contained within the annual report for 2015, the group supports causes based on the following three criteria:

- Projects should be for a good cause and operate in an area relevant to us
- Financial involvement should be for the benefit of the good cause
- Projects should offer alignment with our strategic priorities

It would appear that Brit employees select the charities that receive support. During 2015, they selected ten charities, nine of which were based in the UK and the remaining one in the USA. The charities benefitted from an initial one-off donation and support continued throughout the year in the form of fundraising activities and events, including a quiz night.

Employees are also supported in their charitable involvement in their local areas and there is a 'cross-functional' Social Committee which organises, among other things, community and charitable events.

Main locations

Brit has an office in the City of London, as well as offices in various locations overseas.

Community contributions

The 'Social and community' report states that 'during 2015, Brit donated US $0.3m under its charitable initiatives'. We have taken the figure declared – approximately £243,500 – as our figure for the group's worldwide cash donations. We believe the majority of this to have been given in the UK (nine of the ten charities supported were UK based); however, we could not determine the exact amount.

We were unable to determine the value of the time taken by employees for volunteering purposes.

We could not find details of the selected beneficiary charities.

In-kind support

Employee time

Employees are given two days of paid leave for volunteering activities with registered charities in their local areas. During 2015, 66 employee volunteering days were taken.

Employee-led support

Employee volunteering

The group's Social Committee organises a range of community and charitable events for employees, including volunteering days.

Payroll giving

Employees can support good causes through a payroll giving scheme.

Matched funding

Money raised by employees through charitable activities is matched by Brit.

Applications

It would appear that charities are selected by Brit employees.

British Airways PLC

Aviation

Correspondent: Community Relations, HBBG, Waterside, Harmondsworth, Middlesex UB7 0GB (tel: 0870 850 9850; email: community.branch@britishairways.com; website: www.ba.com)

Directors: Alison Reed; Baroness Kingsmill; Baroness Symons; Jim Lawrence; Keith Williams, Chief Financial Officer; Ken Smart; Maarten van den Bergh; Martin Broughton, Chair; Rafael Sánchez-Lozano Turmo; Willie Walsh, Chief Executive (women: 3; men: 7)

Year end	31/12/2015
Turnover	£11,333,000,000
Pre-tax profit	£2,628,000,000

Nature of business: Principal activities: the operation of international and domestic scheduled and charter air services for the carriage of passengers, freight and mail and the provision of ancillary airline and travel services.

Company registration number: 1777777

Subsidiary undertakings include: The Mileage Company, OpenSkies and BA European Ltd.

Focus of giving: Education, overseas projects, children, young people, community/social welfare.

Community involvement	✓
Community contributions	✓
CSR report	✓
Cash donations declared	✓
Charity partner(s)	✓
Employee-led support	✓
Gifts in kind	✓
Overseas giving	✓
Payroll giving	✓

Charitable donations

Total UK (cash and in kind):	2015	£7,670,000
Total worldwide (cash and in kind):	2015	£7,670,000

Community involvement

The company's community work focuses on four specific areas:

- Flying Start – the partnership with Comic Relief
- Colleague volunteering
- The British Airways Community and Conservation programme (BACC)
- The Community Learning Centre which provides airline specific activities for schools and colleagues across the Heathrow community

Charity Partners: Comic Relief

Main locations

The group's head office is in Harmondsworth.

Community contributions

In 2015 British Airway's charitable donations amounted to £7.67 million (€9 million).

In-kind support

British Airways' Community and Conservation Programme

British Airways has 40 community and conservation partners all of which are UK-registered charities, based in communities across its worldwide network. The main focus is on education, youth development and conservation. The company provides flight bursaries, excess baggage allowances and cargo transportation services to support these partners in their work.

Employee-led support

Flying Start

In 2010 British Airways launched Flying Start, a charity partnership with Comic Relief. The aim was to raise £6 million and 'change the lives of children worldwide'. By the end of 2014 the scheme had raised over £7 million.

Volunteering

In July 2013 the volunteering programme was formalised which means employees can now volunteer both in the UK and overseas 'within a structured framework contributing to their own development'. Volunteering priorities are centred around; education and youth development, colleague development and engagement, as well as sustained communities and conservation. During the year 1,810 employees donated a total of 14,828 hours.

Payroll giving

Over 3,000 current and retired colleagues donate to charity through the company's payroll giving scheme. In 2015 the payroll giving scheme raised £689,000 (€806,000) for employee-chosen charities.

Commercially led support

The British Airways Community Learning Centre

Opened in 1999, the centre provides learning opportunities for young people from schools and colleges across the Heathrow community and further afield. The team of specialist trainers provide insights into the world of work and the airline industry. To date over 100,000 young people have benefitted from this initiative.

Apprentices and work placement positions

A small number of students from local schools are given five-day work placements in a variety of departments across the airline.

Applications

Apply in writing to the correspondent.

British American Tobacco PLC

Tobacco

Correspondent: UK Social Reporting Manager, Globe House, 4 Temple Place, London WC2R 2PG (tel: 020 7845 1000; fax: 020 7240 0555; website: www.bat.com)

Directors: Ann Godbehere; Ben Stevens, Finance Director and Chief Information Officer; Christine Morin-Postel; Dimitri Panayotopoulos; Dr Gerard Murphy; Dr Marion Helmes; Dr Pedro Malan; Kieran Poynter; Nicandro Durante, Chief Executive; Richard Burrows, Chair; Savio Kwan; Sue Mair (women: 4; men: 8)

Year end	31/12/2015
Turnover	£13,104,000,000
Pre-tax profit	£6,045,000,000

Nature of business: Principal activities: the manufacture, market and sale of cigarettes and other tobacco products.

Company registration number: 3407696

Subsidiary undertakings include: British American Tobacco (1998) Ltd, B.A.T. International Finance PLC., B.A.T Capital Corporation and BATMark Ltd.

Brands include: Benson and Hedges; Dunhill; Lucky Strike; Rothmans.

Total employees: 50,000

Focus of giving: General charitable purposes, education, environment, heritage, overseas projects, arts, culture.

Membership: BITC

Community involvement	✓
Community contributions	✓
CSR report	✓
CSR or charity committee	✓
AF Covenant	✓
FTSE 100	✓
Overseas giving	✓

Charitable donations

Cash worldwide:	2015	£11,100,000

Community involvement

The company's approach towards corporate social investment (CSI) is seen as an end in itself, rather than as a way to promote itself. However, it is recognised that local community needs are diverse. As a result, within the parameters of this guidance and guidelines on focus of spend, CSI is managed locally to ensure the most appropriate projects are supported.

Charity partners

At group level, the major activities supported by the company are the British American Tobacco Biodiversity

Partnership and the Eliminating Child Labour in Tobacco Growing Foundation.

There is an annual Sustainability Report. The report does not contain information on community programmes as it is considered that this information is more relevant locally and global data is not collected.

According to the company's website:

> We provide our companies with guidance on selecting, managing and evaluating major CSI activities and ask them to calculate their contributions using the London Benchmarking Group (LBG) model, used by over 100 businesses. This includes cash contributions, in-kind donations and employee volunteering in company time.
>
> In recent years, we have concentrated on a smaller number of large projects that are focused on our key themes. We believe this means that our community investments have greater impact in the areas that really count.
>
> We are encouraging our companies to focus their CSI activities around three key themes:
>
> - Sustainable agriculture and environment
> - Empowerment
> - Civic life

The group's corporate social responsibility (CSR) performance is monitored through a Board CSR Committee and at regional and local levels through combined audit and CSR committees. This structure is said to support the embedding of CSR and sustainability principles across the group and allows performance against those principles to be monitored.

Main locations

Main UK location – London.

The company has various locations worldwide.

Community contributions

The company's global CSI expenditure in 2015 was £11.1 million as defined by the London Benchmarking Group criteria for charitable donations.

We could find no information regarding the UK cash or in-kind contributions, although in the past the company has declared this information.

Exclusions

No support can be given for causes outside the company's areas of focus.

Applications

Apply in writing to the correspondent.

British Land Company PLC

Property

Correspondent: Joanne Hammond, Charity & Volunteering Executive, York House, 45 Seymour Street, London W1H 7LX (tel: 020 7486 4466/020 7467 3452; fax: 020 7935 5552; email: joanne.hammond@britishland.com; website: www.britishland.com/sustainability/strategy/community)

Directors: Aubrey Adams; Charles Maudsley; Chris Grigg, Chief Executive; Elaine Williams; John Gildersleeve, Chair; Laura Wade-Gery; Lord Turnbull; Lucinda Bell, Chief Financial Officer; Lynn Gladden; Simon Borrows; Tim Roberts; Tim Score; William Jackson (women: 4; men: 9)

Year end	31/03/2016
Turnover	£590,000,000
Pre-tax profit	£1,331,000,000

Nature of business: British Land is a real-estate investment trust with a portfolio of office and residential properties in London and retail and leisure properties across the UK.

Company registration number: 621920

Subsidiary undertakings include: British Land City Offices Ltd; British Land Property Advisors Ltd; Liverpool One Management Services Ltd.

UK employees: 589

Total employees: 589

Focus of giving: Education, enterprise/training, small groups, local groups, arts, culture, children, young people, community/social welfare.

Membership: BITC, LBG

Community involvement	✓
Community contributions	✓
CSR report	✓
CSR or charity committee	✓
Directors have other relevant posts	✓
Cash donations declared	✓
Charity partner(s)	✓
Company gives to smaller charities	✓
Employee-led support	✓
FTSE 100	✓
Gifts in kind	✓
Matched funding	✓
Payroll giving	✓
Pro bono	✓

Charitable donations

Cash UK (latest available):	2016	£1,370,000
Total UK (cash and in kind):	2016	£1,680,000
Cash worldwide:	2016	£1,370,000
Total worldwide (cash and in kind):	2016	£1,680,000

Community involvement

British Land Company PLC supports national, regional and local initiatives in the areas around its properties and developments, with a particular focus on those that benefit:

- Young people and education
- Employment and training
- Local regeneration of community infrastructure and facilities

The company takes a structured and transparent approach to community contributions and its policy and processes are outlined in a document available to download from the website. Titled 'Charity and Community Funding Guidelines', the document explains that the majority, although not all, of the organisations supported by the company are registered charities, and that favour is given to requests that:

> - Help address specific local issues in communities where our major properties and developments are located.
> - Present opportunities for our local teams to become engaged and actively involved, for instance through volunteering
> - Deliver best value in terms of meaningful, measurable impacts in the local community
> - Offer long-term opportunities for partnership, so we can create long-term impacts and nurture mutually beneficial relationships. We may choose to pilot initiatives in the first year, before committing to ongoing funding

In addition to funding projects within these guidelines, British Land also supports its employees' charitable involvement by providing matched funding for their payroll giving and fundraising efforts.

Community partnerships

British Land develops partnerships with organisations in order to connect with its local communities. Examples of partnerships, outlined in the 2016 'Sustainability Update for Colleagues and Suppliers', include:

- National Literacy Trust's Young Readers Programme: this partnership, which has run for more than five years, sees literacy events take place in shopping centres owned by the company, and has so far benefitted 17,000 schoolchildren
- Construction Youth Trust's Budding Brunels, Reading Real Estate Foundation's Pathways to Property and Urban Land Institute's UrbanPlan UK: during the year, more than 900 young people gained an insight into careers in the built environment industry

- Elk Mill, Oldham: British Land commissioned the sculptor Emma Hunter to create a series of four permanent artworks to celebrate Oldham's heritage as a cotton-spinning town. The initiative included a range of local people, including schoolchildren and former mill workers

Community Day

The company runs an annual 'Community Day' through which, in 2015, 20 community partners were involved and 520 people benefitted. Employees from the head office and other London sites took part in the event, and their activities involved providing charity partners with mentoring support, running mock interviews and providing support for jobseekers; creating outdoor learning spaces for schoolchildren; and organising an afternoon tea dance for older people living in local care homes.

Directors with other relevant posts

Tim Roberts: trustee of LandAid and Chair of its Grants Committee.

Aubrey Adams: Chair of Trustees of Wigmore Hall.

Laura Wade-Gery: trustee of the Royal Opera House and Aldeburgh Music.

Main locations

The group's head office is in London.

Community contributions

The company publishes a detailed breakdown of its community contributions in the form of sustainability accounts, which can be downloaded from the website.

The sustainability accounts show that, in 2015/16, the company made community contributions totalling £1.68 million. As is our usual practice, we have not included the figure for management costs in our total for the company's community contributions.

The following helpful breakdown of the company's community contributions during 2015/16 was given in the accounts, according to London Benchmarking Group framework:

Cash	£1.37 million
British Land management costs	£605,500
British Land employee time	£251,500
In-kind contributions	£57,500
Total	**£2.29 million***

*This contribution equates to 0.63% of pre-tax profits.

In addition, the accounts also provide a breakdown of 'leveraged' community investment. We have taken this to represent contributions from, for example, employees and suppliers and, as is our usual practice, have not counted it in the total of the company's contributions made during the year. This amounted to £2.06 million (£1.9 million in cash and £153,500 in 'Key supplier workforce time').

A breakdown of the company's community programme contributions in various regions of the UK was also provided. It is important to note that this breakdown includes not only direct contributions from the company, but also leveraged contributions (from staff, suppliers, etc.). It does not include management costs. We have included this information as it provides some indication to the degree to which the company has an involvement with communities in specific regions across the UK.

London	£2.46 million
Yorkshire and the Humber	£337,000
'Corporate'	£304,000
Midlands and the East England	£175,000
Scotland	£138,000
North West England and Wales	£121,500
South West England	£85,500
South East England	£59,500
North East England	£53,500
Northern Ireland	£1,800

In total, almost 29,500 beneficiaries – including apprentices, jobseekers, and schoolchildren – were reached through the company's community programmes: 14,517 in well-being, culture and leisure; 14,513 in education; and 452 in employment and training.

In-kind support

Staff time

In 2015/16 the value of employee time contributed by the company through volunteering amounted to £251,500.

Employee-led support

Match funding

The company supports employees' charitable involvement with matched funding in three ways:

- 50% matched funding is given for all staff payroll giving donations, up to a maximum of £5,000 per employee per year
- Up to £750 is given in matched funding for money raised by staff based at British Land's head office and London-based office estates
- Each year, the company matches two fundraising initiatives at each of the company's retail properties, up to a value of £750 per initiative per year

Employee volunteering

Through the programme, in 2015/16, employees spent 2,658 hours volunteering for charity and community causes, an average of 10.1 hours per employee. During the year, 84% of British Land employees volunteered. Of the volunteering work carried out by employees, 16% was skills based (e.g. mentoring).

Exclusions

The funding guidelines state that British Land does not make donations to political organisations, nor will it:

- Support programmes outside the regions in which it operates
- Subsidise government funding
- Provide commercial sponsorship
- Support religious causes

Applications

In the first instance, read the helpful 'Charity and Community Funding Guidelines' which are available to download from the website. The document can be located on the 'Governance and policies' area of the website under the heading 'Community' (www.britishland.com/sustainability/governance-and-policies/policies).

If your initiative falls within the funding guidelines, contact either:

- The Building Manager of your local British Land shopping centre, retail park or office estate (the locations of these can be found at www.britishland.com/our-places). It is stressed in the guidelines that the company believes 'that local issues and partnerships are best identified by local people and so local funding requests must have the support of its local teams'
- For all regional and national funding requests, the correspondent who is the Secretary of British Land's Charity and Community Committee

The Charity and Community Committee meets to consider requests on a quarterly basis.

British Sky Broadcasting Group PLC

Media

Correspondent: The Bigger Picture Team, Grant Way, Isleworth, Middlesex TW7 5QD (tel: 0333 100 0333; fax: 0333 100 0444; email: biggerpicture@bskyb.com; website: corporate.sky.com)

Directors: Adine Grate Axen; Andrew Griffith; Andrew Sukawaty; Charles Carey; Christopher Taylor; David Darroch; James Murdoch; John Nallen; Katrin Wehr-Seiter; Martin Gilbert; Matthieu Pigasse; Tracy Clarke (women: 3; men: 9)

Year end	30/06/2015
Turnover	£7,820,000,000
Pre-tax profit	£1,516,000,000

Nature of business: Sky is Europe-wide entertainment company. In the UK and Ireland the group provides paid television, broadband and streaming services. BSkyB launched its digital television services in the UK on 1 October 1998.

Company registration number: 2247735

Subsidiary undertakings include: Bonne Terre Ltd; British Sky Broadcasting Ltd; BSkyB Finance UK PLC; Hestview Ltd; NGC Network International LLC; Sky In-Home Service Ltd.

Total employees: 30,714

Focus of giving: Environment, arts, culture, sport, recreation, children, young people, community/social welfare.

Membership: BITC, LBG

Community involvement	✓
Community contributions	✓
Company reports on anti-slavery	✓
CSR report	✓
Cash donations declared	✓
Gifts in kind	✓
Matched funding	✓
Payroll giving	✓
Sponsorship	✓

Charitable donations

Cash worldwide:	2015	£13,200,000
Total worldwide (cash and in kind):	2015	£19,800,000

Community involvement

The Bigger Picture

This is the group's community programme focusing on the arts, education, environment, sport, health and taking social responsibility for its activities. Sky continues to align its community investment to the wider goals of the business and its customers and utilises its brand, platform and technology in community investment.

Current initiatives undertaken under the Bigger Picture Programme include: Sky Academy; Cycling; and Sky Rainforest Rescue.

Sky Academy

The programme was launched in 2013. The website states: 'Sky Academy uses the power of TV, creativity and sport to unlock the potential of young people. Since the launch of Sky Academy in the UK and Ireland in 2013, more than 370,000 young people have been involved.'

Cycling

In an ongoing partnership with British Cycling Sky aims to transform cycling at all levels, from grassroots through to the elite. In 2008, Sky set out with the aim of increasing participation at all levels of the sport. Sky has been inspiring the nation to get back on their bikes for the past eight years and 2016 has been a great year with Team Sky winning its fourth Tour de France and the milestone of more than one million participants taking part in the Sky ride.

For a more detailed description of the programmes and most recent updates see an informative Sky's website.

Sky Rainforest Rescue

Delivered in partnership with WWF the initiative seeks to help save around three million hectares of forest from deforestation in Brazil. During the year a total of £4 million was fundraised which Sky matched to reach a total of over £8 million to support the project. The group raises awareness of the issue through its media platforms.

In September 2015, Sky celebrated the completion of Sky Rainforest Rescue, and its six-year partnership with WWF, through which Sky helped to raise over £9 million, save one billion trees in the Amazon and raise awareness of deforestation among 7.3 million people. This unique partnership between Sky and WWF started in 2009 with the ambition to save one billion trees, because deforestation and forest degradation cause up to a fifth of all greenhouse gas emissions globally. Over the duration of the partnership Sky customers and employees, schools and the general public all came together to raise funds and awareness. This made it possible to support a range of conservation work in Acre, Brazil, designed to give local people ways of making a sustainable living from the rainforest without having to cut down trees.

Main locations

Various locations throughout the UK and worldwide.

Community contributions

The group values its community contribution (based on London Benchmarking Group model) at £19.8 million. A further breakdown is given on the group's website which details the following information:

Cash	£13.2 million
Management	£3 million
In-kind support	£2.4 million
Time	£1.2 million

However, we were unable to determine how much was given in the UK and how much wordwide.

In-kind support

Sky Sports Living for Sport

According to the 2015 Bigger Picture Report, 3 Sky Sports Living for Sport has a team of over 135 athlete mentors delivering multi-week and one-day sports projects with Sky's partner Youth Sports Trust. The initiative reaches one-third of secondary schools, inspiring more than 114,000 young people a year. 85% of students felt their skills had improved as a direct result of taking part last year.

Employee-led support

Volunteering

About 10% of Sky employees engage in volunteering activities, particularly participating in the Sky's Bigger Picture programmes, such as Sky Academy. We know that in the past Sky employees were entitled to two days of paid time off annually.

Payroll giving

Employees give to charity through payroll giving or matched funding.

Matched funding

The group matches employee fundraising efforts pound to pound.

Commercially led support

Sponsorship

Over the past 20 years Sky has contributed more than £10 billion to British and Irish sports organisations, covering a wide range of sports, such as cycling, rugby, golf and cricket. Cycling is one of the main group's sponsorships with the collaboration with British Cycling, the Sky Ride campaign and support of elite cycling through Team Sky, a professional British road-racing team.

Exclusions

Our research suggests that support is not generally given for animal welfare charities, appeals from individuals, older people, heritage, medical research, overseas projects, political or religious appeals.

Applications

Apply in writing to the correspondent.

Britvic Soft Drinks PLC

Drinks manufacture

Correspondent: Sustainable Business Committee, Britvic PLC, Breakspear Park, Breakspear Way, Hemel Hempstead HP2 4TZ (tel: 0121 711 1102; email: info@britvic.co.uk; website: www.britvic.co.uk)

Directors: Ben Gordon; Euan Sutherland; Gerald Corbett, Chair; Ian McHoul; Joanne Averiss; John Daly; Matthew Dunn; Simon Litherland, Chief Executive; Sue Clark (women: 2; men: 7)

Year end	27/09/2015
Turnover	£1,300,100,000
Pre-tax profit	£137,600,000

Nature of business: Britvic is the largest supplier of branded still soft drinks and the number two supplier of branded carbonated soft drinks in Great Britain, and it is an industry leader in Ireland and France. Through franchising, export and licensing, Britvic has also been growing its reach into other territories, particularly the United States. Britvic is listed on the London Stock Exchange under the code BVIC.

Company registration number: 5604923

Subsidiary undertakings include: Britannia Soft Drinks Ltd; Britvic Finance No. 2 Ltd; Britvic International Ltd; Britvic Property Partnership.

Brands include: J20; Pepsi; Red Devil; Robinsons.

Focus of giving: Education, environment, health, ill health, community/social welfare.

Membership: BITC, LBG

Community involvement	✓
Community contributions	✓
CSR report	✓
CSR or charity committee	✓
Charity partner(s)	✓
Employee-led support	✓
Gifts in kind	✓

Charitable donations

Total UK (cash and in kind):	2015	£822,500
Total worldwide (cash and in kind):	2015	£822,500

Community involvement

The company's support for communities ranges from global projects via charity partners in countries from which it sources materials to local initiatives via its community fund. As part of its overall policy on corporate responsibility and long-term corporate vision of supporting local communities, Britvic established the Britvic Community Fund administered by the Essex Community Foundation. The fund focuses on supporting charities and voluntary groups in Essex, with a particular focus on those working with families in the Chelmsford area. Grassroots projects, such as local breakfast clubs and local charities, receive funding.

Charity partner

The company's website states:

> At Britvic we are committed to supporting charitable organisations that align with our business strategy. We have been involved with numerous different charities over the years all supporting important social and environmental challenges. During 2015 we raised over £822,000 for a wide variety of corporate and employee chosen charities, and this year we have appointed The Wildlife Trusts and Sported Foundation as our long-term corporate charity partner.

Main locations

Various locations throughout the UK and worldwide.

Community contributions

In 2014/15 'total cash-led' contributions totalled £822,500. This included cash donations directly to charitable organisations and other investment in support of community programmes, including volunteering time and in-kind donations. We do not have a separate breakdown of cash donations from the company.

In-kind support

Learning Zones

In 2009 Britvic's first Learning Zone was launched in Beckton to provide a dedicated space in which to help teachers connect classroom learning with an understanding of business. Since then, Learning Zones have been opened across the company's manufacturing sites and its head office in Hemel Hempstead. The company continues to run its enterprise learning module in partnership with The British Soft Drinks Association (BSDA), as well as its new Young People Employability workshops. An online educational toolkit has also been updated and is available at: www.britviclearningzone.co.uk

The company's annual report for 2015 states:

> We are committed to building upon the foundations set by our Learning Zone programme and next year will evolve the programme to focus on building impactful relationships between industry and the education sector through career inspiration days. The programme will be aimed at those studying either STEM subjects looking for careers in engineering or business studies where they are perhaps considering a career in marketing.

Volunteering

The company encourages people to support local communities by offering three paid days a year or two hours per month to volunteer. In 2015 nearly 50% of employees volunteered.

Employee-led support

In 2015 nearly 60% of Great Britain employees volunteered. The company has estimated that nearly 4,000 hours of volunteering have been dedicated.

Applications

Apply in writing to the correspondent.

Bruntwood Group Ltd

Property

Correspondent: The Directors, City Tower, Piccadilly Plaza, Manchester, Greater Manchester M1 4BT (tel: 0161 236 1647; email: info@bruntwood.co.uk; website: www.bruntwood.co.uk)

Directors: Andrew Butterworth; Chris Oglesby, Chief Executive; Chris Roberts; Jessica Bowles; John Marland; Katharine Vokes, HR Director; Kevin Crotty, Chief Financial Officer; Michael Oglesby, Chair; Peter Crowther; Richard Burgess; Rowena Burns (women: 3; men: 8)

Year end	30/09/2015
Turnover	£108,178,000
Pre-tax profit	£13,500,000

Nature of business: Bruntwood is a family-owned and family-run property investment, development and management group with over 110 properties in four UK cities. It provides office space, serviced and virtual offices and meeting rooms and retail premises to companies across a range of business sectors.

Company registration number: 2825044

Subsidiary undertakings include: Afflecks Ltd; Alderley Park Ltd; Salford Innovation Park.

UK employees: 538

Focus of giving: Education, environment, health, ill health, heritage, inner cities, medical research, arts, culture, children, young people, community/social welfare.

Community involvement	✓
Community contributions	✓
CSR report	✓
Directors have other relevant posts	✓
Cash donations declared	✓
Charity partner(s)	✓
Corporate charity	✓
Employee-led support	✓
Gifts in kind	✓
Pledge 1%	✓
Sponsorship	✓

Charitable donations

Total UK (cash and in kind):	2015	£2,900,000
Total worldwide (cash and in kind):	2015	£2,900,000

Community involvement

The group focuses its community contributions primarily in the communities in which its business operates, particularly Greater Manchester. It donates 10% of annual profits to charitable, cultural, environmental and medical causes.

Partners

Bruntwood sponsors cultural events and has a long-standing partnership with the Manchester School of Art. The company also partners with Forever Manchester, the community foundation for Greater Manchester.

The Oglesby Charitable Trust (Charity Commission no. 1026669)

The trust supports a variety of charitable causes and normally makes grants of £5,000 to over £500,000 to registered charities primarily in the North West, with some preference for Greater Manchester. Donations have been made to charities based elsewhere in the UK and to projects which the trustees have become aware of in East Africa and Northern India.

The trust focuses on work to address health inequalities at a community level, but also supports: artistic development, both at an individual and a group level;

educational grants, bursaries and building projects; environmental projects; medical aid and research; and challenging social inequality, especially projects in which individuals and communities are encouraged to be self-supporting.

Examples of support include a research project to investigate how people across the region can take greater ownership of their own health outcomes. The report from this project was published in 2015. More recently the trust has focused on the development of a health foundation, called Shared Health, to facilitate networks to improve the health and welfare of disadvantaged people in the region.

The Bruntwood Charity (Charity Commission no. 1135777)
Through the Bruntwood Charity five nominated charitable causes are supported across the regions the group operates in. Charities are selected on the basis of the real difference they can make to the lives of people in these communities. Bruntwood employees devise their own ways of raising money to reach fundraising targets and the company itself also makes donations. Employees raise an average of £120,000 each year. The charity does not take any unsolicited requests for funding.

Charity partners: Claire House Children's Hospice (Liverpool); Onside (Manchester); St Gemma's Hospice (Leeds); The Factory Youth Zone (Manchester); and Whizz-Kidz (Birmingham).

Directors with other relevant posts
Katharine Vokes is a trustee of the Oglesby Charitable Trust (Charity Commission no. 1026669), The Bruntwood Charity (Charity Commission no. 1135777) and The Factory Youth Zone (Manchester) Ltd (Charity Commission no. 1134580).

Chris Oglesby is a trustee of the Oglesby Charitable Trust (Charity Commission no. 1026669) and The Grange School Hartford Ltd (Charity Commission no. 525918).

Michael Oglesby is a trustee of Chetham's Library (Charity Commission no. 526054), the Chetham's School of Music (Charity Commission no. 526702), Oglesby Charitable Trust (Charity Commission no. 1026669) and the Nicholls Hospital Trust (Charity Commission no. 526407). He is also on the steering board of the Manchester Cancer Research Centre and Vice-President of the Liverpool School of Tropical Medicine.

Peter Crowther is a trustee of The Bruntwood Charity (Charity Commission no. 1135777) and The Oldham Coliseum Theatre Ltd (Charity Commission no. 508829).

Chris Roberts is a governor of Cheadle Hulme High School.

Main locations
The company operates in the following areas: Birmingham; Cheshire; Greater Manchester; Leeds; and Liverpool.

Community contributions

The group donates 10% of its annual profits each year to charitable causes. In 2014/15 the total value of fundraising, sponsorship and charitable activities was £2.9 million.

Employee-led support

Employee fundraising
Bruntwood sets a fundraising target each year via The Bruntwood Charity to challenge its employees to raise funds for local charities.

Employee volunteering
The group has a scheme called Bruntwood Cares where employees are entitled to two days per year to volunteer for community projects. In 2015 a total of 162 employees devoted 1,150 hours to volunteering for local charitable causes. Examples included: mentoring young people; tree planting; helping with the Manchester International Festival; or sitting on a board or committee.

Commercially led support

Sponsorship
According to the website, the group sponsors a variety of organisations and cultural events 'that add to the vibrancy of the cities' in which it operates.

Bruntwood have supported Manchester International Festival since 2005. In 2015 this involved the group collaborating with a local digital agency to create a data visualisation project, ManchesterInFlux, to give festival's attendees a unique insight into the festival.

In 2016 the group became the headline sponsor of the Royal Horticultural Flower Show in Tatton Park, Cheshire East.

The group has also for the past decade provided a platform to showcase creative talent by encouraging writers, through The Bruntwood Prize for Playwriting. The prize came about through a long-standing partnership between the group, the Oglesbury Charitable Trust and the Royal Exchange Theatre. In 2016 the partners commissioned playwrights from seven different countries to write new plays on the subject of birth to promote discussions around global health inequalities.

Previous sponsorship activity includes:

- 2004 Cow Parade
- The Bruntwood Awards for Arts & Business
- The Royal Exchange Theatre
- The 2004 Commonwealth Games
- Birmingham Repertory Theatre
- Superlambanana
- West Yorkshire Playhouse
- Manchester Art Gallery
- The Lowry Theatre
- The Birmingham Hippodrome

Corporate charity

Oglesby Charitable Trust (Charity Commission no. 1026669) and The Bruntwood Charity (Charity Commission no. 1135777).

Exclusions

A list of eligibility criteria and exclusions for the trust can be found on: www.oglesbycharitabletrust.co.uk/eligibility.

Applications

According to the Charity Commission's record, **The Bruntwood Charity's** funds are fully committed and they do not seek unsolicited requests for funding. Enquiries can be addressed to Kathryn Graham, Trustee of the Bruntwood Charity, Bruntwood Ltd, York House, York Street, Manchester M2 3BB.

The Oglesby Charitable Trust has an application form on its website; however, the site currently notes 'that this form should only be used when requested by Trustees and any unsolicited requests will not be acknowledged and are unlikely to be read'. Visit www.oglesbycharitabletrust.co.uk for further information.

Individuals can apply to **The Bruntwood Prize for Playwriting** via the website. The prize is a biennial event, check the site for the latest deadline dates: www.writeaplay.co.uk.

Any other enquiries regarding community involvement and contributions can be addressed to the directors at the company's head office.

BT Group PLC

Telecommunications

Correspondent: Corporate Responsibility Team, BT Group Communications, 81 Newgate Street, London EC1A 7AJ (tel: 020 7356 5000; email: yourviews@bt.com; website: www.btplc.com/Betterfuture)

Directors: Gavin Patterson, Chief Executive; Iain Conn; Isabel Hudson; Jasmine Whitbread; Karen Richardson; Mike Inglis; Nick Rose; Sir Michael Rake, Chair; Tim Höttges; Tony Ball; Tony Chanmugam, Group Finance Director (women: 3; men: 8)

Year end	31/03/2016
Turnover	£18,909,000,000
Pre-tax profit	£3,473,000,000

Nature of business: The provision of fixed lines, broadband, mobile and TV products and services, and networked IT services.

Company registration number: 4190816

Subsidiary undertakings include: BT (International) Holdings Ltd; EE Ltd; Plusnet PLC.

Brands include: BT Sport; EE; Plusnet.

UK employees: 80,975

Total employees: 102,500

Focus of giving: General charitable purposes, education, enterprise/training, environment, fundraising events, large national appeals, overseas projects, poverty and social exclusion, science technology, sport, recreation, children, young people, community/social welfare.

Membership: BITC, LBG

Community involvement	✓
Community contributions	✓
Company reports on anti-slavery	✓
CSR report	✓
CSR or charity committee	✓
Directors have other relevant posts	✓
AF Covenant	✓
Charity partner(s)	✓
Employee-led support	✓
FTSE 100	✓
Gifts in kind	✓
Humanitarian aid: overseas	✓
Market-led giving	✓
Matched funding	✓
Overseas giving	✓
Payroll giving	✓
Pro bono	✓
Shared-value alliances	✓
Sponsorship	✓

Charitable donations

Total worldwide (cash and in kind):	2016	£29,400,000

Community involvement

BT looks to support communities in the UK and overseas by sharing skills, supporting fundraising and providing technology. Its goals include Improving Lives, which aims to use BT's skills and technology to raise more than £1 billion for good causes around the world, and Connected Society, which helps to contribute to society by promoting digital connections. It also works in partnership with a number of charities, particularly by supporting large fundraising appeals, and offers in-kind support.

Partnerships

The group has long-standing relationships with Children in Need, Comic Relief and Sport Relief, offering in-kind support for telethons, as well as staff volunteering and fundraising.

The group also works in partnership with NSPCC's ChildLine (Charity Commission no. 216401), providing the free phone line, employee volunteering and pro bono support for online and mobile communications.

The group also supports the Disasters Emergency Committee (Charity Commission no. 1062638) through its MyDonate platform and telethon support.

Young people and education

The group works with schools to deliver technology training for teachers and children, in partnership with the British Computer Society and the National Schools Partnership. The Barefoot Computing Programme is aimed at supporting teachers in primary schools to deliver computer-science lessons, and was delivered to 344,000 children during the 2014/15 school year.

Working in partnership with Unicef, the group also delivers an internet safety programme in schools, called The Right Click.

The group is also part of Movement to Work, an initiative aiming to tackle youth unemployment, by offering traineeships, skills development and work experience to disadvantaged young people.

The Supporters Club

Administered by Comic Relief, BT Sport raises money through donations from customers and the funds raised are used to make grants to projects for young people in the UK and abroad, with a particular focus on sport. In 2015/16 nine new charities received funding from the scheme, four of which were in the UK.

More information on the scheme can be found at www.thesupportersclub.org.

Digital inclusion

One of the group's goals is to support better digital inclusion. Initiatives include: Digital Inclusion for Social Housing, providing low cost internet for housing associations; Wi-fi in our Community, an initiative in partnership with Barclays providing free Wi-fi in libraries and community centres in disadvantaged communities; working with SOS Children's Villages to connect villages in Africa via satellite technology.

Directors with other relevant posts

Iain Conn is a member of the council of Imperial College London. Isabel Hudson is an ambassador for Scope (Charity Commission no. 208231). Jasmine Whitbread was previously Chief Executive of Save the Children International (Charity Commission no. 1076822) and is now Chief Executive of London First. Gavin Patterson is also a trustee of the British Museum. Iain Conn is a trustee of Movement to Work (Charity Commission no. 1160325).

Main locations

The group has offices throughout the UK and across the world.

Community contributions

According to the 2015/16 annual report, the group 'invested £35 million to accelerate a number of environmental and societal priorities' during the year, including environmental work, cash donations, volunteering time and in-kind support, equating to around 1.1% of the previous year's adjusted pre-tax profit. The 2015/16 Delivering our Purpose report states that the group estimates that around 84% of this amount corresponds with the London Benchmarking Group criteria.

During the year, £94 million was raised for good causes, including: funds raised through MyDonate by fundraising, telethons and appeals; employee fundraising and volunteering during working hours; sponsorships; in-kind and pro bono support; matched funding; donations; partnerships; fundraising activities run by the company; and investment in infrastructure such as MyDonate.

Beneficiaries included: Comic Relief; Lord's Taverners; NSPCC ChildLine; SOS Children's Villages.

In-kind support

Pro bono

BT's employees assist charities by contributing their skills and expertise. For example, through BT Troubleshooter, charities can 'borrow' a small team of volunteers with the appropriate skills and experience free of charge for a day or half a day.

Connected Society

As part of the Connected Society element of its Better Future programme, BT runs Get IT Together programmes in conjunction with the charity Citizens Online. The regional programmes help to develop people's computer literacy and confidence. Through BT Digital Champions young people are encouraged to share their online knowledge with people in their community.

Around the world BT works with charities helping to improve IT education through local initiatives.

The group has entered into a three-year partnership with Unicef UK to support the provision of face-to-face online safety training to parents, children and teachers. The partnership, which runs until 2017, provides in 600 schools across the UK.

Gifts in kind

BT contributes in-kind support to charities through technology and fundraising assistance, including:

- BT MyDonate – a free platform for online fundraising
- Support to telethons and large-scale fundraising appeals
- A limited number of free places at the BT Tower Dining Club for charities to use as prizes in fundraising appeals
- BT Community Web Kit – a free service for charities to host and manage their own website

Employee-led support

Payroll giving

Employees are able to donate to charities through the Give As You Earn scheme.

Employee volunteering

BT group encourages employees to get involved in local communities. It provides a wide range of volunteering opportunities and offers up to three days a year for staff to participate in volunteering activities. According to the annual report for 2016, in that year over 27% of staff spent nearly 45,000 days volunteering their time to support charities and community groups around the world. BT volunteers were involved in raising £8.5 million for Children in Need and £2.9 million for Sport Relief.

Commercially led support

The group offers reduced call rates to charities, and low-cost internet to housing associations.

Applications

BT Group

Apply in writing to the correspondent.

MyDonate

For more details of the MyDonate service, including the registration form and an email contact form, visit the website: www.btplc.com/mydonate/index.aspx.

BT Supporters Club

Grants from the Supporters Club are administrated by Comic Relief; for further information, visit the website: www.thesupportersclub.org.

BTG PLC

Pharmaceuticals

Correspondent: Corporate Responsibility Department, 5 Fleet Place, London EC4M 7RD (tel: 020 7575 0000; fax: 020 7575 0010; email: info@btgplc.com; website: www.btgplc.com)

Directors: Dame Louise Makin, Chief Executive; Dr Susan Foden; Garry Watts, Chair; Giles Kerr; Graham Hetherington; Ian F. R. Much; Jim O'Shea; Richard Wohanka; Rolf Soderstrom, Chief Financial Officer (women: 2; men: 7)

Year end	31/03/2016
Turnover	£367,800,000
Pre-tax profit	£57,500,000

Nature of business: BTG is an international specialty pharmaceuticals company that is developing and commercialising products targeting critical care, cancer, neurological and other disorders.

Company registration number: 2670500

Subsidiary undertakings include: BTG International Ltd; EKOS Corporation; Protherics UK Ltd.

Total employees: 1,209

Focus of giving: Health, ill health, overseas projects, science technology, children, young people, disability.

Community involvement	✓
Community contributions	✓
Company reports on anti-slavery	✓
CSR report	✓
CSR or charity committee	✓
Directors have other relevant posts	✓
Cash donations declared	✓
Employee-led support	✓
Matched funding	✓
Payroll giving	✓

Charitable donations

Cash UK (latest available):	2016	£27,000
Total UK (cash and in kind):	2016	£27,000
Cash worldwide:	2016	£27,000
Total worldwide (cash and in kind):	2016	£27,000

Community involvement

Directors with other relevant posts

Dame Louise Makin is also a trustee of the Outward Bound Trust and an honorary fellow of St John's College, Cambridge.

Main location

Various locations throughout the UK and worldwide.

Community contributions

According to the 2015/16 annual report, charitable donations totalling £27,000 were made.

Each year corporate charities are chosen locally by employees at each of the company's major sites.

According to the group's website, during 2015, the group made donations to a number of charities.

Beneficiaries included: American Heart Association and American Stroke Association (US); Children's Hospital of Eastern Ontario (Canada); Disability Challengers (UK); Frimley Hall Cystic Fibrosis Unit (UK); Great Ormond Street Hospital Children's Charity (UK); HeartKids South Australia and Northern Territory (Australia); Macmillan Cancer Support (UK); Wales Air Ambulance (UK).

Employee-led support

Previous research indicates that the company operates a Give As You Earn scheme in the UK. This enables employees to efficiently donate, so money that would normally be given in tax goes to their chosen charity instead.

Each year employees at each of the major sites choose corporate charities that support one of the diseases or conditions relevant to BTG, or that benefit the local communities where the company operates.

Matched funding

BTG encourages employees to support charitable events by matching funds raised by individuals up to a designated cap.

Applications

Apply in writing to the correspondent referenced 'UK Charitable Giving'.

Bunzl PLC

Distribution, print/paper/packaging

Correspondent: Julia Battyll, Bunzl Communities Co-ordinator, York House, 45 Seymour Street, London W1H 7JT (tel: 020 7725 5000; fax: 020 7725 5001; website: www.bunzl.com)

Directors: Brian May; David Sleath; Eugenia Ulasewicz; Frank van Zanten; Jean-Charles Pauze; Patrick Larmon; Philip Rogerson, Chair; Vanda Murray (women: 2; men: 6)

Year end	31/12/2015
Turnover	£6,489,700,000
Pre-tax profit	£322,700,000

Nature of business: Distribution and outsourcing group, primarily of plastic and paper-based products.

Company registration number: 358948

Subsidiary undertakings include: Bunzl Australia Holdings Pty Ltd; Bunzl Finance PLC; Bunzl Holding Danmark A/S; Bunzl Holdings France SNC; Bunzl Outsourcing Services BV; Bunzl UK Ltd; Bunzl USA Holdings LLC.

Total employees: 13,750

Focus of giving: Education, environment, health, ill health, overseas projects, disability.

Community involvement	✓
Community contributions	✓
CSR report	✓
CSR or charity committee	✓
Cash donations declared	✓
Employee-led support	✓
FTSE 100	✓
Gifts in kind	✓
Matched funding	✓
Overseas giving	✓

Charitable donations

Cash worldwide:	2015	£631,000

Community involvement

Main locations

London and various locations worldwide.

Community contributions

Across the group, Bunzl donated a total of £631,000 to charitable causes during 2015. This does not include in-kind donations or employee fundraising. Bunzl assisted a variety of projects for charities supporting healthcare and the environment, and funded a mobile first-aid vehicle for St John Ambulance and a seed-collection trip for Kew's Millennium Seed Bank.

In-kind support

Bunzl encourages employees to volunteer to assist organisations in their local communities and to raise funds for local charities of their own choice.

Where appropriate, to assist charitable organisations and to reduce the need to send obsolete stock to landfill, Bunzl will donate stock free of charge.

Employee-led support

The company supports its employees in their charitable fundraising. Examples include a cycle challenge raising money for Northern Ireland Hospice, as well as supporting projects of healthcare and environmental charities, such as sponsoring Kew Gardens' Millennium Seed Bank's field trips to the Atacama Desert in Chile to collect seeds from rare plants flowering due to unusual weather conditions.

Exclusions

No support can be given for political and religious appeals.

Applications

Apply in writing to the correspondent.

Bupa Ltd

Healthcare, insurance

Correspondent: Lauren Young, UK Sustainability Manager, BUPA House, 15–19 Bloomsbury Way, London WC1A 2BA (tel: 0800 600500/020 7656 2000; website: www.bupa.co.uk)

Directors: Clare Thompson; Evelyn Bourke, Chief Executive Officer; Janet Voute; Joy Linton, Chief Financial Officer; Julian Sanders, Company Secretary; Lawrence Churchill; Lord Leitch, Chair; Martin Houston; Prof. Sir John Tooke; Roger Davis; Simon Blair (women: 4; men: 7)

Year end	31/12/2015
Turnover	£9,828,400,000
Pre-tax profit	£374,300,000

Nature of business: Bupa is an international healthcare group offering health insurance and medical subscription products. It runs care homes, retirement villages, hospitals, primary-care and diagnostic centres and dental clinics. Bupa also provides workplace health services, home healthcare, health assessments and long-term condition management services. Bupa has 29 million customers in 190 countries. With no shareholders, Bupa reinvests its profits to provide more and better healthcare and fulfil its purpose. Bupa employs 84,000 people, principally in the UK, Australia, Spain, Poland, New Zealand and Chile, as well as Saudi Arabia, Hong Kong, India, Thailand, and the USA.

Company registration number: 2306135

Subsidiary undertakings include: Bupa Insurance Ltd; Sanitas, SA de Seguros (99% holding); Bupa Australia Pty Ltd; Australia Bupa Care Homes (BNH) Ltd; Bupa Asia Pacific Pty Ltd; Bupa (Asia) Ltd; Bupa Investments Overseas Ltd Bupa Occupational Health Ltd; Grupo Bupa Sanitas SL; UK Care No. 1 Ltd.

UK employees: 32,000

Focus of giving: Health, ill health, medical research, overseas projects, older people, children, young people.

Membership: BITC

Community involvement	✓
Community contributions	✓
CSR report	✓
Cash donations declared	✓
Charity partner(s)	✓
Corporate charity	✓
Employee-led support	✓
Gifts in kind	✓
Matched funding	✓
Overseas giving	✓
Payroll giving	✓

Charitable donations

Total UK (cash and in kind):	2015	£341,500
Cash worldwide:	2015	£341,500
Total worldwide (cash and in kind):	2015	£341,500

Community involvement

Main locations

Bupa has locations throughout the UK, details can be found on the company's website.

Community contributions

In April 2015 the Bupa UK Foundation (Charity Commission no. 1162759) was incorporated to replace Bupa's previous corporate charity – The Bupa Foundation. This new foundation is entirely funded by Bupa UK and at the outset it announced that in 2015 up to £1 million would be available for grant-making and that this figure would be reviewed annually.

The foundation funds practical projects to tackle specific challenges in health and social care and make a direct impact on people's health and well-being. Initially the focus is on two funding programmes: Mid-life Mental Health and Caring for Carers. Once a specific funding programme is announced applications can be made at any time before the stated closing date and will be reviewed in order of the submission date.

The foundation's accounts show that in the financial year April–December 2015 the actual donation figure was £460,500 made up of a services donation of £119,000 and a cash donation of £341,500 – the figure we have used in our financial section. Under the grant agreement with Bupa the donation income is received from the company when grants payable have been approved by the trustees. There is evidence of Bupa's continued support to the foundation as at the time of writing (December 2016) the company's website stated that since the foundation's inception Bupa had donated over £1 million. The foundation's website notes that through the first programme they ran – Mid-life Mental Health – 24 grants were made totalling £834,000. The second programme – Caring for Carers – was closed for applications at the time of writing but details of the awards had not yet been published.

In-kind support

Bupa provided services to the Bupa UK Foundation in 2015 with a value of £119,000.

Employee-led support

In February 2015 Bupa announced a two-year partnership with the Age UK. Money raised by employees, customers and suppliers will enable the charity to deliver a national wellness programme of activities, support, information and advice to empower more older people to live well and age well. The aim is for £1 million to be raised during the partnership.

Matched funding

In the UK Bupa matches up to £250 per employee, when they fundraise for health and/or adult social care charities.

Payroll giving

The company operates a Give As You Earn scheme.

Corporate charity

Bupa UK Foundation (Charity Commission no. 1162759).

Exclusions

The company does not support appeals from individuals, political appeals or religious appeals.

Applications

The Bupa UK Foundation operates specific funding programmes, details of which are given on the company's website. When a funding programme is open, applicants should apply through the online form on the website after checking that they meet the specific criteria for that particular programme and reading the FAQ section which provides further details of what types of projects that can be funded.

Burberry Group

Clothing manufacture, retail – clothing and footwear

Correspondent: Catherine Sukmonowski, Horseferry House, Horseferry Road, London SW1P 2AW (email: enquiries@burberryfoundation.com; website: www.burberryplc.com/corporate_responsibility/our_communities)

Directors: Carol Fairweather, Chief Financial Officer; Christopher Bailey, Chief Executive Officer; Dame Carolyn McCall; Fabiola Arredondo; Ian Carter; Jeremy Darroch; John Smith; Matthew Key; Philip Bowman; Sir John Peace, Chair; Stephanie George (women: 4; men: 7)

Year end	31/03/2016
Turnover	£2,514,000,000
Pre-tax profit	£421,000,000

Nature of business: The company designs, develops, makes and sells products under the Burberry brand. Product design and development are centred in Burberry's London headquarters. Fabrics and other materials are bought from, and finished products manufactured at, both company-owned facilities in the UK and through an external supplier network, predominantly located in Europe.

Company registration number: 3458224

Focus of giving: Children, young people.

Accredited Living Wage Employer	✓
Community involvement	✓
Community contributions	✓
Company reports on anti-slavery	✓
Cash donations declared	✓
Charity partner(s)	✓
Corporate charity	✓
FTSE 100	✓
Gifts in kind	✓

Charitable donations

Total worldwide (cash and in kind):	2016	£4,200,000

Community involvement

The Burberry Foundation

The Burberry Foundation (Charity Commission no. 1154468) is a philanthropic organisation dedicated to helping young people realise their dreams through the power of their creativity.

Directors with other relevant posts

Matthew Key (non-executive director)is also Chair of the Dallaglio Foundation (Charity Commission no. 1130353), which is a charity focused on disengaged young people.

Main location

London and various locations throughout the UK and worldwide.

Community contributions

Burberry continued to donate 1% of the group's adjusted profit before tax (which was £4.2 million in 2015/16) to charitable causes. Examples include supporting innovative youth charities through the Burberry Foundation and nurturing emerging creative talent through the Burberry Design Scholarship at the Royal College of Art and an apprenticeship programme at the British Fashion Council. We take the figure of £4.2 million as the company's overall worldwide charitable contribution.

In-kind support

Burberry's in-kind donations range from one-off gifts of non-trademark fabric and materials to assist young people enrolled in creative courses, to donations of smart business clothing to support vulnerable people enrolled in employability programmes and preparing for interviews.

Employee-led support

Volunteering

Employees worldwide are encouraged and empowered to take part in impactful community projects during working hours. Volunteering activities include anything from career inspiration events and employability workshops to long-term mentoring programmes and community revitalisation projects. During 2015/16 alone, 2,300 employees in 74 cities around the world dedicated nearly 12,000 hours to supporting their local communities.

Corporate charity

The Burberry Foundation (Charity Commission no. 1154468).

Applications

Apply in writing to the correspondent.

Cadbury

Confectionery

Correspondent: Kelly Farrell, Community Affairs Manager Northern Europe, Cadbury Ltd, PO Box 12, Bournville, Birmingham B30 2LU (0121 787 2421; email: kelly.farrell@mdlz.com; website: www.cadbury.co.uk/cadbury-foundation)

Year end	31/12/2015

Nature of business: Cadbury is one of the largest confectionery brands in the world. In 2010 it was acquired by US-based Kraft Foods Inc. which was later restructured into two companies: the spin-off company became Kraft Foods Group Inc., specialising in grocery products, and the remaining company was renamed Mondelēz International Inc., focusing on confectionery and snacks. Cadbury is now owned by Mondelēz International.

Given Cadbury's historical and recognisable links to philanthropy, we have made the decision to name this record using the brand name 'Cadbury', rather than the name of the Mondelēz holding company whose annual report and accounts declared charitable donations for 2015. See 'Community involvement' for more information.

Brands include: Dairy Milk; Freddo; Green and Black's.

Focus of giving: Education, enterprise/training, marginalised people, overseas projects, poverty and social exclusion, children, young people, community/social welfare.

Membership: BITC

Community involvement	✓
Community contributions	✓
Company reports on anti-slavery	✓
Cash donations declared	✓
Charity partner(s)	✓
Corporate charity	✓
Employee-led support	✓
Gifts in kind	✓
Matched funding	✓
Overseas giving	✓
Pro bono	✓

Charitable donations

Cash UK (latest available):	2015	£600,000
Total UK (cash and in kind):	2015	£642,000
Cash worldwide:	2015	£600,000
Total worldwide (cash and in kind):	2015	£642,000

Community involvement

Philanthropy is intertwined with the Cadbury name. In 1893 the owners of the company, George and Richard Cadbury (who were sons of its founder) began building at their own expense the Bournville Model Village. The village was part of a broader factory expansion, as described on the Cadbury World website (www.cadburyworld.co.uk). The website states: 'The Cadbury brothers not only built a brand new factory but improved the lives of their workers by building sixteen houses. They named this new village Bournville and over time added additional homes, a school, and a hospital. By late 1900, the village had grown to 313 houses on 330 acres of land and George Cadbury established the Bournville Village Trust to care for, and maintain this growing community.'

Although the Cadbury brothers Richard and George died in 1899 and 1922 respectively, Cadbury's dedication to philanthropy continued, notably with the founding of its charitable trust in 1935. Now known as The Cadbury Foundation (Charity Commission no. 1050482), the foundation continues to receive support in the form of cash donations and services from Mondelēz UK Holdings and Services Ltd (formerly named Cadbury Holdings Ltd) which is a subsidiary company of Cadbury Ltd.

The Cadbury Foundation
The foundation supports communities where the company (Mondelēz International) operates so that, according to its annual report for 2015, 'where possible donations can be backed up with employee volunteering work and gifts in kind'. The trustees currently focus funding on four 'pillars' outlined in the annual report as follows:

- Skills development: 'giving an awareness of the world of work and enhancing the ability of young people and disadvantaged adults to gain and sustain employment'
- Olympic and Paralympic legacy: 'to build stronger, healthier communities through sport'
- Source projects: 'supporting the development of sustainable cocoa growing communities where Mondelēz International sources its cocoa beans'
- Employee passions: 'some funds are reserved for employee-related grants and cash match where company volunteers can either have their fundraising efforts matched, or where they can bid for a grant to support the work of a chosen charity'

The foundation's trustees are proactive in their grant-making, preferring to award more substantial grants to charities within its chosen areas of activity (these grants are usually of between £10,000 and £30,000, with larger donations of up to £100,000 awarded to 'flagship' charities). The foundation has supported charities such as The British Paralympic Association, Help for Heroes, The Prince's Trust and Youth Sports Trust, as well local causes in line with the interests of employees.

Main locations
Mondelēz International has sites in Birmingham, Chirk (Wrexham), Crediton (Devon), Marlbrook (in Herefordshire), Reading, Sheffield, Uxbridge and the Republic of Ireland.

Community contributions

The 2015 annual report and accounts of Mondelēz UK Holdings and Services Ltd, a company whose immediate parent undertaking is Cadbury Ltd, states: 'During the year, the company contributed £600,000 (2014 – £750,000) to the not-for-profit Cadbury Foundation, which gives grants to projects and partner organisations, mainly in the fields of education and employment.' We have taken this as Cadbury's cash donations for the year.

The Cadbury Foundation's annual report and accounts further show that, in 2015, it also received 'Donated services' to the value of £42,000. We have taken this to represent 'costs of seconded staff' of almost £32,000 and 'fees for audit services of £10,000 which are met by the company as part of its Community Affairs Programme'.

Beneficiary: The Cadbury Foundation.

In-kind support

The Cadbury Foundation's charity partners are supported with donations of gifts in kind including IT equipment, office space and advice provided by the finance department.

Employee-led support

Matched funding
Employees can have their charitable fundraising efforts matched by The Cadbury Foundation.

Employee-related grants
Employees can apply to the foundation for funding to support a chosen charity.

Corporate charity

The Cadbury Foundation (Charity Commission no. 1050482).

Applications

The Cadbury Foundation does not accept unsolicited applications. Its annual report for 2015 explains:

> The Trustees' approach is to actively seek projects to support and therefore do not accept unsolicited applications for funding on an ad hoc basis. It is partly the elimination of 'token' grants in response to applications that has enabled the Foundation to provide more substantial support – and 'really make a difference' – in its chosen areas of activity.

Cadogan Group Ltd

Furniture manufacture, property

Correspondent: Paul Loutit, Company Secretary & Correspondent to the Trustees, 10 Duke of York Square, London SW3 4LY (tel: 020 7730 4567/ 020 7881 1032 or 020 7730 4567; fax: 020 7881 2300; email: paul.loutit@cadogan.co.uk; website: www.cadogan.co.uk)

Directors: Charles Ellingworth; Francis Salway; Hugh Seaborn, Chief Executive; John Gordon; Richard Grant, Finance Director; The Hon. James Bruce; Viscount Chelsea, Chair (women: 0; men: 7)

Year end	31/12/2015
Turnover	£135,415,000
Pre-tax profit	£650,587,000

Nature of business: The principal activity of the group is property investment. Cadogan Group Ltd is the holding company for the UK property investment business of the family of Earl Cadogan. The company is ultimately owned by a number of charitable and family trusts.

Company registration number: 2997357

Subsidiary undertakings include: Cadogan Estates Ltd; Chelsea Land Ltd.

Focus of giving: General charitable purposes, animal welfare, health, ill health, housing, homelessness, local groups, armed forces, religion, sport, recreation, children, young people.

Community involvement	✓
Community contributions	✓
Directors have other relevant posts	✓
Cash donations declared	✓
Charity partner(s)	✓
Corporate charity	✓
Employee-led support	✓
Gifts in kind	✓
Matched funding	✓
Sponsorship	✓

Charitable donations

Cash UK (latest available):	2015	£77,000
Total UK (cash and in kind):	2015	£77,000
Cash worldwide:	2015	£77,000
Total worldwide (cash and in kind):	2015	£77,000

Community involvement

The Cadogan Group supports charity and community projects in the area in which it operates through making corporate donations and via The Cadogan Charity. In 2015 the company supported cultural events and attractions, arts for children, and a charity working with people experiencing homelessness.

The Cadogan Charity (Charity Commission no. 247773)
The charity supports a variety of local and national organisations involved in: community/social welfare; medical research; education; the environment; animal welfare; and military charities. Particular preference is given to those based, or operating, in London and Scotland.

Sponsorship
Significant contributions have included:

- Sponsor of Team GB at 2012 Olympics
- Sponsor of the Thames Diamond Jubilee Foundation
- Sponsor of the Royal Philharmonic Orchestra, based at Cadogan Hall
- Lead sponsor of the Prince's Foundation for Children and the Arts Carol Concert
- Sponsor of Chelsea Gardens Exhibition by the Chelsea Society
- Organising and running Chelsea in Bloom, in alliance with the Royal Horticultural Society, held during Chelsea Flower Show
- Sponsor of Chelsea Festival of Music
- Funding and erecting of the Christmas lights in and around the Estate
- Support for several local churches
- Financial support to the National Army Museum
- Ongoing financial support to the Royal Court Theatre on Sloane Square

Directors with other relevant posts
Viscount Chelsea is a trustee of The Cadogan Charity (Charity Commission no. 247773) and St David's College Trust (Charity Commission no. 1075705).

Main locations
The group operates in London.

Community contributions

In 2015 the company declared £77,000 (2014: £213,000) in charitable donations, together with a donation to The Cadogan Charity which received £2.48 million (2014: £2.2 million) from the annual dividend received from Cadogan Group Ltd. The charity received other income but this was not derived from the company's shares.

Beneficiaries included: Glassdoor; The Prince's Foundation for Children and the Arts.

In-kind support

The company donates land and buildings around Chelsea for charitable and community purposes. This has included: churches; schools; and social housing. It also donates surplus furniture, bedding and crockery from its hotels to charitable causes.

Employee-led support

Employee fundraising
Cadogan's employees fundraise for local charities, which is then 100% matched by the company.

Commercially led support

Each year the company funds the Santa's Grotto and Christmas light displays on Sloane Square, Duke of York Square and Sloane Street in Chelsea. Donations from the Grotto are given to the company's charity partner, The Prince's Foundation for Children and the Arts.

Corporate charity

The Cadogan Charity (Charity Commission no. 247773).

Exclusions

The Cadogan Charity does not make any grants to individuals.

Applications

Applications can be made in writing to the correspondent, who represents both the company and its charity.

Cairn Energy PLC

Oil and gas/fuel

Correspondent: Christian Goodbody, 50 Lothian Road, Edinburgh EH3 9BY (tel: 0131 475 3000; email: Christian.Goodbody@cairnenergy.com; website: www.cairnenergy.com)

Directors: Alexander Berger; Iain McLaren; Ian Tyler; James Smith; Keith Lough; M. Jacqueline Sheppard; Peter Kallos; Simon Thomson; Todd Hunt (women: 1; men: 8)

Year end	31/12/2015
Turnover	(£498,000,000)

Nature of business: Cairn is one of Europe's leading independent oil and gas exploration and development companies. Cairn has its headquarters in Edinburgh (Scotland) and operational offices in London (UK), Stavanger (Norway) and Dakar (Senegal).

Company registration number: SC226712

Total employees: 151

Focus of giving: General charitable purposes.

Membership: Arts & Business

Community involvement	✓
Community contributions	✓
Company reports on anti-slavery	✓
CSR report	✓
CSR or charity committee	✓
Cash donations declared	✓
Employee-led support	✓
Matched funding	✓

Charitable donations

Cash UK (latest available):	2015	£229,500
Total UK (cash and in kind):	2015	£229,500
Cash worldwide:	2015	£229,500
Total worldwide (cash and in kind):	2015	£229,500

Community involvement

The Charities Committee evaluates applications based on its selection criteria. The company also supports local communities in regions where it is operationally active, through charitable donations and social investment. This activity is co-ordinated and managed in-country by the regional directors.

In 2015 Cairn provided charitable funding to a wide range of organisations as part of its commitment to give something back to the communities in which it works.

Case study
The following case study is taken from the company's website:

> Scottish Ballet's 'The Close' is an innovative way of inspiring marginalised and at-risk young people, positively affecting their lives by building confidence, exploring their own creativity and directly contributing to their ability to cooperate with each other through the arts. Cairn Energy's donation supported the project's costs for two school groups, providing participant tickets to the ballet, workshop delivery costs, professional staff fees and film creation.

Cairn supports charities across a number of categories including young people, communities, health, environment, arts and culture, and education and learning. Cairn looks to support charities that, first and foremost, share its core values of 'Respect', 'Relationships' and 'Responsibility'.

Main locations
UK locations – Edinburgh and London.

Cairn also has offices worldwide.

Community contributions

The Charity Committee donated over £229,500. The Cairn Charities Committee's primary focus is on distributing its annual budget among charities based in Edinburgh and the Lothians area, where Cairn is headquartered.

In the 2015 CSR report, charitable giving in the UK was broken down as follows:

Children	£108,500
Culture	£35,000
Health	£25,000
Community development	£15,000
Environment	£15,000
Other	£11,000
Disaster relief	£10,000
Education	£10,000

We take the total of £229,500 as the figure of Cairn's charitable giving in the UK.

Beneficiaries included: St Columba's Hospice and The Yard.

Employee-led support

Volunteering

The company encourages staff to participate in volunteering opportunities and provides up to three days of paid leave a year for volunteering. In 2015 a number of staff participated in two team charity events. These events included a 50-mile cycle from Glasgow to Edinburgh to raise money for Bowel Cancer UK and a 26.2-mile walk over the hills in the annual Pentland Push, raising funds for St Columba's Hospice. In total, £15,000 was raised.

Matched funding

Cairn continues to support staff and contractors in fundraising for a variety of good causes through matched funding.

Exclusions

Note that Cairn does not fund the following: charities with religious or political affiliations; political parties; places of worship; labour unions; organisations where there is a potential conflict of interest; organisations that discriminate; or individual sponsorship.

Applications

The Cairn Charities Committee's primary focus is on distributing its annual budget among charities based in Edinburgh and the Lothians area, where Cairn is headquartered. The committee evaluates applications based on its selection criteria. Cairn also looks to support charities that encourage the behaviours it values in its own organisation, such as teamwork, fostering individual potential and encouraging entrepreneurial spirit.

The company's regional directors co-ordinate and manage charitable donations and social investment.

All requests for funding are required to be submitted using the application form, which available from the Cairn website.

Calor Gas Ltd

Oil and gas/fuel

Correspondent: Sustainability Team (Community), Athena House, Athena Drive, Tachbrook Park, Warwick CV34 6RL (tel: 01926 330088; email: sustainability@calor.co.uk; website: www.calor.co.uk)

Directors: A. Thompson; G. Goddard; M. Hicken; S. Rennie; T. Collins

Year end	26/12/2015
Turnover	£418,000,000
Pre-tax profit	£79,000,000

Nature of business: The principal activity of the company is the processing, marketing and distribution of liquefied petroleum gas in the UK.

Company registration number: 303703

Focus of giving: General charitable purposes, education, environment, health, ill health, children, young people.

Membership: BITC

Community involvement	✓
Community contributions	✓
CSR report	✓
Employee-led support	✓
Gifts in kind	✓
Market-led giving	✓

Community involvement

In 2011 Calor created the Calor Wood at its Stoney Stanton site in Leicestershire. Around 400 people including local schoolchildren, Calor staff and their families planted 2,500 saplings on two hectares of unused scrubland in support of the Woodland Trust's MOREwoods scheme.

Charity partner/Charity of the Year

The company states on its website that it has found it more valuable and effective to focus support on the work of one charity as a means of engaging staff around a central cause. A national charity, for which the majority of corporate fundraising efforts are undertaken, is chosen through an all-staff voting process and typically for a three-year period. Following a successful partnership with Make-A-Wish Foundation UK, the new corporate charity is Alzheimer's Society. It is hoped to raise £100,000 through staff fundraising and company donations.

Main location

Various locations throughout the UK.

Community contributions

In 2015 the company did not declare its charitable donations and only the cash donations raised by staff were detailed on the website. We do not know the costings of in-kind giving as no information was provided as to the financial aspect of this.

In-kind support

A partnership has been established with Warwickshire's Myton School to increase students' knowledge of the workplace and improve their employability skills. As part of Calor's involvement in the Business in the Classroom Initiative by the Confederation of British Industry, the company offered students from years 7, 8, 9 and 12 the opportunity to obtain a better understanding of business by spending a day in the workplace and undertaking a long-term real-life business project.

Employee-led support

Start From the Heart

This is a scheme which gives employees one day's paid leave each year to do something which can make a difference to their community. Employees can choose to either participate in an event co-ordinated by Calor or take part in their their own Start From the Heart activity, as long as it meets the criteria of education and sustainability.

Commercially led support

The company has a Gift of the Gas scheme whereby it pledges to donate £5 (subject to terms and conditions) to its partner charity for every disused Calor cylinder returned to an approved Calor outlet.

Applications

Apply in writing to the correspondent.

Camelot UK Lotteries Ltd

Gaming

Correspondent: See 'Applications', Tolpits Lane, Watford, Hertfordshire WD18 9RN (tel: 01923 425000; website: www.camelotgroup.co.uk)

Directors: Andy Duncan, Chief Executive; David Kelly; Jane Rowe; Jo Taylor, Chair; Rob Rowley; Sir Patrick Brown; Tony Illsley (women: 1; men: 6)

Year end	31/03/2016
Turnover	£7,595,200,000
Pre-tax profit	£96,700,000

Nature of business: Camelot is the operator of the UK National Lottery and has a licence to run it up to 2023. The company changed its status during 2011, from a public limited company to a private limited company.

Company registration number: 2822203

Subsidiary undertakings include: Camelot Lotteries Ltd; CISL Ltd; National Lottery Enterprises Ltd.

UK employees: 644

Total employees: 644

Focus of giving: General charitable purposes, education, environment, health, ill health, heritage, arts, culture, poverty and social exclusion, sport, recreation, community/social welfare.

Membership: BITC

Community involvement	✓
Community contributions	✓
Company reports on anti-slavery	✓
CSR report	✓
Directors have other relevant posts	✓
Charity partner(s)	✓
Community Mark	✓
Employee-led support	✓
Gifts in kind	✓
Market-led giving	✓
Matched funding	✓
Payroll giving	✓

Community involvement

Camelot is the operator of the National Lottery which, since it was established in 1994, has benefitted more than 490,000 community projects in the UK. The company supports its employees' charitable and community involvement through schemes for employee volunteering, matched funding and payroll giving. Employees are encouraged to work with Camelot's current Lottery-funded charity partners.

Charity partners

Current Lottery-funded charity partners listed on Camelot's website are The Prince's Trust, The Silver Line, TCV: The Conservation Volunteers, and Media Trust.

Directors with other relevant posts

Andy Duncan: trustee of the Media Trust and of Oasis Trust.

Main locations

The group's head office is in Watford and there are also offices in London and Liverpool. There is a global office in Chicago, USA.

Community contributions

The company did not declare its charitable donations for 2015/16.

As is our usual practice, we consider funding raised from product sales (in this case, sales of National Lottery games) to be commercially led support and, therefore, have not included it in the total for the company's charitable contributions.

In-kind support

Employee time

All permanent employees can spend two days each year volunteering. Further time is available if the volunteering is linked to an employee's personal development.

Recycling

IT equipment that is no longer needed is recycled and any money raised from this is given to charity.

Employee-led support

Employee volunteering

40% of Camelot staff take part in the employee volunteering scheme.

Matched funding

Money raised by Camelot employees for registered charities can be matched up to a total of £500 for each employee per year.

Payroll giving

Employees can donate to a charity in a tax-efficient way directly through the Give As You Earn scheme.

Commercially led support

The National Lottery

Proceeds from the National Lottery games (including Lotto, Euromillions and scratch cards) help to raise an average of £36 million for good causes each week. There are currently 12 independent distributors of the National Lottery funding: Arts Council England; Arts Council of Northern Ireland; Arts Council of Wales; BFI (The British Film Institute); Big Lottery Fund; Creative Scotland; Heritage Lottery Fund; Sport England; Sport Northern Ireland; Sport Wales; sportscotland; and UK Sport.

Applications

It would appear, based on the information available, that community involvement from Camelot is led principally by employees, through their volunteering and fundraising activities.

Camelot plays no role in how funds raised through the National Lottery are allocated. For more information on how these funds are distributed to charitable and community causes, see www.lotterygoodcauses.org.uk.

Canary Wharf Group PLC

Property

Correspondent: Emma Warden, One Canada Square, Canary Wharf, London E14 5AB (tel: 020 7418 2000/020 7418 2448; email: emma.warden@canarywharf.com; website: group.canarywharf.com/corporate-responsibility)

Directors: A. Peter Anderson II; Anthony Jordan; Camille Waxer; Christopher Henderson; Clifford Bryant; Cormac MacCrann; Howard Dawber; Ian Ferguson; John Garwood; Richard Archer; Russell Lyons; Sir George Iacobescu, Chief Executive Officer (women: 1; men: 11)

Year end	31/12/2015
Pre-tax profit	(£60,695,000)

Nature of business: The group is involved in property development, investment, and management.

Company registration number: 4191122

Focus of giving: Education, enterprise/training, health, ill health, local groups, arts, culture, sport, recreation.

Membership: BITC

Community involvement	✓
Community contributions	✓
CSR report	✓
CSR or charity committee	✓
Corporate charity	✓
Employee-led support	✓
Gifts in kind	✓
Matched funding	✓
Payroll giving	✓
Sponsorship	✓

Charitable donations

Total UK (cash and in kind):	2015	£2,870,000
Total worldwide (cash and in kind):	2015	£2,870,000

Community involvement

The group's community work covers nine main areas of activity:

- Representation and corporate leadership
- Corporate charitable support
- Employment and training
- Employee volunteering
- Community engagement and support
- Educational engagement and research
- Economic development – support for local businesses
- Sports sponsorship
- Arts and events

Education

The company works directly with schools to run projects such as breakfast clubs and after-school sports projects. As well as working directly with schools the group has also partnered with the local authority to sponsor the Tower Hamlets Down Syndrome Conference and The Canary Wharf Group Paralympics. Other educational projects the group has supported include the Architecture in Schools Programme and Code Club which provides after-school coding classes all to children aged between 9 and 11 in Tower Hamlets' primary schools.

Canary Wharf Film Fund

Instead of charging a location fee for professional filming and photography in the Canary Wharf locations, the group asks crews to make a donation, half of which goes to the Canary Wharf Film Fund (CWFF), and the other half to local charities. The fund 'fosters film making and media in the local community, investing in equipment, training and projects that encourage young people to acquire the passion and skills that may eventually see them employed in the growing media sector in Canary Wharf and East London'. Projects recently funded by CWFF include digital video equipment for local schools and a summer training programme to introduce young people to film-making.

The Tower Hamlets and Canary Wharf Further Education Trust (Charity Commission no. 1002772)

The trust began in 1990 from a £2.5 million endowment 'to fund grants for local people to access further and higher education'. It provides approximately £250,000 each year to local people who need additional support to access college, university or professional courses.

The Canary Wharf Achievement Fund

The fund of £50,000 a year was set up in 1997 'to support a series of initiatives designed to improve local educational results through innovative programmes'. Some of the projects carried out through this programme have included: After School Clubs; Getting Ready for Reading and Talking Time; CommTAP.org; and Singing Playgrounds.

Canary Wharf Contractors Fund (Charity Commission no. 1097007)

The fund is a registered charity that was set up in 2001 and is administered by trustees and committee members from both Canary Wharf Contractors and the supply chain. Its primary aim is to help people in the construction industry that are in need as well as community organisations in East London. In recent years it has supported organisations such as Chickenshed, SPLASH, St Joseph's Hospice and Whizz-Kidz.

Main locations

East Docklands, Tower Hamlets and the South Bank.

Community contributions

According to the Sustainability Report for 2015, during the year the group spent a total of £2.87 million in 'community investment'. Assistance was provided to over 150 local organisations.

In-kind support

During the year 1,156 hours of labour was donated to pro bono projects in the community. Office space is also made available to local organisations when possible.

Employee-led support

Volunteering

Employees are given two volunteering days per year. Projects which have been supported include cooking at a local homeless shelter, delivering Christmas presents and refurbishing a community centre.

Commercially led support

Sports sponsorship

Sponsorship has been provided to a range of local sports groups as well as the British Heart Foundation for its Canary Wharf Jog. The annual event involves more than 1,000 fun-runners, raising over £100,000 for the charity.

Individuals athletes are supported through the Investing in Talent Fund.

Arts and Culture Sponsorship

The group has assisted a number of events and programmes for the national youth charity UK Youth, the London Festival of Architecture, the National Youth Theatre, and the Jewish Association of Business Ethics. It has been involved in a five-year programme helping Heritage of London Trust's work to restore and protect historic structures and provides an ongoing support to the Museum of London Docklands.

Awards

The groups sponsor the Canary Wharf Sports Personality of the Year Awards and the Canary Wharf Community Champions Awards.

Corporate charity

Canary Wharf Contractors Fund (Charity Commission no. 1097007).

Applications

The group

Apply in writing to the correspondent.

The charities

The contact for the educational trust is David Stone (tel: 020 7364 4888; email: david.stone@towerhamlets.gov.uk) at London Borough of Tower Hamlets, Mulberry Place, 5 Clove Crescent, London E14 2BG.

The contact for the contractors' fund is Alan Ruddy at Ruddy Joinery, Enterprise Way, Flitwick, Bedford MK45 5BS.

Capita Group PLC

Professional support services

Correspondent: Juliet Jones, Corporate Responsibility Manager, 71 Victoria Street, Westminster, London SW1H 0XA (tel: 0117 311 5757; fax: 020 7799 1526; email: Juliet.Jones@capita.co.uk; website: www.capita.co.uk)

Directors: Andrew Williams; Andy Parker; Dawn Marriott-Sims; Gillian Sheldon; Ian Powell; John Cresswell; Maggi Bell; Martin Bolland, Chair; Nick Greatorex; Paul Bowtell; Vic Gysin (women: 3; men: 8)

Year end	31/12/2015
Turnover	£4,674,000,000
Pre-tax profit	£585,500,000

Nature of business: The group provides a range of white-collar integrated professional support services to clients in local and central government, education, and the private sector. Services include: administrative services; consultancy; IT and software services; and human resource provision.

Company registration number: 2081330

Subsidiary undertakings include: Capita Holdings Ltd; Capita Business Services Ltd; Capita Trust Company Ltd.

Focus of giving: Children, young people.

Community involvement	✓
Community contributions	✓
Company reports on anti-slavery	✓
CSR report	✓
CSR or charity committee	✓
Cash donations declared	✓
Charity partner(s)	✓
FTSE 100	✓
Matched funding	✓
Pro bono	✓
Sponsorship	✓

Charitable donations

Cash worldwide:	2015	£388,000

Community involvement

Pro bono

The group builds long-term relationships with charities, small and medium enterprises, and voluntary organisations and supports them through the community programmes as well as providing pro bono advice and mentoring.

Main locations

London and various locations worldwide.

Community contributions

In 2015 corporate contributions totalled £388,000. The 2015 CSR report states: 'We donated money to good causes through support for our charity partner, our matched funding scheme, other community initiatives and disaster appeals.'

We take the figure of £388,000 to represent the company's worldwide charitable giving.

Employee-led support

The group has a corporate charity partnership, chosen by employees. Since 2014 the group has been supporting The Prince's Trust which works to support disadvantaged young people, including those in care. The company's CSR report for 2015 notes: 'Our employees also fundraise for the charity and have raised over £500,000 since the partnership began.'

Matched funding

The company provides matched funding to support employees in their individual charitable efforts.

Exclusions

No support can be provided outside that being given to Capita's chosen charities.

Applications

Apply in writing to the correspondent.

Capital & Counties Properties PLC

Property

Correspondent: Jill Pett, Director of CR & HR, 15 Grosvenor Street, London W1K 4QZ (tel: 020 3214 9150; fax: 020 3214 9151; email: cr@capitalandcounties.com; website: www.capitalandcounties.com/responsibility/corporate-responsibility/charity)

Directors: Andrew Strang; Anthony Steains; Demetra Pinsent; Gary Yardley;

Gerry Murphy; Graeme Gordon; Henry Staunton; Ian Durant, Chair; Ian Hawksworth, Chief Executive; Soumen Das, Managing Director and Chief Financial Officer (women: 1; men: 9)

Year end	31/12/2015
Pre-tax profit	£459,900,000

Nature of business: Capital & Counties, which is also known as Capco, is a London-based property company with two key assets located at Earls Court and Covent Garden.

Company registration number: 7145051

Subsidiary undertakings include: Capco Covent Garden Residential Ltd; Capital & Counties Asset Management Ltd; Olympia Management Services Ltd.

UK employees: 303

Total employees: 303

Focus of giving: Education, enterprise/ training, housing, homelessness, local groups, armed forces, children, young people.

Community involvement	✓
Community contributions	✓
CSR report	✓
Directors have other relevant posts	✓
Armed forces personnel	✓
Charity partner(s)	✓
Employee-led support	✓
Gifts in kind	✓
Matched funding	✓
Pro bono	✓
Sponsorship	✓

Community involvement

Capco, according to its website, works to develop long-standing relationships with selected charities in areas near to its assets at Earls Court and Covent Garden. Areas of special interest include young people, youth employment, homelessness and former members of the armed forces. The group also works with schools in Earls Court and Covent Garden to deliver an educational programme for schoolchildren based around issues affecting their local areas. Employees are actively involved in Capco's corporate responsibility activities, including through volunteering.

Some examples of Capco's community and educational programmes include:

- Volunteering programme with The Connection at St Martin's: One of Capco's commitments in 2016, as described on its website, was to launch a volunteer programme with this homelessness charity based in the City of Westminster
- Fulham Boys School: Capco has funded equipment, educational and sporting facilities at the school which are used to deliver a number of benefits for the local community. Children from the West Kensington and Gibbs Green Estates were able to attend educational and sports activities at the facilities free of charge
- Capco Education Programme: This programme, which informs schoolchildren about the history of their local areas, is delivered in conjunction with the Hammersmith and Fulham Urban Studies Centre. In 2016 Capco aims to extend the number of schools involved in the programme
- Spear: In 2015, Capco sponsored students to participate in the charity's programme, which has a focus on youth unemployment

Directors with other relevant posts

Gerry Murphy: non-executive member of the Department of Health board.

Main locations

The group operates in London. It also has offices in South Africa.

Community contributions

The Corporate Responsibility report for 2015, which is contained within the annual report and accounts, states: 'This year we have developed close ties with selected charities which align with our overarching CR strategy and have donated over £388,000 to charitable causes.' We were unable to determine if this figure included funds raised by employees or those given as sponsorship.

Employee-led support

Employee CR engagement

Staff members at Capco are each given a CR objective as part of their performance review. During 2015, Capco employees exceeded their collective target of 400 hours dedicated to CR-related activities, committing a total of 607 hours.

Employee fundraising

Capco employees take part in a range of fundraising activities including sponsored bike rides and bake-offs.

Matched funding

The website explains that funds raised by employees are often matched by the 'Capco staff recognition fund'.

Commercially led support

Sponsorship

Examples of sponsorship in 2015 included:

- Little Architect: a project delivered in partnership which The Architectural Association School of Architecture. The project includes design sessions and mentoring by Capco employees in order to help introduce children living in Earls Court and Covent Garden with the built environment
- Maggie's Cultural Crawl: Capco sponsored the night-time cultural walk around West London, which helps to raise funds for Maggie's cancer centres

Applications

Direct CR queries to the correspondent.

Capital One (Europe) PLC

Financial services

Correspondent: UK Community Relations Team, Trent House, Station Street, Nottingham NG2 3HX (website: www.capitalone.co.uk)

Directors: Amy Lenander; Chris Newkirk, Head of International; Karen Bowes; Neil Herbert, International Chief Financial Officer; Rob Harding; Rupert MacInnes; Victoria Mitchell, Chief Operating Officer (women: 3; men: 4)

Year end	31/12/2015
Turnover	£490,460,000
Pre-tax profit	£98,333,000

Nature of business: The company provides a range of financial services in the UK primarily comprising credit-card lending.

Company registration number: 3879023

Subsidiary undertakings include: Capital One Homeowner Loans Ltd; Capital One Loans (UK) Ltd; Capital One Mortgages Ltd; Castle Credit Card Securitisation Funding Ltd; Tenby Castle Funding Group Ltd; Sherwood Castle Holdings Ltd.

Focus of giving: Education, local groups, children, young people.

Membership: BITC, LBG

Community involvement	✓
Community contributions	✓
Cash donations declared	✓
Charity partner(s)	✓
Community Mark	✓
Employee-led support	✓
Market-led giving	✓
Matched funding	✓
Payroll giving	✓

Charitable donations

Cash UK (latest available):	2015	£1,000,000
Total UK (cash and in kind):	2015	£1,000,000
Cash worldwide:	2015	£1,000,000
Total worldwide (cash and in kind):	2015	£1,000,000

Community involvement

The company wants to help young people develop behaviours and skills that will help them become more employable and allow them to achieve their potential.

Partnerships

Capital One has a had a partnership with YouthNet since 2012. The company has helped improve the work and study provided by the charity as well as helping with the development of online services.

Main locations

The group has offices in London and Nottingham.

Community contributions

During the year 2015 the company made charitable contributions of £1 million directly benefitting around 25,000 individuals from nearly 500 charitable organisations.

In-kind support

Cheese Matters

This programme, developed and run in partnership with two other businesses and Businesses in the Community, brings secondary school pupils closer to the reality of financial management. It is a financial capability programme that follows the story of a young man who has got himself into debt, explores the consequences and then lets the students make decisions about what the outcome should be.

Employee-led support

Employee volunteering

Employees are encouraged to take at least one day a year – or the equivalent in hours – to get involved with the company's community activities. They use their skills to benefit local charitable organisations, for example assisting with business plans, websites or databases and providing financial consultancy.

Employee donations

The company has several donation schemes for employees:

- A 'Pound for Pound' scheme whereby the company matches 100% of the money raised for charity
- A volunteer grant is available for employees who work on a regular basis for a local community group
- A 'Pennies From Heaven' scheme helps employees automatically donate the odd pence in their salaries to Macmillan Cancer Support
- The Give As You Earn programme gives employees a tax-efficient way of donating to their favourite charity straight from their salary

Commercially led support

The company has been supporting local schools, namely Bulwell Academy and Big Wood School (both in Nottingham), for many years. It focuses its contribution on delivering employability workshops and financial capability sessions through Cheese Matters (see 'Commercially led support'). Work experience is available for students at partner schools, which teaches students about the company, the world of credit and what it takes to be successful in the world of work.

Additionally, tours are available under the company's AWE (Aspirational Work Experience) initiative to local primary schools. These are one-day experiences which cover the basics of financial management, an introduction to the world of work and a fun insight into what the company does. The sessions are facilitated by volunteer employees.

Applications

Apply in writing to the correspondent.

Cargill PLC

Commodity traders, distribution, food services, shipping

Correspondent: Cargill Cares, Velocity V1, Brooklands Drive, Weybridge, Surrey KT13 0SL (tel: 01932 861000; website: www.cargill.co.uk/en/corporate-responsibility/index.jsp)

Directors: Melanie Pollard; Paul Kingston; Peter de Braal; Richard Nield (women: 1; men: 3)

Year end	31/05/2016
Turnover	£957,600,000
Pre-tax profit	£28,400,000

Nature of business: The company trades commodities, and processes and distributes foodstuffs.

Company registration number: 1387437

Subsidiary undertakings include: Cargill Chocolate UK Ltd; Cargill Cotton Ltd; Sun Valley Foods Ltd.

UK employees: 652

Total employees: 150,000

Focus of giving: Education, environment, health, ill health, local groups, humanitarian help, overseas projects, poverty and social exclusion, science technology, children, young people.

Community involvement	✓
Community contributions	✓
Company reports on anti-slavery	✓
CSR report	✓
CSR or charity committee	✓
Cash donations declared	✓
Charity partner(s)	✓
Employee-led support	✓
Gifts in kind	✓
Humanitarian aid: UK including food banks	✓
Market-led giving	✓
Matched funding	✓
Overseas giving	✓

Charitable donations

Cash UK (latest available):	2016	£148,000
Total UK (cash and in kind):	2016	£148,000
Cash worldwide:	2016	£148,000
Total worldwide (cash and in kind):	2016	£148,000

Community involvement

Corporate support is complemented by employee volunteering, with a focus on health, education and environment.

Cares Councils

Cargill's five UK Cares Councils support initiatives and projects in the areas of health, education and environmental stewardship.

Examples of support include: supporting Lincolnshire Businesses for Breakfast, providing breakfasts and advice on health and nutrition to local schools; funding and creating a wildlife garden for a school in Witham St Hughs; working in partnership with Concern Universal to promote water conservation.

Partnerships

The group works with a range of different partners worldwide to deliver its corporate responsibility programmes.

In the UK, since 2009, the group has been working in partnership with the charity FareShare. The website states that between 2009 and 2014, the group provided funding totalling £400,000 to the charity and signed a new commitment of £225,000 to support FareShare North West and FareShare Merseyside, which it helped to establish.

The group also works with the organisation Bright Crop, to promote careers in food and farming to young people in the UK.

Main locations

The group has operations in 22 locations in England, which are listed on the website. It operates in 70 countries worldwide.

Community contributions

The 2015/16 accounts state that charitable contributions during the year totalled £148,000.

In 2014 the group made a two-year commitment of £225,000 to support FareShare North West and FareShare Merseyside.

Employee-led support

Employee volunteering

Employees volunteer with activities to support projects in the areas of health, education and environmental stewardship. These have included: establishing a vegetable garden at a homeless shelter in Manchester; running food science workshops with Salford Education Business Partnership; providing support with reading sessions in local schools in Manchester; volunteering through Bright Crop to promote STEM education; supporting FareShare depots in Liverpool and Manchester.

Exclusions

The group will not support:

- Organisations without charitable status
- Capital campaigns
- Core costs
- Religious or political activities
- Sports events
- Medical research
- Individuals
- Advertising or media
- Fundraising events or sponsorship

Applications

According to the company's website:

> Cargill businesses and facilities and their employees give through 350 employee-led, worldwide Cargill Cares Councils. The councils provide support for local charitable and civic organizations and programs such as food relief agencies, schools and youth programs, and local environmental projects.

The following information was taken from the Cargill Inc. website: 'If your program or project is in a Cargill community contact the Cargill manager or Cargill Cares Council. They are typically responsible for reviewing local grant requests and making funding decisions.'

There is also an online form and guidelines for the group's global corporate giving, which focuses on food security and nutrition, education, and environmental stewardship: www.cargill.com/corporate-responsibility/community-engagement/charitable-giving.

Carillion PLC

Building/construction

Correspondent: Sustainability Department, 84 Salop Street, Wolverhampton WV3 0SR (tel: 01902 422431; email: sustainability@carillionplc.com; website: www.carillionplc.com/sustainability)

Directors: Alison Horner; Andrew Dougal; Ceri Powell; Keith Cochrane; Philip Green, Chair; Richard Adam, Group Finance Director; Richard Howson, Group Chief Executive (women: 2; men: 5)

Year end	31/12/2015
Turnover	£4,587,000,000
Pre-tax profit	£155,100,000

Nature of business: Providing expertise in commercial and industrial building; and refurbishment; civil engineering; road and rail construction and maintenance; mechanical and electrical services; facilities management; and PFI (Private Finance Initiative) solutions.

Company registration number: 3782379

Subsidiary undertakings include: Carillion (AMBS) Ltd; Carillion (Aspire Construction) Holdings No. 2 Ltd; Carillion (Aspire Services) Holdings No. 2 Ltd.

Focus of giving: Economic generation, education, enterprise/training, environment, housing, homelessness, armed forces, overseas projects, poverty and social exclusion, children, young people, community/social welfare.

Membership: BITC

Community involvement	✓
Community contributions	✓
Company reports on anti-slavery	✓
CSR report	✓
CSR or charity committee	✓
AF Covenant	✓
Armed forces personnel	✓
Cash donations declared	✓
Gifts in kind	✓
Overseas giving	✓
Payroll giving	✓
Sponsorship	✓
STEM-focused	✓

Charitable donations

Total worldwide (cash and in kind):	2015	£1,900,000

Community involvement

Carillion supports the communities in which it has a presence by contributing to local causes the equivalent of 1% of its pre-tax profits. This total includes cash donated to communities, financial cost of employee time and total cost of donations in kind.

Directors with other relevant posts

Philip Green is Chair of Trustees for Sentebale. This charity helps vulnerable children, the forgotten victims of poverty and Lesotho's HIV/AIDS epidemic. In 2015 ten Carillion volunteers helped to complete building work on the Mamohato Children's Centre, which is a flagship centre for Sentebale's work.

Armed forces

The company aims to enhance its recruitment of veterans in Canada and the UK. Working with the Ministry of Defence and the military the company helps find careers for talented ex-forces personnel.

Main locations

Carillion's UK headquarters are in Wolverhampton; however, the company has various locations worldwide.

Community contributions

In 2015 charitable and community giving through a combination of employees' time, cash and in-kind donations totalled £1.9 million. Carillion's two-year national partnership with Barnardo's drew to a close in December 2015. The staff at Carillion raised over £155,000 and gave over 1,800 hours of volunteering time during the partnership, contributing to five major national projects that supported 727 children leaving care. In addition, during 2015 a total of 160 charities were nominated by the company's employees to receive £500 each via the Employee Nomination Fund. We were unable to determine the amount of charitable giving provided solely by the company itself.

Charity partner

Hospice UK, has been selected by employees to be the next strategic charity partner for two years. The partnership focuses on fundraising and volunteering opportunities in 2016 and 2017.

In-kind support

Staff time

Carillion's Special Leave Policy allows employees six days of leave per year to be spent volunteering in their local communities.

Employee-led support

Employee volunteering

Globally, 19% of Carillion employees volunteer in their communities. UK employees can register on a national database to volunteer in local schools through Inspiring the Future, which encourages young people to further their careers aspirations, and can also volunteer as mentors on the Ready for Work scheme.

Commercially led support

Employment and education

Carillion helps to engage marginalised groups such as long-term unemployed and homeless people, ex-offenders and wounded service personnel. According to the 2015 sustainability report:

> We have offered over 1,000 ready for work placements over the last eight years...We've directly employed 130 people from the scheme, of whom 12% were ex-offenders, and 270 more have secured jobs with other employers...we piloted a project to extend ready for work to women looking to return to work. Twenty female employees mentored eight long-term unemployed women. Four have since found jobs.

Building relationships with schools: Carillion is a partner for Your Life to promote STEM studies, and in 2015 supported nearly 45,000 children by volunteering over 8,000 hours of employees' time in schools.

Applications

Apply in writing to the correspondent.

Carrs Group PLC

Engineering, food manufacture, agriculture

Correspondent: Corporate Responsibility Team, Old Croft, Stanwix, Carlisle CA3 9BA (tel: 01228 554600; email: info@carrsgroup.com; website: www.carrsgroup.com)

Directors: Alistair Wannop; Chris Holmes, Chair; Ian Wood; John Worby; Neil Austin, Group Finance Director; Robert Heygate; Tim Davies, Chief Executive Officer (women: 0; men: 7)

Year end	29/08/2015
Turnover	£411,565,000
Pre-tax profit	£17,467,000

Nature of business: Carr's Group has three divisions: agriculture; food; and engineering.

Company registration number: 98221

Subsidiary undertakings include: Carrs Agriculture Ltd; Carrs Billington Agriculture (Sales) Ltd; Carrs Engineering Ltd.

Total employees: 1,101

Focus of giving: Education, enterprise/training, local groups, poverty and social exclusion, children, young people, community/social welfare.

Community involvement	✓
Community contributions	✓
CSR report	✓
Directors have other relevant posts	✓
Charity partner(s)	✓
Company gives to smaller charities	✓
Employee-led support	✓
Gifts in kind	✓
Pro bono	✓
Sponsorship	✓

Charitable donations

Total UK (cash and in kind):	2015	£44,000
Total worldwide (cash and in kind):	2015	£44,000

Community involvement

The group provides support through its fund with Cumbria Community Foundation for rural communities, young people, and people who are disadvantaged. It also supports other charitable activities through partnerships and employee engagement.

Carr's Group Fund

During 2015, the group established a grant-making fund with Cumbria Community Foundation (Charity Commission no. 1075120). According to the website, the fund supports charitable groups in Cumbria that focus on:

- Supporting rural and farming activities
- The needs of people who are disadvantaged
- Supporting young people and those wanting to develop skills; in particular, activities that raise aspirations, promote the development of life skills and support people to fulfil their potential
- Improving 'knowledge of countryside matters'

Grants are given at a minimum of £500, although most are around £1,000, for one year. The fund made £10,000 available in the first year of grant-making.

Other partners

The 2014/15 annual report states that the fund offers long-term support to Carlisle Youth Zone, a young people's charity in Carlisle.

The group also, jointly with the Biotechnology and Bioscience Research Council, funds a PhD student at Lancaster University.

Directors with other relevant posts

Chris Holmes is also Chair of Trustees of Carlisle Youth Zone (Charity Commission no. 1134974).

Main locations

The group has operations throughout the UK and across the world. Its head office is based in Carlisle.

Community contributions

In 2014/15 the group's total charitable contribution in the UK was £44,000. Of this, £35,000 was given to establish the Carr's Group Fund with Cumbria Community Foundation.

Employee-led support

Employee engagement

The group's 2014/15 annual report states that employees engage in the group's community activities through volunteering, mentoring and fundraising.

Exclusions

The Carr's Group Fund will not provide grants for: the purchase of computers, photocopiers, or vehicles; individuals; political purposes; promotion of religion.

Applications

Carr's group

Apply in writing to the correspondent.

Carr's Group Fund: Cumbria Community Foundation

Applications for the fund can be made using the form on the Cumbria Community Foundation's website, where deadlines and guidelines are also provided: www.cumbriafoundation.org.

Queries should be directed to Ellen Clements on 01900 825760 or ellen@cumbriafoundation.org.

CEMEX UK Operations Ltd

Building/construction

Correspondent: Paula Goodall, Community Fund Administrator, CEMEX House, Coldharbour Lane, Thorpe, Egham, Surrey TW20 8TD (tel: 01932 568833; email: paula.goodall@cemex.com; website: www.cemex.co.uk/cemexfoundation.aspx)

Directors: Carlos Uruchurtu Bustamante; Christopher Lesse; Hector Tassinari Eldridge; Jesus Gonzalez Herrera; Larry Zea Betancourt; Lex Russell; Vishal Puri (women: 0; men: 7)

Year end	31/12/2015
Turnover	£824,000,000
Pre-tax profit	£65,000,000

Nature of business: CEMEX is a global building-materials company with a presence in more than 50 countries. CEMEX UK Operations Ltd is the principal Cemex trading company in the UK.

Company registration number: 658390

Subsidiary undertakings include: Cemtrade Ltd; Buxton Rail Ltd; Russell Coal Ltd.

Focus of giving: Education, environment, community/social welfare.

Community involvement	✓
Community contributions	✓
Company reports on anti-slavery	✓
CSR report	✓
Charity partner(s)	✓
Corporate charity	✓
Employee-led support	✓
Matched funding	✓

Community involvement

CEMEX UK Foundation

The company channels its charitable contribution through the CEMEX UK Foundation (which is not a registered charity). It was created to provide a single point of focus for the company's charitable, community support and employee engagement activities. Both in-kind and financial support is available. The foundation will consider small community and environmental projects near the areas where the company operates. Projects that help educate children, students and stakeholders on CEMEX's business and the construction industry will also be considered.

Rugby Group Benevolent Fund (Charity Commission no. 265669)

This fund was established in 1955 with the aim of supporting employees and former employees of Rugby Group Ltd, and their dependants. The Rugby Group is now a part of CEMEX UK but the fund has kept its independence and is managed by a group of employees and former employees.

Today, the fund maintains the same objectives with which it was established but has broadened its scope to include charitable causes in communities where employees, former employees and their dependants are resident. These are: Barrington (Cambridgeshire); Chinnor (Oxfordshire); Kensworth (Bedfordshire); Lewes (Sussex); Rochester (Kent); Rugby and Southam (Warwickshire); South Ferriby (North Lincolnshire); and Tilbury (Essex).

Partnerships

The company works with Groundwork UK to improve communities where the company operates. CEMEX UK has also had a partnership with the RSPB since 2009 which aims to create 2,000 hectares of priority habitat by 2020. The company's staff also participate in wildlife initiatives and habitat maintenance schemes.

Main locations

CEMEX UK has sites throughout the UK. A searchable list can be found on: www.cemexlocations.co.uk.

Community contributions

We were unable to determine CEMEX UK's contributions for the year.

Employee-led support

In the UK, volunteers from local CEMEX UK sites volunteer on RSPB wildlife initiatives and habitat-maintenance schemes.

Matched funding

The foundation provides matched funding to employees that are raising money for charities and their communities up to a maximum of £200 per year.

Corporate charity

CEMEX UK Foundation (not a registered charity) and The Rugby Group Benevolent Fund Ltd (Charity Commission no. 265669).

Applications

CEMEX UK Foundation

Application forms are available from the company's website: www.cemex.co.uk/community-support.aspx.

Rugby Group Benevolent Fund (Charity Commission no. 265669)

Applications can be made through the fund's website: www.rugbygroupbenevolentfund.org.uk.

Center Parcs Ltd

Leisure

Correspondent: Corporate Social Responsibility Team, One Edison Rise, New Ollerton, Newark, Nottinghamshire NG22 9DP (website: www.centerparcs.co.uk)

Directors: K. O. McCrain; Martin Dalby, Chief Executive Officer; Paul Inglett, Finance Director; V. Aneja; Z. B. Vaughan

Year end	21/04/2016
Turnover	£420,200,000
Pre-tax profit	£57,300,000

Nature of business: Center Parcs is a network of holiday villages. In August 2015 it was purchased by Canadian asset-management company Brookfield.

Company registration number: 1908230

UK employees: 7,646

Focus of giving: Environment, health, ill health, children, young people.

Community involvement	✓
Community contributions	✓
Company reports on anti-slavery	✓
CSR or charity committee	✓
Charity partner(s)	✓
Employee-led support	✓
Gifts in kind	✓

Charitable donations

Cash UK (latest available):	2016	£16,500
Total UK (cash and in kind):	2016	£71,500
Cash worldwide:	2016	£16,500
Total worldwide (cash and in kind):	2016	£71,500

Community involvement

Community Fund

The Community Fund allows each village and the head office to sponsor local projects. During the year £16,500 was donated to community projects.

Charity partnerships

The group currently has partnerships with ChildLine and The Wildlife Trusts. Over £96,000 has been raised during 2015/16 through guest donations, matched funding and fundraising events from Center Parcs. In June 2016 a new partnership was formed with Together for Short Lives, a charity that raises money for children's hospices throughout the UK.

Main locations

Center Parcs has villages in Cumbria, Nottinghamshire, Suffolk, Bedford and Wiltshire.

Community contributions

In 2015/16 cash donations were not specified in the group's annual accounts. The value of in-kind donations in the form of short breaks totalled £56,000 and the Community Fund made donations totalling £16,500.

In-kind support

In-kind support is given in the form of holiday breaks to disadvantaged families going through difficult times, including families whose children are seriously ill.

Employee-led support

The group encourages staff to volunteer at local community projects by giving them a day a year for this purpose. Staff volunteer at schools, community groups and nature projects.

Payroll giving raised £3,400 for local charities.

Applications

Apply in writing to the correspondent referenced 'Charitable giving' or write to the 'Employee Representative Council' at your nearest Center Parcs.

Central England Co-operative

Retail – department and variety stores, retail – miscellaneous, retail – supermarkets

Correspondent: Community Dividend Selection Committee, Central House, Hermes Road, Lichfield, Staffordshire WS13 6RH (website: communities.centralengland.coop)

Directors: Dave Ellgood; Elaine Dean, Vice President; Graeme Watkins; Jane Avery; Maria Lee, President; Marta Mayhew; Martyn McCarthy; Max Hunt; Paul Singh; Rachel Wilkinson; Richard Bickle; Sean Clothier; Sue Rushton; Tanya Noon (women: 7; men: 7)

Year end	23/01/2016
Turnover	£806,847,000
Pre-tax profit	£8,763,000

Nature of business: The society's principal business activities are retail food stores (responsible for around 70% of the total turnover), petrol filling stations, funeral services and property investment. The society also has trading interests in travel shops, coffin manufacture and optical services.

The company's website states:

> Central England Co-operative is one of the largest independent retailers in the UK, with over 400 trading outlets, a family of around 8,600 colleagues and more than 330,000 regular trading members. We're independent from The Co-operative Group, but we're part of the wider co-operative movement, working together to provide all sorts of benefits for our members and customers. Central England Co-operative trades across 16 counties from the Midlands to the East Coast.

Company registration number: IP10143R

Subsidiary undertakings include: Anglia Co-operative (Food) Ltd; Co-operative Funeral Service (Anglia) Ltd; Shaws Petroleum Ltd.

UK employees: 8,639

Total employees: 8,639

Focus of giving: General charitable purposes, education, environment, health, ill health, small groups, local groups, humanitarian help, older people, arts, culture, religion, sport, recreation, children, young people, community/ social welfare, disability.

Membership: BITC

Community involvement	✓
Community contributions	✓
CSR report	✓
CSR or charity committee	✓
Charity partner(s)	✓
Company gives to smaller charities	✓
Employee-led support	✓
Gifts in kind	✓
Humanitarian aid: UK including food banks	✓
Sponsorship	✓

Charitable donations

Cash UK (latest available):	2016	£141,000
Total UK (cash and in kind):	2016	£141,000
Cash worldwide:	2016	£141,000
Total worldwide (cash and in kind):	2016	£141,000

Community involvement

Central England Co-operative invests in communities where it has a trading presence, redistributing 1% of its trading profit each year. The society supports local charities and community causes through financial support, volunteering and partnerships.

Community Dividend Scheme

Through the 'Making a Difference' Community Dividend, Central England Co-operative makes charitable donations of between £100 and £5,000 to a wide range of local community groups in its trading area.

According to the guidance provided on the website, support is given 'for four broad types of projects':

- Contributions towards the fundraising efforts of a school, college, community organisation or group, residential or day-care facility or hospital project.
- Contributions towards a voluntary, self-help or 'not-for profit' organisation other than those listed above.
- Donations to a local charity or cause, or the local branch of a national charity, that will benefit the local community, for example the provision of equipment, enhancement of the physical environment, training or education programme.
- Contributions to environmental and social projects that will enhance the local community or raise awareness of environmental issues amongst local residents.

Examples of projects recently supported are given on the website.

Charity partners

As well as making charitable donations to local community groups, the society also holds events to help raise money for its colleague-nominated corporate charity partner. The company's website states that the society's current corporate charity is the Newlife Foundation for Disabled Children which it has partnered since 2012, helping to raise more than £1 million. Other charity partners in 2015 included Alzheimer's Research UK, Dementia Support South Lincolnshire and Louise Hamilton Centre.

Food bank policy

The society has developed a food bank policy in response to a growing number of requests to support the work food banks carry out in local communities. More than 60 of its food stores now have permanent collection points where members and customers can donate food items from their weekly shop or from home. Representatives from food banks are also invited into stores on a quarterly basis to discuss their work with local people, recruit volunteers and request donations of food items.

Main locations

The geographical area where support is given can be broken down into three regions: Western (West Midlands, Staffordshire, Warwickshire and Worcestershire); Central (Leicestershire, Derbyshire, Nottinghamshire, South Yorkshire and West Yorkshire); and Eastern (East and South Leicestershire, Lincolnshire, Northamptonshire, Cambridgeshire, Norfolk and Suffolk).

Community contributions

The 'My Co-op Community' website states that £141,000 was 'invested in 2015 to help local communities'. The society's annual report for the year states that 102 grants were awarded. We were unable to determine the value of other support given by the society in its local communities.

Recent beneficiaries detailed on the website include: Willoughby School (£5,000); Sight Support Derbyshire (£4,500); Groundwork East (£4,400); Flash Ley Community Primary School (£1,000); Whitwick Parish Council (£700); Lutterworth Photographic Society (£400); Serenade Women's Community Choir (£100).

In-kind support

Employee volunteering

As part the society's Corporate Responsibility strategy, it has recently launched a colleague volunteering scheme which allows all employees to volunteer for up to three days each year.

Healthy Eating Initiatives

Central England Co-operative has a responsible business focus on reducing food and drink waste and promoting sustainable behaviour in relation to the environment among local people. In partnership with the Waste and Resources Action Programme (WRAP), the society has delivered workshops to school pupils in Birmingham with the aim of educating and engaging them in food-waste prevention. More information about the society's involvement in the campaign, which involves a wide range of other businesses and organisations in ten cities across the UK, is available from www.centralengland.coop/yourfoodyourwaste.

SENse to Aspire – Selly Oak Trust School

For a number of years, Central England Co-operative has partnered Selly Oak Trust School in Birmingham to help provide opportunities for sixth-form students with special educational needs to develop employment skills and experience. The scheme allows the students to take up work experience placements at local food stores or on floral teams, CV and floristry masterclasses and mock interview practice. They are also partnered with a store colleague who provides support and guidance. The scheme was developed as part of Business in the Community's Business Class programme which creates long-term partnerships between businesses and schools.

Journey to a Job

Working alongside Jobcentre Plus, the society's Journey to a Job scheme offers two-day workshops to help young people between the ages of 16 and 24 find, get and keep a job. Through the scheme, there are also opportunities for participants to gain work experience in one of the society's stores. In 2015 Journey to a Job supported 84 young people.

Employee-led support

Employee fundraising

Colleagues nominate and fundraise for the society's corporate charity partners.

Employee volunteering

Colleagues are involved with a wide range of volunteering activities. Examples from 2016 detailed on the website include: ten colleagues who helped out with a project at Hadhari Day Centre in Derby, painting day rooms and providing goody bags, vouchers and snacks donated by the society to the users of the centre; and six colleagues from the Business Support Centre in Lichfield who worked alongside other businesses to run a Fit for Fun event.

Commercially led support

Sponsorship

In 2016 the society sponsored Lichfield Food Festival for the fourth time.

Exclusions

The website states that support cannot be given for:

- Start-up costs
- Awards that benefit one individual (for example, personal equipment, bursaries or scholarships)
- Awards for one-off events such as fetes or festivals
- Awards for running costs such as staff costs or room hire

Applications

Applications for Community Dividend grants should preferably be made online where full information, including guidance and closing dates, can be found. Application forms can also be printed off from the website and submitted by post or handed in to your local Central England Co-operative store. Applicants who do not have access to a printer can obtain a Community Dividend application form by requesting one from a colleague in store. Applications are considered every three months and applicants are normally informed of the decision 12–16 weeks after the closing date.

There are limited funds available and the demand for awards is extremely high; the website states: 'Do not be too disappointed if your application is unsuccessful, but be assured that it will have received our full and proper consideration.'

Centrica PLC

Oil and gas/fuel

Correspondent: Ivor Gibbons, Corporate Responsibility Manager, Millstream, Maidenhead Road, Windsor, Berkshire SL4 5GD (tel: 01753 494000; fax: 01753 494001; email: responsibility@centrica.com; website: www.centrica.com)

Directors: Carlos Pascual; Ian Conn, Chief Executive; Ian Meakins; Jeff Bell, Group Chief Financial Officer; Lesley Knox; Margherita Della Valle; Mark Hanafin; Mark Hodges; Mike Linn; Rick Haythornthwaite, Chair; Steve Pusey (women: 2; men: 9)

Year end	31/12/2015
Turnover	£28,000,000,000
Pre-tax profit	£1,127,000,000

Nature of business: Centrica's principal activities are the provision of gas, electricity and energy-related products and services in the UK, Ireland and North America. The group also operates gas fields and power stations.

Company registration number: 3033654

Subsidiary undertakings include: Lincs Wind Farm Ltd, Energy America, Scottish Gas Ltd.

Brands include: British Gas; Direct Energy; Dyno.

UK employees: 32,387

Total employees: 38,848

Focus of giving: Economic generation, animal welfare, education, enterprise/training, environment, health, ill health, overseas projects, humanitarian help, arts, culture, community/social welfare.

Membership: BITC, LBG

Community involvement	✓
Community contributions	✓
CSR report	✓
Charity partner(s)	✓
Employee-led support	✓
FTSE 100	✓
Gifts in kind	✓
Humanitarian aid: overseas	✓
Overseas giving	✓

Charitable donations

Total UK (cash and in kind):	2015	£3,320,000
Cash worldwide:	2015	£3,000,000
Total worldwide (cash and in kind):	2015	£4,720,000

Community involvement

According to the Community and Local Impact Policy available on the company's website, Centrica invests in the local communities around the world in which it operates. This includes charitable donations, in-kind support and employee volunteering. Centrica particularly focuses on the following five areas:

- Climate change and the environment – particularly energy efficiency and investing in renewable power
- Fuel poverty and social inclusion – by working with public and voluntary sector partners to support Centrica's most vulnerable customers, particularly those affected by fuel poverty
- Health and safety
- Education, skills and employability – by investing in education to promote learning about energy-related issues as well as supporting skills and training development
- Employee involvement – by encouraging charitable giving and volunteering

Centrica's website has up-to-date news stories on the kind of projects it invests in, as well as details about types of in-kind support and donations: www.centrica.com/newsroom/responsibility-news.

Main locations

Centrica operates in various locations throughout the UK and Ireland. It also operates worldwide in: Canada; Israel; Netherlands; Norway; Trinidad Tobago; USA.

Community contributions

According to the 'Data Centre' section of the company's website, in 2015 Centrica contributed £4.72 million to charitable causes. This includes £3 million in cash donations made to organisations around the world; there was no figures available regarding cash donations made in the UK. Out of the £4.72 million made in contributions, £3.32 million went to UK organisations, £680,000 to North America and £160,000 went to organisations based elsewhere in the world. All contributions were broken down as follows:

Type of support	Total
Community investment	£2.8 million
Charitable gifts	£860,000
Management costs	£560,000
Commercial initiatives	£500,000

Investment methods	Total
Cash donations	£3 million
Cost of volunteering time*	£780,000
In-kind donations	£370,000

*This relates only to volunteering conducted within work hours.

Donations were also broken down by sector as follows, although this accounts for only £4.3 million worth of contributions:

Social welfare	£1.97 million
Education and young people	£1.02 million
Health	£520,000
Economic development	£520,000
Environment	£90,000
Arts and culture	£80,000
Emergency relief	£70,000
Other	£20,000

According to the 2015 annual report, Centrica's community contributions totalled £228.1 million. However, over £220 million of this was spent due to mandatory government programmes in the UK and is not open to applications. Out of the total community contributions, Centrica made donations to charities (as detailed above) and £11.6 million in mandatory contributions for customers and non-customers to the independent charity British Gas Energy Trust. This trust operates separately from Centrica and makes donations to charities such as Shelter, with whom the trust works in strategic partnership.

Centrica also made donations of £8 million to 12 social enterprises through Ignite, a UK corporate impact investment fund focused on energy. Further details can be found on

Centrica's website: www.centrica.com/responsibility/our-focus-areas/people-partners.

Exclusions

Note that the company is unable to provide assistance for projects that fall outside its Community and Local Impact Policy, available under the 'Responsibility' heading under the 'Contact Us' section of the website. See the 'Community involvement' section of this entry for further information.

Applications

Apply in writing to the correspondent. Note that the company has a preference for working in long-term partnerships with community organisations and charities that are closely aligned with its business principles.

The Corporate Responsibility team manages group-wide community investments while business units oversee brand community initiatives and business sites co-ordinate local engagement. Contact the correspondent for further details.

Channel 4 Television Corporation

Telecommunications

Correspondent: Corporate Responsibility Team, 124 Horseferry Road, London SW1P 2TX (tel: 020 7396 4444; email: CRin4@channel4.co.uk; website: www.channel4.com)

Directors: Charles Gurassa, Chair; Christopher Holmes; Dan Brooke; David Abraham, Chief Executive; Jay Hunt; Jonathan Allen; Josie Rourke; Mary Teresa Rainey; Paul Geddes; Paul Potts; Roly Keating; Simon Bax; Stewart Purvis (women: 3; men: 10)

Year end	31/12/2015
Turnover	£56,000,000
Pre-tax profit	£26,000,000

Nature of business: Channel 4 is a publicly owned, commercially funded public service broadcaster. It does not receive any public funding and has a remit to be innovative, experimental and distinctive. Channel 4 works across television, film and digital media to deliver its public service remit, as outlined in the 2003 Communications Act and the 2010 Digital Economy Act.

Company registration number: 1533774

Subsidiary undertakings include: 4 Ventures Ltd; E4 Television Ltd; Film Four Ltd.

Brands include: E4; More4; Film4.

UK employees: 819

Total employees: 819

Focus of giving: Education, enterprise/training, equal opportunities, medical research, arts, culture, science technology, children, young people, disability.

Community involvement	✓
Community contributions	✓
CSR report	✓
CSR or charity committee	✓
Directors have other relevant posts	✓
Charity partner(s)	✓
Employee-led support	✓
Gifts in kind	✓
Matched funding	✓
Payroll giving	✓
Pro bono	✓
Shared-value alliances	✓

Charitable donations

Cash UK (latest available):	2015	£1,500,000
Total UK (cash and in kind):	2015	£1,500,000
Cash worldwide:	2015	£1,500,000
Total worldwide (cash and in kind):	2015	£1,500,000

Community involvement

The group has a focus on supporting education, training and equal opportunities in the creative, film, television and media industries. Support is provided through funding, partnerships and in-kind support. Employees are also encouraged to fundraise and volunteer for charitable causes.

Partnerships

The group works in partnership with a number of organisations to support training and skills in creative, film, television and media industries, including Creative Skillset and BRITDOC. In 2016 the group donated £1.5 million to the National Film and Television School, £1 million of which will support the expansion of the school's new Creative Industries Skills Academy and £500,000 of which will fund a bursary aimed at improving social mobility in the creative industries. The group also supports the RTS Technology Bursary scheme, which helps undergraduates from low-income backgrounds.

The group also has a focus on diversity. In 2015 it worked with the charity Scope to create a series of short videos titled 'What Not To Do', aimed at challenging prejudice and awkward behaviour around disability.

Stand Up To Cancer

Channel 4's Stand Up to Cancer TV fundraising event raises money for Cancer Research UK. In 2016 over £15.7 million was raised for the charity from the event.

Directors with other relevant posts

Charles Gurassa is a trustee of Migration Museum (Charity Commission no. 1153774) and of The English Heritage Trust (Charity Commission no. 1140351). Stuart Purvis is a trustee of The Services Sound and Vision Corporation (Charity Commission no. 233480). Maria Teresa Rainey is Vice-Chair of Creative Skillset (Charity Commission no. 1015324) and David Abraham is also a trustee of the charity. Roly Keating is a trustee of Turner Contemporary (Charity Commission no. 1129974). Dan Brooke is a trustee of the Mass Extinction Monitoring Observatory.

Main locations

The group's head office is based in London and it also has an office in Glasgow.

Community contributions

No figure was given for the group's total charitable contributions. However, the 2015 annual report states that during the year the group donated £1.5 million to the National Film and Television School.

In-kind support

Channel 4 has worked in partnership with Disaster Emergency Committee (DEC) for a number of decades, broadcasting international crisis appeals free of charge. The group has also offered the use of its premises and resources as in-kind support to charities.

Employee-led support

Employee fundraising and volunteering

Channel 4 employees can make tax-free donations to charities through the group's Give As You Earn scheme. The group also supports staff teams to fundraise for charities by offering up to £2,500 in matched funding for team charitable fundraising efforts.

The 2015 annual report states that the group supports employee volunteering as part of its contributions to the community and to staff personal development.

Applications

Apply in writing to the correspondent.

Close Brothers Group PLC

Financial services, banking

Correspondent: Rebekah Etherington, Group Head of Human Resources, 10 Crown Place, London EC2A 4FT (tel: 020 7655 3100; fax: 020 7655 8917; email: enquiries@closebrothers.com; website: www.closebrothers.co.uk)

Directors: Bridget Macaskill; Elizabeth Lee; Geoffrey Howe; Jonathan Howell, Finance Director; Lesley Jones; Oliver Corbett; Preben Prebensen, Chief Executive; Stephen Hodges; Strone Macpherson, Chair (women: 3; men: 6)

Year end	31/07/2015
Turnover	£689,500,000
Pre-tax profit	£219,900,000

Nature of business: Close Brothers is the parent company of a group of companies involved in merchant banking.

Company registration number: 520241

Subsidiary undertakings include: Armed Services Finance Ltd; Close Securities (Germany) Ltd; Lion Nominees Ltd; Winterflood Securities Ltd.

UK employees: 2,784

Focus of giving: General charitable purposes, health, ill health, medical research, arts, culture, community/social welfare, disasters.

Community involvement	✓
Community contributions	✓
CSR or charity committee	✓
Charity partner(s)	✓
Employee-led support	✓
Matched funding	✓
Payroll giving	✓

Community involvement

The company makes donations to a variety of charitable causes in the UK at a local level and to its charity partners.

Charity partner

Cancer Research UK continues to be the group's lead charitable partner, which is nominated by staff, although a number of additional charities are also supported by its local businesses. The company also partners with the Prince's Foundation for Children and the Arts to sponsor the National Schools Art Competition.

Matched funding

The group provides matched funding for money raised by employees, matching 50% of funds raised by staff or donating £8 for each hour of voluntary time given by employees. In 2015 this accounted for 44% of the company's charitable contributions.

Directors with other relevant posts

The Chair of the Board of Directors, Strone Macpherson, is a trustee of the King's Fund (Charity Commission no. 1126980), a charity focused on health and health care. He is also a trustee of the GPS Macpherson Charitable Settlement (Charity Commission no. 261045), a grant-making charity with general charitable purposes.

Main locations

The group's main office locations are as follows: Doncaster; East Sussex; London; Manchester.

Community contributions

In 2014/15 the group's charitable cash donations in the UK totalled £261,000 (2014: £251,000), raised through ongoing fundraising activities and company contributions through matched funding.

Employee-led support

Employee fundraising

Employees are actively encouraged to participate in a range of events held during the company's designated charity week, and throughout the year, including sponsored fitness initiatives, dress-down days, baking competitions and quizzes.

Employee volunteering

The company has launched a Trustee Leadership Programme to give its employees the skills necessary to join a charity as a board member, with a particular focus on encouraging younger trustees. According to the 2015 annual report, 60 employees had signed up for the programme.

A local primary school has also been supported by the company since 2013. Volunteers from the company spend their lunch break helping children improve their reading skills.

Payroll giving

Employees are also encouraged to donate to charities of their own choice through the Workplace Giving scheme. The group maintained its Payroll Giving Quality Mark Gold Award for the fifth consecutive year in recognition of the ongoing strong participation rate of 17% (2014: 11%) in the scheme.

Exclusions

No support is given for political appeals.

Applications

Apply in writing to the correspondent. The CSR committee is chaired by the company's group head of human resources and supported by employees across the group. There are also a number of local CSR committees which run initiatives to raise funds for charity.

CMC Markets PLC

Financial services

Correspondent: CSR Team, 133 Houndsditch, London EC3A 7BX (tel: 020 7170 8200; website: www.cmcmarkets.com/group)

Directors: David Fineberg; Grant Foley; James Richards; Malcolm McCaig; Manjit Wolstenholme; Peter Cruddas, Chief Executive Officer; Simon Waugh, Chair (women: 1; men: 6)

Year end	31/03/2016
Turnover	£186,397,000
Pre-tax profit	£53,376,000

Nature of business: CMC offers online financial trading. Its head office is in London but it also has offices in 13 other countries.

Company registration number: 5145017

Subsidiary undertakings include: CMC Markets Holdings Ltd; CMC Spreadbet PLC; Information Internet Ltd.

Total employees: 596

Focus of giving: Education, enterprise/training, marginalised people, poverty and social exclusion, children, young people, community/social welfare.

Community involvement	✓
Community contributions	✓
CSR report	✓
Directors have other relevant posts	✓
Cash donations declared	✓
Corporate charity	✓
Employee-led support	✓
Matched funding	✓
Pledge 1%	✓

Charitable donations

Cash UK (latest available):	2016	£540,000
Total UK (cash and in kind):	2016	£540,000
Cash worldwide:	2016	£540,000
Total worldwide (cash and in kind):	2016	£540,000

Community involvement

The group donates 1% of its pre-tax profit to charity, most of which goes towards its corporate charity, which supports projects for disadvantaged young people. The group also provides matched funding for employee fundraising initiatives.

Peter Cruddas Foundation

The Peter Cruddas Foundation (Charity Commission no. 1117323) was established by Peter Cruddas, Chief Executive and founder of CMC Markets. The foundation's income is comprised of donations from the group and from Peter Cruddas. The foundation makes grants in support of projects providing support for disadvantaged young people in England and Wales, particularly: support to get young people into education, training or employment; work experiences and skills projects for young people; youth work in London. The foundation also provides mentoring support for charities.

Beneficiaries have included: Barnardo's; Duke of Edinburgh Trust; Great Ormond Street Hospital; Stroke Association; University College London Horizons Programme.

Directors with other relevant posts

Simon Waugh is also a trustee of Age UK (Charity Commission no. 1128267). Peter Cruddas is a trustee and the founder of the Peter Cruddas Foundation (Charity Commission no. 1117323). He is also a trustee of the Royal Opera House (Charity Commission no. 211775).

Main locations
The group's UK office is based in London, and there are also offices in: Auckland; Beijing; Madrid; Milan; Oslo; Paris; Singapore; Stockholm; Sydney; Toronto.

Community contributions

The 2015/16 annual report states that, during the year, the group donated 1% of its pre-tax profit to charity, which amounted to £540,000. Of this, £450,000 was donated to The Peter Cruddas Foundation.

Employee-led support

Matched funding
The group provides matched funding for employee fundraising efforts.

Corporate charity

The Peter Cruddas Foundation (Charity Commission no. 1117323).

Applications

Group
Apply in writing to the correspondent.

Peter Cruddas Foundation
Application forms are available to download from the foundation's website (www.petercruddasfoundation.org.uk) along with guidance notes. There are two deadlines per year: 1 March and 1 September. Applications are only accepted from registered charities in England and Wales. Any queries before or during the submission of an application should be directed to Stephen Cox, the Foundation Administrator: s.cox@petercruddasfoundation.org.uk or 020 3003 8360.

Cobham PLC

Defence, aerospace, electronics/computers, engineering, aviation

Correspondent: Eleanor Smith, Corporate Responsibility & Sustainability Manager, Brook Road, Wimborne, Dorset BH21 2BJ (tel: 01202 882020; fax: 01202 840523; email: crs@cobham.com; website: www.cobham.com)

Directors: Alan Semple; Alison Wood; Birgit Nørgaard; David Flint; John Devaney, Chair; Mark Ronald; Mike Hagee; Mike Wareing; Robert Murphy, Chief Executive Officer; Simon Nicholls, Chief Financial Officer (women: 2; men: 8)

Year end	31/12/2015
Turnover	£2,072,000,000
Pre-tax profit	(£39,800,000)

Nature of business: Provides technologies and services to solve challenging problems across commercial, defence and security markets, such as: air-to-air refuelling; aviation services; audio, video and data communications, including satellite communications; defence electronics; life support; and mission equipment.

Company registration number: 30470

Subsidiary undertakings include: Air Précision SA; Axell Wireless Ltd; Chelton Ltd; Omnipless Manufacturing (Pty) Ltd.

Total employees: 11,505

Focus of giving: Education, enterprise/training, health, ill health, medical research, armed forces, science technology, children, young people, disability, disasters.

Membership: BITC

Community involvement	✓
Community contributions	✓
CSR report	✓
CSR or charity committee	✓
Employee-led support	✓
Gifts in kind	✓
Humanitarian aid: overseas	✓
Matched funding	✓

Charitable donations

Cash worldwide:	2015	£228,000

Community involvement

The group states on its website that it invests in charitable causes that are relevant to its business and where the company can apply its skills and experience. Its focus is on supporting science, technology, engineering and maths (STEM) education; ex-services personnel; causes in communities in which the company operates; and disaster relief appeals. The group will, on occasion, promote particular charitable causes across the company.

Ethics
Cobham has voluntarily engaged with Transparency International (TI), a non-governmental organisation that works with government and businesses to put in place measures to tackle corruption. In 2015 Cobham was benchmarked within Band A in TI's Defence Companies Anti-Corruption Index. The company also has a Responsible Supply Chain Management policy which gives preference to suppliers that demonstrate responsible and sustainable business practices.

Main locations
The group has a variety of business locations in the south of England, particularly London and the South East, and one location in Blackburn. Worldwide, it has various business locations in: Australia; Denmark; Finland; France; Germany; Republic of South Africa; Sweden; and the USA.

Community contributions

According to the Social Performance Data report available on the website, during 2015 Cobham donated £228,000 to charitable causes worldwide. No details were available regarding how much was donated in the UK.

Previous beneficiaries have included: Air League Trust; Combat Stress; Cancer Research UK; Help for Heroes; Make-A-Wish Foundation; and Red Cross Hurricane Sandy Appeal.

In-kind support

The company has previously provided in-kind support for charities. This includes supplying computer monitors for schools in Zimbabwe, teaching in India, supporting the Air Ambulance Service in the UK's Thames Valley and helping to equip Project Kaisei for the Pacific Ocean clean-up.

Disaster relief
Previously Cobham has fundraised for worldwide disasters such as the 2012 hurricane Sandy and 2010 Haiti earthquake. As well as donating directly to charities, the company provides equipment and expertise such as helping to reinstate communications systems.

Employee-led support

In 2015 employees raised funds for charities supporting the Nepal earthquake and the company matched contributions of up to £2,500. An Employee Activities Committee in the US also organised events to raise additional funds. In the UK employees are involved in the annual Big Battlefield Bike Ride on behalf of the charity Help for Heroes, as well as fundraising for various charities that are important to them. Fundraising efforts can then be matched by the company.

Exclusions

No support is provided for political appeals or for causes that are not relevant to the group's business (see 'Community involvement' for further information).

Applications

Apply in writing to the correspondent. The central Corporate Responsibility and Sustainability (CR&S) team is overseen by the CR&S Committee chaired by the CEO.

Coca-Cola Holdings (United Kingdom) Ltd

Drinks manufacture

Correspondent: Liz Lowe, Corporate Responsibility & Sustainability Manager, Coca-Cola Great Britain, 1A Wimpole Street, London W1G 0EA (tel: 020 8237 3000; email: lilowe@coca-cola.com; website: www.coca-cola.co.uk/sustainability)

Directors: Alison Beadle; Anil Rajbhandary; David Canham; Denis Kearney; Jonathan Woods; Sarah Hutton; Scott Roche (women: 2; men: 5)

Year end	31/12/2015
Turnover	£23,100,000
Pre-tax profit	£3,700,000

Nature of business: Coca-Cola's business in Great Britain is made up of two separate companies with different roles. Together, these companies manufacture, distribute and market its range of drinks.

The companies are Coca-Cola Great Britain (CCGB), which is a wholly owned subsidiary of The Coca-Cola Company, and Coca-Cola Enterprises Ltd (CCE), which is part of Coca-Cola Enterprises Inc. These two companies form the business in Great Britain. CCGB markets and develops new and existing brands. CCE manufactures and distributes soft drinks for both The Coca-Cola Company and other brand owners.

Company registration number: 1724995

Subsidiary undertakings include: Coca-Cola International Sales Ltd; Beverage Services Ltd.

Brands include: Coca-Cola; Fanta; Schweppes.

UK employees: 4,000

Focus of giving: Education, enterprise/training, environment, health, ill health, humanitarian help, overseas projects, science technology, sport, recreation, women's issues, children, young people, disasters.

Membership: BITC, LBG

Community involvement	✓
Community contributions	✓
CSR report	✓
CSR or charity committee	✓
Charity partner(s)	✓
Employee-led support	✓
FTSE 100	✓
Gifts in kind	✓
Humanitarian aid: overseas	✓
Humanitarian aid: UK including food banks	✓
Market-led giving	✓
Sponsorship	✓

Charitable donations

Total UK (cash and in kind):	2015	£1,200,000
Total worldwide (cash and in kind):	2015	£1,200,000

Community involvement

The group has a number of charitable partnerships and community programmes and focuses on three priority areas: supporting skills and employability for young people; encouraging people to get active; protecting the environment. Support is also given through the international Coca-Cola Foundation.

Coca-Cola Foundation

The group has a global corporate charity based in the US, with 19 local or regional foundations which make grants to support communities, particularly in the areas of environment, recycling, active lifestyles and education. According to the list of grants made in 2015, available on the website, it appears that two grants were made in the UK during the year. Further information can be found online (www.cocacolacommunityrequest.com), including FAQs, eligibility quiz, exclusions and the online application form.

Partnerships and programmes

The group works with a number of different partners to deliver its community involvement activities.

ParkLives and StreetGames

The group works in partnership with the charity StreetGames to provide opportunities to disadvantaged young people through sport, such as supporting the charity's Neighbourhood Festivals and setting up the StreetGames Training Academy, which provides training for community sport coaching qualifications.

The group's ParkLives programme provides free outdoor activities in parks in cities across the UK, encouraging people to be more active. The group is working with StreetGames to expand this scheme, providing activities for 14- to 25-year-olds in disadvantaged communities.

The ParkLives programme involves work with a range of partners, including local authorities and ukactive.

5by20

One of Coca Cola Group's global programmes, 5by20 aims to empower five million female entrepreneurs by 2020. While it is internationally focused, in 2016 the group launched a project in Dundee under this programme. Working in partnership with local charity Showcase the Street, which helps women establish their own catering business, the group set up a cafe to provide training, experience and opportunities for local women to develop their skills.

Special Olympics

The group is a long-standing supporter of Special Olympics GB, providing funding to cover running costs, as well as employee involvement through fundraising and volunteering with local clubs.

WWF

The group also works in partnership with WWF to achieve its environmental goals. In 2015 the partnership was extended for a further three years.

FareShare

The group donates surplus mislabelled or unsellable drinks to FareShare, which redistributes them to charities and community groups. In 2016 the group also ran a Christmas campaign to fundraise for the charity (see 'Market-led giving').

Education

The group runs five education centres, which offer the opportunity for students at local schools to experience industry, take part in enterprise activities and hear about career options. On International Women's Day in 2016, the group ran activities to encourage female students to engage with STEM subjects.

The group also runs an annual competition, the Real Business Challenge, in which students were challenged to develop a litter-awareness campaign, with representatives from CCE, Keep Britain Tidy, Keep Wales Tidy, Keep Scotland Beautiful, Hubbub and Clean Up Britain involved in providing support to the teams and judging the winners.

Main locations

There are six manufacturing sites in the UK, which are located in: East Kilbride; Edmonton; Milton Keynes; Morpeth; Sidcup; Wakefield. The group has offices in Uxbridge and the City of Westminster.

Community contributions

According to its 2015/16 corporate responsibility report, the group's contributions to community and education programmes during the year amounted to £1.2 million.

Note: The charitable contributions figure is from 2015/16; the other financial information is taken from the company's 2015 accounts (year end 31 Dec 2015).

According to the website, the international Coca-Cola Foundation made grants or in-kind donations totalling $32.7 million (around £25.6 million) in 2015, across the world. Of this, two grants appear to have been made in the UK – a grant of $250,000 (around £196,000) for the University of Edinburgh USA Development Trust Inc., to fund international scholarships; and a grant of $515,000 (around £404,000) for WWF UK, to support sustainable agriculture efforts.

Employee-led support

Employee fundraising and volunteering

The group's employees fundraise and volunteer for its partner charities and community programmes. For example, 120 employees volunteered to support students in the Real Business Challenge in 2015/16, while other employees volunteered with and fundraised for Special Olympics GB athletes. Every year the group holds an international CRS in Action Week, during which employees are encouraged to get involved in charitable and sustainability activities.

Commercially led support

Market-led giving

In 2016 the group ran its Designated Driver scheme for the ninth year, in partnership with the UK government's Department for Transport THINK! road safety campaign. The group provided a special offer on soft drinks for those who are not driving, at participating venues. The group's Christmas campaign in 2016 focused on FareShare, with the group donating 25p for every picture of a promotional bottle that was uploaded to the group's website.

Sponsorship

Sponsorships include the London Eye, the Olympic and Paralympic Games and the Rugby World Cup.

Exclusions

A list of exclusions for requests to the Coca-Cola Foundation can be found on the website: www.cocacolacommunityrequest.com.

Applications

UK group

Queries about the group's UK CSR activities can be sent to Coca-Cola Great Britain's Corporate Responsibility and Sustainability Manager: lilowe@coca-cola.com.

Coca-Cola Foundation

Requests for support from the international Coca-Cola Foundation should be made online, following the eligibility quiz: www.cocacolacommunityrequest.com.

Any applications sent by post or fax will be returned. Organisations applying from outside the US must have charitable status in the country in which they are based.

Compass Group PLC

Retail – restaurants/fast food

Correspondent: Celine Ricord, Corporate Responsibility Manager, Compass House, Guildford Street, Chertsey, Surrey KT16 9BQ (tel: 01932 573000; fax: 01932 569956; email: global.HSE@compass-group.com; website: www.compass-group.com)

Directors: Carol Arrowsmith; Dominic Blakemore; Don Robert; Gary Green; Ireena Vittal; John Bason; Johnny Thomson, Finance Director; Mark White; Nelson Silva; Paul Walsh, Chair; Richard Cousins, Chief Executive; Stefan Bomhard; Susan Murray (women: 3; men: 10)

Year end	30/09/2015
Turnover	£17,843,000,000
Pre-tax profit	£1,159,000,000

Nature of business: The principal activity is the provision of contract food services to business and industrial organisations around the world. The company also provides support services such as cleaning, reception services and building maintenance.

Company registration number: 4083914

Subsidiary undertakings include: Bon Appetit Management Co.; Coffee Partners Ltd; Eurest Services; Hospital Hygiene Services Ltd.

Brands include: Caffè Liscio; Deli Marche/So Deli; Zona Mexicana. Franchises include: Burger King; Costa; Starbucks.

UK employees: 60,000

Total employees: 515,864

Focus of giving: Education, enterprise/training, environment, health, ill health, local groups, overseas projects.

Membership: BITC

Community involvement	✓
Community contributions	✓
Company reports on anti-slavery	✓
CSR report	✓
CSR or charity committee	✓
Charity partner(s)	✓
Employee-led support	✓
FTSE 100	✓
Overseas giving	✓

Charitable donations

Cash UK (latest available):	2015	£370,000
Cash worldwide:	2015	£7,900,000

Community involvement

The company operates in over 50 countries and receives many requests from non-governmental organisations (NGOs) for support. The company engages with NGOs and states that as a result the organisation has benefitted from expert advice and guidance in the areas of animal welfare, environmental performance, sustainable supply chain initiatives and human rights.

Community engagement

The 2015 Corporate Responsibility report states that the company operates and supports community initiatives that:

- Encourage healthy lifestyles
- Tackle social exclusion
- Improve employment opportunities
- Promote sustainability and diversity

The company's 2014/15 annual report notes that charitable donations and support are focused on improving the environment, education, health and well-being, community engagement and responsible business practice.

Partnerships

The company has developed partnerships with a variety of organisations with a focus on those that help the company with improving its corporate responsibility performance. It has a long-standing partnership with Cancer Research UK, which the company raises funds for.

In 2015 the Corporate Responsibility report stated that the company also partnered with the following charitable organisations: Charities Aid Foundation; Carbon Disclosure Project; Children's Food Trust; Compassion in World Farming; Fairtrade Foundation; Hospitality Action; Linking Environment and Farming; Marine Conservation Society; Marine Stewardship Council; Soil Association; Springboard; Sustainable Restaurant Association; United Nations Global Impact; Waste and Resources Action Programme.

Directors with other relevant posts

The following members of the board of directors are also trustees of charities:

- Carol Arrowsmith is a trustee of Northern Ballet Ltd (Charity Commission no. 259140)
- John Bason is a trustee of Voluntary Service Overseas (Charity Commission no. 313757), FareShare (Charity Commission no. 1100051) and Weston Provident Fund (Charity Commission no. 283311)
- Don Robert is a trustee of Education and Employers Taskforce (Charity Commission no. 1130760)

Susan Murray is also a fellow of the Royal Society of Arts.

Charitable work in Australia

In 2015 the company received the INPEX World Environment Day Initiatives Award for its work tackling food waste in Australia. The company invested in a dehydrator which turns food waste into a sterile, nutrient-rich garden compost and used to create green spaces for residents in some of the country's village gardens.

The company also partnered with Beyondblue, an Australian mental health organisation, to engage and raise awareness among its employees of mental health issues.

Main locations

The group has offices in: Birmingham; Chertsey; London; Northampton; Uxbridge.

Community contributions

In 2014/15 the group made worldwide charitable donations totalling £7.9 million. The company stated that approximately £370,000 was raised and donated for UK charities through various fundraising activities.

According to the 2015 Corporate Responsibility report, since 2012 the company has raised £1.7 million for its UK charity partner Cancer Research.

Employee-led support

The 2015 Corporate Responsibility report states that the company's employees use their skills to support community initiatives in areas where the company has a presence.

Exclusions

The company does not support advertising in charity brochures, animal welfare, individuals, the arts, older people, heritage, medical research, overseas projects, political or religious appeals and science/technology.

It is the group's policy not to make donations to political parties; however, the 2014/15 annual report states that it is possible that certain routine activities undertaken by the company might unintentionally fall within the wide definition of political donations. This includes donations to EU political organisations. The company does not make any cash donations to political parties.

Applications

The website states that letters of appeal are forwarded onto to the General Counsel and Company Secretary (Mark White) at the company's registered address.

Computacenter PLC

Information Technology

Correspondent: The Charity Committee, Hatfield Avenue, Hatfield Business Park, Hatfield AL10 9TW (tel: 01707 631000; email: charity@computacenter.com; website: www.computacenter.com)

Directors: Greg Lock, Chair; Mike Norris, Chief Executive; Minnow Powell; Peter Ogden; Philip Hulme; Philip Yea; Regine Stachelhaus; Tony Conophy, Chief Finance Officer (women: 1; men: 7)

Year end	31/12/2015
Turnover	£3,057,615,000
Pre-tax profit	£126,767,000

Nature of business: Computacenter is a leading independent provider of IT infrastructure services in Europe offering services and solutions at every stage of infrastructure investment.

Company registration number: 3110569

Subsidiary undertakings include: Amazon Computers Ltd; Compufix Ltd; Digica Group Finance Ltd.

UK employees: 5,971

Total employees: 12,993

Focus of giving: General charitable purposes, health, ill health, armed forces, children, young people.

Community involvement	✓
Community contributions	✓
Company reports on anti-slavery	✓
CSR report	✓
CSR or charity committee	✓
Armed forces personnel	✓
Charity partner(s)	✓
Employee-led support	✓
Gifts in kind	✓
Matched funding	✓
Payroll giving	✓
Sponsorship	✓

Charitable donations

Cash UK (latest available):	2015	£145,000
Cash worldwide:	2015	£190,000

Community involvement

Charity policy

In the UK Computacenter's charity policy is to support three charities for a two-year period. At the end of that period, employees are asked to select alternatives from a shortlist that includes the current charity partners. Selected charities must be registered in the UK and are approved by the charity committee. Each of the charities will receive considerable support from Computacenter in this period. Funds collected via fundraising activities within the programme are in most instances matched by Computacenter.

The group also engages in charitable activities elsewhere in the world where its offices are based. In 2015 the group donated 50,000 euros to support refugee integration projects, which were selected in 2016 by the company's German employees.

Charity partners

According to the 2014/15 Corporate Sustainable Responsibility (CSR) report, the three charity partners for that year, as nominated by the company's employees, were Alzheimer's Society, Prostate Cancer UK and the Teenage Cancer Trust.

The 2015 annual report also notes that the company has a strong partnership with Mind UK, which has helped foster employee engagement in mental health issues. For example, employees have access to webinars and there is a programme of education for the group's Management team to support them in recognising and managing stress and mental health issues within their teams.

Contribution to the community

The company focuses on providing opportunities for employment and education through a number of programmes in local schools and colleges. In 2014/15 a number of UK employees trained as ambassadors for the Hertfordshire Chamber of Commerce under the organisation's People Like Me campaign, where they will be running programmes in schools to encourage girls to get into technology and science-based activities.

The company also supports the Career Transition Partnership, which provides support for people leaving the armed services.

Directors with other relevant posts

Philip Yea is a trustee of the Francis Crick Institute (Charity Commission no. 1140062), which operates and manages a centre for biomedical research.

Main locations

The company has a variety of offices across England, plus an office in Cardiff and Edinburgh. Worldwide, the company operates in: Europe; Malaysia; Mexico; South Africa; and the USA.

Community contributions

In 2015 employees in the UK raised over £145,000 (2014: £130,000) for the chosen charity partners, which was matched by the company bringing the total to £290,500. Details about the group's total worldwide contributions were not available, although at least £45,000* was donated to support refugee integration projects in Germany.

*Note, the original figure was 50,000 euros but we have converted this to sterling using currency exchange rates available at the time of writing (October 2016).

Employee-led support

Employees raise money each year for the company's chosen partners, which is usually matched by the company. In 2015 one example of employee-led fundraising involved a team of 15 raising over £2,000 each by taking part in a sponsored 10-day trek in Peru. In the UK Simon Burman, Resource Manager, is the main events organiser in the company's Charity Committee.

Applications

Apply in writing to the company's Charity Committee. The committee is comprised of a cross section of employees throughout the company and any enquiries about the programmes and fundraising activities or suggestions can be sent via email.

Co-operative Group Ltd

Insurance, legal, pharmaceuticals, retail – department and variety stores, banking, retail – supermarkets

Correspondent: Jim Cooke, Foundation Manager, 1 Angel Square, Manchester M60 0AG (tel: 0161 834 1212/0843 751 9251; fax: 0161 833 1383; email: jim.cooke@co-operative.coop; website: www.co-operative.coop/corporate)

Directors: Allan Leighton; Christopher Kelly; Hazel Blears; Ian Ellis; Margaret Casely-Hayford; Paul Chandler; Peter Plumb; Richard Pennycook; Ruth Spellman; Simon Burke; Stevie Spring; Victor Adebowale (women: 4; men: 8)

Year end	02/01/2016
Turnover	£9,301,000,000
Pre-tax profit	£23,000,000

Nature of business: The Co-operative Group is the UK's largest mutual business, owned not by private shareholders but by over six million consumers. The business areas of the group are: food retail and convenience store operation; financial and legal services; funeral care; travel; property investment; electrical products; and banking.

Company registration number: 525R

Subsidiary undertakings include: Brompton Homes Ltd; Co-op Cruise Holidays Ltd; Co-operative Foodstores Ltd; Cumbria Group and Business Travel Ltd.

Brands include: CIS Co-operative Insurance; Co-operative Bank; Co-op e-store; smile; Shoefayre; Travelcare; Somerfield; Britannia.

Focus of giving: General charitable purposes, education, environment, local groups, overseas projects, sport, recreation, children, young people, community/social welfare.

Membership: BITC, LBG

Community involvement	✓
Community contributions	✓
Company reports on anti-slavery	✓
CSR report	✓
CSR or charity committee	✓
Cash donations declared	✓
Corporate charity	✓
Gifts in kind	✓
Matched funding	✓
Sponsorship	✓

Charitable donations

Cash UK (latest available):	2016	£1,600,000
Total UK (cash and in kind):	2016	£3,400,000

Community involvement

The Co-operative Community Investment Foundation

Known as The Co-operative Foundation, this registered charity was established by the Co-op with the aim of helping people living in disadvantaged communities by putting co-operative values into practice. At the time of writing (March 2017) the foundation had recently identified three new priorities as part of its 2017–19 strategy. According to the foundation's web page, these are:

- To champion young people's ability to contribute positively to their communities and help strengthen their sense of belonging
- To invest in disadvantaged communities' capacity to overcome social, economic or environmental challenges
- To build its reputation as a trusted charity with a co-operative difference, uniting with others to make sustainable impact in communities

Local Community Fund

Each time a Co-op member buys the group's own-brand products and services, 1% of what they spend is given to the Local Community Fund. Income received by the fund, which is also generated through the sales of carrier bags, is distributed to good causes in the local community. Members can choose a local cause to receive their 1% and local causes can also apply to be considered to receive support from the fund.

Main locations

Various locations throughout the UK.

Community contributions

The group's Sustainability Report for 2015 provides the following breakdown of community investment during the year:

Leverage	£2.2 million
Cash	£1.6 million
Employee time	£1 million
Gifts in kind	£800,000
Management costs	£200,000

As is our usual practice, we have not included the amounts given in 'Leverage' or 'Management costs' in our figure for the group's community contributions. We have, therefore, calculated the total of the group's UK contributions to be £3.4 million.

In addition to community investment in the UK, £1.1 million was given in support for communities overseas; however, as this figure also includes leveraged funds, we have not included it in the group's worldwide total contributions.

In-kind support

The group can provide in-kind contribution. Staff volunteering time and fundraising efforts are available.

Employee-led support

Volunteering

During 2015, colleagues from across the businesses took part in community activities during work time, equating to a donation of time worth £1 million. This includes formal volunteering through the volunteer programme, delivered in partnership with The Co-operative Community Investment Foundation; colleagues setting up and running community projects; and locally organised activity throughout the businesses.

Commercially led support

Cause-related marketing

The group has undertaken commercially led initiatives whereby donations were made based on the amount spent in store or upon a purchase of a specific product.

Fairbourne Springs Water

For every bottle of water purchased money is donated to fund clean water projects in Africa.

Carrier bags

The Sustainability Report states that in 2015 through the carrier bag levy, funds for 570 good causes in local communities have been raised.

Applications

The Co-operative Foundation

The Foundation Manager informed us that the foundation's current web page (coop.co.uk/foundation) is expected, in the near future, to develop into a full website with much more detailed guidance for charities.

Local Community Fund

More information on the fund is available from the website (coop.co.uk/membership/local-community-fund).

Costain Group PLC

Building/construction, engineering

Correspondent: Catherine Warbrick, CR Director & Trustee of the Charitable Foundation, Costain House, Vanwall Business Park, Maidenhead, Berkshire SL6 4UB (tel: 01628 842444; email: costainfoundation@costain.com; website: costain.com/our-culture/the-costain-charitable-foundation)

Directors: Alison Wood; Andrew Wyllie, Chief Executive; David McManus; Dr Paul Golby, Chair; James Morley; Jane Lodge; Tony Bickerstaff, Finance Director; Tracy Wood (women: 3; men: 5)

Year end	31/12/2015
Turnover	£1,316,500,000
Pre-tax profit	£29,900,000

Nature of business: A provider of engineering and technology-led solutions operating in the rail, highway, power, oil and gas, water and nuclear sectors.

Company registration number: 1393773

Subsidiary undertakings include: Construction Study Centre Ltd; Costain Civil Engineering Ltd; County and District Properties Ltd.

UK employees: 3,956

Total employees: 4,005

Focus of giving: General charitable purposes, education, environment, health, ill health, large national appeals, older people, children, young people, community/social welfare.

Membership: BITC

Community involvement	✓
Community contributions	✓
Company reports on anti-slavery	✓
CSR report	✓
Directors have other relevant posts	✓
Cash donations declared	✓
Charity partner(s)	✓
Corporate charity	✓
Employee-led support	✓
Gifts in kind	✓
Matched funding	✓
Sponsorship	✓
STEM-focused	✓

Charitable donations

Cash UK (latest available):	2015	£523,000
Total UK (cash and in kind):	2015	£523,000
Cash worldwide:	2015	£523,000
Total worldwide (cash and in kind):	2015	£523,000

Community involvement

Costain Group set up The Costain Charitable Foundation (Charity Commission no. 1159056) at the end of 2014 in celebration of the group's 150th birthday the following year. The foundation acts as a vehicle for the majority of the group's charitable donations and also benefits from the fundraising activities of Costain employees. In 2016 the group also launched Hour Pledge, an employee volunteering initiative.

The Costain Charitable Foundation and the 150 Challenge

In 2015 Costain launched the 150 Challenge, a fundraising campaign with a target of £1 million, to commemorate the group's 150th anniversary. The year-long challenge – in which employees, supporters and the company all took part – managed to raise more than £1.1 million, exceeding its target.

Funds raised through the challenge were allocated to four organisations selected as The Costain Charitable Foundation's 'chosen charities'; they were: the British Heart Foundation; Macmillan Cancer Support; The Prince's Trust; and Samaritans.

In 2016 funds raised for the foundation benefited the following organisations: Age UK; Macmillan Cancer Support; The Prince's Trust; and The Wildlife Trust.

Directors with other relevant posts

Dr Paul Golby: Chair of the Engineering and Physical Sciences Research Council and Pro-Chancellor of Aston University.

Jane Lodge: trustee of Bromsgrove School Foundation.

Tracy Wood: director of The Costain Charitable Foundation.

Reporting on anti-slavery

The group's 'Modern Slavery and Human Trafficking Policy' is available to download from the website.

Main locations

The group has offices in: Aberdeen; Coventry; London; Maidenhead; Manchester.

Community contributions

The 'Targets and progress' section of the Costain website states that charitable donations amounted to £523,000.

We believe that this figure includes the £500,000 received from the group by The Costain Charitable Foundation. The website further states: 'We continue to support various charities local to our operations and via the Costain Community Chest, where small donations are made by the Company to support employee charity involvement.'

Beneficiaries included: The Costain Charitable Foundation.

In-kind support

Hour Pledge

In 2016 Costain launched the Hour Pledge initiative, the purpose of which is to encourage employees to contribute 10,000 hours of their working time to support causes in their local communities through volunteering. The 'News releases' section of the website explains: 'Volunteering can take place for any charity or good cause and Costain will regularly communicate volunteering opportunities from the charities.'

Heysham M6 link 'welly walks'

Costain worked alongside Lancashire County Council to organise 'welly walks' along the route before it was opened to traffic. More than 5,000 local people took part, raising £20,000 for St John's Hospice and the Costain 150 Challenge.

Employee-led support

Employee volunteering

One example of volunteering provided on the Costain website is the efforts of five employees who spent two days clearing ground and laying foundation stones for a new garden of remembrance at Immingham Cemetery in Lincolnshire.

Employee fundraising

Costain employees played a central role in the 150 Challenge to raise funds for Costain's four charity partners. Activities included climbing Mont Blanc, skydiving and baking cakes.

Commercially led support

Sponsorship

Costain is a founding sponsor of the London Design and Technology UCT (University Technical College).

Corporate charity

The Costain Charitable Foundation (Charity Commission no. 1159056).

Applications

For information on how to apply to become a charity partner, in the first instance, see www.costain.com/our-culture/the-costain-charitable-foundation.

Note that charity partners are selected according to criteria that are strategically aligned to Costain Group PLC's code of ethics and corporate governance. The following guidance was obtained from the website:

> To be considered as one of the Foundation's sponsored charities the following requirements must be satisfied:
>
> - All recipients of the Foundation must be designated or registered as a charity or non-profit organisation; and are
>   - Not involved in the abuse of human rights
>   - Do not have employment policies or practices that discriminate on grounds of race, creed, sexual orientation, religion, gender, disability or age
>   - Do not discriminate unfairly in the allocation of their support according to race, creed, sexual orientation, religion, gender, disability or age
>   - Are not directly involved in gambling, recreational or illegal drugs, tobacco, armaments or alcohol (with the exception of those charities and organisations specifically dedicated to tackling addiction or drug abuse)
>   - Do not cause harm to animals for the purposes of either sport or entertainment
>   - Do not have, as their main purpose, the dissemination of political or religious information and do not otherwise use their charitable work to encourage support for political or religious causes
>   - Do not have activities which involve significant damage to the environment
>   - Fully disclose all relevant corporate and personal conflicts of interest
> - The Costain Charitable Foundation's preference is to only support charities and other non-profit organisations that have long-term goals and objectives

Costcutter Supermarkets Group Ltd

Retail – supermarkets

Correspondent: See 'Applications', Harvest Mills, Common Road, Dunnington, York YO19 5RY (tel: 01904 488663; website: www.costcutter.co.uk/community)

Directors: Bibby Bros and Co. (Management) Ltd; Daniel Quest; Darcy Willson-Rymer, Chief Executive Officer; David Thompson; Huw Edwards; Jenny Wilson; Matthias Seeger, Finance Director (women: 1; men: 5)

Year end	26/12/2015
Turnover	£699,116,000
Pre-tax profit	(£13,907,000)

Nature of business: The Costcutter Supermarkets Group is a franchise operation, with convenience stores throughout the UK.

Costcutter Supermarkets Group is a wholly owned subsidiary of Bibby Line Group and part of the Bibby Retail Services division. The 200-year-old family-owned business bought Costcutter Supermarket Group in 2011 and operates a diverse portfolio of business across sectors including distribution, financial services, off-shore, shipping and retail services.

Company registration number: 2059678

Subsidiary undertakings include: Ebor Foodmarkets Ltd; PDQ Ltd; Simply Fresh Ltd.

Brands include: Costcutter; Kwiksave; Mace; SuperShop.

UK employees: 290

Total employees: 290

Focus of giving: General charitable purposes, health, ill health, small groups, local groups, sport, recreation, community/social welfare.

Community involvement	✓
Community contributions	✓
Cash donations declared	✓
Company gives to smaller charities	✓
Market-led giving	✓

Charitable donations

Cash UK (latest available):	2015	£71,500
Total UK (cash and in kind):	2015	£71,500
Cash worldwide:	2015	£71,500
Total worldwide (cash and in kind):	2015	£71,500

Community involvement

During 2014/15, Costcutter supported medical and sports charities by making donations. In January 2016, the company also launched a new charity initiative called 'Local Pride', with the aim of facilitating its stores to support good causes in their local areas.

Local Pride

Through this programme, stores owned by Costcutter select a local charity partner. Chosen charities benefit from an agreed proportion of proceeds from the sale of specially selected items, as well as other fundraising initiatives such as in-store collection tins, proceeds from carrier bag sales, and donations through stores' online fundraising pages.

According to the Costcutter website at the time of writing (October 2016), £100,000 had already been pledged through the programme to more than 140 charities.

Main locations

There are branches across the UK. The head office is in York.

Community contributions

The company's annual report and accounts for 2014/15 declared charitable donations of £71,500. These were awarded to medical and sports charities.

Applications

Apply in writing to your local store.

Coutts & Co.

Banking

Correspondent: Kay Boland, The Coutts Charitable Foundation, 440 Strand, London WC2R 0QS (tel: 020 7753 1000/ 020 7957 2822; email: kay.boland@coutts.com; website: www.coutts.com)

Directors: Francesca Barnes; Mark Lund; Mike Regan, Finance Director; Peter Flavel, Chief Executive; The Rt Hon. Lord Waldegrave of North Hill, Chair (women: 1; men: 4)

Year end	31/12/2015

Nature of business: Banking and allied financial services. Coutts is the private banking arm of the Royal Bank of Scotland Group. The bank's main location is London, but there also international offices.

Company registration number: 36695

Brands include: RBS; Coutts.

Total employees: 1,833

Focus of giving: Overseas projects, children, young people.

Community involvement	✓
Community contributions	✓
Company reports on anti-slavery	✓
Corporate charity	✓
Sponsorship	✓

Charitable donations

Cash UK (latest available):	2015	£630,000
Total UK (cash and in kind):	2015	£630,000
Cash worldwide:	2015	£630,000
Total worldwide (cash and in kind):	2015	£630,000

Community involvement

Coutts Charitable Foundation (Charity Commission no. 1150784)

According to the foundation's annual report for 2016, its mission is: 'to support sustainable approaches to tackle the causes and consequences of poverty, focusing on the communities where Coutts has a presence.'

'This mission builds on the legacy of Angela Burdett-Coutts, the grand-daughter of Thomas Coutts, who was a progressive 19th century philanthropist who was concerned with breaking the cycles of poverty and the provision of basic human needs.'

The foundation makes significant contributions to a small number of organisations. The foundation is currently focused on supporting organisations that help women and children in the UK.

Directors with other relevant posts

Francesca Barnes is the Chair of Trustees for Penny Brohn Cancer Care.

Main locations

Offices throughout the UK and overseas.

Community contributions

The total amount given for charitable purposes, via the foundation, by the company and its subsidiary undertakings during the year 2015 was £630,0000. The figure we have used for UK charitable cash contributions is that received by the Coutts Charitable Foundation for the 2014/15 period.

Commercially led support

Sponsorship is provided to exhibitions and festivals such as the RHS Chelsea Flower Show and the London Design Festival.

Corporate charity

Coutts Charitable Foundation (Charity Commission no. 1150784).

Applications

According to the website:

> The Coutts Foundation adopts a proactive approach to its philanthropy and in its identification of organisations to support. It is especially interested in organisations that are developing innovative solutions and/or those whose successful work has the potential to be scaled up.
>
> At this stage, the Foundation does not accept unsolicited proposals for funding.

If you would like to bring to the foundation's attention information about your organisation or programmes that fit its funding priorities, you can complete the information submission form, which is available to download from the website. The completed form can be returned to the correspondent by email or post. The foundation will contact you should it wish to learn more about your organisation.

Coventry Building Society

Building society

Correspondent: Alison Readman, Coventry BS Charitable Foundation, Economic House, PO Box 9, High Street, Coventry CV1 5QN (tel: 0845 766 5522/ 024 7643 5231; email: alison.readman@thecoventry.co.uk; website: www.thecoventry.co.uk)

Directors: Alasdair Lenman; Catherine Doran; Ian Geden; Ian Pickering, Chair; Janet Ashdown; John Lowe; Mark Parsons; Peter Ayliffe; Peter Frost; Roger Burnell (women: 2; men: 8)

Year end	31/12/2015
Turnover	£369,000,000
Pre-tax profit	£216,000,000

Nature of business: Building Society.

Company registration number: FCA – 150892

Focus of giving: General charitable purposes, health, ill health, armed forces, older people, poverty and social exclusion, children, young people, community/social welfare, disability.

Community involvement	✓
Community contributions	✓
CSR report	✓
Directors have other relevant posts	✓
Armed forces personnel	✓
Cash donations declared	✓
Charity partner(s)	✓
Company gives to smaller charities	✓
Corporate charity	✓
Employee-led support	✓
Gifts in kind	✓
Market-led giving	✓
Matched funding	✓

Charitable donations

Cash UK (latest available):	2015	£1,900,000
Cash worldwide:	2015	£1,900,000

Community involvement

Community Partner programme

Local support is key to the Community Partner programme. Branch and head office teams choose a local charity to work with and there are now 60 partnerships in place. As well as the support provided by local teams the society also help these community partners by raising money at a society level and using this to provide small but very valuable grants. Furthermore, nearly two-thirds of employees took part in the community programme through volunteering or fundraising.

The company also offers support to schools; this can range from executives providing strategic advice as governors, helping improve financial literacy to providing careers support. In each case employees are encouraged to volunteer.

Coventry Building Society Charitable Foundation

The Coventry Building Society Charitable foundation (Charity Commission no. 1072244) was launched in 1998. It is entirely funded by Coventry Building Society and is an independent entity with a board of trustees who determine the criteria according to which grants are made. The foundation makes donations only to registered charities that are based or active within the region covered by Coventry Building Society's branch network.

Directors with other relevant posts

Peter Ayliffe (non-executive director) is currently a trustee of The Pennies Foundation (Charity Commission no. 1122489), which promotes the voluntary sector by encouraging and facilitating charitable giving through the use of technology.

Main location

The company is based in Coventry. There are branches across the West Midlands as well as in the East Midlands; Bath, Bristol and Somerset; Gloucestershire and Monmouthshire; Oxfordshire; Wiltshire; and Yorkshire.

Community contributions

In 2015 the society provided donations of £1.9 million to charitable organisations. This included £1.7 million to The Royal British Legion's Poppy Appeal, £60,000 to the Coventry Building Society Charitable Foundation, and £140,000 to Cancer Research UK from the society's Race for Life Bond. In 2015 the total contribution through the society's charitable activities reached £2.5 million, including affinity savings accounts. We take the figure of £1.9 million as the society's contribution.

In-kind support

The society promotes employees' charitable efforts and has a volunteering database.

Employee-led support

Matched funding

If a member of staff participates in a sponsored event to raise money for a cause or charity, the society matches what they raise up to £200.

Volunteering database

To support employee volunteering in local communities the company launched its new skills-based volunteering database which aims to match the professional skills that employees have with local charities, community groups, and schools that do not have access to such skills.

The enthusiasm and commitment of employees means that the company is supporting more organisations than ever before, from national events like Children in Need to a range of local charitable groups.

In 2015 employees volunteered more than 3,625 hours.

Commercially led support

The society is a provider of charitable affinity accounts. In 2015 the society donated £1.7 million to The Royal British Legion's Poppy Appeal. The contribution to this appeal since 2008 now totals £12.6 million.

Corporate charity

Coventry Building Society Charitable Foundation (Charity Commission no. 1072244).

Exclusions

No grants can be given outside the Midlands area. The following are not eligible for support:

- Large charities which enjoy national coverage
- Charities with no base within the branch area
- Charities with an annual donated income in excess of £250,000
- Charities with assets over £500,000
- Projects requiring an ongoing commitment
- Large capital projects
- Maintenance or building works for buildings, gardens or playgrounds
- Major fundraising
- Projects which are normally the responsibility of other organisations (such as the NHS, Education Department and local authorities)
- Sponsorship of individuals
- Requests from individuals
- Replacing funds that were the responsibility of another body
- Educational institutions, unless for the relief of disadvantage
- Sporting clubs or organisations, unless for the relief of disadvantage
- Medical research and equipment
- More than one donation for the same organisation in any one year – further applications will be considered after three years
- Animal welfare
- Promotion of religious, political or military causes

No contributions were made for political purposes.

Applications

Coventry Building Society Charitable Foundation

According to the society's website: 'Any small charities or community groups operating within reach of our branch network can apply. We don't donate to charities or community groups with an annual income in excess of £250,000.'

Priority is given to groups or activities aimed at improving the quality of life among groups which are disadvantaged or deprived, the consequence of which may otherwise lead to social exclusion.

Applications are welcomed from small grassroots charities and community groups that focus on:

- Young people, particularly those who are disadvantaged
- Vulnerable groups such as frail older people, people with physical disability, people with learning difficulties or those who are mentally ill
- Small neighbourhood groups in areas experiencing the greatest disadvantage
- Supporting communities and voluntary organisations through assisting them in the achievement of social and community development

The foundation wishes to support as many charities as possible and so does not offer large sums and, in exceptional circumstances, may offer up to £2,000; however, the grants will tend to be smaller than this.

If you have any queries about the application process contact your local branch of the foundation directly.

The grants panel from each branch of the foundation meet on a bimonthly or quarterly basis to consider applications. The panel will consider your application to see if, in its opinion, it meets the objectives of the Coventry Building Society Charitable Foundation. All applications will be acknowledged.

Unfortunately, it may not always be possible to support all applications even if they fully meet the Coventry Building Society Foundation's criteria.

Community grants

Staff members who are involved with a community-based group – such as a local charity, school, children's sport club, old people's home, or a scout group – are able to apply to the society for a grant of up to £250 to help support the group.

Cranswick PLC

Food services

Correspondent: Corporate Social Responsibility Department, 74 Helsinki Road, Sutton Fields Industrial Estate, Kingston upon Hull HU7 0YW (tel: 01482 372000; email: info@cranswick.co.uk; website: cranswick.plc.uk)

Directors: Adam Couch, Chief Executive; Jim Brisby; Kate Allum; Mark Bottomley, Finance Director; Mark Reckitt; Martin Davey, Chair; Steven Esom (women: 1; men: 6)

Year end	31/03/2016
Turnover	£1,069,604,000
Pre-tax profit	£65,700,000

Nature of business: Cranswick is one of the largest food producers in Britain with products spanning retail shelves and restaurant menus across the country and internationally. The company has farms across Yorkshire and East Anglia.

Company registration number: 1074383

Subsidiary undertakings include: Kingston Foods Ltd; Mulberry House Foods Ltd; The Harts Corner Natural Sausage Company Ltd.

Brands include: Bodega; Simply Sausages; Yorkshire Baker.

UK employees: 8,885

Focus of giving: Health, ill health, armed forces, overseas projects.

Community involvement	✓
Community contributions	✓
Company reports on anti-slavery	✓
CSR report	✓
Employee-led support	✓
Gifts in kind	✓
Overseas giving	✓
Sponsorship	✓

Charitable donations

Cash UK (latest available):	2016	£20,000
Total UK (cash and in kind):	2016	£20,000
Cash worldwide:	2016	£20,000
Total worldwide (cash and in kind):	2016	£20,000

Community involvement

Charitable activities

The company engages in charitable activities predominantly in the UK but also elsewhere in the world. It does this through charitable donations, sponsorship and by encouraging its employees and businesses to engage with their local communities.

In 2015 the group became a Platinum Food for Good Sponsor, joining with other food and hospitality companies to raise funds to create sustainable farming opportunities for people living in Eastern Africa to help end hunger. No details were available regarding how much the company donated to this cause during the year.

The group continues to be involved with the Red Lion Brand, a business which donates all of its post-tax profits to armed forces charities.

Sponsorship

In 2015 the company sponsored the arts stage of the Hull Freedom Festival and provided food to some of the performers. In 2016 the company became the main sponsor of the event. The company intends to support Hull in becoming UK City of Culture in 2017 by running a series of events and activities to get its employees involved.

Main locations

The company operates in the following locations in the UK: Barnsley; Denbigh; Hull; Manchester; Milton Keynes; Norfolk; North and West Yorkshire; Preston.

Community contributions

In 2015/16 the company's various UK sites raised over £115,000 for 26 charities, mostly through employee-led fundraising efforts. A further £20,000 was given in charitable donations by the company during the year.

In-kind support

According to the 2015/16 CSR report, the company donates hampers and food parcels to charitable causes and local community events on a regular basis.

Employee-led support

Employees working at the company's various sites in the UK nominate local and national charities to support via a voting system and are encouraged to fundraise through sponsored events, Name the Bear competitions and cake sales. In 2015/16 a total of 26 charities were supported, which included: Bluebell Children's Hospice; Macmillan; Marie Curie; Tickled Pink Campaign; Yorkshire Air Ambulance.

Exclusions

The company does not make donations to political causes.

Applications

Apply in writing to the correspondent.

Credit Suisse

Banking

Correspondent: Kate Butchart, Credit Suisse EMEA Foundation, One Cabot Square, London EC14 4QJ (email: emea.corporatecitizenship@credit-suisse.com; website: www.credit-suisse.com/uk/en)

Directors: Alison Halsey; Christopher Horne; David Mathers; Eraj Shirvani; Noreen Doyle; Paul Ingram; Robert

Arbuthnott; Robert Endersby; Stephen Dainton (women: 2; men: 7)

Year end	31/12/2015
Turnover	£892,000,000
Pre-tax profit	(£427,000,000)

Nature of business: Credit Suisse is a global financial services group based in Switzerland, with operations in 50 countries worldwide.

Note: Financial information for the group was converted from USD at the time of writing (November 2016).

Company registration number: 891554

Subsidiary undertakings include: Credit Suisse Client Nominees Ltd; Credit Suisse First Boston Trustees Ltd; Redwood Trust I.

Total employees: 48,200

Focus of giving: Economic generation, education, enterprise/training, environment, financial education, older people, arts, culture, overseas projects, sport, recreation, children, young people, community/social welfare.

Community involvement	✓
Community contributions	✓
CSR report	✓
CSR or charity committee	✓
Charity of the Year	✓
Charity partner(s)	✓
Corporate charity	✓
Employee-led support	✓
Gifts in kind	✓
Market-led giving	✓
Matched funding	✓
Overseas giving	✓
Pro bono	✓
Sponsorship	✓

Community involvement

The group has three areas of focus for its social commitments: education; microfinance; and employee engagement. The group has a global strategy for social commitments, which is implemented at a regional level depending on local needs, in co-operation with local partners. The group works with more than 700 partner organisations internationally.

Credit Suisse Foundation

The group has a global Credit Suisse Foundation, which allocates funds to the group's Global Education Initiative, and manages the Disaster Relief Fund and Jubilee Fund. It also has a number of regional foundations:

Credit Suisse EMEA Foundation (Charity Commission no. 1122472)

The group's foundation in Europe, the Middle East and Africa focuses on education, employability and aspirations among disadvantaged young people. Funding is given to organisations supporting these aims in the countries where Credit Suisse has offices. The foundation also supports the Charity of the Year scheme, and charities nominated by employees. In 2015 the group made eight grants totalling almost £1.5 million.

Disaster relief

The group's Disaster Relief Fund, which is managed by the Credit Suisse Foundation, provides short- and long-term financial support to areas affect by disaster. For example, in 2015, the foundation supported the relief efforts following the earthquake in Nepal, by matching employee donations and bringing the total amount donated to $600,000 (around £480,000) to Habitat for Humanity.

The group is also a member of the Corporate Support Group for the International Committee of the Red Cross, offering financial contributions as well as support through expertise in areas like human resources or IT skills.

Education

The group supports education at local and regional levels, as well as through its Global Education Initiative, which worked with a total of 830 schools in 2015. Activities include a financial programme for girls, in partnership with Plan International and Aflatoun, providing financial education and life skills support to girls in Brazil, China, India and Rwanda, as well as working with Room to Read and Teach for All.

In 2015 the group launched its second Higher Education Note, providing support for students with promising academic potential who do not have access to funding for higher education.

Social enterprise

The corporate responsibility report states that the group provides support for small and medium-sized social enterprises. Examples in the UK include supporting Teach First with their Innovation Award, which benefitted 32 organisations in 2015.

Microfinance

The group provides microfinance – small loans or other financial services – to disadvantaged households or enterprises in low- and middle-income countries. The group works with partners such as Habitat for Humanity, FINCA International and Women's World Banking on its Microfinance Capacity Building Initiative (MCBI), which currently focuses on small-holder farmers, home construction, education and financial services for women and people with disabilities.

Youth unemployment

The group has a well-established programme to support young people who are unemployed, focusing on providing professional training through its Check Your Chance scheme.

Main locations

In the UK, Credit Suisse is based in London. The group operates in over 50 countries internationally.

Community contributions

No figure was given for the charitable contribution of the group in the UK.

The Credit Suisse EMEA Foundation received almost £1.7 million in 2015 from Credit Suisse AG (the group registered in Switzerland). The foundation made grants totalling almost £1.5 million during the year to organisations across its area of benefit.

In-kind support

Global Citizens Programme

This is a leadership development scheme which allows employees to contribute their expertise to projects run by partner organisations, particularly in low- and middle-income countries.

Employee-led support

Employee volunteering

According to the 2015 corporate responsibility report, over 20,000 employees volunteered during the year. The group prefers to complement financial support that it provides to partner organisations with employee volunteering. All employees are entitled to four days of paid volunteering leave each year to contribute to partner organisations' projects in the areas of health, education, social issues and environment.

The group also rolled out its Board Training Programme in 2015, which started in the US, providing training for employees who are interested in becoming a trustee or board member of a charitable organisation.

In the UK, examples of employee volunteering include employees working as mentors to volunteers for City Year UK, as part of a five-year partnership with the education charity.

Commercially led support

Sustainable or philanthropic products and services

The group offers services to charities and other not-for-profit organisations through 'strategic philanthropy' advice. This can include support with drafting a grant-making policy, support with charitable structure for individuals or families, and managing the operation of charitable foundations on behalf of clients. The group provides services for sustainable investment, impact investment and philanthropy. For example, its Nature Conservation Notes initiative allows investment in conservation and sustainable bonds, supporting conservation activities in 10–15 countries.

Sponsorship
The group's sponsorship focuses on sports and arts. Examples include the National Gallery in London, Sydney Symphony Orchestra and Roger Federer, tennis player.

Corporate charity

Credit Suisse EMEA Foundation (Charity Commission no. 1122472).

Exclusions

The Credit Suisse EMEA Foundation will not support:

- Replacement or subsidation of statutory funding, or activities that are the responsibility of statutory funders
- General administration costs that are not specific to the project
- Individuals
- Promotion of religious or political causes
- Holidays
- Retrospective requests
- General appeals
- Animal welfare
- Festivals, sports and leisure activities

Applications

Credit Suisse EMEA Foundation
Apply in writing to the correspondent.

The company
Enquiries can be emailed to the Corporate Citizenship team at: responsibility.corporate@credit-suisse.com.

P. Z. Cussons PLC

Household, pharmaceuticals

Correspondent: Ngozi Edozien, Board Director & Chair of Good4Business Committee, 3500 Aviator Way, Manchester Business Park, Manchester M22 5TG (tel: 0161 435 1000; email: pzccommunications@pzcussons.com; website: www.pzcussons.com/en_int/csr)

Directors: Alex Kanellis, Group Chief Executive; Brandon Leigh, Chief Financial Officer; Caroline Silver, Chair; Chris Davis; Helen Owers; John Nicolson; Ngozi Edozien; Prof. John Arnold (women: 3; men: 5)

Year end	31/05/2016
Turnover	£821,200,000
Pre-tax profit	£103,000,000

Nature of business: Principal activities of the group are the manufacture and distribution of soaps, toiletries, cleaning agents, pharmaceuticals, refrigerators and air conditioners.

Company registration number: 19457

Subsidiary undertakings include: PZ Cussons Beauty LLP; Seven Scent Ltd; St Tropez Holdings Ltd.

Brands include: Carex; Imperial Leather; Pampers.

Total employees: 4,998

Focus of giving: Education, health, ill health, arts, culture, overseas projects, children, young people, community/ social welfare, disability.

Membership: BITC

Community involvement	✓
Community contributions	✓
CSR report	✓
CSR or charity committee	✓
Directors have other relevant posts	✓
Charity partner(s)	✓
Employee-led support	✓
Gifts in kind	✓
Market-led giving	✓
Overseas giving	✓

Community involvement

P. Z. Cussons supports local communities and charities in the places where it operates, with a particular focus on: children and families; education; well-being and hygiene; social welfare; people with disabilities; the arts and music.

Most support is given through The Zochonis Charitable Trust (Charity Commission no. 274769), a shareholding trust. Contributions are also made through staff time, fundraising and gifts in kind. In Manchester, where the global head office is based, the group supports the Seashell Trust, Manchester Halle and the Manchester International Festival.

Charity partner
The group is in a long-term partnership with the Seashell Trust, a charity for children, young people and adults with disabilities. In 2015/16 the group supported the charity's fundraising appeal to build an educational facility. This support has been in the form of employee-led fundraising and volunteering, as well as corporate/brand support, although we do not have any figures to say if the group itself directly donated.

International contributions
In Indonesia the group runs health and education programmes for schoolchildren and donates books and computers.

In Australia the group supports the charity Sports Without Borders.

In Nigeria the group works with The Forest Trust, farmers and co-operatives on a smallholder programme to help farmers develop traceable and sustainable sources of palm oil.

P. Z. Cussons Nigerian Foundation
The foundation was established in 2007 and supports projects in Nigeria that improve education, health, water access and infrastructure. Support appears to be mainly in the form of in-kind donations (such as product packs) and employee volunteering and fundraising.

Directors with other relevant posts
Caroline Silver is a trustee of the Victoria and Albert Museum.

Professor John Arnold is a trustee and chair of Feelgood Theatre Productions (Charity Commission no. 1092907).

Helen Owers is a non-executive director of The Eden Project (Charity Commission no. 1093070).

Office locations
The group has offices based in: Manchester, Salford and London; New York, USA; Athens, Greece; Warsaw, Poland; Jakarta, Indonesia; Bangkok and Pathum Thani, Thailand; Melbourne, Australia; Dubai, United Arab Emirates; Lagos, Nigeria; Tema, Ghana; and Nairobi, Kenya.

Community contributions

In 2015/16 the group did not declare figures for its charitable contributions.

Beneficiaries included: Global Hand Washing Day; Manchester Halle; Manchester International Festival; Teach First; The Seashell Trust.

Employee-led support

The group embarked on a three-year association with Teach First in 2015/16 in which selected employees are being trained as coaches then paired with a teacher to mentor and support them during their two-year teacher training programme.

Commercially led support

Brand charitable support
The group looks to support charitable causes through its various brands.

Each year, the team at the group's Carex brand host activities in support of Global Hand Washing Day in Asia, Africa and Europe. In the UK, the Hands Up for Hygiene education programme provides resources to complement the school curriculum.

In 2015/16 the Imperial Leather brand raised funding for the group's charity partner, the Seashell Trust.

Applications

Applications can be made by writing to the group's Good4Business Committee (formerly known as the CSR committee), which is chaired by one of the board's directors. The Company Secretary, Mr Plant, is secretary to this committee.

CYBG PLC

Banking

Correspondent: Corporate Support Team, 20 Merrion Way, Leeds, West Yorkshire LS2 8NZ (website: www.cybg.com)

Directors: Adrian Grace; Clive Adamson; David Bennett; David Browne; David Duffy, Chief Executive Officer; Debbie Crosbie; Dr Teresa Robson-Capps; Fiona MacLeod; Ian Smith, Chief Financial Officer; James Pettigrew, Chair; Paul Coby; Richard Gregory; Tim Wade (women: 3; men: 10)

Year end	30/09/2015
Turnover	£998,000,000
Pre-tax profit	(£352,000,000)

Nature of business: CYBG is a banking group that owns Clydesdale Bank, established in Glasgow, and Yorkshire Bank, founded in Halifax, West Yorkshire. Both banks date back to the 19th century. The banks were previously owned by National Australia Bank; CYBG PLC, a newly formed holding company, began trading in 2016.

Clydesdale Bank operates across Scotland, while Yorkshire Bank concentrates mainly on the north of England and the Midlands.

Company registration number: 9595911

Subsidiary undertakings include: Clydesdale Bank Asset Finance Ltd; CYB Intermediaries Holdings Ltd; Yorkshire Bank PLC.

UK employees: 6,718

Total employees: 6,718

Focus of giving: General charitable purposes, education, environment, animal welfare, health, ill health, medical research, older people, arts, culture, poverty and social exclusion, sport, recreation, children, young people, community/social welfare.

Membership: Arts & Business, BITC

Community involvement	✓
Community contributions	✓
CSR report	✓
CSR or charity committee	✓
Directors have other relevant posts	✓
Charity partner(s)	✓
Corporate charity	✓
Employee-led support	✓
Gifts in kind	✓
Matched funding	✓
Payroll giving	✓
Sponsorship	✓

Community involvement

The group offers support to charities through its foundation, which supports a wide range of causes in local communities. Employees offer support through payroll giving and through fundraising for the group's partner charity, both of which are backed by matched funding from the group. Employees volunteer days to contribute to associated projects, particularly in the area of education, and there are also grants available for charities that employees volunteer with in their spare time.

Yorkshire and Clydesdale Bank Foundation (OSCR no. SC039747)

The group's corporate charity, the Yorkshire and Clydesdale Bank Foundation (YCBF) provides grants to charities and voluntary organisations for a wide range of charitable purposes. Grants to the group's partner charity are also made through the foundation. The foundation also runs Spirit of the Community Awards to recognise the vital contributions of grassroots community projects.

In 2014/15 the foundation made grants to 358 organisations totalling £865,000, in the following areas: health; citizenship or community development; education; sports; environment; relief in need; arts, heritage, culture or science; animal welfare; saving of lives.

Charity partner

The group's charity partner since 2008 has been Hospice UK. The group fundraises for both the national body and local hospices.

Education

The group's employees volunteer with local schools, delivering the Number Partners and Right to Read programmes run by Business in the Community. The group also works in partnership with Leeds City Council and Glasgow Life to deliver the Count Me In 123 and Count Me In Primary programmes, providing books and games for parents and teachers to help build numeracy skills.

Directors with other relevant posts

David Browne is a trustee of London Youth Rowing (Charity Commission no. 1122941). Richard Gregory is a director of Sheffield Children's Hospital NHS Foundation Trust and Interim Chair of Derbyshire Healthcare NHS Foundation Trust.

Fiona MacLeod is Chair of Trustees of the Women's Fund for Scotland (part of Foundation Scotland, OSCR no. SC022910) and is a member of the Development Fund Board for Pancreatic Cancer UK (Charity Commission no. 1112708).

Debbie Crosbie is also a trustee of the Yorkshire and Clydesdale Bank Foundation.

Main locations

The group's head office is in Leeds. Yorkshire Bank has over 150 branches in the north of England and the Midlands, and Clydesdale Bank has over 120 branches across Scotland.

Community contributions

No figure was given for the group's charitable contributions.

According to the Yorkshire and Clydesdale Bank Foundation's 2014/15 annual report, the group donated £752,000 to the foundation during the year.

Note: The financial information for the group is from the year 2015/16. The latest accounts available for the foundation were the 2014/15 accounts.

Employee-led support

Payroll giving and matched funding

Around 20% of the group's employees support charities through the payroll giving scheme and the bank matches funds every donation. The group is part of the Geared for Giving campaign, which promotes payroll giving.

Employee volunteering

Employees are entitled to two days of paid leave for volunteering on a bank-led volunteer activity. Examples include: team challenges, such as events organised by Business in the Community; supporting schoolchildren through the Number Partners and Right to Read education programmes run by BITC; mentoring young people in the Career Ready programme; and sharing skills through charity boards or school governance.

In 2014/15 employees volunteered a total of over 14,500 hours. Through the group's partnership with Hospice UK, employees have volunteered a total of 35,000 hours with local hospices since 2008.

The group also has an Employee Volunteer Grant Programme, providing grants of up to £500 to charities that employees volunteer with in their own time. These grants are awarded quarterly.

Employee fundraising

Employees organise fundraising initiatives for the group's partner charity, Hospice UK, with matched funding from the group. £5 million has been raised since 2008.

Commercially led support

Sponsorship

Clydesdale Bank sponsors the Royal Zoological Society of Scotland's outreach programme, Wild about Scotland, with a bus that takes wildlife and environmental activities to schools across Scotland. The bank also sponsors and supports Scotland's Charity Air Ambulance.

Yorkshire Bank sponsors Cycle Yorkshire's bike libraries. The libraries allow people to donate unwanted bikes for reuse, providing a network of bikes that are free to hire.

Corporate charity

Yorkshire and Clydesdale Bank Foundation (OSCR no. SC039747).

Applications

The group

Apply in writing to the correspondent.

The foundation

See the foundation's web page on the company's website for more information. The group's Corporate Support Team is responsible for the day-to-day running of the foundation.

Daejan Holdings PLC

Property

Correspondent: M. R. M. Jenner, Company Secretary, Freshwater House, 158–162 Shaftesbury Avenue, London WC2H 8HR (tel: 020 7836 1555; fax: 020 7497 8941; email: mark.jenner@highdorn.co.uk; website: www.daejanholdings.com)

Directors: A. M. Freshwater; Benzion Freshwater, Chair and Chief Executive; D. Davies; R. E. Freshwater; Solomon Israel Freshwater (women: 0; men: 5)

Year end	31/03/2016
Turnover	£148,564,000
Pre-tax profit	£173,242,000

Nature of business: Property investment and trading, with some development activities. The major part of the group's property portfolio comprises commercial, industrial and residential premises throughout the UK and in the US. Approximately 25% of the group's property portfolio is located in the US.

Company registration number: 305105

Subsidiary undertakings include: Agecroft Estates Ltd; Coineagle Ltd; Kintsilk Investments Ltd.

Focus of giving: Education, health, ill health, medical research, poverty and social exclusion.

Community involvement	✓
Community contributions	✓

Charitable donations

Cash UK (latest available):	2016	£150,000
Total UK (cash and in kind):	2016	£150,000
Cash worldwide:	2016	£150,000
Total worldwide (cash and in kind):	2016	£150,000

Community involvement

The company makes cash donations, mainly to educational charities, in the areas in which the business operates.

Directors with other relevant posts

The following charities have some of the group's directors as trustees:

- Beth Jacob Grammar School for Girls Ltd (Charity Commission no. 248708) – trustees are: Benzion Freshwater and D. Davis
- Mayfair Charities Ltd (Charity Commission no. 255281) – Benzion Freshwater, D. Davis and Solomon Freshwater
- Regent Charities Ltd (Charity Commission no. 1059253) – Benzion Freshwater and D. Davis
- Sassov Beis Hamedrash (Charity Commission no. 1102303) – Benzion Freshwater and Solomon Freshwater
- Service to the Aged (Charity Commission no. 1001916) – Benzion Freshwater and Solomon Freshwater
- The Raphael Freshwater Memorial Association (Charity Commission no. 313890) – Benzion Freshwater, D. Davis and Solomon Freshwater
- The Union of Orthodox Hebrew Congregations (Charity Commission no. 1158987) – Benzion Freshwater
- Vendquot Ltd (Charity Commission no. 284984) – D. Davis

Main locations

The company's head office and the vast majority of its properties are based in London. The company also has properties across the UK and in the USA.

Community contributions

In 2015/16 the group made donations totalling £150,000 (2014/15: £150,000) mainly to educational charities. The company also passed on dividend payments of £909,000 (2014/15: £847,000) from shares that were donated some years ago to charitable companies.

Exclusions

Organisations dealing with professional fundraisers, large overhead expenses and expensive fundraising campaigns are avoided. Support is not given to the arts, enterprise or conservation.

Applications

Apply in writing to the correspondent. There is no donations or CSR committee.

Dairy Crest Group PLC

Dairy products

Correspondent: Sue Farr, Chair of the Corporate Responsibility Committee, Claygate House, Littleworth Road, Esher, Surrey KT10 9PN (tel: 01372 472200; fax: 01372 472333; website: www.dairycrest.co.uk)

Directors: Adam Braithwaite; Andrew Carr-Locke; Mark Allen, Chief Executive Officer; Richard Macdonald; Robin Miller, Company Secretary; Stephen Alexander, Chair; Sue Farr; Tom Atherton, Finance Director (women: 1; men: 7)

Year end	31/03/2016
Turnover	£422,300,000
Pre-tax profit	£57,700,000

Nature of business: Dairy Crest is a dairy company, processing and selling fresh milk and branded dairy products in the UK and Europe.

Note: In November 2014 Dairy Crest agreed to sell its dairies' operations to Müller UK and Ireland Group and this process was completed in December 2015.

Company registration number: 3162897

Subsidiary undertakings include: Dairy Crest Ltd; Coombe Farm Dairies Ltd; Morehands IP Ltd.

Brands include: Cathedral City; Country Life; Frijj; Willow.

Total employees: 1,180

Focus of giving: General charitable purposes, economic generation, education, enterprise/training, environment, health, ill health, local groups, armed forces, poverty and social exclusion, community/social welfare, disasters.

Membership: BITC

Community involvement	✓
Community contributions	✓
CSR report	✓
CSR or charity committee	✓
Charity partner(s)	✓
Company gives to smaller charities	✓
Employee-led support	✓
Gifts in kind	✓
Sponsorship	✓

Charitable donations

Cash UK (latest available):	2016	£100,000
Total UK (cash and in kind):	2016	£100,000
Cash worldwide:	2016	£100,000
Total worldwide (cash and in kind):	2016	£100,000

Community involvement

Community programme

The group's 2015/16 annual report notes that its community programme supports four key strategic aims: looking after the countryside; promoting healthy living and well-being; supporting education and employability; and engaging with local communities. Through the Local Community programme, support is given to:

- Local good causes that make a positive and direct contribution to the communities where the group's workplaces are based
- Good causes that improve health, education, the environment or countryside

Charity partners

Dairy Crest (together with other businesses and the Prince of Wales) contributed to setting up The Prince's Countryside Fund in 2010 to protect, improve and promote the British countryside and the businesses which work within it. The group has since maintained a long-term relationship with the charity, raising funds through brand partnerships, sponsored events and employee-led fundraising. In 2016 the group co-sponsored a racing day at Ascot for the second year running to raise money for the fund. The charity then distributes the funds in the form of grants, which in 2015/16 totalled over £1.5 million, and also in emergency funding to supported people affected by flooding in the north of England and Scotland.

The group is also a long-term supporter of GroceryAid, a food-industry charity that provides welfare assistance to people who are currently working or who have worked in the food industry. In 2015 the group was given the Gold Award at the GroceryAid Achievement Awards.

The group has supported the charity Pub is the Hub since 2010. The charity encourages local authorities, local communities, licensees and pub owners to work together to support, retain and locate services within rural pubs. The group provides funding and assists pubs with setting up rural shops with the support of the local milkman.

Education

The group helps to fund community educational programmes, including food-science placements at Reading and Nottingham Universities.

The Prince's Rural Action Programme and The Dairy Initiative

The group supports the Prince's Rural Action Programme, which is run by Business in the Community. Its purpose is to engage businesses to make a positive difference to rural communities, through the way in which they do business, in order to sustain the rural economy, protect and enhance the environment and protect the nation's cultural heritage and landscape. One programme set up in 2011 as a result of the group's support is The Dairy Initiative, which aims to help the most vulnerable dairy farms become more economically and environmentally sustainable. The pilot with 74 dairy farms was run in 2012 and the group was expecting to help a further 300 farms in 2016.

The Rural Action Award

The group sponsors the Dairy Crest Rural Action Award, run by Business in the Community. The award recognises companies that are helping to address issues faced by rural communities in order to maintain a vibrant, sustainable rural economy.

Directors with other relevant posts

The Chief Executive, Mark Allen, is a trustee of The Prince's Countryside Fund (Charity Commission no. 1136077).

Stephen Alexander, is also the Chair of Look Ahead Housing and Care, a London-based charitable housing association under the Co-operative and Community Benefit Societies Act (no. 21004R).

Sue Farr was formerly a trustee of Historic Royal Palaces (Charity Commission no. 1068852), but stepped down from this role in 2013.

Richard Macdonald is a trustee of The National Institute of Agricultural Botany (Charity Commission no. 1064230) and Farm Africa Ltd (Charity Commission no. 326901). He is also a governor of The Royal Agricultural College Cirencester (Charity Commission no. 311780).

Main locations

There are offices or operations in: Esher, Surrey (head office); Cornwall; Frome; Kent; Kirkby; Newport; Nuneaton.

Community contributions

No details were available regarding the total amount of funds the group donated to charitable causes in 2015/16; however, its annual report notes that the group donated over £100,000 during the year to The Prince's Countryside Fund.

Beneficiaries included: GroceryAid; The Prince's Countryside Fund.

There were no further details available regarding other charitable organisations that the group supported; however, in 2014 the group supported the following: Age UK; Bedworth Cricket Club; Bowel Cancer UK; Butterflies Children's Hospice; Claygate Flower Show; Hinchley Wood School; Royal Cornwall Hospital Truro; Walking with Giants; Weddington Allotment Association.

In-kind support

The group donates products to assist charitable organisations. For example, in 2015 the group donated over 8,500 litres of milk to the homelessness charity Crisis at Christmas, and 40kg of Cathedral City cheddar for Chelsea pensioners over the Christmas period.

Employee-led support

Local Community programme

The Local Community programme (also see 'Community involvement' section) is the fourth strand of Dairy Crest's community strategy and is owned and run by the staff. Each site where the company operates has a community committee made up of about five to six employees. Each committee has a community budget to distribute to local charitable causes. In 2015/16 over 60 local causes were supported through financial donations.

Employee fundraising

Dairy Crest employees also fundraised for the charity partner, the Prince's Countryside Fund. In 2015 before the group sold its dairy business, the milk&more milkmen and customers raised £60,000 for the fund through an envelope drop.

Quids In

Employees of the group can also nominate charitable causes they wish to support through the money raised as a result of the staff lottery called Quids In. About £1,500 is donated to charitable causes each month through this scheme.

Meals on Wheels

The group supports staff who wish to volunteer to deliver fresh food to vulnerable people in their local communities through Meals on Wheels.

Commercially led support

Brand partnerships

The group had brand partnerships with Davidstow cheddar and Country Life butter in order to raise £100,000 for The Prince's Countryside Fund in 2015/16.

Exclusions

Political donations are not made.

Applications

Apply in writing to your local site referenced 'Local Community Committee', or to the correspondent for corporate CSR enquiries.

De La Rue PLC

Print/paper/packaging

Correspondent: Corporate Responsibility Team, De La Rue House, Jays Close, Viables, Basingstoke, Hampshire RG22 4BS (tel: 01256 605000; fax: 01256 605004; email: webcontact@delarue.com; website: www.delarue.com)

Directors: Andrew Stevens; Jitesh Sodha, Chief Financial Officer; Maria de Cunha; Martin Sutherland, Chief Executive Officer; Nick Bray; Philip Rogerson, Chair; Rupert Middleton; Sabri Challah (women: 1; men: 7)

Year end	26/03/2016
Turnover	£454,500,000
Pre-tax profit	£54,900,000

Nature of business: The company operates in commercial and government sectors as security printer and papermaker, involved in the production of over 150 national currencies and a wide range of security documents. De La Rue provides cash-handling equipment and solutions to banks and retailers, and supplies a range of identity systems to governments worldwide.

Company registration number: 3834125

Subsidiary undertakings include: De La Rue Consulting Services Ltd; De La Rue International Ltd; Portals Group Ltd.

Total employees: 3,566

Focus of giving: Education, small groups, overseas projects, poverty and social exclusion, community/social welfare.

Community involvement	✓
Community contributions	✓
Company reports on anti-slavery	✓
CSR report	✓
CSR or charity committee	✓
Directors have other relevant posts	✓
Charity of the Year	✓
Company gives to smaller charities	✓
Corporate charity	✓
Employee-led support	✓
Humanitarian aid: overseas	✓
Matched funding	✓
Payroll giving	✓
STEM-focused	✓

Community involvement

The group states in its annual report that sites within the group tend to focus their support on smaller, local charities where employees can be involved. The group's corporate charity provides funding for international development; education; disasters; local charities and community projects; and charities benefitting employees or ex-employees.

The De La Rue Charitable Trust (Charity Commission no. 274052)

The group's corporate charity, The De La Rue Charitable Trust, supports causes both in the UK and abroad, with an emphasis on education, relief in need, international development and sustainability. The website states that grants are made to registered charities for the following purposes:

- Well-researched causes in under-developed countries, preferably through UK charities to secure both financial control and tax relief
- Educational charities which promote relevant skills and international understanding, particularly for the benefit of disadvantaged and underprivileged students
- Disaster funds
- Local charities or community projects, particularly if employees are involved
- Charities for the benefit, directly or indirectly, of employees or ex-employees

The latest accounts available at the time of writing (November 2016) were for 2014/15, when the trust made grants totalling £56,500. The trust's income comes from investments.

Beneficiaries included: African Prisons Project; Maternity Worldwide; Proteus Theatre; Resolve International; St Michael's Hospice.

Charity of the Year

The group's head office supports a Charity of the Year, which employees vote to select annually.

Education

The group works with charities and schools to promote STEM subjects and employability. It also provides Caribbean scholarship programme, supporting students studying economics, finance and actuarial sciences in Barbados, East Caribbean, Jamaica and Trinidad and Tobago.

Directors with other relevant posts

Sabri Challah is a trustee of the Contemporary Art Society (Charity Commission no. 208178). Nick Bray is a member of the Technology Sector Group for The Prince's Trust (Charity Commission no. 1079675).

Main locations

The group has offices or operations in the following UK locations: Bathford; Basingstoke; Debden; Gateshead; Overton; Westhoughton. There are also sites in Kenya, Malta, and Sri Lanka.

Community contributions

No figure was given for the group's charitable contribution.

Employee-led support

Employee fundraising

Employees organise fundraising initiatives to support the group's Charity of the Year, which is elected through an annual vote. For example, in 2015/16, for the fifth year, teams of employees competed in the Three Peaks Challenge

Matched funding

The De La Rue Charitable Trust provides matched funding of up to £500 for each of the employees undertaking their own fundraising initiatives.

Payroll giving

Employees can also choose to donate through a payroll giving scheme.

Corporate charity

The De La Rue Charitable Trust (Charity Commission no. 274052).

Exclusions

The De La Rue Charitable Trust will not support:

- Party political causes
- Organisations that do not benefit a community in a place where De La Rue does business
- Individuals
- Grant-makers
- National charities
- Military organisations
- Religious organisations

Applications

De La Rue Charitable Trust

Applications should be made in writing to the Trust Administrator to be considered at the trustees' meetings which take place around three times a year. Applications should include the information specified on the website: www.delarue.com/about-us/corporate-responsibility/relationships/de-la-rue-in-the-community/charitable-trust.

The trust regrets that it is not able to reply to every unsuccessful application.

The group

Apply in writing to the correspondent.

Debenhams PLC

Retail – department and variety stores

Correspondent: Lisa Hunt, Correspondent to the Trustees, 10 Brock Street, Regent's Place, London NW1 3FG (tel: 020 7408 4444 or 020 3549 6000/020 3549 7891; fax: 020 3549 7744; email: lisa.hunt@debenhams.com; website: www.debenhamsplc.com)

Directors: Dennis Millard; Mark Rolfe; Martina King; Matt Smith, Chief Financial Officer; Peter Fitzgerald; Sergio Bucher, Chief Executive; Sir Ian Cheshire, Chair; Stephen Ingham; Suzanne Harlow, Group Trading Director; Terry Duddy (women: 2; men: 8)

Year end	29/08/2015
Turnover	£2,322,700,000
Pre-tax profit	£113,500,000

Nature of business: Debenhams is an international, multi-channel brand which trades out of 248 stores across 27 countries. It is available online in 60 countries.

Company registration number: 5448421

Subsidiary undertakings include: A&D Pension Services Ltd; Aktieselskabet Th. Wessel and Vett Magasin du Nord; Debenhams Retail PLC; Debenhams Properties Ltd.

Brands include: Faith; Red Herring; The Collection.

Total employees: 28,127

Focus of giving: General charitable purposes, environment, political appeals, health, ill health, armed forces, children, young people, community/social welfare, disability.

Membership: BITC

Community involvement	✓
Community contributions	✓
Company reports on anti-slavery	✓
CSR report	✓
CSR or charity committee	✓
Charity partner(s)	✓

Corporate charity ✓
Employee-led support ✓
Gifts in kind ✓
Humanitarian aid: overseas ✓
Payroll giving ✓

Community involvement

The company states on its sustainability website (www.sustainability.debenhamsplc.com) that it supports local and national charities and community groups through volunteering and fundraising. Employees are encouraged to be involved in local community activities.

Debenhams Foundation

In 2011, following a charity audit by the company, the Debenhams Foundation (Charity Commission no. 1147682) was established through which all charitable giving is channelled. The aim of the foundation is to raise funds for its key charity partners.

The objects of the foundation are to preserve and protect health and relieve financial hardship, as well as to further general charitable purposes. These objects will be achieved primarily through grant-making. The foundation operates worldwide and will also provide relief aid through the Disasters Emergency Committee (DEC). The foundation's trustees also manage the annual donation of funds from Debenhams PLC to the Debenhams Retirement Association.

Many charities are supported by Debenhams at a local level including children's charities, schools, sports clubs, animal and wildlife charities, old people's homes, hospitals, hospices and medical charities. The food services division is a corporate member of the Anaphylaxis Campaign and fully supports the great work they do, helping people with severe allergens and persuading the food industry (including catering) of the need to provide detailed and accurate allergen information.

The foundation's charity partners 2014/15: BBC Children in Need; Breast Cancer Now; Help for Heroes; Fashion Targets Breast Cancer.

Partners

The 2014/15 annual report notes that the company has partnered with the charity TRAID (Charity Commission no. 297489), which works to stop textiles and footwear being thrown to landfill.

The company has a recycling initiative at its head office for staff to dispose of samples and their own clothing, footwear and accessories. Debenhams aims to operate a customer-facing option for stores and online in 2015/16. Any financial gain from this will be donated to Supporting the Children of Garment Workers in Bangladesh, which is run with ChildHope UK (Charity Commission no. 328434) whose Bangladeshi partner is Nagorik Uddyog.

In 2015 the group also established a partnership with Swasti (www.swasti.org) for the charity's Life Skills for Empowering Women programme. Its purpose is to strengthen the life skills of female workers by using a peer-education approach.

Directors

Dennis Millard is a trustee of the Holy Cross Children's Trust (Charity Commission no. 1095593), which supports orphaned children in South Africa.

Sir Ian Cheshire is a trustee of Business in the Community (Charity Commission no. 297716). He is also on the Council of Ambassadors for the WWF (Charity Commission no. 108247), Chair of the Prince of Wales Corporate Leaders Group on Climate Change, Honorary President of the Business Disability Forum (Charity Commission no. 1018463), Chair of the Advisory Board for the Cambridge Institute for Sustainability Leadership and Chair of Medicinema (Charity Commission no. 1058197).

Terry Duddy is a trustee of the Retail Trust (Charity Commission no. 1090136).

The company also sits on the government's Body Confidence Advisory Committee, following its sponsorship of the Be Real! Campaign for Body Confidence and being awarded a charity B-eat Beacon Award in 2014/15.

Community contributions

In 2014/15 the group did not declare any charitable donations in its annual report and accounts. The report does note, however, that the Debenhams Foundation raised £1.68 million during the year. This includes £457,500 raised through the company's Think Pink initiative, which has now been disbanded.

The foundation's beneficiaries included: BBC Children in Need (£478,000); Breakthrough Breast Cancer, Breast Cancer Campaign, Breast Cancer Now, Breast Cancer Ireland and Pink Ribbon Foundation (£457,500 split between the charities); Help for Heroes (£378,500); Disasters Emergency Committee for the Nepal Earthquake (£14,000).

In-kind support

The group provides legal, accounting and marketing support to the foundation at no cost.

The group also donates products to be recycled. For example, the company has previously donated 24 tonnes of faulty/damaged products to the Salvation Army in 2014/15 for processing in the charity's recycling outlets and in 2013 Debenhams gave away its Christmas decorations to charities to sell in their outlets.

Employee-led support

The Debenhams Foundation was launched in 2012, to give clear visibility of the money raised for good causes and to channel Debenham's company, staff and customers' giving. The foundation's aim is to raise funds through store and head office's fundraising and through product sales. All monies raised through staff and customer fundraising goes via the foundation.

Corporate charity

Debenhams Foundation (Charity Commission no. 1147682).

Exclusions

It is the group's policy not to make donations to political organisations or independent election candidates, or incur political expenditure.

Applications

Apply in writing to the correspondent for grant-giving or to the local store for community projects, gifts in kind, etc. Most of the group's charitable giving is directed through its associated foundation – see 'Community involvement' section.

Dechra Pharmaceuticals PLC

Pharmaceuticals

Correspondent: The Corporate Responsibility Team, 24 Cheshire Avenue, Cheshire Business Park, Lostock Gralam, Northwich CW9 7UA (tel: 01606 814730; website: www.dechra.com)

Directors: Anne-Francoise Nesmes, Chief Financial Officer; Dr Christopher Richards; Ian Page, Chief Executive Officer; Ishbel Macpherson; Julian Heslop; Michael Redmond, Chair; Tony Griffin (women: 2; men: 5)

Year end	30/06/2015
Turnover	£203,480,000
Pre-tax profit	£25,806,000

Nature of business: Dechra Pharmaceuticals is an international specialist business in veterinary pharmaceuticals and related products. It specialises in the development, manufacturing, sales and marketing of products exclusively for veterinarians worldwide. Over 725 people work for the group in its European sites.

Company registration number: 3369634

Subsidiary undertakings include: Albrecht GmbH; Dechra Ltd; Eurovet Animal Health BV.

Brands include: Felimazole; DermaPet; Sedator; Soludox; Specific.

Total employees: 869

Focus of giving: Environment, animal welfare, health, ill health, small groups, local groups, overseas projects, children, young people, community/social welfare.

Community involvement	✓
Community contributions	✓
CSR report	✓
Company gives to smaller charities	✓
Employee-led support	✓
Gifts in kind	✓
Humanitarian aid: overseas	✓
Overseas giving	✓

Charitable donations

Cash UK (latest available):	2015	£10,350
Cash worldwide:	2015	£26,100

Community involvement

Donations policy

The group operates a donations policy where employees can nominate a charitable organisation to receive cash donations from the company. This is normally taken from a budget of £10,000 each year set aside for this purpose; however, in 2014/15 due to the increase in number of nominations from employees the group decided to double the donation's fund.

Directors with other relevant posts

Julian Heslop is a trustee of The Royal Academy of Arts (Charity Commission no. 1125383).

Main locations

There are offices in Cheshire; Skipton, Yorkshire; and Hadnall, Shropshire.

Community contributions

According to the annual report, in 2014/15 the group donated £20,000 split between ten charitable causes chosen by employees in line with the donations policy. Five of these charities were based in the UK. A further £6,100 was donated by the group's various business units to local community groups and charities, of which £350 was given to local and national UK charities. We, therefore, estimate that total contributions made to UK charitable causes were approximately £10,350.

Beneficiaries included: Coalition to Unchain Dogs (US); Cuan Wildlife Animal Rescue (UK); Cystic Fibrosis Trust (UK); Heifer International (international); Help Street Animals of Morocco (Morocco); Inges Kattehjem (Denmark); Love Underdogs (Romania); Manchester and Cheshire Dogs Home (UK); Skipton Extended Learning for All (UK); SOS Children's Villages (£815 – international); Stichting WensAmbulance Brabant (Netherlands); The Children's Hunger Project (US); The Good Will Cause (UK); The Joshua Tree Charity (UK).

In-kind support

The group donates veterinary supplies to animal charities worldwide. In 2014/15 the group donated products to Manchester and Cheshire Dogs home following a fire at the Manchester site. They also gave supplies to the charity Help the Street Cats of Morocco and wound care products to Love Underdogs in Romania.

Exclusions

No donations are made to political organisations.

Applications

Organisations should contact the local company's site nearest to where their project is based. These are located on the group's website: www.dechra.com/contact-us/locations.

All other enquiries should be directed to the Corporate Responsibility Team at the head office.

Deloitte

Accountants

Correspondent: Director of Community Investment, Stonecutter Court, 1 Stonecutter Street, London EC4A 4TR (tel: 020 7936 3000; fax: 020 7583 1198; website: www.deloitte.co.uk)

Directors: Anna Marks; Chris Loughran; Chris Powell; David Sproul, Senior Partner and Chief Executive; Denis Woulfe; Emma Codd; John Maxey; Mark Fitzpatrick; Maxine Saunders; Nick Edwards; Nick Owen, Chair; Paul Robinson; Reto Savoia; Zahir Bokhari (women: 3; men: 11)

Year end	31/05/2015
Pre-tax profit	£620,000,000

Nature of business: Audit, tax, corporate finance and management consultancy services.

Company registration number: 2400371

Focus of giving: Education, enterprise/training, medical research, sport, recreation, children, young people.

Membership: BITC, LBG

Accredited Living Wage Employer	✓
Community involvement	✓
Community contributions	✓
CSR report	✓
AF Covenant	✓
Cash donations declared	✓
Gifts in kind	✓
Matched funding	✓
Pro bono	✓

Community involvement

According to the website: 'Every office has a Corporate Responsibility Champion who organises local activities alongside our calendar of centrally managed events and challenges. Additionally, each year the firm allocates a matched funded amount for staff fundraising.'

Main locations

Deloitte has various offices based throughout the UK and worldwide.

Community contributions

According to the 2015 Impact report, this year £1.7 million was raised in support of a range of charities, including £913,000 for the company's national charity partners.

We were unable to determine how much of this was contributed by the company.

Beneficiaries included: Alzheimer's Society; Prostate Cancer UK; Mind.

In-kind support

According to the 2015 Impact report, in the course of that year Deloitte provided charitable organisations and social enterprises with 13,458 hours of pro bono services.

Employee-led support

In order to raise funds for charity, staff have participated in one of four challenges across four continents including trekking Kilimanjaro, a rafting, hiking and biking challenge in Borneo, a walk across the Sierra Nevada and a volcano climb in Ecuador.

Exclusions

No support is given for advertising in charity brochures, appeals from individuals, overseas projects or political/religious appeals.

Applications

Apply in writing to the correspondent. However, few ad hoc or unsolicited requests for funding are approved.

According to the Deloitte website (November 2016):

> The focus of our support until 31 May 2016 is on our three national charity partners, voted for by staff: Alzheimer's Society, Mind and Prostate Cancer UK. Regional charities selected by regional offices are also supported through the partnership scheme.
>
> Applications for our new society partnerships programme (2016–2019) have now closed. If you have submitted your entry to the programme and we have confirmed receipt, we will be in touch with you towards the end of March.

Derwent London PLC

Property

Correspondent: John Davies, Head of Sustainability, 25 Savile Row, London W1S 2ER (tel: 020 7659 3000/020 7659 3000; email: sustainability@derwentlondon.com; website: www.derwentlondon.com)

Directors: Cilla Snowball; Claudia Arney; Damian Wisniewski, Finance Director; David Silverman; John Burns, Chief Executive Officer; Nigel George; Paul Williams, Sustainability Director; Richard Dakin; Robert Rayne, Chair; Simon Fraser; Simon Silver; Stephen Young; Stuart Corbyn (women: 2; men: 11)

Year end	31/12/2015
Turnover	£4,954,500,000
Pre-tax profit	£779,500,000

Nature of business: Derwent London is an office specialist property regenerator and investor. The group's investment portfolio comprises 6.2 million square feet, of which 98% is located in central London, specifically the West End and areas bordering the City of London.

Company registration number: 1819699

Subsidiary undertakings include: City Shops Ltd; Kensington Commercial Property Investments Ltd; Urbanfirst Ltd.

UK employees: 116

Total employees: 116

Focus of giving: General charitable purposes, economic generation, education, enterprise/training, environment, equal opportunities, health, ill health, individuals, non-registered charities, small groups, local groups, older people, arts, culture, sport, recreation, children, young people, disability.

Community involvement	✓
Community contributions	✓
CSR report	✓
CSR or charity committee	✓
Company gives to smaller charities	✓
Employee-led support	✓

Charitable donations

Total UK (cash and in kind):	2015	£266,000
Total worldwide (cash and in kind):	2015	£266,000

Community involvement

Fitzrovia Community Fund

The company has operated a community fund since 2013 supporting community projects in Fitzrovia, central London. In 2015 the company received 12 applications to the fund, of which five were successful and received a grant. During the year the company decided to extend the duration and scope of the fund, committing a further £150,000 to the fund until 2018.

Examples of projects previously supported by the fund include: community gardens; programmes, such as dance lessons and holistic well-being classes, for older people; after-school youth football club and arts club; community events and parties; and music workshops.

Tech Belt Community Fund

In 2016 the company launched a new community fund to engage with communities based in in the vicinity of one of its major property portfolios. The Tech Belt Fund will benefit small community projects based in Islington, Shoreditch, Whitechapel, Clerkenwell, Holborn and Old Street. Applicants can collaborate with national or non-local organisations if these organisations are supporting the project or providing complementary services.

The company has allocated £150,000 to the fund until 2018. Local community groups, residents and business owners are invited to apply to the fund, further details of which can be found in the 'Community' section of the company's website.

The company is particularly interested in community projects that are focused on: local events; increasing employment opportunities for disadvantaged local people; health and well-being; small public space improvements; arts and culture; and educational projects.

Directors with other relevant posts

Robert Rayne is a trustee of The Rayne Trust (Charity Commission no. 207392), a charity that makes grants in Israel, and The Rayne Foundation (Charity Commission no. 216291), a charity that makes grants in the UK with an interest in communities, arts, health, well-being and education.

Cilla Snowball is a trustee of Comic Relief (Charity Commission no. 326568) and also Chair of the Women's Business Council.

Simon Silver is an honorary fellow of the Royal Institute of British Architects (Charity Commission no. 210566).

Paul Williams is director of The Paddington Partnership.

Claudia Arney is a non-executive director of the Premier League.

Main locations

There are offices in London and Glasgow.

Community contributions

In 2015 the company gave £66,000 via its Fitzrovia Community Fund to five organisations.

Beneficiaries were: All Souls Clubhouse; Fitzrovia Community Centre; Fitzrovia Neighbourhood Association; Fitzrovia Youth in Action; Upbeat Music and Mental Health.

In addition to the community fund, the company also donated in excess of £200,000 to a range of charitable organisations.

Beneficiaries included: Cancer Research UK; Norwood; Teenage Cancer Trust.

Employee-led support

The company's employees are entitled to one paid day per year to volunteer for a charity or community project. Many staff volunteer for projects already supported by the company, including the community funds. In 2015 a total of 36% of employees participated in the volunteering programme undertaking a total of 239 hours of volunteering.

Exclusions

Applications to either the Tech Belt or Fitzrovia Community Fund must be from applicants based within the specified local areas at which each of the funds is directed. Applicants based just outside the target area may be considered if their project benefits people living in the target area. See the 'Community involvement' section for more details. The community funds will also not consider funding the following:

- Core costs
- Commercial costs
- Political activities and campaigns
- Religious activities
- Activities where people are excluded on the grounds of religious beliefs, ethnicity, sexual orientation or disability

Applications

Applications to the Tech Belt and Fitzrovia Community Funds can be made via an application form available to download from the company's website under the 'Community' section under the 'Sustainability' tab and should be addressed to the company's Community Team. In 2016 registered charities could apply for up to £5,000 and other organisations, businesses and individuals could apply for up to £2,000. Check the website for the latest details, including application deadlines.

Further information about each of the funds can be obtained by calling the company or emailing community@derwentlondon.com.

Organisations that wish to enquire about the company's volunteering programme are advised to contact Susannah Woodgate by email at fitzrovia@derwentlondon.com.

Deutsche Bank

Banking

Correspondent: Sabira Rouf, Charities & Fundraising, Corporate Citizenship UK, Winchester House, 1 Great Winchester Street, London EC2N 2DB (tel: 020 7545 5194; email: sabira.rouf@db.com; website: www.db.com/unitedkingdom/responsibility.html)

Directors: Christian Sewing; Dr Marcus Schenck, Chief Financial Officer; Garth Ritchie; Jeffrey Urwin; John Cryan, Chief Executive; Karl Von Rohr; Kimberley Hammonds; Nicolas Moreau; Stuart Lewis; Sylvie Matherat; Werner Steinmüller (women: 2; men: 9)

Year end	31/12/2015
Turnover	£28,613,000,000
Pre-tax profit	(£5,204,000,000)

Nature of business: Deutsche Bank is the holding company of a group providing international merchant banking and investment management services.

Company registration number: BR000005

Subsidiary undertakings include: Abbey Life Assurance Company Ltd; Cardales UK Ltd; DB Group Services (UK) Ltd.

Total employees: 101,104

Focus of giving: Education, enterprise/training, environment, equal opportunities, heritage, housing, homelessness, financial education, arts, culture, poverty and social exclusion, science technology, sport, recreation, children, young people, community/social welfare.

Membership: BITC, LBG

Community involvement	✓
Community contributions	✓
CSR report	✓
CSR or charity committee	✓
Cash donations declared	✓
Charity of the Year	✓
Charity partner(s)	✓
Company gives to smaller charities	✓
Employee-led support	✓
Gifts in kind	✓
Humanitarian aid: overseas	✓
Matched funding	✓
Payroll giving	✓
Pro bono	✓

Charitable donations

Total UK (cash and in kind):	2015	£2,300,000

Community involvement

The group supports charitable organisations and projects with a focus on education; social investment; and art and music. The current corporate citizenship programme, 'Born to Be', focuses on supporting young people to fulfil their potential.

Partnerships and programmes

The bank works in partnership with a number of organisations to deliver programmes supporting its 'Born to Be' initiative, focusing on education, young people and youth unemployment.

Sporteducate

Working in partnership with the charity Sported, the bank has helped to develop a programme for disadvantaged young people which aims to provide education, employability skills and personal development through sport. The programme has been delivered by 33 sports clubs in London and employees also volunteer to support the programme.

Playing Shakespeare with Deutsche Bank

This programme offers educational workshops, tickets to performances and learning resources for school students in London and Birmingham to experience and engage with Shakespeare's plays.

Design Ventura

Working in partnership with the Design Museum, Design Ventura gives school students the opportunity to learn about design and produce their own product in a competition, with the winning design going on sale for charity in the museum's shop.

Deutsche Bank Awards for Creative Design

The bank provides awards for students and recent graduates to pursue creative enterprise.

StreetSmart

The bank works in partnership with the StreetSmart and SleepSmart campaigns for homelessness charities, fundraising and covering administration costs for the campaign.

Charities of the Year

The group supports two charities each year, which are voted for by employees and support the 'Born to Be' focus on young people. The group prioritises small charities and provides unrestricted funding, supported by employee fundraising. In 2016/17 the group is supporting Autistica and Hope and Homes for Children. In 2016 the group decided that the Charities of the Year will be supported for a two-year period, to enable a bigger impact.

Small grants fund

The bank provides small grants to local small charities and community groups in London and Birmingham whose work is related to the goals of the 'Born to Be' initiative, supporting young people to fulfil their potential. In 2015 ten organisations received small grants. The grants are administered by London Community Foundation and further details can be found on the website: www.londoncf.org.uk.

Social enterprise and investment

The group's global enterprise programme, Made for Good, provides funding and expertise to help social entrepreneurs develop and grow their entrepreneurial ideas. The group also has an impact investment fund which invests in bodies which provide funding for social enterprises.

Arts

The group also supports a number of initiatives relating to arts and music in the UK and globally. In 2016 the bank sponsored an exhibition at Tate Modern in London, as part of an ongoing partnership with the gallery. It also sponsors the Frieze Art Fair in London.

Main locations

In the UK, the bank's head office is based in London. There are also offices in Birmingham and Bournemouth. The group's global headquarters are in Frankfurt, Germany and it operates in 70 countries worldwide.

Community contributions

The group's 2015 corporate responsibility report states that its global investments in corporate citizenship totalled €76.8 million (around £65.5 million). Of this, 12% was in the UK – around €9.2 million (or £7.9 million). It is unclear whether this includes employee fundraising.

The report states that Corporate Citizenship UK commitments totalled €2.7 million (around £2.3 million) in 2015.

In 2015 employees raised £1.9 million for the Charities of the Year.

At a global level, the group's global community investments were broken down as follows:

Social investments	43%
Education/'Born to Be'	27%
Art and music	22%
Employee engagement	8%

Employee-led support

Employee fundraising

The bank runs an annual summer series of cycling events which employees can take part in to raise money for the Charities of the Year. The group also runs a Donate One Day initiative in a number of countries including the UK, where employees are encouraged to donate a day's salary to charity. There is also a payroll giving scheme and matched funding available.

Employee volunteering

In 2015 more than 17,000 of the bank's employees worldwide volunteered. Employees in the UK are entitled to up to two working days per year to undertake volunteering, and many volunteer with a number of the group's charitable projects under the 'Born to Be' programme. Examples include: volunteers meeting groups of 16- to 18-year-olds in London and Birmingham on a monthly basis to discuss current affairs and economics issues; employees mentoring school students through Volunteering Matters; female employees volunteering as mentors to encourage female students to engage with STEM subjects and careers. Employees also provide pro bono support and take part in team challenges in the local community.

Exclusions

The guidelines on the bank's website state that it cannot support:

- Animal welfare projects
- Drugs-related projects
- Emergency funding
- Heritage projects
- Medical causes or medical research
- Capital projects
- Individuals
- Sponsorship of events/tables for projects not associated with core community development activities
- Charities or initiatives with religious or political objectives

Applications

Charities of the Year

The selection process for Charities of the Year to be supported in 2018–19 opens in May 2017 – details are provided on the website.

Small grants fund

The website states that for information about the bank's small grants and whether they are currently available, you should contact The London Community Foundation: enquiries@londoncf.org.uk.

Contact details

A helpful list of relevant contacts within the bank's UK CSR team is provided on the website: www.db.com/unitedkingdom/content/en/contact_us.html.

DFS Furniture PLC

Retail – DIY/furniture

Correspondent: The Company Secretary, 1 Rockingham Way, Redhouse Interchange, Adwick-le-Street, Doncaster DN6 7NA (website: www.dfscorporate.co.uk/responsibility/community)

Directors: Gwyn Burr; Ian Filby, Chief Executive Officer; Julie Southern; Luke Mayhew; Nicola Bancroft, Chief Financial Officer; Richard Baker, Chair (women: 3; men: 3)

Year end	01/08/2015
Turnover	£706,100,000
Pre-tax profit	£10,700,000

Nature of business: DFS specialises in the retail of upholstered furniture with more than 100 stores across the UK and the Republic of Ireland. DFS also has a presence in mainland Europe.

Company registration number: 7236769

Subsidiary undertakings include: Coin Furniture Ltd; DFS Trading Ltd; The Sofa Workshop Ltd.

Brands include: Dwell; House Beautiful; Sofa Workshop.

Total employees: 3,717

Focus of giving: Health, ill health, small groups, local groups, children, young people.

Membership: BITC

Community involvement	✓
Community contributions	✓
CSR report	✓
Directors have other relevant posts	✓
Cash donations declared	✓
Charity partner(s)	✓
Company gives to smaller charities	✓
Employee-led support	✓
Gifts in kind	✓
Market-led giving	✓

Charitable donations

Cash UK (latest available):	2015	£264,000
Total UK (cash and in kind):	2015	£264,000
Cash worldwide:	2015	£264,000
Total worldwide (cash and in kind):	2015	£264,000

Community involvement

DFS works in partnership with three national charities and also supports local charities and initiatives in the communities where its stores are based. There is a particular emphasis on those that promote opportunities for young people.

Charity partners

During 2014/15, DFS continued its partnerships with:

- British Heart Foundation (BHF): DFS promotes the charity's furniture-collection scheme to its customers. According to the website, more than £10 million has been raised by customers who have recycled their old sofas since 2012. Customers in the Republic of Ireland can also take part in a similar scheme with the Irish Red Cross. New and existing DFS employees are trained in CPR skills as part of BHF's Nation of Lifesavers campaign
- BBC Children in Need: Customers and staff helped to raise £700,000 through a wide range of activities. DFS runs monthly competitions for customers to have the chance of winning their order for free; customers donate £5 to enter the competition, with all proceeds going to support the charity
- Duke of Edinburgh's Award: DFS is a Gold Partner of the charity and its apprentices complete the award as part of their training. In the Republic of Ireland, DFS takes part in a similar scheme, Gaisce – The President's Award

Directors with other relevant posts

Richard Baker is an independent director of the Lawn Tennis Association (LTA).

Ian Filby is a trustee of The Pennies Foundation (Charity Commission no. 1122489) and of The Paquita Filby Trust (Charity Commission no. 1139689).

Luke Mayhew is a trustee of BBC Children in Need.

Main locations

There are stores across the UK and the Republic of Ireland. The head office is in Doncaster.

Community contributions

In 2014/15 DFS made charitable donations amounting to £264,000.

The annual report and accounts for the year also state that 'Ian Filby [CEO] waived his entitlement to a pension contribution from the Group and a donation of £50,000 (2014: £50,000) has instead been made to a registered charity of which he is one of the trustees'. We understand that this amount has been included in the figure for charitable donations stated in the annual report and accounts. We believe that the recipient charity was The Paquita Filby Trust, which works to promote the education of children from Spanish-speaking countries in Latin America.

Employee-led support

Employee fundraising

One of the ways in which employees helped to raise money for DFS charity partner, BBC Children in Need, was by carrying out their own take of the Three Peaks Challenge, carrying sofas weighing 75kg.

Applications

We would suggest that requests are directed to your local DFS store.

Dhamecha Holdings Ltd

Cash 'n' Carry, wholesale

Correspondent: Pradip Dhamecha, Trustee of The Laduma Dhamecha Charitable Trust, 2 Hathaway Close, Stanmore, Middlesex HA7 3NR (tel: 020 8903 8181; email: info@dhamecha.com; website: www.dhamecha.com)

Directors: J. Patel; K. R. Dhamecha; S. R. Dhamecha (women: 0; men: 3)

Year end	31/03/2015
Turnover	£668,930,000
Pre-tax profit	£13,080,000

Nature of business: The principal activities are wholesale food cash and carry, property dealings and the manufacture and sale of paper disposable products.

Company registration number: 6519903

UK employees: 497

Total employees: 497

Focus of giving: Education, health, ill health, arts, culture, overseas projects, poverty and social exclusion, community/social welfare.

Community involvement	✓
Community contributions	✓
Directors have other relevant posts	✓
Cash donations declared	✓
Corporate charity	✓
Overseas giving	✓

Charitable donations

Cash UK (latest available):	2015	£400,000
Total UK (cash and in kind):	2015	£400,000
Cash worldwide:	2015	£400,000
Total worldwide (cash and in kind):	2015	£400,000

Community involvement

The company makes its charitable contributions through The Laduma Dhamecha Charitable Trust (Charity Commission no. 328678). According to its Charity Commission record, the trust makes grants to charities working in the following areas: the provision of medicine and medical research; education projects; cultural activities; the relief of poverty; and community projects. The majority of donations are made in support of overseas causes, with a small proportion given in the UK.

Directors with other relevant posts

Two of the directors, K. R. Dhamecha and S. R. Dhamecha, are also trustees of the associated charitable trust.

Main locations

The head office is in Wembley, London. There are stores across Greater London and in Leicester.

Community contributions

In 2014/15 the company declared cash donations totalling £400,000, which were paid to The Laduma Dhamecha Charitable Trust.

Corporate charity

The Laduma Dhamecha Charitable Trust (Charity Commission no. 328678).

Applications

Applications to the trust should be made in writing to the correspondent who is a trustee of the Laduma Dhamecha Charitable Trust.

Diageo PLC

Food manufacture, brewers/distillers

Correspondent: Sustainability and Responsibility Team, Lakeside Drive, Park Royal, London NW10 7HQ (tel: 020 8978 6000 (main switchboard); email: csr@diageo.com; website: www.diageo.com)

Directors: Alan Stewart; Betsy Holden; David Harlock, Company Secretary; Deirdre Mahlan; Dr Franz Humer, Chair; Emma Walmsley; Ho Kwon Ping; Ivan Menezes, Chief Executive Officer; Javier Ferran; Kathryn Mikells, Chief Financial Officer; Lord Davies of Abersoch; Nicola Mendelsohn; Peggy Bruzelius; Phillip Scott (women: 6; men: 8)

Year end	30/06/2016
Turnover	£15,641,000,000
Pre-tax profit	£2,858,000,000

Nature of business: The group's principal activity is the manufacture and distribution of spirits, wines and beer. The group has presence in over 180 countries around the world. In 2015/16 the group had 10,752 employees in Europe, Russia and Turkey.

Company registration number: 23307

Subsidiary undertakings include: Diageo Capital PLC; Diageo Great Britain Ltd; United Spirits Ltd.

Brands include: Baileys; Captain Morgan; Smirnoff.

Total employees: 32,078

Focus of giving: Education, enterprise/training, environment, health, ill health, overseas projects, women's issues, children, young people, community/social welfare, disasters.

Membership: BITC

Community involvement	✓
Community contributions	✓
CSR report	✓
CSR or charity committee	✓
Directors have other relevant posts	✓
Charity partner(s)	✓
Corporate charity	✓
Employee-led support	✓
FTSE 100	✓
Gifts in kind	✓
Humanitarian aid: overseas	✓
Matched funding	✓
Overseas giving	✓
Payroll giving	✓
Sponsorship	✓

Charitable donations

Total worldwide (cash and in kind):	2016	£16,300,000

Community involvement

Programmes

Diageo invests in a variety of long-term programmes that address challenges facing the communities where it sources, makes and sells its products. The programmes the group supports align with the following UN Global Goals:

- Enabling entrepreneurship, employability and skills
- Improving health and well-being, including through access to clean water, sanitation and hygiene
- Helping to empower women

In 2015/16 the group launched a new Social Impact Framework (SIF), developed with three of its partner NGOs in 11 countries, to measure and evaluate the impact of their programmes. The results from SIF will be reported on in 2017. The group's current programmes are as follows:

Water of Life

Established in 2006 this programme has worked in 18 countries in Africa and focuses on access to water, sanitation and hygiene, particularly in rural areas that supply raw materials to the group's sites. Through the programme Diageo invests in infrastructure and sanitation in local communities where the group operates. In 2015/16 the group provided access to sanitation and safe water to 351,700 people living in Africa. The group has sites in areas of Africa that are water-stressed and the annual report for that year states that 21% of total water used in final product by the group in these areas was replenished.

Learning for Life

The programme provides education and vocational training in the hospitality, retail, entrepreneurship and alcohol industries to young unemployed people. According to the annual report and accounts, participants benefit from advice, in areas such as interview preparation, teamwork and communication, as well as ongoing mentoring and assistance to guide them during both the training and the job application process. The programme is run in over 40 countries, principally in Latin America and the Caribbean, and more recently in Scotland, Germany and Ireland.

Plan W

The programme was launched in 2012 and is run in Asia Pacific. Its aim is to empower women, both employees and those in the group's wider supply chain, which also includes educating men on issues that concern women. Since its inception work has been undertaken with 90,575 women in 15 countries in partnership with 13 organisations. Further information can be found on the programme's website: www.diageoplanw.com.

Partnerships

In 2015/16 the group agreed new partnerships with several organisations, including the following:

- WaterAid – to improve safe access to water and sanitation in Africa
- United States Agency for International Development – on a joint programme supporting veterans with learning skills in Colombia, and on farmer training in South Sudan
- United Nations Institute for Training and Research – on a programme to reduce traffic deaths and injuries caused by drink-driving and to improve global road safety

The Diageo Foundation (Charity Commission no. 1014681)

The Diageo Foundation was established in 1992 with the aim to create positive, long-term change in the community. It focuses on areas of humanitarian need, primarily in financially developing countries in Africa, Latin America and Asia. The foundation provides kick-start funding and expertise in establishing local projects, some of which are run in partnership with local businesses.

It is funded entirely by Diageo and makes charitable donations in support of projects or causes proposed by Diageo businesses and externally, matches employee fundraising in the UK and provides longer-term social investment in areas where it can make the most difference.

Directors with other relevant posts

Lord Davies of Abersoch is a trustee and Chair of The Royal Academy Trust (Charity Commission no. 1067270).

Nicola Mendelsohn is the director of the Bailey's Women's Prize for Fiction and Co-chair of the Creative Industries Council. She was also formerly a trustee of The White Ribbon Alliance for Safe Motherhood (Charity Commission no. 1143376) and Chair of the Corporate Board for Women's Aid (Charity Commission no. 1054154), although she stepped down from these positions in 2013.

Betsy Holden is a trustee of Duke University in the US.

Main locations

There are offices in London and Edinburgh.

Community contributions

The 2015/16 annual report states that during the year the group invested £16.3 million (0.6% of operating profit) to charitable projects that address critical local needs. The Sustainability and Responsibility Performance Addendum explains that community investment includes contributions (via cash, in-kind donations or employee time) from the group and that contributions are made to charitable organisations, non-branded responsible drinking programmes that benefit charities, and management costs associated with the Diageo Foundation. The group uses the principles of the London Benchmarking Group to estimate its community investment. The charitable giving data also includes donations made through the independent Diageo Foundation.

The annual report and accounts give the following breakdown of community investment by focus area:

Community aspects of responsible-drinking projects*	46%
Brand-led and local community spend**	21%
Learning for Life	20%
Water of Life	7%
Plan W	6%

* This forms a sub-section of the total responsible-drinking budget.

** This includes cause-related brand campaigns, local market giving and disaster relief.

Community investment was also broken down in the annual report by region as follows:

North America	38%
Europe and global functions	26%
Asia Pacific and Global Travel and Middle East (GTME)	14%
Latin America and Caribbean	14%
Africa	8%

Note that the community investment figures above exclude the group's £10.2 million legacy commitment to the Thalidomide Trust (in the UK) and the Thalidomide Foundation Ltd (in Australia) which has operated over the last few years.

At the time of writing (August 2016) the accounts for the The Diageo Foundation were unavailable from the Charity Commission for both 2014/15 and 2015/16. The only information available showed that in 2014/15 the foundation had an income of £676,500 and expenditure of £867,000. Based on the donations made in previous years, we estimate that Diageo PLC donated approximately £600,000 to the foundation during this year. The foundation then distributes grants worldwide to charitable organisations.

We could not distinguish between worldwide and UK charitable giving. The figure of £16.3 million represents the group's total worldwide contributions; however, we were unable to deduct management costs from this figure. We were unable to separate direct cash giving from other types of investment worldwide.

In-kind support

The group acknowledges that while financial contributions are important, the giving of time and skill by its staff or surplus products and other in-kind donations can often achieve more. Staff members provide accounting and administration support to the foundation.

Employee-led support

Diageo's employees are involved in volunteering and fundraising activities for good causes.

Commercially led support

Sponsorship

The group undertakes good-cause sponsorship, including sport events, for example Ryder Cup and National Basketball Association (NBA).

Responsible Drinking

Part of Diageo's focus is responsible-drinking programmes and responsible marketing strategies (including mandatory standards) aimed at preventing and addressing the negative aspects of the business activity. In 2015/16 the group supported 335 responsible-drinking programmes, 25.4% of which were based in Europe, Russia and Turkey. Programmes include focusing on preventing drink-driving, underage drinking and excessive drinking. Further details on responsible-drinking promotion can be found on Diageo's website.

Brand-led programmes

The group recognises that its brands provide an opportunity to engage consumers around the world in social and environmental causes. Examples include: the Arthur Guinness Fund (established in 2009) which supports social entrepreneurs; and Bell's campaign to raise money for Help for Heroes which has run since 2012.

Corporate charity

The Diageo Foundation (Charity Commission no. 1014681).

Exclusions

Political donations are not made in the UK or to EU political organisations or for EU political expenditure.

Applications

The company: Apply in writing to the correspondent.

The Diageo Foundation: The website states that the foundation is no longer accepting unsolicited applications. The foundation now sources new investments through recommendations from experts, donors and existing partners and through detailed research.

Diploma PLC

Industrial products/services

Correspondent: Corporate Responsibility Department, 12 Charterhouse Square, London EC1M 6AX (tel: 020 7549 5700; fax: 020 7549 5715; website: www.diplomaplc.com)

Directors: Andy Smith; Anne Thorburn; Bruce Thompson, Chief Executive Officer; Charles Packshaw; Iain Henderson, Chief Operating Officer; John Nicholas, Chair; Marie-Louise Clayton; Nigel Lingwood, Group Finance Director (women: 2; men: 6)

Year end	30/09/2015
Turnover	£333,800,000
Pre-tax profit	£59,600,000

Nature of business: Diploma PLC is an international group of businesses supplying specialised technical products and services. The group operates worldwide in the following sectors: life sciences (supplying products and services to the healthcare and environmental industries); seals (supplying various components for heavy mobile machinery and industrial equipment); and controls (supplying specialised wiring, connectors, fasteners and control devices for technically demanding applications).

Company registration number: 3899848

Subsidiary undertakings include: Hitek Ltd; FPE Seals NCL Ltd; IS Rayfast Ltd; Hawco Refrigeration Ltd.

Total employees: 1,505

Focus of giving: Health, ill health, sport, recreation, children, young people.

Community contributions	✓
CSR report	✓
Employee-led support	✓
Sponsorship	✓

Charitable donations

Cash worldwide:	2015	£35,500

Community involvement

Main locations

The head office is in London.

Community contributions

In 2015 the group made donations of £35,500 to causes and charities local to worldwide sites in which the group operates. We were unable to determine how much was donated to UK-based charitable causes.

Employee-led support

The group encourages and supports some community activities and events that are managed by local management teams. In Europe, in 2014/15, this included the following:

- A fundraising day for Breast Cancer Now charity held by Speciality Fasteners
- FPE held a team fundraising event for a Down's Syndrome charity, supported a breast cancer charity and sponsored a new strip for a local junior football team
- IS-Rayfast held various charitable events such as supporting Movember

Exclusions

The group tends not to make any political donations.

Applications

For donations from the group apply in writing to the correspondent. For sponsorship or donation from one of the group's local sites contact the local site close to which your organisation is based. Contact details can be found on the group's website under 'Contact Us' and 'Business Contacts'.

Direct Line Insurance Group PLC

Insurance

Correspondent: Ashley Taylor, Group Sustainability Manager, Churchill Court, Westmoreland Road, Bromley, Kent BR1 1DP (tel: 0113 292 0667; email: enquiries@directlinegroup.co.uk; website: www.directlinegroup.com)

Directors: Andrew Palmer; Clare Thompson, Chair of Corporate Social Responsibility Committee; Dr Richard Ward; Jane Hanson; John Reizenstein, Chief Financial Officer; Mike Biggs, Chair; Paul Geddes, Chief Executive Officer; Priscilla Vacassin; Sebastian James (women: 3; men: 5)

Year end	31/12/2015
Turnover	£3,269,800,000
Pre-tax profit	£507,500,000

Nature of business: The group provides a variety of insurance services such as motor, home, rescue and other personal lines and commercial insurance.

Company registration number: 2280426

Subsidiary undertakings include: DL Insurance Services Ltd; UK Assistance Accident Repair Centres Ltd; UK Insurance Ltd.

Brands include: Churchill; Green Flag; Privilege.

UK employees: 10,310

Total employees: 10,310

Focus of giving: Health and safety.

Community involvement	✓
Community contributions	✓
CSR report	✓
CSR or charity committee	✓
Directors have other relevant posts	✓
Charity partner(s)	✓
Employee-led support	✓
FTSE 100	✓
Gifts in kind	✓
Matched funding	✓
Payroll giving	✓
Sponsorship	✓

Charitable donations

Cash UK (latest available):	2015	£148,000
Total UK (cash and in kind):	2015	£148,000
Cash worldwide:	2015	£148,000
Total worldwide (cash and in kind):	2015	£148,000

Community involvement

Corporate Social Responsibility Strategy

The group's current CSR strategy focuses on the following four areas:

- Helping to make society safety – this is focused on road safety initiatives, particularly those aimed at young drivers. The group develops partnerships with organisations to meet this strategic aim, see below for further details
- Proud to be here – to improve employee engagement such as the development of volunteer groups like the Community and Social Committees. See the 'Employee-led support' section for further details
- Being recognised as part of local communities – this includes group targets for volunteering, fundraising and matched payroll giving
- Reduce, reuse, recycle

Partners

In 2015 the group partnered with various organisations to address road safety, in line with the group's CSR strategy under the strand 'helping to make our society safer'. One such partnership is with the road safety charity Brake (Charity Commission no. 1093244). The group has partnered with Brake for the past 13 years and has produced survey reports covering several aspects of safer driving, which Brake then uses in its wider outreach work. The group also sponsors Brake events, such as the Brake Parliamentarian of the Year Award.

In 2015 the group also partnered with PACTS, the Parliamentary Advisory Council for Transport Safety, (Charity Commission no. 1068607) and launched the Road Safety Dashboard. The group also sponsored the charity's Road Safety Summit.

Grants

The group makes grants of £250 to organisations that its employees regularly volunteer or raise funds for in their own time.

Directors with other relevant posts

John Reizenstein is a trustee of Farm Africa Ltd (Charity Commission no. 326901).

Sebastian James is a trustee of The Save the Children Fund (Charity Commission no. 213890) and The DSG International Foundation (Charity Commission no. 1053215).

Andrew Palmer is a trustee of The Royal School of Needlework (Charity Commission no. 312774) and Cancer Research UK (Charity Commission no. 1089464).

Main locations

There are offices across England and Scotland; see: www.directlinegroupcareers.com/About-Us/Our-Locations.

The head office is in Bromley.

Community contributions

In 2015 the group's employees donated £144,000 via payroll giving, which was matched with a further £97,000 by the group itself. The group also donated £51,000 in grants to organisations with which its employees already have a connection.

Employee-led support

Community and Social Committees

The group supports and funds a network of Community and Social Committees (CASCs) which its employees run on a voluntary basis. The CASCs create their own programme of events and activities at their local sites, including fundraising and building relationships with local charities and voluntary organisations. Examples of CASC support to charities in 2015 include: 450 employees volunteering on the phone lines for Comic Relief; a masquerade ball in Leeds to fundraise for Cancer Research, Leeds Mind, Sue Ryder and Leeds Haven; and 50 Manchester-based employees taking part in a sponsored 10-kilometre run for local causes.

Volunteering

The group encourages individual and team volunteering through the One Day Initiative where a team can spend a day engaging in a practical task for a charity or local community group.

The annual report for 2015 notes that 32% of employees fundraised or volunteered for charitable organisations during the company's time.

Applications

Applications can be made in writing to the local employee-run Community and Social Committees in the various sites in which the group's companies are based. Alternatively, applications can be made in writing to the correspondent at the head office.

Dixons Carphone PLC

Retail – miscellaneous, telecommunications

Correspondent: Corporate Responsibility Department, 1 Portal Way, London W3 6RS (tel: 0370 111 6565; email: CR@dixonscarphone.com; website: www.dixonscarphone.com)

Directors: Andrea Gisle Joosen; Andrew Harrison; Baroness Sally Morgan of Huyton; Gerry Murphy; Graham Stapleton; Humphrey Singer, Group Finance Director; Jock Lennox; Katie Bickerstaffe; Lord Ian Livingstone of Parkhead; Sebastian James, Group Chief Executive; Sir Charles Dunstone, Chair; Tim How; Tony DeNunzio (women: 3; men: 10)

Year end	30/04/2016
Turnover	£9,738,000,000
Pre-tax profit	£263,000,000

Nature of business: Independent retailer of electrical and telecommunications devices and services.

Company registration number: 3253714

Subsidiary undertakings include: Carphone Warehouse Europe Ltd; Currys Group Ltd; Mastercare Service and Distribution Ltd.

Brands include: Currys PC World; Dixons Travel; Simplify Digital.

UK employees: 27,608

Total employees: 41,847

Focus of giving: Poverty and social exclusion, science technology, children, young people.

Community involvement	✓
Community contributions	✓
Company reports on anti-slavery	✓
CSR report	✓
Directors have other relevant posts	✓
Cash donations declared	✓
Charity partner(s)	✓
Employee-led support	✓
FTSE 100	✓
Gifts in kind	✓
Humanitarian aid: overseas	✓
Matched funding	✓
Payroll giving	✓
Sponsorship	✓

Charitable donations

Cash UK (latest available):	2016	£654,500
Total UK (cash and in kind):	2016	£654,500
Cash worldwide:	2016	£678,000
Total worldwide (cash and in kind):	2016	£678,000

Community involvement

The group, through its company Carphone Warehouse, has a long-term partnership with a single charity with whom it delivers its local and in-store charitable activities. The charity the company supports, Get Connected, merged with YouthNet in 2015 to create a new charity The Mix, which provides support services for young people. The company assists The Mix with cash donations, gifts in kind and employee fundraising.

The group was also supporting Techknowledge for Schools (formerly known as Tablets for Schools); however, in February 2016 this charity closed down due to meeting its objectives. The group then invested in a project in May 2016 to progress the findings from its work with Techknowledge. Known as Project Blupoint, this scheme will trial and evaluate technology that can provide educational content in resource-starved schools in Durban, South Africa.

The Dixons Carphone Foundation

This fundraising account was established under the Charities Aid Foundation to enable the group to facilitate its employees' applications for matched funding and one-off donations to emergencies and disaster funds.

The DSG International Foundation

This charity (Charity Commission no. 1053215) was established by the group in 1996 to distribute funds, primarily to charitable organisations concerned with children's welfare through Children in Need. The foundation is funded by the group; however, from 2016/17 the group's charitable activities will be directed through The Dixons Carphone Foundation.

Directors with other relevant posts

Sebastian James is a trustee of the Save the Children Fund (Charity Commission no. 213890) and The DSG International Foundation (Charity Commission no. 1053215).

Sir Charles Dunstone is Chair of Royal Museums Greenwich and was formerly Chair of The Prince's Trust from 2009 to 2015.

Graham Stapleton is a trustee of the Make-A-Wish Foundation (Charity Commission no. 295672).

Jock Lennox is a trustee of the Tall Ships Youth Trust (Charity Commission no. 314229).

Baroness Morgan of Huyton is an advisor to the board of the children's charity ARK (Charity Commission no. 1095322) and a trustee of the following charities: Education Policy Institute (Charity Commission no. 1102186); Future Leaders Charitable Trust Ltd (Charity Commission no. 1116801); Schools and Teachers Innovating for Results (Charity Commission no. 1149143); and Teaching Leaders (Charity Commission no. 1146924).

Tim How is a director of the Norfolk and Norwich University Hospitals NHS Foundation Trust.

Andrew Harrison was a trustee of Techknowledge for Schools (Charity Commission no. 1156905) until it closed in 2016.

Main locations

The group's head office is based in London but the business operates in various locations across the UK and Ireland. Worldwide, the group has business locations in: Denmark; Finland; Greece; Norway; Spain; Sweden; and the USA.

Community contributions

In 2015/16 the group donated £447,500 to its charity partner, The Mix, and £207,000 to Techknowledge for Schools.

Outside the UK the group's company Elkjøp donated £23,500 to the Red Cross Water for Life Project.

Employee-led support

Employee fundraising

Employees take part in fundraising events in aid of the company's charity partner, The Mix, and the group's fundraising account, The Dixons Carphone Foundation. In 2015 a total of 230 employees took part in the Race to the Stones ultramarathon raising £69,000 for The Mix. The group's executives also took part in a charity tennis tournament to raise £63,000 for the foundation.

Matched funding

Employees support a variety of charities and local causes through fundraising activities that are matched by the group. The group donates up to £100 or £300 for a team fundraising event.

Commercially led support

The company sponsors the UK's biggest ultramarathon, Race to the Stones, which raises funds for a variety of charitable causes.

Applications

Any corporate responsibility enquiries should be directed to the Corporate Responsibility team via email.

Dow Corning Ltd

Chemicals and plastics

Correspondent: Community Relations Co-ordinator, Dow Corning Ltd, Cardiff Road, Barry, Vale of Glamorgan CF63 2YL (tel: 01446 732350; fax: 01446 747944; website: www.dowcorning.com/content/about/aboutcomm/Barry_Community_donations.asp)

Directors: Bridget Sparrow; David Brookes; Helen McCulloch; Peter Cartwright; Steven Dopp (women: 2; men: 3)

Year end	31/12/2015
Turnover	£514,500,000
Pre-tax profit	£3,723,000

Nature of business: Dow Corning Ltd specialises in the manufacture and marketing of silicone products. Its ultimate parent undertaking and controlling party is Dow Corning Corporation, a company incorporated in the USA.

Company registration number: 486170

UK employees: 500+

Focus of giving: Education, environment, health, ill health, small groups, local groups, older people, safety and crime prevention, science technology, children, young people, community/social welfare.

Community involvement	✓
Community contributions	✓
CSR report	✓
CSR or charity committee	✓
Company gives to smaller charities	✓
Employee-led support	✓
Gifts in kind	✓
STEM-focused	✓

Community involvement

Dow Corning targets investment in communities where its employees work and live. Its corporate giving programmes operate at major sites in Asia, Europe, and the Americas, with each site managing its own programme.

In the UK the company operates from Barry, South Wales. The Dow Corning website has a section dedicated to the Barry site which provides, among other information, details of the site's community involvement. We obtained the following information from this section of the website.

Community donations and sponsorship

The Barry site regularly receives requests for donations of equipment, sponsorship or practical support from employees from community groups. Requests are considered by a small community donations team made up of employees, which meets monthly. The website explains that priority is given to requests received from local groups and that 'the team tries to make sure that any donation the company makes helps as many people as possible and has a long-term benefit'. The website helpfully sets out the following guidelines in line with the company's donations policy.

The community donations team will consider requests that meet the following criteria:

- Projects that are local to the Barry, South Wales site and benefit people locally with preference given to requests from Barry and Sully areas and then the Vale of Glamorgan
- We prefer to make donations to properly established organizations rather than to an informal group
- Donations must have a wide benefit ensuring a good number of people can be impacted by the funding

If a request meets the above criteria, it must also fall within the following, more specific, criteria:

- activities that will help young people learn more about science, math and technology, or skills that they will need in their future careers, or to make them better citizens
- ideas that will help organizations or communities to improve safety or the local environment
- activities or projects that help improve the local community's health and wellbeing
- projects that help improve the local biodiversity (nature, wildlife, etc.)
- projects that promote good citizenship
- projects that can help the elderly

Support for education

The Barry site works with local schools to support science, maths and technology activities for pupils, helping them to develop the skills they require for their future careers. The website provides the information regarding the site's flagship programmes, which are:

- **National Science and Engineering Week**: Each year since 1997, the site has hosted science workshops and experiments for primary school pupils through this national programme. The website states that in 2015 more than 250 children aged nine and ten took part in the programme at the site
- **Math mentoring**: Since 2012 this initiative has provided 'hundreds of young people' with the opportunity to strengthen their maths skills
- **Nature and Education Centre**: This 29-acre reserve, which is located next to the Barry site, runs environmental programmes linked to the curriculum for schools and groups in the community

Community Advisory Panel (CAP)

The Dow Corning Sustainability Report for 2015 states that, during the year:

> Each of Dow Corning's major manufacturing sites regularly convenes a Community Advisory Panel (CAP). A Responsible Care® initiative, CAPs bring together site management and a cross section of community members, some of whom may represent such fields or interests as business, academia, health care, non-profit organizations, clergy and agriculture.

In Barry a CAP has been set up in conjunction with nearby chemical companies.

The Dow Corning Foundation

This foundation – which is an endowed fund supported by donations from Dow Corning Corporation and Hemlock

Semiconductor Group – does not operate in the UK. It makes grants in support of communities in the US, where Dow Corning is headquartered.

Main locations
The UK manufacturing site is located in Barry, Wales.

Community contributions

The annual report and accounts for 2015 did not declare a figure for charitable donations.

In-kind support

One of the ways in which the Barry site supports its local community is through contributions of equipment and practical support from employees.

Employee-led support

Employee volunteering
Employees are encouraged to become involved in supporting their local communities through practical help. A major part of this is the active programme the company has in supporting students and teachers in local schools in the areas of science, maths and technology.

Exclusions

Information provided on the company's website notes that support is not given for:

- Raffle prizes
- Individuals (such as sponsorship for travel or individual fundraising)
- Donations to central funds of charities, political or religious groups
- Contributions to an organisation's running costs or funding for someone's salary
- One-off events such as fetes, parades, shows, tournaments, concerts, awards ceremonies (even if any of these are annual events)
- Group travel expenses for excursions or overseas adventures
- Medical research
- General fundraising appeals where Dow Corning funding is not used on specific projects or purchases
- Uniforms or kits for sports teams
- National or international appeals
- Advertising
- Requests that make Dow Corning a corporate sponsor

Applications

Apply in writing to the correspondent explaining what the request is for, who will benefit, how much you are requesting and any other supporting information. Only written requests will be considered. Only requests that meet the criteria will be reviewed and discussed by the donations team.

Drax Group PLC

Electricity

Correspondent: Ann Gray, Community Relations Co-ordinator, Drax Power Station, Selby, North Yorkshire YO8 8PH (tel: 01757 618381/01757 612933; fax: 01757 612192; email: ann.gray@drax.com; website: www.draxgroup.plc.uk)

Directors: Andy Koss; David Lindsell; Dorothy Thompson, Chief Executive; Philip Cox, Chair; Tim Cobbold; Tony Thorne; Will Gardiner, Chief Financial Officer (women: 1; men: 6)

Year end	31/12/2015
Turnover	£3,065,000,000
Pre-tax profit	£59,000,000

Nature of business: Drax Group has three principal activities: sourcing fuel (including sustainable biomass); electricity production; and electricity sales to the wholesale market and business customers.

Company registration number: 5562053

Subsidiary undertakings include: Drax Power Ltd; Haven Power Ltd; Morehouse BioEnergy LLC.

UK employees: 1,451

Total employees: 1,451

Focus of giving: Economic generation, education, environment, heritage, non-registered charities, small groups, arts, culture, sport, recreation, children, young people, community/social welfare.

Membership: BITC

Community involvement	✓
Community contributions	✓
Directors have other relevant posts	✓
Company gives to smaller charities	✓
Sponsorship	✓
Unregistered charities/NFP	✓

Charitable donations

Cash UK (latest available):	2015	£155,000
Total UK (cash and in kind):	2015	£155,000
Cash worldwide:	2015	£155,000
Total worldwide (cash and in kind):	2015	£155,000

Community involvement

The company's community involvement takes the form of sponsoring a variety of local charities and fundraising events and maintaining open communication channels and good working relationships with the region's key opinion formers. The group also promotes its own campaigns focusing on education and the environment and supports sporting, community and charity activities.

Project Reinvent
The company uses its community fund to support local projects under its programme Project Reinvent. The company welcomes applications from not-for-profit organisations that:

- Reinvent learning (by supporting the education and employability of young people)
- Reinvent places (by improving local community spaces, buildings or the natural environment)
- Reinvent opportunities (by improving the skills and prospects of local people)

Sponsorship
The company has sponsored The Drax Cup since 2007. It is a Yorkshire-based cricket competition for children under the age of nine. For more information visit www.yorkshireccc.com/draxcup.

The company also sponsors a variety of other local events such as the annual Drax Art in the Community competition, which showcases the artwork of children from local schools, and the Selby and Goole Community Pride Awards.

Directors with other relevant posts
David Lindsell is a trustee of Cancer Research UK (Charity Commission no. 1089464) and Imperial Cancer Research Fund (Charity Commission no. 209631). He is also the Deputy Chair of Governors for the University of the Arts, London.

Tony Thorne is Chair of the South East Coast Ambulance Service (Charity Commission no. 1059933).

Will Gardiner is a member of the Board and Treasurer of Groton School, a private Episcopal college preparatory boarding school in Massachusetts.

Main locations
The group's main UK site is in Selby, North Yorkshire. There are also operations in Ipswich, Liverpool and London.

Community contributions

In 2015 the group gave financial support totalling £296,000 (2014: £228,000) to a range of charitable and non-charitable community causes. Of that amount, £155,000 (2014: £154,000) was given as charitable donations. This includes £2,800 that was donated to the winning schools of the annual Drax Art in the Community competition.

Commercially led support

Education
A state-of-the-art visitor centre is open for people to explore the properties of electricity, discover how a power station works and consider the environmental issues related to electricity generation.

Another visitor opportunity exists at the company's nature reserve situated at its ash-disposal site. Established as a sanctuary for over 100 species of wildlife, it is specially designed to help schoolchildren understand more about the natural habitats and ecology of the area.

Applications

Applications for Project Reinvent can be made by contacting the Community Relations Co-ordinator. Organisations wishing to apply for this programme must have been in existence for at least six months and be able to start the project within three months of receiving funding. The organisation or project must be based within 30 miles of Drax's sites.

Duchy Originals Ltd

Food manufacture

Correspondent: See 'Applications', Clarence House, St James's Palace, London SW1A 1BA (website: www.waitrose.com/home/inspiration/about_waitrose/about_our_food/our_brands/duchy_originals.html)

Directors: Andrew Wright; Craig Sams; Michael Jary, Chair; Stephen Nelson (women: 0; men: 4)

Year end	31/03/2015
Turnover	£3,160,000
Pre-tax profit	£3,020,000

Nature of business: The ownership of a range of premium organic food and drink products under the 'Duchy Originals' brand. The company's ultimate controlling party is The Prince of Wales's Charitable Foundation (Charity Commission no. 1127255).

Company registration number: 2478770

Brands include: Waitrose Duchy Organic.

UK employees: 1

Total employees: 1

Focus of giving: General charitable purposes, education, enterprise/training, environment, health, ill health, small groups, armed forces, older people, arts, culture, overseas projects, religion, children, young people, community/social welfare, disasters.

Community involvement	✓
Community contributions	✓
Armed forces personnel	✓
Cash donations declared	✓
Company gives to smaller charities	✓
Corporate charity	✓
Humanitarian aid: overseas	✓
Overseas giving	✓

Charitable donations

Cash UK (latest available):	2015	£3,020,000
Total UK (cash and in kind):	2015	£3,020,000
Cash worldwide:	2015	£3,020,000
Total worldwide (cash and in kind):	2015	£3,020,000

Community involvement

The Prince of Wales founded Duchy Originals in 1990 to promote sustainable produce and champion organic foods. Products produced by the company are distributed through a partnership with Waitrose and, since 2015, have been sold under the Waitrose Duchy Organic brand. The range now has more than 300 different products which, as Waitrose's website describes, are sold under the shared principles of 'Good Food, Good Farming, Good Causes'.

The Prince of Wales's Charitable Foundation

The foundation receives its funding from the profits made by Waitrose Duchy Organic and Highgrove Enterprises products (Highgrove is another trading company of the charitable foundation), and from the proceeds of tours of the gardens at Highgrove.

The work carried out by the foundation is described on its website as two-fold:

1. A grant making body that supports a wide range of causes, the primary areas of interest being the built environment, responsible business and enterprise, young people and education, and global sustainability.*
2. An incubator for initiatives and projects that fall within the Charitable Foundation's primary areas of interest, mentioned above, such as the International Sustainability Unit and Accounting for Sustainability

Grants are made to UK-registered, independent, non-profit organisations. The foundation is keen for the awards it makes to have a significant impact on people and their communities and particularly welcomes small grant applications from grassroots, community-based projects in the UK.

Applications for amounts of up to £5,000 (the average grant is £1,500) are accepted through the foundation's small grants programme. The foundation also awards grants of more than £5,000 through its major grants scheme; however, unsolicited applications are not accepted through this programme.

*In the most recent year for which financial information was available for the foundation (2014/15), grants awarded were broken down into the following categories: environment; culture; education; children and young people; overseas; medical welfare; and 'other'.

Community contributions

In 2014/15 a total of £3.02 million was donated to the company's ultimate controlling party, The Prince of Wales's Charitable Foundation.

Corporate charity

The Prince of Wales's Charitable Foundation (Charity Commission no. 1127255).

Exclusions

As is stated on its website, The Prince of Wales's Charitable Foundation does not make grants to:

- Individuals
- Public bodies
- Organisations that mainly distribute grants to other organisations
- Organisations that are looking to deliver similar projects to any of The Prince's Charities (please visit The Prince's Charities page for further project details)
- Organisations with an income of £1 million or more
- Organisations with political associations or interests
- Cover capital expenditure with the exception of community-based, religion-related and heritage restoration projects

The foundation does not support sponsorship.

Applications

For more information about the work of The Prince of Wales's Charitable Foundation, as well as full eligibility criteria and how to apply for a small grant, visit www.princeofwalescharitablefoundation.org.uk.

Dunelm Group PLC

Retail – clothing and footwear, retail – department and variety stores

Correspondent: Corporate Social Responsibility Team, Watermead Business Park, Syston, Leicestershire LE7 1AD (tel: 0116 264 4400; email: enquiries@dunelm.com; website: www.dunelm-mill.com)

Directors: Andy Harrison, Chair; Dawn Durrant; John Browett, Chief Executive Designate; Keith Down, Finance Director; Liz Doherty; Marion Sears; Peter Ruis; Simon Emeny; Will Adderley, Chief Executive; William Reeve (women: 3; men: 7)

Year end	04/07/2015
Turnover	£835,805,000
Pre-tax profit	£122,622,000

Nature of business: Specialist out-of-town homewares retailer providing a comprehensive range of products to a wide customer base, under the brand name Dunelm Mill.

Company registration number: 4708277

Subsidiary undertakings include: Dunelm Estates Ltd; Dunelm (Soft Furnishings) Ltd; Zoncolan Ltd.

Brands include: Dorma.

UK employees: 8,856

Total employees: 8,856

Focus of giving: Health, ill health, armed forces, overseas projects, children, young people.

Community involvement	✓
Community contributions	✓
Company reports on anti-slavery	✓
CSR or charity committee	✓
Charity of the Year	✓
Employee-led support	✓
Gifts in kind	✓
Matched funding	✓
Sponsorship	✓

Charitable donations

Cash UK (latest available):	2015	£98,000
Total UK (cash and in kind):	2015	£98,000
Cash worldwide:	2015	£98,000
Total worldwide (cash and in kind):	2015	£98,000

Community involvement

Charity of the Year

The company adopts a Charity of the Year for which collections are made in-store, specific fundraising events are organised and the group makes its own donations.

According to the 2014/15 annual report, the company's Charity of the Year was Barnardo's with funds raised in a variety of ways. Barnardo's was also supported in 2013/14. The report noted that during 2015/16 the Roald Dahl's Marvellous Children's Charity would be the Charity of the Year.

Regular donations

Regular local donations include supporting schools, communities and the town of Syston where the Dunelm Store Support Centre is based.

Sponsorship

The company is the main sponsor of the 7days 7irons challenge, supporting an individual to complete seven triathlons in seven days.

Main locations

There are stores across the UK. The head office is in Leicestershire.

Community contributions

In 2014/15 the total value of donations made by the company was £98,000 (2013/14: £206,000, which includes £129,000 donated by Will Adderley in lieu of an annual bonus). In addition, £366,000 was raised by employees (2014: £352,000).

Beneficiaries* included: Barnardo's; Blesma; Cancer Research; East African Playgrounds; Leicester Hospice Charity; Macmillan.

*This may include both donations made by the company and fundraising efforts by its employees.

Employee-led support

Employees are involved in fundraising events and activities, which are often matched by the company, and many take a day's paid leave to volunteer for local charities. Each store has a designated Charity Champion who organises fundraising for local and national charitable causes, including for the company's Charity of the Year.

Commercially led support

Funds raised from carrier bag sales are donated to the charity GroundWork.

Exclusions

The company does not make any political donations.

Applications

Applications can be made by writing to the correspondent. If you have local fundraising and events enquiries, contact the Charity Champion at your local store.

Dyson Ltd

Domestic appliances, engineering

Correspondent: Kevin Walker, The James Dyson Foundation, Tetbury Hill, Malmesbury, Wiltshire NS16 0RP (tel: 01666 827272/01666 828416; email: jamesdysonfoundation@dyson.com; website: www.dyson.co.uk)

Directors: James Shipsey; Max Conze

Year end	31/12/2015
Turnover	£351,300,000
Pre-tax profit	£22,600,000

Nature of business: Manufacture of domestic appliances. The company began in 1978 when James Dyson invented the bagless vacuum. The group now operates in over 65 countries.

Company registration number: 2627406

Subsidiary undertakings include: Dyson International Ltd; Dyson Overseas Distribution; Dyson Technologies (Shanghai) Ltd.

Focus of giving: Education, enterprise/ training, health, ill health, medical research, arts, culture, science technology, children, young people, community/social welfare.

Community involvement	✓
Community contributions	✓
Charity partner(s)	✓
Corporate charity	✓
Employee-led support	✓
Gifts in kind	✓
Market-led giving	✓
Matched funding	✓
Pro bono	✓
Sponsorship	✓
STEM-focused	✓

Charitable donations

Cash worldwide:	2015	£5,400,000
Total worldwide (cash and in kind):	2015	£5,400,000

Community involvement

The James Dyson Foundation

The company's support is channelled through The James Dyson Foundation (Charity Commission no. 1099709). The foundation works internationally to encourage young people to engage with design in engineering, through resources and workshops for schools and universities, scholarships, and competitions, such as the James Dyson Award, an international design and engineering award for university students. The foundation also supports medical and scientific research charities through grants and employee-led fundraising. The foundation offers an annual scholarship to one A-level student at Malmesbury School for studying a STEM subject at university and funds a professorship at the University of Bath. It also supports some major capital projects such as engineering facilities in universities, as well as working with educational institutions to develop courses and other activities.

In 2015 The James Dyson Foundation also made grants towards the establishment of four new Dyson family charities: The James and Deidre Dyson Trust; The Star and Storm Foundation; The Mimosa Trust; and The Blue Surf Trust.

Main locations

The UK head office is in Malmesbury, Wiltshire. The company also operates internationally in over 65 countries.

Community contributions

In 2015 Dyson Ltd donated £5.4 million to The James Dyson Foundation. The foundation made grants totalling almost £2.4 million during the year, which were distributed as follows:

Education and training	£2.2 million
Science and medical research	£106,500
Social and community welfare	£7,200

Beneficiaries included: Cambridge University (£1.4 million); Bath Schools Design Education Programme (£93,000); Royal College of Art (£50,000); Malmesbury School Project (£42,000); The Unicorn Press (£7,200); The Blue Surf Trust and The Star and Storm Foundation (£5,000 each); Imperial College London (£200).

In-kind support

Design engineers from Dyson host workshops at schools and universities throughout the country and the foundation provides free resources to design and technology teachers throughout the UK. The company provides an information pack for teachers and lecturers which can be used in conjunction with the Dyson Education Box and both are free of charge.

Each year, the company donates a number of Dyson vacuum cleaners to charitable causes within the James Dyson Foundation's objectives.

Each year, the company donates a number of Dyson vacuum cleaners to charitable causes within the James Dyson Foundation's objectives.

Employee-led support

Dyson employees in Malmesbury, Wiltshire, also contribute to the foundation and take an active role in selecting projects and fundraising, especially for Dyson's charity partnerships. In 2015 employees nominated and fundraised for the charities Alzheimer's Research UK and Sparks and the foundation provided matched funding.

Commercially led support

The James Dyson Award

The annual James Dyson Award inspires students from around the world to engineer a solution to an everyday problem and elevates their work on a global platform. Contenders have included folding plugs, sprinkler taps, emergency rescue devices, water purifiers and airless tyres. International and national winners' prizes range from £2,000 to £30,000, with the successful students' universities receiving a share.

Corporate charity

The James Dyson Foundation (Charity Commission no. 1099709).

Exclusions

The foundation does not provide support for political purposes and local appeals not in areas of the company's presence.

Applications

Apply in writing to the correspondent at The James Dyson Foundation.

easyJet PLC

Aviation

Correspondent: Charity Committee, Hangar 89, London Luton Airport, Luton, Bedfordshire LU2 9PF (email: easyjet@mailnj.custhelp.com; website: www.easyjet.com)

Directors: Adèle Anderson; Andrew Findlay, Chief Financial Officer; Andy Martin; Carolyn McCall, Chief Executive; Charles Gurassa; Dr Andreas Bierwirth; François Rubichon; John Barton, Chair; John Browett; Keith Hamill (women: 2; men: 8)

Year end	30/09/2015
Turnover	£4,686,000,000
Pre-tax profit	£686,000,000

Nature of business: Airline operators.

Company registration number: 3034606

Subsidiary undertakings include: easyJet Airline Company Ltd; easyJet Switzerland S.A.; Dawn Licensing Ltd.

Total employees: 9,811

Focus of giving: Health, ill health, small groups, sport, recreation, women's issues, children, young people.

Community involvement	✓
Community contributions	✓
CSR report	✓
CSR or charity committee	✓
Directors have other relevant posts	✓
Charity partner(s)	✓
Company gives to smaller charities	✓
Employee-led support	✓
FTSE 100	✓
Gifts in kind	✓
Sponsorship	✓
STEM-focused	✓

Charitable donations

Cash UK (latest available):	2015	£40,000
Total UK (cash and in kind):	2015	£74,500
Cash worldwide:	2015	£40,000
Total worldwide (cash and in kind):	2015	£74,500

Community involvement

Partners

The company has partnered with Unicef for several years and has so far raised £5 million for the organisation via employees' fundraising and donations from customers. Customers are encouraged to donate spare change and leftover foreign currency when on board the planes.

The 2014/15 annual report notes that the company has decided to continue this partnership for a further three years with the aim to raise a further £5 million.

Charity Committee

The company has a Charity Committee that is comprised of airline employees. The company funds the committee which supports either charitable activities by employees or charities that are important to employees. Charities supported tend to be smaller and located in areas where employees live. The committee makes awards of either flight vouchers or cash donations of up to £250. Preference is normally given to health charities, particularly cancer, and to organisations that support children. Charities in the Luton area may be preferred as this is where a large number of the company's employees are based.

Community support

easyJet is a long-term supporter of Luton Town Football Club and was the main shirt sponsor of the team in 2014/15. The company also partially funds the club's children's sports project.

The company is also a patron of Love Luton, an organisation that seeks to improve and promote the local town.

Directors with other relevant posts

Carolyn McCall is a member of the Advisory Board for Unicef's Children in Danger campaign. She was also formerly Chair of Opportunity Now (2005–09) and President of Women in Advertising and Communications London (2002–03).

Charles Gurassa is a trustee of The English Heritage Trust (Charity Commission no. 1140351) and the Migration Museum Project (Charity Commission no. 1153774).

Adèle Anderson is a trustee of The Save the Children Fund (Charity Commission no. 213890) and chairs its Audit Committee.

Main locations

The head office is in Luton.

Community contributions

In 2014/15 the partnership with Unicef raised £2.5 million; however, of this amount £2.4 million was donated by customers. Approximately £400,000 was raised for Unicef through other fundraising activities, including a donation totalling £40,000 from the company itself.

The company also donated £34,500 in cash donations and flight vouchers to the employees' Charity Committee, which then distributed this among 138 beneficiaries.

In-kind support

easyJet have supported the charity Aerobility for a number of years. In 2014/15 the company provided a flight free of charge to enable the charity to hold a fundraiser on the flight while viewing the Northern Lights.

Employee-led support

Following feedback from customers and employees, the company has also decided to increase its charitable work locally. This has involved focusing on the Luton area around the company's head office, for example by partnering with Connecting Enterprising Women. This partnership is focused on matching the company's female managers with young women in education in order to provide mentoring and careers advice.

Applications

Applications can be made by writing to the correspondent.

Ecclesiastical Insurance Group PLC

Insurance

Correspondent: Chris Pitt, Group CR Manager, Beaufort House, Brunswick Road, Gloucester GL1 1JZ (0345 777 3322; fax: 0345 604 6398; email: information@ecclesiastical.com; website: www.ecclesiastical.com)

Directors: Caroline Taylor; David Henderson; Denise Wilson; Edward Creasy, Chair; Ian Campbell, Group Chief Financial Officer; Jacinta Whyte, Deputy Group Chief Executive; John Hylands; Mark Hews, Group Chief Executive; The Venerable Christine Wilson; Tim Carroll; Tony Latham (women: 4; men: 7)

Year end	31/12/2015
Turnover	£308,199,000
Pre-tax profit	£53,605,000

Nature of business: Owned by a registered charity, Allchurches Trust Ltd (Charity Commission no. 263960), Ecclesiastical is a unique financial services organisation. With its main operations and headquarters in the UK, Ecclesiastical also operates in Australia, Canada and Ireland. Ecclesiastical is a specialist insurer of the faith, heritage, fine art, charities, education and private client sectors. Founded in 1887 to provide insurance for the Anglican Church, the company now offers a wide range of commercial insurances, as well as home insurance, selling through brokers and directly. The Ecclesiastical Group also includes broking and advisory businesses and an investment management business, EdenTree, which provides a range of ethically screened investment funds.

Company registration number: 1718196

Subsidiary undertakings include: Ecclesiastical Insurance Office PLC; Ecclesiastical Life Ltd; South Essex Insurance Holdings Ltd.

UK employees: 806

Total employees: 997

Focus of giving: General charitable purposes, heritage, small groups, local groups, less popular charitable purposes, arts, culture, overseas projects, poverty and social exclusion, religion, community/social welfare, disability.

Membership: BITC

Accredited Living Wage Employer	✓
Community involvement	✓
Community contributions	✓
CSR report	✓
CSR or charity committee	✓
Directors have other relevant posts	✓
Cash donations declared	✓
Charity partner(s)	✓
Community Mark	✓
Company gives to smaller charities	✓
Corporate charity	✓
Employee-led support	✓
Gifts in kind	✓
Humanitarian aid: overseas	✓
Matched funding	✓
Overseas giving	✓
Payroll giving	✓
Pro bono	✓
Unpopular causes	✓

Charitable donations

Cash UK (latest available):	2015	£20,377,000
Total UK (cash and in kind):	2015	£20,377,000
Cash worldwide:	2015	£20,604,000
Total worldwide (cash and in kind):	2015	£20,604,000

Community involvement

In 2014 the group launched its vision to donate £50 million to charity in a three-year period. In March 2016 the group announced that it had reached its target almost a year ahead of schedule donating almost £53 million in total. The group has now set an ambition to give £100 million to charity by 2020.

The group gives its available profits to its charitable owner Allchurches Trust. The object of the trust is to promote the Christian religion and to contribute to the funds of any charitable institutions, associations, funds or objects and to carry out any charitable purpose. Applicants to Allchurches should visit www.allchurches.co.uk.

The Ecclesiastical Group also supports charitable causes in its own right – through charity partnerships, donations and employee-supported giving. The group has established a 'Greater Good' initiative to oversee, manage and drive its CR practices and community investment approach.

Charity partnerships

Ecclesiastical's offices all over the UK have partnerships with local charities, as do its overseas businesses in Canada and Australia. Examples of charity partnerships include:

The Landmark Trust: In 2016 Ecclesiastical established a partnership with the Landmark Trust to repair and restore a historic property on the at-risk register.

The Nelson Trust: In 2015 Ecclesiastical's Gloucester office established a partnership with The Nelson Trust, a national charity based in Gloucestershire which provides drug and alcohol rehabilitation and services for women and families. Support given to the trust through the partnership has included: a clothing and toiletries appeal through which 3,000 donations were collected; fundraising; and employee volunteering and skills.

IT Schools Africa: Ecclesiastical's UK IT Support Team connected with the IT Schools Africa (ITSA) Project, 'replacing, boxing and shipping' old monitors to help make a positive difference to the lives of schoolchildren in Africa. More than 350 monitors were donated in 2015 and a further 150 were set to be donated in 2016.

Directors with other relevant posts

John Hylands is a governor of the Royal Conservatoire of Scotland and a school governor.

Christine Wilson is the Archdeacon of Chesterfield in the Diocese of Derby and in 2013 was elected as the East Midlands female regional representative to the House of Bishops. She has also previously chaired several charities.

Denise Wilson is the CEO for the Lord Davies Review of Women on Boards and Chair of the Friends Board at the Royal Academy of Arts.

Main UK locations

Gloucester (head office); London; Manchester; Birmingham; Eastbourne; South Essex; Newcastle.

Community contributions

In 2015 Ecclesiastical gave £20.6 million to charity, including £20 million in grants to Allchurches Trust Ltd and £600,000 in donations via the Greater Giving programme.

Note that the above figures refer to cash donations only; Ecclesiastical also made in-kind contributions, namely in the form of employee volunteering time and skills, the values of which are not included in these figures.

Beneficiaries included: Allchurches Trust Ltd (£20 million).

Recent examples of the ways in which Ecclesiastical contributes financially to charities include:

Christmas 2016: Instead of sending out Christmas cards, Ecclesiastical split a donation of £25,000 between three charities. The share of donations was decided by an employee and partner vote. The three supported charities were: Crisis (40% of votes, £10,000); Great Ormond Street Hospital (30% of votes, £7,500); Age UK (30% of votes, £7,500).

Disaster relief: Ecclesiastical has given to Disasters Emergency Appeals for several years: in 2016 it gave £25,000 to the Yemen appeal. In Canada the company gave nearly $10,000 Canadian dollars (including employee donations and matched funding from the company and the government) to the Fort McMurray Wildfire Appeal.

In-kind support

Volunteering time and skills

Every employee is given a day's leave to take for volunteering purposes. Employees are also encouraged to share their practical and professional skills with charities.

Employee-led support

Employee volunteering

In 2016 a total of 60% of Ecclesiastical's employees gave their practical and professional support through volunteering time.

Payroll giving

Ecclesiastical has a Gold standard Payroll Giving Quality Mark. The Mark is supported by the Cabinet Office, the Institute of Fundraising and the Association of Payroll Giving Organisations.

Matched funding

Ecclesiastical matches all money employees fundraise or donate through payroll giving.

Personal grant scheme

Every employee is given a personal grant of £125 which they can donate to a charity of their choice. Employees who volunteer with the same cause have their grant doubled. In 2016 this programme distributed nearly £250,000 through small personal grants.

Corporate charity

Allchurches Trust Ltd (Charity Commission no. 263960).

Exclusions

The trustees of the Allchurches Trust do not make grants to charities with political associations. Support is not normally given to individuals, appeals for running costs and salaries, or more than one appeal from an organisation within a 24-month period.

Applications

Enquiries about or applications for charitable partnerships with the Ecclesiastical Insurance Group should be emailed to information@ecclesiastical.com. Applications for grants are not considered by the company but by the trustees of the Allchurches Trust Ltd, which owns the group. Applications should be submitted via the trust's online tool. If you have difficulty in doing this, contact the trust via details on their website. Look at the 'Statement and Policy' page on the trust's website for details about its policies and other guidelines before completing your application.

Economist Newspaper Ltd

Business services, media

Correspondent: Mathew Hanratty, Corporate Communications Manager, 25 St James's Street, London SW1A 1HG (tel: 020 7830 7000; fax: 020 7839 2968; email: mathewhanratty@economist.com; website: www.economist.com)

Directors: Baroness Tessa Jowell; Brent Hoberman; Chris Stibbs, Chief Executive; Dr Alex Karp; Lady Lynn Forester de Rothschild; Lady Suzanne Heywood; Rupert Pennant-Rea, Chair; Sir David Bell; Sir Simon Robertson; Zanny Minton Beddoes (women: 4; men: 6)

Year end	31/03/2016
Turnover	£330,900,000
Pre-tax profit	£54,100,000

Nature of business: The publication of The Economist and specialist publications.

Company registration number: 236383

Subsidiary undertakings include: Economist Digital Services Ltd; The Economist Books Ltd; The Television Consultancy Ltd.

Total employees: 1,372

Focus of giving: Economic generation, education, enterprise/training, health, ill health, arts, culture, overseas projects, children, young people, community/social welfare, disasters.

Community involvement	✓
Community contributions	✓
Company reports on anti-slavery	✓
CSR or charity committee	✓
Directors have other relevant posts	✓
Charity partner(s)	✓
Corporate charity	✓
Employee-led support	✓
Gifts in kind	✓
Matched funding	✓
Payroll giving	✓
Sponsorship	✓

Charitable donations

Cash UK (latest available):	2016	£104,000
Total UK (cash and in kind):	2016	£104,000
Cash worldwide:	2016	£104,000
Total worldwide (cash and in kind):	2016	£104,000

Community involvement

The Economist Charitable Trust (Charity Commission no. 293709)

The group channels its charitable activities through its corporate charity, The Economist Charitable Trust. The trust's 2015/16 accounts state the following:

> 50–60% of the trust's donations go to charities in the fields of communication, education, literacy and re-training for individuals and groups who are disadvantaged in some way. Approximately 30–40% of funds are used to match donations made by employees of The Economist Group. Remaining funds are utilised to make small donations to small and local charities.

The Economist Educational Foundation (Charity Commission no. 1147661)

The foundation works to give young people, particularly those who are disadvantaged, the opportunity to engage with current affairs and have their say on topical issues. It runs two programmes: the Burnet News Club, setting up clubs in schools to discuss issues in the news and think critically; and the Policy League, a debate and negotiation competition for sixth-form students focusing on complex social, political and economic challenges.

Directors with other relevant posts

Sir David Bell is a trustee of a number of charities, including Girl Effect (Charity Commission no. 11411155) and Sadler's Wells (Charity Commission no. 279884), of which he is Chair. Lady Suzanne Heywood is a trustee of a number of charities, including Royal Opera House (Charity Commission no. 211775) and Royal Academy of Music (Charity Commission no. 310007). Sir Simon Robertson is a trustee of the Royal Opera Endowment Fund 2000 (Charity Commission no. 1089928). Baroness Tessa Jowell is a trustee of The Tennis Foundation (Charity Commission no. 298175) and The Ditchley Foundation (Charity Commission no. 309657). Lady Lynn Forester de Rothschild is a trustee of the The Eranda Rothschild Foundation (Charity Commission no. 255650).

Main locations

The group's UK offices are based in London. The group also has offices in a number of countries internationally.

Community contributions

According to the 2015/16 accounts for The Economist Charitable Trust, The Economist Newspaper Ltd donated £104,000 during the year.

The 2014/15 accounts were the latest available for The Economist Educational Foundation at the time of writing (January 2017); they state that the foundation received a donation from the group and some costs were paid on behalf of the foundation, but the amount is not specified.

Employee-led support

Payroll giving and matched funding

There is a payroll giving scheme and the group provides matched funding through The Economist Charitable Trust for employees' donations of both time and money to charities. Employees are also entitled to time out of work to take part in charitable and community activities.

Corporate charity

The Economist Charitable Trust (Charity Commission no. 293709).

Exclusions

Previous research has suggested that The Economist Charitable Trust does not support appeals from non-registered charities, circular appeals, applications of a chain-letter type, gala charity events, advertising in charity brochures, appeals from individuals, larger national appeals, church restoration appeals, politically sensitive organisations, organisations of a religious or denominational nature, single service (among forces) charities, arts sponsorship or appeals from ordinary educational establishments (e.g. schools or university building funds). Special schools or projects for students with disabilities are the exception to this rule.

Animal welfare appeals are supported via staff matched funding only. Fundraising events are only supported by gifts in kind, and these are usually bought from other voluntary organisations. Sport appeals are only supported if for people with disabilities.

Applications

The Economist Charitable Trust

Apply in writing to the correspondent, with a simple letter and the latest annual report and accounts. There is an advisory panel which decides how 50–60% of the trust's funds are allocated and monitors employee matched funding. The panel's decisions are approved by the trustees.

Our research shows the company has previously stated that multiple approaches are wasteful and counter-productive, particularly when they are addressed to directors who retired some time ago, indicating use of out-of-date lists. A few applications each year are rejected simply because they are badly presented. Many more fail because their deadlines for events are far too close when they apply. Applicants are also advised that if they are asked for additional information, this is a sign of interest in the project and not the opposite. Unsigned, circular appeals will not receive a response.

EDF Energy PLC

Electricity

Correspondent: Sustainability Team, 40 Grosvenor Place, Victoria, London SW1X 7EN (tel: 020 7242 9050; email: sustainability@edfenergy.com; website: www.edfenergy.com)

Directors: Robert Guyler; Vincent de Rivaz, Chief Executive (women: 0; men: 2)

Year end	31/12/2015
Turnover	£8,440,000,000
Pre-tax profit	(£296,000,000)

Nature of business: EDF Energy (the group) is an integrated energy company with over 15,000 employees. It generates and supplies electricity and gas for the UK from a nuclear, coal, gas and renewable energy portfolio.

Company registration number: 2366852

Subsidiary undertakings include: British Energy Direct Ltd; EDF Energy Investments; Northern Power Ltd.

Focus of giving: Education, environment, health, ill health, financial education, poverty and social exclusion, science technology, children, young people, community/social welfare, disability.

Membership: BITC

Accredited Living Wage Employer	✓
Community involvement	✓
Community contributions	✓
Company reports on anti-slavery	✓
CSR report	✓
CSR or charity committee	✓
Armed forces personnel	✓
Charity partner(s)	✓
Corporate charity	✓
Employee-led support	✓
Gifts in kind	✓
Matched funding	✓
Sponsorship	✓
STEM-focused	✓

Charitable donations

Cash UK (latest available):	2015	£7,800,000
Total UK (cash and in kind):	2015	£7,800,000
Cash worldwide:	2015	£7,800,000
Total worldwide (cash and in kind):	2015	£7,800,000

Community involvement

The group offers support through the EDF Energy Trust to individuals in need and through grants to organisations providing financial and debt advice and support. The group also supports charities through three-year partnerships and by matching employee fundraising, and has an extensive education programme, the Pod, which focuses on sustainability and STEM.

EDF Energy Trust (Charity Commission no. 1099446)

The company supports customers facing financial difficulties through the EDF Energy Trust, which was the first energy trust to be established in the UK. Grants are awarded by the trust to vulnerable domestic customers of EDF Energy who are in debt with or struggling to pay their gas or electricity charges, or need help with other essential household debts or essential household items.

Receiving donations from EDF Energy since 2003, the trust is independent of its donor company and is governed by the usual board of trustees. However, the administration of the trust is undertaken by Charis Grants Ltd (Charis) on their behalf.

Charis exists to facilitate charitable and corporate giving by designing, developing and managing a range of services in support of vulnerable members of society. Grant management is undertaken by Charis awarding grants to EDF Energy Trust's beneficiary group for utility debt and other essential household bills and costs.

The EDF Trust, through Charis, actively encourages applications from customers for grants, as part of the 'Shared Programme of Giving' with other utility providers, meaning that only one application is needed to be considered for any of the grants schemes within the programme. Contact: admin@charisgrants.com for further information.

According to the trust's 2015 annual report, 3,751 grants were made from the Individuals and Families Grants programme during the year, totalling £2.7 million.

The EDF Trust also provides grants to organisations for: the provision of money and debt advice; supporting customers to apply for support; developing partnerships for referrals with local organisations; raising awareness of energy debt. According to the 2015 annual report, the trust has been providing funding for a number of years for Plymouth Citizens Advice, Citizens Advice Thanet and Talking Money (Bristol). In 2015 grants totalled £276,000.

Beneficiaries included: Plymouth Citizens Advice (£106,000); Talking Money (£88,000); Citizens Advice Thanet (£82,000).

Charity partner

The group's chosen charity partner during 2013–2016 was Marie Curie. Employees voted in late 2016 to support Breast Cancer Now, with an aim of raising £450,000 over a three-year partnership.

The Pod Programme for greener schools

The Pod is EDF's award-winning sustainable schools programme which has reached over 50% of all schools (over 21,000 schools) in the UK. Established in September 2008, the Pod aims to engage young people in energy, science and sustainability. It provides free curriculum-linked resources and runs campaigns to teach young people (aged 4–14) about these issues, empower them to act on their learning, and enable them inspire others with their achievements.

The programme provides a wide range of resources for schools including lesson and assembly plans for different age groups, practical activity guides, films, games and resources linked to campaigns such as the Pods Waste Week and Switch Off Fortnight. Pod campaigns are designed to help get the whole school, parents and the local community engaged in living more sustainable lifestyles.

EDF works closely with a number of partners on the Pod including: The British Science Association; Eco-Schools; The Met Office; Wastebuster; British Trust for Ornithology; Keep Scotland Beautiful; Step Up to Serve.

Other STEM initiatives

Sites within the group also lead their own activities with local communities. For example, the group's Hinkley Point C site's Inspire Education programme focuses on encouraging local young people in Somerset to engage with STEM subjects.

The group has also launched a programme called Pretty Curious, which specifically aims to encourage girls to engage with STEM subjects and consider STEM careers.

Work Insight programme

The group has a partnership with the Social Mobility Foundation, offering work experience, mentoring and employability skills opportunities to young people from disadvantaged backgrounds.

Main locations

In the UK, the group has offices in London, Barnwood, Crawley, Exeter and Sunderland, as well as power stations around the UK (details can be found on the EDF website). EDF Energy PLC is owned by the French state-owned EDF, with operations worldwide.

Community contributions

During 2015, the group donated £7.7 million to the EDF Energy Trust, £2.6 million of which was part of its obligation under the Warm Home Discount scheme, according to the trust's 2015 annual report. The group also gave £100,000 to Marie Curie as matched funding for the funds raised by employees.

In-kind support

Through the Science in Schools programme, the schools and community groups can gain points for donating unwanted textiles for recycling, which are then exchanged for science equipment.

Employee-led support

Employee volunteering

Employees are entitled to two days of paid volunteering each year, contributing to activities run by The Pod, the group's educational scheme, including STEM activities in schools and Helping Hands, which focuses on community action. In 2015 a total of 8% of the group's employees were engaged in volunteering. 50 employees took part in the Science in Schools campaign, which is run in partnership with Waste Buster and the British Science Association, delivering sessions about recycling in primary schools.

Employee fundraising

Employees fundraise to support the group's partner charity, which is voted on by employees. From 2013 to 2016, they fundraised for Marie Curie, raising almost £1 million over the three years, with a further £300,000 added by the company. In 2016 employees also supported the British Paralympic Association. In late 2016, employees voted to support Breast Cancer Now as the group's partner charity, aiming to raise £450,000 over the next three years, as well as supporting Breast Cancer Awareness Month.

Commercially led support

Sponsorship

EDF is the principal sponsor of the Cheltenham Science Festival and also supports the Generation Science programme (run by Edinburgh International Science Festival) in Scotland. The company has supported The Times Cheltenham Science Festival for 11 years and is the principal sponsor of its Science for Schools programme, which offers educational lectures and interactive science workshops for student visitors.

Corporate charity

EDF Energy Trust (Charity Commission no. 1099446).

Applications

EDF Energy Trust

Organisational grants from the trust: For further information on future grant programmes and deadlines, refer to the trust's website or contact the trust on: edfet@charisgrants.com.

Individual grants from the trust: the easiest way to apply for a grant is via the trust's online application form. Alternatively you can print an application form or request one from the trust to complete by hand and return to the trust's freepost address. Forms may also be available from some advice centres such as Citizens Advice.

The group

You can contact the group in writing to the correspondent, or using the online enquiry form on the EDF website.

EE Ltd (formerly T-Mobile (UK) Ltd)

Telecommunications

Correspondent: Responsibility Team, Trident Place, Mosquito Way, Hatfield, Hertfordshire AL10 9BW (email: responsibility@ee.co.uk; website: ee.co.uk/our-company/corporate-responsibility)

Directors: Bruno Duarte; Ettienne Brandt; Fotis Karonis; Gerry McQuade; James Blendis; Marc Allera, Chief Executive Officer; Max Taylor; Nick Lane; Noel Hamill; Sarah Henly; Simon Frumkin; Stephen Harris, Chief Financial Officer (women: 1; men: 11)

Year end	31/12/2015
Turnover	£6,311,000

Nature of business: UK mobile communications provider. The group, which operates exclusively in the UK, runs EE, Orange and T-Mobile and was formed in April 2010 when France Telecom S.A. and Deutsche Telekom A.G. combined their respective UK mobile businesses as a joint venture.

Company registration number: 2382161

Subsidiary undertakings include: EE (Group) Ltd; Orange Home UK Ltd; Orange Services India Private Ltd; Orange Personal Communications Services Ltd; EE Finance PLC.

Brands include: EE; Orange; T Mobile.

Focus of giving: General charitable purposes, older people, science technology.

Membership: BITC

Community involvement	✓
Community contributions	✓
Company reports on anti-slavery	✓
Directors have other relevant posts	✓
Cash donations declared	✓
Charity partner(s)	✓
Employee-led support	✓
Gifts in kind	✓
Humanitarian aid: overseas	✓
Payroll giving	✓

Charitable donations

Cash UK (latest available):	2015	£240,000
Total UK (cash and in kind):	2015	£424,000
Cash worldwide:	2015	£240,000
Total worldwide (cash and in kind):	2015	£424,000

Community involvement

Much of the charitable activity EE commits to has the aim of promoting digital inclusion. The group is a core founding partner of Go ON UK, a charity formed by eight organisations from the business, charity and public sectors with the aim of bringing 'the benefits of the Internet to every individual and every organisation in every community across the UK'.

Charity partnerships

EE's partnership with Unicef began in 2014 and it has since then helped the organisation to raise over £3.6 million.

Directors with other relevant posts

Marc Allera is a member of the Great Ormond Street Hospital corporate partnerships board and a trustee of Founders for Schools.

Main locations

EE has shops throughout the UK.

Community contributions

There is a downloadable 2014 GRI (Global Reporting Initiative) table on the website and it is from this that we have taken the following information. The group made total contributions of £523,000, of which, management costs amounted to £99,500. The value of cash, in-kind and time contributions totalled £424,000, and was distributed as follows:

Cash donations	£240,000
Time costs	£180,000
In-kind costs	£3,900

A further £684,500 was raised through payroll giving, employee fundraising and customer contributions.

The 2014 Sustainability Report was the latest available at the time of writing (November 2016).

In-kind support

Through partnership with Age UK, EE runs 'Techy Tea Parties' at its stores to help promote digital inclusion. Older people who need help understanding and using digital technology can get free advice from an EE Digital Champion – a specially trained EE employee – over a cup of tea. In 2014 a total of 610 Techy Tea Parties were held, with 3,000 EE employees volunteering to help improve the digital skills of 6,000 people.

Employee volunteering

Employees are able to contribute volunteering time. EE employees are able to spend two days per year volunteering, either for an activity of their choice or on one of the group's volunteering programmes such as EE Digital Champions.

Employee-led support

Employee fundraising

The group supports employees with set-up and top-up costs of fundraising activities. In 2014 employees, with EE's support, raised £131,000 for charitable causes. A further £166,000 was raised through payroll giving.

Applications

Apply in writing to the correspondent.

Electrocomponents PLC

Distribution

Correspondent: Corporate Responsibility Team, International Management Centre, 8050 Oxford Business Park North, Oxford OX4 2HW (tel: 01865 204000; fax: 01865 207400; email: queries@electrocomponents.com; website: www.electrocomponents.com)

Directors: Bertrand Bodson; David Egan, Group Finance Officer; Ian Haslegrave; John Pattullo; Karen Guerra; Lindsley Ruth, Chief Executive Officer; Paul Hollingworth; Peter Johnson, Chair; Rupert Soames (women: 1; men: 8)

Year end	31/03/2016
Turnover	£1,291,100,000
Pre-tax profit	£76,800,000

Nature of business: Founded in 1937, the company is a global distributor of electronics and maintenance products and operates in 32 countries.

Company registration number: 647788

Subsidiary undertakings include: Allied Electronics (Canada) Inc.; Radionics Ltd; RS Components Ltd.

Brands include: Allied Electronics; Design Spark; RS Components.

Total employees: 6,024

Focus of giving: Education, children, young people, community/social welfare, disability, disasters.

Community involvement	✓
Community contributions	✓
Company reports on anti-slavery	✓
CSR report	✓
Directors have other relevant posts	✓
Employee-led support	✓
Gifts in kind	✓
Humanitarian aid: overseas	✓
Matched funding	✓

Community involvement

Support by the group is delivered through employee-led fundraising, employees donating their time and expertise, direct cash contributions, matched funding, and donations of stock. In the UK, the company has been granted patron status of the children's charity, the NSPCC.

Directors

John Pattullo is a trustee of In Kind Direct (Charity Commission no. 1052679) and Chair of NHS Blood and Transplant Trust Fund (Charity Commission no. 1061771).

Main locations

There are branches across the UK. The group's headquarters is in Oxford.

Community contributions

No details were available regarding cash donations made in the UK in 2015/16.

In-kind support

The group provides components and tools for Practical Action, a UK-based charity that uses technology to enable financially developing countries to challenge poverty. In 2015/16 the group also supported the charity with its proposal for UK Aid Match.

The group have also previously supported emergency humanitarian aid initiatives such as in response to the Typhoon Haiyan disaster, by donating end-of-the-line products.

Support is also given, via the donation of products, to universities in the UK, Australia and Germany for the global Formula Student contest run by The Institute of Mechanical Engineers.

Employee-led support

The company supports engagement with its local communities globally and employees are encouraged to be proactive in choosing which organisations/groups to be involved with.

Across the world employees invest their time and money to raise funds for valuable causes, from disaster and cancer charities to community youth projects. During 2015/16 global fundraising reached over £100,000. Some examples of these initiatives include:

- UK employees raising funds for Hearing Dogs for Deaf People
- UK business's call centre supporting Comic Relief and Sport Relief as part of the donation network across the country
- Employees in Germany sponsoring children in Uganda via Plan International
- Employees in France donating to MEDICO Lions Clubs de France
- The Allied business in the USA supporting United Way

Applications

Applications can be made in writing to the correspondent.

EnQuest PLC

Oil and gas/fuel

Correspondent: Charities Committee, 5th Floor, Cunard House, 15 Regent Street, London SW1Y 4LR (tel: 020 7925 4900; email: enquiries@enquest.com; website: www.enquest.com)

Directors: Amjad Bseisu, Chief Executive; Clare Spottiswoode; Dr James Buckee, Chair; Dr Philip Nolan; Helmut Langanger; Jock Lennox; Jonathan Swinney, Chief Financial Officer; Philip Holland (women: 1; men: 7)

Year end	31/12/2015
Turnover	£742,756,000
Pre-tax profit	(£1,096,149,000)

Nature of business: EnQuest is a gas and oil exploration and production company, focusing on the North Sea.

Company registration number: 7140891

Subsidiary undertakings include: EnQuest Global Ltd; EnQuest Thistle Ltd; Stratic UK (Holdings) Ltd.

Focus of giving: Education, environment, health, ill health, local groups, overseas projects, poverty and social exclusion, children, young people, community/social welfare, disability.

Community involvement	✓
Community contributions	✓
Company reports on anti-slavery	✓
CSR report	✓
CSR or charity committee	✓
Directors have other relevant posts	✓
Charity partner(s)	✓
Employee-led support	✓
Gifts in kind	✓
Overseas giving	✓
Pro bono	✓

Community involvement

The group tends to support a selected number of charities to develop a long-term relationship with. In particular, the group supports local charitable projects focusing on: people who are disadvantaged; the environment; health; education; and welfare. The group also supports employees who are involved in charitable activities.

Partnerships

In 2015 the group continued its long-standing relationship with Tullos Primary School in Aberdeen, arranging a visit to the group's helicopter facilities, and also worked with the Paul Lawrie Foundation to bring pop-up sports facilities to the school. The group also supported Archway, a charity in Aberdeen that supports young people and adults with learning disabilities.

Charity committee

The group's charity committee in each of its operational sites reviews requests against the group's criteria and decides which projects should benefit from support.

Directors with other relevant posts

Amjad Bseisu is a trustee of The Amjad and Suha Bseisu Foundation (Charity Commission no. 1118545) and Alfanar (Charity Commission no. 1105048). Jock Lennox is a trustee of the Tall Ships Youth Trust (Charity Commission no. 314229)

Main locations

In the UK, the group's offices are based in London and Aberdeen. It also has offices in Kuala Lumpur and Dubai.

Community contributions

No figure was provided for the group's charitable contributions.

Employee-led support

Employee fundraising and volunteering

The group's charity policy states that it supports charities that employees are involved with. Employees also supported the group's partner charities in 2015; for example, employees fundraised for the charity Archway, and also volunteered to help with refurbishment work for the charity.

Exclusions

The group does not support: political or religious organisations; charitable fundraising; individuals.

Applications

Applications should be made in writing to the local EnQuest operation, where a charity committee will review requests against the group's community and charity policy, which is provided on the website: www.enquest.com/corporate-responsibility/community.

Enterprise Inns PLC

Leisure, property, retail – restaurants/fast food

Correspondent: Charity Committee, 3 Monkspath Hall Road, Solihull, West Midlands B90 4SJ (tel: 0121 733 7700; email: investorrelations@enterpriseinns.com; website: www.enterpriseinnsplc.com)

Directors: Adam Fowle; David Maloney; Marisa Cassoni; Neil Smith, Chief Financial Officer; Peter Baguley; Robert Walker, Chair; Simon Townsend, Chief Executive Officer (women: 1; men: 6)

Year end	30/09/2015
Turnover	£625,000,000
Pre-tax profit	(£71,000,000)

Nature of business: The group includes around 5,000 properties in the UK which are mainly leased and tenanted as pubs.

Company registration number: 2562808

Subsidiary undertakings include: Boldbreak Ltd; Century Inns Ltd; Unique Pubs Ltd.

UK employees: 618

Total employees: 618

Focus of giving: General charitable purposes, education, enterprise/training, fundraising events, health, ill health, local groups, safety and crime prevention, children, young people, community/social welfare.

Community involvement	✓
Community contributions	✓
CSR report	✓
CSR or charity committee	✓
Directors have other relevant posts	✓
Charity partner(s)	✓
Company gives to smaller charities	✓
Employee-led support	✓
Gifts in kind	✓
Market-led giving	✓
Sponsorship	✓

Community involvement

The group offers support to charities through partnerships, and through its charity committee, which decides on donations and sponsors employee initiatives. Individual pubs within the group may also support local charities, and the group offers grants of up to £6,000 for pubs to develop their community activities.

Partnerships

In 2015 the group began a partnership with West Midlands Fire Service, donating £15,000 annually to support Safeside, which runs educational activities focusing on safety.

The group is also working with Stride Ventures, committing £20,000 and offering business and enterprise activities to school pupils in the South East.

Community Heroes Awards

The group runs annual awards to recognise publicans making a difference in their community, offering grants to spend on local community activities. One £6,000 grant is available for the national award winner, £5,000 for second prize, and a further 52 grants of £3,000 available for finalists.

Pub is the Hub campaign

The group supports the Pub is the Hub campaign, which aims to make pubs a centre for communities and invites them to offer additional services to local people and promote collaboration. For example, by developing services such as community cafes or offering support in areas where post offices have closed. In 2016 the group donated £25,000 to the campaign's Community Services Fund, which offers grants to pubs that wish to run a community initiative.

Directors with other relevant posts
David Maloney is Chair of Trustees of the Make-A-Wish-Foundation (Charity Commission no. 295672).

Main locations
The group owns around 5,000 pub properties in the UK. Its head office is located in Solihull.

Community contributions

No figure was provided for the group's overall charitable contributions.

Employee-led support

Charity committee
The group's charity committee, made up of employees, is responsible for allocating the group's contributions to employees' fundraising efforts, as well as organising fundraising events for charities. Donations for challenges such as Cancer Research UK's Race for Life and the Great Birmingham Run totalled £3,000 in 2014/15.

Beneficiaries during the year have included: Comic Relief; Macmillan Cancer Support; The Royal British Legion.

Commercially led support

Alongside the 'finder's fee' that the group offers to any of its publicans that successfully introduce a new publican on a tenancy agreement, the group also donates £500 to a charity chosen by the publican, usually a local charity supported by their pub. Donations under this scheme totalled over £13,000 in 2014/15.

The group have launched a beer with the brewery Charles Wells, for which ten pence is donated to The Royal British Legion from every pint sold.

Applications

Apply in writing to the correspondent.

ERM Group Holdings Ltd

Consultancy, business services

Correspondent: Shona King, Global Manager, ERM Foundation, 2nd Floor, Exchequer Court, 33 St Mary Axe, London EC3A 8AA (tel: 020 3206 5200; email: shona.king@erm.com; website: www.erm.com)

Directors: Andrew Silverbeck, Finance Director; John Alexander, Chief Executive Officer; Mark Pearson.

Year end	31/03/2016
Pre-tax profit	(£7,800,000)

Nature of business: The principal activities of the group are the provision of environmental, social, risk and health and safety consulting services. Environmental Resources Management (ERM) Group operates around the world and has over 150 offices in 40 countries and territories employing more than 4,500 people.

Company registration number: 5593398

Subsidiary undertakings include: Environmental Resources Management; ERM Holdings Ltd; ERM International Services Ltd.

UK employees: 300

Total employees: 4,500

Focus of giving: Education, environment, health, ill health, overseas projects, poverty and social exclusion, women's issues, community/social welfare.

Community involvement	✓
Community contributions	✓
Company reports on anti-slavery	✓
CSR report	✓
Charity partner(s)	✓
Corporate charity	✓
Employee-led support	✓
Gifts in kind	✓
Humanitarian aid: overseas	✓
Matched funding	✓
Overseas giving	✓
Pro bono	✓

Community involvement

The group offers support through its global corporate charity, The ERM Foundation.

The ERM Foundation
The group has a corporate charity, with global reach, The ERM Foundation (Charity Commission no. 1113415). The foundation focuses on the following areas: low-carbon development; conservation and biodiversity; water, sanitation and hygiene; environmental education; empowering women and girls. The foundation's 2015/16 annual review states that it has recently undertaken a realignment of its goals to meet the Sustainable Development Goals, with a focus on research-led and technology-based initiatives. Support is given to charitable organisations and social enterprises through funding, employee volunteering and pro bono technical support.

The foundation also aims to run a flagship project in each of the regions where it operates, in collaboration with partner organisations and led by ERM employees. For example, in the group's Europe, Middle East and Africa operational sites, the foundation is working with the RSPB to protect spring migrant birds.

One of the foundation's main programmes is The Low Carbon Enterprise Fund (LCEF) which supports enterprises in the financially developing world where the entrepreneurs are seeking to build a low-carbon business by providing low-interest loans and equity stakes as well as pro bono support.

It is a practice of the foundation to fund organisations which ERM employees are involved with – the foundation is advised by a committee of specialists from ERM's current staff and alumni. The majority of its income comes from ERM employee donations and other donors through locally organised fundraising events. The company matches a portion of these contributions.

Main locations
Globally, the group has 160 offices in over 40 countries. In the UK, the group has eight offices, which are located in: Aberdeen; Bristol; Edinburgh; Harrogate; London; Manchester; Oxford; Swansea.

Community contributions

The group's 2015/16 sustainability report states that the group contributed over $1 million (around £822,000) to global sustainability initiatives, including the ERM Foundation.

At the time of writing (January 2017), the 2014/15 accounts were the latest available for The ERM Foundation. The accounts state the following about the group's contribution to the foundation during the year: 'ERM Worldwide Ltd supported The ERM Foundation with pro-bono time and matching funds for monies raised by ERM Staff to support Foundation projects. The cost of the audit was borne by ERM Europe Ltd who also provided management and administrative support.'

The 2015/16 annual review of the ERM Foundation, available on the group's website, states that the foundation globally distributed grants to 59 projects in 26 countries, totalling $535,000 (around £429,500), distributed among the following causes:

Environmental education	32%
Water, sanitation and hygiene	28%
Conservation and biodiversity	16%
Low carbon development	16%
Empowering women and girls	8%

Of this, 45% was spent in Europe, Middle East and Africa.

In-kind support

Pro bono support
The group offers pro bono support, in collaboration with partner organisations, where employees have the opportunity to provide support to non-profit organisations and social enterprises. In 2015/16 employees globally contributed over 1,800 hours of pro bono support for charitable organisations, working on 45 projects in 20 countries.

Employee-led support

Employee volunteering and fundraising

The global 2015/16 annual review for the ERM Foundation states that employees are encouraged to participate in volunteering in their local community, particularly in global environmental initiatives such as Earth Day and the International Coastal Cleanup, co-ordinated at a local level.

Employees also offer pro bono or volunteer support to projects supported by the ERM Foundation, as well as the opportunity to apply for matched funding for their own fundraising initiatives.

Corporate charity

The ERM Foundation (Charity Commission no. 1113415).

Applications

Applications to the ERM Foundation should be made in writing to the correspondent.

Esh Group

Building/construction

Correspondent: Added Value Team, Esh House, Bowburn North Industrial Estate, Bowburn, Durham DH6 5PF (tel: 0191 377 4570; fax: 0191 377 4571; email: addedvalue@esh.uk.com; website: www.eshaddedvalue.co.uk)

Directors: Andy Radcliffe, Financial Director; Brian Manning, Chief Executive; Jack Lumsden; John Davies; John Walker; Meg Munn; Michael Hogan, Chair; Tony Carroll Snr (women: 1; men: 7)

Year end	31/12/2015
Turnover	£275,500
Pre-tax profit	£8,603,000

Nature of business: The principal activities of the group are building, construction, civil engineering and property refurbishment.

Company registration number: 3724890

Subsidiary undertakings include: Esh Construction Ltd; Dunelm Homes Ltd; Lumsden and Carroll Construction (Northern) Ltd.

UK employees: 1,231

Total employees: 1,231

Focus of giving: Education, enterprise/training, environment, equal opportunities, health, ill health, small groups, local groups, less popular charitable purposes, poverty and social exclusion, safety and crime prevention, science technology, children, young people, community/social welfare.

Membership: BITC

Community involvement ✓

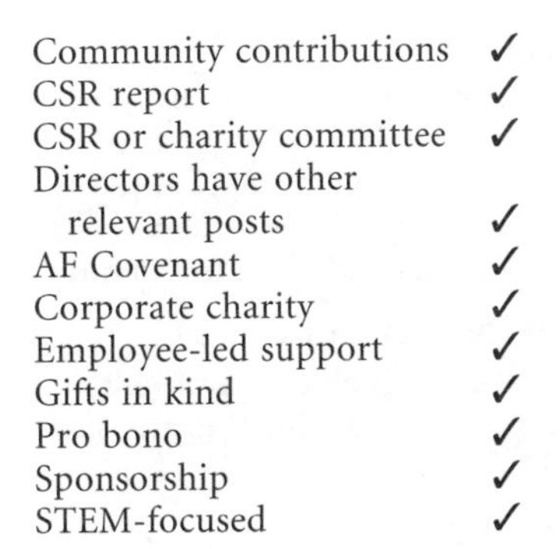

Community contributions ✓
CSR report ✓
CSR or charity committee ✓
Directors have other relevant posts ✓
AF Covenant ✓
Corporate charity ✓
Employee-led support ✓
Gifts in kind ✓
Pro bono ✓
Sponsorship ✓
STEM-focused ✓

Charitable donations

Cash UK (latest available):	2015	£130,000
Total UK (cash and in kind):	2015	£130,000
Cash worldwide:	2015	£130,000
Total worldwide (cash and in kind):	2015	£130,000

Community involvement

The group provides support to charities in communities where it operates through its corporate charity, the Esh Charitable Trust. It also supports employability and STEM education initiatives.

Esh Charitable Trust (registered as Esh Foundation, Charity Commission no. 1112040)

The Esh Charitable Trust (working name) is the group's corporate charity which seeks to support the communities in which the group operates. According to the website, the trust provides grants of up to £1,000 for projects which: improve the quality of life of local residents; support disadvantaged or vulnerable communities; improve employment prospects; or promote equality, engaging minority and hard-to-reach groups. In 2015 the trust made grants totalling £87,000 to 52 projects.

Education and employability

Working in partnership with 71 schools and over 100 partner businesses, the group runs Building My Skills, a year-long programme which aims to equip students with employability skills and provide careers advice. The group also provides work experience opportunities.

The group has created Get into STEM kits in partnership with Northumbria University, providing resources for schools to encourage engagement with STEM subjects. The group also provides site visits and safety talks for schools.

Directors with other relevant posts

Michael Hogan is a trustee of Suubi Africa (UK) (Charity Commission no. 1129595). Brian Manning is a trustee of Changing Lives (Charity Commission no. 500640) and County Durham Community Foundation (Charity Commission no. 1047625). Meg Munn is a patron of the Women's Engineering Society (Charity Commission no. 1008913). Michael Hogan, Jack Lumsden, Tony Carroll and Brian Manning are all trustees of the Esh Foundation (Charity Commission no. 1112040).

Main locations

The group operates in the North East, Yorkshire, the North West and Scotland. Its head office is in Durham, and there are also offices in: Carlisle; Cramlington; Leeds; Livingston; and Newton Aycliffe.

Community contributions

No figure was given for the group's total charitable contributions in 2015. However, the group donated £130,000 to the Esh Charitable Trust during the year.

Employee-led support

Employee volunteering and fundraising

Examples of employee fundraising initiatives during the year include: employees participating in the Great North Run; a Macmillan Coffee Morning; and taking part in the Great North Swim. The group states that it encourages employees to help good causes; employees have volunteered with projects supported by the Esh Charitable Trust.

Commercially led support

Sponsorship

The group is the main sponsor of Newcastle Eagles basketball team, and renewed its sponsorship in 2016 with a three-year commitment. This partnership includes support given through the Esh Charitable Trust for the Eagles Community Foundation, which seeks to grow grassroots basketball participation.

Corporate charity

Esh Charitable Trust (Charity Commission no. 1112040).

Applications

Esh Charitable Trust

Applications can be made using an online form. Information about when applications are open, eligibility criteria and application guidance can be found at: www.eshgroup.co.uk/added-value/community/esh-communities.

Esh Group

Other queries can be directed to the Added Value team. Contact details for members of the Added Value team are provided on the group's website: www.eshgroup.co.uk/added-value/the-added-value-management.

Essentra PLC

Industrial products/services, personal care products, print/paper/packaging

Correspondent: Hugh Ross, Managing Director European Region, Corporate Head Office, Avebury House, 201–249 Avebury Boulevard MK9 1AU (tel: 01908 359100; website: www.essentraplc.com)

Directors: Colin Day, Chief Executive; Jon Green; Lorraine Trainer; Paul Lester, Chair; Peter Hill; Stefan Schellinger, Group Finance Director; Terry Twigger; Tommy Breen (women: 1; men: 7)

Year end	31/12/2015
Turnover	£1,098,100,000
Pre-tax profit	£90,400,000

Nature of business: Essentra is an international supplier of specialist plastic, fibre, foam and packaging products. The company has three business units: Component Solutions; Health and Personal Care Packaging; and Filtration Products. The company operates in 33 countries.

Company registration number: 5444653

Subsidiary undertakings include: ESNT Group Ltd; Essentra (Bristol) Ltd; Essentra International Ltd.

Total employees: 8,866

Focus of giving: Education, enterprise/training, environment, health, ill health, sport, recreation, community/social welfare.

Community involvement	✓
CSR report	✓
Directors have other relevant posts	✓
Employee-led support	✓
Gifts in kind	✓
Sponsorship	✓

Community involvement

Essentra support a number of non-political and non-sectarian projects run by a range of charities and organisations in the locations where the company operates. Charitable support is driven at a local rather than corporate level, and appears to be mostly led by employee involvement. Preference is generally given to causes that relate to: education and enterprise; health and welfare; sports; and the environment. The group's individual businesses support such causes with financial donations, sponsorship, in-kind support and encouraging employee involvement, such as secondment, in the community.

Directors with other relevant posts

Peter Hill is a non-executive director of the Royal Air Force.

Main locations

There are offices in: Aberdeen; Bangor; Bradford; Bristol; Great Harwood; Jarrow; Kidlington; Kilmarnock; Milton Keynes (head office); Newmarket; Newport; Nottingham; and Portsmouth.

Community contributions

No details were available regarding how much the group's individual businesses donated to charitable causes in 2015.

Applications

Charitable and community support is driven at a local rather than corporate level. Organisations are advised to contact the group's individual business local to their cause or project. The group's locations can be found on the website: www.essentraplc.com/site-information/locations.

Euro Packaging UK Ltd

Manufacturing

Correspondent: Nasir Awan, Trustee, Euro Charity Trust, 20 Brickfield Road, Yardley, Birmingham B25 8EH (email: enquiry@europackaging.co.uk; website: www.europackaging.co.uk)

Directors: Martin Higson; Paul Timmins; Sarah Windham Luck; Stephen Flaherty; Zarak Lowe (women: 1; men: 4)

Year end	31/12/2015
Turnover	£100,586,000
Pre-tax profit	£1,015,000

Nature of business: Euro Packaging UK Ltd is a manufacturer and distributor of paper and plastic packaging, allied products, disposable packaging products and consolidated logistics.

Company registration number: 7012425

Total employees: 1,000

Focus of giving: General charitable purposes, economic generation, education, general appeals, overseas projects, poverty and social exclusion, community/social welfare.

Community involvement	✓
Community contributions	✓
Cash donations declared	✓
Corporate charity	✓
Humanitarian aid: overseas	✓

Charitable donations

Cash worldwide:	2015	£2,000,000
Total worldwide (cash and in kind):	2015	£2,000,000

Community involvement

The company appears to make its charitable donations through the Euro Charity Trust (Charity Commission no. 1058460). The mission of the trust is: 'To assist the underprivileged to improve their lives, who in turn can assist their families and communities and live a healthy and dignified way of life.' This mission is met in the main by relieving poverty, providing education and forming partnerships to deliver and sustain projects. No information on the company's CSR activities was provided on the website.

Euro Charity Trust

The trust works to support disadvantaged people and communities, particularly in low- and middle-income countries, through the relief of poverty and hardship, education and provision of basic facilities such as water, electricity and medical resources. It achieves this through grants and loans to charities and religious or educational organisations, as well as educational support for individuals.

In 2015 grants from the trust focused on four organisations with which the foundation has established relationships, working in India and Malawi. 19 students were also supported with educational grants totalling £27,000.

Grants awarded to organisations totalled almost £3.1 million and grants to individuals amounted to nearly £25,000.

Beneficiaries included: Nathani Charitable Trust (£2 million); Maulana Hussain Ahmed Madani Charitable Society and Charitable Trust (£420,000); Mehboob Memorial Centre (£405,000); Imdadul Muslimeen (£300,000).

Main locations

In the UK, the group is based in Birmingham and also has operations in Purfleet and Deeside. The group operates in 20 countries worldwide.

Community contributions

According to the company's 2015 accounts, charitable donations during the year totalled £2 million. It was not specified where these donations were made, but the company appears to support the Euro Charity Trust.

Euro Charity Trust's 2015 accounts report an income of £5.8 million, mainly comprised of donations, and it is stated that the main source of donations was the Alimahomed family, who own Euro Packaging UK Ltd. It is also stated that administration costs were covered by Euro Packaging UK.

Corporate charity

Euro Charity Trust (Charity Commission no. 1058460).

Applications

Euro Charity Trust

Applications to the trust should be made in writing to the correspondent. The 2015 annual report states: 'ECT's Trustees review incoming requests on a case-by-case basis, using their knowledge of the requesting organisations and

ECT's objectives and values as the bases for assessment.'

Euromoney Institutional Investors PLC

Business services

Correspondent: Charity Committee, 8 Bouverie Street, London EC4Y 8AX (tel: 020 7779 8888; email: charity@euromoneyplc.com; website: www.euromoneyplc.com)

Directors: Andrew Ballingal; Andrew Rashbass, Chief Executive; Bashar Al-Rehany; Colin Fordham; Colin Jones, Finance Director; David Pritchard; Diane Alfano; Jane Wilkinson; John Botts; Martin Morgan; Neil Osborn; Sir Patrick Sergeant; The Viscount Rothermere; Tristan Hillgarth (women: 2; men: 12)

Year end	30/09/2015
Turnover	£403,412,000
Pre-tax profit	£123,285,000

Nature of business: Euromoney Institutional Investors PLC is an international business-to-business information company that focuses on the global financial community, metals and commodities sectors. The company provides economic information services, runs investment events and conferences and delivers training to financial institutions, professional firms, corporations and governments.

Company registration number: 954730

Subsidiary undertakings include: Centre for Investor Education (UK) Ltd; Family Office Network Ltd; Steel First Ltd.

Brands include: Euromoney; Institutional Investor; Metal Bulletin; Ned Davis Research.

Total employees: 2,343

Focus of giving: Health, ill health, overseas projects, sport, recreation, children, young people.

Community involvement	✓
Community contributions	✓
CSR report	✓
CSR or charity committee	✓
Directors have other relevant posts	✓
Charity of the Year	✓
Charity partner(s)	✓
Employee-led support	✓
Humanitarian aid: overseas	✓
Matched funding	✓
Overseas giving	✓
Payroll giving	✓

Community involvement

The company makes charitable donations and also matches donations raised by its employees own fundraising efforts for a variety of charitable causes; including: children and young people; health or life-limiting conditions; children's literacy; and overseas development including health, disability, education and sports programmes.

Beneficiaries have included: AbleChildAfrica; Action Against Cancer; Afghan Connection; AMREF; Beanstalk; Haller Foundation; Haven House Children's Hospice; Orbis.

Charity of the Year

The group goes through a selection process to find a company-wide charity to support for 12 to 18 months. Nominations for Charity of the Year are received from employees, which the executive committee then narrows down to a shortlist of three. A final vote from employees secures the Charity of the Year placement.

In 2013 the charity supported was Action Against Cancer; however, in 2014/15 employees voted to support two charities: Afghan Connection, which funds education and sports projects in Afghanistan; and Haven House, which supports families in the UK with children who have life-limiting or life-threatening conditions.

Directors with other relevant posts

David Pritchard is a trustee of The Motability Tenth Anniversary Trust (Charity Commission no. 328160), a disability charity which makes grants and invests in research and projects for people with mobility needs.

The Viscount Rothermere is Chair of the Daily Mail and managing director of the Evening Standard.

Martin Morgan is the Chief Executive of the Daily Mail.

Main locations

The head office is in London. There are also offices in Hong Kong, Montreal, and New York.

Community contributions

In 2014/15 the group raised over £500,000 for local and international charitable causes. However, the annual report notes that these contributions were a combined effort of individual employee fundraising, donations from clients and the company's own charitable budget. There were no details available regarding the amount the company itself actually donated during the year or how much was donated in the UK.

Employee-led support

In 2014/15 employee fundraising efforts included cake sales, office breakfast deliveries, a garden fete, quiz night, an online auction and a golf day. A group of employees from Euromoney also climbed Kilimanjaro, raising over £60,000 for the Haller Foundation.

The company's largest shareholder and parent organisation, Daily Mail and General Trust PLC (DMGT), hosts a Community Champion Awards to encourage the charitable efforts of employees and businesses around the group. The winner of the award receives a £5,000 donation to the charity they fundraise for, and a further £2,500 is awarded to highly commended charities.

Applications

Applications can be made by contacting the Charity Committee by email.

Experian Ltd

Financial services

Correspondent: Corporate Responsibility Department, The Sir John Peace Building, Experian Way NG2 Business Park, Nottingham NG80 1ZZ (tel: 0115 941 0888; fax: 0115 828 6341; website: www.experian.co.uk)

Directors: Brian Cassin, Chief Executive Officer; Deirdre Mahlan; Don Robert, Chair; George Rose; Kerry Williams, Chief Operating Officer; Lloyd Pitchford, Chief Financial Officer; Luiz Fleury; Paul Walker; Roger Davis (women: 1; men: 8)

Year end	31/03/2016
Turnover	£3,639,000,000
Pre-tax profit	£983,580,000

Nature of business: Experian Ltd provides a range of data, analytics and software services across the world. This includes credit services, decision analytics, marketing services and consumer services.

Company registration number: 653331

Subsidiary undertakings include: 192business Ltd; International Communication and Data Ltd; The Royal Exchange Company (Leeds) Ltd.

UK employees: 4,000

Total employees: 17,000

Focus of giving: Enterprise/training, housing, homelessness, non-registered charities, local groups, financial education, overseas projects, older people, poverty and social exclusion, children, young people.

Membership: BITC, LBG

Community involvement	✓
Community contributions	✓
Company reports on anti-slavery	✓
CSR report	✓
CSR or charity committee	✓
Directors have other relevant posts	✓
Cash donations declared	✓
Charity partner(s)	✓
Employee-led support	✓
FTSE 100	✓
Gifts in kind	✓
Overseas giving	✓

Charitable donations

Cash worldwide:	2016	£3,955,000
Total worldwide (cash and in kind):	2016	£4,869,000

Community involvement

Experian PLC contributes to the communities in which it operates around the world with a strong focus on financial education and support. The company utilises its products, services and employees' expertise to provide support and work in partnership with a number of organisations, particularly debt advisory charities, and educational and entrepreneurial organisations.

Partnerships

The company partners with a variety of organisations around the world to support financial education and services. In the UK it partners with Big Issue Invest, the social investment arm of the charity the Big Issue, to run a Rental Exchange programme to enable social-housing tenants to improve their credit scores. In 2015/16 this programme was also extended to private renters.

In Nottingham the company partners with Outreach Solutions, a joint-venture social enterprise created by Age UK, Inprova Group and Volunteering Matters. This partnership involves the company working in the local community to educate older people on how to protect themselves from fraud.

Experian also partnered with Epic Partners to run a programme called Free4All, which supports people experiencing homelessness in Nottingham with donated goods and financial advice.

In the USA the company partners with the Credit Builders Alliance to train housing and social service providers to give financial education to their customers.

Experian also partners with a number of debt advisory charities around the world and provides free credit checks to help individuals in debt.

Education

Experian focuses on education and encouraging entrepreneurship, particularly for children and young people. For example, in the UK the company partners with the charity Young Enterprise to help children have a hands-on experience of creating and running a business.

Experian has also developed online and practical resources, such as interactive storybooks and supporting materials for teachers, to provide financial education for young people in the UK and Ireland. The company also worked with the charity The Mix to launch an online learning tool, Home Truths, to help young people become financially independent at university.

In 2015/16 the company set up a Debt Advice Centre near its head office in Nottingham to provide financial education and debt advice to young people and their families.

Directors with other relevant posts

Don Robert is a trustee of the Education and Employers Taskforce (Charity Commission no. 1130760).

Paul Walker is Chair of the Newcastle Science City Partnership.

Main locations

The company operates in 37 countries around the world and has corporate offices based in: Dublin; London; Nottingham; Brazil; and the USA.

Community contributions

The figures taken from Experian's 2015/16 Corporate Responsibility (CR) report were listed in US dollars, which have been converted here to sterling using the currency exchange rate available at the time of writing (October 2016). The report shows that the company made worldwide charitable contributions that fall within the London Benchmarking Group (LBG) framework totalling £4.87 million. The company also provided a figure for voluntary contributions that fall outside the LBG framework (such as investments in social innovation and monetary commitments to local charities or not-for-profit organisations via a subsidiary) totalling £1.44 million, bringing the total to £6.3 million. As there was no fully detailed breakdown of these voluntary costs, we have used the figure pertaining to the LBG framework, £4.87 million, as the overall total of community contributions made worldwide.

The CR performance data report, available on the company's website, breaks down the company's charitable and voluntary contributions as follows:

Funds from Experian PLC	£2.67 million
Financial donations and investments from Experian subsidiaries	£1.3 million
Employee time volunteered	£1.06 million
Management costs	£780,500
Gifts in kind	£505,500

Employee-led support

Employee volunteering

Employees are encouraged to volunteer their financial expertise to support community initiatives and financial education around the world. In 2015/16 employees devoted 38,000 hours to volunteering. This included: providing financial educational training in the community, for organisations and in schools, and providing group and one-to-one sessions for micro-entrepreneurs.

In the UK in 2015/16 senior leaders volunteered to mentor young entrepreneurs to build social businesses through the Big Issue Invest's Corporate Social Venture Challenge.

In Brazil the company has a long-standing programme called Real Dreams where employees volunteer their time providing financial education in schools and community centres, as well as working with expectant mothers on how to prepare financially.

In Bulgaria, employees volunteer for two charities supporting refugees, providing workshops, language lessons and trips for children.

Commercially led support

Social innovation programme

The company has a social innovation programme to develop and promote products and services that create social and economic community benefits and enable consumers to apply for credit from community lenders and credit unions. The programme also enhances micro-finance opportunities in Africa, Asia and Latin America.

E-links is one such example product developed by the company and its partners to develop and test new products that specifically aim to create social and economic benefits (as well as income for the company), particularly in India.

The company also provides information and tips on managing credit to people all over the world through its call centres, websites and social media channels. In 2015/16 in North America, the company worked with a non-profit organisation, Operation Hope, to support people in understanding their finances.

One Young World

The company runs an annual competition, One Young World, to encourage its younger employees to come up with responsible business ideas that could impact positively in the communities in which the business operates. Examples of ideas that have won this award include: using voice data to help older people gain access to services and avoid fraud, and assisting people in medical debt.

Applications

CR queries can be directed in writing to: Lorena Saez-Bravo, CR and Social Innovation Manager; 80 Victoria Street, 6th Floor, Cardinal Place, London SW1E 5JL; tel. 020 3042 4000.

Fenner PLC

Chemicals and plastics

Correspondent: Corporate Responsibility Team, Hesslewood Country Office Park, Ferriby Road, Hessle, East Yorkshire HU13 0PW (tel: 01482 626500; fax: 01482 626502; website: www.fenner.com/en/people_values/corporate_responsibility_report)

Directors: Vanda Murray, Chair; Mark Abrahams, Chief Executive; John Pratt, Group Finance Director; Geraint Anderson; Chris Surch (women: 1; men: 4)

Year end	31/08/2016
Turnover	£572,500,000
Pre-tax profit	(£30,300,000)

Nature of business: Manufacturer and distributor of conveyor belting and reinforced precision polymer products.

Company registration number: 329377

Subsidiary undertakings include: Fenner Dunlop Ltd; Hallite Ltd; James Dawson and Son Ltd.

Focus of giving: General charitable purposes, education, enterprise/training, general appeals, local groups, older people, overseas projects, poverty and social exclusion, sport, recreation, children, young people, community/social welfare.

Community involvement	✓
Community contributions	✓
Company reports on anti-slavery	✓
CSR report	✓
Cash donations declared	✓
Employee-led support	✓
Gifts in kind	✓
Overseas giving	✓

Charitable donations

Cash worldwide:	2016	£76,000
Total worldwide (cash and in kind):	2016	£76,000

Community involvement

The group's community involvement activities are organised at a local level by individual operating sites. It tends to support initiatives focusing on community, health, or education.

Examples of international activities include: providing bursaries for disadvantaged students in South Africa; housing a transmitter for a local radio station in Canada; and providing work experience opportunities for students in Manheim, USA.

Main locations

In the UK, the group has operations in: Dewsbury; Farington; Hampton; Hull; and Lincoln. Its head office is in Hessle, East Yorkshire.

Community contributions

The group's 2015/16 annual report states that, during the year, charitable donations totalling £76,000 were made to support community and educational purposes in communities local to the group's operating sites. It is not clear how much of this was in the UK. The following breakdown of causes supported was given:

Education	54%
Community	29%
Health	17%

In-kind support

The 2015/16 accounts state that the group's site in Hull allowed the use of its site by building contractors to support the construction of a new classroom for a nearby primary school.

Employee-led support

Employee fundraising

Examples of employee-led fundraising in 2016 include employees of Fenner Precision in the UK, organising a Macmillan Coffee Morning and taking part in a sponsored run to support Cancer Research UK.

Applications

Apply in writing to the correspondent. You can find your local operating site on the group's website: www.fenner.com/en/what_we_do/geographic_locations.

Fenwick Ltd

Retail – department and variety stores

Correspondent: The Company Secretary, Elswick Court, 39 Northumberland Street, Newcastle upon Tyne NE99 1AR (tel: 0191 232 5100; website: www.fenwick.co.uk)

Directors: Christine Cross; Hugo Fenwick; Mark Fenwick; Nicholas Fenwick; Peter King (women: 1; men: 4)

Year end	29/01/2016
Turnover	£302,000,000
Pre-tax profit	£44,189,000

Nature of business: Department stores.

Company registration number: 52411

Subsidiary undertakings include: Bentalls PLC; Williams and Griffin Ltd.

Focus of giving: General charitable purposes, local groups.

Community involvement	✓
Community contributions	✓
Cash donations declared	✓

Charitable donations

Cash UK (latest available):	2016	£152,000
Total UK (cash and in kind):	2016	£152,000
Cash worldwide:	2016	£152,000
Total worldwide (cash and in kind):	2016	£152,000

Community involvement

The group makes donations in support of causes local to its stores.

Main locations

Bond Street; Bracknell; Brent Cross; Canterbury; Colchester; Kingston; Leicester; Newcastle; Tunbridge Wells; Windsor; York.

Community contributions

In 2014/15 the group made charitable donations of £152,000 to causes in the local areas of its stores. We have no information regarding beneficiary groups.

Applications

Apply in writing to your local Fenwick's store, the details of which are available from the website.

FIL Holdings (UK) Ltd (formerly Fidelity Investment Management Ltd)

Financial services

Correspondent: Corporate Citizenship Department, Oakhill House, 130 Tonbridge Road, Hildenborough, Tonbridge, Kent TN11 9DZ (website: www.fidelity.co.uk/investor/about/corporate-citizenship/default.page)

Directors: Andrew Morris; Anthony Lanser; Bruce Wetherill; David Weymouth; Dominic Rossi; John Ford; Kristina Isherwood; Nicholas Birchall; Peter Horrell; Sally Nelson; Simon Haslam (women: 2; men: 9)

Year end	30/06/2015
Turnover	£844,925,000
Pre-tax profit	£27,729,000

Nature of business: Holding company for a group of companies whose principal business is the management and distribution of collective investment funds, the management of defined benefit pension funds, and the management and administration of defined contribution pension funds.

Company registration number: 6737476

Subsidiary undertakings include: FIL Investment Management Ltd; FIL Pensions Management; FIL Retirement Services Ltd.

Focus of giving: General charitable purposes, education, health, ill health, local groups, arts, culture, community/social welfare.

Community involvement	✓
Community contributions	✓
Company reports on anti-slavery	✓
CSR report	✓
Cash donations declared	✓
Corporate charity	✓

Employee-led support ✓
Matched funding ✓
Sponsorship ✓

Charitable donations

Cash UK (latest available):	2015	£10,100,000
Total UK (cash and in kind):	2015	£10,100,000
Cash worldwide:	2015	£10,100,000
Total worldwide (cash and in kind):	2015	£10,100,000

Community involvement

Fidelity directs its community support through three main channels:

Corporate Citizenship Programme

The programme supports local charities and employees in their efforts to contribute to their communities. Employees are encourage to lend their support to good causes through volunteering, fundraising and payroll giving. The group sponsors charity fundraising events and has a small budget from which grants are made to support local charities that are working to benefit the communities in areas where the group has a presence.

The Fidelity UK Foundation (Charity Commission no. 327899)

The foundation was established in 1988 to receive donations from FIL Ltd (FHL's parent company) and its UK subsidiaries. Operating as a grant-maker, the foundation supports UK-registered charities in areas where Fidelity has its corporate offices – London, Kent and Surrey – and applications are also considered from registered charities based and operating in Birmingham and Manchester. Grant-making is directed towards the following sectors: arts and culture; community development; education; and health. Funding is typically directed towards projects in the following categories: capital improvements; information technology upgrades; organisational development; and planning initiatives.

The FIL Foundation

Grants for projects outside the UK are made by the FIL Foundation. The foundation is also funded by FIL International and has similar priorities to the UK foundation. Applications from established international charities serving beneficiaries in Continental Europe, Australia, Bermuda, China, Hong Kong, India, Japan, Korea, Singapore and Taiwan are welcomed.

Main locations

The group's UK offices are in Hildenborough, Kent; Kingswood, Surrey; London; and Newport. There is also an office in Dublin.

Community contributions

In 2014/15 FIL made donations of £10 million to The Fidelity UK Foundation. The group also made donations totalling £100,000 to a wide range of charities, including through the employee grant-matching scheme. A 'substantial' number of individual donations were made to, for example, local children's charities, schools and hospitals.

We have taken our financial information from the annual report and accounts of FIL Holdings (UK Ltd) and have taken our CSR information from the website of FIL Ltd, which is the ultimate parent undertaking and controlling party, registered in Bermuda.

Employee-led support

Fidelity supports and encourages its employees to be active members of their communities.

Grant matching

Through the employee grant-matching programme, funds raised for charitable organisations are matched by the company.

Commercially led support

Sponsorship

Fidelity sponsors charity fundraising events in the areas local to its offices.

Corporate charity

The Fidelity UK Foundation (Charity Commission no. 327899).

Exclusions

Fundraising events sponsorship

Fidelity does not support the following:

- Religious, political and animal-support charities
- Individuals and individual schools
- Events for exclusive audiences, such as black-tie events
- High-risk activities, such as parachute jumps, motor racing and abseiling

Sports events, clubs and teams and advertisements in charity event programmes, diaries or directories are not usually supported.

The foundation: See the foundation's entry on page 360 for a full list of exclusions.

Applications

The Fidelity UK Foundation

Applications to the foundation can be made through an initial letter of enquiry of no more than three pages.

See the foundation's website for further details: www.fidelityukfoundation.org.

Contact the foundation at: Head of Foundations, Oakhill House, 130 Tonbridge Road, Hildenborough, Kent TN11 9DZ; tel: 01732 777364.

Note: Grants for projects outside the UK are awarded by the FIL Foundation, a separate organisations, whose main donor is Fidelity Worldwide Investment. More details are available from the Fidelity UK Foundation website.

Corporate sponsorship and donations

Fundraising events sponsorship

Organisations that fit the following criteria are favoured for sponsorship:

- Support communities within ten miles of any Fidelity office
- Have a good profile locally
- Provide co-branding at their event
- Link the company to related press coverage
- Are registered charities or not-for-profit organisations
- Organise fundraising events that directly benefit their users
- Provide opportunities for employee involvement

The website notes: 'Generally we like to be the sole sponsor of an event, and favour those that benefit the wider community rather than an exclusive audience.'

Small grants for local charities

The group states on its website: 'We have a small dedicated budget to support local organisations who deliver services at a grass roots level. These funds must go to a project that directly benefits the local community.'

For more information on these programmes, contact Fidelity's Corporate Citizenship department: Corporate Citizenship, FIL Ltd, 25 Cannon Street EC4M 5TA; email: corporate.citizenship@fil.com.

FirstGroup PLC

Transport and communications

Correspondent: Charity Committee, 395 King Street, Aberdeen AB24 5RP (tel: 01224 650100; fax: 01224 650140; website: www.firstgroupplc.com/responsibility.aspx)

Directors: Brian Wallace; Drummond Hall; Imelda Walsh; Jim Winestock; Matthew Gregory, Chief Financial Officer; Mick Barker; Tim O'Toole, Chief Executive; Warwick Brady; Wolfhart Hauser, Chair (women: 1; men: 8)

Year end	31/03/2016
Turnover	£5,218,100,000
Pre-tax profit	£168,300,000

Nature of business: The provision of passenger transport services primarily through provision of local bus and coach services and passenger railways. The company operates in the UK and North America.

Company registration number: SC157176

Subsidiary undertakings include: First Caledonian Sleeper Ltd; Great Western Trains Company Ltd; Midland Travellers Ltd.

UK employees: 26,497

Total employees: 113,859

Focus of giving: General charitable purposes, economic generation, education, enterprise/training, environment, health, ill health, medical research, small groups, local groups, overseas projects, older people, sport, recreation, children, young people, community/social welfare, disability.

Membership: BITC, LBG

Community involvement	✓
Community contributions	✓
Company reports on anti-slavery	✓
CSR report	✓
CSR or charity committee	✓
Directors have other relevant posts	✓
Charity of the Year	✓
Charity partner(s)	✓
Company gives to smaller charities	✓
Employee-led support	✓
Gifts in kind	✓
Matched funding	✓
Overseas giving	✓
Payroll giving	✓
STEM-focused	✓

Charitable donations

Cash worldwide:	2016	£532,066
Total worldwide (cash and in kind):	2016	£1,420,000

Community involvement

The group supports local and national community and charitable organisations throughout the UK and North America. Support has been given to causes such as: health/ill health; young people, education and unemployment (particularly STEM subjects); people with disabilities; and environmental projects. Many sites where the group operates have developed community engagement plans and the group and its companies work in partnership with charitable organisations. According to the group's website, community investment is focused on the following:

- Developing long-term partnerships with charitable organisations most aligned with the business
- Mobilising employees to support these partnerships through charity committees and charity champion programmes and by encouraging personal commitments like fundraising and payroll giving

Partnerships

The group and its subsidiary companies partner with a variety of charitable causes in the UK and USA.

Prostate Cancer UK is the 2015/16 Charity of Choice for the group in the UK and was chosen following an employee vote. UK employees fundraise and volunteer for this charity and in 2015/16 employees alone raised £25,000 through team and individual challenges. This partnership will last at least three years and aims to raise at least £1 million through employee fundraising, corporate donations, in-kind support (such as free advertising space) and more.

Great Western Railway (GWR) is working in partnership with The Prince's Trust on the Get into Railways project. This project is aimed at young people who are unemployed, underachieving in education or have learning needs or a disability. It aims to support them with gaining their first job within the transport industry.

GWR has also partnered with RNIB and Guide Dogs for the Blind to help improve the experience of using rail services for people with visual impairments.

TransPennine Express works in partnership with the Forestry Commission and has run a Green Grants scheme since 2008. Grants are provided to community-led environmental improvement initiatives in the north of England and south of Scotland. For further information and to see a list of previous grant winners, visit www.tpexpress.co.uk.

In the USA, the Charity of Choice partnership is with the Children's Miracle Network.

First Transit has partnered with Fresh Express, a community project that delivers low-cost fresh produce to areas with little or no transport and no local shops, since 2014. The group has provided a company's bus that has been repurposed into a transportable grocery store.

Greyhound partners with the National Runaway Safeline, providing support through the Home Free programme to enable young people who have run away to safely return home free of charge.

Improvement fund

Great Western Railway runs a £2.2 million Customer and Communities Improvement fund, which supports social needs in the areas where the company provides services. In 2015/16 a total of 40 schemes benefitted from this fund and the programme will run until 2019. A similar fund is being introduced by TransPennine Express.

Education

USA-based First Student makes cash and in-kind donations to charitable organisations that are focused on education and youth work, including contributing to scholarships in areas in which the company operates.

Directors with other relevant posts

Jim Winestock is a trustee of the USA-based Annie E. Casey Foundation, a grant-making organisation that focuses on children's welfare, and a founding member of the MARCH Foundation, which funds social programmes across the USA.

Main locations

The group serves areas across the UK. The headquarters is in Aberdeen.

Community contributions

In 2015/16 the group and its employees donated £1.42 million (2014/15: £1.7 million) to charitable causes, measured by the London Benchmarking Group (LBG) model. These contributions were broken down in the 2015/16 corporate responsibility data document, available from the group's website, as follows:

In-kind support	£534,000
Cash donations	£532,000
Employee fundraising	£171,000
Employee payroll giving	£92,500
Time (e.g. employee volunteering)	£53,500
Other (e.g. donations from customers, suppliers, etc.)	£37,000

The vast majority of community contributions in the year were made by UK-based First Rail and by the group as a whole. No details were available regarding total community contributions made in the UK, although the group made cash donations of approximately £114,000 during the year to its Charity of Choice, Prostate Cancer UK.

In-kind support

The group provides free advertising space for charities on its vehicles and bus and train stations, particularly for the group's Charity of Choice partner. In 2015/16 the group donated advertising space worth over £300,000 to Prostate Cancer UK's Men United campaign.

Free or discounted travel tickets are also donated to organisations. For example, First Rail works with Job Centre Plus to provide discounted travel for jobseekers to help them with getting back into work.

Employee-led support

Employee fundraising

Employees' fundraising efforts for charitable causes are also matched by the group. Support is often focused on local charitable causes or the group's Charity of Choice or other partners.

Volunteering

Employees are supported with volunteering within the company's time. In 2016 TransPennine Express employees volunteered with secondary schools across West Yorkshire with the Make the Grade Programme, run by a social enterprise called the Ahead Partnership. This programme aims to encourage children to become engineers and train drivers in the future by supporting them through mentorships, STEM (science, technology, engineering and maths) workshops, careers advice and talks about safety. A total of 24,000 children have taken part in the programme during the year.

Payroll giving

In 2015/16 over 1,000 UK employees took part in the group's payroll giving scheme, donating £92,000 to charities during the year.

Be First Awards

The group holds an award evening called Be First Awards to celebrate the work of its employees. Winners of the award are given a donation made to a charity of their choice.

Applications

Applications can be made in writing to the correspondent.

For further details and to see how to apply for the Great Western Railway's Customer and Communities Improvement fund, visit: www.gwr.com/about-us/supporting-our-community/customer-and-communities-improvement-fund.

Fisher (James) and Sons

Engineering, marine, oil and gas/fuel

Correspondent: Dr David Jackson, Secretary of The Sir John Fisher Foundation, Fisher House, PO Box 4, Michaelson Road, Barrow-in-Furness, Cumbria LA14 1HR (tel: 01229 615400/ 01229 580349; fax: 01229 836761; email: info@sirjohnfisherfoundation.org.uk; website: www.james-fisher.com)

Directors: Aedamar Comiskey; Charles Rice, Chair; David Moorhouse; Malcolm Paul; Michael Salter; Nick Henry, Chief Executive; Stuart Kilpatrick, Group Finance Officer (women: 1; men: 6)

Year end	31/12/2015
Turnover	£438,930,000
Pre-tax profit	£46,214,000

Nature of business: The group provides marine-related engineering services and is has four divisions: Marine Support; Offshore Oil; Specialist Technical; and Tankships.

Company registration number: 211475

Subsidiary undertakings include: Fender Care Ltd; James Fisher Nuclear Holdings Ltd; James Fisher Subsea Ltd.

Total employees: 2,800

Focus of giving: Education, health, ill health, medical research, local groups, arts, culture, children, young people, community/social welfare, disability.

Community involvement	✓
Community contributions	✓
CSR report	✓
Directors have other relevant posts	✓
Company gives to smaller charities	✓
Corporate charity	✓
Employee-led support	✓

Charitable donations

Cash UK (latest available):	2015	£1,600,000
Total UK (cash and in kind):	2015	£1,600,000
Cash worldwide:	2015	£1,600,000
Total worldwide (cash and in kind):	2015	£1,600,000

Community involvement

As well as fundraising organised by employees or companies within the group, most of the group's charitable support is directed through its corporate charity, the Sir John Fisher Foundation, which gives grants for music; arts; community; maritime projects; disability; and medical research, across the UK, with a preference for Barrow-in-Furness and surrounding areas.

Sir John Fisher Foundation

The group's corporate charity, the Sir John Fisher Foundation (Charity Commission no. 277844), makes grants to organisations in the following categories: maritime; medical and disability; education; music; arts; community projects in and around Barrow-in-Furness. Grants are made across the UK, but there is a preference for projects in Barrow-in-Furness and the surrounding area. Most grants are of less than £10,000, although occasional major one-off or multi-year grants have been awarded.

Beneficiaries in 2014/15 included: Annie Mawson's Sunbeams Music Trust (£100,000); University of Lancaster (£57,000); Furness Carers (£13,300); St John's Hospice (£12,000); Cardigan Bay Watersports (£10,000); Furness Multicultural Community Forum (£4,000); Orchestras Live (£2,000); Motability (£1,000); Blood Pressure UK (£250); Ulverston Pantomime Society (£200).

Directors with other relevant posts

David Moorhouse is a trustee of The Mission to Seafarers (Charity Commission no. 1123613).

Main locations

The group works across 19 countries, and has a number of offices and operations across the UK. Its headquarters is in Barrow-in-Furness.

Community contributions

In 2014/15 the foundation received £1.6 million in income from the group, and made grants to organisations totalling £1.3 million, of which £926,000 was given to local causes and £379,500 to national causes.

Note: While the financial information for the group relates to 2015 (year ending 31 December 2015), the charitable contributions figure relates to 2014/15 (year ending 31 March 2015), as the group has a different accounting year to the Sir John Fisher Foundation.

Employee-led support

Employee fundraising

According to the 2015 annual report, examples of causes supported by employees or companies within the group in 2015 include: Scarborough Engineering Fair; Children's Cancer and Leukaemia Group; Cash for Kids; St Thomas Moore School for special needs; the University of Strathclyde.

Corporate charity

The Sir John Fisher Foundation (Charity Commission no. 277844).

Exclusions

The Sir John Fisher Foundation generally will not fund:

- Individuals
- Sponsorship
- Expeditions
- Promotion of religion
- Places of worship
- Animal welfare
- Retrospective appeals
- Pressure groups
- Community projects outside Barrow-in-Furness and surrounding area (except occasional projects in Cumbria or North Lancashire or if they fall within one of the other categories supported by the foundation)

Applications

The Sir John Fisher Foundation

Applications to the foundation can be made using a form available to download from the foundation's website: www.sirjohnfisherfoundation.org.uk.

Trustees meet at the beginning of May and the beginning of November, and applications should be made at least six weeks in advance of a meeting.

Group

A contact form is provided on the group's website: www.james-fisher.com/contact.

Ford Motor Company Ltd

Motors and accessories

Correspondent: Director, Ford Britain Trust, Room 1/445, Eagle Way, Brentwood, Essex CM13 3BW (tel: 01277 252551; email: fbtrust@ford.com; website: www.ford.co.uk/fbtrust)

Directors: A. Barratt, Chair and Managing Director; C. Bailey; C. Page;

D. Robinson; G. Hoare; J. Skerry; M. Hallward; M. Khan; S. Glanville; T. Holmes (women: 2; men: 8)

Year end	31/12/2015
Turnover	£11,153,000,000
Pre-tax profit	£465,000,000

Nature of business: The Ford Motor Company Ltd is a wholly owned subsidiary of the Ford Motor Company of Dearborn, Michigan, USA.

The company's principal activity is the design, engineering and manufacture of low-carbon technologies, commercial vehicles and automotive components and the sale of motor vehicles and automotive components.

The company and its subsidiaries operate principally in the UK and the Republic of Ireland. It is part of an integrated vehicle manufacturing group of Ford companies throughout Europe.

Company registration number: 235446

Subsidiary undertakings include: Ford Component Sales Ltd; Ford International Liquidity Management Ltd; Ford Retail Group Ltd.

UK employees: 9,214

Total employees: 9,355

Focus of giving: Education, environment, health, ill health, local groups, older people, sport, recreation, children, young people, community/social welfare, disability.

Membership: BITC

Community involvement	✓
CSR report	✓
Corporate charity	✓
Employee-led support	✓

Community involvement

Ford Motor Company Ltd operates the Ford Britain Trust (Charity Commission no. 269410), which makes grants for projects in communities close to Ford's locations, particularly those that focus on the areas of education, environment, children, people with disabilities, activities for young people and projects working to benefit the community. The company also appears to support a small number of charities, including those in the areas of health and sports, some of which are supported on an ongoing basis. Employees are encouraged to contribute to their communities through volunteering efforts.

Main locations

The group works across the UK and worldwide.

Community contributions

The annual report and accounts for 2015 did not declare a figure for charitable donations during the year.

There was a short CSR report included in the annual report and accounts which stated:

> Our commitment to the community is built around the support and encouragement of various employee volunteering efforts, the backing and operating of the Ford Britain Trust and the on-going relationship and support of a range of charitable and altruistic activities including: BEN (Motor and Allied Trades Benevolent Fund); JDRF (Juvenile Diabetes Research Foundation); football's equality and inclusion campaign, 'Kick It Out', Wooden Spoon and Lord's Taverners.

Employee-led support

Employee volunteering

Ford employees are encouraged to contribute to their communities through volunteering their time and skills.

Corporate charity

Ford Britain Trust (Charity Commission no. 269410).

Exclusions

Ford Britain Trust does not make grants for the following purposes:

- Major building works
- Sponsorship or advertising
- Research
- Overseas projects
- Travel
- Religious projects
- Political projects
- Purchase of second-hand vehicles
- Third-party fundraising initiatives (exceptions may be made for fundraising initiatives by Ford Motor Company Ltd employees and retirees)

The trust also only considers grants from projects being undertaken near Ford Motor Company Ltd/FCE Bank PLC UK operations. The trust's website provides details of eligible postcodes and the only exception to this is when initiatives are made by company employees or retirees.

The trust does not provide grants for individuals.

Applications

Ford Britain Trust

Applications can be made in three ways:

- Download the PDF version from the trust's website to print out, complete and return by post to the correspondence address
- Save the Word version to your computer, complete it electronically and return it by email to fbtrust@ford.com
- Request a paper copy on 01277 252551 to complete and return by post to the correspondence address

Applications for large grants should include a copy of the organisation's most recent report and accounts.

Small grant applications are considered in March, June, September and November and should be submitted by the 1st of each month. Applications for large grants are considered in March and September.

Freshfields Bruuckhaus Deringer LLP

Legal

Correspondent: Corporate Responsibility Department, 65 Fleet Street, London EC4Y 1HS (tel: 020 7936 4000; fax: 020 7832 7001; website: www.freshfields.com)

Directors: David Aitman, Managing Partner; Stephen Eilers, Executive Partner; William Lawes, Senior Partner (women: 0; men: 3)

Year end	30/04/2015
Turnover	£1,245,000,000

Nature of business: The provision of legal services through a network of offices in Europe, Asia, the Middle East and the US.

Company registration number: OC334789

Subsidiary undertakings include: A full list of the group's principal investments is given in the annual report and accounts.

UK employees: 1,968

Total employees: 5,446

Focus of giving: Education, enterprise/training, health, ill health, housing, homelessness, overseas projects, children, young people, community/social welfare.

Membership: BITC, LBG

Community involvement	✓
Community contributions	✓
CSR report	✓
CSR or charity committee	✓
Cash donations declared	✓
Charity partner(s)	✓
Employee-led support	✓
Gifts in kind	✓
Humanitarian aid: overseas	✓
Matched funding	✓
Overseas giving	✓
Payroll giving	✓
Pro bono	✓
Sponsorship	✓

Charitable donations

Total worldwide (cash and in kind):	2015	£13,830,000

Community involvement

Scholarships

Determined to do something to address the disproportionally small numbers of black and black mixed race men in large commercial law firms, Freshfields and Doreen Lawrence launched the Freshfields Stephen Lawrence scholarship scheme in 2013. The scheme awards scholarships to exceptionally talented first-year law undergraduates.

Charity partner

Freshfields has supported the British Red Cross and its climate change adaptation project in Bangladesh since 2014. The partnership has grown to include pro bono support, first aid sessions, employee engagement events and fundraising.

Main UK locations

London and Manchester.

Freshfields also has various offices worldwide.

Community contributions

The Responsible Business Update Report 2015 shows that £13.83 million was given in community contributions during the year. This figure includes management costs and we were unable to determine the amount given in cash and pro bono contributions in the UK.

In-kind support

Pro bono

The company works across borders to help global charities and since 2009 has provided 15,722 pro bono hours for Save the Children.

The company offers free-of-charge help for clients from individual asylum seekers to some of the world's biggest charities. The company's website states: 'Our work is focused around our Responsible Business focus areas and underpinned by Article 1 of the Universal Declaration of Human Rights.'

Last year the company gave over 47,000 hours of free legal help and worked on 531 matters for 290 clients.

Employee-led support

Employee volunteering

Employees are encouraged to spend at least one business day a year volunteering with a team for a community challenge sponsored by the firm. Last year almost one in three of employees volunteered for community projects, giving over 22,000 hours of time on top of that donated via pro bono legal advice.

Payroll giving

Aside from their involvement with Freshfields' community investment and pro bono work, employees are also able to support charities through payroll giving. During the year, 5% of UK employees donated through the scheme.

Matched funding

The company has a programme that matches the personal donations that employees make to charity.

Commercially led support

Ready for Work

Through the Ready for Work programme in London the company supports people who face multiple barriers to work such as individuals who are long-term unemployed, care leavers, ex-offenders and those we are who have been at risk of homelessness. Support includes mentoring, offering work experience placements, and making gifts in kind, such as lending rooms.

Applications

Apply in writing to the correspondent.

Fujitsu Services Holdings PLC

Information Technology

Correspondent: Head of Responsible Business, 22 Baker Street, London W1U 3BW (tel: 01235 797711; email: AskFujitsu@uk.fujitsu.com; website: www.fujitsu.com/uk/about/local/corporate-responsibility)

Directors: Duncan Tait; Hidehiro Tsukano; Hidenori Furata; Ichiro Ohama; Lucy Dimes, Chief Executive; Stephen Clayton

Year end	31/03/2016
Turnover	£2,238,300,000
Pre-tax profit	£93,400,000

Nature of business: Holding company of an IT services group.

Note: Number of employees includes the UK and Ireland.

Company registration number: 142200

Subsidiary undertakings include: Fujitsu Services Ltd; Fujitsu Telecommunications Europe Ltd; ICL Ltd.

UK employees: 14,000

Focus of giving: General charitable purposes, economic generation, education, enterprise/training, environment, health, ill health, marginalised people, armed forces, poverty and social exclusion, science technology, children, young people.

Membership: BITC

Community involvement	✓
Community contributions	✓
Company reports on anti-slavery	✓
CSR report	✓
CSR or charity committee	✓
AF Covenant	✓
Armed forces personnel	✓
Cash donations declared	✓
Charity partner(s)	✓
Employee-led support	✓
Gifts in kind	✓
Payroll giving	✓
Pro bono	✓
Sponsorship	✓

Charitable donations

Total UK (cash and in kind):	2016	£190,000
Total worldwide (cash and in kind):	2016	£190,000

Community involvement

The group supports charitable causes mainly through various partnerships and employee-led support, as well as sponsorship. Regional Impact on Society groups, made up of employees, co-ordinate local charitable giving and volunteering.

The group focuses its community involvement on the following areas:

- Youth unemployment
- Digital divide
- Social exclusion
- Disadvantaged children
- Armed forces

Charity partner

From 2016 to 2018, the group is supporting Macmillan Cancer Support as its charity partner. From 2014 to 2016, the group's partner charity was Action for Children; the group raised a total of £350,000 as well as contributing 4,000 hours of volunteering support and other in-kind services such as IT, HR and marketing.

Young people and education

Led by the Impact on Society groups (see 'Employee fundraising and volunteering'), the group works with schools and colleges to promote technology-related education and careers.

The group has a long-standing relationship with The Prince's Trust, as its patron, running CV and interview workshops for young people on the Team programme. The group has also run the Get Into Tech scheme, giving young people the opportunity to gain experience in technology.

The group also takes part in a number of schemes run by Business in the Community and holds events promoting STEM-related careers for young people.

Digital inclusion

One of the group's priorities is enabling more people to access the Internet. The group has worked in partnership with the Post Office to deliver events such as 'Get Online Week' and employees volunteer at local learning centres to help improve digital accessibility and skills in local communities. In Ireland, the group has partnered with Age Action to deliver support to older people.

Other partnerships

The group also takes part in a number of other schemes run by Business in the Community, such as Opportunity Now, aiming to encourage women into leadership positions; Business Class, providing opportunities for disadvantaged young people; and Business Connectors, placing high-achieving individuals in disadvantaged communities on secondment. In 2015 Fujitsu was named as the winner of BITC's Responsible Business of the Year award.

The group is a 'Corporate Friend' partner of SSAFA. Involvement has included raising £121,000 since 2007 for the charity, sponsoring the Ride of Britain (SSAFA's fundraising cycle challenge), and taking part in the installation of the ceramic poppy display at the Tower of London.

Directors with other relevant posts

Duncan Tait is a trustee of Business in the Community (Charity Commission no. 297716).

Main locations

The group has offices across the UK.

Community contributions

According to the 2015/16 accounts, the group's charitable and educational donations during the year totalled £190,000.

In-kind support

As well as through employee fundraising, the group supports Children in Need by staffing one of its call centres to help process donations on appeal night. It has also donated IT equipment to The Prince's Trust.

Employee-led support

Employee fundraising and volunteering

There are six regional Impact on Society (IOS) groups, made up of employees. Each of the groups is allocated a budget and is responsible for: co-ordinating volunteering opportunities; liasing with charity partners, schools and colleges; supporting fundraising events; and dealing with requests for sponsorship or donations in the local area. According to the 2015 Responsible Business report, employees volunteered 3,300 hours during the year for charities of their choice through the IOS group.

Employees fundraise for the group's partner charity, as well as other initiatives such as Children in Need and SSAFA.

Employees are entitled to one day per year of volunteering leave for either local community causes or projects initiated by the group. Examples include volunteering to help older people get online through the group's digital inclusions initiatives, and running CV workshops with young people through The Prince's Trust.

Commercially led support

Sponsorship

The group sponsors SSAFA's Ride of Britain challenge and also the Army Sailing Association's racing yacht, British Soldier. The group is also sponsoring an award for Business in the Community in 2017 – The Fujitsu Award for Responsible Business in the Digital Age.

Applications

Apply in writing to the correspondent. The group has a number of regional Impact on Society (IOS) groups, which co-ordinate charitable activities, including responding to requests. We would, therefore, suggest that local requests should be made in writing to the IOS group at the relevant site.

G4S PLC

Transport and communications

Correspondent: CSR Department, 5th Floor, Southside, 105 Victoria Street, London SW1E 6QT (tel: 020 8770 7000; email: csr@g4s.com; website: www.g4s.com/en/Social%20Responsibility)

Directors: Adam Crozier; Ashley Almanza, Chief Executive; Clare Spottiswoode; Himanshu Raja, Chief Financial Officer; John Connolly, Chair; John Daly; Mark Elliott; Paul Spence; Tim Weller; Winnie Kin Wah Fok (women: 2; men: 8)

Year end	31/12/2015
Turnover	£6,433,000,000
Pre-tax profit	£327,000,000

Nature of business: G4S PLC provides security services, cash services and justice services internationally.

Company registration number: 4992207

Subsidiary undertakings include: G4S Cash Solutions (UK) Ltd; G4S Integrated Services (UK) Ltd; G4S Secure Solutions (UK) Ltd; G4S Security Services (UK) Ltd.

UK employees: 36,500

Total employees: 610,000

Focus of giving: General charitable purposes, education, health, ill health, overseas projects, sport, recreation, children, young people, community/social welfare.

Community involvement	✓
Community contributions	✓
CSR report	✓
CSR or charity committee	✓
Directors have other relevant posts	✓
Charity partner(s)	✓
Employee-led support	✓
Gifts in kind	✓
Matched funding	✓
Overseas giving	✓
Sponsorship	✓

Charitable donations

Total worldwide (cash and in kind):	2015	£1,148,000

Community involvement

G4S community involvement is decentralised and operated on a local level, so the group's businesses can respond to the needs of their local communities and markets. The group supports the health, education and welfare of children and young people by working with community and charity partners. Support is given through cash donations, the provision of in-kind goods and services and contributions of staff time through employee volunteering activities. The group also supports sports organisations through sponsorship.

Sponsorship

G4S UK is the main sponsor of Game On, Scottish Rugby's Street Rugby initiative which is funded by the charity Wooden Spoon. According to the website, the group has contributed a 'six figure investment' in sponsorship in the past three years, although it is not clear whether this was, for example, financial support or in-kind donations.

Partners

G4S UK partners with Crimestoppers in which the company's employees volunteer to deliver a youth-focused crime-reduction programme called Fearless.

The group has partnered with its Indian-based subsidiary G4S India, and Hope Worldwide to fund Shiksha School in Delhi since 2010.

G4S Africa has partnered with Bhubesi Pride since 2013, which is a sports organisation working in nine African countries introducing children to rugby as well as health education and life skills.

G4S USA has partnered with Habitat for Humanity for a number of years. This charitable organisation provides affordable housing across the world. The company provides cash donations and gives employees time off work to volunteer for the charity.

Directors with other relevant posts

John Connolly is a trustee of Great Ormond Street Hospital Children's Charity (Charity Commission no. 1160024).

Adam Crozier was formerly the Chief Executive of the Football Association and is currently the Chief Executive of ITV PLC.

Tim Weller is a non-executive director of the Carbon Trust.

Employee welfare

The group operates an Employees' Trust Fund and other welfare funds to support the long-term welfare and development of employees who live in financially developing countries. This includes support to projects that benefit the group's employees and grants made directly to individuals. In 2015 the group invested £530,000 into these funds, of which £110,000 was given in grants to employees who had experienced hardship following a serious injury, illness or natural disaster. This included £17,000 to employees who experienced difficulties following the earthquake in Nepal and flooding in Chile.

Main locations
The group works across the UK and internationally. Its UK offices are located in London, Sutton, and Belfast.

Community contributions

In 2015 the group contributed cash donations and provided goods and services worth a total of £1.1 million. There were 1,113 community programmes across 65 countries that benefitted from this support. The group also matched £48,000 of employee fundraising for local community causes across the world.

We were unable to determine a figure for cash or in-kind contributions given in the UK.

Employee-led support

Employee volunteering
G4S employees are able to contribute to their local communities through volunteering. In 2015 employees volunteered over 13,000 hours with charitable and local community organisations.

Employee fundraising
The group provides matched funding through 'Match it' scheme, by which it matches employee fundraising efforts up to the value of £500 per application.

Applications

Applications can be made in writing to the correspondent.

Galliford Try PLC

Building/construction

Correspondent: Paul Kirkwood, PR Manager – Corporate Responsibility and more, Cowley Business Park, Cowley, Uxbridge, Middlesex UB8 2AL (tel: 01895 855000/01423 339941; fax: 01895 855298; email: paul.kirkwood@gallifordtry.co.uk; website: www.gallifordtry.co.uk/sustainability)

Directors: Andrew Jenner; Gavin Slark; Graham Prothero, Finance Director; Greg Fitzgerald, Chair; Ishbel Macpherson; Peter Truscott, Chief Executive Officer; Peter Ventress, Deputy Chair; Terry Miller (women: 2; men: 6)

Year end	30/06/2014
Turnover	£2,348,400,000
Pre-tax profit	£114,000,000

Nature of business: Galliford Try PLC is a housebuilding and construction group operating in the UK.

Company registration number: 836539

Subsidiary undertakings include: Fairfield Redevelopments Ltd; Hill Place Farm Developments; Linden Ltd; Schools for the Community Ltd.

Brands include: Linden Homes; Oak Dry Lining; Rock and Alluvium.

UK employees: 5,268

Total employees: 5,268

Focus of giving: General charitable purposes, environment, health, ill health, housing, homelessness, armed forces, community/social welfare.

Membership: BITC

Community involvement	✓
Community contributions	✓
Company reports on anti-slavery	✓
CSR report	✓
Directors have other relevant posts	✓
Armed forces personnel	✓
Employee-led support	✓
Gifts in kind	✓
Sponsorship	✓

Charitable donations

Cash UK (latest available):	2014	£113,000
Total UK (cash and in kind):	2014	£439,500
Cash worldwide:	2014	£113,000
Total worldwide (cash and in kind):	2014	£439,500

Community involvement

The group makes charitable contributions at a group, division, business unit and project level. The group donates time, money and materials and there is some focus on supporting the communities in which the group operates.

Linden Home Foundation
Linden Homes, one of the group's divisions, has set up a foundation to benefit the communities in which the company operates, with a focus on community initiatives and environmental schemes. Examples of support include: refurbishing a war memorial; raising money for local charities; volunteering for a community garden; and sponsoring a local school. Further details can be found here: www.lindenhomes.co.uk/foundation.

Directors with other relevant posts
Terry Miller is a trustee of Invictus Games Foundation (Charity Commission no. 1159482) and International Inspiration (Charity Commission no. 1139074). She is also a director of the British Olympic Association and was formerly General Counsel for The London Organising Committee of the Olympic Games and Paralympic Games.

Greg Fitzgerald is a governor of South Devon College.

Main locations
The group has operations across the UK: www.gallifordtry.co.uk/contacts.

Community contributions

In 2014/15 the group made charitable contributions totalling £439,500, which was broken down in the annual report as follows:

Time	£232,000
Financial	£113,000
In-kind (materials)	£95,000

Beneficiaries included: CRASH; Rowcroft Hospice; The Prince's Regeneration Trust.

Employee-led support

Employee volunteering
The group has a volunteering policy that entitles employees to two days paid leave per year to volunteer for charitable causes. In 2014/15 employees volunteered for a total of 63 days (2013/14: 25 days).

Employee fundraising
Employees raise funds for various charities through events, such as the Land's End to John O'Groats cycle relay.

Applications

Applications can be made in writing to the correspondent or by contacting the division local to where the project takes place.

Game Digital PLC (formerly The Game Group PLC)

Computer software

Correspondent: International Charity Committee, Unity House, Telford Road, Basingstoke, Hampshire RG21 6YJ (tel: 01256 784000; website: www.gamegroup.plc.uk)

Directors: Caspar Wooley; David Hamid, Chair; Franck Tuil; John Jackson; Lesley Watkins; Mark Gifford; Martyn Gibbs, Chief Executive Officer; Pablo Crespo (women: 1; men: 7)

Year end	25/07/2015
Turnover	£866,600,000
Pre-tax profit	£25,800,000

Nature of business: The group is a video games retailer, trading through stores, online and mobile channels.

Previously we have used the details of The Game Group PLC which went into administration in 2012. The business was re-started through Game Digital PLC.

Company registration number: 9040213

Subsidiary undertakings include: Capitex Holdings Ltd; Cherrilux Investments S.à.r.l;.Game Retail Ltd.

Focus of giving: General charitable purposes.

Community involvement	✓
Employee-led support	✓

Community involvement

It seems that currently support is mainly channelled through employees' involvement.

Game recently formed an international Charity Committee which is responsible for running and encouraging charitable activity throughout the company. The committee is tasked with increasing the amount the company does for charity and making it easier for employees to run and ask for support in their own charitable activities.

Main locations

There are stores across the UK. The head office is in Basingstoke.

Community contributions

The annual report and accounts did not seem to declare the amount given in charitable contributions.

In-kind support

Previous research has shown that the group can donate gaming items. We were unable to identify the cost to the company.

Employee-led support

According to the annual report and accounts 2014/15:

> As part of GAME's commitment to community, over the last year we have worked extensively to support charitable causes. Last year we raised funds and donated items to over 500 charities and community projects. Our fundraising ranged from bake sales and raffles to gaming marathons, as well as the more traditional marathons

Applications

Apply in writing to the correspondent.

Genting UK PLC (formerly Genting Stanley PLC)

Gaming

Correspondent: See 'Applications', Genting Club Star City, Watson Road, Birmingham B7 5SA (website: www.gentingcasinos.co.uk/playitsafe)

Directors: Dato' Sri Lee Choong Yan; Lim Keong Hui; Lim Kok Thay; Peter Brooks; Rt Hon. Lord Kenneth Baker (women: 0; men: 5)

Year end	31/12/2015
Turnover	£228,200,000
Pre-tax profit	(£55,800,000)

Nature of business: The main activity of the company is operating casinos.

Company registration number: 1519749

Subsidiary undertakings include: Coastbright Ltd; Genting Casinos UK Ltd; Park Lane Mews Hotel London Ltd.

Total employees: 4,310

Focus of giving: Education, health, ill health, less popular charitable purposes, financial education, children, young people.

Community involvement	✓
Community contributions	✓
CSR report	✓
Charity partner(s)	✓
Employee-led support	✓
Gifts in kind	✓
Market-led giving	✓
Unpopular causes	✓

Charitable donations

Cash UK (latest available):	2015	£202,000
Total UK (cash and in kind):	2015	£202,000
Cash worldwide:	2015	£202,000
Total worldwide (cash and in kind):	2015	£202,000

Community involvement

Genting UK PLC's directors' report for 2016 sets out the group's approach to CSR: 'Genting UK is focused on contributing positively to the development of the economy and the community in all areas where it operates ... As a responsible member of the casino gaming industry, we are resolutely committed to the development of awareness, prevention and counselling programmes for problem and underage gambling, both on our premises and in the wider community in which we operate'.

It is further explained that 'Genting UK PLC is an active contributor to the Responsible Gambling Trust, which funds research and education into problem gambling in the UK. In addition, the Group supports the work of GamCare, a registered charity, and publicises the services they offer to individuals with gambling problems.'

Employees are also encouraged to engage with and fundraise for causes in their local areas. The Genting UK website explains 'This locally based activity is strongly supported by the company in various ways so we can all make a positive and lasting contribution to our local area'.

Main locations

There are sites across the UK.

Community contributions

Genting UK PLC's directors' report for 2015 states that the group made a donation of £202,000 in the year to the Responsible Gambling Trust. We have taken this as the figure for its charitable donations during the year. We were unable to determine a value for the support given to GamCare.

Genting's global business website also explains: 'Other charities supported by Genting UK in 2015 included Cancer Research UK, local children's charities and hospices and Baan Doi, a charity based in Thailand.' However, we were unable to determine whether this support came from the group or from employees.

Beneficiaries included: Responsible Gambling Trust (£202,000); GamCare.

In-kind support

Genting UK promotes the services that GamCare, a registered charity, offers for individuals with gambling problems.

Employee-led support

Employee fundraising

Genting employees are actively involved in raising money for good causes. An example given on the website at the time of writing (October 2016) was a trek of the Great Wall of China by two employees, which raised £1,500 for the Responsible Gambling Trust. The pair won the trip through a competition held for Genting staff. Another example comes from employees at Liverpool's Genting Club Queen Square raised funds for Macmillan Cancer Support.

Commercially led support

Fundraising events

Genting venues hold various charity and fundraising events. The website for Genting's global business states that in 2015:

> Genting UK celebrated the Genting Group's 50th jubilee anniversary with various celebration activities and charity raising events held in all of its casino properties. These included several 60's and James Bond theme nights and 'International Markets vs Home Markets Cricket Match' to support Children's Happiness Involves People – the casino charity which provided wheelchairs for disabled children.

Exclusions

Our research indicates that no support is given for: appeals from individuals; the arts; environment/heritage; fundraising events; overseas projects; political appeals; religious appeals; or science/technology.

Applications

It would appear that charitable supported is directed towards gambling charities. Employees are encouraged to identify charities to support through fundraising.

GKN PLC

Engineering

Correspondent: Lily Xie, Manager of Group Brand and CSR, PO Box 55, Ipsley House, Ipsley Church Lane, Redditch, Worcestershire B98 0TL (tel: 01527 517715/01527 533599 or 07500 973 583; fax: 01527 517700; email: lily.xie@gkn.com or cr@gkn.com; website: www.gkn.com/corporateresponsibility)

Directors: Adam Walker, Finance Director; Angus Cockburn; Jos Sclater; Kevin Cummings; Michael Turner, Chair; Nigel Stein, Chief Executive; Phil

Swash; Richard Parry-Jones; Shonaid Jemmett-Page; Tufan Erginbilgic (women: 1; men: 9)

Year end	31/12/2015
Turnover	£7,231,000,000
Pre-tax profit	£245,000,000

Nature of business: An international engineering group involved in the automotive and aerospace industries.

Company registration number: 4191106

Subsidiary undertakings include: British Hovercraft Corporation Ltd; GKN Defence Ltd; Westland Group PLC.

UK employees: 6,000

Total employees: 56,100

Focus of giving: Education, health, ill health, medical research, science technology, children, young people, community/social welfare.

Community involvement	✓
Community contributions	✓
CSR report	✓
Directors have other relevant posts	✓
Employee-led support	✓
FTSE 100	✓
STEM-focused	✓

Community involvement

GKN supports communities around the globe in which it operates. The group's companies and employees contribute to charitable work and community projects by fundraising and volunteering. Some causes are supported corporately by the group, which also offers a charitable giving scheme, but it appears that the majority are selected and supported by the employees themselves. There is some particular focus on: preparing young people for the world of work, particularly in relation to STEM (science, technology, engineering and maths) subjects; and improving local communities through social projects and charitable donations.

Directors with other relevant posts

Mike Turner is a member of the UK government's Apprenticeship Ambassadors Network.

Angus Cockburn is an Honorary Professor at the University of Edinburgh.

Phil Swash is a honorary fellow of Liverpool John Moores University.

Main locations

The group has sites in Birmingham; Bristol; Filton; Isle of Wight; Leek; London; Luton; Redditch; Portsmouth; Telford; Yeovil.

Community contributions

In 2015 the group made worldwide contributions totalling £1 million to 271 projects mostly supporting young people under the groups Hearts of Gold community scheme. We were unable to determine what form these contributions took, such as cash donations for example, and it is likely that the majority of these contributions were raised and/or delivered by the employees themselves at the group's various sites around the world. We were unable to determine how much the group itself actually donated to charitable causes or how much was contributed in the UK.

Employee-led support

Hearts of Gold

The group launched the Hearts of Gold awards to celebrate the charitable and community contributions made by its employees around the world. These contributions are mostly focused on supporting young people, particularly in the field of STEM (science, technology, engineering and mathematics) subjects. This includes offering work experience and apprenticeships; sponsoring education; and technology institutions and events.

According to the Hearts of Gold website, some examples of employee contributions in the UK include: employees collecting for a local food bank; a team fundraising event for Unicef; and individual employees doing sponsored events. To see further examples of employee support for communities under this scheme, visit: www.gkn.com/heartsofgold.

Employee volunteering

The group provides paid time off for employees to volunteer for community causes.

Commercially led support

The group partners with schools and other academic institutions worldwide to inspire future engineers.

Exclusions

No support is given for political appeals.

Applications

Applications can be made in writing to the correspondent.

GlaxoSmithKline PLC

Healthcare, pharmaceuticals

Correspondent: Global Community Partnerships, GSK House, 980 Great West Road, Brentford, Middlesex TW6 9GS (email: community.partnerships@gsk.com; website: www.gsk.com/en-gb/responsibility)

Directors: Dr Jesse Goodman; Dr Moncef Slaoui; Dr Vivienne Cox; Emma Walmsley, Chief Executive Officer Designate; Judy Lewent; Lynn Elsenhans, Corporate Responsibility Committee Chair; Manvinder Singh Banga; Prof. Sir Roy Anderson; Simon Dingemans, Chief Financial Officer; Sir Andrew Witty, Chief Executive Officer; Sir Philip Hampton, Chair; Stacey Cartwright; Urs Rohner (women: 5; men: 8)

Year end	31/12/2015
Turnover	£23,923,000,000
Pre-tax profit	£10,526,000,000

Nature of business: The group's principal activities are the creation and discovery, development, manufacture and marketing of pharmaceutical products, including vaccines, over-the-counter medicines and health-related consumer products.

Company registration number: 1047315

Subsidiary undertakings include: Glaxo Group Ltd; GlaxoSmithKline LLC; GlaxoSmithKline UK Ltd; Setfirst Ltd; Stiefel Laboratories Inc.; Wellcome Ltd

Brands include: Horlicks; Panadol; Sensodyne.

Total employees: 101,255

Focus of giving: Education, environment, health, ill health, medical research, humanitarian help, overseas projects, science technology, children, young people.

Membership: BITC, LBG

Accredited Living Wage Employer	✓
Community involvement	✓
Community contributions	✓
Company reports on anti-slavery	✓
CSR report	✓
CSR or charity committee	✓
Directors have other relevant posts	✓
Charity partner(s)	✓
Employee-led support	✓
FTSE 100	✓
Gifts in kind	✓
Humanitarian aid: overseas	✓
Humanitarian aid: UK including food banks	✓
Matched funding	✓
Overseas giving	✓
STEM-focused	✓

Charitable donations

Cash UK (latest available):	2015	£3,233,500
Cash worldwide:	2015	£56,600,000
Total worldwide (cash and in kind):	2015	£197,200,000

Community involvement

GlaxoSmithKline looks to improve the well-being of its global communities by supporting programmes that improve healthcare infrastructure, promote science and health education, and assist with humanitarian relief. It works in partnership with numerous organisations with a particular focus on taking a proactive approach towards global health threats and providing community access to healthcare. Cash and in-kind donations are made and employee time is contributed, particularly in response to emergency situations, including investment in re-building and reconstruction following a disaster. Corporate donations are also made to charitable organisations across the world, including those that work in the fields of health, medical research, science education, the arts and the environment.

The website states:

> We are transparent about our charitable giving with data being published in our Annual Report and Corporate Responsibility Report in March each year. We are further increasing transparency by publishing details of our individual charitable grants over £10,000 ($15,000).

Details of GSK's grants awarded can be found on the Responsibility section of the company's website.

GlaxoSmithKline IMPACT Awards

The annual GlaxoSmithKline IMPACT Awards are run in partnership with the King's Fund to recognise and promote excellence in community healthcare.

To be eligible for a GSK IMPACT Award, organisations must be registered, have an annual income of between £25,000 and £2 million, be working in a health-related field, and must have been operating in the UK for at least three years:

- Up to ten winners receive £30,000 of unrestricted funding plus the overall winner will receive an extra £10,000
- Up to ten runners-up receive £3,000
- Organisations do not need to present a new project, and winners decide how to spend the award money
- Winning organisations will be offered free development and training up to the value of £6,000

For further details, visit the King's Fund's website: www.kingsfund.org.uk

Partnerships

The group's main global charity partner is Save the Children. The partnership will last for at least five years and has involved using the charity's local expertise, combining resources and capabilities regarding research and development and providing children with immunisations, treatments and other healthcare interventions. This has resulted in, among other things, a model of services for anti and postnatal and child health in the Democratic Republic of Congo. In 2015 the group provided seed funding to the charity to help it establish an Emergency Health Unit in the UK and Asia Pacific region.

In 2015 the group also partnered with numerous other international organisations, including: AmeriCares; Amref Health Africa; Bill and Melinda Gates Foundation; CARE International; Comic Relief; Direct Relief; IMA World Health; MAP International; Marie Stopes International; National Center for Disaster Preparedness; and Project HOPE.

The 2015/16 partnership with Comic Relief was created with a £17 million donation from the group and a £5 million donation from Comic Relief. The partnership will make grants to frontline organisations working to fight malaria in five countries where it is endemic.

Community health

In the world's least financially developed countries in which the group operates, the group reinvests 20% of its profits from the sale of pharmaceutical and consumer healthcare products to educate and train community health workers and on initiatives to reduce infant and maternal mortality, particularly in rural communities. This has impacted on 35 countries so far and the group is now extending the initiative to other countries in sub-Saharan Africa.

The group supports the UN One Million Community Health Workers Campaign and has funded a pilot to train 1,800 health workers in Ghana.

The group also has an annual US$1 million Healthcare Innovation Award, which rewards initiatives to improve under-five child survival rates in financially developing countries. The award is focused on sustainable and scalable healthcare projects. In 2015/16 winners included initiatives in Africa, Asia and South America, with the overall winner being PATH in South Vietnam.

The group works with community organisations to challenge stigma and discrimination associated with HIV. In 2015 this included a £6.7 million four-year initiative to increase community support for black gay and bisexual men in the USA.

Education

In the UK the group has a Science Education and Early Talent team plus volunteer STEM (science, technology, engineering and mathematics) ambassadors who are employees of the group. These employees demonstrate science and engineering in schools and manage the graduate and apprenticeship programmes.

In Africa, the group invests and collaborates with the Royal Society of Chemistry's Pan African Chemistry Network and universities across Sub-Saharan Africa to train scientists.

Directors with other relevant posts

Dr Vivienne Cox is Lead Independent Director at the UK Government's Department for International Development.

Sir Andrew Witty is Chancellor of the University of Nottingham.

Sir Philip Hampton is Chair of the Women on Board's review.

Professor Sir Roy Anderson is Chair of the Science Advisory Board of the Natural History Museum and a fellow of the Royal Society, the Academy of Medical Sciences and the Royal Statistical Society.

Dr Moncef Slaoui is an advisor to the Qatar Foundation and a director of the International AIDS Vaccine Initiative.

Lynn Elsenhans is a trustee of the United Way of Greater Houston in the USA.

Judy Lewent is a trustee of the Rockefeller Family Trust and a member of the American Academy of Arts and Sciences.

Urs Rohner is a trustee and Chair of the Credit Suisse Research Institute and Credit Suisse Foundation.

Main locations

The group's global headquarters is in Brentford. Other UK sites are located in County Durham; Harlow; Irvine; Maidenhead; Montrose; Slough; Stevenage; Ulverston; Uxbridge; Ware; Weybridge; and Worthing.

Community contributions

In 2015 in the UK, GlaxoSmithKline made donations of £10,000 or more directly to charitable organisations totalling £3.2 million. This includes £618,500 donated under the GSK IMPACT Awards scheme. Over 36 grants were made to organisations working in the fields of health, medical research, science education, the arts and the environment. The company also makes smaller grants, although these are as yet unreported, so the figure we quote here is likely to be higher. No figure was available this year for in-kind support in the UK.

Note that the group do not generally accept unsolicited requests for funding, unless through an application made under the GSK IMPACT Awards.

Beneficiaries of grants in the UK during 2015 included: Tres Cantos Open Lab Foundation (£781,500); Age UK (£585,500); WellChild (£318,000 in four grants); Reach Volunteering (£140,000 in two grants); Music in Hospitals (£125,000); Help for Heroes (£100,000); Cumbria Flood Relief (£50,000); British Lung Foundation and CoolTan Arts (£30,000 each); Thames 21 Ltd (£10,000).

Global contributions

Global contributions during the year totalled £197.2 million, not including £11.1 million spent in management costs:

Product and in-kind	£136.9 million
Cash	£56.6 million
Time	£3.7 million

Contributions were broken down further in the 2015 Responsible Business Supplement as follows:

Cash donations: included £40.8 million on health, well-being and education programmes, including £6.5 million donated primarily for the purposes of training community health workers in financially developing countries. £17 million was also donated to Comic Relief, although it is unclear as to whether this was taken out of the £40.8 million figure.

In-kind gifts: this comprised of donations of medicines, including for the purposes of humanitarian aid. This includes £4.1 million worth of product donations made to five of the group's international partners for the purposes of humanitarian aid.

According to the 2015 Responsible Business Supplement, the group donated £1.1 million to support efforts to address the global refugee crisis.

In-kind support

GlaxoSmithKline makes in-kind contributions in the form of product donations and staff time, particularly for financially developing countries. In 2015 the group donated 644 million albendazole tablets to treat a mosquito–borne worm disease and 258 million tablets to treat intestinal worms.

The group also provides vaccines and medicines at a not-for-profit price and shares its knowledge. For example, the group worked with Save the Children to develop and distribute an antiseptic gel to prevent umbilical cord infections in financially developing countries. The group will offer the gel at a not-for-profit price and will share knowledge with other organisations so that the gel can be manufactured locally.

Employee-led support

Employee volunteering

The company supports employees' charitable and community involvement through two main volunteering programmes:

PULSE Volunteer Partnership – The programme gives GSK employees the opportunity to work with a non-profit organisation full-time for three or six months. Since the initiative was launched in 2009, 560 of the group's employees have worked with 103 non-profit organisations in 62 countries. In 2015 a total of 39 employees' from the UK and USA participated in the programme, as did another 39 employees from elsewhere in the world. The initiative enables employees to develop their leadership skills while lending their skills and expertise to address global healthcare problems. For further information, visit: www.gskpulsevolunteers.com.

Orange Day volunteer programme – Through the Orange Day volunteer programme, employees are able to take one paid day's leave for volunteering purposes each year. Many employees volunteer for activities that promote STEM education to children and young people.

In 2015 the group became a founding partner of IMPACT 2030, in which the UN collaborates with the private sector to use corporate volunteers to contribute to the Global Goals for Sustainable Development.

Employee fundraising

Most employees' fundraising efforts are focused on raising funds for the group's main global charity partner, Save the Children. Donations are then matched by the group.

Applications

For more information on funding requests, contact the correspondent.

However, note the following from the website:

> GSK supports community initiatives in both the developed and the developing world. Identifying the right projects is an important responsibility, and that's why the company takes a strategic, proactive approach and **does not generally support unsolicited requests for funding**.

To apply for a GSK IMPACT Award, read the application guidelines and complete the online form available at: www.kingsfund.org.uk.

The Go-Ahead Group PLC

Transport and communications

Correspondent: Sarah Boundy, Corporate Communications Director, 4 Matthew Parker Street, Westminster, London SW1H 9NP (tel: 020 7799 8983; fax: 07808 568667; email: sarah.boundy@go-ahead.com; website: www.go-ahead.com)

Directors: Adrian Ewer; Andrew Allner, Chair; Carolyn Ferguson; David Brown, Group Chief Executive; Katherine Innes Ker; Nick Horler; Patrick Butcher, Chief Financial Officer (women: 2; men: 5)

Year end	02/07/2016
Turnover	£3,361,300,000
Pre-tax profit	£99,800,000

Nature of business: The principal activity of the group is the provision of rail and bus public transport services. Its subsidiaries provide transport solutions in London and the South East, the South Coast, East Anglia and the North East. The group also has a contract to provide bus services in Singapore.

Company registration number: 2100855

Subsidiary undertakings include: Brighton and Hove Bus and Coach Company Ltd; Go North East Ltd; Metrobus Ltd.

Brands include: London Midland; Southeastern; Plymouth Citybus.

Total employees: 27,566

Focus of giving: General charitable purposes, education, small groups, local groups, children, young people, community/social welfare.

Membership: LBG

Community involvement	✓
Community contributions	✓
Company reports on anti-slavery	✓
CSR report	✓
AF Covenant	✓
Cash donations declared	✓
Charity partner(s)	✓
Company gives to smaller charities	✓
Employee-led support	✓
Gifts in kind	✓
Matched funding	✓
Sponsorship	✓

Charitable donations

Cash UK (latest available):	2016	£233,000
Total UK (cash and in kind):	2016	£525,500
Cash worldwide:	2016	£233,000
Total worldwide (cash and in kind):	2016	£525,500

Community involvement

The Go-Ahead Group's community investment strategy is set out in its 'Community and charitable investment' policy and in its 'Sustainability Report' for 2015/16; both documents are available from the group's website.

The strategy has three strands:

- At a corporate level Go-Ahead supports two international but UK-based charities that have a transport focus and therefore have strong links to our business: Railway Children and Transaid
- Our operating companies support more local initiatives that reflect the concerns and priorities of the communities they serve
- Individuals or groups of employees can also raise money for causes with which they have a personal link. These are supported (for example by sponsorships) by individual operating companies on an ad hoc basis

The group's 'devolved' approach to community involvement allows its operating companies to best respond to their communities and enabling them to 'partner with local charities, community groups as well as schools and colleges to support activities improving the local area and strengthening social cohesion'.

Due to this localised approach and the considerable number of operating companies within the group, we've chosen to focus on examples from just one operating company, London Midland, which produces its own annual sustainability reports. The examples mentioned in this record are taken from the sustainability report for 2015 – the most recent available at the time of writing (November 2016).

Charity partners

As stated above, the group's strategic partners are Railway Children and Transaid. During 2015/16 these partnerships involved both charities attending the group's annual management conference to present interactive sessions from senior management personnel from across the group.

Armed Forces Covenant

Go North East, one of the group's subsidiary companies, is a signatory of the covenant.

Main locations

The group has a head office in the City of Westminster, but has operating companies serving a broad geographical area within England. For more information on the group's companies and where they operate, we would suggest having a look at the operations map on the website (www.go-ahead.com/en/our-companies/our-operations.html).

Community contributions

There is a document available to download from the website containing sustainability data for the group, which includes information on community contributions according to the London Benchmarking Group model.

In 2015/16 the group made community contributions totalling £525,500, which was given in the following forms:

Gifts in-kind	£248,500
Cash contributions	£233,000
Employee time	£43,500

Management time contributed was valued at £175,000, although, as is our usual practice, we have not included this figure in our total for the group's contributions.

Of the total contributed by the group, its rail division gave £272,500 and its bus division £211,500, with a further £41,000 contributed by its head office.

The sustainability data also provides a detailed breakdown of community contributions given by individual operating companies.

In-kind support

Education programmes

Go-Ahead has an online education programme, Go-Learn, which is aimed at helping children and young people between the ages of 4 and 14 to improve their knowledge and confidence about public transport. The group's website explains that 'Mapped against the National Curriculum, the resources can be used by parents and teachers to support literacy, numeracy, citizenship and elements of personal, social and health education'.

Some train operators and bus companies within the group also use locally branded Go-Learn material on certain routes. The programme complements other educational programmes with which Go-Ahead's rail and bus companies are involved; these include Plymouth Citybus's 'Dennis Dart' programme which promotes road safety in primary schools.

Gifts in kind

Our previous research shows that in-kind support is given in the form of the provision of free travel to charities, advertising space, and staff time.

Employee-led support

Employee involvement

The sustainability data available shows that 1,153 employees from across the group were involved in their communities during 2015/16.

Employee fundraising

Staff at London Midland's head office, Snow Hill and West Coast lines took part in a sponsored climb of Mount Snowdon, raising £1,000 for Birmingham Children's Hospital.

Matched funding

The group's individual operating companies support their employees' charitable activities on an 'ad hoc' basis. Support can include matched funding or sponsorships. For example, London Midland's sustainability report for 2015 states that the company contributed £1 for every £2 raised by employees through the London Midland Giving matched funding programme.

Commercially led support

Sponsorship

London Midland sponsored an elephant model, Elmo, at the 2015 Lichfield Festival. The elephant was auctioned for £800 with funds split between the festival and Birmingham Samaritans. The company also sponsored Dr Whoot, a six foot tall model owl, as part of The Big Hoot, a ten week fundraising event in Birmingham. Dr Whoot was auctioned off, raising £10,000 for Birmingham Children's Hospital.

Apprenticeships

In 2015 London Midland took on its first apprentices through The Prince's Trust scheme.

Exclusions

Our research suggests that support is not given for advertising in charity brochures, animal welfare, appeals from individuals, environment/heritage causes, overseas projects and political or religious appeals.

Applications

The group's community involvement is co-ordinated at a local level by its operating companies. For more information about these operating companies and the areas they serve, see the operations map on the group's website (www.go-ahead.com/en/our-companies/our-operations.html).

Goldman Sachs International

Banking, securities/shares

Correspondent: Jenny Evans, Correspondent to the Trustees, Peterborough Court, 133 Fleet Street, London EC4A 2BB (tel: 020 7774 1000; website: www.goldmansachs.com/citizenship/index.html)

Directors: Anthony Grabiner; Brian Griffiths; C. Dahlback; Isabelle Ealet; Jose Barroso; Lord Griffiths of Fforestfach; M. S. Sherwood, Co-Chief Executive Officer; Marius Winkleman; Michael Sherwood; P. D. Sutherland, Chair; Richard Gnodde; Susan Kilsby

Year end	31/12/2015
Pre-tax profit	£2,119,000,000

Nature of business: Provision of investment banking, trading, asset management and securities to corporations, financial institutions, governments and wealthy individuals.

Company registration number: 2263951

Subsidiary undertakings include: Goldman Sachs International Investments Ltd; Goldman Sachs (Cayman) Ltd

Focus of giving: General charitable purposes, education, armed forces, overseas projects, poverty and social exclusion, children, young people.

Membership: BITC

Community involvement	✓
Community contributions	✓
CSR report	✓
AF Covenant	✓
Armed forces personnel	✓
Corporate charity	✓
Gifts in kind	✓
Overseas giving	✓
Sponsorship	✓

Charitable donations

Cash UK (latest available):	2015	£14,300,000
Total UK (cash and in kind):	2015	£14,300,000
Cash worldwide:	2015	£14,300,000
Total worldwide (cash and in kind):	2015	£14,300,000

Community involvement

At a global level, Goldman Sachs' philanthropy includes four major initiatives: Goldman Sachs Gives, a donor-advised fund with which former and current senior employees have an input; Community Teamworks, a worldwide employee volunteering initiative; 10,000 Women, which looks to boost local economies by supporting females entrepreneurs; and 10,000 Small Businesses, which looks to create jobs and economic growth by investing in business education, opportunities and support services for entrepreneurs.

In the UK Goldman Sachs has established two registered grant-making charities:

The Goldman Sachs Charitable Gift Fund (UK) (Charity Commission no. 1120148)

The fund was set up for the advancement of education, the relief of poverty, the advancement of religion and any other purposes charitable in both English and American law.

Goldman Sachs Gives (UK)(Charity Commission no. 1123956)

The charity is a grant-making charity, providing grants to a wide range of charitable projects.

Supporting Veterans

The firm is committed to helping veterans transition to civilian life and work through training and mentoring initiatives. The website states that two-month Goldman Sachs Veterans Integration Program (VIP) 'provides service men and women exiting the military with an opportunity to develop their professional skills, strengthen their understanding of financial services and prepare for careers in the industry'. The Goldman Sachs Veterans Network 'recruits talented troops and fosters their professional development at the firm'.

Main locations

The group's main location is London and there are various offices worldwide.

Community contributions

In 2015 the company donated £14.3 million to Goldman Sachs Gives UK. We have no other information available regarding the company's charitable giving.

In-kind support

Various initiatives are supported on a local basis in the communities in which Goldman Sachs has a presence and the firm contributes its 'ideas, people and resources'.

Employee-led support

Community Teamworks

The volunteer programme is in operation for Goldman Sachs employees around the globe. In 2015 a total of 54 Goldman Sachs offices partnered with over 900 non-profit organisations on nearly 1,600 projects worldwide and contributed over 150,000 hours to communities.

Goldman Sachs Gives

According to the website, this scheme is committed to fostering innovative ideas, solving economic and social issues, and enabling progress in underserved communities globally. Through a donor-advised fund, Goldman Sachs current and retired senior employees work together to recommend grants to qualifying non-profit organisations to help them achieve their goals.

Commercially led support

Citizenship programmes

10,000 Women: This is a global initiative that fosters economic growth by providing women entrepreneurs around the world with a business and management education, mentoring and networking, and access to capital.

10,000 Small Business: This is an investment to help entrepreneurs create jobs and economic opportunity by providing greater access to education, capital and business support services. 10,000 Small Businesses is funded by Goldman Sachs and the Goldman Sachs Foundation.

Sponsorship

Goldman Sachs sponsored The National Portrait Gallery major exhibition of portraits by Pablo Picasso (1881–1973). Goldman Sachs has a long history of supporting arts and culture in the UK.

Corporate charity

Goldman Sachs Gives (UK) (Charity Commission no. 1123956) and The Goldman Sachs Charitable Gift Fund (UK) (Charity Commission no. 1120148).

Exclusions

Our research indicates that grants will not be made to/for: individuals; fraternal organisations; political causes, campaigns or candidates; or fundraising events.

Applications

For company applications contact the Charitable Services Team at the company's address.

For both **The Goldman Sachs Charitable Gift Fund (UK)** and **Goldman Sachs Gives (UK)** Charities Aid Foundation and CAF America, and Ayco Company L.P. review grant eligibility applications and other requests for grant funding on behalf of the directors. Subject to the express approval of each grant application by one of the directors on behalf of the directors, Ayco then distributes funds in furtherance of the fund's objects.

In the first instance, address applications to Mike Housden, a trustee of both charities.

Note: CAF's contact details are:

Charities Aid Foundation, 25 Kings Hill Avenue, Kings Hill, West Malling Kent ME19 4TA (tel: 0300 012 3000, fax: 0300 012 3001, email: enquiries@cafonline.org).

Goodwin PLC

Engineering

Correspondent: Pam Ashley, Company Secretary, Ivy House Foundry, Hanley, Stoke-On-Trent ST1 3NR (tel: 01782 220000/01782 220283; email: investors@goodwinplc.com; website: www.goodwin.co.uk)

Directors: Bernard R. E. Goodwin; Jennifer E. Kelly; John Connolly; John Goodwin; Matthew S. Goodwin; Richard S. Goodwin; Simon R. Goodwin; Steven C. Birks; Tim J. W. Goodwin (women: 1; men: 8)

Year end	30/04/2016
Turnover	£124,000,000
Pre-tax profit	£12,300,000

Nature of business: Founded in 1883 as R. Goodwin and Sons Engineers, specialising in mechanical engineering The company remains under family management and control with over 51% of the voting shares still in the hands of the Goodwin family.

Company registration number: 305907

Subsidiary undertakings include: Goodwin Steel Castings Ltd; Goodwin International Ltd; Easat Antennas Ltd.

UK employees: 848

Total employees: 1,010

Focus of giving: General charitable purposes.

Community contributions	✓
CSR report	✓
Cash donations declared	✓

Charitable donations

Cash UK (latest available):	2016	£48,500
Total UK (cash and in kind):	2016	£48,500
Cash worldwide:	2016	£48,500
Total worldwide (cash and in kind):	2016	£48,500

Community involvement

Little information is available on the company's charitable giving, except on the charitable donation declared.

Main locations

Main UK location: Stoke-on-Trent.

Community contributions

According to the 2015/16 annual report, donations by the group for charitable purposes amounted to £48,500. The majority of these were made to local communities within the group's operating environments.

Exclusions

Funding is not provided for political donations.

Applications

Apply in writing to the correspondent.

Gowling WLG (UK) LLP (formerly known as Wragge Lawrence Graham & Co. LLP)

Legal

Correspondent: Lorna Gavin, Head of Corporate Responsibility, 4 More London Riverside, London SE1 2AU (tel: 020 7759 6963/020 3636 7931; fax: 0370 904 1099; email: lorna.gavin@gowlingwlg.com; website: gowlingwlg.com)

Directors: Andrew Witts, Designated Member; David Fennell, Designated Member

Year end	30/04/2015
Turnover	£181,053,000
Pre-tax profit	£56,374,000

Nature of business: Gowling WLG LLP is an international law firm, formed from the merger of Canadian law firm Gowling and UK-based firm Wragge Lawrence Graham & Co. LLP in 2016. The firm also has offices in Europe, China, the Middle East and Singapore.

Company registration number: OC304378

Subsidiary undertakings include: Ingleby Services; Wragge Lawrence Graham & Co. Services Ltd; Wragge & Co. Ltd.

Focus of giving: General charitable purposes, education, enterprise/training, equal opportunities, health, ill health, housing, homelessness, inner cities, medical research, armed forces, humanitarian help, older people, arts, culture, children, young people, community/social welfare, disability.

Membership: BITC, LBG

Accredited Living Wage Employer	✓
Community involvement	✓
Community contributions	✓
Company reports on anti-slavery	✓
CSR or charity committee	✓
Armed forces personnel	✓
Charity of the Year	✓
Charity partner(s)	✓
Corporate charity	✓
Employee-led support	✓
Gifts in kind	✓
Humanitarian aid: UK including food banks	✓
Matched funding	✓
Payroll giving	✓
Pro bono	✓

Community involvement

The group provides support for a range of causes through its charitable trust, as well as providing volunteer and other support for issues such as homelessness, education and diversity. The group nominates three Charity of the Year partners to support, and also provides pro bono legal advice to a range of charities.

Gowling WLG (UK) Charitable Trust (Charity Commission no. 803009)

Previously known as Wragge & Co. Charitable Trust, the group's corporate charity makes small grants to charities and also provides matched funding for employee fundraising initiatives. The trust supports a wide range of charitable purposes. In 2014/15 the trust made 130 grants totalling £106,000.

Charity of the Year partners

The firm's employees nominate three charities each year – one nationally, and two locally to the London and Birmingham offices. Employees fundraise for the charities and, where possible, pro bono and in-kind support is also provided. In 2016 following the Gowling WLG merger and launch of the new name, the firm pledged to donate 50p per tweet, up to £3,000, for every tweet with a photo of the firm's name and the relevant hashtag. In 2016 the chosen charities were Beyond Food Foundation, Bliss and Help Harry Help Others.

Education and employment

The firm is part of the Legal Social Mobility Partnership, providing work experience opportunities to disadvantaged young people and also works in partnership with Enabling Enterprise, inviting schoolchildren to spend a day in the office and take part in enterprise activities. It also runs the Day in the Life of a Lawyer programme, offering a work placement, mentoring and skills development for young people, aiming to broaden access to the legal profession.

The firm also sponsors a TeachFirst teacher in a school in Birmingham, and offers work placements to individuals through its homelessness support initiatives.

Other partnerships

The firm also supports Free@Last, a charity that works with young people in Birmingham, funding support for young dads and young men to develop leadership and life skills.

Diversity

The firm is also a Stonewall Diversity Champion, with an active LGBTA network for employees, and the firm also sponsors an anti-homophobic bullying scheme through the charity Diversity Role Models in a school in Birmingham.

Suited for Success

The firm is one of the founding partners of the charity Suited for Success (Charity Commission no. 1165131), which provides interview clothing for people in Birmingham who are unemployed.

Main locations

The group has two offices in the UK – Birmingham and London. There are also offices in Belgium; Canada; China; France; Germany; Middle East; Monaco; Russia; and Singapore.

Community contributions

No figure was given for the group's total charitable contributions.

In-kind support

Pro bono

The firm provides pro bono legal advice to charities and community groups and through legal clinics, supporting local and national organisations including NSPCC; Oxfam; Roshni; SIFA Fireside; and The Big Issue Foundation.

Employee-led support

Employee volunteering

The firm's volunteering programme focuses on the issues of homelessness, education and inner city needs. Employees volunteer in a range of activities to support this.

Homelessness

Employees offer support through activities such as CV and interview workshops to help people who are homeless or disadvantaged to gain employability skills and confidence. Employees also provide support through delivering Christmas lunches, donating food and clothing and organising fundraising events. The firm also provides work placements for people in need of experience.

Education

Employees in the firm volunteer with local primary schools in Birmingham and London to help with reading. Over 100 employees have also become school governors through the firm's partnership with the School Governors One Stop Shop.

Inner city needs

Employees can donate to food and clothing banks in the firm's offices, supporting the Trussell Trust as well as local charities SIFA Fireside (in Birmingham) and Spitalfields Crypt Trust and St Giles Trust (in London).

Employee fundraising

Employees raise funds for partner charities and can also donate to charities through a payroll giving scheme. There is also a staff choir which raises money at concerts throughout the year.

Corporate charity

Gowling WLG (UK) Charitable Trust (Charity Commission no. 803009).

Applications

The firm

Enquiries can be directed to Lorna Gavin, Head of Corporate Responsibility.

Gowling WLG Charitable Trust

Applications to the trust should be made in writing to trustee Lee Nuttall (Two Snowhill, Snowhill Queensway, Birmingham B4 6WR; tel: 0121 233 1000)

The trust's 2014/15 annual report states that management of the trust is carried out by the firm, which co-ordinates applications and presents them to the trustees, who consider requests at their meetings throughout the year.

Grainger PLC

Property

Correspondent: Dave Butler, Director of Strategy and Change, Citygate, St James' Boulevard, Newcastle upon Tyne NE1 4JE (tel: 0191 261 1819/020 7940 9500 or 07920 292309; fax: 0191 269 5901; email: dbutler@graingerplc.co.uk; website: www.graingerplc.co.uk/responsibility.aspx)

Directors: Andrew Carr-Lock; Baroness Margaret Ford; Belinda Richards; Helen Gordon, Chief Executive; Nick Jopling; Rob Wilkinson; Tony Wray; Vanessa Simms, Finance Director (women: 4; men: 4)

Year end	30/09/2015
Turnover	£244,100,000
Pre-tax profit	£50,000,000

Nature of business: The group owns, acquires and trades regulated and market-let tenanted properties.

Company registration number: 125575

Subsidiary undertakings include: Atlantic Metropolitan (UK) Ltd; Cambridge Place Management Company Ltd; Park Estates (Liverpool) Ltd.

UK employees: 292

Total employees: 292

Focus of giving: Education, general appeals, housing, homelessness, children, young people, community/social welfare.

Community involvement	✓
Community contributions	✓
CSR report	✓
Directors have other relevant posts	✓
Employee-led support	✓
Gifts in kind	✓
Matched funding	✓
Payroll giving	✓

Charitable donations

Cash UK (latest available):	2015	£31,411
Total UK (cash and in kind):	2015	£39,839

Community involvement

Grainger PLC looks to improve the social, economic and environmental outlook for the communities in which it operates. Charities have been supported through cash donations and employee fundraising and volunteering time. The company is also a foundation partner of the charity Land Aid.

In 2015 the company set up a community grant fund to engage and support its local Wellesley community in Aldershot.

Directors with other relevant posts

Helen Gordon is a board member of the New Covent Garden Market Authority and an advisory board member of the Cambridge University Land Economy Department.

Baroness Margaret Ford is an Honorary Professor of Real Estate at Glasgow University and also sits in the House of Lords as an independent peer.

Main UK locations

Grainger PLC has offices in Newcastle (head office), Altrincham nr Manchester, Harborne in Birmingham, and London Bridge.

Community contributions

During 2014/15 the group made donations of £31,500 (2013/14: £20,400) to charitable causes. In kind giving through staff volunteering time was costed at a further £8,400 (2013/14: £10,000).

Beneficiaries* have included: Alzheimer's Society; Barnabus Homeless Charity; Breast Cancer; Children in Need; Comic Relief; Harry and Jock Appeal; Land Aid; Macmillan Cancer Support; Myeloma UK; Newcastle Society for Blind People; Newcastle United Foundation; Oxfam; Save the Children; Sports Relief; St Ann's Hospice; Useful Vision.

*This includes those who have benefitted through either cash donations or employee volunteering.

In-kind support

The company provides facilities for community organisations, such as rent-free space to The Source's Bike Start initiative in Aldershot.

Employee-led support

Employee fundraising

During 2014/15, Grainger employees raised more than £17,000 for charitable causes through fundraising activities.

Payroll giving

Employees donated a further £13,000 through the payroll giving facility.

Employee volunteering

The group facilitates employee volunteering in the local communities in which it operates and owns properties. During the year 17% of employees participated in the group's volunteering activities. This included collaboration with their partner Kier to undertake a joint team volunteering day.

Applications

Applications can be made in writing to the correspondent.

Great Portland Estates PLC

Property

Correspondent: Janine Cole, Head of Sustainability, 33 Cavendish Square, London W1G 0PW (tel: 020 7647 3000; fax: 020 7016 5500; email: janine.cole@gpe.co.uk; website: www.gpe.co.uk/responsibility.aspx)

Directors: Charles Philipps; Elizabeth Holden; Jonathan Nicholls; Jonathan Short; Martin Scicluna, Chair; Neil Thompson; Nick Sanderson, Finance Director; Toby Courtauld, Chief Executive (women: 1; men: 7)

Year end	31/03/2016
Turnover	£128,800,000
Pre-tax profit	£555,100,000

Nature of business: The main activity of the company is property development and investment. The company's properties are all based in central London.

Company registration number: 596137

Subsidiary undertakings include: B and H S Management Ltd; Collin Estates Ltd; G.P.E. (Bermondsey Street) Ltd.

UK employees: 95

Total employees: 95

Focus of giving: Health, ill health, housing, homelessness, small groups, older people, children, young people, disability.

Community involvement	✓
Community contributions	✓
Company reports on anti-slavery	✓
CSR report	✓
Directors have other relevant posts	✓
Charity of the Year	✓
Company gives to smaller charities	✓
Employee-led support	✓
Gifts in kind	✓
Matched funding	✓

Charitable donations

Cash UK (latest available):	2016	£144,362
Cash worldwide:	2016	£144,362

Community involvement

Great Portland Estates PLC actively participates in associations working to improve central London in various ways. Each financial year, the group's directors and employees nominate four charities, both local and national, to receive support. The Building Managers, in consultation with tenants, also nominate at least two charitable organisations or events to support during the year with fundraising and the use of the buildings. The company also makes regular corporate donations to Land Aid and sponsors other various charitable projects.

Charities of the Year
The company donates £20,000 each year to charities nominated by its employees. In 2015/16 the charities of the year were: Child Bereavement UK; Land Aid; and Thames Reach.

The arts
The company loans the use of properties with empty space to local galleries and charities for temporary exhibitions and presentations. In 2016 it also co-hosted an art competition on 50 years in Soho, along with a local college and one of their contractors.

The company has also supported a theatre event, West End Live, for the past seven years.

Directors with other relevant posts
Charles Philipps is a trustee of The Outward Bound Trust (Charity Commission no. 1128090) and Outward Bound Global (Charity Commission no. 313645).

Toby Courtauld is a member of Imperial College London Council.

One of the company's employee's, Portfolio Director Neil Thompson, is a member of the Willow Foundation Development Board (Charity Commission no. 1106746).

Future plans
The company states on its website that in 2016/17 it will be reviewing its current relationships with charitable organisations with a view of creating longer-term relationships by the 2020s.

Main locations
London (West End)

Community contributions

According to the website, in 2015/16 the company made charitable donations totalling £144,500. This total included an annual donation of £10,000 given to Land Aid.

We were unable to determine the value for the in-kind support given by the group.

2015/16 beneficiaries included: Building Lives; Child Bereavement UK; Land Aid; West End Community Trust; Willow Foundation.

Previous beneficiaries have included: Carers Trust; Children in Need; Handicapped Children's Action Group; Ickle Pickles; Lord Mayor's Appeal; Peter Westropp Memorial Trust; Positive East; ReThink; RNLI; Royal Marsden; Thames Reach; The Fire Fighters Charity; The Institute of Cancer Research; The National ME Centre.

In-kind support

The company provides affordable work space to Islington Council at its 148 Old Street development for the use of small and start-up organisations who may not be able to afford market rents.

Employee-led support

Employee fundraising
The company encourages its employees to participate with charitable activities and matches employee fundraising efforts up to a value of £250 per event. In 2015/16 the company supported 31 employees and their chosen charities in this way.

Commercially led support

The company supports a number of primarily London-based educational establishments through providing on-site tours, presentations, work experience and mentoring. In 2015/16 the company supported: University of Reading; University of Westminster; Westminster Kingsway College.

Exclusions

No support can be given for political appeals or appeals in an area where the company has no presence.

Applications

Applications can be made in writing to the correspondent.

Greene King PLC

Brewers/distillers

Correspondent: Joanna Kreckler, Corporate Communications Manager, Westgate Brewery, Bury St Edmunds, Suffolk IP33 1QT (tel: 01284 763222/ 01284 714123; fax: 01284 706502; email: JoannaKreckler@greeneking.co.uk or corporateresponsibility@greeneking.co.uk; website: www.greeneking.co.uk)

Directors: Gordon Fryett; Kirk Davis, Chief Financial Officer; Lynne Weedall; Mike Coupe; Philip Yea, Chair; Rob Rowley; Rooney Anand, Chief Executive (women: 1; men: 6)

Year end	01/05/2016
Turnover	£2,073,000,000
Pre-tax profit	£256,500,000

Nature of business: Greene King is a leading pub retailer and brewer, running pubs, restaurants and hotels. The company manages 3,035 pubs in the UK, with a focus on the South East (including London) and East.

Company registration number: 24511

Subsidiary undertakings include: Greene King Brewing and Retailing Ltd; Little London Pubs Ltd; Realpubs Ltd.

Brands include: Greene King IPA; Hungry Horse; Loch Fyne Seafood and Grill; Old Speckled Hen.

UK employees: 44,137

Total employees: 44,137

Focus of giving: General charitable purposes, enterprise/training, general appeals, health, ill health, large national appeals, sport, recreation, children, young people, community/social welfare.

Community involvement	✓
Community contributions	✓
CSR report	✓
Directors have other relevant posts	✓
Charity partner(s)	✓
Employee-led support	✓
Sponsorship	✓

Charitable donations

Cash UK (latest available):	2016	£15,000
Cash worldwide:	2016	£15,000

Community involvement

Greene King is currently working in partnership with two charities and also supports the local charities its employees 'most care about'. It makes product donations, supports employee volunteering and operates a payroll giving scheme. The group's employees, licensees and customers help to raise funds for local, national and international causes through a varied range of activities such as sports events, quizzes, raffles, auctions, and karaoke.

Charity partnerships
Macmillan Cancer Support: In 2012 the group launched its first charity partnership with Macmillan Cancer Support with the aim of raising £1 million over three years. Employees and customers managed to raise over £2 million and in 2015/16 the company decided to renew the partnership for a further three years.

The Prince's Trust: In 2015/16 the company partnered with The Prince's Trust to launch a Get into Hospitality programme. The programme aims to give 150 of the UK's most disadvantaged 16- to 25-year-olds the opportunity to develop skills and qualifications in the hospitality sector. The company aims to offer jobs and placements on their apprenticeship scheme for a number of participants who complete the three-week programme.

Great Ormond Street Hospital: The company's Taylor Walker pub brand completed a ten-year partnership with the hospital during the year, and raised £100,000 during that time.

Directors with other relevant posts
Philip Yea is a trustee of The Francis Crick Institute (Charity Commission no. 1140062).

Main UK locations
Greene King's head office is located in Bury St Edmunds. For the location of your nearest Greene King pub, hotel or restaurant, see the pub finder facility on the website (www.greeneking.co.uk/pub-finder).

Community contributions

In 2015/16 the group gave at least £15,000 to charitable causes. This was a donation to Pub is the Hub, a not-for-profit organisation that supports rural pubs in diversifying their services for community benefit. The donation goes towards its Community Services Fund, which provides grants of up to £4,000 to eligible pubs.

Employee-led support

Employee fundraising
Employees across the company's pubs, restaurants and hotels participate in fundraising events and challenges, such as the Yorkshire Three Peaks and London Marathon, to raise funds for charities. Employees also participate in national campaigns, such as the World's Biggest Coffee Morning.

In 2015/16 employees and customers in over 600 of the company's pubs raised £71,000 for Prostate Cancer UK during the Rugby World Cup. Support was also given to ITV's Text Santa fundraising appeal.

Commercially led support

Brand support
The Taylor Walker pub brand supported Prostate Cancer UK in 2015/16 with its Men United movement in late 2015 with fundraising events and with temporarily rebranding some of the pubs into the Men United Arms. The selected pubs were rebranded with the charity's signs, bunting, beer maps, drip trays and team uniforms.

Applications

Contact the correspondent regarding further information about making an application or to enquire about a partnership.

Greggs PLC

Food manufacture, retail – miscellaneous

Correspondent: Richard Hutton, Finance Director, Greggs House, Quorum Business Park, Newcastle upon Tyne NE12 8BU (tel: 0191 281 7721; email: getintouch@greggs.co.uk; website: corporate.greggs.co.uk/social-responsibility)

Directors: Allison Kirkby; Helena Ganczakowski; Ian Durant, Chair; Jonathan Jowett; Peter McPhillips; Raymond Reynolds; Richard Hutton, Finance Director; Roger Whiteside, Chief Executive; Sandra Turner (women: 3; men: 6)

Year end	02/01/2016
Turnover	£835,700,000
Pre-tax profit	£73,000,000

Nature of business: The principal activity of the group is the retailing of sandwiches, savouries and other bakery related products with a particular focus on takeaway food and catering. The majority of products sold are manufactured in house.

Company registration number: 502851

Subsidiary undertakings include: Charles Bragg (Bakers) Ltd; Greggs Properties Ltd; J R Birkett and Sons Ltd.

UK employees: 21,331

Focus of giving: General charitable purposes, education, health, ill health, marginalised people, less popular charitable purposes, humanitarian help, poverty and social exclusion, children, young people, community/social welfare, disasters.

Membership: BITC

Community involvement	✓
Community contributions	✓
CSR report	✓
Directors have other relevant posts	✓
Cash donations declared	✓
Corporate charity	✓
Employee-led support	✓
Gifts in kind	✓
Humanitarian aid: UK including food banks	✓
Market-led giving	✓
Pledge 1%	✓
Sponsorship	✓

Charitable donations

Cash UK (latest available):	2016	£700,000
Cash worldwide:	2016	£700,000

Community involvement

Greggs PLC looks to focus its community involvement through in a number of ways, including through the Greggs Foundation, product and service donations, and employee involvement through volunteering and fundraising activities. The company and foundation tend to support charitable organisations that work with: children and young people, with a focus on education and nutrition; social and community welfare; and food banks/redistribution.

In 2015 the company won the Business of the Year award at the Third Sector Business Charity Awards. This was due to the company's culture of supporting charities at all levels within the organisation.

Greggs Foundation
Each year, Greggs PLC donates at least 1% of its pre-tax profit through its charity, the Greggs Foundation (Charity Commission no. 296590). The foundation supports community initiatives in the North East, such as the Greggs Breakfast Club programme that provides free breakfasts to children in primary schools. In 2015 the programme provided over four million breakfasts in 363 schools. 163 of these clubs are also supported by the company's partner organisations who aim to improve learning opportunities for children in disadvantaged areas.

The foundation helps people in need via its Hardship Fund and contributes to the core running costs of small charitable organisations through the North East Core Funding Programme. In 2015 the foundation awarded a total of £718,000 in community grants.

BITC Business Connector
Greggs has supported Business in the Community's Business Connector initiative since 2011, through which selected employees have undertaken long-term secondments to create a bridge between businesses and community organisations in their local area. The company was given a three-star rating in the BITC CR index scheme during 2015.

Education
In 2015 the company trialled a partnership with the Newcastle Falcons Foundation in which they supported the charity's Tackling Health initiative. The company planned to pilot their own educational initiative, with a focus on nutritional education in schools, in 2016.

Directors with other relevant posts
Richard Hutton is a trustee of the Greggs Foundation (Charity Commission no. 296590) and a member of Business in the Community's Finance and Risk Committee.

Jonathan Jowett is a trustee of The Percy Hedley Foundation (Charity Commission no. 515943).

Main UK locations
Greggs' head office is located in Newcastle. The company operates stores nationwide.

Community contributions

In 2015 the company donated £700,000 to the Greggs Foundation, which also benefitted from additional donations from the proceeds of carrier bag charges, and funds raised in the company's shops and bakeries by employees and customers.

As is our usual practice, we have not included employee or customer-raised funds in our total. We were unable to determine the value of the in-kind or other support not given to the Greggs Foundation.

In-kind support

Donated products

The company donates unsold food at the end of each working day to charitable organisations. In 2015 this amounted to 423.1 tonnes of food. Some of the company's shops have direct links with local organisations to which they distribute unsold food, and the company also partners with the Trussell Trust and FareShare. The company has worked with FareShare over the past ten years and supplies eight of its regional distribution centres.

Donated services

The company assists the Greggs Foundation through the provision of free office space and management staff.

Employee-led support

Employee volunteering

All managers in the company are entitled to one day per year to volunteer with local charitable organisations to share their professional skills, particularly in areas like accounting, administration, legal, marketing, operations and planning. In 2015 this totalled to over 500 days spent volunteering.

Commercially led support

In-store fundraising

The company encourages fundraising in its nationwide outlets and receives donations from customers for a variety of charitable purposes. In 2015 the charities supported this way included: BBC Children in Need; Disasters Emergency Committee (for the Nepal earthquake appeal); North of England Children's Cancer Research Fund; and the Poppy Appeal.

The company donates the proceeds from the carrier bag levy and sales of its Jammy Heart biscuit to the Greggs Foundation.

Sponsorship

The company is the main sponsor of the annual Children's Cancer Run, which is held in aid of the North of England Children's Cancer Research charity. The company gives a free lunch to all who take part in the event.

Corporate charity

The Greggs Foundation (Charity Commission no. 296590).

Exclusions

The company makes no political donations or contributions.

Exclusions for grant programmes administered by the Greggs Foundation can be found on its website.

Applications

The company appears to direct its charitable donations through the Greggs Foundation(Charity Commission no. 296590), which administers a number of grant programmes. Each grant programme has its own criteria, guidelines and application process, all of which are available to view on the foundation's website: www.greggsfoundation.org.uk.

Grosvenor Group

Property

Correspondent: Jane Sandars, The Grosvenor Office, 70 Grosvenor Street, London W1K 3JP (tel: 020 7408 0988; email: westminster.foundation@grosvenor.com; website: www.grosvenor.com)

Directors: Christopher Pratt; Domenico Siniscalco; Jeremy Newsum; Lesley Knox, Chair; Mark Preston, Group Chief Executive; Michael McLintock; Nicholas Scarles, Group Finance Director; Philip Dilley (women: 1; men: 6)

Year end	31/12/2015
Pre-tax profit	£526,600,000

Nature of business: The group's principal activities are property investment, financial services and general management in Britain and Ireland, North America, Continental Europe and Asia Pacific.

Company registration number: 3219943

Subsidiary undertakings include: Grosvenor Investments Ltd; Grosvenor Developments Ltd; Grosvenor Estate Management Ltd; Grosvenor Realty Investments Ltd; Victoria Properties (London) Ltd; Quarrydale Two Ltd.

Focus of giving: Education, enterprise/training, health, ill health, poverty and social exclusion, children, young people, community/social welfare.

Community involvement	✓
Community contributions	✓
CSR report	✓
CSR or charity committee	✓
Cash donations declared	✓
Corporate charity	✓
Employee-led support	✓
Gifts in kind	✓
Matched funding	✓

Charitable donations

Cash UK (latest available):	2015	£2,700,000
Total UK (cash and in kind):	2015	£2,700,000
Cash worldwide:	2015	£2,700,000
Total worldwide (cash and in kind):	2015	£2,700,000

Community involvement

The Westminster Foundation

Most of Grosvenor's community support is routed through the Westminster Foundation (Charity Commission no. 267618) which was established in 1974 as the Grosvenor family's charitable foundation. The foundation's grant-making is currently focused on the issue of poverty in the UK.

The foundation also runs events such as an Impact Assessment workshop attended by 80 charities as well as hosting major events for seven charities.

The Liverpool ONE Foundation

The group also established the Liverpool ONE Foundation in 2009, which is now managed by Community Foundation for Merseyside and awards funding for projects based around children and young people, education and employability in Merseyside, and particularly Liverpool.

The Living Cities Community Fund

The fund was founded by Grosvenor in 2014 and is managed by the London Community Foundation. Grants of between £500 and £5,000 are available to organisations in South Westminster in the areas of health and community cohesion.

Main UK locations

Grosvenor has UK offices in Edinburgh, London and Liverpool.

Community contributions

In 2015 the group made a donation of £2.3 million to the Westminster Foundation. A further £400,000 was given to other charitable causes by the group.

In-kind support

During the year the group supported 144 community events including 77 that they organised.

Occasionally space within the London and Chester offices are made available to charities for fundraising purposes.

Employee-led support

Employee volunteering

The group has introduced a volunteering scheme which gives employees a two day volunteering allowance. During the year 360 volunteering days were logged by staff.

Matched funding

Staff fundraising efforts are supported through the Westminster Foundation. In 2015 the total donated through matched funding was £40,000.

Corporate charity

The Westminster Foundation (Charity Commission no. 267618).

Applications

The Westminster Foundation

Applications can be made through the foundation's website: www.westminsterfoundation.org.uk/how-to-apply/How-to-Apply.aspx.

The Liverpool One Foundation
Applications can be made through the Community Foundation for Merseyside website: www.cfmerseyside.org.uk/funds/liverpool-one.

The Living Communities Fund
Applications can be made through the London Community Foundation website: www.londoncf.org.uk.

Guardian Media Group PLC

Media

Correspondent: See 'Applications', Kings Place, 90 York Way, London N1 9GU (tel: 020 3353 2000; website: www.theguardian.com/sustainability)

Directors: Baroness Gail Rebuck; David Pemsel, Chief Executive Officer; Jennifer Duvalier; Jimmy Wales; John Paton; Judy Gibbons; Katharine Viner; Neil Berkett, Chair; Nick Backhouse; Nigel Morris; Philip Tranter, Company Secretary; Richard Kerr, Chief Financial Officer (women: 4; men: 8)

Year end	03/04/2016
Turnover	£209,500,000
Pre-tax profit	(£173,000,000)

Nature of business: Guardian Media Group PLC (GMG) is one of the UK's leading media organisations.

GMG is solely owned by The Scott Trust Ltd, which was established in 1937 as a trust and in 2008 became a limited company. The Guardian website explains that the main purpose of The Scott Trust is to 'secure the financial and editorial independence of the Guardian in perpetuity, while its subsidiary aims are to champion its principles and to promote freedom of the press in the UK and elsewhere'.

Company registration number: 94531

Subsidiary undertakings include: Guardian Education Interactive Ltd; Guardian News and Media Ltd; Guardian News and Media LLC.

Brands include: The Guardian; theguardian.com; The Observer.

Total employees: 1,813

Focus of giving: Human rights, education, housing, homelessness, large national appeals, small groups, local groups, less popular charitable purposes, older people, overseas projects, poverty and social exclusion, women's issues, children, young people, community/social welfare.

Accredited Living Wage Employer	✓
Community involvement	✓
Community contributions	✓
Company reports on anti-slavery	✓
CSR report	✓
Directors have other relevant posts	✓
Charity partner(s)	✓
Company gives to smaller charities	✓
Employee-led support	✓
Gifts in kind	✓
Humanitarian aid: overseas	✓
Overseas giving	✓
Pro bono	✓
Unpopular causes	✓

Charitable donations

Cash UK (latest available):	2016	£220,000
Total UK (cash and in kind):	2016	£220,000
Cash worldwide:	2016	£220,000
Total worldwide (cash and in kind):	2016	£220,000

Community involvement

Guardian Media Group (GMG) works in partnership with local organisations working in close to its offices and also supports national and international causes through campaigning and promoting issues, fundraising and through its registered charitable foundation.

The Guardian Foundation
GMG makes donations to The Guardian Foundation (Charity Commission no. 1153865), an independent charity which, according to the Guardian website, operates with the following mission: 'to empower journalists and the community to report the truth through education, the promotion of human rights and the right to information'.

The foundation was registered in 2013 as the successor to The Scott Trust Foundation, which transferred its assets and operations to The Guardian Foundation in September 2014. The foundation's principal source of funding is Guardian Media Group PLC.

While, in the past, The Scott Trust Foundation operated as a grant-giver, The Guardian Foundation's current activities are focused on its object of advancing education, research and human rights. There are currently four strands of activity which are outlined in the annual report for 2015/16:

- The operation of The Guardian Education Centre 'provides educational services to a wide variety of schoolchildren, teachers and educational professionals in order to support education in journalism and teaching practices'
- An archive and exhibitions programme 'preserves for the public benefit and makes accessible to the public material of historic, artistic and educational value'
- Bursaries for postgraduate qualifications in print journalism and web journalism are 'provided to the applicants who best satisfy the established criteria, taking account of the desire to encourage graduates from diverse social and/or ethnic backgrounds'
- 'The international programme offers training to overseas journalists and provides educational support to applicants and organisations who best satisfy the established criteria'

The foundation is in the process of expanding existing and establishing new activities, including an outreach educational project which is currently being piloted in UK schools. In 2017 it plans to launch the Hugo Young Award in celebration of young political writing in the UK.

The Guardian Foundation partners
The Guardian Foundation is currently working to achieve its aims in the UK and overseas through partnerships with the following organisations: Article 19; International Media Support; P24.

Community programme
The Guardian has a small-scale community programme designed to promote active engagement in the area local to its office. The 'Living our Values' sustainability report for 2015, which was the most recent available at the time of writing (January 2016) explains that the Guardian partners with local charities, groups and schools working to address a wide range of local issues in its neighbourhood, as well as with organisations involved with media education. The report further states: 'We support our community partners through joint projects, sharing ideas, resources and staff volunteering. Our aim is to build trust and long-term relationships – we have worked with some of our partners for almost 15 years ... Our projects with local partners are individually tailored and developed as needs change over time. Occasionally, we respond to ad hoc requests, such as help with finding space to host an event. We can't always oblige but our feedback surveys make it clear that our partners are very comfortable with asking for extra help when it is needed'. Community partners also benefit from the annual Volunteering Week.

The most recent list of community partners (published in September 2015 on the Guardian website) were grouped under eight headings:

- **Schools: reading, literacy, employability and leadership mentoring** - Elizabeth Garrett Anderson, Richard Cloudesley School and Winton Primary School

- **Older people: helping to tackle isolation and loneliness** – Age UK Camden and Opening Doors London
- **Social mobility** – Bemerton Villages Management Organisation and Team Cally
- **Media education/youth journalism** – Live Mag UK
- **Media education/social exclusion** – Pentonville Prison
- **Homelessness/young people** – New Horizon Youth Centre
- **Environmental/youth leadership and enterprise** – Global Generation
- **Environmental/local habitats** – London Wildlife Trust

The Guardian and Observer Charity Appeal 2016

This charity appeal, which takes place at Christmastime each year, saw 16,000 readers donate a total of almost £1.5 million for the appeal three chosen charities.

The beneficiaries were: The Children's Society; Help Refugees; and Safe Passage.

The Guardian Charity Awards

Since 1993, these awards – which are currently supported by Bates Wells and Braithwaite, The Foundation for Social Improvement, Jigsaw24, the Media Trust, and NCVO – have celebrated the work of small social welfare charities throughout the UK. The Guardian website explains that each year five 'extraordinary' winning charities are awarded with a 'vital boost' in the form of 'a small cash prize, an iPad mini, and a range of tailor-made support'. The five winners in 2016 were: Marsh Community Centre (Lancaster); Music Action International; MyBnk; Refugee and Migrant Centre (the Black Country); TCC – Trefnu Cymunedol Cymru/ Together Creating Communities (North Wales).

Philanthropic partnerships

As part of its commitment to social justice journalism, the Guardian works with charitable funders to help promote issues of particular interest to the paper. Examples of major partnerships include:

- Global Development website (www.theguardian.com/global-development): supported, in part, by the Bill and Melinda Gates Foundation
- Guardian Cities: an online, editorially independent, hub for discussion about urban life: supported by The Rockefeller Foundation
- Modern Slavery in Focus: an online, editorially independent, series covering modern day slavery: supported, in part, by Humanity United
- Women's rights and gender equality in focus: a series launched through the Global Development website to study issues faced by women, girls and transgender people, and the work of women's rights movements. The series received funding from the Ford Foundation and Mama Cash. Mama Cash is also an expert partner for the series, as is the Association for Women's Rights in Development (AWiD)

Directors with other relevant posts

Neil Berkett: trustee of NSPCC.

Nick Backhouse: trustee of Chichester Festival Theatre.

Baroness Gail Rebuck: Chair of both the Cheltenham Literature Festival and Quick Reads; founder of the World Book Day charity; Chair and Pro-Provost of the Royal College of Art.

Jimmy Wales: founder of Wikipedia and on the board of trustees of the Wikimedia Foundation.

Main UK locations

London (Camden) and Manchester.

Community contributions

The annual report and accounts for April 2016 declared that the group paid £220,000 in charitable donations to the Guardian Foundation. We were unable to determine details of other community contributions.

In-kind support

Pro bono

Examples of how pro bono support has benefitted community partners include:

- Community Partners' Workshop: A team of 15 volunteers and five students met with representatives from community partners to discuss ways to deal with a key challenge facing their organisations. They were given a crash course in prototyping and shared their work with the group
- Pentonville Prison: journalists provided skills sessions and software and research training to help with the production of the prison's quarterly magazine and radio station
- Mile End Community Project: the Guardian sports team visited the project to talk to young people, to deliver a tutorial about sports photography and to help them try their hand at live blogging and podcasting

Examples to community partners include:

- Global Generation: event space was provided for a book launch and auction and exhibition
- Opening Doors London: the Guardian prints the charity's monthly newsletter
- The Cally Festival: the Guardian donated books to the festival

Employee-led support

Employee volunteering

GMG's annual Volunteering Week sees staff volunteer with the group's community partners. In 2015/16 the day's theme was #connect and, as the Guardian website explains, '250 people took part as regular volunteers, project managers or project sponsors' with 15 projects (14 in London and one in Manchester) to the benefit of 12 community organisations. Examples included staff from the Guardian Print Centre in Manchester who helped to give Gorse Hill Community Allotment a spring clean and helping out with a community day at New Horizons Youth Centre.

In the 'Living our Values' sustainability report for 2015, it is reported that around one quarter of staff were involved in volunteering activities.

Applications

The group's community contributions appear to be concentrated on The Guardian Foundation and its community partners.

Halfords Group PLC

Motors and accessories, retail – miscellaneous

Correspondent: Community & CSR Manager, Icknield Street Drive, Washford West, Redditch, Worcestershire B98 0DE (tel: 01527 517601; website: www.halfordscompany.com/responsibility/community)

Directors: Claudia Arney; David Adams; Dennis Millard, Chair; Helen Jones; Jill McDonald, Group Chief Executive; Jonny Mason, Chief Financial Officer (women: 3; men: 3)

Year end	01/04/2016
Turnover	£1,021,500,000
Pre-tax profit	£81,500,000

Nature of business: The principal activity of the group is the retailing of auto, leisure and cycling products in the UK and Ireland.

Company registration number: 4457314

Subsidiary undertakings include: Boardman Bikes Ltd; Halfords Ltd; Halfords Autocentres Ltd.

Total employees: 11,036

Focus of giving: Education, less popular charitable purposes, overseas projects, safety and crime prevention, children, young people.

Community involvement	✓
Community contributions	✓
CSR report	✓
CSR or charity committee	✓
Charity partner(s)	✓
Employee-led support	✓

Gifts in kind ✓
Overseas giving ✓
Pro bono ✓

Community involvement

Halfords develops relationships within local communities principally through a range of bicycle-related programmes. Colleagues contribute their time and expertise through these programmes and also take part in fundraising activities for the group's charity partners. Halfords customers take part in bicycle 'trade-in' events, contributing their unwanted bikes which are then used in some of Halfords' community programmes.

Partnerships

Re-Cycle: In 2013 the group entered into a long-term partnership with Re-Cycle, a charity that donates unwanted bikes from the UK to Africa. Re-Cycle has received more than 20,000 bikes donated by the public since the partnership began and Halfords employees have helped to raise more than £295,000 for the charity.

Dallaglio Foundation: During 2015/16, Halfords Autocentres partnered the Dallaglio Foundation to benefit young people who have been excluded from mainstream education.

Breeze: Halfords partners British Cycling's Breeze programme, which looks to encourage more women to take up cycling.

Programmes

Bikes for primary schools: Bikes donated by members of the public at trade-in events held at Halfords stores are reconditioned and given to children at schools in disadvantaged areas in eight 'cycling cities' in the UK. These cities are: Birmingham; Bristol; Cambridge; Leeds; Manchester; Newcastle; Norwich; and Oxford.

Halfords Colleagues also contribute skills, time and expertise through a number of workshop programmes designed for children. These are:

- **Kids' Holiday Bike Club**: Free workshops for children between the ages of 7 and 11 and their parents are held in Halfords stores
- **Gear-Up! School Workshops**: Colleagues run these workshops, which are aimed at promoting bike maintenance and safety, for children who are in their final year of primary school
- **Cub bike workshops**: Halfords has partnered the Scouts Association, helping Cubs to attain their Cyclist Activity badge by attending workshops held in stores

Halfords Academy

Halfords has set up an academy at HMP Onley where prisoners can train to become professional cycle mechanics. Prisoners work on bikes donated by the public at Halfords trade-in events which are then given to schools in disadvantaged areas. The academy also provides prisoners employment opportunities following the completion of their sentences.

Directors with other relevant posts

David Adams is a trustee of Walk the Walk, a charity that raises money for and awareness of breast cancer through power walking challenges.

Main UK locations

Halfords Group PLC's head office is located in Redditch, Worcestershire. There are Halfords branches located nationwide.

Community contributions

The annual report and accounts for 2016 did not declare a figure for charitable donations.

In-kind support

Gifts in kind

As part of its initiative to provide bikes for children in primary schools, Halfords provide new cycle helmets to go with the recycled bikes it donates.

Pro bono

Halfords Colleagues contribute skills, time and expertise through a number of workshop programmes designed for children.

Employee-led support

Employee fundraising

Halfords colleagues take an active role in raising funds for the group's charity partners. As part of the Re-Cycle partnership, for example, employees took part in a number of fundraising initiatives, to help cover the cost of sending bikes to Africa. Colleagues also assisted causes in their local areas. In Penrith for example, colleagues held a collection for unwanted clothing, furniture and essential cleaning items for people whose homes had been affected by flooding caused by Storm Desmond.

Applications

The 'Community' section of the Halfords website (www.halfordscompany.com/responsibility/community) explains: 'As much as we'd like to help everyone who contacts us, we receive an average of five requests for support each day and it's just not possible to help all. So at Halfords we made the decision to make a big difference to one charity and we direct all of our focus there right now by supporting our colleagues in fundraising activities for this charity.'

Bikes for primary schools

Schools in the eight 'cycling cities' (Birmingham, Bristol, Cambridge, Leeds, Manchester, Newcastle, Norwich and Oxford) can apply for a donation of bikes and helmets using the application form which is available to download from the 'Community' page on the Halfords website.

Gear-Up! School Workshops

Teachers can register their interest for the next round of workshops via a link on the 'Community' page.

Cub bike workshops

Cub scouts leaders can find out more about Halfords Cubs workshops at fundraising.scouts.org.uk/halfords.

Hammerson PLC

Property

Correspondent: Charities Committee, Kings Place, 90 York Way, London N1 9GE (tel: 020 7887 1000; email: sustainability@hammerson.com; website: sustainability.hammerson.com/charity-partnerships.html)

Directors: Andrew Formica; David Atkins, Chief Executive; David Tyler, Chair; Gwyn Burr; Jean-Philippe Mouton; Judy Gibbons; Peter Cole; Pierre Bouchut; Terry Duddy; Timon Drakesmith, Chief Financial Officer (women: 2; men: 8)

Year end	31/12/2015
Turnover	£366,400,000
Pre-tax profit	£215,400,000

Nature of business: Owner-manager and developer of retail and office property in the UK and France.

Company registration number: 360632

Subsidiary undertakings include: Grantchester Holdings Ltd; Hammerson Group Ltd; Hammerson SAS.

UK employees: 324

Total employees: 468

Focus of giving: General charitable purposes, education, enterprise/training, health, ill health, local groups, children, young people, community/social welfare.

Membership: LBG

Community involvement ✓
Community contributions ✓
CSR report ✓
CSR or charity committee ✓
Directors have other relevant posts ✓
Charity partner(s) ✓
Company gives to smaller charities ✓
Employee-led support ✓
FTSE 100 ✓
Gifts in kind ✓
Matched funding ✓
Sponsorship ✓

Charitable donations

Cash worldwide:	2015	£150,000
Total worldwide (cash and in kind):	2015	£2,158,000

Community involvement

Hammerson looks to develop relationships in the communities where it has a presence, both at a corporate level and through its locations in the UK and France. It does this through the 'Positive Places' sustainability framework. Support is given to charities in the form of cash, in kind and staff time contributions, and employees also play an active role in their communities through volunteering, fundraising and matched funding schemes.

Community Plans

There are Community Plans for Hammerson's existing assets and developments in the UK and France. The plans are tailored to the needs of different local communities, but do follow four main themes in line with the focus of the group: health and well-being; regeneration; skills and employment for young people; and enterprise. Examples provided on the website include:

- Silverburn Shopping Centre which: developed a long-term relationship with a local food bank, engaging retailers to give donations; worked with local Young Enterprise; and made cash/in-kind contributions of £88,000
- Leeds (Victoria Gate) Development which: worked with a local social enterprise in collaboration with a local food bank to create a healthy recipe book; in celebration of the diversity of Leeds and the Tour de France partnered with Kirkgate Market to organise international-themed tours of the market for local schools
- Croydon Partnership Development which: supported Lives Not Knives, a scheme for young people based around educational workshops, code-club training and advice on employment and training; helped a local social enterprise with business planning and advice; engaged young people with Croydon's development plans in partnership with the Architecture Foundation and Croydon Urban Pioneers; worked in partnership with other businesses and developers in support of the Croydon community; sponsored the Croydon Heritage Festival

Charity partners

Every two years, staff select two charity partners for Hammerson to work with at a corporate level. Firstly, employees make suggestions for possible partners, from which a shortlist is produced. Then, staff vote on the shortlisted charities and two are announced as winners. The 'Positive Places' website explains that chosen charities can benefit from corporate donations as well as an opportunity to build relations with Hammerson and its employees.

The charity partners for 2016–18 are: Alzheimer's Society and Macmillan Cancer Support.

Hammerson Positive Local Places Bursary Scheme

Every year, staff at Hammerson shopping centres choose a local charity to receive a bursary of £5,000 and to develop a relationship with. Work is focused in four areas: health and well-being; young people; skills and employment; and regeneration.

Directors with other relevant posts

Terry Duddy: Chair of the Retail Trust.

Main UK locations

Hammerson's UK office is located in London and it has properties throughout the UK. For details of the whereabouts of Hammerson properties see www.hammerson.com/property.

Community contributions

The Hammerson Corporate Responsibility Report, Data and Disclosure 2016 states that the total value of direct contributions from the group to the community during 2015 was £2.16 million. Unfortunately, unlike in reports from earlier years, a breakdown of the values of cash, in-kind and staff time contributions was not provided. However, the 'Community engagement' section of Hammerson's annual report for 2015 does explain that 'over the course of 2015 the Group contributed more than £150,000 to charitable causes, £34,000 of which went to our two main partners'.

Indirect contributions to the community, which we have taken to represent donations from non-Hammerson sources (charity collections, charity sales, employee contributions, etc.) amounted to a further £383,000, although, as is our usual practice, we have not included this amount in our figure for corporate contributions.

Beneficiaries included: Elifar and Samaritans (charity partners 2014–16).

In-kind support

Staff time

Hammerson's volunteering policy allows staff to spend three paid days volunteering each year, including the annual Community Day. In certain cases, Hammerson may also allow employees to spend a longer time volunteering, an example of which was a working visit paid to a hospital in Haiti.

Employee-led support

Employee volunteering

Employees are involved in a range of volunteering activities for local and national charities. Each year, Hammerson holds a Community Day, both in the UK and France, through which employees are able to select activities to volunteer with. In 2015 these ranged from river clean-ups and organising a fashion show. In the UK, 63% of employees got involved with the 27 activities on offer. In France, an even more impressive 82% of employees volunteered on the day.

The Butterfly Bank

The annual report for 2015 explains that during 2015 Hammerson 'launched a new approach to volunteering, using our own bespoke version of The Butterfly Bank Engagement Platform' as a way to 'inspire and reward volunteering'. The online platform (hammerson.thebutterflybank.co.uk) enables employees to create a profile and then sign-up to volunteering opportunities. Employees who volunteer through the scheme can then 'bank' virtual butterflies as a reward. Those employees who bank the most butterflies as well as those who take up their full volunteering allowance are recognised.

Employee fundraising

Hammerson employees raise funds for charitable causes, including for the company's selected charity partners.

Matched funding

Hammerson matches funds raised by staff up to a value of £250 per employee.

Commercially led support

Sponsorship

Occasionally, Hammerson sponsors sporting, cultural or trade events.

The Prosperity Programme

Hammerson works with partners at a national and local level to deliver employment, skills, training and enterprise schemes across its assets and developments. National partners include National Skills Academy, Retail Trust and Landaid. Partners at a local level include Befriending Scotland, Newham Education Business Partnership and Young Enterprise. The 'Positive Places' website explains: 'Some great examples include our two schemes focused on developing retail skills, in order to optimize the positive local impacts of the major retail development happening over the next five to ten years'.

Exclusions

Charities affiliated with religion or politics are not supported.

Applications

An application form is available to download from the 'Positive Places' website, along with key dates for corporate giving. The form can be completed and returned to request funding either under the Local Positive Places scheme or as a corporate donation. For more information on

Charity Partnerships, contact sustainability@hammerson.com.

Hargreaves Lansdown PLC

Financial services

Correspondent: Danny Cox, The Hargreaves Lansdown Charitable Foundation, One College Square South, Anchor Road, Bristol BS1 5HL (tel: 0117 900 9000; website: www.hl.co.uk/about-us/hl-foundation)

Directors: Chris Barling; Chris Hill, Chief Financial Officer; Chris Worle; David Davies; Ian Gorham, Chief Executive; Ian Hunter; Jayne Styles; Lee Gardhouse; Mark Dampier; Michael Evans, Chair; Rob Byett; Shirley Garrood; Stephen Robertson; Stuart Louden (women: 2; men: 12)

Year end	30/06/2015
Turnover	£395,100,000
Pre-tax profit	£199,000,000

Nature of business: Financial services.

Company registration number: 2122142

Subsidiary undertakings include: Hargreaves Lansdown Advisory Services Ltd; Hargreaves Lansdown Asset Management Ltd; Hargreaves Lansdown Stockbrokers Ltd.

Focus of giving: Health, ill health, children, young people, community/ social welfare.

Community involvement	✓
CSR report	✓
Charity of the Year	✓
Employee-led support	✓
FTSE 100	✓
Sponsorship	✓

Community involvement

The Hargreaves Lansdown Charitable Foundation (Charity Commission no. 1167927) was registered in June 2016 and is Hargreaves Lansdown's channel for charitable involvement. The group also sponsors a small number of local causes in Bristol.

The Hargreaves Lansdown Charitable Foundation

According to the Hargreaves Lansdown website, the mission behind the foundation is 'to utilise the skills and time of our workforce and partners to make a positive, sustainable difference in the world around us'. The foundation focuses on four main areas: the next generation; local communities; health and well-being; and improving lives. Every year, Hargreaves Lansdown employees choose charities working within these areas to support through fundraising activities. The charities are nominated and chosen by employees.

The chosen charities in 2015 were:

- **The next generation**: Youth Adventure Trust and The Prince's Trust
- **Local communities**: Great Western Air Ambulance
- **Health and well-being**: Cancer Research UK
- **Improving lives**: Guide Dogs

Main UK locations

Hargreaves Lansdown is based in Bristol.

Community contributions

A figure for charitable donations was not declared in the group's annual report and accounts for 2014/15.

Employee-led support

Employee fundraising

Employees take part with a range of fundraising activities for their chosen Charity of the Year. In 2015 a number of employees took part with the Brecons 10 Peaks Challenge.

Commercially led support

Sponsorship

According to the Corporate Social Responsibility Report for 2014/15 (contained within the annual report), the group has sponsored a small number of causes local to its head office in Bristol. These were:

- Bristol and West Athletics Club: a donation is made to the club on a monthly basis
- Shaun in the City: Hargreaves Lansdown sponsored a sculpture called 'Dolly' as part of the Shaun the Sheep-inspired arts trail in Bristol. Funds raised from the sculptures' sponsorship benefitted Bristol Children's Hospital's Grand Appeal

Applications

Employees are responsible for selecting beneficiary charities working within the group foundation's chosen areas. Unsolicited applications are not accepted.

Hastings Group Holdings PLC

Insurance

Correspondent: Jay Wootten, Events and Community Relations Manager, Conquest House, Collington Avenue, Bexhill-on-Sea, East Sussex TN39 3LW (website: www.hastingsplc.com)

Directors: Alison Burns; Anthony Leppard; Edward Fitzmaurice; Gary Hoffman, Chief Executive Officer; Ian Cormack; Malcolm Le May; Michele Titi-Cappelli; Mike Fairey, Chair; Pierre Lefèvre; Richard Brewster; Richard Hoskins, Chief Financial Officer; Sumit Rajpal; Teresa Robson-Capps; Thomas Colraine (women: 2; men: 12)

Year end	31/12/2015
Turnover	£481,000,000
Pre-tax profit	£5,000,000

Nature of business: Hastings is a general insurance provider in the UK.

Company registration number: 9635183

Subsidiary undertakings include: Advantage Insurance Company Ltd; Hastings Insurance Group Ltd; Renew Insurance Services Ltd.

Brands include: Hastings Direct; InsurePink; People's Choice.

Focus of giving: General charitable purposes.

Community involvement	✓
Company reports on anti-slavery	✓
CSR report	✓
Charity partner(s)	✓
Employee-led support	✓
Gifts in kind	✓
Market-led giving	✓
Pro bono	✓

Community involvement

Hastings employees play an active role in supporting causes in their communities by taking part in fundraising events for charitable causes. The Hastings website further explains that it 'provides a helping hand to local individuals or groups by providing advice, physical support or small grants to help with fundraising'. The company also builds relationships with school, colleges and universities in its communities.

Partners

Humanutopia; Pink Ribbon Foundation.

Main locations

Bexhill-on-Sea (head office); Leicester; Newmarket.

Community contributions

The annual report and accounts for 2015 did not declare a figure for charitable donations from the company.

We were unable to determine a value for the in kind support given by the company.

In-kind support

Pro bono

In November 2015, the company became involved with a programme called 'Be the Change' in partnership with Humanutopia, a social enterprise, and lovelocaljobs.com. The three-year partnership aims to raise the aspirations of 13-year-old students in the local area by helping them to engage at school and providing them with life skills. Hastings employees take part with the programme as business mentors.

Employee-led support

Employee fundraising

There is a charity events committee made up by employees who volunteer to organise fundraising events for employee-nominated charities. During 2015, £50,000 was raised in support of local organisations.

Employee volunteering
Employees spent 5,500 hours helping out in their communities during 2015.

Commercially led support

InsurePink
From every InsurePink policy sold, £10 is donated to the Pink Ribbon Foundation. More than £100,000 was donated in 2015.

Applications

Apply in writing to the correspondent.

Heathrow Airport Holdings Ltd (formerly BAA Ltd)

Airport operators

Correspondent: Community Relations Team, The Compass Centre, Nelson Road, London Heathrow Airport, Hounslow TW6 2GW (tel: 020 8745 5791; email: community_relations@heathrow.com; website: www.heathrow.com/company/community-and-environment)

Directors: Akbar Al Baker; Ali Bouzarif; Benjamin Bao; Chris Beale; Ernesto Lopez Mozo; Fidel Lopez; Javier Echave, Chief Financial Officer; John Holland-Kaye, Chief Executive; Jorge Gil; Lord Paul Deighton, Chair; Mike Powell; Olivier Fortin; Prof. David Begg; Rachel Lomax; Stuart Baldwin

Year end	31/12/2015
Turnover	£2,767,000,000
Pre-tax profit	£732,000,000

Nature of business: A holding company for a group of companies that provide and manage airport facilities in the UK, including Heathrow, Stansted, Glasgow, Aberdeen International and Southampton International.

Company registration number: 5757208

Subsidiary undertakings include: 9G Rail Ltd; BAA Partnership Ltd; Heathrow Holdco Ltd.

Total employees: 6,714

Focus of giving: Economic generation, education, enterprise/training, environment, local groups, science technology, children, young people, community/social welfare, disability.

Membership: BITC

Community involvement	✓
Community contributions	✓
CSR report	✓
CSR or charity committee	✓
Directors have other relevant posts	✓
Cash donations declared	✓
Charity partner(s)	✓
Corporate charity	✓
Employee-led support	✓
Gifts in kind	✓
Market-led giving	✓
Matched funding	✓

Charitable donations

Cash UK (latest available):	2015	£2,000,000
Total UK (cash and in kind):	2015	£2,000,000
Cash worldwide:	2015	£2,000,000
Total worldwide (cash and in kind):	2015	£2,000,000

Community involvement

The group's charitable support is focused on the areas surrounding Heathrow Airport. The Heathrow Community Fund, which is part of the LHR Airport Communities Trust, makes grants to local projects supporting communities, environment, youth and education. Employees can also volunteer with local projects, and employees and customers contribute to fundraising for the group's partner charity.

Heathrow Community Fund
The community fund is part of the LHR Airport Communities Trust (Charity Commission no. 1058617), which receives funding from Heathrow (including funds raised through fines for breaching aircraft noise levels), as well as other airports in the same group, such as Aberdeen and Glasgow.

The trust also channels support for employee initiatives, including providing matched funding for staff donations.

The Heathrow Community Fund provides grants to community projects in areas local to Heathrow Airport, supporting youth, education and community.

Grants range from £2,000 to £25,000 and are made in the following categories: Communities for Youth – supporting young people's education and skills development; Communities for Tomorrow – projects protecting the environment or promoting environmental education and sustainable development; Communities Together – supporting smaller community-focused projects.

The fund can also offer volunteer support to projects in the local communities.

Further details on each of the grants schemes and what support currently available is given on the website: www.heathrowcommunityfund.com

Charity partnership
Since 2013, the group has been working with Oxfam in a three-year partnership, with a fundraising target of £150,000 per year.

Community investment
The group has a community investment programme which aims to support the economic prosperity of the areas surrounding the airport, through skills development, careers support and engagement with educational institutions and businesses. The areas support are Ealing, Hillingdon, Hounslow, Slough and Spelthorne. For example, in 2015, this included engagement with 50 local primary schools and 15 local secondary schools, running STEM-related challenges; as well as providing support for Duke of Edinburgh challenges and scout groups; and holding a careers fair. The group's Heathrow Academy supports local people with training and employment opportunities.

Directors with other relevant posts
Rachel Lomax is a trustee of The Ditchley Foundation (Charity Commission no. 309657).

Community contributions

The group's 2015 accounts state its total charitable donations during the year totalled £2 million.

Beneficiaries were: Hillingdon Community Trust (£1 million); LHR Airport Communities Trust (£770,000); Green Corridor (£10,000); Dreamflight (£5,000).

Funds were also raised for the group's partner charity, Oxfam, through the support of customers and employees. In 2015 £236,000 was raised through foreign exchange coin collections in the airport, and a further £65,000 was raised by employees.

In-kind support

Employee volunteering
Through the Heathrow Community Fund, the group advertises local community projects looking for volunteer support to employees. Employees also volunteer with local schools – for example, running the Heathrow Primary School Construction Challenge.

Employee-led support

Employee fundraising
The group's employees have been fundraising for Oxfam, the group's partner charity, since 2013. The group provides matched funding for employees engaged in their own charitable fundraising initiatives.

Commercially led support

Market-led giving
Customers can donate spare currency at collection points around the airport for the group's partner charity and for the Heathrow Community Fund. The group also supports collections for Children in Need, Comic Relief and the Poppy Appeal.

Corporate charity

Heathrow Community Fund (Charity Commission no. 1058617).

Exclusions

For guidance notes and exclusions from each of the Heathrow Community Fund's grant schemes, refer to the website: www.heathrowcommunityfund.com.

Applications

Heathrow Community Fund

Information on how to apply to any of the fund's grants schemes is provided on the website, along with deadlines, application forms and guidance notes.

Volunteer support

Local organisations looking for volunteer support can advertise their project to employees by emailing communitiestrust@heathrow.com with the following information:

- Name of organisation
- Location of opportunity
- Dates/times volunteers needed
- What the volunteers are needed for
- How many volunteers are needed

Helical bar PLC

Property

Correspondent: The Company Secretary, 5 Hanover Square, London W1S 1HQ (tel: 020 7629 0113; website: www.helical.co.uk)

Directors: Duncan Walker; Gerald Kaye, Chief Executive; James Moss; Matthew Bonning-Snook; Michael O'Donnell; Michael Slade, Chair; Richard Cotton; Richard Gillingwater; Richard Grant; Susan Clayton; Tim Murphy, Finance Director (women: 1; men: 10)

Year end	31/03/2016
Turnover	£116,500,000
Pre-tax profit	£121,000

Nature of business: Helical Bar is a property development and investment company.

Company registration number: 156663

UK employees: 32

Total employees: 32

Focus of giving: General charitable purposes.

Community involvement	✓
Community contributions	✓
Company reports on anti-slavery	✓
Cash donations declared	✓
Employee-led support	✓
Matched funding	✓

Charitable donations

Cash UK (latest available):	2016	£36,500
Total UK (cash and in kind):	2016	£36,500
Cash worldwide:	2016	£36,500
Total worldwide (cash and in kind):	2016	£36,500

Community involvement

The group engages in community involvement in areas where it has a presence. An example of this was the *Apprentice*-style enterprise challenge it ran for college students in South East Wales.

Main locations

The group is based in London but supports charities throughout the UK.

Community contributions

In the 2015/16 financial year Helical Bar made donations totalling £36,500 to a number of charities. We were unable to locate a value for in kind support given by the group.

Beneficiaries included: Great Ormond Street Hospital; LandAid; The Lord Mayor's Appeal; Muscular Dystrophy UK.

Employee-led support

Employee fundraising

The group holds an annual fundraising day for LandAid which raised £10,400.

Matched funding

The group makes donations to help staff's personal fundraising efforts where appropriate.

Applications

Apply in writing to the correspondent referenced 'Charitable Donations'.

Henderson Group PLC

Financial services

Correspondent: The Company Secretary, 201 Bishopsgate, London EC2M 3AE (tel: 020 7818 1818; website: www.henderson.com/ir/content/corporate-responsibility-ir)

Directors: Andrew Formica, Chief Executive; Angela Seymour-Jackson; Kalpana Desai; Kevin Dolan; Phil Wagstaff; Richard Gillingwater, Chair; Robert Jeens; Roger Thompson, Chief Financial Officer; Sarah Arkle; Tim How (women: 3; men: 7)

Year end	31/12/2015
Turnover	£756,000,000
Pre-tax profit	£167,900,000

Nature of business: The principal activity of the group is the provision of investment management services. The group has businesses in the UK, Europe, Australia, Asia and the USA.

Subsidiary undertakings include: Gartmore Investment Ltd; Henderson Fund Management Ltd; Henderson Global Investors (Australia) Ltd.

Total employees: 955

Focus of giving: General charitable purposes, education, financial education, children, young people, community/social welfare, disasters.

Community involvement	✓
Community contributions	✓
CSR report	✓
Directors have other relevant posts	✓
Charity partner(s)	✓
Employee-led support	✓
Gifts in kind	✓
Humanitarian aid: overseas	✓
Market-led giving	✓
Matched funding	✓
Payroll giving	✓
STEM-focused	✓

Charitable donations

Cash UK (latest available):	2015	£175,500
Total UK (cash and in kind):	2015	£175,500
Cash worldwide:	2015	£175,500
Total worldwide (cash and in kind):	2015	£175,500

Community involvement

Henderson Group PLC looks to support communities in the areas where it operates. The group's website states 'Henderson has a fundamental belief in openness and collaboration – in the power of sharing knowledge'. This belief is embedded in the group's community engagement through financial education initiatives and employee volunteering. As part of the drive to enhance 'Knowledge. Shared', Henderson is aiming to deliver on the following commitments by 2018:

- All offices with an employee headcount of more than 50 to offer a financial education programme within their local communities
- Volunteering and community projects to be integrated into Henderson's learning and development programme

Promoting social mobility is an important part of the group's community involvement and is linked into its volunteering and financial education activities. Henderson is also part of Investment 2020 which aims to promote diversity and talent in investment management.

The Henderson Foundation

In 2012 the group established the Henderson Foundation (not a registered charity) through which it directs support for the charitable activities of its staff and clients, and matches funds raised by employees.

Partnerships

The website explains that 'Henderson believes in developing longstanding relationships with charities'. In 2016 it continued its support of Community

Links in East London, which it has partnered since 1987, and its work with the Isaac Newton Foundation. Hendersons also supports Disasters Emergency Committee with an automatic donation of £10,000 for any appeal. The group's offices in the USA and Asia also have community partners.

Directors with other relevant posts

Sarah Arkle: member of the investment committee at Newnham College.

Tim How: senior independent director of the the Norfolk and Norwich University Hospitals NHS Foundation Trust.

UK locations

London

Community contributions

The group's annual report and accounts for 2015 did not declare a figure for charitable contributions; however, the corporate responsibility report for the year states that the Henderson Foundation charitable spend amounted to £175,500. Based on previous years, we expect that the majority of this amount was given through the employee matched-funding scheme.

Beneficiaries included: Disasters Emergency Committee.

In-kind support

Employee time

Henderson allows staff to take one day's paid leave for voluntary work each year.

Financial education

During the year, the London office hosted four RedSTART Financial Education Days for local school students. The purpose of the days is to increase young people's financial awareness. Financial education and career preparation days were also held at the London and Chicago offices.

Employee-led support

Payroll giving

Henderson Global Investors achieved a Payroll Giving Gold Quality Award for 2016. Requirements for receiving an award include having 10% or more employee participation in payroll giving.

Matched funding

Contributions made through employee payroll giving are matched, as is money from employees' fundraising efforts.

Commercially led support

Investment 2020

Henderson is part of Investment 2020, along with other investment management firms, which looks to create more entry level pathways into the industry.

Applications

Apply in writing to your local Henderson office, referenced 'Charitable support'.

William Hill PLC

Gaming, leisure

Correspondent: Luke Thomas, Secretary to the CR Committee, Greenside House, 50 Station Road, Wood Green, London N22 7TP (tel: 020 8918 3600; fax: 020 8918 3775; website: www.williamhillplc.com)

Directors: Ashley Highfield; David Lowden; Gareth Davis, Chair; Georgina Harvey; Imelda Walsh; James Henderson, Chief Executive Officer; L. Thomas, Company Secretary; Philip Bowcock, Chief Financial Officer; Roy Gardner (women: 2; men: 6)

Year end	31/12/2015
Turnover	£155,200,000
Pre-tax profit	£243,700,000

Nature of business: The principal activities of the group include the operation of licensed betting offices and the provision of telephone, online and interactive television betting and online casino and poker services. The group also operates greyhound stadia.

Company registration number: 4212563

Subsidiary undertakings include: Ad-gency Ltd; Leroy's Horse and Sports Place; Tom Waterhouse N.T. Pty Ltd.

Brands include: William Hill.

Focus of giving: Education, animal welfare, individuals, non-registered charities, small groups, less popular charitable purposes, humanitarian help, arts, culture, overseas projects, safety and crime prevention, community/social welfare.

Community involvement	✓
Community contributions	✓
Company reports on anti-slavery	✓
CSR report	✓
CSR or charity committee	✓
Cash donations declared	✓
Company gives to smaller charities	✓
Employee-led support	✓
Gifts in kind	✓
Humanitarian aid: overseas	✓
Humanitarian aid: UK including food banks	✓
Market-led giving	✓
Matched funding	✓
Overseas giving	✓
Sponsorship	✓

Charitable donations

Cash UK (latest available):	2015	£1,200,000
Total UK (cash and in kind):	2015	£1,200,000
Cash worldwide:	2015	£1,200,000
Total worldwide (cash and in kind):	2015	£1,200,000

Community involvement

William Hill seeks to support the communities in which it operates through charitable donations and other relevant payments, generally 'to organisations involved in areas of greatest relevance to its business'. This can include:

> Promoting a responsible approach to gambling; undertaking research into problem gambling, and providing information, advice and help to those who are at risk or are experiencing difficulties with their gambling; greyhound and racehorse welfare; and supporting disadvantaged individuals in horse and greyhound racing.

Through its two greyhound stadia William Hill assists with greyhound welfare, for example by funding 'an establishment that houses up to 25 dogs for up to three months with the intention of permanently re-homing them'.

The William Hill Foundation (Charity Commission no. 1146270)

The foundation was created in 2011 and registered with the Charity Commission in 2012. It was designed as a hardship fund to support colleagues and their families but now also acts as an umbrella organisation for Project Africa. Four directors administer the £100,000 hardship fund and the donations received from colleagues for Project Africa. Through the Foundation, Project Africa – which was started in 2012 – continues to be supported in its efforts to bring better education, clean water and health facilities to the Ol Maisor village in Kenya. A medical facility for the school and village is currently being completed (August 2016).

In 2015 the foundation provided 17 grants to colleagues and their families at a total cost of £31,000.

Disaster relief

The foundation was also able to help four colleagues in the Philippines following Typhoon Lando and two colleagues in Cumbria following severe flooding.

Examples of local initiatives worldwide are available from the CR Report.

Main locations

The group has betting shops throughout the UK. The group's foundation operates worldwide.

Community contributions

According to the annual report and accounts of the group, in 2015 charitable donations amounted to £1.2 million (including £823,000 given to the Responsible Gambling Trust, £100,000 to the William Hill Foundation and £41,000 in matched funding).

The group supports charities in three main priority areas. The annual report states: 'Helping people get into work is becoming a key theme, as is support for sports like boxing which help local communities and young people. For example, our William Hill Foundation patron, Robbie Savage, is helping us support our partnership with Our Club, where we are working on employment programmes in Swansea and, in due course, London and the North-East.'

Much of William Hill's giving is provided by its employees with over 170 events taking place in 2015.

In-kind support

The group continues its engagement with local communities to combat crime. Working with successful initiatives in the Metropolitan Police area, Northumbria, Strathclyde and Manchester, also Bristol and the West Midlands. In the past the partnership saw campaign literature being sent to postcode districts and posters displayed in William Hill shops and distributed by local Police Community Support Officers.

As part of the Project Africa initiative employee time and skills are donated.

The group is committed to developing women at all levels of their business and has a Springboard programme designed to bring up to 50 women a year through into junior management roles.

Employee-led support

Staff members are supported to volunteer and contribute to good causes through their own fundraising efforts.

Project Africa

This initiative commenced in 2012 to bring better education, clean water and health facilities to the Ol Maisor village in Kenya. In 2015 the project funded a medical facility for the school and village with funds raised by employees and managed and distributed by the William Hill Foundation. The group's annual report states that having largely completed the goals of this project resources will now be refocused on local community work.

Close to HOME

In 2015 nine community projects were piloted with teams from Aberdeen, Birmingham, Bristol, Glasgow, Leeds, London and Swansea with employee teams encouraged to engage with a local charity and support them either financially or through giving time and help. This project will now be rolled out across the Group. Examples of the projects supported include: hospices and centres for the homeless and elderly, repainting a community hall, running customer service workshops for young adults with learning difficulties, creating starter packs of household goods for former homeless people moving into new homes and fundraising to keep a boxing club open for the local community.

Matched funding

There is a proportion of the charitable donations budget used to match funds raised by employees on local charitable initiatives. In 2015 matched donations totalled over £41,000.

Payroll giving

Our research suggests that there has been a payroll giving scheme that allows employees to make donations directly to charities they choose. It has not been possible to determine whether this is still running.

Commercially led support

Partnerships

The group has six partnerships with: Action For Kids, Bobby Moore Fund, Haringey Box Cup, Depaul, Our Club and Tottenham Hotspur Foundation.

Sponsorship

The group also sponsors a number of major sporting events and teams in the UK, Australia and the US. The annual report states that it partnered the 2016 Australian Open with Tennis Australia. The group's sponsorship with the English Football Association comes to an end in 2016, currently it sponsors three Premier League teams: Chelsea, Everton and Tottenham. In Scotland it sponsors the William Hill Scottish Cup and also the PDC's World Darts Championship.

The group sponsors some of the leading greyhound racing events, including the Greyhound Derby and in 2015 made a voluntary donation of £2.2 million to the British Greyhound Racing Fund to help sustain the industry.

Responsible gambling

The main focus of the group is addressing the negative impact of gambling activities. The group donated £823,00 in 2015 to the Responsible Gambling Trust to fund research, education and treatment of problem gambling.

Exclusions

William Hill does not make donations to political parties in the UK.

Applications

The group: Apply in writing to the correspondent.

The William Hill Foundation: This provides grants for financial hardship to employees of the group and their families. Employees can obtain an application form to apply for a grant via William Hill HR teams or by emailing williamhillfoundation@williamhill.co.uk.

Hiscox Ltd

Insurance

Correspondent: Peresha McKenzie, PA to R. Hiscox, Chair of The Hiscox Foundation, 1 Great St Helen's, London EC3A 6HX (tel: 020 7448 6011; website: www.hiscoxgroup.com/responsibility/communities.aspx)

Directors: Anne McDonald; Bronislaw Masojada, Group Chief Executive Officer; Caroline Foulger; Colin Keogh; Ernst Jansen; Gunnar Stokholm; Lynn Carter; Richard Watson, Group Chief Underwriting Officer; Robert Childs, Chair; Robert Macmillan (women: 3; men: 7)

Year end	31/12/2015
Turnover	£1,944,220,000
Pre-tax profit	£216,100,000

Nature of business: Hiscox Ltd specialises in insurance and is registered in Bermuda. We have taken the figure for charitable donations from the annual report and accounts (for the year ending 31 December 2015) of Hiscox PLC, a UK-registered holding company (Registered Company no. 02837811), and from the 2014/15 annual report and accounts of The Hiscox Foundation. Other financial and CSR information relates to Hiscox Ltd.

Company registration number: 38877

Subsidiary undertakings include: Hiscox Insurance Company Ltd; Hiscox PLC; Hiscox Underwriting Ltd.

Focus of giving: Education, health, ill health, medical research, overseas projects, older people, arts, culture, poverty and social exclusion, children, young people.

Community involvement	✓
Community contributions	✓
CSR report	✓
Directors have other relevant posts	✓
Cash donations declared	✓
Charity partner(s)	✓
Corporate charity	✓
Employee-led support	✓
Gifts in kind	✓
Matched funding	✓
Overseas giving	✓
Sponsorship	✓

Charitable donations

Cash UK (latest available):	2015	£500,000
Total UK (cash and in kind):	2015	£530,500
Cash worldwide:	2015	£500,000
Total worldwide (cash and in kind):	2015	£530,500

Community involvement

Hiscox offices around the world play an active role in supporting their communities. In the UK, Hiscox makes an annual donation to The Hiscox Foundation (Charity Commission no. 327635) and works in partnership with other organisations to support programmes in the areas of business, arts, science and technology. Hiscox employees volunteer and fundraise for charitable causes, and are supported in their efforts by matched funding from the foundation.

The Hiscox Foundation

The foundation, which was registered with the Charity Commission in 1987, makes grants principally in support of education, medical science, the arts, and independent living for older, disadvantaged and vulnerable people. During 2015, the foundation continued its support of the Humanitarian Aid Relief Trust (HART) and Richard House Children's Hospice. Priority is given to causes supported by Hiscox employees who can apply to the foundation in support of local charities or charities of personal significance.

Support for the arts, science and technology

Hiscox has worked alongside a number of organisations working in arts, science and technology. These include Royal Academy Schools and the Royal Institution (RI). Hiscox was also a founder of the Public Catalogue Foundation (now known as Art UK). Other involvement in these areas is documented elsewhere in this entry.

Directors with other relevant posts

Robert Childs: trustee of Enham Trust.

Main UK locations

Birmingham; Colchester; Glasgow; London; Maidenhead; Manchester.

Community contributions

The 2015 annual report and accounts for Hiscox Ltd did not include a figure for charitable donations; however, the annual report and accounts for Hiscox PLC, the UK-registered holding company, stated that during the year the company made donations totalling £570,000 to charitable organisations. We believe that the vast majority of this amount was given to The Hiscox Foundation.

The annual report for Hiscox Ltd also explains that, as part of its support for the arts, the Group also provided a bursary for two students through its work with the Royal Academy Schools; however, we were not able to determine the value of this donation.

The Hiscox Foundation

The Hiscox Foundation's 2014/15 annual report explains: 'The level of donation received from Hiscox PLC is dependant on the Hiscox Group's results for the year, and we are grateful for the £500,000 received in March 2015.' Hiscox PLC also donated services costed at £30,500 to the foundation during its 2014/15 financial year (consisting of £21,500 in employee's services and £8,800 in governance costs fees).

During the year, the foundation made grants totalling £228,500 to 84 charities. The ten largest donations accounted for 73% of the grant total and were received by: Humanitarian Aid Relief Trust – HART (£60,000); Richard House Children's Hospice (£25,500); Melanoma Action and Support Scotland, and Whitechapel Gallery (£25,000 each); Royal Academy of Arts (£10,000); St Leonard's Hospice (£7,000); Mind (£5,500); Alzheimer's Society (£3,250); Camphill Blaire Drummond (£3,000); Movember (£2,800). The foundation also contributed £29,000 in support of funds raised.

We were unable to determine a value for cash and in-kind support given by Hiscox to charities other than The Hiscox Foundation.

In-kind support

Hiscox's London office worked alongside The Brokerage Citylink in summer 2015, taking part in The City of London Business Traineeship Programme. The programme gave four students from inner London the opportunity to work at Hiscox over the course of eight weeks, providing them with work experience and the opportunity for skills development.

Employee-led support

Employee fundraising

Employees play an important role in choosing the charities Hiscox supports. In 2015 employees in Colchester raised £15,000 for the Tom Bowdidge Foundation; activities included taking part in the Colchester Half Marathon and a Charity Golf Day. In York, employees have fundraised – more than £5,000 – for two chosen charities, York Mind and Snappy.

Employee volunteering

Hiscox employees volunteered through the City of London's Sculpture in the City project, working with students at Bethnal Green Academy.

Matched funding

The Hiscox Foundation contributes matched funding towards employees' charitable efforts.

Commercially led support

Sponsorship

Hiscox has sponsored the Sunday Times Hiscox Tech Track 100 for five years.

Corporate charity

The Hiscox Foundation (Charity Commission no. 327635).

Applications

The Hiscox Foundation: Apply in writing to the correspondent. Our research suggests that support is mainly given to causes known by the trustees and, according to the annual report for 2015, 'priority is given to any charitable endeavour by members of staff of the Hiscox group to encourage such activity'. The trustees meet quarterly to consider applications.

Home Retail Group PLC

Retail – miscellaneous

Correspondent: Amy Whidburn (Head of Corporate Responsibility) or Megan Kitchen (Corporate Responsibility Manager), 489–499 Avebury Boulevard, Saxon Gate West, Central Milton Keynes MK9 2NW (email: corporate.responsibility@homeretailgroup.com; website: www.homeretailgroup.com/corporate-responsibility/cr-contacts)

Directors: Cath Keers; Ian Durant; Jacqueline De Rojas; John Coombe, Chair; John Walden, Chief Executive; Mike Darcey; Richard Ashton, Finance Director (women: 2; men: 5)

Year end	27/02/2016
Turnover	£4,234,700,000
Pre-tax profit	(£840,300,000)

Nature of business: A UK-based general merchandise retailer.

At the time of writing (August 2016) J Sainsbury PLC was in the process of acquiring Home Retail Group PLC. According to a press release on the Home Retail Group website in June 2016, 'the transaction is currently expected to complete in the third quarter of this calendar year subject to both shareholder and regulatory approvals'.

Company registration number: 5863533

Subsidiary undertakings include: Argos Ltd; Argos Superstores Ltd; Bed Store and More Ltd; Chad Valley Ltd; Habitat Retail Ltd; Jungle.com Ltd; Software Warehouse Holdings Ltd.

Brands include: Argos; Chad Valley; Habitat; Heart of House.

Total employees: 30,489

Focus of giving: General charitable purposes, community/social welfare.

Membership: BITC, LBG

Community involvement	✓
Community contributions	✓
CSR report	✓
Cash donations declared	✓
Charity of the Year	✓
Charity partner(s)	✓
Employee-led support	✓

Gifts in kind	✓
Matched funding	✓
Payroll giving	✓
Pro bono	✓
Shared-value alliances	✓

Charitable donations

Cash UK (latest available):	2016	£389,500
Total UK (cash and in kind):	2016	£687,000
Cash worldwide:	2016	£389,500
Total worldwide (cash and in kind):	2016	£687,000

Community involvement

According to its Corporate Responsibility Annual Summary Report for 2016, Home Retail Group PLC looks to be a 'good neighbour' in the United Kingdom and Republic of Ireland by creating charity partnerships and supporting group colleagues with their charity and community activities through matched funding and volunteering time.

Strategic charity partnerships

In March 2015, the group embarked on a two-year partnership with Macmillan Cancer Support. During the first year, colleagues and customers raised a total of £1.5 million. In addition to holding fundraising events for the charity, a group of employees from Argos volunteered to present a digital skills pilot to cancer patients at Charing Cross Hospital; the pilot's aim was to show patients how to get online and how to use Macmillan digital platforms to access help and advice.

In the Republic of Ireland colleagues and customers raised money for Irish Cancer Society.

Other partnerships

Through its Work Start Programme, which was launched in 2014, the group partnered four charities – Business in the Community, Gingerbread, The Prince's Trust and Remploy – to create work placements for people who want to enter into employment but who face significant barriers. More than 250 work placement opportunities were provided during the year, with 49% resulting in a successful move to employment within the group's stores. Also as part of the Work Start Programme, the group worked with women's prison services to assist female ex-offenders as part of their reintegration back into society.

Argos' Barnardo's Toy Exchange partnership celebrated its fourth year with more than £550,000 raised through the collection and resale of donated toys, taking the cumulative total to £2.5 million.

Main UK locations

Milton Keynes (head office) and stores nationwide.

Community contributions

The group's 'Corporate Responsibility Annual Summary Report 2016' provides a detailed community giving table detailing contributions according to London Benchmarking Group measurement model. Company contributions amounted to £938,000 (together with management costs) and included cash donations totalling £389,500. A full breakdown of contributions is given in the table below:

Cash donations	£389,500
Volunteering	£258,500
'Management resource'	£251,000
Gifts in-kind	£39,000

We have not included management costs in the figure for the group's total contributions.

Donations from colleagues and customers through payroll giving and fundraising amounted to a further £2.9 million.

In-kind support

Pro bono work

The group's legal team participated in Lawyers in Schools, a skills-based programme aimed at improving young people's awareness and understanding of the law.

Employee volunteering time

All colleagues are able to spend two days paid leave volunteering in their local communities.

Employee-led support

Payroll giving

More than 10% of group colleagues are signed up to the group's payroll giving scheme. During financial year ending 2016, employees donated £286,000 to their chosen charities and community groups through the scheme. Home Retail Group matches colleague donations for the first month.

Employee fundraising

Employees are encouraged to support local and national causes through their own fundraising activities. The group supports their efforts with a donation of between £50 and £1,000. In 2015 colleagues raised more than £250,000 through fundraising activities – from organising school or village fairs to supporting national appeals such as Children in Need.

Employee volunteering

According to the group's annual corporate responsibility summary report for 2016, volunteering at the group's Milton Keynes head office is 'co-ordinated and tracked centrally', with around 20% of colleagues at this location having been involved in volunteering in the 2016 financial year.

Exclusions

Applications from overseas charities, political or campaigning groups, or religious organisations that are unable to demonstrate a wider benefit to the community are not considered.

Applications

Home Retail Group makes donations to charities through its community prize draw scheme. Through the scheme, six organisations are selected at random each month to receive a donation in the form of a £100 gift voucher that can be redeemed in Argos stores. Charities, community groups and not-for-profit organisations based in the UK or Republic or Ireland can enter into the draw by completing the form on the website.

Note that Home Retail Group PLC is subject to a possible acquisition by J Sainsbury PLC (see 'Nature of business'). The arrangements of the group's community involvement could change in the future and we recommend that organisations interested in applying for support from the group see the website for updates.

HomeServe PLC

Services

Correspondent: See 'Applications', Cable Drive, Walsall, West Midlands WS2 7BN (website: www.homeserveplc.com/responsibility.aspx)

Directors: Anna Maughan; Ben Mingay; Chris Havemann; J. M. Barry Gibson, Chair; Johnathan Ford, Chief Operating Officer; Mark Morris; Martin Bennett; Richard Harpin, Chief Executive; Stella David (women: 2; men: 7)

Year end	31/03/2016
Turnover	£633,200,000
Pre-tax profit	£82,600,000

Nature of business: HomeServe provides home emergency, repair and heating installation services to more than seven million homes in the UK, the USA, France, Spain and Italy.

Company registration number: 2648297

Subsidiary undertakings include: HomeServe Assistance Ltd; HomeServe Heating Services Ltd; HomeServe International Ltd.

UK employees: 2,489

Total employees: 4,425

Focus of giving: Health, ill health, community/social welfare.

Community involvement	✓
Community contributions	✓
Company reports on anti-slavery	✓
CSR report	✓

Directors have other relevant posts	✓
Charity partner(s)	✓
Employee-led support	✓
Gifts in kind	✓
Sponsorship	✓

Community involvement

According to its corporate responsibility objectives, which are listed on the website, HomeServe PLC looks to build partnerships with charities and community organisations which are aligned closely with its business activities. It seeks to use its 'core skills' to give something back to communities. HomeServe employees take part in fundraising and volunteering activities, using their skills to support their local communities.

Partnerships

Marie Curie Cancer Care: In the UK, HomeServe and its employees have supported the charity through a long-term partnership. Schemes include Pennies for Patients, which allows staff to donate up to 99p in loose change from their monthly wage, as well as clothes collections for local Marie Curie shops and other fundraising events at individual HomeServe locations. A case study on Marie Curie's website also shows that, through the partnership, HomeServe has also developed a 'Patient Policy' to provide 12 months of free household cover for people who have a terminal illness.

HomeServe has also partnered a number of organisation to the benefit of the local area around its West Midlands Head Office:

'Cash for Your Community': HomeServe partnered the Midlands newspaper, the Express and Star, to support more than 100 local community groups. Groups can register to take part with the initiative and then collect tokens printed in the newspaper. The amount they receive depends on the number of tokens collected.

Midland Langar Seva Society: During 2015/16 HomeServe continued support for the society, which works to support homeless people in the West Midlands. Teams of employees volunteered through the partnership.

Directors with other relevant posts

Chris Havemann: governor of London Business School.

Main UK locations

Banbury; London; Preston; Walsall.

Community contributions

A figure for the group's charitable donations was not included in the annual report and accounts for 2015/16.

Employee-led support

Employee volunteering

HomeServe employees volunteer with a range of causes in their communities. An example in 2015/16 included Midland Langer Seva Society, with employees spending a total of 700 hours, serving 8,300 meals and 6,900 food bags to homeless people. In addition, more than 300 volunteers contributed over 1,750 hours to the Sport Relief Campaign, answering 2,369 donation calls and helping to raise more than £70,000.

Employee fundraising

Staff at the group fundraise for a range of good causes, from partners of HomeServe to organisations in their local areas. Examples during the year included the Salvation Army in Banbury and Manchester Children's Hospital, which were supported with donations of presents and food.

Commercially led support

Sponsorship

HomeServe is a principal sponsor of Walsall FC.

Applications

Based on previous research, we would recommend that requests are direct to your local HomeServe location.

House of Fraser (UK and Ireland) Ltd

Retail – department and variety stores

Correspondent: See 'Applications', House of Fraser, 27 Baker Street, London W1U 8AH (website: www.houseoffraser.co.uk/charities/charities,default,pg.html)

Directors: Colin Elliot; Frank Slevin, Chair; Nigel Oddy, Chief Executive Officer; Peter Hearsey (women: 0; men: 4)

Year end	30/01/2016
Turnover	£826,600,000
Pre-tax profit	(£20,200,000)

Nature of business: The group is a multi-branded, multi-channel retailer in the UK and Ireland, trading principally through the House of Fraser brand name.

Company registration number: 5845860

Subsidiary undertakings include: Biba Retail Ltd; House of Fraser Ltd; James Beattie Ltd.

Brands include: Biba; Howick; Linea; Pied a Terre.

Total employees: 4,963

Focus of giving: General charitable purposes, health, ill health, medical research, small groups, local groups.

Membership: BITC

Community involvement	✓
CSR report	✓
Cash donations declared	✓
Charity partner(s)	✓
Employee-led support	✓

Community involvement

House of Fraser supports its chosen charity partners and encourages its retail and support centre employees to organise their own fundraising events for various local and national charities. It would appear that, in recent years, fundraising has been the primary way in which the group has helped to support charities, notably through the annual House of Fraser Charity Golf Day.

Chosen charities

The chosen charities currently detailed on the House of Fraser website are Sparks, Swan UK and Walk the Walk.

Main locations

House of Fraser has stores across the UK.

Community contributions

No charitable donations were made by the group during the year. However, the annual report for 2015/16 does state that the group 'supported various other charities throughout the period, including Walk the Walk and the Retail Trust, and a host of local charities throughout the country'. We were unable to determine a value for this support.

The annual House of Fraser Charity Golf Day helped to raise more than £260,000 for charitable causes, although, as is our usual practice, we have not included this amount in our total figure for corporate cash donations.

Exclusions

Our research suggests that support is not generally given to circular appeals, appeals from individuals, purely denominational (religious or political) appeals, local appeals not in areas of the company's presence or overseas projects.

Applications

Our research indicates that local charities are supported at the discretion of the store managers in their region. It would appear that the majority of initiatives supported by stores and support offices are suggested by staff.

Howden Joinery Group PLC

Furniture manufacture, retail – DIY/furniture

Correspondent: The Company Secretary, Howden Joinery Group PLC, 40 Portman Square, London W1H 6LT (website: www.howdenjoinerygroupplc.com/responsibilities/wider-community/index.asp)

Directors: Andrew Cripps; Geoff Drabble; Mark Allen; Mark Robson, Deputy Chief Executive and Chief Financial Officer; Matthew Ingle, Chief Executive Officer; Michael Wemms; Richard Pennycook, Chair; Tiffany Hall (women: 1; men: 7)

Year end	26/12/2015
Turnover	£1,220,200,000
Pre-tax profit	£219,600,000

Nature of business: The supply of kitchens and joinery products to trade customers, principally small builders.

Company registration number: 2128710

Subsidiary undertakings include: Howden Joinery Ltd; Howden Joinery Properties Ltd; Howden Kitchens Properties Ltd.

Total employees: 8,271

Focus of giving: Education, housing, homelessness, local groups, arts, culture, children, young people, community/social welfare.

Community involvement	✓
Community contributions	✓
CSR report	✓
Directors have other relevant posts	✓
Charity partner(s)	✓
Company gives to smaller charities	✓
Employee-led support	✓
Gifts in kind	✓
Matched funding	✓
Sponsorship	✓

Charitable donations

Total UK (cash and in kind):	2015	£1,900,000
Total worldwide (cash and in kind):	2015	£1,900,000

Community involvement

Individual Howdens depots, manufacturing sites and distribution and support centres are involved in their immediate communities, contributing cash and stock donations. Employees take part in a wide range of fundraising initiatives.

According to the Corporate Social Responsibility report for 2015, support is typically given to 'a broad cross-section of local causes including schools, colleges, sports clubs, care homes, hospices, scouts, guides and youth groups, village halls, and many other community activities and projects'. In 2014 support was extended specifically to include homeless charities and this effort was carried through 2015.

Charity partner

For more than ten years, Howdens has worked in partnership with Leonard Cheshire Disability. During this time, Howdens has funded volunteer training and recruitment initiatives, including 'Can Do' which gives young adults with disabilities the opportunity to find long-term employment or volunteering posts within their local communities, and provides them with support such as individual mentoring and accredited vocational courses.

Other partnerships

Howdens has also worked alongside other organisations to provide apprenticeships and educational support:

- Construction Industry Training Board (CITB): Since 2010, Howdens has worked with CITB to facilitate the Howden Joinery Bursary. The bursary funds the first year of wages for apprentice joiners at companies that would otherwise not be able to afford an apprentice
- Queen Elizabeth Scholarship Trust (QEST): QEST is the charitable division of the Royal Warrant Holders' Association and in 2015, Howdens made its first donation to support its scholarship and apprentice initiatives in the areas of traditional and contemporary crafts
- E-ACT: E-ACT is an independent academy sponsor. In 2015 Howdens has given funding to enable three students in to complete a three year-long, full-time apprenticeship programme. Furthermore, Howdens has pledged £20,000 per year over three years to help with the development of community engagement

Directors with other relevant posts

Mark Allen: trustee for The Prince's Countryside Fund and director on the GLF Schools board.

Main locations

London (head office). There is a local depot search facility on the website.

Community contributions

The CSR report for 2015 states 'This year our staff were responsible for over 3,600 cash and stock donations to local good causes amounting to £1.9 million across the Group'. We believe that this figure includes contributions not only from staff, but from the group and customers too. It has not been possible to separate the group's cash donation from its in kind support or employees' and customers' contributions.

We have taken the figure of £1.9 million to include more than £30,000 in donations from staff, customers and the company which was awarded to 36 homelessness charities across the UK.

Beneficiaries included: Leonard Cheshire Disability.

In-kind support

Gifts in kind

The CSR report for 2015 states that, during the year, Howdens 'supplied and fitted 75 complete kitchens in response to requests from local good causes'.

Employee-led support

Employee fundraising

Employees play an active role in supporting their local communities, principally through fundraising activities. Examples of employee fundraising efforts are listed on the 'Truly Local Timeline' on the Howdens trading website and include marathon runs, organising dancing competitions and taking part in the Bear Grylls Survival Race.

Matched funding

On the 'Truly Local Timeline' described above, there are examples of Howdens contributing cash in support of its employees' fundraising efforts.

Commercially led support

Sponsorship

Details of the group's sponsorship activity is detailed on the trading website. One recent example listed from 2016 was the Kilnsey Show in Skipton which, according to the website, 'showcases Yorkshire's agriculture alongside exhibiting local arts, crafts and rural industries'.

Exclusions

Our research indicates that no grants are given for overseas projects, political or religious appeals, science/technology or local appeals not in areas of the company's presence.

Applications

Requests should be sent to your local Howden depot, manufacturing site or distribution or support centre.

HSBC Holdings PLC

Financial services, banking

Correspondent: Group Corporate Sustainability Department, 8 Canada Square, London EC3R 6AE (tel: 020 7991 8888; website: www.hsbc.com/our-approach/sustainability/communities)

Directors: Ben Matthews; David Nish; Douglas Flint, Group Chair; Heidi Miller; Henri de Castries; Iain Mackay, Group Finance Director; Irene Lee; Jackson Tai; Joachim Faber; John Lipsky;

Jonathan Symonds; Kathleen Casey; Laura Cha; Lord Evans of Weardale; Marc Moses; Paul Walsh; Pauline van der Meer Mohr; Phillip Ameen; Rachel Lomax; Sam Laidlaw; Stuart Gulliver, Group Chief Executive (women: 6; men: 15)

Year end	31/12/2015
Turnover	£47,358,300,000
Pre-tax profit	£16,735,000,000

Nature of business: HSBC is one of the largest banking and financial services organisations in the world, with businesses working in the areas of commercial banking, global banking and markets, global private banking and retail banking and wealth management.

Company registration number: 617987

Subsidiary undertakings include: Endeavour Personal Finance Ltd; HSBC Asset Finance (UK) Ltd; HSBC Private Equity Investments (UK) Ltd.

UK employees: 47,000

Total employees: 264,000

Focus of giving: Education, environment, health, ill health, overseas projects.

Membership: BITC, LBG

Accredited Living Wage Employer	✓
Community involvement	✓
Community contributions	✓
Company reports on anti-slavery	✓
CSR report	✓
CSR or charity committee	✓
Directors have other relevant posts	✓
AF Covenant	✓
Charity partner(s)	✓
Employee-led support	✓
FTSE 100	✓
Gifts in kind	✓
Humanitarian aid: overseas	✓
Matched funding	✓
Overseas giving	✓
Payroll giving	✓
Pro bono	✓
Sponsorship	✓

Charitable donations

Cash UK (latest available):	2015	£18,650,000
Cash worldwide:	2015	£165,700,000
Total worldwide (cash and in kind):	2015	£174,400,000

Community involvement

HSBC's community involvement is based around promoting access to education and natural resources, which the bank's UK website describes as being 'essential to resilient communities'. In 2015 the decision was taken following consultation with employees to add medical charities to the causes supported by the bank.

Through its education programmes, HSBC helps to provide young people with educational and life skills development opportunities they would ordinarily be unable to access. At a global level, the HSBC Water Programme helps to protect vital river systems and to provide access to safe water and sanitation for hundreds of thousands of people.

Community projects and local charities around the world working in the areas of children, education, medical welfare and research, and the environment and wildlife are supported through HSBC's 150th anniversary fund.

HSBC employees take part with various volunteering activities in support of their local communities.

Main locations: HSBC operates around the world. Note that the information on this entry will focus principally on the banking group's community involvement in the UK.

Young People Programme

HSBC's 14 education programmes are known collectively as the Young People Programme and reach 50,000 young people in the UK each year. Examples of two of the programmes HSBC has been involved with are:

- Opportunity Partnership: Now concluded, this £30 million programme, three year programme was created by HSBC and involved four charities: Catch22; St Giles Trust; The Prince's Trust; and Tomorrow's People. The programme helped more than 25,000 young people move into education, training or employment
- The Prince's Trust Fairbridge Programme: This programme was launched by HSBC in 2012, with a commitment of £5 million to The Prince's Trust over five years. The aim of the programme is to assist 3,000 young people who have been excluded from school or are in danger of exclusion return to education, training or employment. After four years, the programme had helped 6,000 young people between the ages of 13 and 17. Employees of the bank help to run workshops through the programme

HSBC 150 Community Fund

To celebrate its 150th birthday in 2015, the bank created the HSBC 150 Community Fund, which will see it contribute $150 million (at the time of writing (October 2016) approximately £122.57 million) to 140 community projects and local charities around the world over the three years from 2015 to 2017. The fund will supplement the contributions HSBC already makes through its community investment programmes.

HSBC employees were consulted on the causes they wanted to benefit from the fund, with more than 50,000 taking part in voting. They decided that projects working to benefit children, education, medical welfare and research, and the environment and wildlife should be prioritised. According to the HSBC global website, teams based in locations around the world have chosen organisations within these areas that 'will provide a positive and sustainable change in their communities'. It is further explained that 'these charities will receive different amounts of funding depending on their plans and requirements'.

ATM donations

In 2006, HSBC became the first bank to enable customers to donate to charity via ATMs and, since then, more than £2.2 million has been raised. Six national charities are selected by employees to benefit through the scheme each year, along with the Disasters Emergency Committee (DEC). For 2016/17, the chosen partner charities are: Alzheimer's Society; Cancer Research UK; Dog's Trust; Mind; Macmillan Cancer Support; and NSPCC.

Directors with other relevant posts

Iain Mackay: trustee of British Heart Foundation.

Rachel Lomax: member of the council of Imperial College, London; trustee of the Ditchley Foundation; and Chair of the corporate responsibility committee of Serco Group.

Sam Laidlaw: Chair of the National Centre for Universities and Business.

Joachim Faber: member of the advisory board for the European School of Management and Technology.

Kathleen Casey: trustee of Pennsylvania State University and a member of the trust fund board of the Library of Congress.

John Lipsky: Co-chair of the Aspen Institute Program on the World Economy; director of the National Bureau of Economic Research and the Center for Global Development; and a member of the advisory board of the Stanford Institute for Economic Policy Research and the Council on Foreign Relations.

Anti-slavery reporting

In its 'UN Global Compact Communication on Progress 2015' document, HSBC states: 'We will integrate the provisions of the Modern Slavery Act 2015 into our business and supply chain, and will report in line with the guidelines published by the UK government.'

Community contributions

HSBC publishes a 'Key facts' document, which is available to download from the website and includes a breakdown of its worldwide cash and in-kind contributions according to geographical region. The following information was obtained from this document.

Worldwide contributions

During 2015 the group made cash donations totalling $205 million (approximately £168.1 million) to charities and non-profit organisations in support of projects benefitting communities around the world. These donations were broken down as follows:

Asia-Pacific	$104 million (£85.1 million)
Europe	$75.2 million (£61.5 million)
North America	$18.6 million (£15.2 million)
Middle East	$4.6 million (£3.76 million)
Latin America	$3 million (£2.45 million)

The global website also provides the following breakdown of how cash donations were allocated according to theme: education (37%); other (35%); environment (28%).

Worldwide, employees spent 304,555 hours volunteering during work time, the value of which is given as $7.3 million (approximately £6 million).

An additional $10.1 million (approximately £8.27 million) was expended in management costs, although, as is our usual practice, we have not included this in the overall total for contributions.

Contributions in the UK

A separate figure for UK contributions was not provided in the 'Key facts' document; however, HSBC's UK website provided the following information, which we have used to inform our total for the group's donations in the UK.

The website states: 'Each year, our education programmes, collectively known as the Young People Programme, reach more than 50,000 young people in the UK through 14 schemes supported by an investment of £14 million.' In addition, during 2015, £653,000 was awarded to 71 local projects in the UK through the employee grants scheme.

HSBC 150 Community Fund

In addition to contributions made through its educational programme and support for employees, HSBC pledged $25 million (approximately £20.4 million) over a period of five years to the Francis Crick Institute, the biomedical research centre located in King's Cross. The donation, which the bank is making through Cancer Research UK, will be funded in part by the HSBC 150 Community Fund. We have estimated the amount given by HSBC to Cancer Research UK during 2015 to be around £4 million; this is based on the overall figure pledged divided by the number of years over which it has been committed.

Another beneficiary of the 150 Community Fund is the University of Aberdeen, where HSBC has established the Sir Thomas Sutherland Scholarship to support students from India, Indonesia, Malaysia and Thailand to complete their undergraduate studies there. According to the university's website, the scholarship is worth £99,000 over four years.

In-kind support

Employee time

Staff are given a day's paid leave each year to enable them to partake with community and charitable projects. Around the world in 2015, HSBC employees spent 304,555 working hours carrying out volunteer work. The 'Key facts' document, available online, provides the following breakdown of hours spent volunteering by geographical region:

Asia-Pacific	177,503
Europe	60,735
Latin America	33,112
North America	28,919
Middle East	4,286

Pro bono

HSBC employees contributed knowledge and expertise to HSBC's community programmes during 2015. An example of this detailed on the UK website is The Prince's Trust Fairbridge Programme, through which employees helped to run workshops based around money management and employability.

Employee-led support

Employee volunteering

HSBC employees are involved in a variety of volunteering initiatives. According to HSBC's UK website, activities range from working with national programmes such as the Opportunity Partnership, Teach First, Young Enterprise and the HSBC Water Programme, to supporting local grassroots organisations. Examples of local projects employees were involved with in 2015 included 'building sensory gardens in hospices, supporting city farms, and working with schools and universities on a 'Stockmarket' project. In the UK in 2015, almost 1,500 HSBC employees volunteered 10,000 hours of their own time.

Matched funding

Staff who volunteer with a registered charity can apply to HSBC for funding to support their cause.

Payroll giving

A payroll giving scheme is in operation.

Commercially led support

Sponsorship

HSBC sponsors organisations in the areas of sport (mainly rugby and golf) and culture.

Exclusions

Our research indicates that no support is given for advertising in charity brochures, animal welfare, appeals from individuals, the arts, older people, fundraising events, political appeals, religious appeals, science/technology, or sports.

Applications

Sponsorship

To apply for sponsorship, complete and submit the online form that can be found at www.hsbc.com/about-hsbc/sponsorship.

Alan Hudson Ltd

Agriculture

Correspondent: David Ball, Trustee, Bevis Lane, Wisbech St Mary, Wisbech, Cambridgeshire PE13 4RR (tel: 01945 583087/01945 461456)

Directors: David Ball, Chair; Stephen Layton; David Wheeler; Sarah Wheeler (women: 1; men: 3)

Year end	31/07/2015
Turnover	£1,000,000

Nature of business: Fruit growers. The company is wholly owned by the Hudson Foundation (Charity Commission no.280332) and donates its taxable profits for the year to the charity by way of Gift Aid.

Company registration number: 613979

Focus of giving: Older people, community/social welfare.

Community involvement	✓
Community contributions	✓
Corporate charity	✓

Charitable donations

Cash UK (latest available):	2015	£130,500
Total UK (cash and in kind):	2015	£130,500
Cash worldwide:	2015	£130,500
Total worldwide (cash and in kind):	2015	£130,500

Community involvement

Giving is made through the Hudson Foundation (Charity Commission no. 280332).

Community contributions

Alan Hudson Ltd is the principal subsidiary of the Hudson Foundation and donates its profits to the foundation by way of gift aid. For 2014/15 it was not clear from either set of accounts what amount was paid by the company to the foundation. We have taken the amount spent in charitable giving to organisations (see the foundation's accounts) as the figure for the cash donations made by the company.

Corporate charity

The Hudson Foundation (Charity Commission no. 280332).

Applications

Apply in writing to the correspondent.

IBM United Kingdom Ltd

Electronics/computers

Correspondent: Corporate Citizenship Team, PO Box 41, North Harbour, Portsmouth, Hampshire PO6 3AU (tel: 0239256 1000; email: ccruk@uk.ibm.com; website: www-05.ibm.com/uk/ondemandcommunity/index.html)

Directors: David Stokes; Sean Tickle; Stephen Leonard; Stephen Smith; Timothy Eagle; Vineet Khurana (women: 0; men: 6)

Year end	31/12/2015
Turnover	£3,658,000,000

Nature of business: IBM United Kingdom Ltd is the UK subsidiary of IBM Corporation. It is involved in the provision of information technology services and solutions, and the development, production and supply of advanced information technology products.

Company registration number: 741598

Focus of giving: Education, local groups, overseas projects.

Membership: BITC

Community involvement	✓
Community contributions	✓
CSR report	✓
Corporate charity	✓
Employee-led support	✓
Gifts in kind	✓
Overseas giving	✓
Pro bono	✓

Charitable donations

Cash UK (latest available):	2015	£89,600
Total UK (cash and in kind):	2015	£89,600
Cash worldwide:	2015	£89,600
Total worldwide (cash and in kind):	2015	£89,600

Community involvement

Charity Skills Masterclasses
IBM has partnered with the Small Charities Coalition to provide charities with an annual series of masterclasses. The masterclasses cover topics such selling techniques, product management, measuring impact, technology, website development, marketing and social media. Further information can be found on the Small Charities Coalition's website.

IBM United Kingdom Trust
The company also makes contributions to its associated charity, IBM United Kingdom Trust (Charity Commission no. 290462), which derives most of its income from the IBM International Foundation and IBM subsidiaries.

The trust's primary areas of focus are:

- To increase the scope, usage and understanding of information technology
- To enable disadvantaged people to acquire skills, particularly through the use of information technology
- To provide aid in the form of technology and technical support for disaster relief
- Promoting volunteering by IBM employees
- Providing support to research universities and other research institutions

Main UK locations
Portsmouth

Community contributions

The company's annual report for 2015 did not declare a figure for charitable donations. However, the IBM United Kingdom Trust's annual accounts for 2014/15 show that it received £896,000 from IBM's subsidiaries and the IBM International Foundation. Of this amount, 10% was sourced from the United Kingdom and we have, therefore, used a figure of £89,600 as IBM's UK cash contributions.

In-kind support

Impact Grants
Impact Grants scheme offers software and pro bono expertise. Organisations should have a UK focus and the resources necessary to implement the consultancy recommendations or software that is provided through the grant.

Employee-led support

Employee volunteering
Through its On Demand Community initiative, IBM encourages and supports employees and retirees to undertake voluntary work, organising its community involvement policies to motivate people to volunteer. The company's intranet site has a database of volunteer opportunities which allows staff to find a good cause which matches their interests.

Corporate charity

IBM United Kingdom Trust (Charity Commission no. 290462).

Applications

Impact Grants and the On Demand Community
Email ccruk@uk.ibm.com for further information on these initiatives.

IBM United Kingdom Trust
Very few unsolicited requests are considered. If you decide to submit an appeal then it should be done by email or in writing and include a brief resumé of the aims of your organisation and details of what assistance is required. Those considering making an application are advised to telephone first for advice.

ICAP PLC

Financial services

Correspondent: The Charity Day Team, 2 Broadgate, London EC2M 7UR (tel: 020 7000 5000; email: charity.day@icap.com; website: www.icapcharityday.com)

Directors: Charles Gregson, Chair; Ivan Ritossa; John Sievwright; Michael Spencer, Group Chief Executive Officer; Robert Standing; Stuart Bridges, Group Finance Director (women: 0; men: 6)

Year end	31/03/2016
Turnover	£1,201,000,000
Pre-tax profit	£89,000,000

Nature of business: The company is the world's largest interdealer broker and is active in the wholesale markets for OTC derivatives, fixed income securities, money market products, foreign exchange, energy, credit and equity derivatives.

Company registration number: 3611426

Subsidiary undertakings include: Garban Group Holdings Ltd; ICAP Group Holdings PLC; Intercapital Ltd

Focus of giving: General charitable purposes, education, environment, health, ill health, heritage, medical research, older people, arts, culture, overseas projects, sport, recreation, children, young people, community/social welfare, disability.

Community involvement	✓
Community contributions	✓
CSR or charity committee	✓
Cash donations declared	✓
Employee-led support	✓
Overseas giving	✓

Community involvement

ICAP PLC donates money raised during its annual 'Charity Day', launched in 1993, to charities across the globe. On this day each year, the group donates its entire revenue, without any cost reductions, to various charities selected by local offices. This unique event sees ICAP donate all revenue, cover all running costs and its brokers contribute 100% of their commission for the day.

Company staff have a significant involvement with Charity Day, which the company sees as having the benefit of contributing to their motivation. Not only do employees contribute personally in a financial way, as described above, but the charities that benefit from the event are selected by ICAP's staff in each region in which it operates. Charity Day also sees significant involvement from ICAP customers and suppliers and celebrities.

Main UK locations
City of London

Community contributions

In 2015 ICAP raised £7.5 million for charities around the world, bringing the total amount raised over Charity Day's 23-year history to almost £127 million.

Beneficiaries included: Advancing Systematic Solutions to end Enslavement and Trafficking (ASSET); Book Aid International; The Brain Tumour Charity; The Cardiac Children Foundation of Thailand; Fundacion Centro Colombiano de Hipoterapia; The Mulberry Bush Organisation; Pertiwi Soup Kitchen; Scope; SportsAid; The Safepoint Trust.

Applications

Organisations with an interest in applying to become a potential beneficiary of ICAP Charity Day can complete an online application form, accessible via the 'Contact us' section of the website (www.icapcharityday.com/contact-us). Applications are accepted throughout the year; however, it is explained on the website that the lists of beneficiaries for Charity Day are generally planned two years in advance 'due to the sheer volume of applications' received.

IG Group Holdings PLC

Financial services

Correspondent: See 'Applications', Cannon Bridge House, 25 Dowgate Hill, London EC4R 2YA (tel: 020 7896 0011; website: www.iggroup.com/about-ig-group/our-vision/corporate-social-responsibility)

Directors: Andy Green, Chair; Jim Newman; June Felix; Malcolm Le May; Paul Mainwaring, Chief Financial Officer; Peter Hetherington, Chief Executive Officer; Sam Tymms; Stephen Hill (women: 2; men: 6)

Year end	31/05/2016
Turnover	£456,300,000
Pre-tax profit	£207,900,000

Nature of business: IG Group is a provider of financial spread betting and CFDs with sales offices in 15 countries, including the UK and Ireland.

Company registration number: 4677092

Subsidiary undertakings include: IG Index Ltd; IG Markets Ltd; IG Finance.

UK employees: 857

Total employees: 1,408

Focus of giving: General charitable purposes.

Community involvement	✓
Community contributions	✓
CSR report	✓
Directors have other relevant posts	✓
Employee-led support	✓
Gifts in kind	✓
Matched funding	✓
Payroll giving	✓

Community involvement

IG Group supports its employees to contribute to a wide range of charitable causes. The group matches funds raised by employees and operates a matched leave policy for employees who spend time volunteering. Through the Charities Aid Foundation (CAF) employees operate their own charity fund and can also donate to charities through payroll giving.

Directors with other relevant posts
Andy Green, Chair: President of UK Space; Co-chair of the Space Leadership Council; member of the Digital Economy Council.

Stephen Hill: trustee and Chair of the Royal National Institute for Deaf People – Action on Hearing Loss; member of the advisory board of the Cambridge Judge Business School; Chair of the Alzheimer's Society.

Community contributions

A figure for charitable donations was not included in the annual report and accounts for 2015/16.

In-kind support

Matched leave
Employees are encouraged to get involved with voluntary work through the group's absence-management policy. Additional leave is given on a like-for-like basis to employees who volunteer, up to a maximum of five days per annual leave cycle.

Employee-led support

Matched funding
Funds raised by employees through sponsored events and activities are matched by the group.

Payroll giving
Employees are able to donate to selected charities from their monthly wage.

Employee charity fund
Through the Staff Charity Fund scheme operated by the Charities Aid Foundation, IG employees are able to operate and contribute to their own charity fund

Applications

It would appear, based on the 'Society and Employee Sponsorship' section of its 2015/16 annual report, that IG Group's community support is employee-led.

IMI PLC

Engineering

Correspondent: The Company Secretary, Lakeside, Solihull Parkway, Birmingham Business Park, Birmingham B37 7XZ (tel: 0121 717 3700; fax: 0121 717 3701; email: info@imiplc.com; website: www.imiplc.com/corporate-responsibility/our-approach.aspx)

Directors: Birgit Nørgaard; Bob Stack; Carl-Peter Forster; Daniel Shook; Isobel Sharp; Lord Smith of Kelvin, Chair; Mark Selway, Chief Executive; Ross McInnes; Roy Twite (women: 2; men: 7)

Year end	31/12/2015
Turnover	£1,557,000,000
Pre-tax profit	£218,700,000

Nature of business: IMI is a diversified engineering group focused on the precise control and movement of fluids in critical applications, delivering engineering solutions to address global trends such as clean energy, energy efficiency, healthcare and increasing automation.

Company registration number: 714275

Subsidiary undertakings include: Engineering Appliances Ltd; Holford Estates Ltd; IMI Hydronic Engineering Ltd.

UK employees: 1,439

Total employees: 11,300

Focus of giving: General charitable purposes, education.

Community involvement	✓
Community contributions	✓
CSR report	✓
Employee-led support	✓

Community involvement

IMI PLC supports charitable and educational programmes in communities in which it has a presence. At a group level there is a charitable donations policy, which benefits a variety of national and international causes and, at a local level, some of its locations develop relationships with local community causes in their areas. Each year on the IMI Way Day, IMI colleagues at its bases around the globe engage with their local communities by taking part in a wide range of activities. Much of the information available on IMI's community involvement focuses on activities around the globe.

Main UK locations
Bristol; Poole; Leeds; Fradley (near Lichfield); Birmingham.

Community contributions

The annual report and accounts for 2015 did not declare a figure for charitable contributions from the group.

Employee-led support

Employee volunteering

An example of employee charitable involvement in the UK was detailed in the Corporate Responsibility report for 2015. Around 200 staff from IMI head office and IMI Critical Engineering and Group spent an afternoon helping with a project at Newlands Bishop Farm, which helps young people and adults who have mental health issues and other disabilities to develop work-related skills in a working environment. Among their activities, the team carried out general maintenance and helped to create a beach garden. Another example that is detailed on the IMI website is the efforts of colleagues at IMI Truflo Marine who spent an afternoon as 'K9 Carers' at Birmingham Dogs Home.

Exclusions

Our research indicates that no support is given for political appeals.

Applications

For national or international appeals, apply in writing to the correspondent. Local appeals should be directed towards the appropriate local IMI facility.

Imperial Tobacco Group PLC

Tobacco

Correspondent: Kirsty Green-Mann, Head of Corporate Responsibility, Winterstoke Road, Bristol BS3 2LL (tel: 0117 963 6636; email: cr@impbrands.com; website: www.imperialbrandsplc.com/Responsibility)

Directors: Alison Cooper, Chief Operating Officer; David Haines; John Downing; Karen Witts; Malcolm Wyman; Mark Williamson, Chair; Matthew Phillips; Michael Herlihy; Oliver Tant, Chief Financial Officer; Steven Stanbrook; Therese Esperdy (women: 3; men: 8)

Year end	30/09/2015
Turnover	£6,300,000,000
Pre-tax profit	£2,615,000,000

Nature of business: Tobacco manufacturer.

Company registration number: 3236483

Subsidiary undertakings include: Imperial Tobacco Holdings (2007) Ltd; Imperial Tobacco Ltd; Imperial Tobacco International Ltd.

Brands include: Davidoff; West; JPS; Gauloises Blondes; Golden Virginia.

Focus of giving: Education, environment, health, ill health, overseas projects, community/social welfare.

Membership: BITC

Community involvement	✓
Community contributions	✓
Employee-led support	✓
Humanitarian aid: overseas	✓
Gifts in kind	✓

Charitable donations

Cash worldwide:	2015	£2,550,000
Total worldwide (cash and in kind):	2015	£2,550,000

Community involvement

Imperial Tobacco Group looks to support community initiatives in markets where it has a presence and contributes funds centrally. Employees of the group also contribute through volunteering activities. The group runs Altadis Foundation, a charity registered with the Spanish Ministry of Culture, which works to improve livelihoods in areas where the group operates, as well as the Leaf Partnership Committee, which aims to supports tobacco farming communities. The majority of the group's charitable contributions appear to be given for overseas causes, either directly or through UK-registered charities.

Main UK locations

Bristol

Community contributions

According to the Directors' Governance Report for 2014/15, £2.55 million was allocated to partnership and community investment. Through the Charities Aid Foundation £1.7 million was given to registered charities, supporting the Eliminating Child Labour in Tobacco Growing Foundation, the group's Altadis Foundation and a small number of UK charities. A further £700,000 was given to leaf sustainability partnerships which help tobacco growing communities, mainly in sub-Saharan Africa.

In-kind support

In-kind support is given in the form of management time, volunteering and gifts.

Employee-led support

Employee volunteering

The group's first global volunteering initiative was launched in 2015 and achieved 50,000 hours of employees' time in support of charitable activities.

Exclusions

Support is not given to individuals, research projects, expeditions or trips.

Applications

Note the following from the website: 'If you represent a charitable or not-for-profit organisation please note that we are not currently looking to fund new partners and we cannot support all appeals.'

Impetus – The Private Equity Foundation

Financial services, professional support services

Correspondent: See 'Applications', 183 Eversholt Street, London NW1 1BU (tel: 020 3474 1000; email: courtney.white@impetus-pef.org.uk; website: www.impetus-pef.org.uk)

Directors: Caroline Mason; Craig Dearden-Phillips; Hanneke Smits; Johannes Huth, Chair; Karl Peterson; Lionel Assant; Louis Elson, Deputy Chair; Marc Boughton; Nat Sloane; Nikos Stathopoulos; Patrick Healey; Prof. Becky Francis (women: 3; men: 9)

Year end	31/12/2015

Nature of business: Impetus – The Private Equity Foundation (PEF) is a venture philanthropy organisation which works with high-potential charities and social enterprises to empower young people from disadvantaged backgrounds to reach their full potential. Its investments packages address the NEET (young people not in education, employment or training) issue and include both financial contributions and pro bono expertise.

Company registration number: 8460519

Subsidiary undertakings include: PEF Trading Ltd; ThinkForward Social Impact.

Focus of giving: Education, enterprise/training, poverty and social exclusion, children, young people.

Community involvement	✓
Community contributions	✓
Cash donations declared	✓
Gifts in kind	✓
Pro bono	✓

Charitable donations

Cash UK (latest available):	2015	£4,700,000
Total UK (cash and in kind):	2015	£11,600,000
Cash worldwide:	2015	£4,700,000
Total worldwide (cash and in kind):	2015	£11,600,000

Community involvement

The current organisation was created following a merger of the Private Equity Foundation (established in 2006) and Impetus (set up in 2002) in 2013. Impetus – PEF is both a private company limited by guarantee and a registered charity (Charity Commission no. 1116139). The organisation normally works with a charity or social enterprise for four to ten years and offers a 'venture philanthropy package' of unrestricted funding, management support and pro bono work to help build, develop and expand their activities. It has a network of over 400 individuals and over 60 companies offering pro bono help.

When selecting charities to work with Impetus – PEF use the following criteria which have been taken from its website:

- Charities or social enterprises working in the UK (including most, if not all, of your operation)
- Who deliver programmes supporting disadvantaged children and young people between the ages of 11–24 to succeed in school and/or work
- The prospect of sustainability and scale is important to us so you need to have an annual income of over £250,000 and help at least 100 young people each year
- You also need ambition; sharing our aspirations to effect far-reaching and lasting change for disadvantaged young people in the UK is crucial
- So too is a desire and commitment to developing robust data and evaluation of your programme to further the impact you're making on the young people you support

Partnerships

Private Equity Foundation 1 Inc. is the Impetus – PEF's independent non-profit sister organisation in the USA. PEF 1 shares the charitable goals and charitable investment approach of Impetus – PEF and supports its charity portfolio.

The Education Endowment Foundation(EEF), set up in 2011 and funded by a £125 million grant from the Department for Education, is overseen by Impetus – PEF and The Sutton Trust.

Impetus – PEF co-operates with government bodies and worldwide partners. The company is a member of the European Venture Philanthropy Association (EVPA), maintains relationships with the Asian Venture Philanthropy Network (AVPN) and is part of the 'best practice' alliance together with New Profit Inc., LIFT Philanthropy Partners and Social ventures Australia (SVA). It is funded through both individual/corporate donations or charities and government departments and agencies.

Main locations

Funding is available throughout the UK.

Community contributions

In 2015 the organisation spent a total of £11.6 million supporting charities, which included strategic grant funding (£4.7 million), pro bono services (£2.3 million), Investment Team support (£2.8 million) and additional funds raised for the portfolio charities (£1.8 million).

Grant beneficiaries included: Tomorrow's People (ThinkForward) (£762,000); Place2Be (£435,500); Street League (£383,500); Workingrite (£356,500); IntoUniversity (£200,000); City Gateway and Brilliant Club (£50,000 each); Dixons (£29,500); Team Up (£25,000); Prison Radion Association (£5,000).

In-kind support

Pro bono work provided by external professionals to the charities in the organisation's portfolio, also other services, including management support.

Applications

The following information was taken from the foundation's website:

> We work mainly through referrals from people and organisations we know who are familiar with our partnership model. But we also carry out our own research, tapping into the latest evidence about what is needed to change the life opportunities of young people.
>
> We don't tend to accept unsolicited applications but if you'd like to find out more about our criteria, please email info@impetus-pef.org.uk
>
> Once we've found the right fit, we carry out some more detailed research, meet with the management team and visit the programme over a number of weeks or even months. This is so that we can develop a deeper understanding of your charity and ensure that you and your team understand and are comfortable with our approach and process.

Inchcape PLC

Motors and accessories, retail – miscellaneous

Correspondent: Marie Giannini, Group Communications Manager, 22A St James's Square, London SW1Y 5LP (tel: 020 7546 0022; fax: 020 7546 0010; email: contact@inchcape.com; website: www.inchcape.com/responsibility)

Directors: Alison Cooper; Coline McConville; John Langston; Ken Hanna, Chair; Nigel Northridge; Nigel Stein; Rachel Empey; Richard Howes, Chief Financial Officer; Stefan Bomhard, Group Chief Executive; Till Vestring (women: 3; men: 7)

Year end	31/12/2015
Turnover	£6,836,000,000
Pre-tax profit	£312,100,000

Nature of business: An automotive retail and services business with a presence in 26 countries around the world, including the UK and emerging markets.

Company registration number: 609782

Subsidiary undertakings include: Chapelgate Motors Ltd; Inchcape Corporate Services Ltd; Normand Motor Group Ltd.

Total employees: 14,691

Focus of giving: Overseas projects, disasters.

Community involvement	✓
Community contributions	✓
CSR report	✓
CSR or charity committee	✓
Employee-led support	✓
Humanitarian aid: overseas	✓
Overseas giving	✓

Charitable donations

Cash worldwide:	2015	£15,000
Total worldwide (cash and in kind):	2015	£15,000

Community involvement

Inchcape supports the local communities in which it operates. The website explains:

> With our extensive international business, we firmly believe in supporting the many different communities and cultures within which we operate, often through sponsorship and support of local charities for local people. These inspirational activities are decided on and driven by our people, who are passionate about the causes and charities they support.

Employees at Inchcape bases in 26 countries support charities in their local areas through fundraising and volunteering activities. The Corporate Responsibility report for 2015 provides a number of case studies about local charitable involvement by Inchcape employees at locations around the world. The example provided in the UK was of an employee from Audi Macclesfield who 'thanks to the Inchcape in the Community scheme and his bosses at Macclesfield Audi ... was given two half days off to be able to deliver two self defence sessions to young adults with learning disabilities'. Unfortunately, we were unable to find further information on the Inchcape in the Community scheme, nor were we able to find any more details of charitable involvement specific to the UK.

During 2015, Inchcape and its subsidiaries also worked to support employees and their local communities in Saipan in the wake of Typhoon Soudelour.

Main UK locations

London (head office)

Community contributions

The annual report and accounts for 2015 did not declare a figure for charitable donations. However, a case study included in the Corporate Responsibility report for 2015 explains that a subsidiary company of the group based in Saipan, Atkins Kroll, and its employees raised funds to assist people affected by Typhoon Soudelour in August 2015.

According to the report:

> An Atkins Kroll (AK) Care Saipan fund was immediately set up with the Inchcape Group donating US $20,000 to kick off the fundraising efforts ...
>
> AK Saipan also provided the charity and the military with additional vehicles and set up a shelter and provided hardship

payments for colleagues affected. They provided emergency transport for customers, who also received discounts on car repair bills and advantageous prices on damaged stock.

We were unable to determine a value for this support and have taken the value of the cash donation given to establish the AK Care Saipan Fund – about £15,000 – as the figure for the group's global contributions.

Applications

Inchcape's community activities are 'decided on and driven by' its employees.

Queries about group responsibility can be addressed to the correspondent or to the Group Company Secretary (Tamsin Waterhouse).

Informa PLC

Business services, information management and communication

Correspondent: The Sustainability Manager, 5 Howick Place, London SW1P 1WG, UK (tel: 020 7017 5000; email: sustainability@informa.com; website: informa.com/sustainability)

Directors: Cindy Rose; David Flaschen; Derek Mapp, Chair; Dr Brendan O'Neill; Gareth Bullock; Gareth Wright, Group Finance Director; Helen Owers; Stephen Carter, Group Chief Executive; Stephen Davidson (women: 2; men: 7)

Year end	31/12/2015
Turnover	£1,212,000,000
Pre-tax profit	£339,700,000

Nature of business: Informa is an international provider of specialist information and services for the academic and scientific, professional and commercial business communities across more than 40 countries.

Company registration number: 8860726

Subsidiary undertakings include: Ashgate Publishing Ltd; eBenchmarkers Ltd; Informa Middle East Ltd.

Total employees: 6,570

Focus of giving: General charitable purposes, education, enterprise/training, local groups, poverty and social exclusion, children, young people, community/social welfare.

Community involvement	✓
Community contributions	✓
Company reports on anti-slavery	✓
CSR report	✓
Cash donations declared	✓
Charity partner(s)	✓
Employee-led support	✓
FTSE 100	✓
Gifts in kind	✓
Humanitarian aid: overseas	✓
Matched funding	✓
Overseas giving	✓
Pro bono	✓
Shared-value alliances	✓

Charitable donations

Cash worldwide:	2015	£246,000
Total worldwide (cash and in kind):	2015	£599,000

Community involvement

Informa develops strategic relationships with community partners, both locally and internationally, by making cash and in-kind donations, and contributing skills and expertise through employee volunteering. Employees also take an active role in fundraising for charitable causes, including disaster appeals which Informa supported during 2015 with matched funding.

UK charity partner

The Prince's Trust

Main UK locations

London (head office) with nine other locations in the south of England and in Midlothian. There is an office locator facility on the website.

Community contributions

According to the Informa Sustainability Report 2015, community contributions during the year totalled £599,000. We were unable to determine how much of this was given in the UK. The CR report provided a breakdown of contributions:

Gifts in kind	£254,500
Cash donations	£246,000
Volunteer programme costs	£98,500

We believe the figure for cash donations to include amounts given in matched funding.

£7.7 million raised at the group's Monaco yacht auction and funds raised by Informa employees (£193,000) have not been included in the total contributions.

Beneficiaries included: British Red Cross.

In-kind support

Employee time

Each year, employees are able to take up to two paid working days for volunteering purposes.

Community partnerships

Informa builds relationships with various community partners, using human and other resources to help deliver on strategic objectives. Examples of this in 2015 are:

- Staff from Taylor and Francis India spent two days setting up a library in the village of Shahabad Mohammadpur in conjunction with the Read India Centre. The library features literature in the form of books, as well as digital content accessible through onsite Kindles and laptops
- Informa's International Roofing Expo, which was held in New Orleans, worked together with local community organisations to hold a Community Service Day, which visitors to the Expo were encouraged to take part in. Volunteers helped to rebuild the homes of disadvantaged people in the city
- In the UK, the group continued its four year relationship with The Prince's Trust. Informa employees ran workshops to help students of the charity improve their CV and interview skills. Work placements in IT, Corporate Communications and Group Strategy were also taken up by students

Employee-led support

Employee volunteering

In 2015 a total of 8% of Informa staff took part in various volunteering activities, including as part of the group's work with its charity partners.

Employee fundraising

In 2015 Informa colleagues helped to raise £193,000 for charitable causes.

The Informa Sustainability Report elaborates: 'Against a tragic backdrop of human crises, 2015 saw a big rise in emergency response giving and match funding'. Informa colleagues raised £35,000 for a range of charities in response to the Ebola campaign, the Nepal Earthquake Appeal and the European Refugee Crisis.

Furthermore, the group held a 'Fitness Challenge' in which 100 teams took part, with the winning team receiving a £4,000 donation for the charity of their choice. A group of 46 colleagues also completed the Three Peaks Challenge, raising £31,000 for Informa's UK partner, The Prince's Trust.

Matched funding

Informa matched funds raised by colleagues for emergency response appeals during the year with a donation for the same amount (£31,000) to the Red Cross.

Commercially led support

Charity auction

The group holds a biannual charity yacht auction at the Monaco Yacht Show.

Exclusions

Support is not given for political appeals.

Applications

The Informa website explains: 'Our businesses have their own sustainability budget to develop partnerships, so that our professional skills and resources can contribute to addressing local, regional and industry challenges'. In the first instance we recommend getting in touch with your local Informa business.

Innocent Ltd

Drinks manufacture

Correspondent: Kate Franks, Foundation Manager, The Innocent Foundation, 342 Ladbroke Grove, London W10 5BU (tel: 020 3235 0352; email: hello@innocentfoundation.org; website: www.innocentfoundation.org)

Directors: Douglas Lamont, Chief Executive; James Davenport; Sandra Mori; Scott Roche (women: 1; men: 3)

Year end	31/12/2015
Turnover	£223,632,000
Pre-tax profit	£11,005,000

Nature of business: The company develops, manufactures and distributes natural healthy drinks.

Innocent Ltd's immediate parent company and immediate controlling company is Fresh Trading Ltd, a company incorporated in the UK. The ultimate parent company and ultimate controlling party is The Coca-Cola Company, a company incorporated in Delaware, USA.

Company registration number: 4007092

Subsidiary undertakings include: Innocent ApS (Denmark); Innocent BV (Netherlands); Innocent SAS (France).

Total employees: 267

Focus of giving: Environment, humanitarian help, overseas projects, poverty and social exclusion, community/social welfare.

Community involvement	✓
Community contributions	✓
Directors have other relevant posts	✓
Cash donations declared	✓
Charity partner(s)	✓
Corporate charity	✓
Gifts in kind	✓
Humanitarian aid: overseas	✓
Humanitarian aid: UK including food banks	✓
Overseas giving	✓

Charitable donations

Cash UK (latest available):	2015	£1,276,000
Total UK (cash and in kind):	2015	£1,267,000
Cash worldwide:	2015	£1,276,000
Total worldwide (cash and in kind):	2015	£1,276,000

Community involvement

Innocent Ltd donates 10% of its annual profits to charitable causes, primarily through its registered charity The Innocent Foundation (Charity Commission no. 1104289).

The Innocent Foundation

The foundation is a grant-making charity supporting charities working around the world. Its mission is 'Helping the World's Hungry'. The founders of innocent – Adam Balon, Richard Reed and Jon Wright – remain as trustees of the foundation, as well as Innocent Ltd's current Chief Executive, Douglas Lamont.

The foundation provides funding for four different types of project which are detailed on the foundation's website:

- **Seed funding**: 'We've given seed funding grants since the very early days of the foundation back in 2004. 795 million people in go hungry every day, and we provide funding for sustainable agriculture projects which help communities in the developing world grow enough to feed and support themselves. These grants are specifically designed to help our partner charities get new projects off the ground, giving them time to refine their model and prove it works.'
- **Local food poverty**: grants are made to charities working on UK food poverty projects
- **Breakthrough development**: 'We are prepared to take risks on great but untested ideas in the hope that we will find new models that over time will become the gold standard to address hunger issues. Our first breakthrough development grant aims to find a better way of treating the 16 million children around the world suffering from severe acute malnutrition.'
- **Emergency hunger relief**: 'When major disasters strike, we are ready to respond. Getting food to people quickly in a humanitarian crisis is essential and a donation from the innocent foundation can have a direct and immediate impact for those affected by natural or man-made disasters. We work with Oxfam to support their emergency relief efforts around the world. Since 2014, we've given £310,000 towards ten emergencies.'

At the time of writing (November 2016), the foundation was accepting applications from UK-registered charities in two of the above areas – seed funding and local food poverty.

Charity partners

Innocent has worked with WWF UK since 2011 by donating money and helping to promote the charity's 'Livewell principles' through the company's 'Five steps for a healthier planet and you'.

Main locations

London.

Community contributions

In 2015 the company made contributions totalling to £1.28 million to charities. The majority of this (£950,000) was given to The Innocent Foundation.

We were unable to identify any other beneficiaries.

In-kind support

Innocent Foundation scholarships

The Innocent Drinks website states that each year someone who works for the company 'gets an extra week's holiday to work with one of our foundation projects'.

Corporate charity

The Innocent Foundation (Charity Commission no. 1104289).

Applications

In the first instance, see The Innocent Foundation's website where more information on the work it is currently supporting can be found, along with eligibility criteria and guidance on how to make an application.

Intercontinental Hotels Group PLC

Hotels

Correspondent: Corporate Responsibility Team, Broadwater Park, North Orbital Road, Denham, near Uxbridge, Buckinghamshire UB9 5HR (tel: 01895 512000; email: companysecretariat@ihg.com; website: www.ihgplc.com)

Directors: Anne Busquet; Dale Morrison; Ian Dyson; Jill McDonald; Jo Harlow; Luke Mayhew; Patrick Cescau, Chair; Paul Edgecliffe-Johnson, Chief Financial Officer; Richard Solomons, Chief Executive Officer; Ying Yeh (women: 4; men: 6)

Year end	31/12/2015
Turnover	£1,429,800,000
Pre-tax profit	£1,119,600,000

Nature of business: Hospitality chain of hotels, soft drinks and public houses.

Company registration number: 3130330

Subsidiary undertakings include: Crowne Plaza LLC; Holiday Inns (UK) Inc.; InterContinental Hotels Group Services Company.

Brands include: Crowne Plaza; Holiday Inn; Staybridge Suites.

Total employees: 350,000

Focus of giving: Economic generation, education, enterprise/training, environment, overseas projects, children, young people, community/social welfare, disasters.

Membership: BITC

Community involvement ✓
Community contributions ✓
Company reports on anti-slavery ✓
CSR report ✓
CSR or charity committee ✓
Directors have other relevant posts ✓
Cash donations declared ✓
Charity partner(s) ✓
Corporate charity ✓
Employee-led support ✓
FTSE 100 ✓
Gifts in kind ✓
Humanitarian aid: overseas ✓
Overseas giving ✓

Charitable donations

Total worldwide (cash and in kind):	2015	£3,300,000

Community involvement

The group provides support through monetary and in-kind donations, as well as partnerships. The group's corporate charity was established in 2016.

Areas of focus

The group's community involvement activities, including partnerships and donations, are based on three areas of focus:

- The environment
- Local economic opportunity
- Disaster relief

Charitable donations

The group's charitable donations policy, on its website, states that contributions are made to registered charities which support its areas of focus. The group can provide support through cash donations, in-kind support, hotel rooms or partnerships.

Community partnerships

The group chooses organisations to support based on the following criteria:

- exhibit a clear purpose and defined need in one of IHG's three areas of focus
- recognise innovative approaches in addressing the defined need
- demonstrate an efficient organisation and detail the organisation's ability to follow through on its proposal
- explain clearly the benefits to IHG and our hotel communities

Local managers and employees are encouraged to use this list as a guide, along with its Code of Ethics, when deciding what is right for local community needs.

IHG® Academy

This initiative focuses on skills, training and employment for local communities, working in partnership with local educational and community organisations. There are also initiatives to support people from a low income backgrounds in China and Brazil to pursue education and career opportunities in the hospitality industry.

Disaster relief

The group works with CARE International to support disaster preparedness and relief in the areas where its hotels operate. There is a designated disaster relief fund which can offer immediate assistance to employees and local communities. In 2015 the group raised more than $775,000 (around £613,500) for the fund and provided support in 17 countries for 27 disasters.

IHG Foundation (Charity Commission no. 1164791)

Registered with the Charity Commission in 2016, the group has established foundations in the UK, the US and China to support its community involvement. The foundation will focus on the following three areas: providing skills for local people; supporting those impacted by disasters; protecting the environment; grassroots community support. Charities supported so far include British Red Cross; The Prince's Trust; and Unseen. Further information can be found on the foundation's website: www.ihgfoundation.org.

Directors with other relevant posts

Patrick Cescau is a trustee of The Leverhulme Trust (Charity Commission no. 1159154). Luke Mayhew is a trustee of BBC Children in Need (Charity Commission no. 802052) and of The National Youth Orchestra of Great Britain (Charity Commission no. 290598).

Main locations

The group has hotels in nearly 100 countries. Its head office is in Denham, Buckinghamshire. There are also regional offices in China, Singapore and the US.

Community contributions

According to the group's accounts, charitable contributions worldwide totalled $4.17 million in 2015 (around £3.3 million), including both monetary donations and in-kind support – it was not clear how much of this was in the UK.

Financial information for the group was converted from US dollars at the time of writing (December 2016).

In-kind support

The group can provide hotel rooms to eligible charities under its donations policy.

Employee-led support

Employee fundraising

The group runs an annual Global Community Fundraising Week, where employees from across the group organise and take part in a range of fundraising events. In 2015 98,000 employees in 76 countries took part.

Corporate charity

IHG Foundation (UK) Trust (Charity Commission no. 1164791).

Exclusions

According to its website, the group does not fund:

- Individuals
- Religious organisations
- General operating support for hospitals and health care institutions
- Capital campaigns
- Endowment funds
- Conferences, workshops or seminars not directly related to its business interests
- Multi-year grants; only the first year of multi-year requests will be assured, with support in subsequent years dependent upon annual evaluation
- Political donations of any kind

Applications

Group

There is an online form for organisations to apply for cash donations, in-kind support or partnerships: www.ihgplc.com/responsible-business/corporate-responsibility/charitable-donations.

Foundation

The foundation's website states that it is focused on supporting a small number of organisations, and so does not accept unsolicited applications.

International Personal Finance

Financial services

Correspondent: Nick Jones, Group Head of Communications, Number Three, Leeds City Office Park, Meadow Lane, Leeds LS11 5BD (tel: 0113 285 6700; email: nick.jones@ipfin.co.uk; website: www.ipfin.co.uk/en/sustainability)

Directors: Adrian Gardner, Chief Financial Officer; Cathryn Riley; Dan O'Connor, Chair; Gerard Ryan, Chief Executive Officer; Jayne Almond; John Mangelaars; Richard Moat; Tony Hales

Year end	31/12/2015
Turnover	£735,400,000
Pre-tax profit	£100,200,000

Nature of business: International Personal Finance is an international home credit business operating using the Provident brand in Poland, the Czech Republic, Slovakia, Hungary, Mexico, Romania, Lithuania and Bulgaria. Its head office is based in Leeds, UK.

Company registration number: 6018973

Subsidiary undertakings include: International Personal Finance Investments Ltd; IPF Holding Ltd; Provident Financial s.r.o.

Total employees: 10,287

Focus of giving: Economic generation, education, enterprise/training, local groups, financial education, overseas projects, poverty and social exclusion, children, young people, community/ social welfare.

Membership: LBG

Community involvement	✓
Community contributions	✓
CSR report	✓
CSR or charity committee	✓
Directors have other relevant posts	✓
Charity partner(s)	✓
Employee-led support	✓
Gifts in kind	✓
Overseas giving	✓
Pro bono	✓

Charitable donations

Total worldwide (cash and in kind):	2015	£571,000

Community involvement

The group tends to support charitable causes in the areas where it operates, with a focus on financial education and social inclusion, as well as encouraging employee volunteering opportunities.

Financial education

The group works with a number of organisations internationally, such as schools, charities and universities, to deliver financial education programmes for communities and financially vulnerable groups.

Social inclusion

In partnership with two educational bodies, the group runs an education and social inclusion scheme in Romania, stARTS, which focuses on supporting teenagers to gain confidence, skills and develop their talents and career prospects.

Directors with other relevant posts

Tony Hales is Chair of Trustees of The Greenwich Foundation for the Old Royal Naval College (Charity Commission no. 1062519) and a trustee of The Services Sound and Vision Corporation (Charity Commission no. 233480) and of Welsh National Opera (Charity Commission no. 221538). Jayne Almond is a member of the council of the University of Oxford. Richard Moat is a trustee of The Peter Jones Foundation (Charity Commission no. 1110288).

Main locations

The group's head office is in Leeds. There are also offices in Australia; Bulgaria; Czech Republic; Estonia; Finland; Hungary; Latvia; Lithuania; Mexico; Poland; Romania; Slovakia; Spain.

Community contributions

The 2015 annual report states that during the year, the group contributed £571,000 in 'community investment'. It was not clear how much of this support was given in the UK.

Employee-led support

Employee volunteering

The 2015 annual report states that 3,400 employees were engaged in community activities during the year, volunteering for a total of 11,300 hours of company time, as well as a further 5,900 hours in their own time. Volunteering is organised at a local level by each branch of the company, to reflect the needs of the community and to allow employees to nominate projects.

Applications

There is a group-wide Sustainability Steering Committee and a Corporate Affairs Group, which discusses sustainability issues and new initiatives. However, many activities are organised at the level of each local branch – for contact details of each branch, refer to the website: www.ipfin.co.uk/en/contact-us.html

The head office is the only branch in the UK; this is based in Leeds.

Interserve PLC

Building/construction, services

Correspondent: Laura Spiers, Group Sustainability Manager, Interserve House, Ruscombe Park, Twyford, Reading RG10 9JU (tel: 0118 932 0123; fax: 0118 932 0206; email: talk.sustainabilities@interserve.com; website: sustainabilities.interserve.com)

Directors: Adrian Ringrose, Chief Executive; Anne Fahy; Bruce Melizan; Dougie Sutherland; Glyn Barker, Chair; Keith Ludeman; Nick Salmon; Russell King; Tim Haywood, Group Finance Director (women: 1; men: 8)

Year end	31/12/2015
Turnover	£3,204,600,000
Pre-tax profit	£79,500,000

Nature of business: Interserve provides advice, design, construction, equipment, facilities management and frontline public services.

Company registration number: 88456

Subsidiary undertakings include: First Security (Guards) Ltd; Interserve (Defence) Ltd; Interserve Healthcare Ltd.

Total employees: 63,570

Focus of giving: General charitable purposes, education, environment, health, ill health, armed forces, community/social welfare.

Membership: BITC

Community involvement	✓
Community contributions	✓
Company reports on anti-slavery	✓
CSR report	✓
Directors have other relevant posts	✓
AF Covenant	✓
Armed forces personnel	✓
Charity partner(s)	✓
Employee-led support	✓
Gifts in kind	✓
Pro bono	✓

Charitable donations

Cash worldwide:	2015	£456,000
Total worldwide (cash and in kind):	2015	£1,287,000

Community involvement

According to the SustainAbilities Progress Update 2015, Interserve builds 'strong relationships at a local level' in areas where it has a presence through cash donations and in kind contributions including employee volunteering time. Employees are supported in their charitable involvement by the Interserve Employee Foundation (Charity Commission no. 1145338). Some Interserve subsidiaries also carry out their own community activities.

Interserve Employee Foundation (IEF)

IEF exists to help connect employees with people living in the communities in which Interserve PLC operates. The foundation receives donations from employee fundraising and from the group, suppliers and customers, which it uses to fund charitable projects run by employees. Foundation ambassadors working across the group promote its aims and help to get employees involved with local projects, particularly through the employee volunteering scheme: Give A Day of Your Time.

SustainAbilities hub

Interserve has a website dedicated to its SustainAbilities plan (sustainabilities.interserve.com). The site includes a blog featuring articles written by Interserve personnel covering various sustainability topics from within the group and the corporate sector more generally.

Directors with other relevant posts

Adrian Ringrose, Chief Executive: adviser to the University of Liverpool.

Tim Haywood, Group Finance Director: member of the sustainability committee of the Institute of Chartered Accountants in England and Wales and a member of the Enterprise Leadership Team of Business in the Community.

Glyn Barker, Chair: Deputy Chair of the English National Opera.

Keith Ludeman: director/trustee of the London Transport Museum.

Bruce Melizan: Chair of Safer London.

Main UK locations
Twyford (head office) with locations across the UK. See the website for details (www.interserve.com/locations/uk-locations).

Community contributions

Based on information included in the SustainAbilities Progress Update for 2015, we believe that almost £1.3 million was given by the group during the year, distributed as follows:

Employee volunteering time	£699,000
Donations to charitable causes	£456,000
In kind contributions	£132,000

We believe, based on previous years, that a small proportion of cash donations (about £25,000) was given to the Interserve Employee Foundation.

A further £345,000 was contributed as 'Interserve leveraged fundraising'; we have taken this to refer to amounts raised by employees for example, and, as is our usual practice, we have not included this in the figure for the group's total contributions.

In-kind support

Employee time

Employee volunteering time is the one of the main ways Interserve contributes to communities. Employees can request to take up to two days paid leave through the Give A Day of Your Time scheme. In 2015 employees spent 3,200 paid days volunteering. The SustainAbilities Progress Update for 2015 provided a helpful breakdown of how these volunteering days were spent:

Building/refurbishing a facility	44%
Improving outdoor space	21%
Raising funds for charity or community projects	16%
Improving lives in deprived communities	11%
Improving education outcomes and business skills	9%

The areas of benefit were (in order): community development; health; education and young people; and environment.

Gifts in kind

Interserve supports charities with gifts in kind. One example of this is £6,000 worth of paint and design time contributed to John Taylor Hospice, where almost 200 Interserve employees volunteered during the year. Spare tyres were also donated to be used as planters at the hospice.

Employee-led support

Interserve Employee Foundation

The Interserve Employee Foundation supports employees, both in the UK and around the world, and facilitates their involvement with charitable activities. Employees raise money for the foundation in support of various charitable projects and the foundation works to inspire employees to get involved in their communities by sharing news of charitable activities from across the Interserve group.

Employee volunteering

During 2015, 5% of employees volunteered in their communities. Interserve has set a target to elevate this to 15% in 2016.

Employee fundraising

Employees fundraise for charities and causes supported by the Interserve Employee Foundation. Examples of this, as described on the foundation's page on the Interserve website, have included:

- Raising £25,000 for a cycle track at Pathways Primary School, a specialist school for children with special needs in Yorkshire
- In the UK, as part of the Big Book Drop for Literacy for Life, employees have collected 50,000 books, which have been given to schools in the Philippines, South Africa, India and Chile – places where Interserve has a presence
- Employees in the Philippines supported the Typhoon Haiyan relief appeal. Among their efforts, fundraising across the group helped to raise more than £20,000 to assist people in finding alternative accommodation and assisted by building a temporary shelter for displaced people

Applications

Interserve's community activities are co-ordinated by the Interserve Employee Foundation. The foundation supports charities nominated by Interserve employees. See the foundation's entry on page 372 in the 'Corporate charities' section for more information.

intu Properties PLC

Property, retail – miscellaneous

Correspondent: Alexander Nicoll, Corporate Responsibility Manager, 40 Broadway, London SW1H 0BT (website: www.intugroup.co.uk/en/about-us/corporate-responsibility)

Directors: Adele Anderson; Andrew Huntley; Andrew Strang; David Fischel, Chief Executive; John Strachan; John Whittaker; Lady Louise Patten; Matthew Roberts, Chief Financial Officer; Patrick Burgess, Chair; Rakhi Goss-Custard; Richard Gordon (women: 3; men: 8)

Year end	31/12/2015
Turnover	£571,600,000
Pre-tax profit	£513,000,000

Nature of business: intu Properties PLC owns and manages shopping centres in the UK and Spain. The company was formerly known as Capital Shopping Centre Group PLC and, before this, Liberty International PLC.

Company registration number: 3685527

Subsidiary undertakings include: Braehead Leisure Partnership; Chapelfield Property Management Ltd; intu Watford Ltd.

Total employees: 2,544

Focus of giving: General charitable purposes, education, enterprise/training, environment, humanitarian help, children, young people.

Membership: BITC, LBG

Community involvement	✓
Community contributions	✓
CSR report	✓
CSR or charity committee	✓
Directors have other relevant posts	✓
Charity partner(s)	✓
Community Mark	✓
Employee-led support	✓
FTSE 100	✓
Humanitarian aid: UK including food banks	✓

Charitable donations

Total UK (cash and in kind):	2015	£1,800,000
Total worldwide (cash and in kind):	2015	£1,800,000

Community involvement

intu Properties shopping centres develop partnerships with organisations in their local areas. Employees are also encouraged to take part with corporate responsibility and community initiatives.

Community partnerships

Examples of partnerships, described in the 2015 corporate responsibility report are:

- intu Trafford Centre: partnered with a local autism charity, the Together Trust, to create an autism-friendly shopping centre – the first in the UK
- intu Derby: through Business in the Community, as part of an effort to create partnerships between businesses and schools, the centre is partnered with the City of Derby Academy, providing employability support and skills development for 160 young people
- intu Watford: has a long-term partnership with Peace Hospice and has worked with The Conservation Volunteers to create the Green Gym, which sees a free outdoor session, based around improving the environment and keeping fit, each week. During 2015, the centre also hosted collections for a local food bank

Directors with other relevant posts
Adele Anderson: trustee of Save the Children UK.

Main locations
See the website for the locations of intu's UK centres.

Community contributions

The Corporate Responsibility report for 2015 states that £1.8 million was the 'cash equivalent of total donations'.

Employee-led support

Employee volunteering
In 2015 a total of 101 employees took part in volunteering activities.

Applications

Approaches should be directed to the appropriate local intu-owned shopping centre.

Investec PLC

Financial services, banking

Correspondent: Donations Committee, 2 Gresham Street, London EC2V 7QP (tel: 020 7597 4000; fax: 020 7597 4070; website: www.investec.com/about-investec/sustainability.html)

Directors: Bernard Kantor; Charles Jacobs; Cheryl Carolus; David Friedland; Fani Titi, Chair; Glynn Burger, Finance Director; Hendrik Du Toit; Ian Kantor; Khumo Shuenyane; Laurel Bowden; Lord Malloch-Brown; Perry Crosthwaite; Peter Thomas; Stephen Koseff, Chief Executive Officer; Zarina Bassa

Year end	31/03/2016
Turnover	£1,934,770,000
Pre-tax profit	£567,399,000

Nature of business: Specialist bank and asset management. The figures for Investec PLC's turnover have been taken from the 'reconciliation from statutory income statement to ongoing summarised income statement' contained in volume one of the 2016 annual report and accounts.

Company registration number: 3633621

Subsidiary undertakings include: Investec Bank PLC; Investec Securities (Pty) Ltd; Investec Wealth and Investment Ltd.

Focus of giving: Education, enterprise/training, environment, overseas projects, children, young people.

Membership: LBG

Community involvement	✓
Community contributions	✓
CSR report	✓
CSR or charity committee	✓
Charity partner(s)	✓
Employee-led support	✓
Gifts in kind	✓
Matched funding	✓
Overseas giving	✓
Payroll giving	✓
Pro bono	✓
Sponsorship	✓

Charitable donations

Total UK (cash and in kind):	2016	£1,575,000
Total worldwide (cash and in kind):	2016	£4,900,000

Community involvement

Investec looks to contribute to the communities in which it has a presence in three core areas – education entrepreneurship, and environment – by forging relationships with local charity partners, principally through employee volunteering, and by making small charitable donations.

Aside from their volunteering efforts, employees support charitable causes through the Give As You Earn scheme and various fundraising activities. They are supported in their activities through a budget allocated to the Donations Committee, which considers applications made by employees to request donations for the charities they personally support.

Partnerships
The sustainability report for 2016 provides numerous and detailed case studies of Investec's partnerships in the communities in which it has a presence. Examples of partnerships under the three areas of support, provided in the sustainability report 2016 are:

Education: Morpeth School
Investec's long-term partnership with the school in east London involves a wide range of activities and support, from one-off events to pupils visiting the Investec offices. Financial support has been given:

- To support a daily breakfast club benefitting more than 100 pupils
- To enable more than 100 young people to take part with Drum Works, a drumming programme held each week
- To provide subsidised residential trips for around 60 students from Years 7, 8 and 9

During the 2015/16 financial year, the school also benefitted from 230 hours of volunteer time, with activities such as:

- Weekly after-school maths sessions for sixth form students
- Young Apprentice, a skills and work experience development programme for Year 9 students, held at Investec

Entrepreneurship: Bromley by Bow Centre
The Bromley by Bow Centre works to promote economic regeneration in Tower Hamlets and, since 2008, has been a partner of Investec. Through the partnership, the Beyond Business programme is delivered and helps to support local people who want to set up their own social enterprise, providing successful applicants with funding and skills support. Volunteers from Investec sit on the *Dragon's Den*-style selection panel and offer advice to shortlisted applicants. Each year, Investec also runs the 'Beyond Business College', providing specialist skills and expertise to entrepreneurs who have benefitted through the programme. The report further explains that 'Twenty volunteers from 11 different business areas volunteered over 95 hours to support the programme'.

Environment
Investec volunteers spent 989 hours helping out with outdoor maintenance projects in areas local to their offices:

- 836 hours spent supporting Newham City Farm, the Bromley by Bow Centre, Trees for Cities and St Mungo's
- 32 hours spent with Edinburgh and Lothians Greenspace Trust
- 70 hours in Reading with Geoffrey Fields School
- 51 hours with Strokestown House in Dublin

Main UK locations
London (head office) with offices located across the UK. See the 'Contact us' section website for the locations of individual offices.

Community contributions

The sustainability report 2016 states that 'CSI' (corporate social investment) spend across the group amounted to £4.9 million, of which £1.57 million was spent in the 'UK and other' and the remaining £3.32 million in Southern Africa. This spend equates to 1% of operating profit before tax.

We have taken the figure for 'UK and other' as our total for UK contributions. Although Investec PLC also has operations in Ireland and Australia, we believe the vast majority of this CSI expenditure benefitted the UK. We believe the £1.57 million (of which £1.13 million was given at a group level) to include both cash donations and in kind contributions. A breakdown of 'UK and other CSI spend' by percentage according to category was provided in the report:

Education	33%
Philanthropic and other	30%
Entrepreneurship	27%
Environment	10%

Employee-led support

Employee fundraising
Employees take part in a range of fundraising activities. An example provided in the sustainability report 2016 was the Investec Ashes Cycle Challenge, which was organised by Investec's Sheffield office in partnership

with the Lord Taverners charity. 100 cyclists took part, including Investec employees from seven offices, and more than £320,000 was raised for local charities and to fund transport for children from special educational needs schools.

Commercially led support

Sponsorship

Investec sponsors a range of individuals, teams and organisations from a wide range of sectors from a local to international level.

Current sponsorship partners include Independent Schools Football Association, Opera Holland Park and the Royal Liverpool Philharmonic Orchestra.

Applications

In the UK, Investec Bank UK makes donations in the three focus areas: education, entrepreneurship and environment.

The following advice has been taken from the 'donations' section of the company's website.

> Before making contact, please note the following criteria: 1. Charities must be UK registered; 2. Charities should not be politically affiliated or religious in nature; 3. Schools may not apply due to our current commitment to Morpeth School; 4. Charities must have been established for at least 12 months; 5. Preference will be given to charities that carry out their work in and around London, or one of our other UK offices; 6.The Committee is likely to favour projects presented by small to medium sized charities; 7. We are unlikely to support projects where fundraising consultancies are involved; 8. Charities that do not provide full details of where the funds requested will be spent will not be considered.

Donation requests can be made using the request form on the 'donations' section of the website. They are considered by the Donations Committee on a quarterly basis.

General corporate sustainability queries can be directed to Susie Steyn, Corporate Sustainability Manager, email: susie.steyn@investec.co.uk, tel: 020 7597 4665).

IP Group PLC

Consultancy, business services, advertising/ marketing, information management and communication

Correspondent: Charitable Donations Committee, 24 Cornhill, London EC3V 3ND (tel: 020 7444 0050; fax: 020 7929 6415; website: www.ipgroupplc.com)

Directors: Alan Aubrey, Chief Executive Officer; David Baynes; Doug Liversidge; Dr Elaine Sullivan; Greg Smith, Chief Financial Officer; Jonathan Brooks; Mike Humphrey, Chair; Mike Townsend; Prof. Lynn Gladden (women: 2; men: 7)

Year end	31/12/2015
Turnover	£98,300,000
Pre-tax profit	£75,100,000

Nature of business: IP Group PLC builds and supports intellectual property-based companies in partnership with, mainly, universities. It specialises in the commercialisation of university intellectual property rights, and works in four main sectors: Biotech; Cleanteach; Healthcare; and Technology.

Company registration number: 4204490

Subsidiary undertakings include: Fusion IP PLC; LifeUK (IP2IPO) Ltd; Wound Genetics Ltd.

UK employees: 63

Total employees: 63

Focus of giving: General charitable purposes, health, ill health, children, young people.

Community involvement	✓
Community contributions	✓
CSR report	✓
CSR or charity committee	✓
Charity of the Year	✓
Charity partner(s)	✓
Employee-led support	✓
Matched funding	✓
Payroll giving	✓
Pledge 1%	✓
STEM-focused	✓

Charitable donations

Cash UK (latest available):	2015	£17,200
Cash worldwide:	2015	£17,200

Community involvement

The group partners with charities and aims to donate 1% of its profits to charitable causes that have particular relevance to the group and its employees.

Charity partners

Charities are selected for corporate and employee support each year by the group's charitable donations committee, which is made up of employees from senior management and the wider team. In 2015 the group's chosen charity partners were: The Multiple Sclerosis Society and The Percy Hedley Foundation.

The group also partners with Career Ready with a programme that gives work experience opportunities to disadvantaged young people who are interested in STEM (science, technology, engineering and maths) or business subjects.

Directors with other relevant posts

Professor Lynn Gladden is a fellow of the Royal Society; Royal Academy of Engineering; Institution of Chemical Engineers; Royal Society of Chemistry and Institute of Physics; and Trinity College, Cambridge. She is also Pro-Vice-Chancellor for Research at the University of Cambridge.

Main UK locations

City of London (head office); Leeds; Newcastle; Oxford.

Community contributions

In 2015 the group donated £17,200 (2014: £27,500) to charitable causes, with most of this going to the group's two main charity partners. Out of this amount, £1,800 was donated to other charities not listed in the annual report.

Beneficiaries included: The Multiple Sclerosis Society; The Percy Hedley Foundation.

Beneficiaries from previous years have included: Candlelighters Charity; Dyslexia Action; Imagineering Foundation; Lend with Care; Macmillan; Sands; Teach First; The Brightside Trust; The Pace Centre; The Prince's Trust; Vauxhall City Farm; Young Enterprise.

Employee-led support

Employee fundraising

Employees take part in fundraising for charitable causes, such as cake sales and challenges, which is often matched with funding from the group. The group also operates a payroll giving scheme in which employees can donate to charities of their choice.

Applications

Enquiries can be made by contacting the Charitable Donations Committee.

ITV PLC

Media

Correspondent: ITV Appeals and Social Action Department, ITV Responsibility, 11th Floor, The London Television Centre, Upper Ground, London SE1 9LT (tel: 020 7157 4833; email: responsibility@itv.com; website: itvresponsibility.com)

Directors: Adam Crozier, Chief Executive; Andy Haste; Anna Manz; Ian Griffiths, Group Finance Director; John Ormerod; Mary Harris; Peter Bazalgette, Chair; Roger Faxon (women: 2; men: 6)

Year end	31/12/2015
Turnover	£2,972,000,000
Pre-tax profit	£843,000,000

Nature of business: Independent television company.

Company registration number: 4967001

Subsidiary undertakings include: Broad Street Films Ltd; ITV News Channel Ltd; Juice Music UK Ltd.

Total employees: 5,558

Focus of giving: General charitable purposes, education, enterprise/training, health, ill health, overseas projects, humanitarian help, arts, culture, poverty and social exclusion, science technology, children, young people, disability, disasters.

Membership: BITC

Accredited Living Wage Employer	✓
Community involvement	✓
Community contributions	✓
CSR report	✓
CSR or charity committee	✓
Directors have other relevant posts	✓
Charity partner(s)	✓
Employee-led support	✓
FTSE 100	✓
Gifts in kind	✓
Humanitarian aid: overseas	✓
Humanitarian aid: UK including food banks	✓
Pro bono	✓

Charitable donations

Total UK (cash and in kind):	2015	£24,000,000
Total worldwide (cash and in kind):	2015	£24,000,000

Community involvement

ITV PLC looks to make a positive social contribution by working in partnership with a range of organisations, charities, NGOs and government. The group has a dedicated 'Responsibility' website which explains that this approach allows it 'to deliver programmes and initiatives to empower our viewers and colleagues to make a positive difference, at regional, national and international scale'. The principal way in which ITV supports its partners is by contributing airtime for appeals and campaigns. Employees are also supported to take an active role in their local communities through paid volunteering time and pro bono work, and ITV viewers also contribute through fundraising appeals such as 'Text Santa'.

Directors with other relevant posts

Sir Peter Bazalgette: Chair of Arts Council England and President of the Royal Television Society.

Roger Faxon: director at The Johns Hopkins University in Baltimore, Maryland.

Mary Harris: member of Remuneration Committee at St Hilda's College, Oxford.

Anna Manz: governor of Haberdashers' Aske's Schools Elstree.

Main locations

South Bank, London.

Community contributions

The ITV Corporate Responsibility Summary Report 2015 stated: 'We contributed more than £24 million in cash and in-kind to support these charities and others through our on-air and off-air activity, equating to 2.8% of our adjusted profit before tax; bolstered by an additional £13.1 million generously donated by the public'. The report did not include a breakdown of how much was given in cash donations. As is our usual practice, we have not included public donations in our figure for total contributions.

Partners have included: The Body and Soul Charity; Do-it Trust; Media Trust.

In-kind support

Employee time

Employees are able to take one day's paid leave per year for volunteering purposes. During 2015, more than 1,160 hours were contributed.

Pro bono

ITV employees contribute their skills and expertise to benefit good causes. Since 2009 this included staff from the legal department supporting The Body and Soul Charity to provide legal advice for people affected by HIV and AIDS.

The CR Summary Report for the 2015 also stated: 'We really want to champion skills-based volunteering and by the end of 2016, aim to mobilise 10% of our workforce to use their area of expertise to benefit local communities and causes.'

Airtime

ITV uses its position as an established commercial TV network to provide charitable causes with airtime. The CR Summary Report explains: 'In 2015 over 30 hours of airtime were dedicated to the charities and causes benefitting from our appeals and campaigns. We ran seven on-air appeals and campaigns raising awareness, items and money for charities'.

ITVinspire

The ITVinspire programme was created to engage young people between the ages of 14 and 17 from communities where ITV has bases (London, Leeds and Manchester). The programme, which was developed using the Business in the Community Work Inspiration framework, in 2015 provided 75 candidates with the opportunity to gain an insight into ITV through workshops, tours and practical activities, and to learn about business areas such as finance, compliance, digital and production.

Employee-led support

Employee volunteering

Employees take part in a range of volunteering activities, including helping out at the 'Text Santa' call centre.

Exclusions

Funds raised by ITV appeals and campaigns cannot be used to support core/running costs, political lobbying or religious campaigns. Partner organisations must meet the criteria set out in the Appeals and Social Action guidelines.

Applications

Organisations that are interested with partnering with ITV, should read the extensive Appeals and Social Action Campaigns guidelines, which act as a framework to ensure that causes supported are 'credible, effective and align' with the group's brand values. The guidelines are available to download from the ITV Responsibility website, where a link to the online application form can also be found.

Jaguar Land Rover Ltd

Motors and accessories

Correspondent: Kate Birkenhead, CSR Communications Officer, Abbey Road, Whitley, Coventry CV3 4LF (email: kbirkenh@jaguarlandrover.com; website: www.jaguar.co.uk/about-jaguar/responsibility/index.html)

Directors: Andrew Robb; Chandrasekaran Ramakrishnan; Cyrus Mistry, Chair; Dr Ralf Speth, Chief Executive Officer; Nasser Munjee (men: 5)

Year end	31/03/2016
Turnover	£22,208,000,000
Pre-tax profit	£1,557,000,000

Nature of business: The design, development, manufacture and marketing of high performance luxury saloons, specialist sports cars, four wheel drive off-road vehicles and related components.

In March 2008, the company was sold by Ford to the Indian company Tata. The 2013/14 annual report and accounts state: 'The immediate parent undertaking is TML Holdings Pte Ltd (Singapore) and the ultimate parent and controlling party is Tata Motors Ltd, India.'

Company registration number: 1672070

Subsidiary undertakings include: Jaguar Racing Ltd; The Daimler Motor Company Ltd; The Jaguar Collection Ltd.

Brands include: Jaguar; Land Rover.

Focus of giving: Education, enterprise/training, health, ill health, local groups, armed forces, overseas projects, humanitarian help, overseas projects, poverty and social exclusion, science technology, children, young people, community/social welfare, disability.

Membership: BITC, LBG

Community involvement	✓
Community contributions	✓
Company reports on anti-slavery	✓
CSR report	✓
CSR or charity committee	✓
AF Covenant	✓
Armed forces personnel	✓
Charity partner(s)	✓
Community Mark	✓
Employee-led support	✓
Gifts in kind	✓
Humanitarian aid: overseas	✓
Humanitarian aid: UK including food banks	✓
Market-led giving	✓
Matched funding	✓
Overseas giving	✓
Payroll giving	✓
Pro bono	✓
Shared-value alliances	✓
Sponsorship	✓
STEM-focused	✓

Community involvement

The group's global CSR programme focuses on the following three areas:

- Education and talent – inspire the workforce of the future
- Design and technology – apply technological innovation for social good
- Well-being and health – support disadvantaged communities

The group supports a number of partner charities, through funding, fundraising and in-kind donations. Employees provide volunteer and pro bono support. The group's operating sites may also offer support to local charities and communities.

Partner charities

The group supports the charities International Federation of Red Cross and Red Crescent Societies (IFRC) and the Born Free Foundation. In 2015/16 the group raised £400,000 to split between the two charities from the sale of a two-millionth Series Land Rover Defender at auction.

The group also has a long-standing relationship with BEN, the automotive industry's benevolent fund. The group supports and organises fundraising initiatives in partnership with other car manufacturers and provides volunteer support.

The group also supports NSPCC, leading the Coventry NSPCC Business Group.

Local community support

Individual operating sites also support charities in their local areas, mainly focusing on employee-led fundraising and supporting charities nominated by employees. Further details are provided on the group's website.

Education

The group is a partner of Premiership Rugby, delivering the HITZ programme, which provides a programme of rugby, skills development and mentoring for disadvantaged young people, particularly those not in education, employment or training.

A central part of the company's CSR programme involves the development of the next generation of engineers. One of the ways in which it does this is through the 'Inspiring Tomorrow's Engineers' (IET) programme. In collaboration with schools and colleges, the programme promotes 'learning and engagement on STEM subjects', with the aim of inspiring young people to take up careers in engineering or manufacturing.

Main locations

The group operates worldwide, but its headquarters and most of its employees are based in the UK, across eight sites – in areas of the West Midlands (Castle Bromwich; Coventry; Gaydon; Solihull; Wolverhampton; Warwick; Whitley) and in Liverpool.

Community contributions

The 2015/16 annual report did not state the group's total charitable contributions.

Beneficiaries during the year included: BEN; Born Free Foundation; International Federation of Red Cross; NSPCC; Royal Geographical Society.

The latest sustainability report available on the group's website at the time of writing (January 2017) was 2014/15. During the year, the group donated a total of £4.1 million through cash and in-kind support to charities globally.

In-kind support

The group provides in-kind support to charity partners – for example, it provides a fleet of Land Rover vehicles to the British Red Cross to help the charity's workers and volunteers to reach isolated or hard-to-reach areas in poor weather conditions.

Employee-led support

Employee volunteering

Employees are entitled to two days a year of volunteering leave, on approved individual or team initiatives. Examples include employees volunteering with the Inspiring Tomorrow's Engineers programme, supporting STEM education; and apprentices in Liverpool providing engineering support to Greenbank Sports Academy. Employees in Coventry and Solihull can also support local eligible charities through a Give As You Earn scheme, for which the group provides matched funding.

Commercially led support

Sponsorship

The group is the primary sponsor – or 'presenting partner' – of the Invictus Games. In 2015 the group also sponsored the Rugby World Cup.

Applications

Volunteer support

The website states that the group provides volunteering support for organisations, with a focus on education, young people or the environment, within a 30-mile radius of a Jaguar Land Rover facility. Requests from organisations meeting these criteria should be send to Dolores Evans, Community Relations Officer, at: devans31@jaguarlandrover.com or, for requests near the Halewood site in Liverpool, to Kate Birkenhead, CSR Communications Officer: kbirkenh@jaguarlandrover.com

Local charity support

The group's plants in the West Midlands and Liverpool can support charities in their local area – for further information, refer to the group's website: www.jaguarlandrover.com/gl/en/responsible-business/charity-fundraising/.

Jardine Lloyd Thompson Group PLC

Insurance

Correspondent: Group Charities Committee, The St Botolph Building, 138 Houndsditch, London EC3A 7AW (tel: 020 7528 4444; website: www.jlt.com/about-jlt/corporate-responsibility/society)

Directors: Adam Keswick; Annette Court; Bruce Carnegie-Brown; Charles Rozes, Group Finance Director; Dominic Burke, Group Chief Executive; Geoffrey Howe, Chair; Jonathan Dawson; Lord Sassoon; Mark Drummond Brady; Nicholas Walsh; Richard Harvey (women: 1; men: 10)

Year end	31/12/2015
Turnover	£1,155,100,000
Pre-tax profit	£155,000,000

Nature of business: JLT is a provider of insurance, reinsurance and employee benefits-related advice, brokerage and associated services. It has offices in more than 40 countries and territories on six continents.

Company registration number: 1679424

Subsidiary undertakings include: Expacare Ltd; Jardine Lloyd Thompson Reinsurance Ltd; Thistle Insurance Services Ltd.

UK employees: 4,109

Total employees: 10,777

Focus of giving: Education, health, ill health, local groups, overseas projects, disasters.

Community involvement	✓
Community contributions	✓
CSR report	✓
CSR or charity committee	✓
Directors have other relevant posts	✓
Cash donations declared	✓
Charity partner(s)	✓
Company gives to smaller charities	✓
Employee-led support	✓
Gifts in kind	✓
Humanitarian aid: overseas	✓
Market-led giving	✓
Matched funding	✓
Overseas giving	✓
Payroll giving	✓
Pro bono	✓
Sponsorship	✓

Charitable donations

Cash worldwide:	2015	£649,000
Total worldwide (cash and in kind):	2015	£649,000

Community involvement

Jardine Lloyd Thompson (JLT) aims to work with strategic charity partners in three areas that complement aspects of its business: sharing the social benefits of specialist knowledge (education); building resilience (disaster preparation); and well-being (healthcare).

According to the group's Corporate Responsibility report for 2015 (included in the annual report), the majority of its charitable giving is conducted on a 'business-by-business' basis, although the Group Charities Committee also manages a central budget, from which funding is allocated in support of strategic partners. A proportion of this budget is set aside to allow for matched funding of employees' fundraising efforts. JLT employees are encouraged to contribute to their communities in a number of ways, including through volunteering time and a payroll giving facility.

Directors with other relevant posts

Lord Sassoon: trustee of the British Museum and Chair of the China-Britain Business Council.

Nicholas Walsh: CEO Champion of the Women's Forum.

Bruce Carnegie-Brown: trustee of Historic Royal Palaces.

UK locations

JLT and its subsidiaries have offices in various locations across the UK. A helpful place to start is the 'Our locations' page on the website (www.jlt.com/our-locations/uk) which has links to the websites of JLT's principal UK businesses.

Community contributions

According to the Corporate Responsibility report for 2015, during the year JLT contributed £649,000 to charitable causes, which we have taken to represent cash donations. We were unable to determine how much of this was given in the UK.

The report did not include a figure for in-kind support given.

Beneficiaries in the UK included: Action on Addiction (where John Lloyd, a founding partner of JLT, is Chair), which receives a 'substantial' annual donation; and Dreams Come True, which was voted to be charity partner by staff at the group's Thistle business.

In-kind support

Volunteering time

Staff in JLT's UK locations are entitled to take one 'Charity Day' in company time per year.

Pro bono

The dedicated community section of the website explains 'At JLT we believe the diverse skills and experience of our workforce can help make a real difference in the communities in which we operate. We have a history of sharing our expertise, time and energy to support the causes about which our people are passionate. We recognise the importance of engaging our colleagues' skills and capabilities with the challenges facing local communities.'. An example of this in 2015 was the involvement employees from JLT India had with charity partner's Udaan India Foundation education project, where they mentored and taught pupils and organised sports events and performances.

Employee-led support

Employee fundraising

An example of employee fundraising activities, detailed in the Corporate Responsibility report for 2015, is the Lord Mayor's inaugural City Giving Day which took place in September and saw employees from the London offices of JLT Management Services, JLT Re, JLT Specialty and JLT Employee Benefits UK get involved with a Break the Cycle team challenge, St Botolph Bake-Off, and one employee take to the stage for a comedy performance.

Matched funding

According to the chair's statement for 2015, fundraising efforts by employees in the UK are matched on a 'pound-for-pound' basis.

Commercially led support

Sponsorship

JLT sponsors a number of sports teams/organisations including JLT Condor (a British UCI continental cycling team), the British Skeleton team and Cheltenham Racecourse.

Lower-cost products for charities

The community section of the website explains that a number of JLT businesses, including in Ireland and Australia, have developed 'specialised products that give lower-cost access to the benefits of risk management solutions to charities and volunteer/community groups, helping to keep community and volunteering sustainable in a risk-averse climate'.

Exclusions

No grants are made for fundraising events, advertising in charity brochures, appeals from individuals or large national appeals.

Applications

The 2015 Chair's Statement explains: 'The Group Charities Committee considers the many requests we receive from charities and takes a particular interest in those charities connected to communities local to our offices'.

JD Sports Fashion PLC

Retail – clothing and footwear

Correspondent: Company Secretary, Hollinsbrook Way, Pilsworth, Bury, Lancashire BL9 8RR (tel: 0161 767 1000; email: info@jdplc.com; website: www.jdplc.com/investor-relations/csr.aspx)

Directors: Andrew Leslie; Andy Rubin; Brian Small, Group Finance Director; Heather Jackson; Martin Davies; Peter Cowgill, Chair (women: 1; men: 5)

Year end	30/01/2016
Turnover	£1,821,652,000
Pre-tax profit	£131,631,000

Nature of business: JD Sports Fashion PLC is a retailer of sports-inspired fashion apparel and footwear. It has operations in the UK and Ireland, France, Spain, Holland and Germany.

Company registration number: 1888425

Subsidiary undertakings include: Mainline Menswear Holdings Ltd; Tiso Group Ltd; Tessuti Group Ltd.

Focus of giving: Health, ill health, children, young people.

Community involvement	✓
Community contributions	✓
CSR report	✓
Cash donations declared	✓
Market-led giving	✓

Charitable donations

Cash UK (latest available):	2016	£22,000
Total UK (cash and in kind):	2016	£22,000
Cash worldwide:	2016	£22,000
Total worldwide (cash and in kind):	2016	£22,000

Community involvement

The JD Foundation (Charity Commission no. 1167090)

The foundation was registered in May 2016 and will distribute the money generated from the carrier bag charge. As well as donations to The Mountain Rescue, the foundation will also support charities working with young people in the UK. The nominated charities for 2016/17 are: The Factory Zone; One Upon a Smile; The Retail Trust; and The Teenage Cancer Trust.

Main UK locations

Bury (head office) and stores nationwide.

Community contributions

In 2015/16 donations were made totalling £26,000. No further information was available.

Beneficiaries included: Once Upon a Smile (£14,000); Cancer Research UK (£8,000); and The Teenage Cancer Trust (£4,000).

Commercially led support

Carrier Bag Charge

During the year £350,000 was generated from the new carrier bag charges which went to the JD Foundation for distribution to good causes. The Mountain Rescue received £258,500 while the remaining £91,500 will be donated to other charitable causes in line with the objects of the charity.

Applications

Apply in writing to the correspondent, referenced 'Charitable donations'.

John Laing PLC

Building/construction, engineering

Correspondent: Chris Waples, Group Managing Director, 1 Kingsway, London WC2B 6AN (tel: 020 7901 3200; fax: 020 7901 3520; email: enquiries@laing.com; website: www.laing.com/corporate_responsibility.html)

Directors: Anne Wade; Caroline Cattermole; David Rough; Dr Jeremy Beeton; Dr Phil Nolan, Chair; Olivier Brousse, Chief Executive Officer; Patrick O'D. Bourke, Group Finance Director; Toby Hiscock (women: 2; men: 6)

Year end	31/12/2015
Turnover	£889,600,000
Pre-tax profit	£106,600,000

Nature of business: John Laing PLC is an international investor and manager of infrastructure projects. Its main focus is on major transport, social and environmental infrastructure projects and renewable energy projects. It works across the world, including the UK, Asia Pacific, Europe and North America.

Company registration number: 1345670

Subsidiary undertakings include: Dreachmhor Wind Farm Ltd; Hyder Investments Ltd; Wimpey Laing Ltd.

UK employees: 196

Total employees: 247

Focus of giving: Children, young people, education, enterprise/training.

Membership: BITC

Community involvement	✓
Community contributions	✓
CSR report	✓
Directors have other relevant posts	✓
Charity partner(s)	✓
Corporate charity	✓
Employee-led support	✓
Matched funding	✓

Charitable donations

Cash UK (latest available):	2015	£70,000
Total UK (cash and in kind):	2015	£70,000
Cash worldwide:	2015	£70,000
Total worldwide (cash and in kind):	2015	£70,000

Community involvement

The group's community investment strategy focuses on education and employment for young people from disadvantaged backgrounds. It does this by offering patronage to partners, encouraging employee engagement with charitable activities and through its own charitable trust. The group supports community-based welfare schemes.

Charity patron

The group has been a patron of The Prince's Trust since 2006 and employees hold regular fundraising days for the charity that are, in most cases, match-funded by the group. The group also provides patronage to The Built Environment Leadership Group, which brings together companies from the built environment sector to help fund and facilitate The Prince's Trust's work experience and employability courses.

Education

The group focuses on supporting educational development in schools in areas of social deprivation. According to the website, the group and its charitable trust support the Paddington Academy in West London and the Nova Hreod School and Isambard Community Colleges in Swindon through the delivery of the following programmes:

- Business Class, which is run by Business in the Community
- Careers Academy UK
- Envision, a year 12 social action project
- The Prince's Teaching Institute, which provides support for headteachers

Employees from the group volunteer to support the programmes.

John Laing Charitable Trust (Charity Commission no. 236852)

The group set up a charitable trust in order to provide welfare support to existing and former employees and their dependants, and to make charitable donations.

The group's employees can make applications to the trust for donations of up to £1,000 for charities they are personally involved with and support, and the trust will also provide matched funding for employees' fundraising efforts up to the value of £1,500. In 2015 employees in the group's offices in the UK, Australia, Canada, New Zealand and the USA successfully applied for charitable donations.

The trust also makes grants to charitable organisations, particularly those that focus on homelessness, disadvantaged young people, education, older people and the regeneration of communities. In 2015 the trust awarded grants to organisations totalling £671,000.

Directors with other relevant posts

Anne Wade is a director of Big Society Capital and also the Heron Foundation, a New York based grant-making organisation.

One of the executive committee members, Chris Waples, is also a trustee of the John Laing Charitable Trust.

Office locations

The group has offices based in: London; Australia; Canada; New Zealand; The Netherlands; and the USA.

Community contributions

No details were provided regarding the group's total charitable contribution in 2015; however, over £70,000 was donated by the group under its annual Star Awards (see 'Employee-led support' section for further information).

Employee-led support

The group's employees are involved in charitable activities that benefit their local communities and environment. This includes volunteering and fundraising events and challenges. In 2015 a team of UK employees took part in a mountain challenge in the Lake District for The Prince's Trust. The money employees raised from sponsorship was then matched by the John Laing Charitable Trust.

The group also has an annual Star Awards in which long-serving employees are rewarded. The winners in 2015 were given up to £1,000 from the group to donate to a charity of their choice.

Corporate charity

John Laing Charitable Trust (Charity Commission no. 236852).

Exclusions

The group makes no political donations.

Applications

To enquire about corporate/employee-led support, contact the correspondent in writing.

John Laing Charitable Trust
The trust generally does not accept unsolicited applications as it prefers to take a proactive approach to grant-making. It does, however, administer funding to some Community Foundations aimed at providing grants of up to £1,000 to smaller organisations. In 2015 the Community Foundations supported were: Lancashire and Merseyside; Leicestershire and Rutland; Wiltshire and Swindon.

Enquiries about the trust can be addressed to Jenny Impey, Trust Director, using the following contact details:

John Laing Charitable Trust, 33 Bunns Lane, Mill Hill, London NW7 2DX (tel: 020 7901 3307; fax: 020 8238 8897; email: jenny.impey@laing.com).

S. C. Johnson Ltd

Household

Correspondent: Faye Gilbert, Trustee, Johnson Wax Ltd Charitable Trust, Frimley Green, Camberley, Surrey GU16 7AJ (tel: 01276 852000; email: givinguk@scj.com; website: www.scjohnson.co.uk)

Directors: John Hayes; Mark Worden; Thomas Howard (women: 0; men: 3)

Year end	03/07/2015
Turnover	£135,419,000
Pre-tax profit	£4,419,000

Nature of business: The company manufactures and markets waxes, polishes, air fresheners and cleaning products for the consumer and industrial markets.

Company registration number: 4166155

Brands include: Autan; Brillo; Duck; Glade; Goddard's; Mr Muscle; Oust; Pledge; Raid; Shout.

Focus of giving: Education, environment, health, ill health, arts, culture, sport, recreation, community/social welfare, disability.

Community involvement	✓
Community contributions	✓
Corporate charity	✓
Employee-led support	✓
Matched funding	✓
Sponsorship	✓

Charitable donations

Cash UK (latest available):	2015	£324,000
Total UK (cash and in kind):	2015	£324,000
Cash worldwide:	2015	£324,000
Total worldwide (cash and in kind):	2015	£324,000

Community involvement

The Johnson Wax Charitable Trust (Charity Commission no. 200332)
The company channels its charitable support through its corporate foundation. The foundation is focuses its giving around the sites of S. C. Johnson in the areas of health, social welfare, community, environment, sport, arts and environment.

Main locations
Frimley Green, Surrey.

Community contributions

In 2014/15 the company donated a total of £324,000 to the Johnson Wax Charitable Trust. Each year about 2.5% of pre-tax profit from S. C. Johnson goes to the trust.

Previous beneficiaries have included: Abbots Hospital; Cancer Research UK; Johnson Wax Charitable Trust; Tongham Community Hall; and Surrey Heath Arts Council.

Employee-led support

Employee Involvement in Local Community

Local Community
Activities undertaken by the staff include: refurbishment/repairs of family respite centre in Frimley; provision of computer equipment for an after school club for teenagers in Camberley; sponsorship of a Women's Aid Refuge; Christmas gifts for older people and families in need at Voluntary Services Surrey Heath; donation towards closure of road for a carnival; update of facilities at St Frances Church Hall in Frimley; donation to Ravenscote School towards the cost of fireworks; and sponsorship of mini bus for BPSA Blackwater Valley Group.

Community Day
One day a year in June the company gives its employees an opportunity to work on local community projects. Previously about 180 volunteers have worked at local schools to help create outdoor classrooms and improve outdoor and indoor areas for local children, including: Church Crookham Junior School; College Town Junior School; Parity for People with Multiple Disabilities; and Surrey Carers Ian Goodchild Centre.

Matched funding
Employee fundraising activities are matched pound-for-pound by the company up to £500 per individual, when they volunteer in their own time and help charities or non-profit organisations.

Samuel C. Johnson Community Service Awards
An award of £3,000 paid to an organisation where a member of staff 'has made a significant contribution through their voluntary work in community service'. Up to three further 'Specially Recognised' awards of £500 are available to an organisation where S. C. Johnson people have made noteworthy contributions.

Commercially led support

The company may provide sponsorships, including in the areas of environment, arts and sports, disability and health causes.

Corporate charity

Johnson Wax Ltd Charitable Trust (Charity Commission no. 200332).

Applications

The Johnson Wax Charitable Trust: Apply in writing to the correspondent.

Sponsorship and company enquiries: can be addressed to the Company Secretary (J. M. Hayes).

Johnson Matthey PLC

Metals

Correspondent: Sustainability Department (Community and Charity), 5th Floor, 25 Farringdon Street, London EC4A 4AB (tel: 020 7269 8400; email: group.charity@matthey.com; website: matthey.com/sustainability/community)

Directors: Alan Ferguson; Chris Mottershead; Colin Matthews; John Walker; Odile Desforges; Robert MacLeod, Chief Executive; Simon Farrant; Tim Stevenson, Chair (women: 1; men: 7)

Year end	31/03/2016
Turnover	£10,714,000,000
Pre-tax profit	£418,200,000

Nature of business: Johnson Matthey PLC is a speciality chemicals and sustainable technologies company that focuses on its core skills in catalysis, precious metals, fine chemicals and process technology.

Company registration number: 33774

Subsidiary undertakings include: Johnson Matthey Precious Metals Ltd; Johnson Matthey South Africa Holdings Ltd; Synetix Ltd.

Total employees: 12,494

Focus of giving: Economic generation, education, environment, health, ill health, overseas projects, poverty and social exclusion, science technology, community/social welfare.

Membership: BITC, LBG

Community involvement	✓
Community contributions	✓
Company reports on anti-slavery	✓
CSR report	✓
CSR or charity committee	✓

Cash donations declared ✓
Charity of the Year ✓
Employee-led support ✓
FTSE 100 ✓
Gifts in kind ✓
Matched funding ✓
Overseas giving ✓
Payroll giving ✓
STEM-focused ✓

Charitable donations

Cash worldwide:	2016	£679,000
Total worldwide (cash and in kind):	2016	£679,000

Community involvement

Johnson Matthey PLC looks to make a positive contribution in the areas in which it operates in the following ways:

Charitable donations

The annual report for 2016 explains: 'We operate a corporate charitable donations programme which represented 44% of the group's total donations in 2015/16. This programme supports organisations in the areas of environment and sustainability, medical and health, science and education, social welfare and economic development'. The group operates a one-off donations scheme by which a single payment is awarded in response to appeals for funding. It also awards donations on an annual basis, providing a 'cycle of regular giving to several chosen charities around the world'.

Educational support

Education forms the central theme of the group's 'Community Investment Policy'. Johnson Matthey promotes STEM (science, technology, engineering and maths) to students in schools and universities. The group's 2016 annual report states: 'The main theme of [the policy] is to support the future growth of our business by encouraging young people to study and exceed in education. As a business reliant upon our expertise in chemistry and its applications, our future depends on the recruitment of excellent science graduates.' The group supports educational causes around the world as well as in the UK, and for a decade has supported three schools in Sri Lanka.

Employees

Employees at Johnson Matthey sites are actively supported by the group in their community efforts through volunteering opportunities, payroll giving and matched funding.

Charity of the Year

The group 'adopts' charities for 12 months or for a longer period of time to benefit from staff support and fundraising efforts. The Charity of the Year benefits from corporate donations and employee fundraising efforts.

Current (2016–17): Plan International

2014–16: Cancer Research UK. The charity had a two-year partnership with Johnson Matthey over which time it received £80,000 including a corporate donation of £30,000. Sites outside the UK were encouraged to support the national cancer charities in their own countries.

Previous Charity of the Year beneficiaries have included: Alzheimer's Society; British Heart Foundation; CLIC Sargent; EveryChild; The International Red Cross and Red Crescent Movement.

Directors with other relevant posts

Chris Mottershead: Vice-Principal, Research and Innovation, at Kings College London; non-executive director at The Francis Crick Institute; governor at King's College Hospital NHS Foundation Trust.

Main UK locations

Johnson Matthey has around 18 sites in England and Scotland. They are displayed on the clickable 'Where we operate' map on the Johnson Matthey website.

Community contributions

In 2014/15 the group donated a total of £679,000 worldwide, which is a considerable increase since the amount given in the last edition (£626,000). The reason for this is explained in the Johnson Matthey annual report for 2016: 'This figure has increased by 11%, mainly due to new legislation in India which requires companies to donate 2% of net profit generated in the country to local good causes'. At least £52,500 of donations was contributed from central group funds through the matched funding scheme.

A figure for UK charitable donations was not included in the annual report and accounts for the year. We were unable to determine the value of the in-kind support given by the group.

In-kind support

Employee time

All employees are able to take two days annual leave for volunteering purposes, subject to their manager's approval.

Employee-led support

Employee volunteering

Johnson Matthey employees participate in charitable and community activities in their local areas. The annual report for 2016 explains that employees are encouraged to take up projects through which their skills can be utilised or they can acquire new knowledge.

Payroll giving

The group operates a payroll giving scheme.

Matched funding

Employees' fundraising efforts for the Johnson Matthey Charity of the Year or other registered charities of their choice, may be matched with central group funds up to £1,000 per individual employee per year. Matched funding is capped at £70,000 per year across the group as a whole. During the year, individual and teams of employees raised £62,000 which were matched with £52,500 in corporate contributions, benefitting 58 charities.

Commercially led support

Promotion of STEM subjects

In the UK, Johnson Matthey sites have worked with local schools through programmes such as Children Challenging Industry, which is organised by the Centre for Industry Education Collaboration.

Applications

The Johnson Matthey website advises organisations seeking charity donations or sponsorship to visit its 'Community and Charity' web page or email group. charity@matthey.com.

Jupiter Fund Management PLC

Financial services

Correspondent: Alicia Wyllie, Head of Corporate Communications & Charity Committee Chair, The Zig Zag Building, 70 Victoria Street, London SW1E 6SQ (tel: 0800 561 4000/020 3817 1638; email: alicia.wyllie@jupiteram.com; website: www.jupiteram.com)

Directors: Bridget Macaskill; Charlotte Jones, Chief Financial Officer; Edward Bonham Carter; John Chatfeild-Roberts; Jon Little; Jonathon Bond; Karl Sternberg; Liz Airey, Chair; Lorraine Trainer; Maarten Slendebroek, Chief Executive Officer; Polly Williams (women: 5; men: 6)

Year end	31/12/2015
Turnover	£403,500,000
Pre-tax profit	£164,600,000

Nature of business: Jupiter Fund Management PLC is a fund management group for institutional and retail clients in the UK, Europe and Asia Pacific region.

Company registration number: 6150195

Subsidiary undertakings include: Jupiter International Holdings Ltd; Knightsbridge Asset Management Ltd; Tyndall Holdings Ltd.

Total employees: 436

Focus of giving: General charitable purposes, general appeals, health, ill health, older people, arts, culture, disasters.

Community involvement ✓
Community contributions ✓
CSR report ✓

CSR or charity committee ✓
Directors have other relevant posts ✓
Cash donations declared ✓
Charity partner(s) ✓
Employee-led support ✓
Humanitarian aid: overseas ✓
Matched funding ✓
Payroll giving ✓
Sponsorship ✓

Charitable donations

Cash UK (latest available):	2015	£102,663
Total UK (cash and in kind):	2015	£102,663
Cash worldwide:	2015	£102,663
Total worldwide (cash and in kind):	2015	£102,663

Community involvement

The group makes various charitable donations as directed by its charity committee, which is made up of various employees. It also provides matched funding for its payroll giving scheme.

Charity partner

In 2015 the group's charity committee selected Alzheimer's Society to be the main charity partner. The group supports the charity with fundraising activities and employee volunteering.

Sponsorship

The group has been a sponsor of the Orchestra of the Age of Enlightenment (Charity Commission no. 295329) since 1999.

Directors with other relevant posts

Polly Williams is a trustee of The Guide Dogs for the Blind Association (Charity Commission no. 209617) and the Westminster Almshouses Foundation (Charity Commission no. 226936).

Office locations

The group has offices in London; across Europe; Hong Kong and Taiwan; and Singapore.

Community contributions

In 2015 the group donated £19,500 to various charitable causes, including a £10,000 donation to the Disaster Emergency Committee's Nepal earthquake appeal. The group also donated £83,000 to match employees' charitable donations through the Give As You Earn scheme.

Beneficiaries included: Alzheimer's Society; Disaster Emergency Committee.

Employee-led support

Employee-led fundraising

The group's employees fundraise for various charitable causes, particularly the charity Movember following the death of a colleague from prostate cancer in 2013.

Give As You Earn

The group operates a payroll giving scheme where employees can donate to charitable causes, which is then matched by the group up to a limit of £800. In 2015 a total of 34% (2014: 30%) of employees took part in the scheme.

Applications

Applications can be made in writing to the group's Charity Committee.

Just Retirement Group PLC

Financial services

Correspondent: CSR and Engagement Manager, Vale House, Roebuck Close, Bancroft Road, Reigate, Surrey RH2 7RU (tel: 01737 233288; website: www.justretirement.com)

Directors: James Fraser; Kate Avery; Keith Nicholson; Michael Deakin; Rodney Cook, Chief Executive Officer; Shayne Deighton; Simon Thomas, Group Finance Director; Steve Melcher; Tom Cross Brown, Chair (women: 1; men: 8)

Year end	30/06/2015
Turnover	£2,567,300,000
Pre-tax profit	(£29,600,000)

Nature of business: The group was formed from the merger of Just Retirement Group and Partnership Assurance Group in 2014. It provides a range of retirement services and products, such as annuity solutions and equity release products.

Company registration number: 8568957

Subsidiary undertakings include: Just Annuities Ltd; Just Retirement Finance PLC; Just Retirement Group Holdings Ltd.

Focus of giving: Environment, health, ill health, medical research, older people, community/social welfare, disability.

Membership: BITC

Community involvement ✓
Community contributions ✓
CSR report ✓
Charity partner(s) ✓
Employee-led support ✓
Gifts in kind ✓
Matched funding ✓
Payroll giving ✓
Shared-value alliances ✓
Sponsorship ✓

Community involvement

The group supports a number of charities, particularly in the areas of older people, medical research and care, through funding and employee support.

Partner charities

The group supports a number of partner charities, including Alzheimer's Research UK; Dementia UK; Meningitis Now; Northern Ireland Hospice; St Catherine's Hospice.

The group also works with other organisations to campaign for better retirement. For example, in 2015, the group signed an open letter, along with a number of charities, calling on the government to tackle issues faced by older people, such as loneliness, poor housing and lack of care and support.

Main locations

The group is based in Reigate, Surrey.

Community contributions

No figure was given for the group's total charitable contributions.

Employee-led support

Employee volunteering

Employees are entitled to company time for volunteering with community projects. In 2014/15 the group participated in Business in the Community's Give and Gain Day, with employees volunteering to decorate a local school. Employees also mentor school students through the charity SATRO.

Payroll giving and matched funding

The group has a payroll giving scheme and provides matched funding for donations made to any of its partner charities.

Commercially led support

Sponsorship

The group sponsors the World Indoor Bowls Championships. In 2014/15 in partnership with the English Indoor Bowling Association, the group also supported a tournament for people with disabilities at Donyngs Indoor Bowls Club, and took 50 members of the club to the World Championships for a day.

In 2014/15 the group also sponsored a garden at RHS Hampton Court Flower Show; as part of this sponsorship, the group funded a garden at St Catherine's Hospice, and also donated flower show tickets to the hospice and to Alzheimer's Research UK for fundraising purposes. The group sold off the plants from the garden, raising £3,600 for Alzheimer's UK, NI Hospice and St Catherine's Hospice.

Applications

Apply in writing to the correspondent.

Keysight Technologies UK Ltd (formerly Agilent Technologies UK Ltd)

Information Technology

Correspondent: CSR Team, 610 Wharfedale Road, Winnersh Triangle, Wokingham, Berkshire RG41 5TP (tel: 0800 026 0637; fax: 0118 927 6855; email: contactcentre_uk@

keysight.com; website: www.keysight.com)

Directors: Christopher Rennie; James Billett; Roy MacNaughton (men: 3)

Year end	31/10/2015
Turnover	£69,242,000
Pre-tax profit	£132,679,000

Nature of business: Keysight Technologies sells to engineers and technicians across industry segments of communications; aerospace and defence; and industrial, computers, and semiconductors.

Keysight has 9,500 employees, R&D centres around the world, and serves customers in more than 100 countries.

The company Agilent Technologies UK Ltd changed its name on 1 August 2014 to Keysight Technologies UK Ltd. It retains the same company number.

Company registration number: 3809903

Subsidiary undertakings include: Anite Ltd; Electroservices Industries Ltd; Micro Movements Ltd.

UK employees: 500

Total employees: 9,500

Focus of giving: Education, environment, overseas projects, science technology, children, young people, community/social welfare.

Community involvement	✓
Community contributions	✓
Company reports on anti-slavery	✓
Employee-led support	✓
Gifts in kind	✓
Matched funding	✓
Overseas giving	✓
STEM-focused	✓

Community involvement

The group's CSR activities focus on the areas where it operates, particularly supporting STEM education.

STEM education

The group has a focus on supporting young people, particularly underrepresented groups such as women, to engage with STEM subjects, working with schools and universities to deliver events and activities. In areas where it has operations, the group runs a programme called Keysight After School, which provides hands-on science activities for children aged 9 to 13, run by employee volunteers.

Main locations

The group's UK sites are in Edinburgh; Fleet, Hampshire; Telford, Shropshire; and Winnersh, Berkshire. It has operations internationally and the headquarters are based in California.

Community contributions

No figure was given for the group's charitable contributions.

In-kind support

Universities

The group supports universities with both grants and in-kind donations of equipment. For example, in 2015, the group donated equipment to the University of Sheffield for its new Electronic Engineering Teaching Lab.

Employee-led support

Matched funding

The Keysight Giving Program allows employees in a number of countries to receive matched funding from the group for their donations to charities, as well as to disaster relief efforts. It is not clear whether this includes the UK.

Employee volunteering

Employees are entitled to four hours of paid leave each month to volunteer with local community causes. The Keysight After School programme is also run by employee volunteers.

Applications

Local appeals should be made in writing to the correspondent.

Kier Group PLC

Building/construction

Correspondent: Gareth Rondel, Head of Group Corporate Responsibility, Kier Group PLC, Tempsford Hall, Sandy, Bedfordshire SG19 2BD (tel: 01767 355000; email: gareth.rondel@kier.co.uk; website: www.kier.co.uk/corporate-responsibility/the-kier-foundation.aspx)

Directors: Adam Walker; Bev Dew, Finance Director; Claudio Veritiero; Constance Baroudel; Haydn Mursell, Chief Executive; Hugh Raven; Justin Atkinson; Kirsty Bashforth; Nick Winser; Nigel Brook; Nigel Turner; Phil White, Chair (women: 2; men: 10)

Year end	30/06/2015
Turnover	£4,112,300,000
Pre-tax profit	(£15,400,000)

Nature of business: Activities span building, civil engineering, opencast mining, facilities management, residential and commercial property investment and PFI project investment. The group operates in England, Wales and Scotland, and also has locations in the Middle East, Asia and Australasia.

Company registration number: 2708030

Subsidiary undertakings include: Kier Construction Ltd; Kier Living Ltd; Kier Property Ltd.

UK employees: 18,354

Total employees: 20,685

Focus of giving: General charitable purposes, health, ill health, armed forces, community/social welfare.

Membership: BITC

Community involvement	✓
Community contributions	✓
Company reports on anti-slavery	✓
CSR report	✓
Directors have other relevant posts	✓
Armed forces personnel	✓
Charity partner(s)	✓
Employee-led support	✓
Gifts in kind	✓
Matched funding	✓
Pro bono	✓

Charitable donations

Cash UK (latest available):	2015	£60,000
Total UK (cash and in kind):	2015	£6,320,000
Cash worldwide:	2015	£60,000
Total worldwide (cash and in kind):	2015	£6,320,000

Community involvement

Kier Group looks to contribute to communities in the areas where the group has a presence. Community contributions are principally made in the form of staff time.

The Kier Foundation (Charity Commission no. 1144803)

This independent foundation was registered in 2011 as Kier Group's 'permanent partner charity'. The group's website explains that the foundation was established with the purpose 'to raise funds for and offer practical assistance to charitable bodies throughout the UK, mainly through the activities of Kier employees and Kier businesses'.

The foundation works to organise fundraising activities in support of Kier Group's corporate charity partner, which is chosen with the help of Kier employees every two years. It also provides funding to assist with employees' fundraising activities, and supports Kier businesses' local community engagement with donations of up to £5,000 for materials and other goods for community projects they are involved with.

The foundation's regular source of income comes from a lottery – the Kier Winners' Club – into which only employees can enter. Lottery members pay the equivalent of £1 per week and income is divided equally between charitable donations and employee prize money. The lottery raised £76,000 for the foundation during 2015/16.

The largest source of income for the foundation is the £10k Board Challenge through which each regional board of directors is challenged to raise £10,000 over the course of the year. During the year, the challenge raised £108,000 for the foundation.

Corporate charity partner: Alzheimer's Society was chosen as the group's partner charity for two years from July

2016 and funds raised will be given to support a research project and dementia support worker hours.

Directors with other relevant posts

Justin Atkinson: member of the audit committee of The National Trust.

Nick Winser: Deputy President of the Institution of Engineering and Technology and Chair of the Power Academy.

Main locations

Kier Group has a presence across England, Scotland and Wales. For a map of specific locations see the website (www.kier.co.uk/get-in-touch/our-locations.aspx#/mapview).

Community contributions

Kier Group's Corporate Responsibility Report 2016 states that, in 2015/16, the group contributed almost £9.6 million in community and social value; however, in addition to cash and in-kind contributions, this figure also includes 'additional social value' generated which we do not include in our figures for corporate contributions.

Helpfully, the group also publishes the Kier Corporate Responsibility Performance Report 'Live' Tracker which is available to download from the website. The 'Live' Tracker tool details up-to-date corporate responsibility information, including values and totals of community contributions. We have used the 'Live' Tracker to calculate our figures for the group's cash and in-kind community contributions during the year.

Although at the time of writing (August 2016) the report already documented helpful information for the 'current' financial year (2016/17) we have taken the figures recorded for 2015/16 as this corresponds with the latest annual report and accounts available and is the most recent complete year.

According to the report, in 2015/16 Kier Group expended £6.32 million on community contributions, which were broken down as follows:

'Value from hours'	£5.19 million
'Cost of activity'	£1.07 million
'Cash donated'	£60,000

We could not find information regarding beneficiary organisations.

The group's Corporate Responsibility Report 2016 explains:

> Our target to generate 10% additional social value, measured as a proportion of Group turnover, is achieved through targeted spending of money to create positive economic ripple effects in the communities where we work. We have started to measure how employment and donation of time, resources and money to good causes contributes to this positive effect.

Employee-led support

Employee fundraising

Employees take part in a wide range of fundraising activities for The Kier Foundation. Examples include the Valentine's Day Cake Bake Off held by employees at Kier's Asset Management services and a fluffy pig racing night.

Employee volunteering

The Corporate Responsibility Report 2016 notes that employees 'gave 272,701 hours on community, employment and skills development'.

Matched funding

Employees are able to apply to the Kier Foundation for up to £200 twice a year to help support their own fundraising activities. In 2015/16 a total of 166 charities benefitted through the scheme.

Applications

Queries about Kier's corporate responsibility activities can be directed to the correspondent.

The Kier Foundation

The website explains: 'The charity partner selection process is based on the charities most supported by Kier's employees and businesses in the previous two years, and therefore The Kier Foundation does not accept applications from external charities.' Furthermore, with regard to the assistance the foundation gives to Kier companies to support their local engagement, it is explained: 'It is encouraged that businesses use this funding to support charitable causes they have a close relationship to, and therefore we do not accept applications for support from external causes.'

Queries about the foundation can be directed to Francesca Campbell, The Kier Foundation Manager, email: info@thekierfoundation.org, tel: 01767 355601).

Kingfisher PLC

Property, retail – DIY/furniture

Correspondent: Net Positive Team, 3 Sheldon Square, Paddington, London W2 6PX (tel: 020 7372 8008; fax: 020 7644 1001; email: netpositiveconversation@kingfisher.com; website: www.kingfisher.com/sustainability)

Directors: Anders Dahlvig; Andrew Bonfield; Clare Chapman; Daniel Bernard, Chair; Karen Witts; Mark Seligman; Pascal Cagni; Rakhi Goss-Custard; Véronique Laury, Chief Executive (women: 4; men: 5)

Year end	31/01/2016
Turnover	£10,300,000,000
Pre-tax profit	£686,000,000

Nature of business: Home improvement retail group with stores located in ten European countries. Kingfisher companies in the UK are B&Q and Screwfix.

Company registration number: 1664812

Subsidiary undertakings include: B&Q PLC; Kingfisher Group Ltd; Screwfix Direct Ltd.

Brands include: B&Q; Castorama; Screwfix.

Total employees: 76,000

Focus of giving: General charitable purposes, small groups, local groups, overseas projects, children, young people, community/social welfare, disability, disasters.

Membership: BITC

Community involvement	✓
Community contributions	✓
Company reports on anti-slavery	✓
CSR report	✓
CSR or charity committee	✓
Cash donations declared	✓
Charity partner(s)	✓
Company gives to smaller charities	✓
Employee-led support	✓
FTSE 100	✓
Gifts in kind	✓
Market-led giving	✓
Matched funding	✓
Overseas giving	✓
Payroll giving	✓
Sponsorship	✓

Charitable donations

Cash worldwide:	2016	£1,001,000
Total worldwide (cash and in kind):	2016	£1,667,000

Community involvement

Kingfisher PLC and its subsidiaries look to make a positive impact in the communities in which they have a presence and in society more generally. Support is given in the form of in kind contributions, cash contributions and employee time. Employees from across the group are actively involved in supporting local charities through volunteering, payroll giving and fundraising, which is supported by matched funding. Customers also contribute through fundraising appeals. Kingfisher companies (in the UK, B&Q and Screwfix) are responsible for their own community and charitable policies.

The Screwfix Foundation

Employees and customers of Screwfix Direct Ltd, a Kingfisher PLC subsidiary company, raise funds for The Screwfix Foundation (Charity Commission no. 1151375). The foundation is a grant-making charity supporting registered local charities in areas where Screwfix stores are located as well as two national charities (according to the foundation's

Charity Commission record at the time of writing (August 2016) these are Barnardo's and Macmillan Cancer Support). According to the foundation's web page, grants are made to organisations working to support people who are in need for environmentally-friendly projects relating to 'the repair, maintenance, improvement or construction of homes, community buildings and other buildings'.

Beneficiaries have included: Children's Hospice South West; Diverse Abilities Plus; The Elizabeth Foundation; Friends Centre.

Main UK locations

Paddington, London (head office). See the Kingfisher PLC website for a group directory. There are store finder searches on both the B&Q and Screwfix websites.

Community contributions

According to the Sustainability Report 2015/16, during the year community contributions in the form of cash, gifts in kind and employee time were given totalling £1.67 million. The report provided the following breakdown:

Cash	£1 million
Gifts in kind	£441,000
Time	£225,000

We were unable to determine the figure of contributions given in the UK.

In 2015/16 employees and customers raised a further £774,000 for good causes although this is not included in the total of contributions for the year.

The report further explained: 'Our total company giving decreased to £1.7 million in 2015/16 (2014/15: £2.3 million), equivalent to 0.24% of pre-tax profits (2014/15: 0.34%). This includes cash donations, employee time and gifts in kind, with product donations valued at cost price. The drop in investment was due to a number of community activities being put on hold as both our business and community strategies were being reviewed'.

In-kind support

Product donations

Kingfisher companies donate products in support of good causes. For example, employees in Swindon who volunteered to improve Hop Skip Jump's outdoor play area (see 'Employee-led support') were provided with B&Q tools to use in their efforts.

Employee time

Kingfisher Corporate Centre employees are able to take one paid day per year for volunteering purposes.

Contact centre use

During charity appeals, contact centres belonging to Kingfisher businesses are provided to take donations from members of the public. In previous years, B&Q and Screwfix contact centres have taken part with this in support of BBC Children in Need.

Employee-led support

Payroll giving

Employees are able to donate to charities through payroll giving schemes.

Employee fundraising

Employees working across the Kingfisher group take part in various fundraising activities.

Staff at Screwfix, for example, helped to raise £80,000 for The Screwfix Foundation, which was then matched by Screwfix. The Kingfisher Sustainability Report describes that fundraising events included 'the Tour de Screwfix, where over 800 staff collectively completed a 6,100 mile cycle relay between every Screwfix UK store'.

According to the Kingfisher Corporate Centre Charities policy standard document, employees at the centre raise funds both for charities selected by a Fundraising Committee through the Kingfisher Charity Fundraising Programme and for charities they choose personally.

Employee volunteering

In 2015/16 employees spent more than 24,000 hours volunteering in their local communities. Examples of this included staff at B&Q who volunteered to assist a charity working with children who have disabilities and special educational needs, Hop Skip Jump, to improve its outdoor play area in Swindon.

Matched funding

Kingfisher Corporate Centre employees can apply to have the funds they raise matched pound for pound up to the value of £500 through the Double It Scheme. Companies within the Kingfisher group also support employee fundraising through matched funding; for example, Screwfix matched the £80,000 raised by employees for the Screwfix Foundation, bringing the total raised to £160,000.

Commercially led support

Product sales

During the Poppy Appeal, B&Q retails 'Flanders poppy seeds' through its website and stores, with £1 from each packet of poppy seeds sold donated to The Royal British Legion and Poppyscotland.

Exclusions

According to the 'Charities policy standard', Kingfisher does not fund:

- Charity advertising space, unless specifically linked to a Kingfisher funded project.
- Arts projects.
- Expeditions, overseas trips of adventure experiences for individuals.
- Support to political parties or political causes.
- Promotion of specific religious ideas or views
- Support to religious bodies, except where the project is for the benefit of the general public and wider community
- Year-end deficits.
- Support or personal appeals by, or on behalf of, individuals.
- A charity's core costs including buildings, salaries general running or management costs.
- Individual overseas projects not linked to current partners.
- Anything that would replace funds provided by government or statutory authorities, and that does not bring additional benefits to people or communities.

B&Q

The B&Q website notes that it does not support the following:

- Political parties or causes
- Religious organisations whose principle aim is to propagate a particular faith or belief
- Charity advertising space, unless linked to an initiative supported by the Kingfisher Group
- Personal appeals by, or on behalf of individuals

Applications

There is a 'Charities policy standard' document available to download from the Sustainability section of the Kingfisher PLC website (under the heading 'Reporting, resources and downloads' and then 'Policies and resources'). This sets out the policy standard, including procedures and guidance on good practices, specifically for employees of the Kingfisher Corporate Centre. Individual operating companies, such as B&Q and Screwfix, set out their own charity policies.

The policy standard, which is reviewed annually, details the following forms of charitable support:

- Kingfisher Charity Cash Sponsorship Programme: Only a small number of charities are selected to receive support in the form of cash funding. These are approved by the Director of Governance and Corporate Services and/or the Director of Corporate Responsibility and are reviewed annually
- Kingfisher Charity Fundraising Programme: A number of charities are agreed by the Fundraising Committee to receive support through Corporate Centre fundraising initiatives. They are reviewed annually (with the exception of a select few national charities)
- Kingfisher Gift Voucher Scheme: This scheme, which is operated and agreed by the Director of Corporate Responsibility, is to allow Kingfisher

to support small requests from local charities and community organisations. The example given in the policy document is raffle prizes

More information is detailed in the document itself.

As mentioned above, Kingfisher companies employ their own policies when it comes to charitable involvement. Kingfisher is represented in the UK in the form of B&Q and Screwfix:

B&Q

The Charity Partnerships page on the B&Q website (www.diy.com/corporate/community/charity-partnerships) explains that charities should direct requests about local fundraising to their local B&Q store. At the time of writing (August 2016) it was also explained on the website that B&Q was not looking to enter into any charity partnerships on a national scale, although this position was due to be reviewed during 2016. See the website for more information and updates.

The Screwfix Foundation

Applications to The Screwfix Foundation can be made using the online application form, accessible via the Screwfix website (www.screwfix.com/help/screwfixfoundation). According to the foundation's Charity Commission record, 'all requests for grants are formally vetted and rated against a strict scoring criteria to ensure all supporting charities meet The Screwfix Foundation's objectives'.

KPMG LLP

Accountants

Correspondent: Corporate Responsibility Team, 15 Canada Square, London E14 5GL (tel: 020 7311 1000; email: corporateresponsibility@kpmg.co.uk; website: home.kpmg.com/uk/en/home/about/corporate-responsibility.html)

Directors: David Matthews; David Sayer; Ian Starkey; Karl Edge; Maggie Brereton; Melanie Richards; Nicola Quayle; Philip Davidson; Richard Heis; Simon Collins, Chair; Stephen Oxley (women: 3; men: 8)

Year end	30/09/2015
Turnover	£1,958,000,000
Pre-tax profit	£383,000,000

Nature of business: The provision of professional services including audit, tax and advisory.

Company registration number: OC301540

Subsidiary undertakings include: KPMG Audit PLC; KPMG IT Advisory Ltd; KPMG Nunwood Consulting Ltd.

Focus of giving: Education, enterprise/training, environment, equal opportunities, poverty and social exclusion, children, young people, community/social welfare.

Membership: BITC, LBG

Accredited Living Wage Employer	✓
Community involvement	✓
Community contributions	✓
Company reports on anti-slavery	✓
CSR report	✓
CSR or charity committee	✓
Directors have other relevant posts	✓
AF Covenant	✓
Cash donations declared	✓
Charity partner(s)	✓
Community Mark	✓
Corporate charity	✓
Employee-led support	✓
Gifts in kind	✓
Payroll giving	✓
Pro bono	✓
Sponsorship	✓

Charitable donations

Total UK (cash and in kind):	2015	£4,800,000
Total worldwide (cash and in kind):	2015	£4,800,000

Community involvement

Social mobility is at the heart of KPMG's community strategy and promotes it in six key ways:

- Preparing young people for the world of work
- Increasing fair access to the profession
- Improving literacy for young people
- Increasing access to affordable and secure housing
- Tackling low pay through the Living Wage
- Encouraging youth leadership

The principal way in which the firm supports these objectives is through pro bono and volunteering work.

Support is also given through The KPMG Foundation(Charity Commission no. 1086518), a grant-making charity.

The KPMG Foundation (Charity Commission no. 1086518)

The group's corporate charity, The KPGM Foundation, focuses on supporting children and young adults who, through social disadvantage, have not achieved their educational potential. According to the website, the foundation focuses on three areas:

- Unlocking potential through early intervention
- Improving outcomes for young people in care
- Engaging in critical issues impacting young people

The KPMG Foundation proactively seeks projects to support and does not accept any unsolicited applications.

Other social mobility initiatives

In 2016 the group was announced as one of the Government's Social Mobility Champions. The group also works with the Social Mobility Foundation, providing work placements for young people, supporting its mentoring programme and hosting other events for the charity. The group has also hosted events for people who have experienced homelessness, including mentoring, skills development and work experience opportunities.

Youth leadership

In line with its efforts to promote greater social mobility, KPMG supports the work of both Enactus and Free the Children. For the second year running the group supported Free the Children's WE' Day, this time with over 340 young people from 11 partner schools attending.

KPMG SPRING

KMPG launched its SPRING approach to corporate responsibility in order to raise awareness about the social mobility and environmental initiatives it supports. There are three aims to this project: to raise awareness and understanding of corporate responsibility issues, through events and seminars; to create an online volunteering portal for employees to find opportunities; to create a community space in the group's offices, with creative installations, where employees, clients and partners from the community can meet and find out about the corporate responsibility initiatives.

Literacy skills

Following a successful national charity partnership between 2012 and 2014, KPMG is now the principal business partner working with the National Literacy Trust to reframe the UK's literacy policy.

KPMG Families for Literacy (KFFL) is a global programme which, to date, has donated two million books to children from low income backgrounds in the US, South Africa, India and Mexico. Launched in the UK in the autumn of 2014, KFFL is helping to improve reading, writing, speaking and listening skills in the UK's most disadvantaged communities.

Directors with other relevant posts

Simon Collins is Chair of Trustees of The KPMG Foundation (Charity Commission no. 1087518).

Main locations

London. KPMG also has a number of offices in the UK and worldwide.

Community contributions

The 2015/16 annual report states that community contributions (including cash, in-kind and time donations, and management costs) during the year totalled £4.8 million. It also states that the group supported a total of 881 organisations during the year.

The latest accounts available from the Charity Commission at the time of writing (January 2017) for The KPMG Foundation were the 2014/15 accounts. During the year, the foundation received a donation of £1.4 million from KPMG LLP, and the group also bore support costs totalling £81,000 for the foundation.

In-kind support

Volunteering and pro bono

KPMG's volunteering and pro bono policy allows staff to spend six days per year volunteering for charities that promote social mobility. Over 83% of KPMG's volunteering is now connected with social mobility, and the remaining proportion is focused on emergency appeals and other causes. In 2015/16 the group seconded a senior manager to work as the Chief Operating Officer of the Social Mobility Foundation.

According to the 2015/16 annual report, 3,156 employees volunteered a total of almost 48,000 working hours during the year.

Commercially led support

'Preparing young people for the world of work'

KPMG are working on a number of initiatives to prepare young people for the world of work and increasing fair access to the law profession. Work Ready is a programme helping Year 9 and 10 students develop employability skills in a fun, interactive way.

Corporate charity

The KPMG Foundation (Charity Commission no. 1086518).

Exclusions

Our research indicates that assistance to private educational establishments, political parties, or primarily evangelical causes and campaigns is not given.

Applications

The KPMG Foundation

The KPMG Foundation proactively seeks projects to support and does not accept any unsolicited applications.

For more information on the KPMG Foundation, contact Jo Clunie (tel: 020 7311 4733, email: jo.clunie@kpmgfoundation.co.uk).

The group

For other queries, there is a contact form on the group's website.

Ladbrokes PLC

Gaming, leisure

Correspondent: Grainne Hurst, Director of Corporate Affairs, Imperial House, Imperial Drive, Rayners Lane, Harrow, Middlesex HA2 7JW (tel: 020 8868 8899; email: grainne.hurst@ladbrokes.co.uk; website: www.ladbrokesplc.com/corporate-responsibility.aspx)

Directors: Christine Hodgson; David Martin; Jim Mullen, Chief Executive Officer; John Kelly, Chair; Mark Pain; Sly Bailey (women: 2; men: 4)

Year end	31/12/2015
Turnover	£1,199,500,000
Pre-tax profit	(£43,200,000)

Nature of business: The group's principal activity is the provision of a range of betting and gaming services.

Company registration number: 566221

Subsidiary undertakings include: Ladbrokes Betting and Gaming Ltd; Ladbrokes Coral Ltd; Ladbroke Group International.

Focus of giving: Education, health, ill health, housing, homelessness, medical research, older people, poverty and social exclusion, sport, recreation, community/social welfare, disability.

Community involvement	✓
Community contributions	✓
CSR report	✓
CSR or charity committee	✓
Charity partner(s)	✓
Corporate charity	✓
Employee-led support	✓
Gifts in kind	✓
Sponsorship	✓

Charitable donations

Total UK (cash and in kind):	2015	£2,130,000
Total worldwide (cash and in kind):	2015	£2,130,000

Community involvement

Ladbrokes supports communities, at a local and national level, principally through the Ladbrokes in the Community Charitable Trust (or Ladbrokes Charitable Trust, also known as LCT; Charity Commission no. 1101804) and the Ladbrokes Community Fund (LCF).

Funds are raised for Ladbrokes Charitable Trust by employees, who play an active role in supporting their communities. The trust makes grants to organisations working in the areas of: health (particularly research/treatment, hospice services and disability support); education/sports (particularly supporting people who are disadvantaged or who have disabilities); and community (with a focus on homelessness, older people and social activity projects for 'those at risk'). Ladbrokes Community Fund makes grants in support of local community clubs and charities in areas where the group operates.

Beneficiaries of LCT in 2015 included: Cancer Research UK (£135,000); Marie Curie Cancer Care (£60,000); Starlight Charity (£50,000).

Charity partners

Ladbrokes bases its partnerships with community organisations around strategic programmes. For example, since 2012 Ladbrokes has supported the Coalfield Regeneration Trust's Family Employment Initiative (FEI), helping people who live in the Dearne Valley back into work. Ladbrokes is in the process of aligning its own apprenticeship programme to complement the needs of of the CRT – new apprenticeship places will be provided in areas of the country where CRT operates.

The CSR report for 2015 also explains: 'All our major charity partnerships are generally designed to engage our customers and employees, for example by using our shop estate to distribute leaflets, carry posters and encourage proactive behaviours, e.g. taking part in online cancer awareness test'.

Ladbrokes is a partner of Crimestoppers and also supports the Responsible Gambling Trust (RGT), which provides funding to gambling charities and for research.

Directors also on trustee bodies

Christine Hodgson: board member of The Prince of Wales' Business in the Community Charity; on audit committee of The Queen Elizabeth Diamond Jubilee Trust.

Mark Pain: trustee of Somerset House.

Community contributions

The Ladbrokes PLC Corporate Responsibility Report for 2015 details some information on the group's community contributions for the year, and shows that the majority of support was given in relation to Ladbrokes in the Community Charitable Trust (LCT).

Contributions by Ladbrokes – time resources given to LCT in the UK	**£1.13 million**
Raised by employees for LCT	£365,500
Donations by LCT in the UK	£348,000
Cash and in-kind support to charitable causes, excluding LCT and donations towards responsible-gambling charities	**£317,000**

The report also states that, during the year, Ladbrokes made cash and in-kind contributions towards responsible gambling charities totalling £682,500.

We believe Ladbrokes to have contributed a total of around £2.13 million during the year – this is taken from the sum of the values of time resources given to LCT, cash and in-kind resources given to charitable causes (excluding LCT and responsible-gambling charities) and cash and in-kind resources to responsible-gambling charities. We were unable to determine a break down of how much was given in cash donations.

As is our usual practice, we have not included funds raised by employees in our total for the group, nor have we included donations given by the Ladbrokes Charitable Trust.

Beneficiaries included: Responsible Gambling Trust (£682,500); Coalfields Regeneration Trust (£32,000)

Employee-led support

Employee fundraising

The group encourages employees to undertake fundraising activities, particularly in support of Ladbrokes Charitable Trust. In 2015 employees raised £365,500 for the trust.

Commercially led support

Sponsorship

In 2015 Ladbrokes became the new sponsor of Rugby League's Challenge Cup and of the Scottish Professional Football Leagues (the Scottish Premiership, Championship and Leagues One and Two).

Corporate charity

Ladbrokes in the Community Charitable Trust (Charity Commission no. 1101804).

Exclusions

Our research indicates that no support is given to appeals for advertising in charity brochures, the arts, appeals from individuals, circular appeals, fundraising events, overseas projects, political appeals, religious appeals, or small, purely local appeals not in an area of the company's presence.

Applications

For **Ladbrokes in the Community Charitable Trust**, the trustees meet each month to consider requests from 'shop and head office fundraisers and charities'. However, it would appear, based on our previous research, that the typical procedure is to secure the support of your local shop in raising funds on behalf of your cause.

Laird PLC

Engineering

Correspondent: J. G. Du Plessis, General Counsel & Company Secretary, 100 Pall Mall, London SW1Y 5NQ (tel: 020 7468 4040; fax: 020 7839 2921; website: www.laird-plc.com/corporate-social-responsibility)

Directors: Dr Martin Read, Chair; Kjersti Wiklund; Mike Parker; Nathalie Rachou; Paula Bell; Sir Christopher Hum; Tony Quinlan, Chief Executive (women: 2; men: 5)

Year end	31/12/2015
Turnover	£630,400,000
Pre-tax profit	(£7,600,000)

Nature of business: Laird PLC is, according to its corporate website, a 'global technology company focused on providing systems, components and solutions that protect electronics from electromagnetic interference and heat, and that enable connectivity in mission-critical wireless applications and antenna systems'.

Company registration number: 55513

Subsidiary undertakings include: Laird America Inc.; Laird Group Ltd; Laird Technologies Ltd.

Total employees: 8,593

Focus of giving: Disability, education, children, young people.

Community involvement	✓
Community contributions	✓
Company reports on anti-slavery	✓
CSR report	✓
Cash donations declared	✓
Employee-led support	✓
Gifts in kind	✓
STEM-focused	✓

Charitable donations

Cash worldwide:	2015	£34,500
Total worldwide (cash and in kind):	2015	£34,500

Community involvement

Individual Laird sites develop relationships within their local communities, supporting community organisations and schools with contributions of staff time and other gifts in kind. They also have access to a 'charities budget' which is approved by the Laird PLC board each year.

Case study: DEMAND (Design and Manufacture for Disability)

The Corporate Responsibility Report for 2015 explains that, during the year, Laird helped to fund a student placement at DEMAND, a charity that works to promote solutions for the daily challenges faced by people with disabilities.

UK locations

City of Westminster (headquarters) and Wooburn Green, Buckinghamshire.

Community contributions

The Corporate Social Responsibility Report for 2015, which is contained within the annual report and accounts, states that cash charitable donations amounted to £34,500. We were unable to determine how much of this was given in the UK.

A figure for the value of in-kind support, principally staff time, was not included in the report.

Applications

Apply in writing to your local Laird PLC location.

Lancashire Holdings Ltd

Insurance

Correspondent: Donations Committee, 29th Floor, 20 Fenchurch Street, London EC3M 3BY (tel: 020 7264 4000; fax: 020 7264 4077; website: www.lancashiregroup.com/en/responsibility/lancashire-foundation.html)

Directors: Alex Maloney, Chief Executive Officer; Elaine Whelan, Chief Financial Officer; Peter Clarke, Chair; Robert Lusardi; Samantha Hoe-Richardson; Simon Fraser; Tom Milligan (women: 2; men: 5)

Year end	31/12/2015
Turnover	£493,478,000
Pre-tax profit	£132,161,000

Nature of business: Lancashire is a global provider of specialty insurance products operating in Bermuda and London.

Subsidiary undertakings include: Cathedral Capital Holdings Ltd; Lancashire Insurance Company Ltd; Lancashire Insurance Marketing Services Ltd.

Brands include: Cathedral; Kinesis; Lancashire.

Total employees: Focus of giving: Overseas projects, children, young people, community/social welfare.

Accredited Living Wage Employer	✓
Community involvement	✓
Community contributions	✓
Company reports on anti-slavery	✓
CSR report	✓
CSR or charity committee	✓
Directors have other relevant posts	✓
Charity partner(s)	✓
Corporate charity	✓
Employee-led support	✓
Matched funding	✓
Overseas giving	✓
Pro bono	✓

Community involvement

Lancashire Holdings Ltd supports communities in the UK, Bermuda and around the world through The Lancashire Foundation (Charity Commission no. 1149184).

The Lancashire Foundation

The Lancashire Foundation is central to Lancashire's corporate social responsibility efforts – something that's reflected in its board of trustees, which is made up of group employees and non-executive board members. It usually receives an annual cash donation from the company as well as dividends on Lancashire warrants that were given when it was established. According to the annual report for 2015, the foundation now owns 330,713 common shares in the company.

The foundation directs its resources to addressing the needs of communities, both those local to where the group has a presence and international communities. There is a particular focus on supporting young people and people who are severely disadvantaged.

There is a page on the main group's website dedicated to the foundation, from where the following helpful information is taken:

> The Foundation recognises the financial pressure that charities face and therefore its donations are generally not tied or restricted to particular programmes or activities. We believe that the benefitting charities themselves are best placed to direct funds in the most efficient and effective way to ensure their sustainability and to meet their beneficiaries' needs. We seek to enter into multi-year arrangements with the charities we support to assist in their sustainability.

The foundation facilitates 'key flagship' charity partnerships and also supports some smaller charities that have been nominated by Lancashire staff. Very occasionally the foundation can give emergency funding and sometimes also funds charities nominated by others in its marketplace. More than 40 charities in the UK, Bermuda and elsewhere were supported by the foundation during 2015.

Charity partners detailed on the website are: Family Centre; International Care Ministries; Médecins Sans Frontières; St Giles Trust; Tomorrow's Voices.

Other beneficiaries in 2015 were: Action Medical Research; Back Up Trust; Batten Disease Family Association; National Brain Appeal; Prostate Cancer Research Centre; Skiing with Heroes.

Directors with other relevant posts

Peter Clarke: Chair of the National Teaching Awards Trust and member of the Treasury Committee at King's College London.

Samantha Hoe-Richardson: Head of Environment and Sustainability at Network Rail.

Robert Lusardi: board member of Oxford University's 501(c)3 charitable organisation.

Main UK locations

City of London (head office)

Community contributions

The directors' report for 2015 states: 'During 2015 the Company facilitated a donation of $2.5 million to the Lancashire Foundation from a third party. In view of this substantial donation, the Company decided not to make any further donation to the Foundation during 2015.' At the time of writing (September 2016) $2.5 million equated to approximately £1.9 million.

It is also explained that:

> The Foundation held warrants in the Company, which were exercised in May 2015, and the dividend equivalent payments received on the warrants, which had been an important income stream for the Foundation, will be taken into account when considering the appropriate level of donations to be made by the Company in the future. The Foundation now owns 330,713 common shares in the Company and will receive any dividends declared on those shares.

The annual report and accounts further state that donations made to the foundation during the year amounted to $3.2 million (approximately £2.46 million) we have taken this figure to represent the third-party donation and dividends. As is our usual practice, we have not included the value of dividends in our total for contributions.

Employee-led support

Employee volunteering

All staff are encouraged to take part with volunteering days. According to the website, in 2015 employees' charitable activities included: sorting through items at a warehouse for Noah's Ark Hospice charity shops; helping with food redistribution for FareShare; and carrying out essential maintenance work on animal enclosures at Vauxhall City Farm. Employees also supported key charity partners in a variety of ways, including acting as mentors for staff at St Giles Trust. Each year, eight employees are also given the opportunity of travelling to the Philippines to work with International Care Ministries.

Matched funding

Funds raised by employees can be matched by The Lancashire Foundation.

Corporate charity

The Lancashire Foundation (Charity Commission no. 1149184).

Applications

The foundation principally channels its funding through key partner charities and those nominated by staff of the Lancashire group. Its page on the Lancashire group's website explains:

> Prospective charitable organisations are asked to provide a grant application form to the staff Donations Committee, which considers their funding proposals and, if agreed, provides a recommendation to the Trustees of the Foundation for their approval to release funds accordingly. Donations Committee members and other members of staff act as advocates for the charitable organisations that the Foundation supports throughout the year.

Land Securities Group PLC

Property

Correspondent: Caroline Hill, Head of Sustainability, 5 Strand, London WC2N 5AF (tel: 020 7413 9000/020 7024 5462; fax: 020 7925 0202; email: caroline.hill@landsecurities.com; website: www.landsecurities.com/sustainability/jobs-opportunities/activities/charity)

Directors: Chris Bartram; Cressida Hogg; Dame Alison Carnwath, Chair; Edward Bonham-Carter; Kevin O'Byrne; Martin Greenslade, Chief Financial Officer; Robert Noel, Chief Executive; Simon Palley; Stacey Rauch (women: 3; men: 6)

Year end	31/03/2016
Turnover	£942,500,000
Pre-tax profit	£1,335,600,000

Nature of business: Land Securities is the largest UK property group, involved in both property development and investment, and property outsourcing.

Company registration number: 4369054

Subsidiary undertakings include: City and Central Shops Ltd; Land Securities (Hotels) Ltd; The City of London Real Property Company Ltd.

UK employees: 459

Total employees: 459

Focus of giving: Education, enterprise/training, housing, homelessness, small groups, local groups, less popular charitable purposes, poverty and social exclusion, children, young people, community/social welfare, disability.

Membership: BITC, LBG

Community involvement	✓
Community contributions	✓
CSR report	✓
CSR or charity committee	✓
Directors have other relevant posts	✓
AF Covenant	✓
Charity partner(s)	✓
Company gives to smaller charities	✓
Employee-led support	✓
FTSE 100	✓
Gifts in kind	✓
Pro bono	✓
Sponsorship	✓
Unpopular causes	✓

Charitable donations

Total UK (cash and in kind):	2016	£2,800,000
Total worldwide (cash and in kind):	2016	£2,800,000

Community involvement

Land Securities Group PLC's community involvement is directed through a number of channels under the broader heading 'Creating jobs and opportunities'. These include: charity partnerships and volunteering; education; and community employment.

Charity partnerships and volunteering

According to the group's Sustainability Report 2016, Land Securities seeks to:

- 'Help disadvantaged people to get work experience and jobs'
- 'Support education for young people'
- 'Respond to local inequalities and needs, such as homelessness'

At a group level, Land Securities has one national partner which, since 2014, has been Mencap. In addition, shopping centres and offices belonging to the group develop partnerships with local groups in their communities. Partnerships can see organisations benefit from a wide range of support, such as grants, pro bono assistance, volunteer work or the provision of space for community events.

Mencap partnership: The group's partnership with Mencap was renewed for a third year in 2015/16. During the year, more than £125,000 was raised for the charity, 16 work experience placements were provided or organised and ten jobs were created. The charity also benefitted from volunteering and fundraising activities by Land Securities employees, including on the group-wide Mencap Day, held annually. One particular highlight of the partnership during the year was the Step Up event, which was organised with Mencap, and involved Land Securities hosting a 'vertical rush' fundraising dash up 36 floors to the Sky Garden of its 20 Fenchurch Street property.

Local partnerships: The group's shopping centres and offices build long-term partnerships with groups working to address their area's most vital issues. An example given in the Sustainability Report is that, as London and Oxford have high levels of homelessness, Land Securities has developed relationships with four homelessness charities in London and also supports Aspire Oxford which helps to create work opportunities for individuals in the city who are facing barriers to employment.

Another example is the partnership between the group and the social enterprise Circle Collective, which works to encourage disadvantaged young people to change their lives for the better and influence their communities positively. The report describes how the partnership 'is a great example of the fully rounded package of support we provide to our charity partners. Here it includes pro bono marketing advice from our Head of London Marketing, retail advice from our Retail Operations Manager and strategic support from our Community Manager, who also chairs the Circle Collective advisory board.'

Investing in local communities

Land Securities invests in endowment funds to benefit the local communities, and particularly jobs and opportunities, where it has a presence. The Sustainability Report explains: 'Doing it this way enables us to draw down match funding from partners and government schemes such as Community First.' An example of one of these legacy funds is the 20 Fenchurch Street Legacy Fund – established in collaboration with the Canary Wharf Group, the East End Community Foundation, customers and supply chain organisations – which makes grants to projects and services in Hackney, Newham, Tower Hamlets and the City of London, helping local people to get back into employment. Two other funds are also noted in the report, one with London Community Foundation and the other with Kent Community Foundation.

Education

Land Securities runs a number of education programmes, the aims of which are set out in the Sustainability Report:

- Help young people develop more commercial skills and become more aware of careers in our wider industry
- Attract talent to Land Securities and promote diversity and social mobility within the property industry
- Engage young people and education institutions in the development of our local communities
- Engage our employees and the employees of partner companies in meaningful professional volunteering

As part of its commitment to education, Land Securities is an 'Employer Partner' in the Sir Simon Milton Westminster University Technical College, which educates 14- to 18-year-olds with a focus on the construction and engineering industries. Other educational programmes the group is involved with include:

- Introduction to Property Development Programme, which works with sixth formers at two local schools, Westminster City School and Pimlico Academy and is led by Land Securities employees
- UrbanPlan, which the group sponsors in collaboration with other industry partners to engage school students with the built environment
- Westminster Mentoring Programme, a pilot scheme through which 40 school pupils at Westminster City School were connected with employees at Land Securities and its customer companies, including Microsoft and EDF Trading

Community employment

Land Securities has set itself a target of helping 1,200 disadvantaged people to secure employment by 2020. Examples of how it works towards this are included in the Sustainability Report 2016.

- Bluewater Learning Shop: This 'on-site employment and training hub' is the result of a partnership between Bluewater Shopping Centre, North West Kent College and Jobcentre Plus. The report explains: 'The Learning Shop has brokered employment for more than 46,000 people, trained almost 20,000 people and awarded over 15,000 qualifications'
- 'Girls can do it too': This initiative has the aim of promoting careers in the construction industry to girls, providing practical experience and insight and with activities run by Land Securities, its partners and the Make the Grade programme by Ahead Partnership. Participants with the programme will also benefit through mentoring from women within the sector
- Brixton Prison: Land Securities has supported a new dry lining training centre in the prison. The report states: 'Opened in 2015 and created in partnership with Bounce Back, Lendlease, Measoms, Be Onsite, Knauf and Encon, this is the first centre of its kind in the country. Up to 70 participants can learn skills and gain qualifications on the course, helping them to enter the construction industry when they're released.' It is further explained that a scaffolding centre is being built with the help of Alandale Scaffolding and GKR Scaffolding

Directors with other relevant posts

Robert Noel: trustee of LandAid.

Martin Greenslade: trustee of International Justice Mission UK.

Simon Palley: trustee of the University of Pennsylvania and The Tate Foundation.

UK locations

Land Securities owns properties across the UK. Details of its London and retail portfolios can be seen on the website (www.landsecurities.com/retail-portfolio).

Community contributions

The annual report 2016 states that the equivalent of £2.8 million was given in 'time, promotion and cash investment'.

In-kind support

Pro bono and volunteering

The Sustainability Report 2016 states: 'Volunteering and pro bono expertise are often valued more by community partners than cash. Indeed, it is hard to quantify the effects of this work, but nonetheless the impacts are significant and broad ranging.' Employees make a contribution particularly to the group's education programme, with more than 70 involved with the programme during the year.

An example of the value of pro bono work is the Land Securities Project Director who sits on the board of trustees of the Sir Simon Milton Westminster University Technical College; it is estimated that, through this employee, £45,000 has been contributed in in-kind support.

Employee-led support

Employee volunteering

Land Securities employees are involved in a range of volunteering activities, including pro bono work, and in 2015/16 contributed a total of 6,745 hours. An example of employee volunteering during the year includes 17 employees who spent time refurbishing a care home owned by the group's charity partner, Mencap.

Employee fundraising

In 2015/16 employees helped to raise funds for the group's charity partner, Mencap, by taking part in a range of fundraising activities. Employees participated with the annual Mencap Day held by the group, along with Mencap clients, taking part with Winter Fair-themed activities.

Applications

Local partnership appeals should be directed to the local Land Securities shopping centre or office in your area.

For more information on the legacy funds supported by Land Securities, noted in the Sustainability Report, visit: The 20 Fenchurch Street Legacy fund (www.eastendcf.org); London Community Foundation fund (communityfoundation.london); Kent Community Foundation fund: www.kentcf.org.uk/apply/funding-round). Note that, as with many funds operated by community foundations, these funds are subject to opening and closing dates for applications.

Leeds Building Society

Building society

Correspondent: Ellen Hamilton, Leeds Building Society Charitable Foundation, 105 Albion Street, Leeds LS1 5AS (tel: 0345 050 5075/0113 225 7518; email: ehamilton@leedsbuildingsociety.co.uk; website: www.leedsbuildingsociety.co.uk/your-society/about-us/charitable-foundation)

Directors: Andrew Greenwood; David Fisher; Gareth Hoskin; John Hunt; Karen Wint; Les Platts; Peter Hill, Chief Executive; Philip Jenks; Philippa Brown; Richard Fearon; Robin Ashton, Chair; Robin Litten; Susan Cooklin (women: 3; men: 10)

Year end	31/12/2015
Pre-tax profit	£108,500,000

Nature of business: The provision, to existing and prospective members, of residential mortgages and retail saving products.

FSA registration number: 164992

Subsidiary undertakings include: Headrow Commercial Property Services Ltd; Leeds Building Society Covered Bonds LLP; Leeds Financial Services Ltd.

Focus of giving: General charitable purposes, housing, homelessness, small groups, local groups, older people, poverty and social exclusion, children, young people, community/social welfare, disability.

Membership: BITC

Community involvement	✓
Community contributions	✓
CSR report	✓
Cash donations declared	✓
Charity partner(s)	✓
Company gives to smaller charities	✓
Corporate charity	✓
Employee-led support	✓
Gifts in kind	✓
Market-led giving	✓
Matched funding	✓

Charitable donations

Cash UK (latest available):	2015	£123,000
Cash worldwide:	2015	£123,000

Community involvement

Leeds Building Society makes donations to registered charities in the areas near its branches, principally through Leeds Building Society Charitable Foundation (Charity Commission no. 1074429). It also runs the Lending a Hand employee volunteering scheme and employees are supported in their fundraising efforts through a matched funding scheme. The Society's partner charities, together with the Leeds Building Society Charitable Foundation, received donations totalling £104,500 through the 'Your interest in theirs' and Caring Saver schemes. The Society also makes a donation for each vote cast at the AGM and members can choose from a number of charities to benefit. A total of over £70,000 has been donated to charity since the scheme started.

Partner charities: Age UK; Marie Curie Cancer Care; Variety.

Leeds Building Society Charitable Foundation

The foundation generally considers applications for community-based projects which aim to provide relief of suffering, hardship or poverty, or their direct consequences.

Community Fund

The Community Fund enables the society to support a wide range of smaller charities and community groups around its network of branches. During 2015 around £14,100 was donated by the society to local community organisations. The matched funding scheme looks to support everyone at the society with their fundraising for charities. In 2015 colleagues raised over £50,000 for charity which was matched by a further £14,800.

Main location

Leeds

Community contributions

In 2015 the society made a donation of £100,000 to the Leeds building society charitable foundation which was donated to 124 charities. The Caring Saver account provided further donations of £22,000 to be made to specified charities, although we have classed this as commercially led support. Other charitable donations in the year amounted to £23,000, charitable contributions from colleagues and members totalled £181,000, taking overall donations to charity to £326,000. We take the total of £123,000 as the society's overall contribution. We were unable to determine the value of the in-kind support given by the group.

Beneficiaries: Leeds Building Society Charitable Foundation (£100,000).

In-kind support

Volunteering

All colleagues are encouraged to take up to seven hours paid leave each year to volunteer in their local communities. During 2015 more than 120 people participated in the scheme.

Employee-led support

Matched funding

The society provides matched funding to support employees' fundraising efforts.

The Colleague Charity Group

The group, now in its seventh year, has continued to raise funds for charities chosen by colleagues, currently

Hollybank Trust, Alzheimer's Society, Yorkshire Air Ambulance and Great North Air Ambulance. Almost £67,000 was raised in 2015.

Commercially led support

Caring Saver accounts

Leeds Building Society makes an annual donation equivalent to 1% of the average balance held in all Caring Saver accounts.

Corporate charity

Leeds Building Society Charitable Foundation (Charity Commission no. 1074429).

Exclusions

The foundation is unlikely to make donations for:

- The restoration or upgrading of buildings, including churches
- Environmental charities (unless there is a benefit to a disadvantaged community)
- Administration equipment such as IT equipment for a charity's own use

The foundation is unable to support:

- Projects with religious, political or military purposes
- Overseas charities or projects
- Individuals, including sponsorship of individuals
- Animal welfare projects
- Medical research

Applications

Leeds Building Society Charitable Foundation

Leeds Building Society Charitable Foundation (Charity Commission no - 1074429) was established by the society in 1999 to support the communities around its nationwide network of branches by making donations to charities working in those areas. Since its establishment the foundation has made donations totalling over £1.3 million.

Applications will normally only be considered from registered charities. The foundation may also consider applications from groups affiliated to registered charities.

Generally, the foundation will consider applications for community-based projects which aim to provide relief of suffering, hardship or poverty, or their direct consequences.

Some examples of the areas in which the foundation has made donations include:

- Homeless people
- Adults and children with physical and mental disabilities
- Older people
- Underprivileged families
- Deaf, blind and partially sighted people
- Community projects benefitting local residents
- Victims of natural and civil disasters in the UK; and
- Scout, Guide and play groups

The project must operate in the area of one of the 67 branches.

Church projects will be considered only where they involve community outreach and benefit (e.g. supporting the homeless, disadvantaged families).

Donations are normally in the range of £250 to £1,000. The application must be for capital expenditure. The foundation cannot consider applications towards general running costs.

Applications should be made using the form on the foundation's website.

All applications will be acknowledged. The trustees meet quarterly in March, June, September and November. Following the meeting the foundation will write to you and let you know whether or not your application has been successful.

If you need more information or advice, contact the secretary of the charitable foundation on 0113 225 7518 or email at foundation@leedsbuilding society.co.uk. Because the foundation operates independently of the Building Society, local branch staff are unable to answer questions about the foundation.

Legal & General PLC

Financial services

Correspondent: Sara Heald, Head of Community Involvement, One Coleman Street, London EC2R 5AA (020 3124 2039; email: Sara.Heald@group.landg.com; website: csr.legalandgeneralgroup.com/csr)

Directors: Carolyn Bradley; Julia Wilson; Lesley Knox; Mark Gregory, Chief Financial Officer; Mark Zinkula; Nigel Wilson, Group Chief Executive; Philip Broadley; Richard Meddings; Rudy Markham, Interim Chair; Stuart Popham (women: 3; men: 7)

Year end	31/12/2015
Turnover	£12,701,000,000
Pre-tax profit	£1,414,000,000

Nature of business: The group's principal activities are: the provision of long-term insurance, investment management and general insurance.

Company registration number: 1417162

Subsidiary undertakings include: Adam Kennedy Estate Agents Ltd; Legal & General Property Ltd; Newlife Mortgages Ltd.

UK employees: 7,719

Total employees: 10,148

Focus of giving: Education, enterprise/training, health, ill health, housing, homelessness, children, young people.

Membership: BITC

Accredited Living Wage Employer	✓
Community involvement	✓
Community contributions	✓
Company reports on anti-slavery	✓
CSR report	✓
CSR or charity committee	✓
Directors have other relevant posts	✓
Charity partner(s)	✓
Employee-led support	✓
FTSE 100	✓
Gifts in kind	✓
Matched funding	✓
Payroll giving	✓
Pro bono	✓
Shared-value alliances	✓

Charitable donations

Total UK (cash and in kind):	2015	£857,500
Total worldwide (cash and in kind):	2015	£857,500

Community involvement

Legal & General does not have a Charity of the Year – instead, employees at each location choose charities (mainly in their own local community) to support; however, it does support a number of national charities, such as Comic/Sport Relief, Macmillan Cancer Support, prostate and breast cancer charities, and BBC Children in Need. Each location has an employee 'making a difference' committee, which helps to encourage local involvement. Employees are supported with their charitable commitments through volunteering time, a payroll giving facility, a matched funding scheme and, since 2015, a time matching scheme.

Campaigns

At a group level, Legal & General seeks to develop strategic relationships and partnerships through three group-wide campaigns:

- **Dealing with ill health**: 'the need to understand health trends and innovation'
- **Income in later life**: 'the need to support the retired who are living longer and typically on fixed incomes'
- **Access to housing**: 'the need to create housing opportunities for all'

Legal & General also works alongside other organisations on 'common issues'.

There is more information on these partnerships contained in a helpful document available to download from the Legal & General website, titled 'Groupwide donations for charities, social enterprise and not-for-profit organisations'.

Community and social investment

Examples of the group's community and social investment initiatives include:

- **Financial education – Everyday Money Programme**: Legal & General delivers this programme, which is facilitated by Development Garden, within schools with the aim of encouraging children to consider the financial knowledge they already have, where they got it from and to explore how they can make informed financial decisions once they have the correct information. The programme sees Legal & General employees volunteer as 'table coaches'. In Battle in Sussex, the programme saw parents get involved as volunteers so they could learn alongside their children
- **Social enterprises – SE Assist**: In conjunction with Charities Aid Foundation (CAF), Legal & General provides funding to social enterprises in Sussex, Croydon and Wales in the form of interest-free loans and mentoring. Through this social investment fund, 70 jobs have been created, 15 enterprises have received mentoring and more than £300,000 has been invested
- **'Pennies from heaven'**: Legal & General asked people to vote on which charity should receive funding; Alzheimer's UK was selected

Directors with other relevant posts

Stuart Popham: Chair of the Royal Institute of International Affairs (Chatham House); council member at Birkbeck College, University of London; and Vice-Chair of Royal National Lifeboat Institution.

Richard Meddings: trustee of Teach First.

Carolyn Bradley: non-executive director at The Mentoring Foundation and trustee of Cancer Research UK.

Philip Broadley: on board of governors at Eastbourne College.

UK locations

Birmingham; Cardiff; Hove; Ipswich; London; Kingswood; Surrey; Witham; Essex.

Community contributions

In 2015 Legal & General contributed at least £857,500 through 'charitable investments' in the UK. Expenditure on 'campaign projects and volunteering' was broken down into the following categories:

Health	£203,000
SE Assist – Social Enterprises	£164,000
Income in retirement	£149,500
Volunteering	£143,500
Housing	£122,500
Education – Everyday Money	£75,000

A further £396,000 was expended in 'group costs', including governance. As is our usual practice, we have not included this in our figure for community contributions.

Employee fundraising and matched funding in the UK amounted to an additional £1.43 million; however, we were not able to determine how much of this came directly from the group in matched funding. Employees located overseas in the United States and the Netherlands raised £566,500.

In-kind support

Volunteering time

Legal & General's volunteering policy encourages employees to take time to volunteer during their working day. During 2015, 6,822 hours were spent volunteering.

Employee-led support

Employee fundraising and matching schemes

Employees fundraise for a wide range of charitable causes and are supported in their efforts by the group's matched funding scheme. In 2015 the group also introduced a time matching scheme, which allows employees to turn the time they spend volunteering into cash for their chosen charities.

Payroll giving

Employees are able to donate to registered charities through the Give As You Earn scheme.

Community Awards

Each year, Legal & General holds awards to celebrate employees' community efforts. Awards are given in the following categories: Charity Champions; Charity Fundraiser; Community Spirit; Protecting the Environment; Helping Hands; Inspiring Young People; Youth Engagement; and Charity Ambassador. In 2015 employees from the UK and USA were nominated for the awards and more than 6,500 votes were cast.

Exclusions

According to the donations policy document, Legal & General does not support:

- Organisations that are not recognised as charitable in nature by regulating organisations such as the UK Charity Commission, Charities Aid Foundation or the IRS in the USA
- Religious organisations, except where it can be proven that the project to be undertaken will benefit the community as a whole
- Personal appeals on behalf of individual people, including overseas trips
- Any organisation, which is in conflict with its Bribery and Corruption policy i.e. Political organisations – direct or indirect donations are not permitted
- Donations through Financial Intermediaries such as Independent Financial Advisors, Business Partners or Journalists
- Benevolent Charity Funds
- Events that involve gambling
- Sponsorship requests from individuals

Applications

Decisions on strategic partnerships are made by the Charity Committee. Employees in each location choose, often local, charities to support.

John Lewis Partnership PLC

Retail – department and variety stores, retail – supermarkets

Correspondent: CR Team, 171 Victoria Street, London SW1E 5NN (tel: 020 7828 1000; website: www.johnlewispartnership.co.uk/csr.html)

Directors: Andrew Mayfield; Bérangère Michel; Patrick Lewis; Tracey Killen (women: 2; men: 2)

Year end	30/01/2016
Turnover	£9,749,000,000
Pre-tax profit	£290,000,000

Nature of business: The company trades under the name of John Lewis (full line department stores and smaller 'at home' stores) and Waitrose (food shops, including supermarkets and convenience stores).

The partnership is a retail business run on co-operative principles. All the ordinary share capital is held by a trustee – John Lewis Partnership Trust Ltd – on partners' (employees') behalf. Under irrevocable trusts the balance of profits is available to be shared among all partners after provision for prudent reserves and for interest on loans and fixed dividends on shares held outside. Management is accountable to the general body of partners, in particular through elected councils and through the partnership's journalism.

Company registration number: 233462

Subsidiary undertakings include: Herbert Parkinson Ltd; JLP Insurance Ltd; John Lewis Car Finance Ltd; Waitrose Ltd.

Brands include: John Lewis; Waitrose.

Focus of giving: Education, environment, health, ill health, heritage, housing, homelessness, medical research, overseas projects, older people, arts, culture, children, young people, disability.

Membership: BITC, LBG

Community involvement	✓
Community contributions	✓
Company reports on anti-slavery	✓
Corporate charity	✓
CSR report	✓
CSR or charity committee	✓
Directors have other relevant posts	✓
Charity partner(s)	✓

Employee-led support ✓
Gifts in kind ✓
Humanitarian aid: overseas ✓
Overseas giving ✓

Charitable donations

Cash UK (latest available):	2016	£10,130,000
Total UK (cash and in kind):	2016	£11,580,000
Cash worldwide:	2016	£10,130,000
Total worldwide (cash and in kind):	2016	£11,580,000

Community involvement

During 2015/16, the group delivered programmes, in partnership with national charities and organisations, that complement the school curriculum, empower young people, and provide access to support networks for older people.

The Waitrose and John Lewis Foundations exist to allocate investment in communities overseas in our key sourcing regions. The Waitrose Foundation, supports fresh produce growers in Ghana, Kenya and South Africa and celebrated its tenth year in 2015. Waitrose and the Fairtrade Foundation also announced a new partnership that will see them share best practice and a joint ambition to build upon sustainable supply chain models.

The John Lewis Foundation

The John Lewis Foundation (Charity Commission no. 1118162) is designed to benefit the communities in the UK and overseas in which those who produce products for the John Lewis live and work.

The John Spedan Lewis Foundation

The John Spedan Lewis Foundation (Charity Commission no. 240473) provides finance for charitable purposes reflecting the interests of John Spedan Lewis – notably horticulture, ornithology, entomology and associated environmental and conservation projects.

'Man on the Moon'

To celebrate the popularity of the John Lewis 'Man on the Moon' Christmas advert, partners were involved in a number of fundraising and volunteering events for Age UK. In collaboration with Waitrose as part of its isolation campaign, John Lewis branches also supported Christmas events, such as Christmas lunches at their local Age UK branch.

The Golden Jubilee Trust

The Golden Jubilee Trust is the group's flagship volunteering programme. Partners are given the opportunity to volunteer full or part time with a UK-registered charity for up to six months, on full pay. Since it launched in 2000, partners have dedicated 297,000 hours to over 700 charities. These span causes such as youth education, care for people in need, environmental protection and the arts.

Main locations

Throughout the UK.

Community contributions

In 2015/16 the partnership invested £12.2 million in communities, this included cash, time, in-kind and management costs (equivalent to 4%*of pre-tax profit.) We are unable to determine the amount given specifically to charities.

Employee-led support

Employee (partner) volunteering

At John Lewis, the flagship education programme, Bringing Skills to Life, provides schools with access to curriculum resources and partner volunteering time. It now has 3,000 schools, nurseries and children's groups registered.

Commercially led support

Schools programmes

During 2015/16 Barnardo's and John Lewis united to support young carers and young people leaving care through fundraising activities in branch and special merchandise sales. This will help fund the charity's ongoing work – including staffing costs, extra support for young carers outside care duties and employment advice.

Exclusions

The company does not support: individuals; religious, ethnic or political groups; or third-party fundraising activities.

Applications

Community matters

For more information about the John Lewis Partnership's Community Matters charitable giving scheme operated by local John Lewis and Waitrose stores, see the website (www.johnlewis.com/our-shops/helping-the-community).

The John Spedan Lewis Foundation

According to its website, The John Spedan Lewis Foundation (Charity Commission no. 240473) 'provides finance for charitable purposes reflecting the interests of John Spedan Lewis – notably horticulture, ornithology, entomology and associated environmental and conservation projects'.

The trustees meet biannually to consider funding appeals from registered UK charities. The foundation also sponsors a doctoral studentship.

The website gives application guidelines which suggest that, in order to be eligible for consideration by the trustees, appeals should be no longer than three (single side) pages of A4 and provide information under the following headers:

- Your charity's number as a reference
- How the project fulfils the foundation's criteria
- How the proposed project benefits the public
- How the support will be acknowledged (for instance, the use of logo in newsletters/signage/donations panels)

The guidelines stress that the headers above **must** be included for your application to be eligible.

In addition you should provide as appendices:

- A detailed breakdown of costs of all items requested (please bear in mind that salary and capital building costs cannot be funded by the Foundation)
- An updated summary of financial reporting (1–3 pages) from your charity's annual report. [Please do not send full annual reports]
- The Charity Commission report for your charity (under 'print charity details' 'print report') [Please send the file as PDF, not HTML. Contact the Secretary if you need assistance]

The foundation cannot fund salaries (in any format) nor capital building costs.

The guidelines note:

> All documents should be sent by email as electronic copies in **MS Word or PDF format** to the JSLF Secretary at jslf@johnlewis.co.uk.
>
> If you have difficulties with electronic correspondence, please use our postal address: *Secretary, John Spedan Lewis Foundation, Partnership House, Carlisle Place, London SW1P 1BX.* Electronic correspondence is preferred however – enabling documents to be shared among our Trustees and reducing our running costs and environmental impact.

PhD studentships

The website specifies that the foundation funds one PhD studentship over consecutive three-year periods. It is further noted: 'Natural history research topics are chosen by the Trustees and invitations are sent out to research organisations with expertise in the chosen topic. The Foundation does not respond to unsolicited requests for PhD funding.'

John Lewis Foundation

The John Lewis Foundation was launched in 2010. It funds projects based in its supplier communities overseas with a particular focus on India as a key sourcing country. Following a pilot in 2013 with Geosansar, the Foundation has committed to investing in further financial literacy training and access to bank savings accounts for factory workers in Delhi. The aim of the project is to empower workers to plan and control their finances.

Linklaters LLP

Legal

Correspondent: Louise Smith, Global Corporate Responsibility Manager, One Silk Street, London EC2Y 8HQ (tel: 020 7456 2000; website: www.linklaters.com)

Directors: Charles Jacobs, Senior Partner; Gideon Moore, Firm-wide Managing Partner

Year end	30/04/2015
Turnover	£1,263,805,000
Pre-tax profit	£420,122,000

Nature of business: Linklaters is an international law firm.

Company registration number: OC326345

Total employees: 4,810

Focus of giving: Education, enterprise/training, local groups, children, young people, community/social welfare.

Membership: BITC, LBG

Community involvement	✓
Community contributions	✓
Company reports on anti-slavery	✓
CSR report	✓
CSR or charity committee	✓
Charity partner(s)	✓
Community Mark	✓
Employee-led support	✓
Gifts in kind	✓
Payroll giving	✓
Pro bono	✓

Community involvement

The group's community investment activities focus on young people and capacity building of charitable organisations. The group prefers to work in partnership with charities over a number of years, mainly offering support through pro bono work. The group also reviews its activities in relation to the UN Sustainable Development Goals.

Charity partners

The group prefers to develop a relationship with charities, working together through partnerships over the course of at least three years. Examples include: Camfed, which the group has worked with since 2011, supporting the charity with its governance review, as well as funding an educational programme for 2,000 girls; and Pop Up, a literacy charity that the group works with on developing a website, supporting its programmes in Hackney and providing pro bono advice. The group also has a long-term partnership with the School for Social Entrepreneurs, providing bursaries and mentoring opportunities to entrepreneurs and pro bono advice to the charity.

Education

The group runs a Raising Aspirations programme with partner schools in Hackney, providing support through initiatives such as mentoring, careers advice and development activities. It also works in partnership with The Access Project, to encourage students from disadvantaged backgrounds to reach the top universities.

Main locations

The group has 29 offices in 20 countries. The group's head office is based in London.

Community contributions

No figure was given for the group's charitable contributions.

In-kind support

Pro bono

The group has a focus on providing pro bono support to charitable organisations, and contributes over 25,000 of pro bono work each year. As well as providing access to support and services, the group also funds full-time secondments for employees. Pro bono work generally falls into the following categories: supporting local access to justice; human rights; advancing the rule of law; social finance; international development. More information can be found in the pro bono report available to download on the website.

Employee-led support

Employee volunteering

In total, globally, the group's employees contributed almost 35,000 volunteering hours during 2014/15. The group has a strong focus on volunteering, particularly through pro bono work with charitable organisations.

Payroll giving and employee fundraising

The group is a founding member of the campaign Geared for Giving, which aims to encourage payroll giving.

Teams of employees also take part in the Wildhearts Micro-Tyco challenge, an international event in which teams aim to grow £1 of seed funding, supporting micro-loans to women in financially developing countries.

Exclusions

The group does not generally give support for speculative appeals, appeals from individuals or local appeals not in areas of the company's presence.

Applications

Apply in writing to the correspondent.

Liontrust Asset Management PLC

Financial services

Correspondent: Mark Jackson, Company Secretary, 2 Savoy Court, London WC2R 0EZ (tel: 020 7412 1700; email: info@liontrust.co.uk; website: www.liontrust.co.uk)

Directors: Adrian Collins; Alastair Barbour; George Yeandle; John Ions; Mike Bishop; Vinay Abrol (men: 6)

Year end	31/03/2015
Pre-tax profit	£7,300,000

Nature of business: Liontrust is a fund management company and has five teams that invest in UK, European, Asian and Global equities and Global credit and a team running multi-manager multi-asset portfolios.

Company registration number: 2954692

Focus of giving: Animal welfare, health, ill health.

Community involvement	✓
Community contributions	✓
CSR report	✓
Charity partner(s)	✓
Sponsorship	✓

Community involvement

Main locations

City of Westminster (head office) and Chelmsford, Essex.

Community contributions

According to the 2014/15 annual report, in addition to making some small donations in response to staff requests, Liontrust Assets Management PLC will enter into partnerships with charities and charitable endeavours that the company believes will make a difference at both global and local levels. Currently we have no financial information regarding the company's charitable contribution.

Commercially led support

Sponsorship

The company sponsors the ZSL's Lions500 campaign to protect the last remaining Asiatic lions in the wild as well as building a new conservation and breeding centre at ZSL London Zoo. Liontrust also sponsors the Old Colfeians rugby club in Lee, South East London. This support helps to fund the club as a whole, including the Colts teams and junior teams. In addition to this, Liontrust supports Richard Farquhar's Walking the Courses to raise money for Pancreatic Cancer and Racing Welfare.

Applications

Apply in writing to the correspondent.

Liverpool Victoria

Financial services, insurance

Correspondent: The Regional Community Committee, County Gates, Bournemouth, Dorset BH1 2NF (tel: 01202 292333; website: www.lv.com/about-us/lv-cares)

Directors: Caroline Burton; Cath Keers; David Neave; James Dean; John Edwards; John O'Roarke; Mark Austen, Chair; Michael Rogers, Group Chief Executive; Philip Moore, Group Finance Director; Richard Rowney (women: 2; men: 6)

Year end	31/12/2015
Pre-tax profit	£124,000,000

Nature of business: The society is an incorporated Friendly Society which carries out insurance and financial services business in the UK.

FSA registration number: 110035

Subsidiary undertakings include: Frizzell Financial Services Ltd; Highway Insurance Company Ltd; LV Protection Ltd.

UK employees: 6,000

Focus of giving: General charitable purposes, health, ill health, children, young people.

Community involvement	✓
Community contributions	✓
Company reports on anti-slavery	✓
CSR report	✓
CSR or charity committee	✓
Charity partner(s)	✓
Employee-led support	✓
Gifts in kind	✓
Market-led giving	✓
Matched funding	✓
Payroll giving	✓
Sponsorship	✓

Charitable donations

Cash UK (latest available):	2015	£198,000
Total UK (cash and in kind):	2015	£618,000
Cash worldwide:	2015	£198,000
Total worldwide (cash and in kind):	2015	£618,000

Community involvement

Liverpool Victoria supports charities and communities in the locations in which it has a presence through donations, community sponsorship and by supporting its employees' fundraising and volunteering efforts. The group has also partnered national charities through sponsorship and fundraising support.

LV gives charitable support in various ways. These include:

'Regional community committees'

A network of employee-led committees based at the group's 16 offices decides where the company can contribute its support most effectively. During the year, more than 300 local charities, good causes and projects benefitted from contributions from these committees.

Member Community Fund

Four times a year a good cause, charity or individual nominated by a member of the group receives a donation of £10,000. Nominations are assessed by a small independent committee of members.

Member Support Fund

Established in 2001 to support members and their families 'who have fallen on hard times' by way of hardship grants.

Partnerships

The group's partnership with Age UK supports their Call in Time programme. Employees are given 30 minutes a week to make calls to people who are lonely or isolated. The group also works with Fields in Trust to preserve recreational outdoor spaces near its major offices.

UK locations

Bournemouth; Brentwood; Bristol; Croydon; Exeter; Hitchin; Huddersfield; Ipswich; Leeds; London.

Community contributions

In 2015 the group 'raised, donated or invested' more than £1 million in UK communities, which was broken down into the following categories in its annual report: Community investment, £490,000; Community partnerships, £109,000; Community fundraising, £265,000; member relations £178,000.

We have taken the figure for 'Community investment' to include both cash and in kind donations. Our figure for cash contributions takes into account the following figures provided in the annual report and accounts: donations from **Member Support Fund** (£58,000); **Member Community Fund** donations (£50,000); and a donation to The Rainbow Trust raised by AGM votes (£20,000). These figures were included in the total provided for 'Community investment', the remainder of which we have taken as the value of in kind support. Additionally, we have also included £70,000 given through the 'charity matching scheme'. In the annual report this figure was included in the total for 'Community fundraising', the remainder of which we have taken as employee-raised funds.

As is our usual practice, we have not included the amount for 'Community sponsorship' in our figures for cash donations or total contributions.

Beneficiaries included: Cancer Research UK; Comic Relief; Leeds Community Committee; Fields in Trust.

In-kind support

Over 3,400 hours of employee time was donated during the year.

Employee-led support

Matched funding

Over 250 employees used the matched funding scheme which resulted in £150,000 being raised, £70,000 of which came from the company.

Volunteering

In 2015 a new employee volunteering hub was launched which has provided additional opportunities for staff to volunteer.

Payroll giving

The company has a Pennies for Charity scheme and a Give You Earn Scheme which together raised £60,000 in 2015.

Commercially led support

Community sponsorship

During the year, the group continued its support of:

LV=Streetwise, which saw 8,000 children visit an interactive safety centre which teaches about 'dangers in and outside the home'.

LV=KidZone, a beach safety scheme, helped 116 lost children find their families in Bournemouth during the summer months.

The group also sponsors the entrance pavilion at the Mary Rose Museum in Portsmouth.

Applications

Apply in writing to your nearest regional committee, locations and contact details of which are available from the website. Details of your project, charity or community initiative should be included, along with the type of support (funding or volunteering) you are looking for.

Lloyd's

Insurance

Correspondent: The Corporate Responsibility Managers, One Lime Street, London EC3M 7HA (tel: 020 7327 1000; email: communityaffairs@lloyds.com; website: www.lloyds.com/lloyds/corporate-responsibility)

Directors: Andy Haste; Dominic Christian; Dr Fred Hu; Inga Beale, Chief Executive Officer; John Nelson, Chair; Julian James; Karen Green; Lawrence Holder; Matthew Fosh; Michael Deeny; Michael Watson; Neil Maidment; Paul Jardine; Philip Swatman; Robert Childs; Simon Beale; Sir David Manning (women: 2; men: 15)

Year end	31/12/2015

Nature of business: Lloyd's is a specialist insurance and reinsurance underwriter.

Company registration number: 3189123

Principal subsidiary undertakings: Additional Securities Ltd; Centrewrite Ltd; Lloyd's Insurance Company (China) Ltd.

UK employees: 806

Total employees: 1,026

Focus of giving: General charitable purposes, education, enterprise/training, environment, health, ill health, individuals, armed forces, science technology, sport, recreation, children, young people, community/social welfare, disability, disasters.

Membership: BITC

Accredited Living Wage Employer	✓
Community involvement	✓
Community contributions	✓
CSR report	✓
Directors have other relevant posts	✓
AF Covenant	✓
Armed forces personnel	✓
Cash donations declared	✓
Corporate charity	✓
Employee-led support	✓
Humanitarian aid: overseas	✓
STEM-focused	✓

Charitable donations

Cash UK (latest available):	2015	£455,000
Total UK (cash and in kind):	2015	£455,000
Cash worldwide:	2015	£455,000
Total worldwide (cash and in kind):	2015	£455,000

Community involvement

Lloyd's focuses its community contributions primarily within the local communities in which it operates around the world. It gives support through its four grant-making charities and supports the community in east London, where it is based, through the Lloyd's Community Programme.

The group's 2015 CSR report states it also wants to utilise its expertise to help communities build resilience against disasters, including the effects of climate change and extreme weather events.

Lloyd's charities

Lloyd's Charities Trust (Charity Commission no. 207232)

The trust has supported local, national and international causes on Lloyd's behalf for more than 60 years. The Lloyd's website states that charitable giving from the trust is focused on the following areas:

- Global communities at risk from disasters and emergencies:
  - Donations are given to charities responding to disasters and emergencies, to help relieve suffering and rebuild lives
  - In areas prone to natural disasters, funding is given to disaster risk reduction initiatives aiming to build resilience into these communities
- To spread the economic and social benefits of the Lloyd's market by supporting projects that tackle disadvantage and foster opportunity
- To support the individual and collective charitable efforts of those working in the Lloyd's market and the City of London

The partner charities the trust is working with until 2019 are: Build Change; Mayor's Fund for London; RedR UK; Whizz-Kidz.

In 2015 the charity supported the training of aid workers in 91 countries and new urban-specific training courses developed and delivered in the UK, Jordan and Pakistan.

Lloyd's Patriotic Fund (Charity Commission no. 210173)

Lloyd's has a long history, over 200 years, of providing support to the UK armed forces community. This fund was established to make grants to serving and ex-service personnel and their families. It also provides support to a number of armed forces organisations with a particular focus on those working to help those in the military community who have disabilities or face poverty, illness and hardship.

Lloyd's Benevolent Fund (Charity Commission no. 207231)

This fund financially and practically assists those who have worked in the Lloyd's community who are in need and, at the discretion of the trustees, their dependants. The fund can be contacted at the group's head office or by contacting: raymond.blaber@lloyds.com or 020 7327 6453.

Lloyd's Tercentenary Research Foundation (Charity Commission no. 298482)

This charity was established to mark the tercentenary of Lloyds in 1988. The following information was taken from the website:

> Since then, it has funded over 100 years of academic research in the fields of engineering, science, medicine, business and the environment through the provision of post-doctoral fellowships and business scholarships.
>
> Today, through its partnership with the Insurance Intellectual Capital Initiative and UK Research Councils, Lloyd's Tercentenary Research Foundation continues its work of funding top flight academic research by supporting new programmes of research on risk related issues.

Support for the armed forces

Lloyd's is a signatory to the Armed Forces Covenant and has also operated The Lloyd's and City Branch of The Royal British Legion for the past 75 years. The branch fundraises for Legion-approved charities that work to support and improve the lives of military veterans and their families.

Directors with other relevant posts

John Nelson is a trustee of the Chichester Harbour Trust (Charity Commission no. 1096308) and the National Gallery.

Paul Jardine is a trustee of The Sick Children's Trust (Charity Commission no. 284416).

Robert Childs is a trustee of the Enham Trust (Charity Commission no. 211235), a charity for people with disabilities.

Dominic Christian is a trustee of the Juvenile Diabetes Research Foundation (Charity Commission no. 295716) and Lloyd's Tercentenary Foundation (Charity Commission no. 298482). He is also Chair of the University of East Anglia's Campaign Advisory Board.

Karen Green is a trustee of the Lloyd's Charities Trust (Charity Commission no. 207232) and Chair of the Development Council for the Almeida Theatre Company.

Lawrence Holder is a trustee of the Lloyd's Charities Trust (Charity Commission no. 207232).

Dr Fred Hu is a trustee of the Yale-China Association, Co-chair of the Nature Conservancy Asia Pacific Council and member of the US Council on Foreign Relations' Global Board of Advisors.

Sir David Manning is Chair of the Advisory Board of IDEAS at the London School of Economics and is on the Panel of Senior Advisors at the Royal Institute of International Affairs, Chatham House.

Main locations

The group's head office is based in London, but it also has offices all over the world in: Africa and the Middle East; Asia and Pacific; Europe; Latin America; North America.

Community contributions

In its annual report and accounts for 2015 the group declared charitable donations of £455,000 (2014: £433,000).

In 2015 the Council of Lloyd's made a donation of £250,000 to the Lloyds Charities Trust general fund, and £150,000 to the Lloyd's Community Programme. The Council also makes an annual donation of £200,000 to the Lloyd's Patriotic Fund.

Employee-led support

Lloyd's Together

In 2015 the group launched this new programme to provide support and encouragement for employees to take on community and charitable activities, with a focus on:

- Education and employability
- Environment and sustainability
- Social welfare and health
- Disaster preparedness and relief

During the year 18 offices took part in the programme with initiatives ranging from providing solar lamps in East Africa to building affordable housing in Canada.

Lloyd's Community Programme

Through the programme, employees are able to contribute their time and skills to community projects in East London. More than 2,600 employees volunteered through the scheme in 2015 (2014: 2,100). Participants can choose to volunteer with projects in one of the programme's four focus areas:

- Employability skills – helping young people from Tower Hamlets secondary school and sixth form with mentoring and employability workshops
- Reading and numbers – helping local primary schoolchildren to develop their literacy and numeracy skills
- Neighbourhood games – helping to run sports tournaments for young people in Tower Hamlets
- Team challenges – practical team tasks such as giving a community centre a makeover or helping to cook breakfasts for homeless people

Lloyd's Market Charity Awards

The Lloyd's website states that anyone who works in the Lloyd's market can apply for a donation to a charity or community organisation in which they are actively involved through the Lloyds Market Charity Awards scheme. Employees can win a donation of £2,000 for their chosen charity and winners are selected by the trustees of the Lloyd's Charities Trust.

Corporate charity

Lloyd's Charities Trust (Charity Commission no. 207232).

Applications

All of Lloyd's charities can be contacted by emailing communityaffairs@lloyds.com. Any other corporate social responsibility enquiries can be addressed to either of the two Corporate Social Responsibility Managers: Michaele Hawkins (tel: 020 7327 5484, email: michaele.hawkins@lloyds.com); or Suzanna Nagle (tel: 020 7327 6144, email: suzanna.nagle@lloyds.com).

Lloyds Charities Trust – Note the following from the website: 'Lloyd's Charities Trust will be supporting our partner charities for the next three years (2016–2019) and we are not accepting any new funding submissions at this time.'

Lloyd's Patriotic Fund – Note the following from the website: 'Lloyd's Patriotic Fund works with a number of long-standing partners through which funds are administered. Individuals wishing to apply for a welfare grant should contact their local branch of SSAFA Forces Help.'

Lloyd's Tercentenary Research Foundation – For more information on the scholarships available, visit the Lloyd's website: www.lloyds.com/ltrf.

The Lloyd's and City Branch of The Royal British Legion can be contacted using the following details: c/o Mark Drummond Brady, Jardine Lloyd Thompson Group PLC, The St Botolph Building, 138 Houndsditch London EC3A 7AW (tel: 020 7558 3569; email: Mark_Drummond-Brady@jltgroup.com).

Lloyds Banking Group

Financial services, banking

Correspondent: Responsible Business Team, 25 Gresham Street, London EC2V 7HN (tel: 020 7626 1500; website: www.lloydsbankinggroup.com/our-group/responsible-business)

Directors: Alan Dickinson; Anita Frew; Anthony Watson; António Horta-Osório, Group Chief Executive; Deborah McWhinney; George Culmer, Chief Financial Officer; Juan Colombás; Lord Blackwell, Chair; Nick Luff; Nick Prettejohn; Sara Weller; Simon Henry; Stuart Sinclair (women: 3; men: 10)

Year end	31/12/2015
Turnover	£17,637,000,000
Pre-tax profit	£1,644,000,000

Nature of business: Lloyds Banking Group is one of the largest financial services companies in the UK, covering retail banking, commercial and corporate banking, mortgages, life assurance and pensions, general insurance, asset management, leasing, treasury and foreign exchange dealing. (Lloyds TSB Group PLC was renamed Lloyds Banking Group on 19 January 2009, following the acquisition of HBOS PLC.)

Company registration number: 2065

Subsidiary undertakings include: Bank of Scotland PLC; Halifax Group Ltd; Lloyds Bank PLC.

Focus of giving: Economic generation, education, enterprise/training, small groups, local groups, financial education, poverty and social exclusion, sport, recreation, children, young people, community/social welfare, disability.

Membership: BITC

Community involvement	✓
Community contributions	✓
Company reports on anti-slavery	✓
CSR report	✓
CSR or charity committee	✓
Directors have other relevant posts	✓
Cash donations declared	✓
Charity of the Year	✓
Charity partner(s)	✓
Company gives to smaller charities	✓
Corporate charity	✓
Employee-led support	✓
FTSE 100	✓
Gifts in kind	✓
Matched funding	✓
Pro bono	✓
Sponsorship	✓

Charitable donations

Cash UK (latest available):	2015	£27,000,000
Total UK (cash and in kind):	2015	£64,000,000
Cash worldwide:	2015	£27,000,000
Total worldwide (cash and in kind):	2015	£64,000,000

Community involvement

Lloyds Banking Group (LBG) has one of the largest community programmes in the UK. Through its Helping Britain Prosper Plan the group has a range of commitments aimed at helping communities across the UK. These are outlined on the website as including: 'colleague volunteering'; 'support for community organisations'; donations to the group's four foundations; and fundraising for the Charity of the Year. LBG also runs community investment programmes which fall under three key themes – education, employability and enterprise. These programmes are supported by colleagues, who are encouraged to dedicate their time and expertise. Examples of LBG's community programmes and commitments include:

Corporate foundations

Lloyds Banking Group supports registered charities across the UK and the Channel Islands through its four corporate foundations – Lloyds Bank Foundation for England and Wales, Bank of Scotland Foundation, Halifax Foundation for Northern Ireland and Lloyds Bank Foundation for the Channel Islands.

The foundations support charities that enable people, particularly those who are disadvantaged or who have disabilities, to play a fuller role in society. Applications are only accepted from registered charities that fit the grant-giving criteria.

Charity of the Year

BBC Children in Need was chosen as the Charity of the Year for 2015 and 2016. Lloyds also became the charity's first 'principal partner' and 'exclusive schools partner' until 2017.

Community sports programmes

Bank of Scotland works in partnership with the Scottish Football Association and Midnight League to promote football participation among young people. The bank also partners the Great Scottish Run, Scotland's in which 30,000 people take part.

Supporting Credit Unions

Lloyds Banking Group has launched a fund in partnership with the Credit Union Foundation and the Association of British Credit Unions (ABCUL) which, according to the website, will 'help Credit Unions, with strong, sustainable proposals for growth, improve their capital base'. The fund is worth £4 million over the four years from 2014 to 2017.

Lloyds Scholars

This programme is a partnership with eight universities in the UK and is aimed at supporting students from lower income households with, according to the website, 'a complete support package, helping them manage the financial strain of University while improving their employability'. Students are given financial support, a mentor from Lloyds Banking Group, skills sessions and paid internship opportunities. The participant university are: University College London; University of Bath; University of Birmingham; University of Bristol; University of Edinburgh; University of Oxford; University of Sheffield; and University of Warwick.

Go ON UK

Lloyds Banking Group is a founding partner of this digital skills charity and works alongside nine other organisations (Age UK, Argos, BBC, Big Lottery Fund, E.ON, EE, Post Office, Sage Group and Talk Talk) to promote basic digital skills.

Halifax libraries partnership

One example of this is the partnership between Halifax and the Society of Chief Librarians which is aimed at improving the digital literacy of more than six million adults who have never used the Internet, helping to get them online, emailing and connected. More than 2,000 members of staff at Halifax who have committed themselves to be 'Digital Champions' help out with IT taster sessions already being provided through public libraries in England Wales and Northern Ireland.

The Lloyds Bank and Bank of Scotland Social Entrepreneurs Programme

This year long programme is delivered in partnership with the School for Social Entrepreneurs and The Big Lottery Fund. It provides participants with financial support ('Start-up' grants of £4,000 and 'Scale-up' grants of £15,000), a learning programme run by the School for Social Entrepreneurs and mentoring support from a Lloyds Banking Group expert.

Money for Life

This scheme has two main strands – Money for Life Qualifications and the Money for Life Challenge – and is aimed at helping young people and adults develop the ability and skills they need to manage their finances. There is a particular focus on those who are in further education, work or community-based learning.

Directors with other relevant posts

Lord Blackwell: governor of The Yehudi Menuhin School.

Alan Dickinson: governor of Motability.

Simon Henry: member of the Advisory Board of the Centre for European Reform.

Deborah McWhinney: trustee of the California Institute of Technology and trustee of the Institute for Defense Analyses.

Nick Prettejohn: Chair of the Britten-Pears Foundation and the Royal College of Music.

Sara Weller: board member at the Higher Education Funding Council.

António Horta-Osório: Chair of the Wallace Collection.

Community contributions

In 2015 Lloyds Banking Group contributed a total of £64 million in community investment. The Responsible Business Report 2015 offers the following breakdown:

Cash donations	£27 million
Colleague time	£20 million
Gifts in-kind	£239,500

We believe that these figures include the £17 million donated to tackle disadvantage through its four foundations, as well as more than £1 million invested through the Money for Life scheme.

In addition, in 2015 Lloyds colleagues and customers helped in raising £5.7 million for BBC Children in Need.

In-kind support

Employee time

Colleagues are able to spend one paid day per year volunteering. In 2015 more than 40,000 volunteering days were taken.

Pro bono

The Responsible Business update for 2015 explains that, during the year, 20% of colleagues who volunteered supported 'skills based projects, including: employability skills; literacy and numeracy teaching for children; mentoring SMEs; and providing business advice for charities'. Colleagues are encouraged to use their time and expertise in support of LBG's community programmes.

Employee-led support

Employee volunteering

LBG colleagues are able to volunteer with a charity or community project of their own choosing through the group's volunteering programme.

In 2015 a total of 8,000 LBG colleagues took part with the UK's largest employee volunteering day, Give and Gain Day. Activities have included helping out with community sports events, running employability workshops and helping to rebuild flood-hit communities.

Employee fundraising

Colleagues raise funds for the Charity of the Year which, in 2015, was BBC Children in Need. More than £5 million, including matched funding, was raised and activities included colleagues climbing 24 peaks in the Lake District in 24 hours.

Matched funding

LBG matches funds raised by colleagues for good causes.

Commercially led support

Sponsorship

Lloyds Banking Group sponsors and is part of Business in the Community's Business Connectors Programme, which is aimed at using businesses' expertise to benefit communities. The programme helps to build relations between businesses and communities through 'Business Connectors'. The Responsible Business update explains: 'By the end of 2015, the equivalent of 60 full-time employees had been seconded as Connectors in some of the most deprived communities across Britain, including our first Connector in Scotland.'

Corporate charity

Halifax Foundation for Northern Ireland (Northern Ireland Charity no. 101763–0), Lloyds Bank Foundation for England and Wales (Charity Commission no. 327114), Lloyds Bank Foundation for the Channel Islands (Charity Commission no. 327113), Lloyds TSB Foundation for Scotland (OSCR no. SC009481), The Bank of Scotland Foundation (OSCR no. SC032942).

Exclusions

Only UK-registered charities are supported. See the relevant foundation's website for further details of exclusions.

Applications

Corporate foundations

Details of grant-giving policies and guidelines are available on the website of the relevant foundation for your region:

- Lloyds Bank Foundation for England and Wales Pentagon House
  - 52–54 Southwark Street, London SE1 1UN
  - telephone: 0870 411 1223; email: enquiries@lloydsbankfoundation.org.uk
  - website: www.lloydsbankfoundation.org.uk
- Halifax Foundation for Northern Ireland
  - 2nd Floor, 14 Cromac Place, Gasworks, Belfast BT7 2JB
  - 028 9032 3000; email: grants@halifaxfoundationni.org
  - website: www.halifaxfoundationni.org
- Lloyds Bank Foundation for the Channel Islands
  - Sarnia House, Le Truchot, St Peter Port, Guernsey GY1 4EF
  - telephone: 01481 706360; email: jlepoidevin@lloydsbankfoundation.org.uk
  - website: www.lloydsbankfoundationci.org.uk
- Bank of Scotland Foundation
  - The Mound, Edinburgh EH1 1YZ
  - telephone: 0131 655 2599; email: enquiries@bankofscotlandfoundation.co.uk
  - website: bankofscotlandfoundation.org

General queries

The website notes that queries or comments about Lloyds Banking Group's community programmes, environmental activities or approach to responsible business more generally can be directed to the correspondent in writing.

London Stock Exchange Group PLC

Financial services

Correspondent: See 'Applications', 10 Paternoster Square, London EC4M 7LS (tel: 020 7797 1000; website: www.lseg.com/about-london-stock-exchange-group/london-stock-exchange-group-foundation)

Directors: Andrea Munari; David Nish; David Warren, Chief Financial Officer; Donald Brydon, Chair; Jacques Aigrain; Lex Hoogduin; Mary Schapiro; Paul Heiden; Raffaele Jerusalmi; Stephen O'Connor; Xavier Rolet, Chief Executive (women: 1; men: 11)

Year end	31/12/2015
Turnover	£1,324,700,000
Pre-tax profit	£516,400,000

Nature of business: International financial markets infrastructure group. The group has a presence in locations including the UK (London), Italy, Sri Lanka, France, and the USA.

Company registration number: 5369106

Subsidiary undertakings include: FTSE International Ltd; LCH.Clearnet Group Ltd; London Stock Exchange PLC.

Focus of giving: Education, enterprise/training, overseas projects, children, young people.

Membership: LBG

Community involvement	✓
Community contributions	✓
Company reports on anti-slavery	✓
CSR report	✓
CSR or charity committee	✓
Cash donations declared	✓
Charity partner(s)	✓
Employee-led support	✓
FTSE 100	✓
Gifts in kind	✓
Overseas giving	✓
Pro bono	✓

Charitable donations

Cash worldwide:	2015	£2,154,000
Total worldwide (cash and in kind):	2015	£2,285,000

Community involvement

London Stock Exchange Group (LSEG) supports programmes making a positive difference in communities in which it has a presence. The majority of the group's charitable involvement is channelled through the London Stock Exchange Group Foundation, which was established in 2010 through the Charities Aid Foundation (CAF). Employees are also actively involved in their communities through the foundation's work.

London Stock Exchange Group (LSEG) Foundation

According to the LSEG Corporate Responsibility Report for 2015, the foundation has four main sources of income:

- Employee donations and fundraising events
- An annual charity trading day. The report explains that the group 'donates the equivalent of all equity trading fees raised on London Stock Exchange, Turquoise and Borsa Italiana during their annual charity trading day'. November 2015 saw the fifth annual trading day event which raised £452,000
- Corporate donations from other companies in the group
- Money raised through fines levied by LSEG

The foundation's giving is based around the group's brand values and, according to the LSEG website, focuses on supporting 'significant endeavours' that help 'young and disadvantaged people to reach their full potential, through the development of life skills and business enterprise'. The foundation's beneficiaries are mainly based in the UK; however, support is also given to charities in Italy, Australia, France, the USA and Sri Lanka.

Charity partners

Unicef: In 2015 the LSEG Foundation entered into partnership with Unicef as part of an effort to expand charitable involvement from only the communities in which LSEG has a presence to disadvantaged communities all over the world. The foundation will support a community investment programme in Zambia which will work to develop the business skills of teenage girls over a period of three years.

Ellen MacArthur Cancer Trust (EMCT): LSEG subsidiary LCH.Clearnet has partnered the Ellen MacArthur Cancer Trust since 2012. In that time, the trust has benefitted from corporate donations, employee fundraising and employee volunteering at sailing days.

Directors with other relevant posts

Donald Brydon: Chair of Chance to Shine and Chair of the Science Museum Foundation.

Xavier Rolet: member of Colombia Business School Board of Overseers.

Main UK locations

City of London (head office)

Community contributions

The London Stock Exchange Group's Corporate Responsibility Report for 2015 shows that the group gave a total of £2.5 million during the year in community investment. A breakdown of community investment was provided as follows:

Cash donations	£2.15 million
Management costs	£219,000
In-kind donations	£131,000

We have not included management costs in our figure for the group's total charitable contributions.

We were not able to determine how much of the group's community investment was given in the UK. However, the CR report did explain that, of the £2.15 million given in cash donations, about half (£1.07 million) was awarded directly to charities (this funding came mainly from FTSE Russell and LCH.Clearnet, subsidiaries of LSEG), with the remainder given to the

London Stock Exchange Group Foundation.

The report states the following regarding the level of cash donations during the year:

> This was a 7% increase compared to the prorated amount for 2014. The donations for 2015 are equivalent to £479 per employee (including Russell). This is 24% higher than the prorated benchmark calculated by the London Benchmarking Group, which showed that the average amount donated per employee by leading corporate donors was £387 in 2015.

The CR report further specifies that, of the beneficiaries supported by the LSEG Foundation, 75.1% were UK organisations, with the remaining 24.9% based in Italy, Australia, France, the USA and Sri Lanka. During the year, the foundation made grants to 33 charities (20 of which were in the UK) and, along with donations to global and regional partner charities, made grants totalling £835,000.

Examples of funded organisations, detailed on the LSEG website include: Bright Ideas Trust; Broadway Homelessness and Support; FareShare; Lord Mayor's Show; The Prince's Trust; St Paul's Cathedral; Westminster Boating Race.

In-kind support

Venue hire

Charities in the UK and Italy can hire venues at the group's premises free of charge.

Pro bono

In Sri Lanka, MillenniumIT employees were involved in a number of activities; these included 'creating teaching content for IT syllabus development' and training workshops for teachers in collaboration with the Ministry of Education. A group of volunteers also 'built a technology platform to connect NGOs and the Government with the corporate sector with the aim of undertaking development projects'.

'Business and beekeeping'

In the UK, LSEG collaborated with The Golden Company to offer a 'business and beekeeping course' to 37 young people from East London. The course involved visiting the rooftop bee hives at the LSEG building accompanied by employees, learning about the Stock Exchange, and carrying out paid shifts.

Employee-led support

Employee fundraising

Employees are involved with fundraising initiatives and provide one of the four principal sources of funding for the London Stock Exchange Group Foundation. In 2015 fundraising events included a mixed Touch Rugby Tournament organised in collaboration with the Rugby Football Union (RFU). The event helped to raise more than £54,000 for the LSEG Foundation and All Schools, a programme encouraging more rugby participation in schools.

Employee volunteering

LSEG employees in the group's various global locations volunteer in their local communities. In the UK, employees took part in the Reading Buddies programme through Tower Hamlets Education Business Partners. Based in London, the programme sees LSEG employees partner school pupils and provide them with one-to-one tuition once a week to help improve the students' reading skills and to raise their aspirations. As a member of the East London Business Alliance (ELBA) of almost ten years, FTSE Russell employees have volunteered to help with reading and numeracy for pupils at a local school and have taken it in turns to visit the school each week. During 2015, two employees also joined the board of a local youth charity and volunteers have acted as mentors at universities.

Applications

The LSEG website explains: 'One of the main principles of the Foundation's approach is to focus our charitable efforts on a small number of charities. In this way we can make the biggest difference'. More can be found out about the work carried out by the foundation by emailing LSEGFoundation@lseg.com.

LondonMetric Property PLC

Property

Correspondent: Communities & Charity Working Group, One Curzon Street, London W1J 5HB (tel: 020 7484 9000; fax: 020 7484 9001; email: info@londonmetric.com; website: www.londonmetric.com/our-company/responsible-business)

Directors: Alec Pelmore; Andrew Jones, Chief Executive; Andrew Livingston; Andrew Varley; Charles Cayzer; James Dean; Mark Stirling; Martin McGann, Finance Director; Patrick Vaughn, Chair; Philip Watson; Rosalyn Wilton; Valentine Beresford (women: 1; men: 11)

Year end	31/03/2016
Pre-tax profit	£82,742,000

Nature of business: Property development and investment.

Company registration number: 7124797

Subsidiary undertakings include: LondonMetric Liverpool Ltd; Metric Property Investments PLC; Riverway Estates Ltd.

UK employees: 35

Total employees: 35

Focus of giving: Small groups, local groups.

Community involvement	✓
Community contributions	✓
Company reports on anti-slavery	✓
CSR report	✓
CSR or charity committee	✓
Directors have other relevant posts	✓
Cash donations declared	✓
Charity partner(s)	✓
Company gives to smaller charities	✓
Employee-led support	✓
Gifts in kind	✓
Matched funding	✓
Pro bono	✓
Sponsorship	✓

Charitable donations

Cash UK (latest available):	2016	£20,000
Total UK (cash and in kind):	2016	£20,000
Cash worldwide:	2016	£20,000
Total worldwide (cash and in kind):	2016	£20,000

Community involvement

LondonMetric Property PLC looks to make a positive contribution to communities in areas local to its properties. Support is given in the form of cash donations and in-kind support, including pro bono work. Employees of the company take part with volunteering and LondonMetric matches their charitable giving and work. The 2016 Responsible Business Report explains that, during the year, the company formed a Communities and Charity Working Group 'to formalise our approach to community activities and charitable giving'.

An example of how a LondonMetric property contributed to its local area was provided in the Responsible Business Report. Kirkstall Bridge Retail Park in Leeds:

- Collaborated with Re'New to recruit staff
- Sponsored Kirkstall Festival for the fifth year
- Staff volunteering and pro bono work

Future plans

In the near future, the group has plans to extend its community and charitable involvement, at the same time as continuing with its local community engagement. The Responsible Business Report for 2016 explains that LondonMetric will publish a communities policy 'over the next year' to enable it to achieve the following charitable objectives:

> - Increased targeted giving to community causes local to our assets
> - Support of LandAid events and one employee-led charity event per annum

- Matching by LondonMetric of employee charity giving and work
- Encouragement of pro bono work and employee volunteering

Directors with other relevant posts
Rosalyn Wilton: trustee of the University of London, Vice-Chair of the Harris Federation and Chair of Governors of Harris Girls Academy.

Main locations
The company has an office in Mayfair, London, and properties in England, Scotland, Wales and the Isle of Man. For details of the whereabouts of properties, see the properties map on the website.

Community contributions

In 2015/16 the group made charitable donations totalling £20,000.

We could not determine a value of the group's in-kind contributions.

Applications

Apply in writing to the correspondent.

Lush Cosmetics Ltd

Health/beauty products

Correspondent: Charity Pot Team, 29 High Street, Poole, Dorset BH15 1AB (tel: 01202 641001; email: charitypot@lush.co.uk; website: www.lush.co.uk/tag/our-policies)

Directors: A. Gerrie; Karl Bygrave; M. Constantine; Ms M. Constantine

Year end	30/06/2015
Turnover	£326,456,000

Nature of business: The production and retail of cosmetic products.

Company registration number: 4162033

Subsidiary undertakings include: Lush Dublin Ltd; Lush (Ireland) Ltd; Lush Ltd; Lush Manufacturing Ltd; Lush (New Zealand) Ltd; Lush Retail Ltd.

Focus of giving: Human rights, environment, animal welfare, overseas projects.

Accredited Living Wage Employer	✓
Community involvement	✓
Community contributions	✓
CSR report	✓
CSR or charity committee	✓
Cash donations declared	✓
Employee-led support	✓
Gifts in kind	✓
Humanitarian aid: overseas	✓
Overseas giving	✓
Unregistered charities/NFP	✓

Charitable donations

Cash UK (latest available):	2015	£833,500
Cash worldwide:	2015	£4,800,000

Community involvement

Lush Cosmetics focuses its charitable giving on supporting small, grassroots organisations working in the areas of environment, human rights and animal protection. Lush looks to support less popular causes and organisations using education, campaigns and activism as a way to address global issues. Aside from supporting registered charities, Lush also supports non-violent campaign groups and other organisations not registered with the Charity Commission. Lush prefers to support projects looking to create a long-term change, which address the root causes of social issues. Funding is also given to projects that provide aid and support, such as an animal shelter or refugee support and advice groups.

Charity Pot
The principal manner in which Lush supports charities and good causes is through sales of its Charity Pot product, although it also runs various other initiatives in line with its charitable interests, such as a self-imposed Carbon Tax and the Lush Prize for research against animal testing.

Main locations
Various locations worldwide.

Community contributions

According to the 2014/15 annual report, Lush partners worldwide donated a total of £6.3 million to charities and other good causes (of the total amount donated, £4.9 was from Lush group and associate companies). The website notes that of the total amount donated in the last financial year, customers in the UK and Ireland raised £833,500 for vital and important grassroots campaigns and charities by buying Charity Pot. We have no other UK financial information available and take £833,500 as the UK figure.

Lush raises most of its funds through the sale of Charity Pot body lotion, which is sold in various sizes online and in shops. 100% of the retail price of the product, less VAT, goes to a variety of good causes. In this financial year Charity Pot was sold in thirty four countries. Lush also sell limited edition products, which raise funds for specific charities and campaigns. In the UK the May Day bath bomb raised £135,000 for badger conservation groups.

In addition to Charity Pot and limited-edition charity products, the UK, Sweden, Japan Hong Kong and Korea continued the carbon tax fund. A total of £246,000 was raised and £130,000 was donated from carbon tax funds. Money raised from the carbon tax is used to fund environmental campaign groups.

The Sustainable Lush (SLush) fund grew considerably where a total of £1.5 million was raised as a percentage of buying budgets in the UK and North America. Of this £909,000 was donated through the North American and UK funds mainly to permaculture farms and lush suppliers, to enable them to become more sustainable.

The Lush prize ran for another year and £250,000 was donated to the winners, all of which are working in the fields of research against animal testing.

In-kind support

Product donations
Individual Lush shops occasionally donate unwanted products to charities in their local areas which require products for their beneficiaries (for example, to women's refuges or homeless shelters).

Employee-led support

Volunteering
Staff volunteer their time through the company's Employee Volunteer Program. They also frequently participate in volunteer days with Charity Pot partners local to their shops or offices.

Through volunteer support and Charity Pot donations, the company is able to help both humans and animals who were impacted by hurricane Sandy in 2012 and the devastating 2011 earthquake and tsunami in Japan. The company co-ordinates efforts with charities to offer funding, volunteers and direct action to help others in times of need.

Commercially led support

Product sales
The FunD currently supports grassroots charities creating safe places for children to play in Japan, after the earthquake in 2011 caused a rupture at a nuclear plant, contaminating the area and making it too dangerous for children to play outside. For every bar of 'Fun' soap Lush sells, 10p will go into the FunD. This money is granted to projects providing fun and recreational activities for children living in challenging environments.

Exclusions

According to the funding guidelines, Lush does not support organisations that:

- Promote or support violence, aggression or oppression towards others
- Deny the human rights of others
- Are involved in cruelty or subjugation of animals, including testing on animals for research or using animals for human gain
- Force or coerce others to change their religious beliefs
- Harbour racism, prejudice or judge others on anything other than their own actions
- Are not making the effort to be environmentally responsible

In addition to the above exclusions, funding is not provided for schools or individual student expeditions and no contributions are made to sponsored walks/runs, fundraising initiatives or sponsor events.

Applications

Charity Pot grants

To apply for funding from the Charity Pot, an online application form must be completed. See the company's website for more details and funding guidelines.

If your application is successful you will be contacted in due course. Leave six to eight weeks to hear whether your application has been shortlisted or not.

Lush no longer accept applications on old forms emailed directly. Instead, use the new online application process.

Full details: www.lush.co.uk/article/charity-pot-funding-guidelines.

Man Group PLC

Financial services

Correspondent: Angeline Boothroyd, Company Secretarial Executive, Riverbank House, 2 Swan Lane, London EC4R 3AD (tel: 020 7144 1737; email: charitable.trust@man.com; website: www.man.com/GB/man-charitable-trust)

Directors: Andrew Horton; Dev Sanyal; Emmanuel Roman, Chief Executive; John Cryan; Jonathan Sorrell, Chief Financial Officer; Lord Livingstone of Parkhead, Chair; Matthew Lester; Nina Shapiro; Phillip Colebatch; Richard Berliand (women: 1; men: 9)

Year end	31/12/2015
Turnover	£866,351,000
Pre-tax profit	£140,481,000

Nature of business: The company is a global provider of alternative investment products and solutions.

Company registration number: 8172396

Subsidiary undertakings include: AHL Partners LLP; GLG Partners LP; Man Investments Ltd.

Total employees: 1,230

Focus of giving: Education, small groups, local groups.

Community involvement	✓
Community contributions	✓
CSR report	✓
Directors have other relevant posts	✓
Charity of the Year	✓
Charity partner(s)	✓
Company gives to smaller charities	✓
Corporate charity	✓
Employee-led support	✓
Gifts in kind	✓
Matched funding	✓
Payroll giving	✓
Pro bono	✓
Sponsorship	✓

Community involvement

The majority of Man Group PLC's community involvement is through its associated charity, Man Group PLC Charitable Trust (Charity Commission no. 275386).

Man Group PLC Charitable Trust

Man Group PLC Charitable Trust has two activities. Firstly, it supports organisations working to raise literacy and numeracy levels in the UK by making grants, either in response to applications or through partnerships with chosen charities. Secondly, it supports the charitable involvement of Man Group employees by providing volunteering opportunities and matched funding for employee fundraising activities and Give As You Earn donations.

According to its annual report, the trust focuses on supporting activities providing assistance 'directly to individuals, families and communities as well as those that increase the capacity of organisations and individuals'. The trust prefers to concentrate on supporting 'smaller charities where its donations make a material difference and where it can work in partnership with charities that are less likely to obtain support from the general public'. Preference is given to charities working in deprived areas of London.

Charity of the Year

The employee-nominated charity for 2014/15 was Children's Cancer Recovery Project.

Directors with other relevant posts

Dev Sanyal: member of Board of Advisors at The Fletcher School of Law and Diplomacy; Vice-Chair of the Centre for China in the World Economy at Tsinghua University.

Main UK locations

The group has two offices in London: its head office located in the City of London, and another office in Mayfair.

Community contributions

Man Group PLC's annual report and accounts for 2015 did not declare a figure for its community contributions.

In-kind support

Employee time

According to the annual report for 2015, through the 'Mankind Programme' employees are able to take 'the opportunity to take two additional days paid leave per annum to volunteer with charities supported by the Man Charitable Trust or with a charity of their choice'.

Employee-led support

Employee volunteering

Employees are encouraged to take up volunteering opportunities either with charities supported by Man Group or charities of their own choice. During 2015, employees volunteered in support of good causes in their local communities, and examples in the annual report include running programmes promoting financial literacy and reading sessions for pupils at primary schools, working to transform outdoor spaces and helping out at a local food bank.

Employee volunteering

Employees take part in a variety of fundraising activities. In 2015 these included skydiving, baking cakes and holding a Christmas jumper day in support of Man Group's annual charity, the Children's Cancer Recovery Project.

Payroll giving

The Give As You Earn scheme is in operation.

Matched funding

The Man Group PLC Charitable Trust matches, up to an agreed limit, contributions made by employees to any registered charities through fundraising or payroll giving.

Commercially led support

Sponsorship

The company has sponsored the Man Booker Prize for Fiction since 2002 and also sponsors the Man Booker International Prize. It is explained on the website that 'sponsorship of the prizes underscores Man Group's charitable focus on literacy and education as well as the firm's commitment to excellence and entrepreneurship'.

Partnerships

Man Group PLC has partnered SEO London and Investment2020 as part of its diversity agenda. SEO London is a not-for-profit organisation which, according to its website, works to promote educational and career opportunities for young people from 'under-represented and under-served backgrounds'. Investment2020 is a programme through which careers in investment management are promoted to a diverse range of people.

Corporate charity

Man Group PLC Charitable Trust (Charity Commission no. 275386).

Exclusions

According to the guidelines, Man Group PLC Charitable Trust does not generally support:

- Large national charities
- Charities which use external fundraising agencies

- Charities primarily devoted to promoting religious beliefs
- Endowment funds
- Requests to directly replace statutory funding
- Individual beneficiaries
- General media campaigns or campaigning or advocacy work to influence policy debates
- Applicants which have been successful during the last twelve months
- Work which has already been completed
- Capital projects and appeals
- Sponsorship or funding towards marketing appeals or fundraising events
- Organisations or projects whose primary purpose is political

Applications

See the trust's page on the Man Group website (www.man.com/GB/man-charitable-trust) where criteria and information on how to apply is available.

Manchester Airport Group PLC

Airport operators

Correspondent: Jack Carnell, CSR Manager, M.A.G Sustainability, 6th Floor, Olympic House, Manchester Airport, Manchester M90 1AA (tel: 0871 271 0711; email: jack.carnell@magairports.com; website: www.magworld.co.uk)

Directors: Angela Spindler; Baroness Elizabeth Symons; Charlie Cornish, Group Chief Executive; Christian Seymour; James Wallace; Ken O'Toole; Kieran Quinn; Manoj Mehta; Neil Thompson, Chief Financial Officer; Robert Napier; Sir Adrian Montague, Chair; Sir Richard Leese; Vanda Murray (women: 3; men: 11)

Year end	31/03/2016
Turnover	£778,800,000
Pre-tax profit	£117,200,000

Nature of business: The group is comprised of Manchester Airport; East Midlands Airport; Bournemouth Airport; and London Stansted Airport.

Company registration number: 4330721

Subsidiary undertakings include: Manchester Airport PLC; Ringway Developments PLC; Stansted Airport Ltd.

UK employees: 4,986

Total employees: 4,986

Focus of giving: Economic generation, education, enterprise/training, environment, animal welfare, small groups, local groups, older people, arts, culture, playgroups, children, young people, community/social welfare.

Membership: BITC, LBG

Community involvement	✓
Community contributions	✓
Company reports on anti-slavery	✓
CSR report	✓
CSR or charity committee	✓
Directors have other relevant posts	✓
Cash donations declared	✓
Charity partner(s)	✓
Community Mark	✓
Company gives to smaller charities	✓
Corporate charity	✓
Employee-led support	✓
Gifts in kind	✓
Pro bono	✓
Sponsorship	✓

Charitable donations

Cash UK (latest available):	2016	£735,416
Cash worldwide:	2016	£735,416

Community involvement

Each of the group's airports has a community fund through which grants are made to local causes. The group also sponsors arts initiatives and works with educational institutions in areas local to its airports.

Community funds

Each of the group's airports have a Community Fund, which provide grants to local charities and community groups. In 2015/16 grants made by the four community funds totalled £291,500 altogether.

Manchester Airport Community Trust Fund (Charity Commission no. 1071703)

Grants of up to £3,000 are awarded to charitable organisations for projects which are 'community, socially or environmentally focused' and benefit communities within a ten-mile radius of Manchester Airport.

East Midlands Airport Community Fund

Grants are available to community organisations in the specified area of benefit (refer to the map provided online) for projects which benefit the local community or environment.

Bournemouth Airport Community Fund

Grants of up to £2,000 are available to community organisations in the borough of Christchurch for projects which are focused on: bringing the community together through sport, recreation or leisure activities; environment or heritage conservation; environmental education; wildlife conservation.

Stansted Airport Community Trust (Charity Commission no. 1111200)

Grants are available for capital projects that benefit the local community within a ten-mile radius of Stansted Airport in a social, economic or environmental way.

More information on each of the community funds, including guidelines and application forms, are available on their respective websites – see 'Applications'.

Charity partner

The group's first national charity partner chosen by employees in 2015/16 is CLIC Sargent. The group has set a goal of raising £1 million for the charity.

Education

At Manchester, East Midlands and Stansted airports, the group has education centres called Aerozones, working in collaboration with local educational institutions, offering STEM activities to young people.

The group also works in partnership with schools such as Manchester Enterprise Academy, where it provides opportunities such as shadowing placements to students. There is also a focus on promoting international cultures and languages through school partnerships.

Arts

The group also provides sponsorship for arts initiatives in the regions where it operates (North West; Essex; Bournemouth; East Midlands). According to the website, the group particularly supports outreach projects, organisations that encourage wider community access to the arts, and projects with an 'international flavour'. In 2015/16 arts sponsorship totalled £370,000.

Directors with other relevant posts

Sir Richard Leese is leader of Manchester City Council. Vanda Murray is Chair of the Board of Governors of Manchester Metropolitan University. Robert Napier is Chair of Trustees of St Mungo's (Charity Commission no. 1149085) and a trustee of the Royal College of Surgeons (Charity Commission no. 212808) and treasurer of Watts Gallery (Charity Commission no. 313612). Kieran Quinn is leader of Tameside council and a trustee of The Mechanics Centre Museum of Labour and Trade Union History Trust (Charity Commission no. 519213). Baroness Elizabeth Symons is a former Deputy Leader of the House of Lords and is a trustee of The British Egyptian Society (Charity Commission no. 1134721).

Main locations

The group's airports are in Bournemouth; East Midlands; Greater Manchester; London Stansted.

Community contributions

The 2015/16 annual report states that charitable donations and sponsorships made by the group and its subsidiaries to local and national charities during the year totalled £735,500. This includes £291,500 given through the group's four community funds.

Employee-led support

Employee volunteering

In 2015/16 a total of 16% of the group's employees volunteered a total of 10,427 hours. Manchester and Stansted airports have established Airport Community Networks, which bring together other airport businesses to co-ordinate community activities and support already established initiatives.

Corporate charity

Manchester Airport Community Trust Fund (Charity Commission no. 1071703) and Stansted Airport Community Trust (Charity Commission no. 1111200).

Exclusions

Refer to the websites for exclusions from each of the community funds or from the group's arts sponsorship scheme.

Applications

Manchester Airport Group

The website states that if you have any questions or would like to get in touch with one of the local airport teams, you should contact the CSR team on jack.carnell@magairports.com.

Community funds

Application forms and guidelines are available on the website of each of the airport community funds.

Manchester Airport Community Trust Fund: www.manchesterairport.co.uk/community/working-in-our-community/community-trust-fund

East Midlands Airport Community Fund: www.eastmidlandsairport.com/community/supporting-the-local-community/charitable-giving

Bournemouth Airport Community Fund: www.bournemouthairport.com/community/community-support/community-fund

Stansted Airport Community Trust: www.stanstedairport.com/community/community-support/community-funds

Arts sponsorship

Arts sponsorship application forms are available online at: www.manchesterairport.co.uk/community/working-in-our-community/sponsoring-the-arts/arts-sponsorship-form.

Marks and Spencer Group PLC

Financial services, retail – clothing and footwear, retail – department and variety stores, retail – DIY/furniture, retail – supermarkets

Correspondent: Mike Barry, Director of Sustainable Business (Plan A), Waterside House, 35 North Wharf Street, London W2 1NW (tel: 020 7935 4422; website: corporate.marksandspencer.com/plan-a)

Directors: Alison Brittain; Amanda Mellor; Andrew Fisher; Andy Halford; Helen Weir, Chief Finance Officer; Laura Wade-Gery; Miranda Curtis; Patrick Bousquet-Chavanne; Richard Solomans; Robert Swannell, Chair; Steve Rowe, Chief Executive; Vindi Banga (women: 5; men: 7)

Year end	02/04/2016
Turnover	£10,555,400,000
Pre-tax profit	£488,800,000

Nature of business: The principal activities of the group are retailing clothes, beauty products, home products, food and the provision of financial services.

Company registration number: 214436

Subsidiary undertakings include: Marks and Spencer International Holdings Ltd; Marks and Spencer Outlet Ltd; Marks and Spencer PLC; Per Una Group Ltd; St Michael (Textiles) Ltd.

Brands include: Autograph; Blue Harbour; Per Una; Simply Food.

Total employees: 80,000+

Focus of giving: Education, enterprise/training, environment, health, ill health, housing, homelessness, overseas projects, humanitarian help, poverty and social exclusion, community/social welfare.

Membership: BITC, LBG

Community involvement	✓
Community contributions	✓
Company reports on anti-slavery	✓
CSR report	✓
CSR or charity committee	✓
AF Covenant	✓
Cash donations declared	✓
Charity of the Year	✓
Charity partner(s)	✓
Community Mark	✓
Company gives to smaller charities	✓
Employee-led support	✓
FTSE 100	✓
Gifts in kind	✓
Humanitarian aid: overseas	✓
Market-led giving	✓
Matched funding	✓
Overseas giving	✓
Payroll giving	✓
Pro bono	✓
Shared-value alliances	✓

Charitable donations

Cash UK (latest available):	2016	£9,900,000
Total UK (cash and in kind):	2016	£15,500,000
Cash worldwide:	2016	£9,900,000
Total worldwide (cash and in kind):	2016	£15,500,000

Community involvement

Marks and Spencer PLC (M&S) supports charities in the areas local to its stores and, at a corporate level, builds strategic partnerships with a number of fundraising partners. M&S stores can select either a 'Local Charity of the Year' or one of the company's corporate partners to raise funds for. Furthermore, each store has its own charity budget which can be used to support local charities with donations of up to £50. Employees and customers contribute to fundraising and employees are supported in their community involvement through volunteering time, payroll giving and matched funding.

Partner charities

The company has a particular focus on fundraising for health and well-being charities and has a commitment to raising £20 million by 2020; during 2015/16 a total of £5.25 million was raised. In October 2015, a new appeal was launched with Breast Cancer Now, with a total of £2.4 million raised through carrier bag sales and other fundraising activities. M&S cafes, food halls and Simply Food stores also participated in Macmillan Cancer Support's World's Biggest Coffee Morning which, along with other activities, raised more than £2.2 million, including £1 million by employees.

M&S also runs an initiative called 'Shwopping' in conjunction with Oxfam. Through the scheme, customers can donate items of clothing they no longer want. The initiative also ties in with the Sparks membership card scheme (see 'Commercially led support' for more information).

Other charity partners include: Collectively; Great Ormond Street Hospital; Marine Conservation Society; Newlife; Prostate Cancer UK; Shelter; The Royal British Legion; Unicef; Woodland Trust; WWF.

Employability programmes

Youth employment initiatives (which can be divided into two categories: Youth employment at M&S and Youth employment outside M&S) make up a central part of the company's community involvement. Its flagship work experience programme, Marks and Start, focuses on people from disadvantaged groups – including young unemployed people, people with disabilities, single parents, and people at risk of homelessness – and the company has also worked in partnership with The Prince's Trust on a programme called Make Your Mark. In total, M&S was able to provide more than 3,100 work placements in 2015/16. M&S, along with suppliers, partners and other companies, is also part of Movement to Work, which creates vocational training and work experience placements for young people.

M&S Community Energy Fund

M&S seeks to enable more communities in Great Britain to 'generate renewable energy and become environmentally and financially sustainable' through the fund, which was launched in July 2015. The website (www.mandsenergyfund.com) where more information is available, explains:

> If you've got a not for profit project that wants to use renewable energy to provide community benefits, this is your chance to secure funding! Whether you're a community energy group, a sports club or simply an organisation that wants to have a positive impact on the environment, we want to hear from you.

Directors also on trustee/other bodies

Robert Swannell: advisory board member of The Sutton Trust; trustee of the SpringBoard Boarding Bursary Foundation; and of the Kew Foundation.

Patrick Bousquet-Chavanne: board member of Collectively.org.

Helen Weir: independent non-executive director of the Rugby Football Union; trustee of Marie Curie Cancer Care.

Laura Wade-Gery: director of Royal Opera House Covent Garden Ltd

Miranda Curtis: board member of the Institute for Government and the Royal Shakespeare Company; Chair of Camfed.

Vindi Banga: on the governing board of the Indian School of Business

Community contributions

According to the Plan A Report 2016, Marks and Spencer made community contributions totalling £15.5 million. Based on previous years, we believe the majority of this was given in the UK. Contributions were distributed as follows:

Cash	£9.9 million
In-kind	£1.7 million
Time	£3.9 million

An additional £8 million was raised in leveraged funds, which are described in the report as being 'additional funds raised from other sources as a result of M&S activities'. We have taken this to represent funds raised by employees, customers and suppliers and so have not included this in our overall total for contributions.

We have taken cash donations to include £400,000 awarded from the M&S Community Energy Fund. In its inaugural year, there were 246 applications received by the fund, from which 132 projects were shortlisted to compete in a public vote. A total of 51,000 votes were cast and 21 winners were decided. Awards included two national prizes, one of £40,000 and another of £20,000, and 19 smaller awards of £12,500 each for regional projects.

Beneficiaries included: Hartlepool Community Solar for Schools (£40,000); Just Around the Corner (£20,000); Comunn Eachdraidh Nis, Dunvant Rugby Club, Hayle Swimming Pool, Penketh Scouts and Guides and The Easterside Partnership (£12,500 each).

In-kind support

Gifts in-kind

M&S donates unsold clothing, food and unwanted equipment to a range of charity partners. As of March 2016, all M&S operated stores in the UK can take part in a programme to donate surplus food to charities through the Neighbourly social network. The programme puts stores in contact with local charities that redistribute food.

Employee time

All colleagues in the UK and Republic of Ireland are allowed to take one day's paid leave to volunteer in their local communities. From 2015, the company will aim for at least 5,000 days to be contributed each year. In the first year, the company was successful in meeting this goal, with 5,000 colleagues taking part in the scheme.

Pro bono

During the year, 50 M&S data analysts took part in a 36 hour 'data dive', during which charity partners were helped to improve their use of data.

Employee-led support

Employee volunteering

Colleagues are encouraged to volunteer and fundraise for charities in their local communities and are given one day's paid time for volunteering purposes each year. At a national level, in 2015/16, more than 3,000 employees took part in The Big Beach Clean-Up, and more than 1,000 helped through Marks and Spencer's Spark Something Good Community Days in London, Dublin, Manchester, Swansea and Edinburgh.

Matched funding

Groups of employees (of five or more) who are fundraising can apply to have funds matched.

Payroll giving

The company operates a payroll giving scheme.

Commercially led support

Product sales

Each year, charities are selected from the company's existing list of partners to benefit from funds raised from charitable Christmas cards.

In October 2015 M&S also launched a re-usable shopping bag designed by the fashion designer Barbara Hulanicki. Made from upcycled hotel linen, the bags helped to raise funds to protect children in danger with profits donated to Unicef.

Sparks card

On registering for the Sparks loyalty card scheme, customers can choose a cause from a selected list of charities. Each time they make a transaction at M&S, their Sparks card can be scanned and M&S makes a donation of 1p to their chosen charity. Sparks members can also earn points by taking part in the Oxfam Shwopping scheme.

Exclusions

M&S stores are not able to help:

- Personal appeals on behalf of individual people, including overseas trips
- Advertising or goodwill messages
- Political parties
- Third-party fundraising on behalf of a charity
- Religious bodies, except where the project provides non-denominational, non-sectarian support for the benefit of the general project
- By supplying clothing, other than in exceptional circumstances, as they already give clothes to Newlife and Shelter

Applications

Small donations

Each store has a limited budget from which small donations of up to £50 can be made in support of local community causes. The company's website advises interested organisations to visit their local store and ask to speak with a manager.

Food redistribution

Charities that wish to take part in the recently-introduced M&S surplus food redistribution scheme need to create a profile on the website neighbourly.com, where more information is available.

M&S Community Energy Fund

In the first instance, see the fund's website (www.mandsenergyfund.com).

Initial applications are usually made online and are then considered by a team of judges who produce a shortlist. The shortlist of projects is then voted on by the public and the project with the most validated votes in each region will secure the funding. According to the fund's website, prizes are also given to projects the judges feel were inspiring and 'went the extra mile for their community' but didn't win the public vote. At the time of writing (August 2016) the applications round for 2016 had closed.

Marsh Ltd

Insurance

Correspondent: Corporate Social Responsibility Team, 1 Tower Place West, Tower Place, London EC3R 5BU (tel: 020 7357 1000; website: www.marsh.com/uk/about-marsh/corporate-social-responsibility.html)

Directors: Alexander Alway; Colin Kiddie; Jane Barker, Chair; John Hirst; Joseph Grogan; Mark Chessher; Mark Weil, Chief Executive Officer; Peter Box; Roy White; Sally Williams; Victoria Davison (women: 3; men: 8)

Year end	31/12/2015
Turnover	£776,100,000
Pre-tax profit	£197,300,000

Nature of business: Marsh is a global provider of insurance broking and risk management services with a presence in more than 130 countries.

The company is a wholly owned subsidiary of Marsh and McLennan Companies, Inc., incorporated in Delaware, USA.

Company registration number: 1507274

Subsidiary undertakings include: Central Insurance Services Ltd; Guy Carpenter and Company Ltd; Professional Claims Handling Ltd.

Focus of giving: Humanitarian help.

Membership: BITC

Community involvement	✓
Community contributions	✓
CSR report	✓
Cash donations declared	✓
Charity partner(s)	✓
Employee-led support	✓
Gifts in kind	✓
Humanitarian aid: UK including food banks	✓
Matched funding	✓
Payroll giving	✓

Charitable donations

Cash UK (latest available):	2015	£48,500
Total UK (cash and in kind):	2015	£48,500
Cash worldwide:	2015	£48,500
Total worldwide (cash and in kind):	2015	£48,500

Community involvement

The theme of Marsh's and its parent company's (Marsh and McLennan Companies – MMC) corporate social responsibility programmes is 'Helping People and Communities at Risk'. According to Marsh's UK website, philanthropy and employee volunteering are two of the central elements of its CSR programmes.

Donations: Marsh partner charities
The company administers its charitable donations programme centrally. It works closely with the Charities Aid Foundation to select eight national charities that fit into its core theme of 'Helping People and Communities at Risk'. Marsh's website explains how the chosen charities 'when viewed in the aggregate, address a broad spectrum of human need'. The company develops multi-year partnerships with the charities and agrees with each at the beginning of its involvement a specific project or activity which its donation will fund. Marsh then works with the charity to ensure the project or activity is achieved.

British Red Cross partnership
MMC and the British Red Cross joined forces in 2014 with the aim of raising £250,000 to provide emergency response vehicles, equipment and training across the UK. The British Red Cross website states that MMC employees have so far raised a combined amount of £130,000. The Marsh website further explains that 'MMC are committed to building more resilient communities by offering colleagues the opportunity to train in First Aid and volunteer their time and skills through selected projects'.

Main UK locations
The company has offices throughout the UK. Details of where they are located are available at www.marsh.com/uk/contact-us/office-locator.html.

Community contributions

In 2015 the company made donations to charitable organisations in the UK totalling £48,500. We believe this was received by the company's chosen national charities as well as through the matched funding scheme.

We were unable to determine costings for the in-kind support given by the company.

National charity beneficiaries for 2013–16 were: Business in the Community; Centre for Social Justice Awards; Genetic Alliance; London Symphony Orchestra; The Maritime London Officer Cadet Sponsorship; Over the Wall; Special Olympics Great Britain; Trees for Cities.

In-kind support

Employee time
Through Marsh's volunteering policy, employees can take one day per year to spend on an activity or programme that supports their community.

Employee-led support

Employee volunteering
Employees are involved in a range of volunteering activities their communities. These range from one day 'Team Challenges' to individual activities such as one-to-one mentoring. The Marsh website also details that: 'In addition, Marsh colleagues in our Bristol, Witham and London offices spend one lunchtime per week visiting local schoolchildren and helping them with their literacy and numeracy skills. In London, we have had a relationship with the Halley School since 1997.'

MAGIC (Matching and Giving for Involvement with Charities)
Through this programme Marsh matches employee fundraising efforts up to £300 per employee per year.

Payroll giving
Employees are able to contribute to charities of their choice through the Give As You Earn scheme. Payroll donations are topped up by 10% by Marsh.

Applications

Marsh's charitable donations programme is administered centrally, with beneficiaries proactively selected by Marsh through its work with the Charities Aid Foundation. More information on Marsh's community and charitable activities in the UK is available from the company.

Marshall of Cambridge (Holdings) Ltd

Defence, engineering, motors and accessories, aviation, property

Correspondent: Julie Ingham, Administrator of D. G. Marshall of Cambridge Trust, Airport House, The Airport, Newmarket Road, Cambridge CB5 8RY (website: www.marshall-group.co.uk)

Directors: Alex Dorrian, Chair; Christopher John Sawyer; James Buxton; Peter Harvey; Philip Yea; Robert Marshall, Group Chief Executive; Sarah Moynihan; Sean Cummins, Chief Financial Officer; Steve Fitz-Gerald (women: 1; men: 8)

Year end	31/12/2015
Turnover	£1,585,732,000
Pre-tax profit	£22,231,000

Nature of business: Marshall of Cambridge (Holdings) Ltd is the private holding company of the Marshall family. The Marshall group operates in four business sectors; it has three wholly owned businesses – Marshall Aerospace and Defence Group, Marshall Fleet Solutions and Marshall Group Property

– and is a majority shareholder of Marshall Motor Holdings PLC, an independent public company.

Company registration number: 2051460

Subsidiary undertakings include: Marshall Group Properties Ltd; Marshall of Cambridge (Engineering) Ltd; Marshall of Cambridge Aerospace Ltd.

Total employees: 4,767

Focus of giving: General charitable purposes, education, health, ill health, small groups, local groups, poverty and social exclusion, religion, science technology, children, young people, community/social welfare, disability.

Community involvement	✓
Community contributions	✓
CSR report	✓
Directors have other relevant posts	✓
AF Covenant	✓
Cash donations declared	✓
Company gives to smaller charities	✓
Corporate charity	✓
Employee-led support	✓
Gifts in kind	✓
Sponsorship	✓
STEM-focused	✓

Charitable donations

Cash UK (latest available):	2015	£191,000
Total UK (cash and in kind):	2015	£191,000
Cash worldwide:	2015	£191,000
Total worldwide (cash and in kind):	2015	£191,000

Community involvement

Marshall of Cambridge looks to make an active contribution in the communities in which it operates and principally in the area surrounding its group head office in Cambridge. Marshall's 'Code of Business Ethics' document explains that support in the form of cash and in-kind contributions is directed 'primarily to causes with educational, engineering and scientific objectives, as well as to social objectives connected with our business and our place in the wider community'.

The Group Strategic Report for 2015 further explains:

> At a Company level, we are proud to be members of the Percent Club and to be involved, at a senior level, often as trustees or directors with a number of local and national charities, including: BEN, the benevolent charity of the motor industry; the Addenbrooke's Charitable Trust; The East Anglian Air Ambulance; Ely Cathedral; and the Cambridgeshire Community Foundation.
>
> Marshall is also actively engaged with local organisations and membership groups which seek to sustain the success and growth of the greater Cambridge area, such as: Cambridge Network; Cambridge Ahead; Cambridgeshire Chambers of Commerce; Cambridge City Deal; and the Greater Cambridge Greater Peterborough Local Enterprise Partner.

Marshall does not have a chosen charity but rather encourages employees from across the group and at all levels to select their own community causes to support.

It would appear that much of Marshall's charitable support is channelled through D.G. Marshall of Cambridge Trust (Charity Commission no. 286468).

D.G. Marshall of Cambridge Trust

The trust was established in December 1982 by its settlor Marshall of Cambridge Aerospace Ltd (referred to in the trust's annual report and accounts as 'the Company'), Marshall of Cambridge (Holdings) Ltd and Marshall Motor Group Ltd. The trust's annual report for 2014/15 explains that 'initially the trust capital was £100 but since then further donations have been paid into the Trust by the settlor'.

The trust's primary objectives are to support:

- People who are in need, particularly those who are employees or ex-employees of 'the Company or any subsidiary or associated company' and their dependants
- Local charities
- Local educational institutions of a charitable nature

Grants are made to support local charities in Cambridgeshire as well as UK national charities.

According to the trust's annual report and accounts for 2014/15, during the year £46,000 was awarded in grants to around 40 charities in the following categories: aviation; disability, health and life threatening conditions; education; hospitals and related organisations; churches; children's charities; and local community.

STEM – LaunchPad

In 2015 Marshall established LaunchPad, a programme aimed at encouraging more young people between the ages of 8 and 18 to make decisions that could result in opportunities for careers in engineering and related industries. The Group Strategic Report 2015 states: 'This is not a recruitment tool but rather a scheme helping on a local level to address the woeful lack nationally of young people choosing to study STEM (science, technology, engineering and maths) subjects, especially among young girls ... We are committed to achieving a 50:50 spilt between boys and girls on the programme.' The programme is delivered through local schools in the Cambridge area, and is led by a group of young engineers and apprentices from Marshall. Participants benefitted from talks from LaunchPad 'ambassadors', visits to Marshall and various engineering-themed activities and competitions. In its inaugural year, the programme reached 650 children and young people; in 2016 the programme doubled in size to reach 15 schools and was expected to engage with more than 1,500 pupils.

Directors with other relevant posts

Robert Marshall: trustee of the D.G. Marshall of Cambridge Trust.

Sarah Moynihan: trustee of the Royal Aeronautical Society and governor of The Fields Children's Centre.

Christopher John Sawyer: trustee of Tomorrow's Company think-tank.

Philip Yea: trustee of The Francis Crick Institute.

Armed Forces Covenant

Marshall Aerospace and Defence Group is a signatory of the Armed Forces Covenant.

Main UK locations

Cambridge

Community contributions

In 2015 the group made charitable donations totalling £191,000. We believe that the majority of this amount was given to the D.G. Marshall of Cambridge Trust. We have taken this figure to also include donations made by group's subsidiary company Marshall of Cambridge Aerospace Ltd; these donations totalled £3,000, the largest of which was awarded to Children in Need.

Beneficiaries included: D.G. Marshall of Cambridge Trust; Children in Need.

In-kind support

Marshall of Cambridge (Holdings) Ltd provides accounting and administration service free of charge to the D.G. Marshall of Cambridge Trust.

Company time and resources

Marshall's 'Code of Business Ethics' document explains that employees can seek its support with their voluntary community involvement, in the form of time or resources, as long as they have received permission to do so.

Employee-led support

Employee volunteering

Employees at all levels are encouraged to be involved with their communities. The Group Strategic Report for 2015 explains:

> Involvement with extra-curricular activities directly benefits our employees and the Company, helping them to develop and nurture skills in a variety of environments and helping the Company to be an integral and active part of the various communities in which we operate. All employees are actively encouraged to be involved in the community, whether that be as a Reserve in the Armed Forces, a Governor in a school, a youth group leader, a charity fundraiser or trustee, a

parish councillor, a reading assistant, or any other similar role.

Employee fundraising
Employees of Marshall and its subsidiary companies raise funds for a wide range of charitable causes.

Commercially led support

Sponsorship
Marshall was a 2016 business sponsor of the city fireworks show in Cambridge.

Corporate charity

D.G. Marshall of Cambridge Trust (Charity Commission no. 286468).

Applications

Apply in writing to the correspondent.

Marston's PLC

Brewers/distillers

Correspondent: Corporate Social Responsibilty Committee, Marston's House, Brewery Road, Wolverhampton WV1 4JT (tel: 01902 711811; fax: 01902 429136; website: www.marstons.co.uk/responsibility/charity)

Directors: Andrew Andrea, Chief Financial Officer; Anne-Marie Brennan; Carolyn Bradley; Catherine Glickman; Neil Goulden; Nick Backhouse; Peter Dalzell; Ralph Findlay, Chief Executive Officer; Robin Rowland; Roger Devlin, Chair (women: 3; men: 7)

Year end	03/10/2015
Turnover	£845,500,000
Pre-tax profit	£91,500,000

Nature of business: Brewers and pub management.

Company registration number: 31461

Subsidiary undertakings include: Brasserie Restaurants Ltd; Celtic Inns Ltd; Marston's Pubs Ltd.

Brands include: Brakspear; Burton Bitter; Hobgoblin.

Focus of giving: Health, ill health, disability.

Community involvement	✓
Community contributions	✓
CSR report	✓
CSR or charity committee	✓
Directors have other relevant posts	✓
Employee-led support	✓
Gifts in kind	✓
Market-led giving	✓

Community involvement

Marston's staff and customers support good causes in their local areas in various ways, by taking part in fundraising activities. Marston's pubs assist by helping with collections, sponsored activities, the use of rooms, and publicity. Employees are supported in their fundraising activities by matched funding from the Marston's Inns and Taverns Charitable Trust (not a registered charity). There is also an employee charity fund, Marston's Employees Charity Fund (Charity Commission no. 513282) which is supported by donations from the company and makes grants for equipment to hospitals, schools for children with special educational needs and people with disabilities associated with Marston's.

Directors with other relevant posts
Ralph Findlay: Pro-Chancellor and Chair of the Governing Council at Keele University.

Peter Dalzell: Chair of Marston's Inns and Taverns Charitable Trust.

Nick Backhouse: director of Chichester Festival Theatre.

Carolyn Bradley: non-executive director of The Mentoring Foundation.

Main locations
Wolverhampton (head office). There is a local pub finder facility on the Marston's website (www.marstons.co.uk/pubs/finder).

Community contributions

The annual report and accounts for 2014/15 did not declare a figure for charitable donations. We do know that the company makes contributions to support the Employee Charity Fund, although we weren't able to determine a total figure.

In-kind support

The Marston's website states that its pubs 'assist by helping with collections, sponsored activities, the use of its rooms and publicity'.

Employee-led support

Employee fundraising
Marston's staff fundraise for a variety of local causes. According to the website, employees at Marston's Head Office take part with 'give back days' which feature activities such as cake sales and auctions.

Matched funding
Funds raised by Marston's employees are matched by the Marston's Inns and Taverns Charitable Trust. In 2015 these matched contributions amounted to £15,000.

Payroll giving
According to the website, employees give to the Marston's Inns and Taverns Charitable Trust voluntarily through their 'salary credit'.

Commercially led support

Market-led giving
In association with Help for Heroes, Marston's has produced a blonde ale which is on sale in 384 Tesco stores and in Marston's pubs. For each bottle sold in Tesco, five pence will be contributed to the charity and six pence will be donated from the sale of each pint of the ale in pubs. According to the Marston's website, sales of the ale have raised £49,000 for the charity.

Sponsorship
Marston's sponsors Pub is the Hub, a not-for-profit organisation working to support rural pubs and communities.

Applications

Apply in writing to the correspondent.

Mascolo Ltd

Health/beauty products, personal care products

Correspondent: Michela Lodovichi, 58–60 Stamford Street, London SE1 9LX (website: toniandguy.com/charity)

Directors: Christian Mascolo; Giuseppe Mascolo; Pauline Mascolo; Pierre Mascolo; Sacha Mascolo-Tarbuck (women: 2; men: 3)

Year end	31/08/2015
Turnover	£11,900,000
Pre-tax profit	£2,358,000

Nature of business: Hairdressing and other beauty treatments.

Company registration number: 770236

Subsidiary undertakings include: TONI&GUY Ltd.

Focus of giving: Health, ill health.

Community involvement	✓
Community contributions	✓
Corporate charity	✓

Charitable donations

Cash UK (latest available):	2015	£42,500
Total UK (cash and in kind):	2015	£42,500
Cash worldwide:	2015	£42,500
Total worldwide (cash and in kind):	2015	£42,500

Community involvement

Mascolo Ltd is the parent company of the 200 or so TONI&GUY hair salons in the UK, some of which are franchised or partially-owned by the company. The company's charitable giving, both cash and in kind, appears to be directed through the TONI&GUY Charitable Foundation (Charity Commission no. 1095285).

Community contributions

The TONI&GUY Charitable Foundation's accounts state that, in 2014/15, £42,500 was given through 'donated services' Mascolo Ltd, which we have taken to be the company's cash contributions for the year.

Employee-led support

Staff appear to be involved with the various initiatives led by the company's charitable foundation.

Corporate charity

TONI&GUY Charitable Foundation Ltd (Charity Commission no. 1095285).

Exclusions

The foundation does not make grants to individuals.

Applications

Those applying for grants to the TONI&GUY Charitable Foundation Ltd should write directly to Michela Lodovichi, Charity and Fundraising Co-ordinator, via email: charitablefoundation@mascolo.co.uk.

Mazars LLP

Accountants

Correspondent: The Company Secretary, Tower Bridge House, St Katherine's Way, London E1W 1DD (tel: 020 7063 4000; fax: 020 7063 4001; website: www.mazars.co.uk/Home/About-us/Corporate-Responsibility)

Directors: Antonio Bover; Dr Christopher Regierer; Hervé Helias; Hilton Saven; Liwen Zhang; Phil Verity; Philippe Castagnac, Group Chief Executive Officer; Victor Wahba (women: 1; men: 7)

Year end	31/08/2015
Turnover	£1,252,701,000
Pre-tax profit	£188,000

Nature of business: Mazars specialises in audit, tax and advisory services around the world.

Company registration number: OC308299

UK employees: 1,600

Total employees: 15,462

Focus of giving: General charitable purposes, local groups, overseas projects, poverty and social exclusion, community/social welfare.

Membership: BITC

Community involvement	✓
Community contributions	✓
Company reports on anti-slavery	✓
Directors have other relevant posts	✓
Cash donations declared	✓
Corporate charity	✓
Employee-led support	✓
Overseas giving	✓

Charitable donations

Cash UK (latest available):	2015	£250,000
Total UK (cash and in kind):	2015	£250,000
Cash worldwide:	2015	£250,000
Total worldwide (cash and in kind):	2015	£250,000

Community involvement

Mazars LLP donates a proportion its annual profits to various charities. It would appear that the way the group directs this charitable giving is through its corporate charity, the Mazars Charitable Trust (Charity Commission no. 1150459).

The Mazars Charitable Trust

The trust makes grants to charities that have been nominated by teams of employees. Grants typically range from £50 to £25,000. Examples of support in 2015 include a project to improve sanitary facilities and education in Kenya, and to a women's social and economic empowerment programme in Afghanistan.

LGBT

In 2014 Mazars set up a LGBT Champions network and entered the Stonewall Workplace Equality Index in 2015.

Business for good

Mazars is part of the Business for Good initiative. As part of this initiative in 2015, the group co-developed and launched the UN Guiding Principles Reporting Framework, a guide for companies to report on human rights issues.

Directors with other relevant posts

Phil Verity is a trustee of the Mazars Charitable Trust (Charity Commission no. 1150459), Access Accountancy (Charity Commission no. 1165776) and Milton Keynes Christian Centre (Charity Commission no. 1119304).

Main locations

The group operates in about 250 offices all around the world, 19 of which are based in the UK.

Community contributions

The 2015 UK review states that the group donated £250,000 to the Mazars Charitable Trust.

Employee-led support

Employee volunteering

Employees volunteer in their communities in Mazars Community Days, where employees can take a day away from the office to participate in community projects as a team. In 2015 teams were involved in over 30 different local charitable causes.

Employee fundraising

Individual Mazars employees raise funds through taking part in charitable events. For example, in 2015 a team of Mazars' employees took part in the Lloyd's of London rugby 7s charity tournament. The group's team wore rainbow laces in support of Stonewall's Kick it Out campaign.

Corporate charity

Mazars Charitable Trust (Charity Commission no. 1150459).

Applications

Charities cannot apply directly for funding but, rather, are nominated by Mazars partners and employees. Unsolicited applications will receive no response.

Sir Robert McAlpine Ltd

Building/construction, engineering

Correspondent: The Sustainability Team, Eaton Court, Maylands Avenue, Hemel Hempstead, Hertfordshire HP2 7TR (tel: 01442 233444; email: sustainability@srm.com; website: www.sir-robert-mcalpine.com)

Directors: Boyd McFee; Gavin McAlpine; Hector McAlpine; Jacqueline Mitchell-Innes; Mark Williamson; Martin Pitt; Miles Shelley; Robert McAlpine (women: 0; men: 8)

Year end	31/10/2015
Turnover	£782,000,000

Nature of business: The principal activities of the company include provision of building construction, civil engineering, design and project development services, also renewable energy systems.

Company registration number: 566823

Focus of giving: General charitable purposes, education, local groups, children, young people.

Community involvement	✓
Community contributions	✓
CSR report	✓
Cash donations declared	✓

Charitable donations

Cash UK (latest available):	2015	£716,500
Total UK (cash and in kind):	2015	£716,500
Cash worldwide:	2015	£716,500
Total worldwide (cash and in kind):	2015	£716,500

Community involvement

The company invests in the communities it operates in and seeks to establish links with local organisations, charities, schools, businesses and social enterprises. The Sustainability Report for 2015 states that over 200 community initiatives were undertaken during the year.

Charity partnership projects

The company provided support to The Prince's Trust's Get Into Construction scheme aimed at 18- to 25-year-olds, offering work placements with the company.

The Robert McAlpine Foundation (Charity Commission no. 226646)

The foundation generally supports charities with an income of less than

£1 million working in sectors it wants to support.

The McAlpine Educational Endowment (Charity Commission no. 313156)
This charity is aimed at 13- to 18-year-olds who have sound academic ability, show leadership potential and are facing financial hardship. The trustees favour ten particular schools, with referrals coming from the headteachers.

UK office locations
Birmingham; Bristol; Cardiff; Edinburgh; Glasgow; Manchester; Newcastle; Leeds; London.

Community contributions

In 2014/15 The Robert McAlpine Foundation received a donation of £500,000 from the company and paid a total of £681,000 in charitable grants.

In 2014/15 The McAlpine Educational Endowment received a donation of £75,000 from McAlpine and spent £90,000 in grants.

The Sustainability Report for 2014/2015 states that £141,500 was donated to charity. We have, therefore, used a figure of £716,500 for cash donations.

Commercially led support

The company is a founding partner of the Supply Chain Sustainability School (SCSS) – a free online educational tool for the registered members (currently 350) of the company's supply chain.

Applications

Apply in writing to the correspondent.

Applications to the charities
Enquiries regarding the two charities should be addressed to Gillian Bush, the charities' administrator (email: g.bush@srm.com).

McCain Foods (GB) Ltd

Food manufacture

Correspondent: Company Director, Marketing and Corporate Affairs, Havers Hill, Scarborough, North Yorkshire YO11 3BS (tel: 01723 584141; website: www.mccain.co.uk/about-mccain/our-community)

Directors: A. R. Bridges; Allison D. McCain, Managing Director; G. Dent; M. C. McCain; M. Hodge, Marketing Director; N. I. Vermont; R. A. Hunter; R. Jones; R. Smelt; S. N. Amin, Finance Director; S. W. Herd; W. A. Bartlett (women: 2; men: 10)

Year end	30/06/2015
Turnover	£440,066,000
Pre-tax profit	£63,714,000

Nature of business: Manufacturer and supplier of frozen and ambient food products principally in the UK.

Company registration number: 733218

Brands include: McCain.

Total employees: 1,373

Focus of giving: Economic generation, education, enterprise/training, environment, health, ill health, arts, culture, sport, recreation, children, young people, community/social welfare.

Membership: BITC

Community contributions	✓
Employee-led support	✓
Gifts in kind	✓
Humanitarian aid: UK including food banks	✓
Sponsorship	✓

Charitable donations

Total UK (cash and in kind):	2015	£31,000
Total worldwide (cash and in kind):	2015	£31,000

Community involvement

The company's community support programme focuses resources on local issues concentrating on: encouraging healthy, active lifestyles; educating the next generation and reducing food waste. McCain Foods also runs an engineering apprenticeship scheme and a scholarship programme for employees' children.

Main locations
Scarborough, Hull, Peterborough, Wolverhampton and Montrose.

Community contributions

According to the 2014/15 annual report, the company made charitable donations of £31,000. We have no information regarding the beneficiaries but have been advised previously that support is only given to charities and organisations in the company's local area.

In-kind support

During the year, McCain supported FareShare and in 2014 donated the equivalent of over 30,000 meals.

Employee-led support

Employees' voluntary work is supported by McCain Community Stars grant scheme. No details as to how this scheme operates could be found.

Applications

Applications should be made in writing to the correspondent.

McColl's

Retail – supermarkets

Correspondent: Paul Weaver, Company Secretary, McColl's House, Ashwells Road, Brentwood, Essex CM15 9ST (tel: 01277 372916; website: www.mccolls.co.uk)

Directors: Angus Porter; Georgina Harvey; James Lancaster, Chair; Sharon Brown (women: 2; men: 2)

Year end	29/11/2015
Turnover	£932,200,000
Pre-tax profit	£21,100,000

Nature of business: McColl's is a leading community retailer serving the Convenience and Newsagent sectors with a strong national presence throughout the UK. McColl's comprises over 1360 stores including over 950 convenience stores. Trading under our shop names of McColl's, Martin's and RS McColl.

Company registration number: 8783477

Subsidiary undertakings include: Martin McColl Group Ltd; Martin the Newsagent Ltd; Martin CTN Group Ltd; NSS Newsagents Ltd.

Focus of giving: General charitable purposes, health, ill health.

Community involvement	✓
Community contributions	✓
CSR report	✓
CSR or charity committee	✓
Cash donations declared	✓
Charity partner(s)	✓
Gifts in kind	✓

Charitable donations

Cash UK (latest available):	2015	£330,000
Total UK (cash and in kind):	2015	£330,000
Cash worldwide:	2015	£330,000
Total worldwide (cash and in kind):	2015	£330,000

Community involvement

Main locations
The company has various store locations throughout England; Scotland and Wales. The main office is based in Essex.

Community contributions

According to the 2014/15 annual report, the company raised £330,000 for local and national causes. We take this figure as the company's overall contribution. Unfortunately we have no information regarding the company's beneficiaries.

In-kind support

The company takes part in the Making A Difference Locally (MADL) campaign. The money raised goes to local good causes chosen by each store's manager and their customers.

Turning plastic bags into charity funds
The company raises charity funds through the mandatory 5p charge on plastic bags. Since the extension of this rule in October 2015 to include the whole of the UK, the company has been able to raise even more money for good causes. According to the 2014/15 annual report: 'We are currently set to raise around £600,000 a year in this way. So far, we have donated over £66,000 to St George's, University of London, and over £68,000 to various charities.'

Employee-led support

Colleagues and customers across the group took part in a range of fundraising events and made in-store donations for Halloween. In the year reported 2014/15 they raised over £195,000 for St Georges, University of London, to help fund research. McColl's has been raising money over the past few years every Halloween by way of colleagues and customers across the company taking part in a range of fundraising events. The money raised goes for research into sudden death in young adults.

Applications

Apply in writing to the correspondent.

McDonalds Restaurants Ltd

Retail – restaurants/fast food

Correspondent: Corporate Affairs Manager, 11–59 High Road, East Finchley, London N2 8AW (website: www.mcdonalds.co.uk/ukhome/Ourworld.html)

Directors: Douglas Goare; Jason Clark; John Park; Malcolm Hicks; Michael Flores; Paul Pomroy, Chief Executive Officer (men: 6)

Year end	31/12/2015
Turnover	£1,500,000,000
Pre-tax profit	£270,800,000

Nature of business: The principal activity of the company is the franchising and operation of a chain of limited menu quick service restaurants.

Company registration number: 1002769

Subsidiary undertakings include: Jardin Valley Restaurants; West One Restaurants Ltd.

UK employees: 35,879

Focus of giving: Education, environment, health, ill health, sport, recreation, children, young people, community/social welfare, disability.

Community involvement	✓
Community contributions	✓
AF Covenant	✓
Cash donations declared	✓
Charity partner(s)	✓
Employee-led support	✓
Gifts in kind	✓
Market-led giving	✓
Sponsorship	✓

Charitable donations

Cash UK (latest available):	2015	£422,000
Total UK (cash and in kind):	2015	£422,000
Cash worldwide:	2015	£422,000
Total worldwide (cash and in kind):	2015	£422,000

Community involvement

The group focuses supports on its corporate charity, Ronald McDonald House Charities. It also promotes children's reading and grassroots football through partnership initiatives, sponsorship and market-led giving.

Ronald McDonald House Charities

McDonald's UK makes its charitable contribution to its own charity, the Ronald McDonald House Charities (UK) (Charity Commission no. 802047), which provides free 'home away from home' accommodation for families of children in hospital and hospices across the UK. RMHC UK is one of a network of RMHC 'chapters' operating in countries throughout the world. The group also raises money for the charity through customer and employee-led fundraising activities.

Grassroots football

The group's Better Play initiative supports grassroots football. As a sponsorship partner of the four UK Football Associations, the group has a scheme to provide free kits to grassroots football teams and also runs community awards to recognise the contributions of volunteers.

Main locations

The group operates throughout the UK and worldwide. Its UK head office is in London.

Community contributions

In 2015 the group donated £1.2 million to Ronald McDonald House Charities (UK), of which £778,000 came from plastic carrier bag levies from Wales and Scotland. We have not included carrier bag levies in the total figure for the group's contributions. The group also provided in-kind support and office facilities.

The charity's 2015 accounts state that it also received £3.2 million from donations made by customers in collection boxes at McDonald's restaurants, which is its largest source of voluntary income.

Commercially led support

Sponsorship

In 2016 the group established a partnership with the Nuffield Farming Trust, sponsoring a scholarship for studying agriculture, land management, horticulture or the food chain.

The group also sponsors the Football Associations of England, Northern Ireland, Scotland and Wales and in 2016 sponsored the Rio Olympic Games.

Market-led giving

The group's Happy Readers campaign encourages families to read together, offering free book extracts in its Happy Meal products. In 2016 McDonald's announced a new partnership with the National Literacy Trust, Penguin Random House and author Jeff Kinney, to give away 11 million books during 2016, including extracts from Jeff Kinney's Diary of a Wimpy Kid series. In 2015 the group also worked with the Roald Dahl Literary Estate to provide extracts from Roald Dahl books in its Happy Meals.

Applications

The group's website states that it is fully committed to supporting Ronald McDonald House Charities so does not respond to unsolicited requests.

Mears Group

Services

Correspondent: Judith Herbert, Trustee of The Mears Foundation, Mears Group PLC Unit 1390, Montpellier Court, Gloucester Business Park, Brockworth, Gloucester GL3 4AH (tel: 0870 607 1400/ 01452 634600; email: mearsfoundation@mearsgroup.co.uk; website: www.mearsgroup.co.uk)

Directors: Alan Long; Andrew C. M. Smith; David J. Miles; David L. Hosein; Geraint Davies; Julia Unwin CBE; Michael G. Rogers; Peter F. Dicks; Robert Holt OBE; Rory Macnamara (women: 1; men: 9)

Year end	31/12/2015
Turnover	£881,100,000

Nature of business: Mears provide rapid response and planned maintenance services to Local Authorities and registered Social Landlords and provide flexible care for older people and individuals with disabilities.

Company registration number: 3232863

Total employees: 12,000

Focus of giving: General charitable purposes, children, young people.

Community involvement	✓
Community contributions	✓
CSR report	✓
CSR or charity committee	✓
Directors have other relevant posts	✓
Charity partner(s)	✓
Corporate charity	✓
Gifts in kind	✓

Community involvement

The Mears Foundation (Charity Commission no. 1134941)

The foundation supports many projects focusing on loneliness and gave grants to smaller UK charities with a particular focus on children and young people and older people. Volunteers have carried out a variety of fundraising events, including sponsored walks, buckets collections, bake sales and auctions.

Funds are targeted to those projects that are enabling isolated people to establish social networks. The specific aim of the foundation is to provide support through volunteering and hands-on help rather than solely providing financial support.

Partnerships
The group has a partnership with the Percy Hedley Foundation (Charity Commission no. 15943) which has ensured that Mears provides services for people with disabilities and their families. They now have work placements in their branches with the aim to develop employment opportunities for people with disabilities. According to the 2015 social value report, Mears have secured a corporate partnership with The Prince's Trust. The partnership will focus on the group's commitment to creating chances.

Directors with other relevant posts
Julia is Chief Executive of the Joseph Rowntree Foundation and the Joseph Rowntree Housing Trust. She has significant experience in the social housing sector.

Main locations
Birmingham; Bristol; Chippenham; Devizes; Dudley; Gloucester; Stroud; Swindon; Witney.

Community contributions

Our research suggest that the group's charitable giving is directed through its associated foundation; however, little information was identified regarding the group's charitable contributions to the foundation. It appears that most of the foundation's funds are raised through employee fundraising.

In-kind support

The group supports staff volunteering and fundraising.

Employee-led support

Fundraising
Due to the efforts of employees thousands of pounds have been raised for the Mears Foundation, to target projects that are enabling isolated people to establish social networks.

According to the social value report, the number of volunteering hours undertaken by staff from January to December 2015 totalled 11,000. The group's social value report explains in depth the fundraising events that staff have contributed to in support of various local charities. Examples included: the Exeter branch supervisor who raised more than £4,000 after completing a three-day, 150km trek in the Sahara desert for Devon Hospice Care; and Mears Gateshead Big Bake Day which raised funds for Metro Radio's Cash for Kids appeal.

Corporate charity

The Mears Foundation (Charity Commission no. 1134941).

Applications

Our research suggests that the group's charitable giving is directed through its associated foundation – see 'Community involvement' section.

Meggitt PLC

Engineering

Correspondent: Marina Thomas, Company Secretary, Atlantic House, Aviation Park West, Bournemouth International Airport, Christchurch, Dorset BH23 6EW (tel: 01202 597597; website: meggittinvestors.com/corporate-responsibility)

Directors: Alison Goligher; Brenda Reichelderfer; Colin Day; Doug Webb, Chief Financial Officer; Guy Berruyer; Paul Heiden; Philip Green; Sir Nigel Rudd, Chair; Stephen Young, Chief Executive (women: 2; men: 7)

Year end	31/12/2015
Turnover	£1,647,200,000
Pre-tax profit	£310,300,000

Nature of business: Meggitt PLC is a global engineering group specialising in extreme environment components and sub-systems for aerospace, defence and energy markets

Company registration number: 432989

Subsidiary undertakings include: Avica Ltd; Meggitt Aerospace Ltd; Microponents Ltd.

UK employees: 2,999

Total employees: 11,926

Focus of giving: Education, local groups, overseas projects.

Membership: BITC

Community involvement	✓
Community contributions	✓
CSR report	✓
Directors have other relevant posts	✓
Employee-led support	✓
Gifts in kind	✓
Overseas giving	✓
Sponsorship	✓
STEM-focused	✓

Community involvement

Meggitt supports communities in which it operates by providing cash or in-kind contributions to organisations benefitting the community. There is priority placed on educational initiatives and the group works with schools, colleges, universities and other programmes local to its facilities. Employees are also involved in supporting charities and community organisations.

Due to Meggitt's global presence, much of the Corporate Responsibility report for 2015 focuses on community activities in overseas locations, principally the United States. However, the report does provide a number of examples of how Meggitt supports initiatives in Dorset, where its UK head office is located:

- Poole Hospital NHS Foundation Trust: Meggitt is a long-standing funder of annual excellence awards for staff and, in 2015, Philip Green, an executive director at Meggitt, joined its board
- Dorset Community Foundation: according to the report, Meggitt regularly supports the foundation
- Julia's House: Meggitt supports the hospice which provides assistance across Dorset and Wiltshire to children who have life-limiting or life-threatening conditions and their families

Support of STEM subjects
Meggitt is a contributing sponsor of The Arkwright Scholarships Trust, which works to promote education in engineering in the UK through its scholarship scheme. Through its involvement with the trust, Meggitt provides mentoring to scholarship students.

Directors with other relevant posts
Philip Green: non-executive director of Poole Hospital NHS Foundation Trust.

Guy Berruyer: member of the Council of the University of Southampton.

Doug Webb: member of the Investment Advisory Committee of Fitzwilliam College, Cambridge University.

Main UK locations
Dorset (head office); Basingstoke; Birmingham; Coventry; Dunstable; Fareham; Loughborough; Rugby; Shepshed; Stevenage.

Community contributions

The annual report and accounts for 2015 did not declare a figure for charitable donations made during the year.

Applications

We suggest that requests are directed to your local Meggitt site, referenced 'Charitable support'.

John Menzies PLC

Distribution, logistics

Correspondent: Charity Fund Administrator, 2 Lochside Avenue, Edinburgh Park EH12 9DJ (tel: 0131 225 8555; website: www.johnmenziesplc.com/responsibility.aspx)

Directors: David Garman; Dermot Jenkinson; Dr Demot Smurfit, Chair; Forsyth Black; Geoff Eaton; Giles Wilson, Chief Finance Officer; Paul Baines; Silla Maisey (women: 1; men: 7)

Year end	31/12/2015
Turnover	£1,993,000,000
Pre-tax profit	£38,200,000

Nature of business: Logistics support services group.

Company registration number: SC34970

Subsidiary undertakings include: Menzies Distribution Ltd; Menzies Group Holdings Ltd; Princes Street (Jersey) Ltd; John Menzies Finance Ltd; Menzies Aviation PLC; Menzies Aviation Holdings Ltd.

Total employees: 25,600

Focus of giving: General charitable purposes, education, local groups, overseas projects.

Community involvement	✓
Community contributions	✓
CSR report	✓
CSR or charity committee	✓
Cash donations declared	✓
Employee-led support	✓
Overseas giving	✓
Payroll giving	✓

Charitable donations

Cash UK (latest available):	2015	£100,000
Total UK (cash and in kind):	2015	£100,000
Cash worldwide:	2015	£100,000
Total worldwide (cash and in kind):	2015	£100,000

Community involvement

The group looks to contribute to communities particularly in places where it has a presence. Apart from contributing 'skills and expertise' in its local areas, the group also makes charitable donations through its two funds, the Charities Fund and the John M. Menzies Community Fund. The group actively supports its employees' fundraising and volunteering activities.

Charities Fund

The group's Charities Fund supports a small number of charities which have been nominated by each operating division. Each dvision nominates charities based on efficiency, integrity and effectiveness criteria, specified in the 2015 annual report.

John M. Menzies Community Fund

The fund makes cash donations of up to £350 per individual or £700 per team for employees who are involved with a charity or community project. During the year over £10,000 was donated through this fund.

Community contributions

In 2015 cash donations from the group totalled £100,000. Of this, £45,000 was donated to support children's education, development and well-being across the company's areas of operation.

Beneficiaries included: Room to Read

Employee-led support

Payroll giving

The group supports its employees in their charitable activities and operates a payroll giving scheme.

Employee fundraising

The group actively supports employees in their fundraising activities. During the year a team of employees raised £4,700 for the British Heart Foundation by walking 96 miles along the Westhighland Way.

Applications

Unsolicited applications are not considered. Nominations are made by the group's divisions.

Merck Sharp & Dohme Ltd

Pharmaceuticals

Correspondent: Grants Committee, Hertford Road, Hoddesdon, Hertfordshire EN11 9BU (tel: 01992 467272 (switchboard); email: grantscommittee@merck.com; website: www.msd-uk.com/responsibility/ethics-and-transparency/home.xhtml)

Directors: Gertraud Polz; Louise Houson; Richard Robinski; Simon Nicholson (women: 2; men: 2)

Year end	31/12/2015
Turnover	£596,815,000
Pre-tax profit	£31,015,000

Nature of business: MSD is the UK subsidiary of Merck and Co., Inc., which is headquartered in Kenilworth, New Jersey in the United States and specialises in discovering, developing, manufacturing and marketing pharmaceutical products for human and animal use.

There are four MSD sites in the UK: Hoddesdon, Hertfordshire (headquarters and pharmaceutical research and development laboratories); Cramlington, Northumberland (manufacturing); Milton Keynes, Buckinghamshire (animal health headquarters); and London (business development and licensing hub for Europe, the Middle East and Africa).

Company registration number: 820771

Subsidiary undertakings include: Continuum Professional Services Ltd; Nourypharma Ltd; Safe Patient Systems Ltd.

Total employees: 1,134

Focus of giving: Education, environment, health, ill health, medical research, science technology.

Community involvement	✓
Community contributions	✓
CSR report	✓
CSR or charity committee	✓
Gifts in kind	✓
Pro bono	✓
Sponsorship	✓

Charitable donations

Cash UK (latest available):	2015	£439,000
Total UK (cash and in kind):	2015	£440,000
Cash worldwide:	2015	£439,000
Total worldwide (cash and in kind):	2015	£440,000

Community involvement

Merck Sharp & Dohme Ltd (MSD) supports academic, charitable and government organisations, with the aim of 'bringing about better health outcomes for patients'. The company also works with and supports patient organisations 'to enable people to make informed choices about their health'.

UK locations

MSD has four sites in the UK, at: Hoddesdon, Hertfordshire; Cramlington, Northumberland; Milton Keynes; and London.

Community contributions

The company's annual report and accounts for 2015 did not declare charitable donations. However, there are two downloadable PDF documents available from the website which provide a breakdown of payments and donations made during the year. The first provides a breakdown of 'payments & donations to academic and other non-patient organisations' and the second provides a breakdown of 'payments to patient organisations'. We have used the information in these documents to calculate the company's charitable contributions during the year.

Academic and other non-patient organisations

In 2015 MSD gave financial support to academic and non-patient organisations totalling about £323,000. Note that this figure consists of grants paid in GBP totalling around £52,500, and grants paid in USD totalling $337,000 (approximately £270,000). We have not included expenditure such as membership fees or payments to think tanks in our total. The document further states that MSD donated a used fire engine, with an estimated value of £1,000, to the Whitewebbs Museum of Transport which we have taken to represent in kind support.

Beneficiaries included: European Calcified Tissue Society (approximately £84,500 'with a New Investigator Research Grant'); Liverpool School of Tropical Medicine (approximately £58,000 'to fund an HIV and Hepatitis C drug interactions website'); Newcastle University (approximately £40,000 'to fund projects aimed at educating school children and the local community about health-related issues, as part of the "Neighbour of Choice" grants programme'); Family Planning Association (£20,000 'to support the updating of "Unprotected Nation: The Financial Impact of Restricted Contraception Services" ').

Patient organisations

In 2015 the company gave financial support to patient organisations amounting to about £116,000. Note that this figure consists of payments given in GBP totalling around £104,000 and payments given in USD totalling $15,000 (approximately £12,000). We have not included expenditure such as membership fees or sponsorship in our total.

Beneficiaries included: Heart UK (£39,000 for 'the development and launch of a report assessing cardiovascular disease prevention across health & wellbeing strategies in north west England'); Melanoma UK (£10,000 'to support the development of and information resource database/ spreadsheet on hospitals'); National Ankylosing Spondylitis Society (£10,000 'to fund the initial development of material and activities for "Wellbeing and AS" '); Arthritis and Musculoskeletal Alliance (£3,000 'to co-fund a seminar for clinical networks on the delivery of integrated, patient-centred care for people with musculoskeletal disorders')

For a complete list of grant recipients and projects supported by the company, view the document at www.msd-uk.com/ responsibility/ethics-and-transparency/ home.xhtml.

In-kind support

Pro bono

In previous years, MSD has provided staff to carry out work on behalf of other organisations. An example of this came in 2013 when a Patient Research Manager was provided to conduct a research project on behalf of North West London NHS Hospital Trust over the course of ten days.

Commercially led support

Sponsorship

Included in the 2015 payments documents detailed in the 'community contributions' section are examples of sponsorships. These include: £2,100 given to sponsor the National AIDS Trust's website migration and hosting from 2015 to 2017; £5,000 paid as annual corporate sponsorship of the Arthritis and Musculoskeletal Alliance; and £7,000 paid to sponsor the Positively UK patient conference.

Applications

To apply for a grant, email your request with details of your project to the correspondent.

Merlin Entertainments

Leisure

Correspondent: CSR Director, 3 Market Close, Poole, Dorset BH15 1NQ (tel: 01202 666900; website: www. merlinentertainments.biz)

Directors: Andrew Carr, Chief Financial Officer; Charles Gurassa; Fru Hazlitt; Ken Hydon; Nick Varney, Chief Executive Officer; Sir John Sunderland, Chair; Søren Thorup Sørensen; Trudy Rautio; Yun (Rachel) Chiang (women: 3; men: 6)

Year end	26/12/2015
Turnover	£1,278,000,000
Pre-tax profit	£237,000,000

Nature of business: This is an entertainment company, running 115 attractions in 23 countries, in 4 continents. Examples of attractions in the UK include Alton Towers; Chessington World of Adventures; and Warwick Castle.

Company registration number: 5022287

Subsidiary undertakings include: Chessington World of Adventures Ltd; London Dungeon Ltd; The Millennium Wheel Company Ltd.

Brands include: LEGOLAND; Madam Tussauds; SEA LIFE.

Focus of giving: Education, environment, animal welfare, health, ill health, individuals, small groups, local groups, poverty and social exclusion, children, young people, community/ social welfare, disability.

Community involvement	✓
Community contributions	✓
CSR report	✓
Directors have other relevant posts	✓
AF Covenant	✓
Employee-led support	✓
FTSE 100	✓
Gifts in kind	✓
Pro bono	✓

Community involvement

The group's CSR strategy is called 'Being a Force for Good' and focuses mainly on support given through the group's two corporate charities, Merlin's Magic Wand, which provides days out and facilities for children in need, and the Sea Life Trust, which focuses on marine conservation. The group's attractions also provide local community outreach through in-kind support.

Corporate charities

The group has two corporate charities: Merlin's Magic Wand, and Sea Life Trust.

Merlin's Magic Wand (Charity Commission no. 1124081)

The charity provides days out at the group's attractions for children who are seriously ill or disadvantaged or who have disabilities, and their families. The charity also creates 'Merlin's Magic Spaces' for organisations such as hospices and hospitals for children who cannot visit Merlin attractions.

In 2015 the charity provided days out for almost 53,000 children; travel grants totalling £44,600; delivered four 'Magic Spaces'; and undertook 50 community outreach visits.

Sea Life Trust (Charity Commission no. 1149058)

The trust supports conservation projects focusing on oceans and marine life. The trust's areas of focus include: increasing marine protection; reducing plastic litter; combating overfishing.

Young people

The website states that the group also works with charities such as The Prince's Trust, Street League and Teens and Toddlers, providing mentoring, placements and careers support for disadvantaged young people.

Directors with other relevant posts

Charles Gurassa is a trustee of The English Heritage Trust (Charity Commission no. 1140351) and Migration Museum Project (Charity Commission no. 1153774), and he is a former trustee of Whizz-Kidz (Charity Commission no. 802872). Fru Hazlitt is a trustee of Downe House School (Charity Commission no. 1015059) and is also Chair of the Women's Leadership Group for The Prince's Trust (Charity Commission no. 1079675).

Main locations

Attractions in the UK are based in Alton, Staffordshire; Birmingham; Blackpool; Brighton; Chertsey, Surrey; Chessington, Surrey; Edinburgh; Gweek, Cornwall; Great Yarmouth; Hunstanton; Loch Lomond; London; Manchester; Oban; Scarborough; Warwick; Weymouth; Windsor; York. There are also attractions in North America; Europe; and Asia Pacific locations.

Community contributions

No figure was provided for the group's charitable contributions.

In-kind support

Community outreach

The group's attractions have various initiatives to involve their local communities. For example, Sea Life Brighton provides tickets to young people with additional needs through the local Gully's Days Out scheme; Legoland Windsor hosts visits and a Christmas party for children from a local hospice and provides annual passes for looked-after children.

Employee-led support

Employee volunteering and fundraising

Employees support Merlin's Magic Wand through helping with outreach activities and organising fundraising initiatives

Applications

Apply in writing to the correspondent.

Michelin Tyre PLC

Motors and accessories

Correspondent: See 'Applications', Campbell Road, Stoke-on-Trent, Staffordshire ST4 4EY (website: michelindevelopment.co.uk/support-community-organisations-charities)

Directors: François d'Avout; Geoffrey Alderman; Gillian Duddy; Guy Heywood; John Reid; John Young; Keith Shepherd; Philippe Berther (women: 1; men: 7)

Year end	31/12/2015
Turnover	£800,243,000
Pre-tax profit	(£41,077,000)

Nature of business: The manufacture and sale of tyres, tubes, wheels and accessories, maps and guides, and mobility support services.

Company registration number: 84559

Subsidiary undertakings include: Michelin Development Ltd; Michelin Solutions UK Ltd; Michelin Travel Partner UK Ltd.

UK employees: 2,343

Total employees: 2,343

Focus of giving: Education, environment, health, ill health, small groups, local groups, financial education, arts, culture, safety and crime prevention, science technology, children, young people, community/social welfare.

Membership: BITC, LBG

Community involvement	✓
Community contributions	✓
Charity of the Year	✓
Company gives to smaller charities	✓
Employee-led support	✓
Gifts in kind	✓
Pro bono	✓
STEM-focused	✓

Community involvement

Through its Community Involvement Programme, Michelin Tyre PLC looks to build relationships with charities, educational establishments and not-for-profit organisations that work to benefit the local communities in which it operates.

Priority is given to organisations working in Michelin's core focus areas, which are described on the website:

- **Education**: 'We are committed to developing creative thinkers for tomorrow's workplace. We foster and support programmes that build reading, literacy and numeracy skills within local schools. We also promote scientific and technical professions and encourage youth development through sport and culture. We believe these programmes nurture creativity and develop important life and work skills.'
- **Mobility, safety and environment**: 'We are committed to support programmes that reduce the impact of our activities on the environment. In addition, we look to support programmes that sustain our natural environment and promote green mobility. We work to educate, raise awareness of and sustain better mobility through road safety initiatives.'
- **Community enhancement**: 'We are committed to supporting programmes that enrich the quality of life for individuals and our communities as a whole. Providing support in Health and Human services should be considered and we also believe the Arts and our heritage are a powerful way to expose people to different cultures and celebrate the diversity of all people.'

Support can be given in the form of cash donations, in-kind contributions or 'personnel resources'. It is further explained that 'support is generally awarded for specific activities, not general operating costs, however some operating costs may be allocated for the administration of a project'. Charities with a national presence or which work on a national basis can also be supported.

Charity of the Year

In 2015 Michelin's Stoke-on-Trent team raised more than £10,000 for its Charity of the Year, Approach, which works with people affected by dementia and mental health problems.

Main UK locations

Ballymena; Dundee; Stoke-on-Trent.

Community contributions

A figure for charitable donations was not included in the annual report and accounts for 2015.

Employee-led support

Employee fundraising

Michelin employees in Stoke-on-Trent took part in a range of team and individual activities to raise funds for the 2015 Charity of the Year, Approach. Examples of activities and events included a staff breakfast club, a cycling challenge, a fashion show, the Approach 'Walk to Remember' and the Potteries Marathon.

Commercially led support

Michelin Development

A subsidiary of the company is Michelin Development Ltd, which was established to support the creation of sustainable employment in the areas around Michelin's operations. Through Michelin Development, small and medium-sized businesses (SMEs) can apply for either financial assistance in the form of unsecured loans at subsidised interest rates, or business advice and expertise, or both. The Michelin Development website (michelindevelopment.co.uk – where full information is available) explains that 'support is available to viable projects that can demonstrate the potential to create quality sustainable jobs'.

Exclusions

According to the website, the Community Involvement Programme does not support requests which relate to:

- Organisations that do not have tax-exempt status
- Individuals
- Political organisations, candidates or lobby organisations
- Organisations with a limited constituency or membership
- Travel costs for groups or individuals
- Advertising
- Organisations outside the United Kingdom
- Activities that are not in line with Michelin's corporate values and image

Support is not given for general operating costs, although some operating costs may be given for the administration of a project.

Applications

All applications must be supported by a completed application form, which is available to download from the website. Organisations must make sure that they meet the eligibility criteria before submitting an application. Forms should be returned to the relevant correspondent by email, along with any supporting evidence

Each Michelin UK site has its own community involvement contact:

- Ballymena: Ballymena-PRM@michelin.com
- Dundee: dawn.duncan@michelin.com
- Stoke-on-Trent: michelin.requests@michelin.com

National appeals can be submitted to christine.reynolds@michelin.com. Note that this 'National' contact should only be used for organisations that have a national presence or work on a national basis.

Applicants should allow 30 days for their request to be processed and responded to. Applications are acknowledged in writing. A new application must be submitted each year for ongoing projects.

Micro Focus International PLC

Business services

Correspondent: CSR Team/Charity Committee, The Lawn, 22–30 Old Bath Road, Newbury, Berkshire RG14 1QN (tel: 01635 565200; website: www.microfocus.com/about/responsibility/index.aspx)

Directors: Amanda Brown; David Maloney; Karen Slatford; Kevin Loosemore, Chair; Mike Phillips, Chief Financial Officer; Nick Braukmann; Stephen Murdoch; Steve Shuckenbrock; Tom Virden (women: 2; men: 7)

Year end	30/04/2015
Turnover	£834,539,000
Pre-tax profit	£91,427,000

Nature of business: Micro Focus provides software that enables companies to develop, test, deploy, assess and modernize enterprise applications.

Company registration number: 5134647

Subsidiary undertakings include: Micro Focus Group Ltd; Micro Focus Holdings Ltd; Micro Focus Ltd.

Focus of giving: Education, children, young people, community/social welfare.

Community involvement	✓
Community contributions	✓
CSR report	✓
CSR or charity committee	✓
Cash donations declared	✓
Charity of the Year	✓
Employee-led support	✓
FTSE 100	✓
Humanitarian aid: overseas	✓
Matched funding	✓

Charitable donations

Cash worldwide:	2015	£77,000
Total worldwide (cash and in kind):	2015	£77,000

Community involvement

Micro Focus supports its employees' participation in charitable activities through a matched-funding scheme and employee volunteering time. All initiatives supported follow the 'core themes of education and local community support'. In 2014/15 the company's fundraising focus was on Doctors Without Borders for the first six months before switching to a broad range of local charities and initiatives supported around Micro Focus operations.

The company has a local 'project grants' initiative through which 12 charity or community organisations 'with wide geographic spread across Micro Focus operations worldwide' benefitted during the year.

Main locations

The group has offices throughout the world with UK operations based in Berkshire.

Community contributions

In 2014/15 over $102,000 (£77,000) was raised and contributed by the company and its employees. $39,700 (£30,000) was given to local causes across seven countries, $49,600 (£37,500) was given to international causes, and $12,800 (£9,500) was donated to national causes in the UK, the USA and the Philippines. Employee-raised funds are not normally counted in our total figure for donations; however, a breakdown of corporate cash donations given in the UK was not included in the 2014/15 annual report.

Currency conversions were calculated at the time of writing (October 2016).

In-kind support

Employee volunteering

A number of employee days are allocated each month so that teams or individuals can volunteer for a selected charity or a community initiative.

Employee-led support

Matched funding

The company provides matched funding for selected employees' charity initiatives.

Applications

Apply in writing to the correspondent.

Microsoft Ltd

Computer software

Correspondent: UK Community Affairs Team, Microsoft Campus, Thames Valley Park, Reading RG6 1WG (email: ukprteam@microsoft.com; website: www.microsoft.com/en-gb/about/charities-communities)

Directors: Benjamin Orndorff; Cindy Rose, Chief Executive; Keith Dolliver (women: 1; men: 2)

Year end	30/06/2016
Turnover	£956,000,000
Pre-tax profit	£111,200,000

Nature of business: Microsoft Ltd is a subsidiary company of Microsoft Corporation – based in Redmond, Washington State, USA. It markets and supports systems, devices and applications software for business, professional and home use.

Company registration number: 1624297

Focus of giving: Education, enterprise/training, overseas projects, safety and crime prevention, science technology, children, young people, community/social welfare, disability, disasters.

Community involvement	✓
Community contributions	✓
Company reports on anti-slavery	✓
CSR report	✓
Charity partner(s)	✓
Employee-led support	✓
Gifts in kind	✓
Humanitarian aid: overseas	✓
Market-led giving	✓
Matched funding	✓
Overseas giving	✓
Payroll giving	✓
Pro bono	✓
Sponsorship	✓
STEM-focused	✓

Charitable donations

Cash worldwide:	2016	£108,000,000
Total worldwide (cash and in kind):	2016	£844,000,000

Community involvement

The group provides in-kind technological support, matched funding and payroll giving, and has a focus on young people and education.

Young people

Microsoft's YouthSpark initiative aimed to create opportunities for 300 million young people by 2015.

The group works in partnership with the charity UK Youth on its Generation Code programme, which teaches 16,000 'hard-to-reach' young people how to code, and gives them the opportunity to enter a national competition, The Generation Code Challenge, designing an app with a social action purpose in their community.

Microsoft IT Youth Hubs
In conjunction with its UK charity partner, UK Youth, Microsoft has funded 30 youth clubs, through which young people are trained as IT champions and peer-educate others in their communities.

Get On
The group's Get On programme aims to encourage young people to develop digital skills and introduce them to technology-based career opportunities. This is provided through its work with UK Youth as well as online resources and initiatives.

Online safety
The group works in partnership with the Internet Safety Foundation and the Child Exploitation and Online Protection Centre to promote internet safety.

For example, through its Safer Families initiative, Microsoft provides online support for parents as well as offering workshops run by a volunteer advisor in workplaces.

Education
The group has a number of initiatives to promote STEM education, working in partnership with schools, businesses and organisations such as Computing At School to provide resources for teachers and schools.

Digital inclusion
To promote online accessibility and inclusion, the group developed Microsoft Digital Literacy, a programme designed to teach and assess basic computer technology skills to people so that they can use them in day-to-day life and can access new social and economic opportunities.

Main locations
The group's UK head office is in Reading. There are also offices in Cambridge; Edinburgh; London; and Manchester.

Community contributions

No figure was given for the group's UK charitable contributions.

The worldwide 2015 CSR report states that globally, the group donated more than $922 million (around £736 million at the time of writing – January 2017) through in-kind technology donations to more than 120,000 charitable organisations and cash donations totalled $135 million (around £108 million) worldwide.

In-kind support

Hardware and software
Since 2006, Microsoft has been one of the companies working with the Technology Trust to provide software donations to eligible UK charities. The website states that it also offers charities and educational organisations subsidised refurbished PCs through the Microsoft Registered Refurbisher programme, and offers software design and development tools free of charge to students and educational organisations through Microsoft Imagine.

Office 365 for charities
Eligible UK charities may apply for Office 365 as a donation. A range of subscription plans are available, some of which provide the programme free of charge and others offer the programme at a discounted price.

Humanitarian support
Globally, the group provides technological support, in-kind and cash donations to assist with humanitarian efforts, such as the Nepal earthquake in 2015. The group supports organisations including Red Cross, Oxfam, Mercy Corps and International Rescue Committee.

Employee-led support

Employee volunteering and fundraising
Employees are encouraged to volunteer in their communities through the employee volunteering policy operated by the company. There is a worldwide corporate giving programme, through which employees donated $177 million (around £141 million) in 2015.

Matched funding
Microsoft will match funds raised for charity up to a value of £7,500 per employee.

Commercially led support

Sponsorship
Microsoft sponsors the Scouts' IT badge.

Applications

Software donations
Microsoft makes its software donations through Technology Trust. For more information see www.tt-exchange.org.

Office 365 options for charities
For more details of Office 365 donations or discounts see products.office.com/en-GB/nonprofit.

Low cost hardware
Microsoft runs a PC refurbishment scheme through which charities and educational establishments are able to access low-cost Windows devices. For more information see www.microsoft.com/refurbishedpcs.

Microsoft Digital Literacy Curriculum
Instructor Resources to support the teaching of the Microsoft Digital Literacy Curriculum are free online or to download from www.microsoft.com/digitalliteracy.

Note that Microsoft is only able to donate cash to selected major charity projects.

The Midcounties Co-operative

Financial services, miscellaneous, retail – supermarkets

Correspondent: Community Team, Co-operative House, Warwick Technology Park, Gallows Hill, Warwick CV34 6DA (01902 492235; email: communityteam@midcounties.coop; website: www.midcounties.coop/community)

Directors: Barbara Rainford; Bernadette Connor; Clive Booker; Donald Morrison; Ellie Freeman; Helen Wiseman, Vice President; Irene Kirkman; Jean Nunn-Price; Judith Feeney; Louise Pevreal; Matthew Lane; Olivia Birch; Patrick Gray, Vice President; Ruth FitzJohn, President; Steve Allsopp; Vivian Woodell (women: 10; men: 6)

Year end	23/01/2016
Turnover	£926,705,000
Pre-tax profit	£6,411,000

Nature of business: The Midcounties Co-operative is registered as an Industrial and Provident Society and has more than 500 trading sites operating within the food, travel, healthcare, funeral care, childcare, energy, post offices and flexible benefits business sectors. The society's website describes its 'heartlands' as being Oxfordshire, Gloucestershire, Buckinghamshire, Shropshire, Staffordshire, the West Midlands, Wiltshire, and Worcestershire. The society also trades in the surrounding counties and its energy, childcare, travel and flexible benefits businesses trade UK-wide.

Company registration number: IP19025R

Subsidiary undertakings include: Co-op Travel Services Ltd; Harry Tuffin Ltd; West Midlands Co-operative Chemists Ltd.

Brands include: Co-operative Food; Co-operative Funeralcare; Co-operative Travel.

UK employees: 8,693

Total employees: 8,693

Focus of giving: General charitable purposes, economic generation, children, young people, education, enterprise/training, environment, health, ill health, medical research, small groups, local groups, overseas projects, humanitarian help, poverty and social exclusion, women's issues, community/social welfare.

Membership: BITC

Community involvement	✓
Community contributions	✓
CSR report	✓
Directors have other relevant posts	✓
Charity partner(s)	✓
Community Mark	✓
Company gives to smaller charities	✓
Employee-led support	✓
Gifts in kind	✓
Humanitarian aid: overseas	✓
Humanitarian aid: UK including food banks	✓
Market-led giving	✓
Overseas giving	✓
Pro bono	✓
Sponsorship	✓

Charitable donations

Cash UK (latest available):	2016	£268,000
Total UK (cash and in kind):	2016	£651,500
Cash worldwide:	2016	£268,000
Total worldwide (cash and in kind):	2016	£651,500

Community involvement

As a co-operative business, Midcounties Co-op places great emphasis on supporting the communities in which it has a presence. The society's board has four key social goals which, according to the guidelines for its community fund, are:

- Supporting communities
- Defending the environment
- Developing young people
- Developing co-ops

Community Fund

Community groups and organisations can apply for grants of up to £2,000 from the society's Community Fund. The society's website explains: 'You must be a member of The Midcounties Co-operative and your group must be working in a community where there is a Midcounties store.'

Groups located within the following counties can apply for support: Staffordshire; Shropshire; West Midlands (Walsall, Wolverhampton, Sandwell and Dudley); Worcestershire; Gloucestershire; Oxfordshire; Buckinghamshire; Northamptonshire; and Swindon. Funding can also be given for groups located within specific postcodes in the following areas: Warwick CV5, CV8, CV10, CV36; and Birmingham B43, B62, B72, B90, B94, B97. The Community Fund's guidelines state that groups should be based 'no more than five miles away from the nearest Midcounties trading branch'.

The guidelines further outline examples of expenditure grants can be given to assist with:

- The purchase of equipment
- The costs of putting on a local event or workshop
- Staff costs to enable the employment of individuals, contribution to rent costs (related to activities/service delivery)
- The cost of attending a conference or event which provides training for volunteers
- Additional activities to expand an existing funded project
- Activities that meet an identified need in the local community, funding to support an organisation to achieve a quality or other standard, relevant to their activities
- Assisting the development of a local service or venue for the good of the community

See 'Applications' for information on how to apply.

Regional Communities

In 2015 the society worked with its members and colleagues to develop its Regional Community strategy. The Social Responsibility Report 2015/16 explains: 'Our programme works by colleagues and members working together to identify relevant local community opportunities, and collectively taking action to make a positive difference in the community.' The programme is focused on 'the real Co-operative Difference' to 'put members at the heart of everything we do'. There were 20 Regional Community set up at the time of the Social Responsibility Report being written.

According to the Social Responsibility Report 2015/16, during the year, Midcounties Co-op colleagues and members worked together to make a difference in their Regional Communities in a range of ways, including:

- 9,000 colleague volunteering hours completed on focused Regional Community activity
- Over 1,000 young people have been engaged in our Regional Community activity, ranging from fairtrade workshops to learning about employability skills
- Our members, colleagues and customers have donated over 24,000 products to foodbanks, providing meals for over 450 families in need
- 40 members actively involved in supporting Regional Community projects, ranging from strategic input on local Steering Groups to supporting community events

Examples of the Regional Communities programme in action include:

- The Midcounties Co-operative's Oxley food store in Wolverhampton where colleagues joined together to collect hats, scarves, gloves, and toiletries, worth £100, which were given to P3, a charity working with people experiencing homelessness in the UK
- The food store in Highworth provides Highworth Community Clean Up with free storage space and has presented the group with £750 from carrier bag charges to purchase new cleaning equipment. The store has a close relationship with Highworth Community Clean Up, having provided refreshments for clean up activities and had colleagues volunteer with litter-picking activities

Charity partners

Between 2005 and 2015, more than £1.4 million has been raised for the society's charity partners, which have included Help the Hospices, the Outward Bound Trust, Teenage Cancer Trust and Women's Aid. Other examples of partnerships include:

- Midcounties Co-operative Funeralcare joined with the children's bereavement charity CHUMS to produce a series of DVDs designed to help parents, teachers, carers and other professionals support children to cope with the loss of a loved one
- The society is working with The Travel Foundation and Just a Drop to provide travel and tourism students at Walsall College Academy with lessons on sustainable tourism
- Since 2013, Midcounties Co-op has also supported the provision of clean drinking water to Sokoloko village in Zambia through a project run by Just A Drop's local partner Kaloko Trust. The well is now maintained by a local co-operative committee which fundraises within the community

Individual Midcounties Co-op trading branches can also support local charity partners.

Developing young people

In 2015 Midcounties Co-operative provided 189 work experience placements for young people across all of its trading groups. Furthermore, 90 young people completed the Green Pioneers programme which provided them with the opportunity to learn about co-operative values and sustainability. The Green Pioneers conference, held for the very first time during the year, was attended by 69 young people.

Directors with other relevant posts

Steve Allsopp: governor of Oaktree Nursery and Primary School (Swindon) and trustee of Buckhurst Community Centre.

Olivia Birch: governor of Tettenhall Special School (Wolverhampton).

Ruth Fitzjohn: Chair of 2gether NHS Foundation Trust; trustee of the Diocese of Clifton and Catholic Safeguarding Commission; trustee of Cheltenham Town Football Club Sporting and Educational Trust; trustee of Gloucestershire GP Educational Trust; patron of The Aston Project.

Ellie Freeman: governor of Coppice Junior School (Solihull, West Midlands).

Barbara Rainford: board member of Young Enterprise, Shropshire.

Main locations
See the 'Nature of business' section for information.

Community contributions

The annual report and accounts for 2015/16 state that £1.2 million was invested in community or co-operative initiatives during the year. Included in this figure is 'the money given out as grants, the amount raised for local charity partners, the value of our volunteering work and our annual investment in co-operative initiatives'. As we do not typically include funds raised by colleagues, members or customers (such as those in the examples below) or contributions for non-charitable purposes in our totals for corporate contributions, we have instead calculated a figure using on alternative figures that were available.

Cash donations and in-kind contributions
In a note to the financial statements titled '2.4 Payments to and on behalf of members', which is contained within the society's 2015/16 annual report and accounts, it is stated that £268,000 was given in charitable donations to community projects during the year. We have taken this figure to include the £140,500 noted in the Social Responsibility Report 2015/16 as having been distributed from the society's Community Fund 'to support grassroots community organisations across its trading area'.

The 'Community Volunteering' section of the society's website further states: 'Last year over 26,000 hours were volunteered by colleagues across our Society. If this work had been paid for it would have cost the beneficiaries a whopping £383,492.' We have attributed this contribution to the society. We were unable to determine the value of other in-kind contributions given by the society during the year.

Recent beneficiaries have included: FC Newlands – a football club in Cannock (£1,400); 1st Churchstoke Brownies; Bloodwise; Churchstoke Over 60's Club.

Member and customer fundraising
The annual report and accounts for 2015/16 state that members and customers raised more than £70,000 in aid of the Nepal earthquake appeal. Furthermore, an annual fun day held at the Churchstoke store in Powys raised £56,000 for local causes and the inaugural fun day in Cheltenham raise more than £17,000 for local charity partner, Riding for the Disabled.

In-kind support

Colleague volunteering programme
Every Midcounties Co-op colleague is entitled to take up to three days each year, within their usual working hours, for volunteering purposes.

Provision of free space
Highworth Community Clean Up is provided with free storage space by the Highworth food store.

Employee-led support

Colleague volunteering
The society's website explains that employees take part with a wide range of volunteering activities in their communities – 'anything from painting a church hall, to supporting employability events or one-to-one mentoring for young people from The Prince's Trust' can be considered.

Commercially led support

Sponsorship
Midcounties Co-operative sponsors the football kit of Walsall College's Supported Learning Football Team.

Exclusions

The guidelines document for Community Fund grants states that support cannot be given for the following:

- Non-members or where membership has not been in place for at least three months prior to application
- Individuals
- Groups which are currently a Midcounties Co-operative Local Fundraising Partner (exclusion only applies during the term of the partnership)
- Statutory (Government funded) organisations, including PCTs and schools*
- Religious worship – The Community Fund welcomes applications from religious or faith groups for projects that are designed to benefit the wider community. However, projects that are deemed to promote a particular religion are excluded from the scheme. For example, an application to refurbish a building that is owned by a particular religious group, but is open to members of the community outside that group, would be considered. An application for prayer mats or new bibles would not be supported
- Groups who are not constituted
- To fund trips abroad or overseas activities
- To fund improvements to property not owned by the applicant, or leased to the applicant for a period of less than 15 years
- Third party applications (groups who distribute funding to others)
- Party political activity

Grants cannot be awarded to groups which have received funding from The Midcounties Co-operative Community Fund within a certain period of time (refer to the guidelines for specific details).

*Independent groups within schools, such as PTAs, *can* apply.

Applications

Community Fund
In the first instance, it is essential to read the funding criteria, which is available to download from the website, to ensure that your group is eligible to apply for support. Eligible groups can then contact the community team (tel: 01902 492235; email: communityfund@midcounties.coop) to request a copy of the application form by post.

Note the following information which was obtained from the guidelines:

> To apply for funding the *applicant (individual submitting the form) must be a member of The Midcounties Co-operative and membership should have been in place for at least three months prior to application. Further details on membership can be obtained www.midcounties.coop/membership
>
> *The applicant must have proven personal involvement with the group applying for funding i.e. be a Member of the Group/ Group's Management Committee, is a service user, paid member of staff or a volunteer.

Community volunteering
Groups can find out more about the society's community volunteering scheme by contacting the community team (community.team@midcounties.coop).

Regional Communities
More information on the Regional Communities programme is available from the website (www.midcounties.coop/community/regional-communities).

Mitchells & Butlers PLC

Retail – restaurants/fast food

Correspondent: Sally Ellson, External Communications Manager, 27 Fleet Street, Birmingham B3 1JP (tel: 0121 498 4000/0121 498 4000; email: csr@mbplc.com; website: www.mbplc.com/responsibility)

Directors: Bob Ivell, Chair; Colin Rutherford; David Coplin; Eddie Irwin; Imelda Walsh; Josh Levy; Phil Urban, Chief Executive; Ron Robson; Stewart Gilliland; Tim Jones, Finance Director (women: 1; men: 9)

Year end	26/09/2015
Turnover	£2,101,000,000

Nature of business: Operator of managed pubs and pub restaurants.

Company registration number: 4551498

Subsidiary undertakings include: Mitchells & Butlers Retail Ltd; Mitchells

& Butlers Leisure Retail Ltd; Mitchells & Butlers Finance PLC.

Brands include: All Bar One; Browns; Crown Carveries; Harvester; Sizzling Pubs; Toby Carvery.

Total employees: 43,332

Focus of giving: General charitable purposes.

Community involvement	✓
Community contributions	✓
CSR report	✓
AF Covenant	✓

Charitable donations

Total UK (cash and in kind):	2015	£20,000
Total worldwide (cash and in kind):	2015	£20,000

Community involvement

Mitchells & Butlers looks to contribute to the local communities in which it operates, in the main, by supporting its employees in their fundraising for charities and good causes. The group and its brands have also supported charities through various initiatives including the sale of charity products and the organising of fundraising events.

Good Cause Fund

Retail employees can apply for a donation towards a community or charity event they are taking part in. During the year, the group donated £20,000 to a number of local charities and groups.

Main locations

The company has pubs and restaurants throughout the UK.

Community contributions

In 2014/15 the group donated at least £20,000 to charitable causes through the Good Cause Fund. A further £362,000 was raised by staff and employees through the Poppy Appeal, Daffodil Appeal and the Bake-A-Wish initiative.

Commercially led support

Over 200 Harvester restaurants participated in the Bake-A-Wish initiative which sees a donation from every dessert sold go to charity.

Applications

Apply in writing to the correspondent.

Mitie Group PLC

Business services

Correspondent: Sustainability Steering Group, 1 Harlequin Office Park, Fieldfare, Emersons Green, City of Bristol BS16 7FN (tel: 0117 970 8800; website: www.mitie.com/sustainability)

Directors: Jack Boyer; Larry Hirst; Mark Reckitt; Roger Matthews, Chair; Ruby McGregor-Smith, Chief Executive; Suzanne Baxter, Group Finance Director (women: 2; men: 4)

Year end	31/03/2016
Turnover	£2,232,000,000
Pre-tax profit	£96,800,000

Nature of business: The company provides facilities, property and asset management for public and private sector businesses.

Company registration number: SC 19230

Subsidiary undertakings include: Mitie Facilities Services Ltd; Mitie Cleaning and Environmental Services Ltd; Mitie Security Holdings Ltd.

Focus of giving: Enterprise/training, children, young people.

Membership: BITC

Community involvement	✓
Community contributions	✓
Company reports on anti-slavery	✓
Cash donations declared	✓
Charity partner(s)	✓
Corporate charity	✓
Employee-led support	✓
Gifts in kind	✓

Charitable donations

Cash UK (latest available):	2016	£477,500
Total UK (cash and in kind):	2016	£986,500
Cash worldwide:	2016	£477,500
Total worldwide (cash and in kind):	2016	£986,500

Community involvement

Mitie Group supports charities and communities through donations, gifts in kind and employee volunteering time. The majority of the group's charitable involvement is through The Mitie Foundation (Charity Commission no. 1148858), which looks to 'create opportunities for people of all backgrounds to join the world of work'. Grant-making is not the primary focus of the foundation and very few grants are made.

Though a definitive list of beneficiaries was not given, we know that individuals, schools and further education colleges across the UK have benefitted from the group's contributions.

Main locations

Bristol

Community contributions

In 2015/16 the group gave a total of £986,500 in charitable and community contributions, of which £477,500 was given in cash donations to charities. A considerable portion of this cash total was given to The Mitie Foundation.

Among its non-cash contributions, the group also gave gifts in kind worth £15,500 and contributed employee time, which was costed at £338,000.

In-kind support

In 2015/16 the group gave gifts in kind in the form of materials to its seven skills centres across the country. A total of 1,309 employee volunteering days were also contributed.

Corporate charity

The Mitie Foundation (Charity Commission no. 1148858).

Applications

The group is increasingly making its charitable contributions through its corporate charity, The Mitie Foundation, which does not accept any unsolicited applications, but instead actively seeks 'like-minded' organisations. For more details on the foundation, its work and partner organisations, see the web page (www.mitie.com/sustainability/the-mitie-foundation).

Moneysupermarket.com Group PLC

Miscellaneous

Correspondent: Community Team, Moneysupermarket House, St David's Park, Ewloe, Chester CH5 3UZ (tel: 01244 665700; email: community@moneysupermarket.com; website: corporate.moneysupermarket.com/company/csr.aspx)

Directors: Andrew Fisher; Bruce Carnegie-Brown, Chair; Darren Drabble; Genevieve Shaw; Matthew Price, Chief Financial Officer; Peter Plumb, Chief Executive Officer; Rob Rowley; Robin Freestone; Sally James (women: 2; men: 7)

Year end	31/12/2015
Turnover	£281,700,000
Pre-tax profit	£79,800,000

Nature of business: Price comparison websites.

Company registration number: 6160943

Subsidiary undertakings include: Moneysupermarket.com Financial Group Ltd; Moneysupermarket.com Ltd; MoneySavingExpert.com Ltd.

Focus of giving: General appeals, health, ill health, poverty and social exclusion, children, young people, community/social welfare, disability.

Community involvement	✓
Community contributions	✓
CSR report	✓
CSR or charity committee	✓
Charity of the Year	✓
Employee-led support	✓
Gifts in kind	✓

Charitable donations

Cash UK (latest available):	2015	£130,000
Total UK (cash and in kind):	2015	£130,000
Cash worldwide:	2015	£130,000
Total worldwide (cash and in kind):	2015	£130,000

Community involvement

Moneysupermarket.com PLC and its employees supported more than 30 charities and community groups during 2015 through the .Community initiative and a staff volunteering scheme. The group tends to support charities within a few miles of their offices in Flintshire. The group and its employees also select a Charity of the Year to support on an annual basis.

Main locations
Flintshire

Community contributions

During 2015, the group made £6,000 available each month for its .Community initiative, which was 'channelled via the Charities Aid Foundation, enabling the group to make gross donations to registered charities'. A further £58,000 was donated by the group to its Charity of the Year, The National Autistic Society. Therefore, we believe that the group made charitable donations totalling £130,000 during the year.

Costings for the in-kind support given by the group were not included in the report.

Beneficiaries included: Citizens Advice for Flintshire; Flintshire Deaf Children's Society; Flintshire Young Carers; Mold Alex U8s Football Team; North Wales Super Kids; Wepre PTA.

In-kind support

The group gives a total of 60 days a year through its staff volunteering scheme.

Employee-led support

Moneysupermarket.com employees play an active role in researching and finding local charitable causes for the group to help support. Each month, a volunteer group of employees meets to discuss requests for donations and to allocate funds in line with agreed guidelines.

Employee fundraising
During the year 19 employees took part in the Four Highest Peaks in Africa challenge to raise money for the Charity of the Year. In total employees helped to raise £48,500 for the group's Charity of the Year, the National Autistic Society.

Charity of the Year
In 2015 the National Autistic Society benefitted from corporate donations and employee fundraising worth a total of £58,000.

Applications

Apply in writing to the correspondent.

Morgan Advanced Materials PLC

Manufacturing

Correspondent: Paul Bolton, Company Secretary and General Counsel, Quadrant, 55–57 High Street, Windsor, Berkshire SL4 1LP (tel: 01753 837000; email: company.secretariat@morganplc.com; website: www.morganadvancedmaterials.com)

Directors: Andrew Shilston, Chair; Douglas Caster; Helen Bunch; Laurence Mulliez; Peter Raby, Chief Executive Officer; Peter Turner, Chief Financial Officer; Rob Rowley

Year end	31/12/2015
Turnover	£911,800,000
Pre-tax profit	£59,000,000

Nature of business: The group is an international provider of materials and products for its target niches, including aerospace, defence and protection, power generation, medical, petrochemical and iron and steel markets.

Company registration number: 286773

Subsidiary undertakings include: Morgan Advanced Materials Canada Inc.; Morganite Crucible Inc.; Morgan Korea Company Ltd.

UK employees: 1

Total employees: 6

Focus of giving: Health, ill health, medical research, arts, culture, children, young people, community/social welfare, disability.

Community involvement	✓
Community contributions	✓
CSR report	✓
Gifts in kind	✓
Sponsorship	✓

Charitable donations

Cash worldwide:	2015	£84,000
Total worldwide (cash and in kind):	2015	£840,000

Community involvement

According to the company's website, community engagement is focused at site level and involves initiatives that are relevant to the business and the local community. Business and group support is available.

In the past support has been provided to the Army Cadet Force Association (ACFA) Outreach Project (£60,000 over three years); continued support to the joint Barnardo's/Outward Bound initiative which provides opportunities for young people to develop life skills at a centre in Ullswater; and helping British Heart Foundation and a number of other sports and health-related charities and appeals.

Main locations
Berkshire

Community contributions

In 2015 a total of £84,000 was given in charitable donations. We could not determine what proportion of this figure was awarded in the UK.

Beneficiaries included: The Outward Bound Trust (£13,000).

In-kind support

Employee time and skills may be available.

Commercially led support

Sponsorship totalled £24,000 in 2015.

Applications

Apply in writing to the correspondent. Grant decisions are made by a donations committee which normally meets quarterly.

The group welcomes feedback on the community-related policies, systems, performance, reports and communications via email or post.

Morgan Stanley International Ltd

Financial services

Correspondent: Anish Shah, Morgan Stanley International Foundation, 25 Cabot Square, Canary Wharf, London E14 4QA (tel: 020 7425 1302; email: communityaffairslondon@morganstanley.com; website: www.morganstanley.com/globalcitizen/community_affairs.html)

Directors: C. E. Woodman; Christopher Castello; D. A. Russell; D. O. Cannon; E. J. W. Gieve; I. Plenderleith, Chair; J. Horder; Lee Guy; M. C. Phibbs; R. P. Rooney; T. Duhon

Year end	31/12/2015

Nature of business: The group's principal activity is the provision of financial services to corporations, governments and financial institutions.

Company registration number: 3584019

Subsidiary undertakings include: Morgan Stanley and Co. International PLC; Morgan Stanley and Co. Ltd; Morgan Stanley Bank International Ltd.

Focus of giving: Education, enterprise/training, health, ill health, housing, homelessness, medical research, overseas projects, arts, culture, children, young people, community/social welfare, disability.

Membership: BITC

Accredited Living Wage Employer	✓
Community involvement	✓
Community contributions	✓
CSR report	✓

Cash donations declared	✓
Gifts in kind	✓
Matched funding	✓
Overseas giving	✓
Pro bono	✓
Sponsorship	✓

Charitable donations

Cash UK (latest available):	2015	£2,900,000
Total UK (cash and in kind):	2015	£2,900,000
Cash worldwide:	2015	£2,900,000
Total worldwide (cash and in kind):	2015	£2,900,000

Community involvement

Morgan Stanley supports organisations in regions where it has a presence through the **Morgan Stanley International Foundation** (Charity Commission no. 1042671). This includes the boroughs of Tower Hamlets and Newham in London, Glasgow, as well as continental Europe, the Middle East and Africa. Grants are made to organisations focusing on children's health and education.

Morgan Stanley Foundation

The principal objective of the foundation is to make a sustainable impact to children's welfare in disadvantaged communities. Focusing primarily on child health and education, the foundation works in partnership with charitable organisations to direct funding and utilise expertise of Morgan Stanley employees to benefit the communities in which the group operates.

Main locations

Main UK locations – Glasgow and London. Morgan Stanley also has various locations worldwide.

Community contributions

The annual report and accounts for 2015 explain that during the year the group made donations to various charities totalling $3.6 million (£2.9 million), of which $1.8 million (£1.4 million) was donated to the Morgan Stanley International Foundation. We take the figure of £2.9 million as the group's worldwide charitable giving.

Exclusions

The website states that:

> MSIF does not make contributions to organisations that fall within the following criteria:
>
> - Organisations which are not registered as a non profit organisation with the appropriate regulatory agencies in their country (unless a state funded school)
> - National or International charities which do not operate in the regions we are located
> - Grants will not be made to either political or religious organisations, 'pressure groups' or individuals outside the Firm who are seeking sponsorship either for themselves (e.g. to help pay for education) or for onward transmission to a charitable organisation
> - Programmes that do not include opportunities for Morgan Stanley employee volunteer engagement.

Applications

It appears that the majority of the group's giving is through its charitable foundation.

The Morgan Stanley International Foundation

The foundation does not accept unsolicited proposals.

According to the website:

> If you think your organisation is a match for the criteria set out below, send an email to communityaffairslondon@morganstanley.com with the following information:
>
> - Program description, including mission, goals and numbers served
> - Measurement strategies
> - Geographic scope
>
> Note that due to the large number of quality proposals we receive, only applications that have been reviewed and are considered to fit within the MSIF priorities will be contacted directly.

Wm Morrison Supermarkets PLC

Retail – supermarkets

Correspondent: Sam Burden, Charity & Sponsorship Co-ordinator, Hillmore House, Gain Lane, Bradford BD3 7DL (0845 611 5364; email: foundation.enquiries@morrisonsplc.co.uk; website: www.morrisons-corporate.com/policy/charitable-giving-and-sponsorship)

Directors: Andrew Higginson, Chair; Belinda Richards; David Potts, Chief Executive Officer; Neil Davidson; Paula Vennells; Rooney Anand; Trevor Strain, Chief Financial Officer (women: 2; men: 5)

Year end	02/02/2015
Turnover	£16,122,000,000
Pre-tax profit	£217,000,000

Nature of business: Manufacture and retail distribution of goods through nationwide network of supermarkets.

Company registration number: 358949

Subsidiary undertakings include: Farmers Boy Ltd; Safeway Ltd; Wm Morrison Product Ltd.

UK employees: 120,913

Total employees: 120,913

Focus of giving: General charitable purposes, education, health, ill health, housing, homelessness, small groups, local groups, humanitarian help, older people, poverty and social exclusion, children, young people, community/social welfare, disability, disasters.

Membership: BITC

Community involvement	✓
Community contributions	✓
Company reports on anti-slavery	✓
CSR report	✓
CSR or charity committee	✓
AF Covenant	✓
Charity partner(s)	✓
Company gives to smaller charities	✓
Corporate charity	✓
Employee-led support	✓
FTSE 100	✓
Gifts in kind	✓
Humanitarian aid: UK including food banks	✓
Market-led giving	✓
Matched funding	✓

Charitable donations

Cash UK (latest available):	2015	£100,000
Total UK (cash and in kind):	2015	£100,000
Cash worldwide:	2015	£100,000
Total worldwide (cash and in kind):	2015	£100,000

Community involvement

Morrisons has a number of corporate programmes through which it supports charities and local community organisations throughout the UK.

The Morrisons Foundation

The foundation was set up in 2015 to provide financial support to registered charities in England, Scotland and Wales, with the aim of making a 'positive difference' in people's lives. Beneficiaries have included disability charities, educational projects, homeless shelters and hospices. As Morrisons has its roots in Bradford, charities in the city are particularly encouraged to apply. Morrisons' colleagues can also apply to the foundation for matched funding to support their fundraising activities.

The foundation receives its income from a number of sources and is the main beneficiary of funds raised through carrier bag sales in Morrisons' stores in England. It also receives income from carrier bag sales in Scotland and Wales. The foundation also benefits from some of the revenue generated by charity scratch cards and clothing banks at Morrisons' stores.

'Raise a Smile' National Charity partnership

The company's website explains:

> 'Raise a Smile' provides an overarching identity for our Charity Partnerships. It helps define our approach to developing and delivering effective partnerships with our chosen charities. Raise a Smile aims to do exactly what is says – for our customers, our colleagues and, of course, for the charities and their beneficiaries.

In February 2014, Sue Ryder became Morrisons' national charity partner. As of May 2016, customers and colleagues had managed to raise £5 million to help provide community healthcare services in areas where they are most needed.

Other national charities

In addition to the national charity partner, Morrisons helps to raise funds for other national charities and campaigns such as Children in Need, the Poppy Appeal and Movember. The Corporate Responsibility Review for 2015/16 explains: 'Last year we also supported the Walking with the Wounded Walk of Britain, a 1,000 mile trek to raise funds to support injured veterans to get back into work and achieve independence.'

Directors with other relevant posts

Andrew Higginson, Chair: non-executive director of the Rugby Football Union (RFU).

Paula Vennells: non-executive director and trustee for Hymns Ancient and Modern Group.

Modern Slavery Act 2015

The CR Review for 2015/16 states: 'Customers expect us to take responsibility for fair supply chain working conditions, protection of workers' rights and good relationships with our suppliers. This is a challenging and fast moving agenda to manage; highlighted by recent media coverage concerning hidden exploitation and the introduction of the UK Modern Slavery Act 2015'. Morrisons intends to publish a slavery and trafficking statement in line with the Modern Slavery Act 2015 Transparency in Supply Chains clause.

Main locations

Morrisons has supermarkets throughout the UK and the foundation makes grants across the country.

Community contributions

The annual report and accounts for 2015/16 did not declare a figure for charitable donations, nor could we determine a figure for the value of in-kind support given by the group. At the time of writing (November 2016), the Morrisons Foundation's annual report and accounts for the year were not yet available to view at the Charity Commission.

The Corporate Responsibility Review for 2015/16 states that £2.5 million was donated through the Morrisons Foundation 'to hundreds of local charities'; however, we were unable to determine how much of this was given directly by the group.

The review also explains that Morrisons donated £100,000 to support victims of the winter floods in 2015, which we have taken as the group's charitable donations for the year.

Furthermore, the review states that, in 2015/16, £20 million was raised in stores to support local and national causes – we believe this to include £2.5 million raised during the year for the national charity partner, Sue Ryder. As is our usual practice, we have not included funds raised by colleagues and customers in our figure for the group's charitable donations.

In-kind support

Surplus food

Morrisons works with partners – Company Shop, Community Shop and His Church – to ensure unsold food that is still safe to eat is redistributed to people who need it. Donations include fresh food as well as tinned and packeted goods. All Morrisons' stores can now take part in the programme. The Corporate Responsibility Review for 2015/16 explains: '0.5 million products donated in the first few months of the programme to over 400 community groups. 459 stores connected with a local charity with 428 donating on a weekly basis.'

Let's Grow

Since its launch in 2008, this programme – which closed in 2015/16 – provided schools with £20 million worth of gardening and cooking equipment.

Love Food Hate Waste (LFHW)

The CR Review for the year states that Morrisons supports WRAP's (The Waste and Resources Action Programme) campaign through its 'social media channels, website and internal communications' as well as providing 'information, hints and tips on how best to plan food shopping, store food and utilise leftovers to save money and reduce waste'.

Employee-led support

Community Champions

Each Morrisons store has a 'Community Champion' – a colleague who manages engagement between the store and groups and charities in its local community. Community Champions organise activities to help raise funds for local causes, as well as for the Morrisons' national charity partner. The company's website explains that 'the Community Champion co-ordinates in store fundraising for our national charity partnership, organises community bag packs, school and community tours and looks to support local events – plus a whole host of other activity, bespoke to each store'.

In 2015 Community Champions have also played an important part in the development of Morrisons' unsold food redistribution programme, developing relationships with community groups and organising food collections. During the year, the CR Review explains, Community Champions also took part in a training programme 'covering key aspects of the role and offering support, advice and guidance' and became Dementia Friends.

According to the review, £10 million was raised through Community Champion activity during the year.

Employee fundraising

Colleagues from Morrisons' stores, sites and head office raise funds through a varied range of activities – from individual running challenges to national in-store events such as Morrisons to the Moon and Communi-Tea Parties.

Matched funding

The Morrisons Foundation matches funds raised by colleagues for good causes (up to £1,000, two times per year).

Commercially led support

Product sales

Morrisons donates money from the sales of certain products to charitable causes.

Corporate charity

The Morrisons Foundation (Charity Commission no. 1160224).

Exclusions

The Morrisons Foundation only supports charities registered with the Charity Commission or OSCR.

Applications

The Morrisons Foundation

Applications for support can be made through the foundation's website (www.morrisonsfoundation.com), where more information is available.

Local opportunities

Enquiries regarding local support or in-kind contributions can be directed to your local store's Community Champion.

'Raise a Smile' National Charity partnership

The partnership between Morrisons and Sue Ryder came to an end in February 2017. The process for selecting a new partner ran between May and October 2016. The website explains: 'We are not currently looking for further sponsorship opportunities.'

Sponsorship

The Morrisons Foundation's website states: 'Unfortunately we're unable to support requests for sponsorship, although your local store may be able to provide a raffle prize, or food or drink for an event.'

Requests and comments that fall outside the above areas can be submitted via the contact form on the Morrisons' website.

Motorola Solutions UK Ltd

Electronics/computers, telecommunications

Correspondent: See 'Applications', Jays Close, Viables Industrial Estate, Basingstoke, Hampshire RG22 4PD (website: www.motorolasolutions.com/en_us/about/company-overview/corporate-responsibility.html)

Directors: Ian McCullagh; John Wozniak; Philip Jefferson; Tetyana Vasylevska (women: 1; men: 3)

Year end	31/12/2015
Turnover	£113,900,000
Pre-tax profit	£2,100,000

Nature of business: Motorola Solutions is a global provider of communication infrastructure, devices, accessories, software and services.

This record refers to Motorola Solutions UK Ltd, a UK-registered subsidiary company whose ultimate parent company and ultimate controlling party is Motorola Solutions, Inc., which is incorporated in the United States of America.

Company registration number: 912182

Subsidiary undertakings include: Motorola Solutions Services Ltd.

Brands include: ASTRO; MOTOTRBO; WAVE.

UK employees: 402

Total employees: 14,000

Focus of giving: Education, overseas projects, humanitarian help, science technology, disasters.

Community involvement	✓
Community contributions	✓
Company reports on anti-slavery	✓
CSR report	✓
Cash donations declared	✓
Employee-led support	✓
Gifts in kind	✓
Humanitarian aid: overseas	✓
Humanitarian aid: UK including food banks	✓
Matched funding	✓
Overseas giving	✓
STEM-focused	✓

Charitable donations

Cash UK (latest available):	2015	£3,000
Total UK (cash and in kind):	2015	£3,000
Total worldwide (cash and in kind):	2015	£10,270,000

Community involvement

Motorola Solutions UK Ltd supports community causes in the form of cash and product donations, as well as employee volunteering and fundraising activities. The company's community involvement, which is supported by the work of the Motorola Solutions Foundation, is part of the commitment Motorola Solutions Inc. (a global company incorporated in the USA) has in the communities in which it has a presence worldwide.

Motorola Solutions Foundation

According to the Motorola Solutions website, this US-based foundation was established in 1953 as the 'charitable and philanthropic arm' of Motorola Solutions. Each year, the foundation 'donates millions of dollars to science, technology, engineering and math education as well as public safety programs and disaster relief'. The foundation also facilitates employee matched giving programmes, both in the USA and around the globe.

The foundation operates several grants programmes across its chosen areas, including 'Innovation Generation (STEM) Grants' and 'Public Safety Grants' for organisations in North America. Organisations based outside North America are supported through the foundation's international grants programme.

The website explains: 'The International grant program supports programs that improve students' skills in science, technology, engineering and math (STEM) through hands-on activities or provide safety education and training to first responders, their families and the general public outside North America.'

More information on the international grants programme and the work carried out by the foundation can be found on the Motorola Solutions website.

According to the Motorola Solutions UK Ltd annual report, in 2015 the Motorola Solutions Foundation organisations supported by the foundation in the UK included:

- University of Bristol – support was given to the university's Enterprise Competition which helps find 'the newest technology entrepreneurs'
- University of Southampton – 'which received a grant to support robotics research among schoolchildren'
- Royal Academy of Engineering – 'to help fund a programme to create role models for young women in Engineering'
- Greenpower Education Trust – 'a charity with the goal to advance education in the subjects of sustainable engineering and technology to young people and to change current views about engineering, presenting it as a fascinating, relevant and dynamic career choice for any young person'

Main locations

Motorola Solutions has offices worldwide. Its UK office is located in Basingstoke, Hampshire.

Community contributions

According to the 2015 Corporate Responsibility Report, at a global level Motorola Solutions and the Motorola Solutions Foundation made corporate contributions, in the form of cash and product donations, totalling $12.6 million (approximately £10.27 million). This included 'employee matching gifts/volunteerism' contributed to a value of $1.4 million (approximately £1.14 million).

Of the total amount contributed by Motorola solutions worldwide, $1.2 million (approximately £978,000) was given in the Europe and Africa region, with the vast majority of contributions being made in the Americas.

Currency conversions were calculated at the time of writing (January 2017).

The annual report and accounts of Motorola Solutions UK Ltd 2015 declared donations to UK charities amounting to £3,000. We were unable to determine a value for in-kind donations given in the UK, nor were we able to determine if contributions from the Motorola Solutions Foundation were also included in this amount. It is, therefore, possible that the total amount contributed to charitable causes in the UK exceeded the figure declared in the annual report and accounts.

In-kind support

Support is given in the form of product donations and employee volunteering.

Employee-led support

Employee fundraising

During 2015, Motorola Solutions employees raised £3,000 for their chosen charities which included Comic Relief, the Diana Award, Macmillan Cancer Support and Save the Children. Worldwide, employees raised $900,000 (approximately £732,000) for charities.

Employee volunteering

The CR page on the Motorola Solutions global website states that 'more than 3,200 employees around the world dedicated 40,000 hours to their communities last year, serving as mentors, tutors, firefighters, science fair judges and more'. The global CR report states that 23% of employees took part with volunteering programmes.

We were unable to determine how many hours were contributed by employees in the UK, or the percentage of UK employees involved with volunteering activities.

Matched funding
According to the website, the Motorola Solutions Foundation provides 'employees with matching programs in the United States and globally'. We were unable to determine specific details of such activities in the UK.

Applications

In the first instance, see the Motorola Solutions Foundation page on the Motorola Solutions website where more information about the foundation and its international grants programme, including guidelines and dates of application rounds, are given.

National Express Group PLC

Transport and communications

Correspondent: The Employee Charity Panel, National Express House, Mill Lane, Digbeth, Birmingham B5 6DD (tel: 0845 013 0130; website: www.nationalexpressgroup.com/our-way)

Directors: Chris Muntwyler; Dean Finch; Dr Ashley Steel; Jane Kingston; Joaquín Ayuso; Jorge Cosmen; Lee Sander; Matthew Ashley; Matthew Crummack; Mile McKeon; Sir John Armitt (women: 2; men: 9)

Year end	31/12/2015
Turnover	£1,919,800,000
Pre-tax profit	£150,100,000

Nature of business: Principally the provision of passenger coach, bus and train services, operating in the UK, North America, Spain, Morocco and Germany.

Company registration number: 2590560

Subsidiary undertakings include: National Express Ltd; Euroline (UK) Ltd; Airlinks Airport Services Ltd; The Kings Ferry Ltd; West Midlands Travel Ltd; c2c Rail Ltd

Focus of giving: Enterprise/training, environment, overseas projects, children, young people.

Accredited Living Wage Employer	✓
Community involvement	✓
Community contributions	✓
CSR report	✓
Charity partner(s)	✓
Employee-led support	✓
Gifts in kind	✓
Overseas giving	✓

Charitable donations

Total UK (cash and in kind):	2015	£530,500
Total worldwide (cash and in kind):	2015	£530,500

Community involvement

The National Express Foundation (Charity Commission no. 1148231)
The foundation was launched in 2012 and is a key part of the group's community support in the UK, making grants to charitable and community groups working to 'support young people and promote cross-community cohesion'. The group's companies also conduct their own community initiatives in their respective countries.

The group's employees play a central role in its community involvement through volunteering, fundraising activities and a payroll giving scheme. In 2009 the group launched the Employee Charity Panel, which meets quarterly to identify and allocate funds to charities in the UK.

Partnerships
The group works with The Prince's Trust to provide transport for its Palace to Palace cycle ride as well as providing mentoring and work placements to young people. Similar work placements are also offered to young people from Whizz-Kidz.

Main locations
London

Community contributions

Across the group as a whole, charitable donations amounted to £530,500 during the year. The Employee Charity Panel, which supports UK employees who carry out fundraising or volunteer for community groups made 53 awards during the year.

The National Express Foundation also continued to provide bursaries to individuals and grants to organisations. In 2016 the group will give £150,000 to the foundation.

In-kind support

National Express Group donates surplus buses to community organisations.

Employee-led support

National Express Group actively encourages its employees to give charitably through 'volunteering and fundraising for local initiatives'. In the UK, employees can apply to the Employee Charity Panel for funding for charitable and community initiatives with which they are personally involved.

During the year the UK Bus section appointed community champions in each garage. The employees in each garage were also asked to select a charity which would become the beneficiary of any fundraising.

Applications

The company
Apply in writing to the correspondent.

National Express Foundation
Applications to the National Express Foundation can be made through its website: www.nationalexpressgroup.com/our-way/national-express-foundation.

The National Farmers Union Mutual Insurance Society Ltd

Insurance

Correspondent: James Creechan, NFU Mutual Charitable Trust, Tiddington Road, Stratford upon Avon, Warwickshire CV37 7BJ (tel: 01789 204211 (main swithboard); email: nfu_mutual_charitable_trust@nfumutual.co.uk; website: www.nfumutual.co.uk)

Directors: Adam Quinney; Brian Duffin; Chris Stooke; Christine Kennedy OBE; Eileen McCusker; Jim McLaren; John Elliot; Kim Arif; Lindsay Sinclair; Nick Turner; Richard Percy; Sally-Ann Hibberd; Steve Bower (women: 3; men: 10)

Year end	31/12/2015
Pre-tax profit	£410,000,000

Nature of business: National Farmers Union Mutual Insurance Society Ltd a mutual company providing insurance, pension and investment products and services.

Company registration number: 111982

Subsidiary undertakings include: Avon Insurance PLC; NFU Mutual Management Company Ltd; NFU Mutual Select Investments Ltd; NFU Mutual Risk Management Services Ltd.

Focus of giving: Economic generation, education, enterprise/training, environment, health, ill health, individuals, local groups, poverty and social exclusion, children, young people, community/social welfare.

Community involvement	✓
Community contributions	✓
CSR report	✓
Directors have other relevant posts	✓
Cash donations declared	✓
Charity partner(s)	✓
Corporate charity	✓
Employee-led support	✓
Gifts in kind	✓

Charitable donations

Cash UK (latest available):	2015	£532,000
Cash worldwide:	2015	£532,000

Community involvement

The NFU Mutual Charitable Trust (Charity Commission no. 1073064)
Established in 1998, the NFU Mutual Charitable Trust promotes and supports charitable causes in agriculture and rural development within the UK. In 2015 the

trust made donations of more than £200,000 to alleviate hardship, support future farming generations and improve the knowledge of the value of farming.

Charity partnership

In 2015 a new charity partner – Guide Dogs – was voted by employees with the target of £125,000 to be raised. By the end of 2015 the company's current and retired employees, and agents and their staff had exceeded the annual target and had raised more than £145,000.

The Community Giving Fund

The Community Giving Fund was set up in 2005 to support local initiatives and charitable events within the communities in which NFU Mutual operates. The Community Giving Fund (CGF) has donated in excess of £110,000 to help numerous community groups, charities, local hospices, schools and sports clubs. During 2015 more than £12,000 was donated to such groups across the UK.

Directors with other relevant posts

Chris Stooke is Chair of Chaucer Syndicates Ltd and Miles Smith Ltd, a non-executive director at Kings College Hospital, and a trustee and member of Council of the Royal School of Needlework.

Main location

Main office location is in Warwickshire.

Community contributions

Charitable donations during 2015 amounted to £532,000, which included a donation to the NFU Mutual Charitable Trust of £250,000 (which distributes awards at its discretion), £250,000 to the Farm Safety Foundation and £32,000 to the Community Giving Fund and charity matching fund.

In-kind support

Employee volunteering time and fundraising efforts.

Employee-led support

Fundraising

2015 saw the start of the new two-year charity partnership with Guide Dogs. During the year, NFU Mutual staff have raised £145,000 for the charity.

Employee volunteering

Each member of NFU Mutual staff is offered the opportunity to volunteer one day a year, along with their colleagues, to work on projects facilitated by one of the company's volunteering partners, including The National Trust, and its corporate charity. The 2015 annual report states that during the year 247 members of staff voluntarily gave 1,729 hours of their collective time to benefit communities close to their place of work, at the same time learning new skills, promoting collaborative working and gaining a sense of shared achievement.

Corporate charity

The NFU Mutual Charitable Trust (Charity Commission no. 1073064).

Applications

The NFU Mutual Charitable Trust

The NFU Mutual Charitable Trust (Charity Commission no. 1073064) was set up in 1998, to promote and support charities in the United Kingdom working in agriculture, rural development and insurance.

The application form is available from the website.

According to the website:

> Applications for funding for projects and initiatives falling within the Objects of the Trust can be made in writing to:
>
> The NFU Mutual Charitable Trust, Tiddington Road, Stratford upon Avon, Warwickshire CV37 7BJ; Email: nfu_mutual_charitable_trust@nfumutual.co.uk
>
> When making an application, details should be included of:
>
> - The project, initiative or organisation for which funding is sought
> - An indication of the amount of the donation requested
> - Any business plans
> - Details of any other funding sought and or obtained
> - Any recognition which would be given to the Trust in recognition of its support
> - Confirmation of whether or not the applicant is a registered charity
>
> Following a recent strategic review, the Trustees have indicated that in future, the Trust will focus on providing funding to larger initiatives, which would have a significant impact on the rural community. The Trustees are particularly interested in initiatives in the areas of education of young people in rural areas and relief of poverty within rural areas. The Trustees meet twice a year to consider applications received. These meetings are currently held in June and November.

The Centenary Awards: Further details on applications for Centenary Awards (for individuals) can be found online.

National Grid PLC

Electricity

Correspondent: Caroline Hooley, Corporate Responsibility and Sponsorships Manager, National Grid House, Warwick Technology Park, Gallows Hill, Warwick CV34 6DA (email: caroline.hooley@nationalgrid.com; website: www2.nationalgrid.com/responsibility)

Directors: Andrew Bonfield, Finance Director; Dean Seavers; John Pettigrew, Chief Executive; Jonathan Dawson; Mark Williamson; Nicola Shaw; Nora Mead Brownell; Paul Golby; Ruth Kelly; Sir Peter Gershon, Chair; Therese Esperdy (women: 4; men: 7)

Year end	31/03/2016
Turnover	£15,115,000,000
Pre-tax profit	£3,032,000,000

Nature of business: The principal operations of the group are the ownership and operation of regulated electricity and gas infrastructure networks in the UK and the US.

Company registration number: 4031152

Subsidiary undertakings include: National Grid Electricity Transmission PLC; National Grid Gas PLC; National Grid Holdings One PLC.

Total employees: 25,068

Focus of giving: Education, enterprise/training, environment, community/social welfare.

Membership: BITC, LBG

Community involvement	✓
Community contributions	✓
Company reports on anti-slavery	✓
CSR report	✓
Cash donations declared	✓
Employee-led support	✓
FTSE 100	✓
Gifts in kind	✓
Sponsorship	✓

Charitable donations

Total UK (cash and in kind):	2016	£7,985,000
Total worldwide (cash and in kind):	2016	£14,554,500

Community involvement

National Grid focuses a large part of its community involvement, both in the UK and the US, on education and skills development for young people in the form of cash donations, staff volunteering and sponsorship.

Community fund

Grants of up to £20,000 are available to charities and community organisations in areas where the work of National Grid impacts on communities.

Education

National Grid takes part in Careers Lab which is a programme for 11- to 16-year-olds which tries to make careers advice more relevant and inspiring for young people. The company also has an Energy Education Centre in London and supports the Queen Elizabeth Prize for Engineering.

Fuel poverty

Affordable Warmth Solutions CIC was set up by National Grid in 2009 and provides assistance to those in fuel poverty in deprived areas.

Charity of the Year

National Grid has recently come to the end of a two-year partnership with Macmillan Cancer Support.

Membership organisations
National Grid is a member of Business in the Community, Volunteering Matters and The Corporate Responsibility Group.

Main locations
London; Warwick; Wokingham; Leeds; Castle Donnington; Solihull; Manchester; Hinckley; Newark.

Community contributions

In 2015/16 community engagement and investment in education totalled £14.6 million. Of this figure £8 million was given in the UK; £6.6 million in the United States; and £3,100 in other countries. The London Benchmarking measurement framework was used to provide the figure which includes employee volunteering time, employee fundraising and support given to charity partners.

National Grid's Bringing Energy to Life Fund has made grants totalling £184,000 since its inception in December 2015.

In-kind support

Pro bono
National grid employees shared their time and expertise, giving more than 18,000 hours in aid of community causes, including towards environmental initiatives and projects for young people to improve their STEM skills.

Employee-led support

Employee volunteering
In 2015/16 over 14,000 hours of voluntary support was given to community projects across the UK.

Employee fundraising
Employees participated in various fundraising activities during the year. Over £600,000 was raised for Macmillan Cancer Support, which provided 3,121 emergency fuel grants to people affected by cancer. The Special Olympics GB was also supported with a donation of over £17,000.

Applications

For more information on community projects and volunteering, contact Kate Van Der Plank, Head of Community Investment (email: kate.vanderplank@nationalgrid.com.

For more information on corporate responsibility and sponsorships, contact Caroline Hooley, Corporate Responsibility and Sponsorships Manager (email shown above).

Applications to Bringing Energy to Life, the National Grid's community grants programme, can be made through its website: betl.nationalgrid.com.

Nationwide Building Society

Building society

Correspondent: The Nationwide Foundation, Nationwide House, Pipers Way, Swindon SN38 2SN (01793 655113; email: enquiries@nationwidefoundation.org.uk; website: your.nationwide.co.uk/your-news/articles/Pages/corporate-responsibility.aspx)

Directors: Chris Rhodes; David Roberts; Joe Garner; Kevin Parry; Lynne Peacock; Mai Fyfield; Mark Rennison; Mitchel Lenson; Rita Clifton; Tim Tookey; Tony Prestedge (women: 3; men: 8)

Year end	04/04/2015
Pre-tax profit	£1,044,000,000

Nature of business: The group provides a comprehensive range of personal financial services.

FSA registration number: 106078

Subsidiary undertakings include: Derbyshire Home Loans Ltd; E-MEX Home Funding Ltd; Nationwide Syndications Ltd; The Mortgage Works (UK) PLC.

UK employees: 17,500+

Total employees: 17,500+

Focus of giving: Economic generation, education, housing, homelessness, financial education, older people, poverty and social exclusion, community/social welfare.

Membership: BITC, LBG

Accredited Living Wage Employer	✓
Community involvement	✓
Community contributions	✓
CSR report	✓
CSR or charity committee	✓
Directors have other relevant posts	✓
Cash donations declared	✓
Charity partner(s)	✓
Community Mark	✓
Corporate charity	✓
Employee-led support	✓
Gifts in kind	✓
Matched funding	✓
Payroll giving	✓
Pro bono	✓
Sponsorship	✓

Charitable donations

Cash UK (latest available):	2015	£2,200,000
Total UK (cash and in kind):	2015	£3,400,000
Cash worldwide:	2015	£2,200,000
Total worldwide (cash and in kind):	2015	£3,400,000

Community involvement

Nationwide's community involvement is directed towards four areas of focus:

- Offering innovative and simple savings products
- Addressing low levels of numeracy and financial capability through education
- Encouraging young people to establish a savings habit
- Helping people to avoid and manage problem debt

Nationwide supports charities and community projects which have a 'tangible' impact on the communities close to its branches or admin centres. Support is given in the form of funding or of pro bono work. Preference is given to projects focused on the areas of housing, financial education and money management, and particularly projects where Nationwide's support has the potential to help unlock further funding or where its employees' skills and knowledge are useful.

Charity partners: Macmillan Cancer Support, Shelter.

The Nationwide Foundation
Nationwide is the main benefactor of The Nationwide Foundation (Charity Commission no. 1065552) which makes grants and social investment to create decent affordable housing for people who are in need. The Nationwide Foundation is a registered charity which was set up in 1997. Nationwide agreed to give a quarter of its 1% of pre-tax profit to donate to charitable causes from April 2008.

Directors with other relevant posts
Michael Jary (non-executive director) is Chair of Fairtrade Foundation (Charity Commission no. 1043886).

Main locations
Main UK location – Swindon.

Nationwide Building Society also has a number of branches throughout the UK.

Community contributions

According to the 2014/15 accounts, donations were made totalling £2.2 million including £1.5 to the Nationwide foundation. In addition the society has contributed employee time for volunteering programmes at a cost of £1.2 million, resulting in a total commitment to the community of £3.4 million.

In-kind support

Numeracy programmes
National Numeracy: A four-year partnership that aims to improve the numeracy skills of more than one million adults.

Talking Numbers: An educational programme to improve the everyday number skills of over 200,000 young people by 2017. The society works with teachers and partner organisations and has created a wide range of interactive activities.

Employee-led support

Employee fundraising

According to the 2014/15 accounts, fundraising for national and local charities totalled £1.7 million.

Matched funding

Nationwide matches employee fundraising.

Corporate charity

The Nationwide Foundation (Charity Commission no. 1065552).

Exclusions

No response is given to circular appeals. Support cannot be provided for advertising in charity brochures, animal welfare, appeals from individuals, medical research, overseas projects, political appeals, religious appeals, or for commercial (as opposed to community-related) sponsorship.

The foundation will not consider funding for the following:

- Charities with unrestricted reserves which exceed 50% of annual expenditure, as shown in their accounts
- Charities which are in significant debt as shown in their accounts
- Promotion of religion or politics
- Charities which have been declined by the foundation within the last 12 months
- Applications which do not comply with the foundation's funding criteria/guidelines

Applications

There are online forms through which charities can be nominated to receive funding or can request employee volunteers. They can be found on the 'Get involved' page on the 'Your Nationwide' section of the website: your.nationwide.co.uk/your-society/get-involved.

The Nationwide Foundation

For applications to the Nationwide Foundation (Charity Commission no. 1065552), further information can be obtained from the foundation's website (www.nationwidefoundation.org.uk). However, at the time of writing (November 2016) the foundation's website stated:

> Currently, the Nationwide Foundation is not accepting any new applications for funding. We are preparing for the next phase of our Decent Affordable Homes strategy, therefore organisations looking for funding should revisit the website to find out more in early 2017.

Nestlé UK Ltd

Drinks manufacture, food manufacture

Correspondent: Community Relations, 1 City Place, Gatwick, West Sussex RH6 0PA (tel: 020 8686 3333; email: community.relations@uk.nestle.com; website: www.nestle.co.uk)

Directors: D. Hix; David McDaniel; Fiona Kendrick, Chair and Chief Executive; M. McKenzie; N. Stephens; P. Hagmann; S. Stewart (women: 2; men: 5)

Year end	31/12/2015
Turnover	£1,579,085,000
Pre-tax profit	£112,714,000

Nature of business: Holding company of some of the interests of Nestlé SA businesses operating in the UK. Nestlé manufactures and sells food products, pet food products and associated activities. In the UK, the principal operating companies are Nestlé UK Ltd and Nespresso UK Ltd.

Company registration number: 51491

Subsidiary undertakings include: Buxton Mineral Water Ltd; Nespresso UK Ltd; Nestlé UK Ltd; Nestlé Waters (UK) Holdings Ltd; Purlaw Company; Vitaflo International Holdings Ltd

Brands include: Aero; Dolce-Gusto; Milky Bar; Nescafe; Purina Petcare.

Focus of giving: Education, health, ill health, overseas projects, children, young people, community/social welfare.

Membership: BITC

Accredited Living Wage Employer	✓
Company reports on anti-slavery	✓
CSR report	✓
Charity of the Year	✓
Charity partner(s)	✓
Company gives to smaller charities	✓
Employee-led support	✓
Humanitarian aid: overseas	✓
Humanitarian aid: UK including food banks	✓
Overseas giving	✓
Pro bono	✓
STEM-focused	✓

Community involvement

Nestlé supports the communities in which its 22 sites in the UK and Ireland operate. The company regularly joins forces with charities and other community partners to support good causes.

It works alongside community groups to promote healthier lifestyles and better education and runs three principal initiatives: Nestlé Academy in the Community; Nestlé Healthy Kids global programme; and a Charity of the Year scheme ('Charity of Choice').

Examples of relationships in the community include the group's direct engagement with local schools to promote the uptake of science, technology, engineering and maths subjects, raising awareness of good nutritional practices in schools via the PhunkyFoods programme, and support for local flood relief efforts as in York, Dalston and Tutbury. It is also involved in local charities, such as Nestlé Purina's involvement in the Wisbech Reads initiative to promote literacy.

Main locations

Nestlé operates in 22 sites across the UK and Ireland.

Community contributions

Nestlé Healthy Kids global programme (and PhunkyFoods partnership)

Nestlé launched its global programme in 2009 and, in 2012, partnered the organisation PhunkyFoods in an initiative to help teach children about healthy eating. The website states that Nestlé has pledged to invest more than £800,000 in the programme over three years to fund:

- The roll-out of the PhunkyFoods curriculum in local primary schools near our UK locations
- A team of nutritionists to help local schools to deliver the PhunkyFoods programme
- The development of a new PhunkyFoods website and online tools for parents
- A major research project by Leeds Metropolitan University to measure the impact of regular healthy lifestyle lessons on children's health

Charity of choice

Between 2012 and 2015 the company had a three-year partnership with Action for Children, which was selected by employees and raised £700,000. Employees selected Macmillan Cancer Care for 2016.

In-kind support

Pro bono

As part of Nestlé Ireland's partnership with the Jack and Jill Foundation, staff, in addition to fundraising, provided strategic advice for an advertising awareness campaign.

Nestlé is also involved in the community through a number of programmes:

Nestlé Academy in the Community

The Nestlé Academy was launched in 2012 to use its expertise to help young people in its communities. The programme has seen the company's involvement with a number of educational initiatives. Note that some of these initiatives appear to qualify also as being 'Commercially led'.

FareShare partner
Nestlé donated 185 tonnes of surplus food in 2015 to FareShare which contributed to 440,485 meals for people in need.

Employee-led support

Employee fundraising
During the year, employees raise funds for the company's Charity of Choice. In 2012–15 this was Action for Children and through a variety of activities including running and baking cakes £700,000 was raised. We were unable to ascertain the amount raised in 2015. For 2016 there is a new Charity of Choice – Macmillan Cancer Care.

Employee donations
The York site has its own employee charitable trust, which raises funds from employees to be donated in small grants to local organisations in which employees hold an interest. The trust is The Nestlé Rowntree York Employees Community Fund Trust (Charity Commission no. 516702).

Exclusions

Previous research indicates that no support is given towards student expeditions, individuals, political causes, third-party fundraising events or the purchase of advertising space in charity programmes.

Applications

Applications should be made to nearest local site. Our research indicates that few national financial donations are given.

Network Rail Infrastructure Ltd

Engineering, transportation

Correspondent: Charities Panel, Network Rail, 1 Eversholt Street, London NW1 2DN (email: charitablegiving@networkrail.co.uk; website: www.networkrail.co.uk/charities)

Directors: Bridget Rosewell; Chris Gibb; Jeremy Westlake, Chief Financial Officer; Mark Carne, Chief Executive; Michael O'Higgins; Richard Brown; Rob Brighouse; Sharon Flood; Sir Peter Hendy, Chair (women: 2; men: 7)

Year end	31/03/2016
Turnover	£6,098,000,000
Pre-tax profit	£411,000,000

Nature of business: Network Rail owns operates and maintains Britain's railway infrastructure.

Company registration number: 2904587

Subsidiary undertakings include: Network Rail (High Speed) Ltd; Network Rail Consulting Ltd; Network Rail Insurance Ltd.

UK employees: 37,481

Focus of giving: General charitable purposes, environment, health, ill health, non-registered charities, small groups, local groups, marginalised people, children, young people, community/social welfare.

Membership: BITC

Community involvement	✓
Community contributions	✓
Company reports on anti-slavery	✓
CSR or charity committee	✓
Directors have other relevant posts	✓
Charity of the Year	✓
Charity partner(s)	✓
Company gives to smaller charities	✓
Employee-led support	✓
Gifts in kind	✓
Payroll giving	✓
Unregistered charities/NFP	✓

Charitable donations

Total UK (cash and in kind):	2016	£1,969,000
Total worldwide (cash and in kind):	2016	£1,969,000

Community involvement

Network Rail's 2015/16 annual report states that the company is revising its approach to charitable giving from 2016/17 onwards. The company will now offer support through gifts in kind (time, premises, spare advertising hoardings, etc.) rather than making cash donations. Staff fundraising, payroll giving, and charity bucket collections will still continue to be supported.

The company supports communities through its Charity of Choice partnership, allowing charity bucket collections at stations, supporting local charities close to its routes, and offering disused land for the use of voluntary groups.

Charity of Choice
The company's employees nominate a charity to be supported over a number of years. Currently, the company's Charity of Choice until March 2019 is Barnardo's. Support given to the charity includes fundraising, payroll giving and employee volunteering.

The company's previous Charity of Choice partnership, with CLIC Sargent, ended in 2015/16.

Supporting local charities
Employees working on the company's eight routes (Anglia; Freight; London North Eastern and East Midlands; London North Western; Scotland; South East; Wales; Wessex; Western) organise fundraising and volunteering activities for local charities.

Note that the Route Charity Funding has now been discontinued. However, route panel members still facilitate local community investment through promoting volunteering opportunities, fundraising and payroll giving and are looking for local projects to support.

Partnership
Network Rail works with Samaritans to address the issue of attempted suicide on its network. For full information visit: www.samaritans.org/your-community/saving-lives-railway/suicide-and-railways/working-prevent-railway-suicide.

Directors with other relevant posts
Sir Peter Hendy is a trustee of the London Transport Museum (Charity Commission no. 1123122).

Rob Brighouse is a trustee of LIFE Trust (Charity Commission no. 1162380) and a director of Motionhouse Dance Theatre.

Sharon Flood is a trustee of the Science Museum Group and was formerly a trustee of Shelter (Charity Commission no. 263710), but left this position in 2015.

Mark Carne is a governor of Falmouth University.

Michael O'Higgins is Chair of the NHS Confederation.

Main locations
Network Rail operates throughout the UK. Its head office is in London.

Community contributions

The 2015/16 annual report shows that employees volunteered for a total of 11,500 hours during the year. The company has calculated this as being worth £168,500 based on the average salary rate. The report also notes that the company contributed the equivalent of £1.8 million to its Charity of Choice partner for the year, CLIC Sargent. This contribution is likely to have included donations, fundraising, volunteering time, gifts in kind and payroll giving. No details were available regarding how much the company contributed in cash donations alone.

In-kind support

Collections
Charities can apply to hold cash collections free of charge at the company's railway stations. This includes some of the busiest stations in Britain (Birmingham New Street; Bristol Temple Meads; Cannon Street; Charing Cross; Edinburgh Waverley; Euston; Glasgow Central; King's Cross; Leeds; Liverpool Lime Street; Liverpool Street; London Bridge; Manchester Piccadilly; Paddington; Reading; St Pancras; Victoria; and Waterloo).

Community scheme
The community scheme enables voluntary groups to utilise disused land owned by the company, such as old platforms, land adjoining stations and land underneath viaducts. Examples of

schemes include: litter picking; painting over graffiti; creating gardens, wildlife areas or food growing; and murals and artwork. The scheme is open to anyone, including: residents; transition towns; charities; rail partnerships; and local authorities.

Employee-led support

Employee volunteering

The company gives all employees up to five days of volunteering leave annually to enable work with UK-registered charities and Network Rail-led community engagement activity such as Community Safety work, early engagement and Community Rail work.

In 2015/16 employees gave 11,500 (2014/15: 11,000) hours as volunteers. Examples of volunteering activity included causes related to: hospices; homelessness; disability; STEM (science, technology, engineering and maths) support in schools; heritage railways; and environmental issues.

Exclusions

Support is not normally given to non-registered charities or for political appeals.

Applications

For national charities or enquiries about partnerships or the Charity of Choice, applications can be made by emailing the correspondent.

Local charities

To request more information on gaining support from the company, applicants must find their local route and contact the appropriate person as listed on the Network Rail website. These contacts are currently listed in the table at the bottom of the page.

Community scheme

To apply for a scheme to work on disused land owned by the company, call the 24-hour helpline on 0345 711 4141.

Charity Collections

For registered charities wishing to host a bucket collection in a Network Rail-operated station, download and complete the appropriate forms from the Network Rail website and return to the correspondent.

Promotional activities

Charities wishing to hold a promotional activity at a station (including flyers, leafleting, events, stands and stalls) are advised to contact Space and People via email: NetworkRail@spaceandpeople.co.uk.

Newcastle Building Society

Building society

Correspondent: Corporate Social Responsibility Team, Newcastle Building Society, FAO Corporate Social Responsibility, Portland House, New Bridge Street, Newcastle upon Tyne NE1 8AL (tel: 0191 232 0505; email: csr@newcastle.co.uk; website: www.newcastle.co.uk)

Directors: Andrew Haigh, Chief Executive; Angela Russell, Finance Director; Damian Thompson; David Buffham; Ian Ward; John Morris; Karen Ingham; Patrick Ferguson; Phil Moorhouse, Chair; Richard Bottomley; Ron McCormick (women: 2; men: 9)

Year end	31/12/2015
Turnover	£50,100,000
Pre-tax profit	£5,400,000

Nature of business: A building society based in the North East.

Company registration number: FCA No. 156058

Subsidiary undertakings include: Newcastle Financial Services Ltd; Newcastle Portland House Ltd; Newcastle Systems Management Ltd.

UK employees: 875

Total employees: 875

Focus of giving: General charitable purposes, education, enterprise/training, health, ill health, housing, homelessness, small groups, local groups, financial education, humanitarian help, older people, poverty and social exclusion, children, young people, community/social welfare, disability.

Membership: BITC

Community involvement	✓
Community contributions	✓
CSR report	✓
CSR or charity committee	✓
Directors have other relevant posts	✓
Charity of the Year	✓
Charity partner(s)	✓
Company gives to smaller charities	✓
Employee-led support	✓
Gifts in kind	✓
Humanitarian aid: UK including food banks	✓
Market-led giving	✓
Sponsorship	✓

Community involvement

The group supports charities and community groups in the areas where it operates, through its Community Fund. It also supports a group-wide partner charity and branches within the group support their own Charity of the Year. Employees provide support through volunteering and fundraising initiatives.

Newcastle Building Society Community Fund

Administered by Community Foundation Tyne and Wear and Northumberland (Charity Commission no. 700510), the Newcastle Building Society Community Fund awards grants to charities and community groups local to the group's branches. The fund's income is linked to one of the group's accounts products, the Newcastle Community Saver, receiving 0.1% of the total balances held in these accounts, in addition to income from employee fundraising. Customers can nominate projects to be considered for funding.

Partner charity

The group supports the Percy Hedley Foundation, through staff volunteering and fundraising.

Charity of the Year

Individual branches may adopt a charity to support with employee fundraising as their Charity of the Year. For example, the website states that the group's branch in Morpeth supported a local food bank in 2016, while the Carlisle Street Branch has previously supported The Glenmore Trust.

NETWORK RAIL INFRASTRUCTURE LTD

Route	Name	Email
Anglia	Chrissy Alderson	AngliaCharitiesPanel@networkrail.co.uk or Chrissy.Alderson@networkrail.co.uk
London North Eastern and East Midlands	Shannen Thorp	Shannen.Thorp@networkrail.co.uk
London North Western	Shelley Quinton-Hulme	Shelley.Quinton-Hulme@networkrail.co.uk
Scotland	Ben Hall or Kirstein Wright	Ben.Hall@networkrail.co.uk or Kirstein.Wright@networkrail.co.uk
South East	Angus McConchie	Angus.McConchie@networkrail.co.uk
Wales	Claire Partridge or Sarah Reardon	Claire.Patridge@networkrail.co.uk or Sarah.Reardon@networkrail.co.uk
Wessex	Kat O'Malley	Kathleen.O'Malley@networkrail.co.uk
Western	Caroline Matcham	Caroline.Matcham@networkrail.co.uk

Financial education

The group has a number of initiatives to promote financial education in the local community.

The Boardroom Charity Challenge programme provides education about managing money for children in schools across the North East and Cumbria, along with a competition to develop a business idea, with each team mentored by a Branch Manager. The winning team receives a £1,000 prize to put their idea into action, with proceeds going to a local charity.

The group also provides financial planning seminars for adults and young adults on a wide range of topics.

Cornerstone Awards

The group also hosts annual Cornerstone of the Community Awards, which recognise the charitable endeavours of individuals and groups in the local community.

Directors with other relevant posts

Andrew Haigh is a trustee of Community Foundation Tyne and Wear and Northumberland (Charity Commission no. 700510).

Main locations

The group has branches across the North East and Cumbria; there is also a branch in Dumfries, Scotland and a branch in Gibraltar. The head office is in Newcastle.

Community contributions

No figure was given for the group's total charitable contributions during the year.

Beneficiaries of the Community Fund in 2016 included: Daisy Chain Project (£3,000); Henry Dancer Days (£1,500); MS Research and Relief Fund (£1,500); Nathan's Needs (£1,100); Whickham Hermitage Community Garden (£1,900).

Employee-led support

Employee volunteering

The group's branch managers volunteer to offer careers advice in local schools, providing support such as interview practice, and opportunities such as careers fairs. In 2015 the group launched a new staff volunteering policy, offering two days of paid leave, which up to 80 employees took up during the year.

Employee fundraising

Employees also fundraise to support charities chosen by their branch or for the group's Community Fund. Examples of fundraising initiatives in 2015 and 2016 include a racing night to support a local charity; a bake sale for Children in Need and a Coffee Morning for Macmillan Cancer Support; a 'Tour de Branch' fundraising cycle; employees taking part in the Great North Run. Staff can also nominate charities for support from the Community Fund.

Commercially led support

Market-led giving

The group has a long-standing relationship with the Sir Bobby Robson Foundation, which supports cancer research and facilities, particularly in the North East. Money is raised through the group's Sir Bobby Robson savings account, paying 0.1% of the total balance held in the accounts to the foundation. The Community Fund is funded in the same way with its own savings account.

Sponsorship

The group also sponsors The Chronicle Champions' Community Champion Award, recognising individuals who have made a significant contribution to their community.

Exclusions

Grants are made for specific projects, not general ongoing costs. Grants are not made for religious, political or commercial activities.

Applications

Community Fund

For information on grants currently available, or details of the next funding round, refer to the group's website: www.newcastle.co.uk/about-us/community-and-charity.

Applications are made using the online form. Customers, employees and members can nominate a charity or community group for support using the online form or by visiting their local branch.

Next PLC

Retail – clothing and footwear

Correspondent: Corporate Responsibility Manager, Legislation and Environment Department, NEXT PLC, Desford Road, Enderby, Leicester LE19 4AT (tel: 0333 777 4577; website: www.nextplc.co.uk/corporate-responsibility/community.aspx)

Directors: Amanda James, Finance Director; Caroline Goodhall; Dame Diane Thompson; Francis Salway; Jane Shields; John Barton, Chair; Jonathan Bewes; Lord Wolfson of Aspley Guise, Chief Executive; Michael Law; Steve Barber (women: 4; men: 6)

Year end	25/01/2016
Turnover	£4,149,700,000
Pre-tax profit	£821,300,000

Nature of business: The principal activities of the group are high-street retailing, home shopping, customer services management and financial services.

Company registration number: 4521150

Subsidiary undertakings include: Next Group PLC; Next Retail Ltd; Lipsy Ltd.

Focus of giving: Health, ill health, non-registered charities, sport, recreation, children, young people, community/social welfare, disability.

Membership: BITC

Community involvement	✓
Community contributions	✓
Company reports on anti-slavery	✓
CSR report	✓
Cash donations declared	✓
Employee-led support	✓
FTSE 100	✓
Gifts in kind	✓
Market-led giving	✓
Sponsorship	✓

Charitable donations

Cash worldwide:	2016	£1,155,000
Total worldwide (cash and in kind):	2016	£4,581,000

Community involvement

Next PLC worked with over 350 charities of various sizes in 2015/16. Support is also provided to organisations without charitable status and local sporting teams, especially where there is direct employee involvement. Resources are focused on projects that benefit communities in the UK and Ireland in the areas of children; care for the sick; people with disabilities; healthcare; medical research; and community support.

According to the website, rather than supporting one Charity of the Year, NEXT instead:

> Supports a wide range of registered charities and other groups and organisations without charitable status, providing donations of financial support or the offer of products which can be used to realise additional funding via charitable spend, gifts in kind and charity linked sales.

Main locations

UK

Community contributions

During 2015/16 Next PLC gave financial support to: registered charities amounting to £1 million; individual requests, local and national groups and organisations amounting to £63,000; and commercial support and sponsorship amounting to £80,000.

Financial support has been complemented with the following fundraising activities to generate additional funds for registered charities, individuals, groups or organisations: gifts in kind – donations of products (£3.4 million); charity-linked sales (£403,000); Next charity events (£64,000); employee fundraising (£43,000).

The figures we use for the company's UK and worldwide contributions do not include commercial sponsorship, charity link sales and employee fundraising (as is our usual practice); however, they are noted here to provide full information.

Beneficiaries included: Doncaster Refurnish; Oxfam; WWF-UK.

In-kind support

NEXT supports charities and community organisations through gifts in kind, mainly in the donation of furniture and clothes which are unsellable or no longer needed.

NEXT Charity Event

NEXT hosted a charity golf day, which helped to raise funds for Bowel Cancer UK.

Employee-led support

Employee fundraising

NEXT employees have raised funds for a range of charities through activities such as 'running, cycling, sky diving, playing football, cake sales' and growing moustaches in support of Movember.

Commercially led support

Commercial sponsorship

Next offers commercial sponsorship to a small number of organisations. Local sporting teams are also supported and especially those with which an employee has a direct involvement.

Applications

Apply in writing to the correspondent.

Northern Powergrid Holdings Company (formerly CE Electric UK Funding Company)

Electricity

Correspondent: Stakeholder & Customer Engagement Team, Lloyds Court, 78 Grey Street, Newcastle upon Tyne NE1 6AF (tel: 0800 011 3332; email: general.enquiries@northernpowergrid.com; website: www.northernpowergrid.com/about-us)

Directors: Douglas Anderson; Dr John France; Dr Philip Jones, Chief Executive Officer; Gregory Abel, Chair; John Reynolds; Patrick Goodman, Chief Financial Officer; Ronald Dixon (women: 0; men: 7)

Year end	31/12/2015
Turnover	£776,300,000
Pre-tax profit	£384,000,000

Nature of business: Northern Powergrid Holdings Company (formerly CE Electric UK Funding Company) is responsible for delivering electricity to properties across the North East, Yorkshire and northern Lincolnshire.

Company registration number: 3476201

Subsidiary undertakings include: Northern Powergrid UK Holdings; Yorkshire Power Group Ltd.

Total employees: 2,547

Focus of giving: Education, environment, local groups, humanitarian help, poverty and social exclusion, safety and crime prevention, science technology, children, young people, community/social welfare.

Membership: BITC

Community involvement	✓
Community contributions	✓
CSR report	✓
CSR or charity committee	✓
Directors have other relevant posts	✓
Charity partner(s)	✓
Employee-led support	✓
Gifts in kind	✓
Humanitarian aid: UK including food banks	✓
Market-led giving	✓
Matched funding	✓
Pro bono	✓
Shared-value alliances	✓
Sponsorship	✓
STEM-focused	✓

Community involvement

The group's community investment strategy, developed in 2015/16 focuses on five areas: vulnerability to power cuts; public safety and education; energy affordability; employee engagement; and strengthening communities. The group works in partnerships with a range of charitable and voluntary organisations to deliver its activities, and also provides funding through the Community Foundation for Tyne and Wear and Sunderland.

Northern Powergrid Fund

The group has a fund which provides grants through the Community Foundation for Tyne and Wear and Northumberland, supporting education, environment and safety, with a focus on rural and ex-industrial areas in the region. Grants of between £500 and £5,000 are available to support projects, with a particular focus on young people, aspiration and skills, and the environment. In 2015/16 the fund made grants to five projects totalling £16,000.

Beneficiaries were: Blyth Resource and Initiative Centre and Northern Learning Trust (£4,500 each); Cramlington Voluntary Youth Project Ltd (£3,000); Wayout in Gateshead (£2,200); LookwideUK (£1,800).

Community Energy Seed Fund

The group has also awarded grants through its Community Energy Seed Fund with the Community Foundation for Tyne and Wear and Northumberland, supporting the development of community energy projects in the North East, North Lincolnshire and Yorkshire and Humber. In 2015/16 the group awarded grants to seven groups totalling £50,000.

Beneficiaries were: Allen Valleys Enterprise Ltd; Hartlepool Power CIC; International Community Organisation of Sunderland; Seaton Valley Community Partnership; Syrian Community of Leeds; Yorkshire Energy Doctor CIC; Yorkshire Energy Partnership.

For information on what funds are currently available, refer to the Community Foundation's website: www.communityfoundation.org.uk.

Charity partnerships – vulnerable customers

The group works in partnership with a number of charities to support its vulnerable customers through the group's Priority Services Register. This initiative aims to support customers that are particularly vulnerable – for example, by providing 'winter warmer packs' and support services in the event of a power cut. It also runs a number of local, targeted initiatives in areas of deprivation to promote this support and reach those in need.

The group works in partnership organisations including the British Red Cross, Citizens Advice and National Energy Action to deliver this support. For example, the group works with The Children's Society to support vulnerable children and families in the Tees Valley area. In Leeds, the group works with the Trussell Trust and Groundwork on the Green Doctors scheme, to assist those at risk of fuel poverty.

Education

The group has a number of educational programmes.

The group visits schools to promote safety around electricity, and has a website, the Fusebox (thefusebox.northernpowergrid.com), which provides activities and resources. It also works in partnership with the social enterprise Ahead Partnership to deliver a STEM-focused programme called Make the Grade, encouraging students in schools in the North East and Yorkshire to engage with STEM subjects and develop skills for STEM-related careers.

The group has also commissioned My Green Investment CIC to deliver its Energy Heroes activities to schools. The programme encourages awareness of how to save energy. The group also takes part in Crucial Crew, an education initiative which aims to teach children to avoid dangerous situations.

Social Issues Expert Group

The group's community investment activities are informed by a panel known as the Social Issues Expert Group. The group includes representatives from National Energy Action, Citizens Advice, British Red Cross and Voluntary Organisations Network Northeast.

Directors with other relevant posts
Dr Philip Jones is a trustee of Five Towns Christian Fellowship (Charity Commission no. 1152389).

Main locations
In the UK, the group's offices are located in Castleford; Houghton-le-Spring; Newcastle (two offices); and Stockton-on-Tees.

Community contributions

No figure was given for the group's total charitable contributions.

In-kind support

At Christmas in 2015, the group donated food and drink hampers to 40 local hospices in the North East, Yorkshire and north Lincolnshire, to support their fundraising initiatives.

Employee-led support

Employee volunteering
Employees volunteer with the group's partners to support its community investment activities. For example, employees volunteer with partners the Trussell Trust and Ahead Partnership, supporting food banks and STEM activities in schools.

The group has previously run a Global Days of Service scheme, providing matched funding for employees to volunteer at local organisations of their choice.

Safety champions
The group's Safety Champions scheme rewards employees for delivering high safety standards by entering them into a draw to win a share of a £10,000 prize fund to donate to a charity chosen by the employee.

Applications

Northern Powergrid Fund grants
To apply for a grant from the Northern Powergrid Fund or the Northern Powergrid Community Energy Seed Fund, refer to the Community Foundation Tyne and Wear and Northumberland website, where guidelines, application forms and deadlines are provided for any funds currently available: www.communityfoundation.org.uk.

Partnerships
The group provides a checklist of how it selects partners to work with to deliver its community investment activities. This can be found in the community investment strategy at: www.northernpowergrid.com/asset/0/document/2014.pdf.

The group
Other enquiries can be submitted using the contact form on the group's website: www.northernpowergrid.com/contact-us.

Northern Shell & Media Group Ltd (entry formerly titled Northern & Shell Network Ltd)

Media

Correspondent: Allison Racher, PA, The Northern & Shell Building, Number 10 Lower Thames Street, London EC3R 6EN (020 8612 7760; email: allison.racher@express.co.uk; website: www.northernandshell.co.uk/philanthropy)

Directors: Digby Rancombe; Dr Paul Ashford; Martin Ellice; Richard Desmond, Chair; Richard Martin; Robert Sanderson (women: 0; men: 4)

Year end	31/12/2015
Turnover	£241,448,000
Pre-tax profit	(£24,838,000)

Nature of business: The ultimate holding company in the Northern & Shell group of companies principally engaged in newspaper publishing and printing, magazine publishing, lottery management services, property investment and the exploitation and further development of intellectual property.

Company registration number: 4086466

Subsidiary undertakings include: Northern & Shell Distribution Ltd; Northern & Shell PLC; Northern & Shell Worldwide Ltd.

Brands include: Daily Express; Daily Star; The Health Lottery.

UK employees: 714

Total employees: 714

Focus of giving: General charitable purposes, health, ill health, older people, poverty and social exclusion, children, young people.

Community involvement	✓
Community contributions	✓
Directors have other relevant posts	✓
Cash donations declared	✓
Corporate charity	✓
Gifts in kind	✓
Market-led giving	✓

Charitable donations

Cash UK (latest available):	2015	£29,000
Total UK (cash and in kind):	2015	£29,000
Cash worldwide:	2015	£29,000
Total worldwide (cash and in kind):	2015	£29,000

Community involvement

Northern & Shell Media Group Ltd supports charities principally through donations made via **The Desmond Foundation** (Charity Commission no. 1014352).

The Desmond Foundation (formerly known as the Richard Desmond Charitable Trust and The R.D. Crusaders Foundation)
The foundation takes the name of Richard Desmond, the Chair of Northern & Shell Media Group. It has been known by a number of different names, including the Richard Desmond Charitable Trust and The R.D. Crusaders Foundation.

The Northern & Shell website describes how the aim of the foundation 'is to use donations in a focused and informed way to realize the greatest possible benefit to recipients. Its strategy is to allocate funds to a large number of smaller charities so that the money goes straight to the people who need it.'

The foundation has, in recent years, focused on supporting UK charities working with children and young people and 'has contributed extensively to further the wellbeing of disadvantaged sections of society'. However, it has also supported larger charities and donations have been made to 'schools, hospitals, old people's homes, carer organisations, hospices and a wide range of medical support groups'. Although children's charities remain the focus of the foundation, the trustees also consider supporting 'worthy causes outside this area, so long as the funds awarded can make a difference'.

Main locations
The foundation supports charities throughout the UK.

Community contributions

The annual report and accounts for 2015 declared charitable donations of £29,000. We have taken this to include £9,000 paid to The Desmond Foundation by Northern & Shell PLC to cover audit fees.

We could not determine a value for the in-kind support given during the year.

In-kind support

Northern & Shell PLC, a subsidiary of the group, provides The Desmond Foundation with free office space and staff time.

Commercially led support

The Health Lottery
The Health Lottery is a scheme managing 51 society lotteries based in different geographical regions in the UK. Proceeds from product sales are distributed to tackle health inequalities in the society lotteries' respective areas.

Corporate charity

The Desmond Foundation (Charity Commission no. 1014352).

Applications

Applications to The Desmond Foundation should be made in writing to the correspondent.

Northumbrian Water Group Ltd (formerly Northumbrian Water Group PLC)

Water

Correspondent: See 'Applications', Abbey Road, Pity Me, Durham DH1 5FJ (tel: 0870 608 4820; website: www.nwl.co.uk/your-home/community.aspx)

Directors: Andrew Hunter; Duncan Macrae; Frank Frame; Heidi Mottram; Hing Lam Kam; Loi Shun Chan; Martin Parker; Tak Chuen Edmond Ip; Wai Che Wendy Tong-Barnes

Year end	31/03/2016
Turnover	£1,050,200,000
Pre-tax profit	£114,000,000

Nature of business: Northumbrian Water Group contains Northumbrian Water Ltd (NWL), which provides water and sewerage services in the north east of England under the brand name Northumbrian Water and water services in the South East under the brand name Essex and Suffolk water.

In October 2011, Northumbrian Water Group PLC was reregistered as a private company and became Northumbrian Water Group Ltd.

Company registration number: 4760441

Subsidiary undertakings include: Ayr Environmental Services Ltd; Caledonian Environmental Services Ltd; Caledonian Levenmouth Treatment Services Ltd; Northumbrian Services Ltd; Northumbrian Water Finance PLC; Northumbrian Water Ltd;

Brands include: Essex and Suffolk Water; Northumbrian Water.

UK employees: 3,209

Total employees: 3,209

Focus of giving: General charitable purposes, education, environment, health, ill health, heritage, overseas projects, older people, sport, recreation, children, young people, community/social welfare.

Membership: BITC

Accredited Living Wage Employer	✓
Community involvement	✓
Community contributions	✓
CSR report	✓
CSR or charity committee	✓
Cash donations declared	✓
Charity partner(s)	✓
Employee-led support	✓
Gifts in kind	✓
Humanitarian aid: overseas	✓
Overseas giving	✓
Sponsorship	✓

Charitable donations

Cash UK (latest available):	2016	£26,500
Total UK (cash and in kind):	2016	£26,500
Cash worldwide:	2016	£26,500
Total worldwide (cash and in kind):	2016	£26,500

Community involvement

The company has developed a partnership with StepChange (Charity Commission no. 1016630), a debt advice charity. The company worked with StepChange to design its SupportPlus tariffs, which launched in January 2015. These schemes incentivise customers to get back into the payment habit and StepChange provides support, advice and access to these support packages. In 2015 more than 2,000 of customers received advice and support to help manage debt from StepChange.

The company provides bottled tap water to charities and not-for-profit groups for use at outside events. Since starting the scheme in 2005, the company has provided more than one million bottles of water to support community events.

In addition to its flagship partnerships and key partners, the company has also supported grassroots community, charitable and environmental activity. Four Community Foundations hold endowment funds that are used to support a range of community and charitable activities across the company's areas of supply. The funds are distributed by a committee from the group, with the advice of the Community Foundations.

WaterAid

Northumbrian Water was one of the water companies that set up the international charity WaterAid (Charity Commission no. 288701) in 1981. WaterAid transforms lives through providing safe water, sanitation and simple hygiene education and the company continues to support the charity as one of its strategic partners. In 2015 Northumbrian Water raised funds aiming to give over 13,000 people in financially developing countries access to clean water and launched a new five-year partnership with WaterAid aiming to raise £1 million to support the delivery of clean water and safe toilets to some of Madagascar's poorest communities.

Main locations

Durham; Essex; Suffolk.

Community contributions

In 2015, through its funds at four Community Foundations, the company donated £26,500 to help 27 different organisations. We take the figure of £26,500 as the company's overall UK giving.

In-kind support

The group's website states that it invested 1.5% of its pre-tax profits in communities through dedicating expertise, employee time, money and facilities.

Employee-led support

Just an Hour

Just an Hour is the group's structured programme of employee involvement in the community and is designed to impact on education, the environment and the general well-being of the community. Since the launch of Just an Hour in 2002, employees have committed more than 100,000 hours in support of the communities and more than half of the group's employees are actively engaged in the programme, supporting 979 organisations with volunteers in 2015.

Exclusions

No donations are given to individuals, exclusive religious projects, organisations outside the company's service area, or to cover wages.

Applications

Apply in writing to the correspondent.

The company's website states: 'If you represent an organisation seeking financial support or equipment for a project we would invite you to apply for a grant through one of our community foundation funds.'

Nottingham Building Society

Building society

Correspondent: Corporate Responsibility Team, Nottingham House, 3 Fulforth Street, Nottingham NG1 3DL (tel: 0344 481 4444; email: dgt@thenottingham.com; website: www.thenottingham.com)

Directors: Andrew Neden; David Marlow, Chief Executive; Guy Thomas; Jane Kibbey; John Edwards, Chair; Keith Whitesides; Mahomed Ashraf Piranie, Finance Director and Deputy Chief Executive; Mary Phibbs; Simon Taylor (women: 2; men: 7)

Year end	31/12/2015
Turnover	£51,400,000
Pre-tax profit	£19,900,000

Nature of business: Independent building society offering a range of financial products and services.

FSA registration number: 200785

Subsidiary undertakings include: Harrison Murray Ltd; HM Lettings Ltd; Nottigham Mortgage Services Ltd.

Focus of giving: General charitable purposes, economic generation, education, enterprise/training, housing, homelessness, large national appeals, local groups, financial education, humanitarian help, poverty and social exclusion, sport, recreation, children, young people, community/social welfare.

Community involvement	✓
Community contributions	✓
CSR report	✓
Directors have other relevant posts	✓
Cash donations declared	✓
Charity partner(s)	✓
Gifts in kind	✓
Humanitarian aid: UK including food banks	✓
Pro bono	✓
Sponsorship	✓

Charitable donations

Cash UK (latest available):	2015	£106,000
Total UK (cash and in kind):	2015	£106,000
Cash worldwide:	2015	£106,000
Total worldwide (cash and in kind):	2015	£106,000

Community involvement

The group's community programme, titled 'Doing Good Together', focuses on the following areas of focus: education; financial capability; housing and homelessness; and employability. Support is given through a grants scheme, partnerships and employee fundraising and volunteering.

Partner charities

The group has long-term partnership with Framework, a small homelessness charity in the East Midlands. Staff and customer support for the charity focuses on its Skills Plus scheme. In 2015 the group held a Do it for Framework Day and a Big Sleep Out.

The group also works with Young Enterprise, providing students at ten schools the opportunity for coaching, mentoring and experience with enterprise and employability skills through the charity's Company Programme.

The group also has a partnership with the charity SportsAid (see 'Sponsorship' section).

Grants scheme

The group's Doing Good Together Grants for Good scheme is managed by Nottinghamshire Community Foundation and provides grants for charities and community groups running projects supporting the group's areas of focus: education, particularly numeracy and literacy; financial security and education; housing and homelessness; and employability. Grants of between £1,000 and £5,000 are provided to organisations within ten miles of one of the group's branches.

Beneficiaries have included: Bugh Community Debt Advice Centre; Hermitage Preschool; Hope Nottingham; Literacy Volunteers; NIDAS; Nottingham Nightstop; Second Chance; The Drop Inn; The New Generation Community Hub; Trussell Trust.

Sponsorship

Through its partnership with the charity SportsAid, the group sponsors aspiring athletes, raising funds for equipment, training and travel costs. In 2015 the group doubled its support to reach 50 athletes, across 28 sports, aged between 12 and 36, and employees raised £15,000 during the year.

The group also sponsors sports teams and events, including Nottinghamshire County Cricket Club and the AEGON Open Nottingham tennis competition.

Directors with other relevant posts

Andrew Neden is a trustee of St Peter's Canary Wharf Trust (Charity Commission no. 1096848) and The Great St Helen's Trust (Charity Commission no. 1089919).

Main locations

The group has offices across Cambridgeshire; Derbyshire; Hertfordshire; Leicestershire; Lincolnshire; Northamptonshire; Nottinghamshire; South Yorkshire. Its head office is in Nottingham.

Community contributions

The 2015 annual report states that charitable donations during the year totalled £106,000.

Employee-led support

Employee volunteering

In 2015 employees volunteered a total of almost 500 hours for local community projects. Staff volunteered 200 hours to mentor and coach students in the Young Enterprise programme.

Employee fundraising

In 2015 employees raised over £10,000 for local charitable causes, including Trussell Trust food banks, Melton Mencap and St Andrew's Hospice, and also raised £15,000 for the athletes sponsored through the company's partnership with SportsAid. A number of the group's offices also collect food bank donations from staff and customers.

Applications

Doing Good Together grants

For information on whether the grants scheme is currently open, refer to the Nottinghamshire Community Foundation website (www.nottscf.org.uk) where deadlines, criteria and application forms are provided.

Volunteer support

Requests for volunteer support from the group can be submitted to dgt@thenottingham.com.

Novae Group PLC

Insurance

Correspondent: Charities Committee, 21 Lombard Street, London EC3V 9AH (tel: 020 7050 9000; email: enquiries@novae.com; website: www.novae.com/about/corporate-responsibility)

Directors: Andrew Torrance; Charles Fry, Chief Financial Officer; John Hastings-Bass, Chair; Justin Dowley; Laurie Adams; Mary Phibbs; Matthew Fosh, Chief Executive Officer (women: 1; men: 6)

Year end	31/12/2015
Turnover	£590,400,000
Pre-tax profit	£55,400,000

Nature of business: Novae Group PLC is the holding company of a group that writes both insurance and reinsurance in the property, casualty and marine, aviation and political risk markets. It has offices in London and Zurich.

Company registration number: 5673306

Subsidiary undertakings include: Novae Bermuda Ltd; Novae Corporate Underwriting Ltd; Novae Management Ltd.

Total employees: 318

Focus of giving: General charitable purposes, education, enterprise/training, environment, health, ill health, medical research, children, young people, community/social welfare, disability.

Community involvement	✓
Community contributions	✓
Company reports on anti-slavery	✓
CSR report	✓
CSR or charity committee	✓
Directors have other relevant posts	✓
Charity partner(s)	✓
Company gives to smaller charities	✓
Employee-led support	✓
Gifts in kind	✓
Matched funding	✓
Pro bono	✓
Sponsorship	✓

Community involvement

The focus of the group's community engagement activities is on young people and education, through its 'Investing in the next generation' programme and its partnership with The Prince's Trust. It also supports small charities chosen by employees and participates in the Lloyd's Community Programme.

Education

Since 2012, the group's 'Investing in the next generation' programme has particularly focused on improving numeracy levels in children and young people, through working with schools.

Partner charity

The group's partner charity is The Prince's Trust. The group supports the charity's xl clubs, which work with 13- to 19-year-olds at risk of exclusion and underachievement in school, and also provides work placements for young people through the trust's Team programme. Novae also sponsors the Educational Achiever of the Year award at the charity's Celebrate Success awards, recognising young people who have overcome barriers and re-engaged with education.

Small charities

As well as supporting its partner charity, the group has a charity committee which supports smaller charities selected by employees.

Directors with relevant posts

Justin Dowley is a trustee of The Dowley Charitable Trust (Charity Commission no. 1081883) and New Schools Network (Charity Commission no. 1132122). Matthew Fosh is a trustee of The Harrow Development Trust (Charity Commission no. 296097). John Hastings-Bass is a trustee of The Landmark Trust (Charity Commission no. 243312).

Main locations

Novae has offices in London and Bermuda.

Community contributions

No figure was given for the group's total charitable contributions.

Employee-led support

Employee fundraising and matched funding

The group provided matched funding for a range of employee-led fundraising initiatives during the year. Beneficiaries included Ambitious about Autism, Colchester Hospitals Charity and Unicef UK.

Employee volunteering

The group's employees volunteer with the partner charity, The Prince's Trust, and also participate in the Lloyd's Community Programme, which supports young people at schools in Tower Hamlets. The group has particularly been involved with the Words and Numbers programme, with employees volunteering to help children develop their literacy and numeracy skills.

Applications

Apply in writing to the correspondent.

Ocado Group PLC

Food services

Correspondent: Charity Committee, Titan Court, 3 Bishop Square, Hatfield Business Park, Hatfield, Hertfordshire AL10 9NE (tel: 01707 227800; email: theocadoway@ocado.com; website: www.ocadogroup.com/our-responsibilities.aspx)

Directors: Alex Mahon; Andrew Harrison; Douglas McCallum; Duncan Tatton-Brown, Chief Financial Officer; Jörn Rausing; Lord Rose, Non-executive Chair; Mark Richardson; Mark Richardson; Neill Abrams; Robert Gorrie; Ruth Anderson; Tim Steiner, Chief Executive Officer (women: 1; men: 11)

Year end	29/11/2015
Turnover	£1,107,600,000
Pre-tax profit	£11,900,000

Nature of business: Online grocer operating home delivery.

Company registration number: 7098618

Subsidiary undertakings include: Jalapeno Partners Ltd; Last Mile Technology Ltd; Ocado Holdings Ltd.

Focus of giving: General charitable purposes, education, enterprise/training, environment, general appeals, health, ill health, children, young people.

Community involvement	✓
Community contributions	✓
Company reports on anti-slavery	✓
Employee-led support	✓
Gifts in kind	✓
Market-led giving	✓
Sponsorship	✓

Charitable donations

Total UK (cash and in kind):	2015	£100,000
Total worldwide (cash and in kind):	2015	£100,000

Community involvement

Ocado appears to focus much of its community involvement on the three key areas of Education and Employment, Environment and Eating Well. It has supported organisations in the form of cash and in-kind donations, sponsorship and product sales. Employees take an active role in the group's charitable initiatives, making up the Charity Committee which, during the year, helped to organise fundraising events in aid of the group's employee-elected Charity of the Year, Macmillan Cancer Support.

The Ocado Foundation

The foundation was established in 2015 to support employees with their personal fundraising and also to be the vehicle for all group fundraising. In its first seven months of operation, £17,500 of matched funding was provided and over £22,000 distributed to charities in communities where employees live and work.

Main locations

Berkshire

Community contributions

In 2014/15 the group made in-kind donations of at least £100,000 through the Donate Food with Ocado scheme but we were unable to determine the value of the rest of the in-kind giving. We were also unable to determine the value of cash donations.

In-kind support

Customers gave almost £100,000 to the Donate Food with Ocado scheme which was matched with groceries provided by Ocado.

Employee-led support

The group's employee-nominated charity, Macmillan Cancer Support, benefitted from funds raised through events organised by the Charity Committee, which is made up of group employees.

Commercially led support

Product sales

Through sales of Duchy branded products, the group was able to make a donation of £145,000 to the Prince of Wales' Charitable Foundation. Through sales of fruit and vegetables the group was also able to support farmers in South Africa and Kenya by making a donation of £30,000 to the Waitrose Foundation.

Carrier bags sales

In 2015/16 the group raised £2.34 million through the sale of carrier bags. The majority of the proceeds were used to support a Bag Buy Back Scheme. The remainder of the proceeds were used to support a number of waste, litter and recycling charities across the UK.

Applications

Apply in writing to the correspondent.

Paddy Power Betfair PLC (record formerly for Betfair Group PLC)

Gaming

Correspondent: Corporate Responsibility Team, Waterfront, Hammersmith Embankment, Chancellors Road (access on Winslow Road), London W6 9HP (tel: 020 8834 8000; website: corporate.betfair.com)

Directors: Alex Gersh, Chief Financial Officer; Breon Corcoran, Chief Executive Officer; Danuta Gray; Gary McGann, Chair; Ian Dyson; Michael Cawley; Pádraig Ó Ríordáin; Peter Jackson; Peter

Rigby; Zillah Byng-Maddick (women: 2; men: 8)

Year end	31/12/2015
Turnover	£974,000,000
Pre-tax profit	£160,000,000

Nature of business: The provision of betting services and online gaming products.

This record previously contained information about the community involvement of Betfair Group PLC. In February 2016, the company merged with Paddy Power and its name was changed to Betfair Group Ltd. We have taken the information in this record from the annual report and accounts of Paddy Power Betfair PLC, a company incorporated in Ireland, which is the immediate and ultimate parent company of Betfair Group Ltd. The majority of the financial information in this record was initially reported in euros.

Subsidiary undertakings include: D. McGranaghan Ltd; Power Leisure Bookmakers Ltd; Paddy Power Online Ltd.

Brands include: Betfair; Paddy Power; Sportsbet.

Total employees: 7,000+

Focus of giving: Education, enterprise/ training, environment, less popular charitable purposes, overseas projects, poverty and social exclusion, sport, recreation, community/social welfare, disability.

Community involvement	✓
Community contributions	✓
CSR report	✓
Charity of the Year	✓
Charity partner(s)	✓
Employee-led support	✓
FTSE 100	✓
Gifts in kind	✓
Overseas giving	✓
Pro bono	✓
Sponsorship	✓
Unpopular causes	✓

Charitable donations

Cash UK (latest available):	2015	£78,000
Total UK (cash and in kind):	2015	£78,000
Total worldwide (cash and in kind):	2015	£652,500

Community involvement

Paddy Power Betfair PLC's Corporate Social Responsibility report states: '2015 was the year we really started to evolve our approach to community investment. We reached out, made some new friends and kicked off some initiatives in the community designed to enable others to achieve their goals. The all new Power Corps launched a call to action to both our own people and those other organisations who were prepared to join our efforts to make the world a little bit better.'

Charities of the Year

The company entered into a two-year partnership with its nominated Charities of the Year, Special Olympics Great Britain and Special Olympics Ireland. During the partnership, the charities benefitted from fundraising efforts led by employees.

Charity partners

Partnerships are central to the company's community involvement. The CSR report for 2015 explains: 'We believe that high quality partnerships matter, and during 2015 we sought out charitable organisations where we could leverage our unique skill base to help make the most positive impact in the service of those who need it most'. The partners included:

Community Links – The Adult Enterprise Programme

Paddy Power Betfair made a three year commitment to Community Links, based in the East End of London. Support, mainly in the form of cash donations, is given for The Adult Enterprise Programme which aims to encourage entrepreneurship among people from disadvantaged backgrounds. In 2015 60 people benefitted from the programme and it was anticipated that a further 100 people would benefit during 2016.

Groundwork London – Neighbourhood Action on Grot Spots (NAGS)

At the end of 2015, the company entered into partnership with the environmental charity Groundwork London to launch NAGS. The initiative supports charities and community groups in London, with the aim of improving the physical environment and getting rid of 'grot spots' which spoil their local areas. The first project supported is The Loop, which tackles the issues caused by fly-tipping on five housing estates across London near to Paddy Power Betfair shops and also creates opportunities for employment.

Gambling charities

The Corporate Social Responsibility report for 2015 states: 'We are pleased to work with a number of external partners who challenge our thinking and help shape our approach to responsible gambling and protecting vulnerable customers. We have long-standing relationships with the Responsible Gambling Trust, Gamble Aware, GamCare, and Gambling Therapy, to help us better understand the issues involved with problem gambling.'

Paddy Power has worked alongside GamCare since 2008. In 2015 the company funded a new organisation, the Young Gamblers Education Trust which aims to provide information to, educate, and protect young people in the UK from problematic gambling and social gaming.

Main locations

UK (it would appear from the information available that the company's community involvement has a particular focus on London); Ireland; Australia.

Community contributions

The Paddy Power Betfair PLC Corporate Social Responsibility report states:

> In 2015, Paddy Power contributed €733,000 [approximately £652,500] to charitable organisations around the world. In addition, our employees raised over €185,000 [approximately £164,500] for our nominated 'Charities of the Year' – Special Olympics Ireland and Special Olympics Great Britain.

We were unable to determine how much of the amount contributed was given in the form of cash donations.

As is our usual practice, we have not included funds raised by employees in our figure for the company's total contributions.

Community contributions in the UK

We were unable to determine the exact amount given by the company to UK charities; however, the CSR report for 2015 does provide some information regarding UK beneficiaries.

During the year, £38,000 was given by the company in the UK as part of the three year commitment to Community Links. In the first two years of the commitment, the company contributed a total of £110,000 to support The Adult Enterprise Programme.

The CSR report for 2015 also states that the first project supported through the Neighbourhood Action on Grot Spots (NAGS) initiative, The Loop, was supported with a donation of £40,000. We have taken this to be included in the total figure for charitable contributions during the year.

In addition, funding was also given to The Young Gamblers Education Trust, although we were unable to find a value for this.

We have taken the sum of the two amounts given above (£78,000) as the total for the company's UK cash donations; however, it is likely that the actual figure exceeds this figure. We were unable to determine the value of in-kind support given in the UK.

Beneficiaries included: The Loop (£40,000); Community Links (£38,000); The Young Gamblers Education Trust (amount not stated).

In-kind support

Annual online marketing day

The CSR report explains that each November members of Paddy Power's Online Marketing Group 'show off to Irish charities keen to use the skills and techniques of online marketing'. More than 50 delegates from a wide range of charities attended the annual online marketing day to learn about search engine optimisation, Pay Per Click and Twitter 'and really make the most of the tools that the modern world has created'. Although this particular instance of community involvement took place in Ireland, rather than the UK, we've included it as a good example of a corporate sharing knowledge and expertise with the charity sector.

Employee-led support

Employee fundraising

Employees managed to raise €185,000 (approximately £165,000) for the company's nominated Charities of the Year by taking part in activities and events including football tournaments, polar plunges, an annual cycle race from Dublin to the Galway Races, a Paddy Power original O'Lympics event, and even walking over hot coals.

Applications

Direct queries to the correspondent.

PageGroup PLC

Professional support services

Correspondent: Corporate Social Responsibility Team, Page House, 1 Dashwood Lang Road, Addlestone, Weybridge, Surrey KT15 2QW (tel: 020 7831 2000; website: www.page.com)

Directors: Danuta Gray; David Lowden, Chair; Kelvin Stagg, Chief Financial Officer; Michelle Healy; Patrick De Smedt; Ruby McGregor-Smith; Simon Boddie; Steve Ingham, Chief Executive Officer (women: 3; men: 5)

Year end	31/12/2015
Turnover	£1,065,000,000
Pre-tax profit	£90,700,000

Nature of business: Michael Page International's business is in professional services recruitment.

Company registration number: 3310225

Subsidiary undertakings include: Michael Page Employment Services Ltd; Sales Recruitment Specialists Ltd; The Page Partnership Ltd.

Brands include: Michael Page; Page Executive; Page Personnel.

UK employees: 1,516

Total employees: 5,835

Focus of giving: Education, enterprise/training, health, ill health, medical research, older people, poverty and social exclusion, children, young people, community/social welfare.

Community involvement	✓
Community contributions	✓
Company reports on anti-slavery	✓
CSR report	✓
Directors have other relevant posts	✓
Charity partner(s)	✓
Employee-led support	✓
Gifts in kind	✓
Matched funding	✓
Payroll giving	✓

Community involvement

The group supports charities in partnerships and employees vote for a charity to support for a two-year commitment. Fundraising for partner charities appears to be mainly employee-led; however, the group does provide matched funding for employee donations through the payroll giving scheme.

Partner charities

The group works with different charities in the countries it operates in.

In the UK, the group supports Smart Works, a charity that provides professional clothing for job seekers, by organising clothing collections.

It also has a partnership with retailTRUST, a charity supporting those in the retail industry, collaborating on fundraising events for the charity and taking part in its forums.

In 2015 employees voted to support Teenage Cancer Trust, and the group established a two-year partnership with the charity, pledging to raise £200,000. Employees previously supported Alzheimer's Research UK.

Education

The group has a schools CSR programme, where employees visit schools and colleges to provide career advice. The group also works with the charity 1000 club to provide work experience placements to students in Tower Hamlets from disadvantaged backgrounds.

Directors with other relevant posts

Steve Ingham is a member of the Corporate Partnerships Board for Great Ormond Street Hospital Charity (Charity Commission no. 1160024).

Main locations

The group works in 35 countries internationally. There are offices across the UK; its head office is in Weybridge, Surrey.

Community contributions

No figure was given for the group's total charitable contributions during the year.

Employee-led support

Employee volunteering

Employees can volunteer to support the group's schools programme, delivering careers advice, and also take part in the group's global CSR day, with co-ordinated activities to support local communities and charities.

Employee fundraising

Employees organise and take part in a variety of fundraising initiatives in support of the group's chosen charity, Teenage Cancer Trust. Examples include participating in the Yorkshire Three Peaks challenge and taking part in street collections. There is also a payroll giving scheme, which the group provides matched funding for.

Applications

Apply in writing to the correspondent.

Paragon Group of Companies PLC

Property

Correspondent: Corporate Social Responsibility Team, 51 Homer Road, Solihull, West Midlands B91 3QJ (tel: 0345 849 4000; website: www.theparagongroup.co.uk/paragon-law/more-about-paragon-law/csr-and-community)

Directors: Alan Fletcher; Fiona Clutterbuck; Hugo Tudor; John Heron; Nigel Terrington, Chief Executive; Peter Hartill; Richard Woodman, Group Finance Director; Robert Dench, Chair (women: 1; men: 7)

Year end	30/09/2015
Turnover	£211,500,000
Pre-tax profit	£134,200,000

Nature of business: Paragon is an independent UK buy-to-let specialist.

Company registration number: 2336032

UK employees: 1,040

Focus of giving: Local groups, children, young people.

Community involvement	✓
Community contributions	✓
Company reports on anti-slavery	✓
CSR report	✓
CSR or charity committee	✓
Cash donations declared	✓
Charity of the Year	✓
Employee-led support	✓

Charitable donations

Cash UK (latest available):	2015	£1,064,000
Total UK (cash and in kind):	2015	£1,064,000
Cash worldwide:	2015	£1,064,000
Total worldwide (cash and in kind):	2015	£1,064,000

Community involvement

The group looks to contribute to registered charities 'relating to financial services or serving the local communities in which it operates'. It has a particular focus on children's and local charities although, it states in its annual report, 'no charity request is overlooked'. The group also supports the employee-run Paragon's Charity Committee.

Employees vote yearly on which charities will benefit from the fundraising activities organised by the committee.

Main locations
London; Solihull.

Community contributions

In 2014/15 the group contributed £1,064,000 to charitable causes. Of this amount, £1,045,000 was donated in support of the Foundation for Credit Counselling, which operates StepChange Debt Charity.

The group made other charitable donations totalling £19,000.

Beneficiaries included: Age UK – Solihull; Army of Angels; The Alzheimer's Society; Chelmsley Colts FC; Children with Cancer; County Air Ambulance; Get Set Girls; Strongbones Charitable Trust; Ward 19 Charity.

Nominated charities (Charity of the Year)

2015: Help Harry Help Others

2014: Libby Mae's Little Angels and Whythall Animal Sanctuary

Employee-led support

Paragon's Charity Committee is made up of volunteer employees who organise fundraising initiatives in aid of charities elected by the group's employees. Around £10,000 is raised for these nominated charitable causes each year. During the year employees also delivered workshops on financial awareness and employability in schools and colleges, donated shoeboxes to Samaritan's Purse Christmas appeal and gave to food banks.

Applications

Apply in writing to the correspondent.

Pennon Group PLC

Water

Correspondent: Sustainability Committee, Peninsula House, Rydon Lane, Exeter EX2 7HR (tel: 01392 446677; website: www.pennon-group.co.uk/sustainability)

Directors: Christopher Loughlin, Group Chief Executive Officer; Gill Rider; Helen Barrett-Hague; Martin Angle; Neil Cooper; Sir John Parker, Chair; Susan Davy, Chief Financial Officer (women: 3; men: 4)

Year end	31/03/2016
Turnover	£1,352,300,000
Pre-tax profit	£508,400,000

Nature of business: Business is carried out through:

Bournemouth Water – provides water services to Dorset, Wiltshire and Hampshire.

South West Water – the provider of water and sewerage services for Devon, Cornwall and parts of Dorset and Somerset.

Viridor Ltd – one of the leading UK recycling, renewable energy and waste management businesses.

Company registration number: 2366640

Subsidiary undertakings include: South West Water Ltd; Viridor Ltd

UK employees: 4,800

Focus of giving: Education, environment, children, young people, community/social welfare.

Community involvement	✓
Community contributions	✓
CSR report	✓
Charity partner(s)	✓
Employee-led support	✓
Sponsorship	✓
STEM-focused	✓

Community involvement

Pennon Group and its subsidiaries support communities and charities in the areas in which they operate.

Our research indicates that South West Water's support focuses on water, the environment and youth education in the South West, while Viridor's business is UK wide and its community support focuses on environmental and science education.

The group's financial involvement in the community is channelled through a number of initiatives, including:

- Community support, sponsorship and donations (South West Water and Viridor)
- Landfill Tax Credit Scheme (Viridor Waste)

Both South West Water and Viridor fundraise for their preferred charities: Breast Cancer Now, Jeans for Genes, Save the Children and Children's Air Ambulance.

Partnerships
In partnership with Red Rose Forest Viridor have started an urban tree-planting project in Manchester. This allows key recycling partners to work with local residents to plant trees in local streets.

Main locations
Support is given throughout the South West.

Community contributions

The annual report and accounts for 2015/16 did not declare a figure for charitable donations. However, the report did include combined figures for 'Community support, sponsorship & donations' which were £136,500 for South West Water and £12 million for Viridor. Note that the £11.8 million of Viridor's community support was paid to Viridor Credits for distribution via the Landfill Communities Fund.

In-kind support

Community programmes
During the year, South West Water continued its support of education by providing talks, resources, work experience placements and by giving lectures at regional universities.

Viridor operates or supports ten educational centres across the UK, which help to promote better understanding and practice of recycling and resource management. During the year, these centres had 17,000 visitors from schools, colleges and community groups.

Employee-led support

Employee fundraising
Employees help to raise funds for the companies' preferred charities.

Employee volunteering
South West Water and Viridor both have active volunteering schemes.

Commercially led support

Sponsorship
Viridor's community sponsorship programme focuses on educational initiatives and particularly those in the areas of STEM (science, technology, engineering and maths) and environment. This has included GO4SET, a Scottish flagship educational initiative with the Engineering Development Trust.

Applications

Apply in writing to the correspondent.

Persimmon PLC

Building/construction

Correspondent: Corporate Responsibility Committee, Persimmon House, Fulford, York YO19 4FE (tel: 0370 703 0178; email: contact@persimmonhomes.com; website: corporate.persimmonhomes.com/corporate-responsibility/our-community/supporting-community-and-charitable-initiatives)

Directors: Dave Jenkinson; Jeff Fairburn, Group Chief Executive; Marion Sears; Mike Killoran, Group Finance Director; Nicholas Wrigley, Chair; Nigel Mills; Rachel Kentleton (women: 2; men: 6)

Year end	31/12/2015
Turnover	£290,000,000
Pre-tax profit	£637,800,000

Nature of business: Principal activities: residential building and development. Persimmon Homes is based in Anglia, Midlands, North East, North West, Scotland, South Coast, South East, South

West, Thames Valley, Wales, Wessex, and Yorkshire.

Company registration number: 1818486

Subsidiary undertakings include: Persimmon Homes Ltd; Charles Church Developments Ltd.

Focus of giving: General charitable purposes, armed forces.

Community involvement	✓
Community contributions	✓
CSR report	✓
Armed forces personnel	✓
Corporate charity	✓
Employee-led support	✓
FTSE 100	✓
Matched funding	✓
Sponsorship	✓

Charitable donations

Cash UK (latest available):	2015	£516,000
Total UK (cash and in kind):	2015	£516,000
Cash worldwide:	2015	£516,000
Total worldwide (cash and in kind):	2015	£516,000

Community involvement

Community Champions

Community Champions is a nationwide scheme where charities can apply for up to £1,000 of matched funding. Every month each of Persimmon's offices are allowed to give away £2,000 giving a total of £60,000 available.

Main locations

Persimmon has offices throughout the UK.

Community contributions

In 2015 the group provided £516,000 in matched funding to local charities and community groups through its Community Champions initiative. A further £156,000 was given directly to charities through group donations and employee fundraising but no breakdown of this figure was provided. This included a final donation of £70,000 to support York Minster's restoration appeal which had been supported since 2006.

Employee-led support

Employee fundraising

Through fundraising activities, Persimmon employees raised some of the £156,000 which was donated to directly to charitable causes by the group during the year, although we were not able to locate a figure.

Corporate charity

The Persimmon Charitable Foundation (Charity Commission no. 1163608).

Applications

Applications to the Community Champions scheme can be made via the website: www.persimmonhomes.com/charity.

Personal Group Holdings PLC

Insurance

Correspondent: Sarah Mace, Trustee, PACT, John Ormond House, 899 Silbury Boulevard, Central Milton Keynes MK9 3XL (tel: 01908 605000; email: sarah.mace@personal-group.com; website: www.personalgroup.com)

Directors: Andrew Lothian; Ashley Doody; David Walker; Deborah Rees; Ken Rooney; Mark Scanlon, Chief Executive; Mark Winlow, Non-executive Chair; Mike Dugdale, Chief Financial Officer; Neil Stride; Rebekah Tapping; Sarah Mace (women: 3; men: 8)

Year end	31/12/2015
Turnover	£59,600,000
Pre-tax profit	£10,400,000

Nature of business: A provider of employee benefits and financial services.

Company registration number: 3194991

Subsidiary undertakings include: Berkeley Morgan Group Ltd; Berkeley Morgan Ltd; Universal Provident Ltd.

Focus of giving: Local groups, overseas projects, community/social welfare.

Community involvement	✓
Community contributions	✓
CSR report	✓
Charity of the Year	✓
Charity partner(s)	✓
Corporate charity	✓
Employee-led support	✓

Charitable donations

Cash UK (latest available):	2015	£100,000
Total UK (cash and in kind):	2015	£100,000
Cash worldwide:	2015	£100,000
Total worldwide (cash and in kind):	2015	£100,000

Community involvement

Personal Assurance Charitable Trust (Charity Commission no. 1023274)

The trust makes grants to organisations recommended by Personal Assurance PLC employees or policyholders.

Charities of the Year

The group chooses several Charities of the Year to benefit from employee fundraising. In 2015 money was raised for Comic Relief; Help For Heroes; the Henry Allen Trust; Milton Keynes Food Bank.

Charity partnership

The group has a partnership with the Memusi Foundation, an African education charity. The group provides financial support as well as assistance on projects from volunteers.

UK locations

Throughout the UK.

Community contributions

Each year Personal Assurance PLC gives around 0.5% of its premium income to its charitable trust. In 2015 donations to the trust totalled £100,000.

Employee-led support

Employee fundraising

During the year, employees raised £2,500 for the group's Charities of the Year. Events included Easter egg hunts, hot dog sales and raffles.

Employee volunteering

There have been several employee volunteering trips to Kenya to work on projects being carried out with their charity partner the Memusi Foundation.

Corporate charity

The Personal Assurance Charitable Trust (Charity Commission no. 1023274).

Applications

Charity of the Year

For applications to the charitable trust, preference is given to recommendations made by policyholders of Personal Assurance PLC and employees of Personal Group Holdings PLC.

Personal Assurance Charitable Trust

Apply in writing to the correspondent.

Pets at Home Ltd

Retail – miscellaneous

Correspondent: See 'Applications', Epsom Avenue, Stanley Green Trading Estate, Handforth, Cheshire SK9 3RN (website: www.petsathome.com)

Directors: Amy Stirling; Brian Carroll; Dennis Millard; Ian Kellet, Chief Executive Officer; Paul Coby; Paul Moody; Tessa Green; Tony DeNunzio, Chair (women: 2; men: 6)

Year end	26/03/2016
Turnover	£793,126,000
Pre-tax profit	£92,142,000

Nature of business: Pets at Home Ltd is a retailer of services and equipment for pets.

Company registration number: 1822577

Subsidiary undertakings include: Farm-Away Ltd; Vets 4 Pets Ltd; Pet City Ltd.

Focus of giving: Animal welfare.

Community involvement	✓
Community contributions	✓
Company reports on anti-slavery	✓
CSR report	✓
CSR or charity committee	✓
Employee-led support	✓
Gifts in kind	✓
Market-led giving	✓

Charitable donations

Total UK (cash and in kind):	2016	£540,000
Total worldwide (cash and in kind):	2016	£540,000

Community involvement

The company's employees raise large amounts for a range of animal welfare charities each year. The company itself makes in-kind donations of dog food as well as supporting employee volunteering.

Main locations

Pets at Home has stores throughout the UK.

Community contributions

In 2015/16 a total of £3.6 million was donated to charity by Pets at Home Ltd customers and employees. The company itself gave gifts in kind of dog food totalling £540,000. No cash donations directly from the company were noted in the annual report.

In-kind support

Dog food worth £540,000 was donated to the Dogs Trust.

Employee-led support

During the year employees raised £1.8 million for Support Adoption for Pets.

Commercially led support

The company runs a VIP (Very Important Pets) loyalty scheme. Every time a member makes a purchase they receive points which can be converted into VIP Lifelines for a charity of their choice. Around 600 animal charities have been supported nationwide including the Dogs Trust, RSPCA, SSPCA, Cats Protection, Blue Cross and Retired Greyhound Trust.

Applications

Contact your local Pets At Home store.

Pfizer Ltd

Chemicals and plastics, agriculture, healthcare

Correspondent: Stakeholder Strategy Team, Ramsgate Road, Sandwich, Kent CT13 9NJ (tel: 01304 616161; website: www.pfizer.co.uk/content/communities)

Directors: Carole Johnson; Darren Noseworthy; Dr Berkeley Phillips; Elizabeth Greenfield; Hendrikus Nordkamp, Managing Director; Ian Franklin; Paula Tully; Thomas Dolan (women: 3; men: 5)

Year end	30/11/2015
Turnover	£1,100,000
Pre-tax profit	(£16,184,000)

Nature of business: The principal activities of the company are the discovery, development, manufacture, marketing and sale of pharmaceutical and animal health products.

Company registration number: 526209

Subsidiary undertakings include: John Wyeth and Brother Ltd; Neusentis Ltd; PZR Ltd.

Brands include: Anadin; Centrum; ThermaCare.

UK employees: 2,189

Focus of giving: General charitable purposes, education, enterprise/training, environment, animal welfare, health, ill health, medical research, local groups, overseas projects, humanitarian help, older people, science technology, sport, recreation, children, young people, community/social welfare, disability, disasters.

Community involvement	✓
Community contributions	✓
CSR report	✓
Cash donations declared	✓
Charity partner(s)	✓
Employee-led support	✓
Gifts in kind	✓
Humanitarian aid: overseas	✓
Humanitarian aid: UK including food banks	✓
Market-led giving	✓
Matched funding	✓
Overseas giving	✓
Payroll giving	✓
Pro bono	✓
Shared-value alliances	✓
Sponsorship	✓
STEM-focused	✓

Charitable donations

Total UK (cash and in kind):	2015	£1,400,000
Total worldwide (cash and in kind):	2015	£1,400,000

Community involvement

The group supports organisations in the field of healthcare, as well as organisations in areas of the company's presence (Sandwich, Walton Oaks, Cambridge and Havant) and STEM education initiatives. The group provides support through financial and in-kind donations, as well as matched funding for employee donations. Employees offer support through volunteering and payroll giving.

Globally, Pfizer has a number of charitable initiatives, such as working in partnership with the WHO on the International Trachoma Initiative, and supporting the Ugandan Infectious Diseases Institute.

Charitable donations

The group's website states that, when allocating its charitable donations, the group gives priority to donations which:

- Improve the quality and availability of healthcare, educate individuals and families about sound health practices in order to empower them to improve their health, and serve those most at risk of health problems, or
- Advance research and knowledge in medicine, healthcare and allied sciences and science education

The group states that it also supports small charitable organisations and projects, including academic, cultural and community organisations, in the areas surrounding its UK operating sites through financial support, in-kind donations and pro bono support from employees.

Strategic community investment initiatives

The group's website explains that it also runs 'strategic community investment initiatives', run by the group, working in partnership with charities and community organisations to meet the group's objectives under its 'Working together for Britain's national health' plan. The website states that these initiatives are not to promote the business, but to address health issues in the UK. Examples include the Pfizer Missed Appointments campaign, which aims to reduce non-attendance of NHS appointments.

Medical and Educational Goods and Services (MEGS) donations

Financial and in-kind donations are made under this category by Pfizer to benefit patient care or the NHS. A full breakdown of these donations, along with the group's educational grants and studentships in 2015, can be found on the website.

STEM education

Pfizer is a member of the Science Industry Partnership, a group of companies working to promote education and careers in STEM subjects. The group also runs a campaign called 'I am Science', which aims to celebrate the achievements of scientists and inspire future generations.

Main locations

The group's head office in the UK is in Walton Oaks, Surrey. There are also operations in Cambridge; Havant; and Sandwich.

Community contributions

The group's website provides the following breakdown of its UK social investment in 2015:

Corporate donations and grants	£1 million
Strategic community investment initiatives	£314,000
Total volunteering time	£105,000
Total value of social investment	**£1.4 million**

'Corporate donations and grants' includes donations to charity and community organisations and matched funding for employee donations, as well as donations to patient groups, but also includes PhD studentships funded by

Pfizer at academic institutions and educational grants to organisations.

'Strategic community investment initiatives' includes programmes managed by the group's corporate responsibility function, working in partnership with charitable and other organisations to address health issues in the UK, through activities which are not designed to promote the business. This also includes the management costs which are associated with charitable donations and community investment activities.

In-kind support

The group provides in-kind donations through the organisation International Health Partners, which provides medical supplies to charities working in humanitarian and disaster relief. In 2015 Pfizer UK donated 127,500 packs of medicine for inclusion in Doctors' Travel Packs.

Employee-led support

Employee volunteering

Pfizer employees are entitled to five days of paid leave for volunteering, which may be done through individual or team initiatives. In 2015 employees in the UK volunteered for a total of almost 3,000 hours. Pfizer employees can volunteer to be SIP Ambassadors, taking part in an 18-month training programme, and working with schools to run science activities and careers workshops with schools. Many employees are also STEMNET ambassadors. Employees can also take part in the Global Health Fellows programme, which places employees with international development organisations, working on short-term projects relating to health services.

Employee fundraising

The group has a payroll giving scheme and also provides matched funding for employee fundraising. The group also has a Christmas giving programme, with employees collecting financial and seasonal food donations to support food banks.

Commercially led support

Studentships and educational grants

The group makes educational grants to areas in which it has an interest, such as medical science or public health policy. It also funds studentships at academic institutions. Grants are provided to organisations, not individuals.

Sponsorship

In 2016 the group sponsored the British Science Festival.

Exclusions

Support is not given to individuals.

Applications

Apply in writing to the correspondent. For local appeals in areas of the company's presence, contact your local Pfizer site.

Phoenix Group Holdings

Financial services

Correspondent: Lucy Symonds, Corporate Responsibility Manager, 1 Wythall Green Way, Wythall, Birmingham B47 6WG (tel: 020 3567 9100; email: corporateresponsibility@thephoenixgroup.com; website: www.thephoenixgroup.com)

Directors: Alastair Barbour; Clive Bannister, Chief Executive; David Woods; Henry Staunton, Chair; Ian Cormack; Isabel Hudson; Jim McConville, Group Finance Director; John Pollock; Kory Sorenson; Nicholas Shott; Rene-Pierre Azria; Wendy Mayall (women: 3; men: 9)

Year end	31/12/2015
Turnover	£692,000,000
Pre-tax profit	£152,000,000

Nature of business: The group is a closed life assurance fund consolidator that specialises in the management and acquisition of closed life and pension funds

Company registration number: 202172

Subsidiary undertakings include: Pearl Group Holdings; National Provident Life Ltd; Opal Reassurance Ltd.

Total employees: 741

Focus of giving: Local groups, financial education, older people.

Community involvement	✓
Community contributions	✓
CSR report	✓
Charity partner(s)	✓
Employee-led support	✓
Gifts in kind	✓
Market-led giving	✓

Community involvement

The group supports charities local to its offices through sponsorship, partnerships, employee fundraising and in-kind giving.

Main locations

The group has offices in Whythall (Worcestershire) and London.

Community contributions

In 2015 the group donated £46,500 to various community initiatives. However, it is not clear how much of this was cash and in-kind donations.

Charity partnerships

The group has partnerships with Midlands Air Ambulance and London's Air Ambulance which are due to run until March 2017.

The group's partnership with The Money Charity meant it was able to deliver financial education workshops to over 300 of 11- to 16-year-olds in local schools.

In-kind support

The group has continued to loan its resources to community groups. Office space and car parking space has been made available to community groups and furniture has been donated to Trident Reach for use in its communal dining areas.

Employee-led support

Employee volunteering

Around 36% of staff took part in the group's volunteering initiative during the year, giving a total of 1,942 in volunteering hours. Charities the group worked with included The Alzheimer's Society, Birmingham Mind, Birmingham St Mary's Hospice and Heart of England Forest.

Employee fundraising

During the year staff raised £169,000 for their charity partners through numerous extreme fundraising challenges. These included staff running 240 miles between the London and Whythall sites as well as a long distance cycle ride across the American plains.

Commercially led support

Sponsorship

During the year the group sponsored Woodrush High School's new community hub as well as the Whythall and Hollywood Fun Run.

Exclusions

Support is not provided to religious or political causes.

Applications

Apply in writing to the correspondent.

Piranha Trading Ltd

Retail – DIY/furniture

Correspondent: Anthony Ponsford, Director, 71–75 Shelton Street, Covent Garden, London WC2H 9JQ (tel: 0330 088 1693; email: info@piranhafurniture.com; website: piranhafurniture.com)

Director: Anthony Ponsford

Year end	30/11/2015

Nature of business: Piranha Trading Ltd is the trading name for Piranha Furniture, a supplier of home/office furniture.

Company registration number: 6546159

Brands include: Piranha.

Focus of giving: General charitable purposes, environment, animal welfare, housing, homelessness, medical research, marginalised people, less popular charitable purposes, armed forces, overseas projects, humanitarian help, older people, poverty and social exclusion, children, young people, disability.

Community involvement ✓
Community contributions ✓

Community involvement

This company was established in 2008 by Anthony Ponsford and has an unusually philanthropic business model. The website gives the following founder's words: 'I strongly believe that people fortunate enough to have more than they need, should use that excess wealth to support charities and other good causes.'

In line with this ideal, the business will donate 25% of its pre-tax profits to UK-registered charities from 2014/15 onwards.

The business model provides for the following: 25% of all profit made from sales on Piranha's website will go to charities nominated by customers (15%), employees (5%) and shareholders (5%).

Every time a customer buys an item from the website, s/he will be given the opportunity to nominate up to three UK-registered charities from a list provided. The customer's chosen charities will receive points, ultimately giving them a larger share of the 15% profit allocation.

Staff of the company and its shareholders will be able to nominate any UK-registered charity to receive a donation (up to 5% in total each of the company's pre-tax profit).

Main locations

Support is given to charities throughout the UK.

Community contributions

The company states on its website that 25% of pre-tax profits is donated to UK-registered charities.

Beneficiaries have included: Alzheimer's Society; Amnesty International UK; Battersea Dogs and Cats Home; British Heart Foundation; British Red Cross; Cancer Research UK; Diabetes UK; Guide Dogs; Help for Heroes; Marie Curie Cancer Care; Macmillan Cancer Support; NSPCC; Oxfam; RNLI; St John Ambulance; Terrence Higgins Trust; The National Trust; The Prince's Trust; The Royal British Legion; The Salvation Army; The Wildlife Trusts; The Woodland Trust; RSPCA; Voluntary Service Overseas (VSO); WaterAid.

Applications

Address any queries to the correspondent and director, Anthony Ponsford who states:

> While 15% of our donations will be given to charities nominated by our customers, 5% will be decided by our shareholders and a further 5% by our employees. If you have a charitable cause that you feel would benefit from our support please get in touch with us and will make sure its passed on to our shareholders and employees.

Playtech PLC

Gaming

Correspondent: The Company Secretary, Ground Floor, St George's Court, Upper Church Street, Douglas, Isle of Man IM1 1EE (website: www.playtech.com)

Directors: Alan Jackson, Chair; Andrew Thomas; John Jackson; Mor Weizer, Chief Executive Officer; Paul Hewitt; Ron Hoffman, Chief Financial Officer (women: 1; men: 5)

Year end	31/12/2015
Turnover	£630,000,000
Pre-tax profit	£142,000,000

Nature of business: Provider of online gaming software.

Company registration number: 008505V

Subsidiary undertakings include: Gaming Technology Solutions Ltd; VS Technology Ltd; Virtue Fusion CM Ltd.

Total employees: 5,000

Focus of giving: Education, poverty and social exclusion, children, young people.

Community involvement ✓
Community contributions ✓
Cash donations declared ✓

Charitable donations

Cash worldwide:	2015	£209,000
Total worldwide (cash and in kind):	2015	£300,000

Community involvement

The group focuses on education and research into the treatment of problem gambling as well as providing donations to various other charities.

Main locations

Support is given throughout the UK. The group has offices in London and Northern Ireland.

Community contributions

In 2015 the group made donations totalling £300,000 (€350,000) to organisations working in the fields of: education; research into vulnerable populations; associations for children with cancer; and other social welfare charities.

Employee-led support

The group's employees support charities through its Social Involvement programme that mainly focuses on providing educational support to disadvantaged children in countries where the group has offices.

Applications

Direct requests to the correspondent.

Premier Foods PLC

Food manufacture

Correspondent: See 'Applications', Premier House, Centrium Business Park, Griffiths Way, St Albans AL1 2RE (tel: 01727 815850; website: www.premierfoods.co.uk/sustainability)

Directors: Alastair Murray, Chief Financial Officer; David Beever, Chair; Gavin Darby, Chief Executive; Ian Krieger; Jennifer Laing; Pam Powell; Richard Hodgson; Tsunao Kijima (women: 2; men: 6)

Year end	02/04/2016
Turnover	£771,700,000
Pre-tax profit	(£13,000,000)

Nature of business: Premier's principal products are bread, shelf stable groceries and chilled foods.

Company registration number: 5160050

Subsidiary undertakings include: British Bakeries Ltd; London Superstores Ltd; Premier Foods Group Ltd.

Brands include: Mr Kipling; OXO; Sharwood's.

UK employees: 3,737

Total employees: 3,737

Focus of giving: General charitable purposes, health, ill health, community/social welfare.

Community involvement ✓
Community contributions ✓
Company reports on anti-slavery ✓
CSR report ✓
Directors have other relevant posts ✓
Charity partner(s) ✓
Employee-led support ✓
Gifts in kind ✓
Market-led giving ✓

Charitable donations

Cash UK (latest available):	2016	£50,000
Total UK (cash and in kind):	2016	£50,000
Cash worldwide:	2016	£50,000
Total worldwide (cash and in kind):	2016	£50,000

Community involvement

Premier Foods PLC, as its website describes, looks to 'make a bigger difference to a single cause' through two year-long corporate charity partnerships. At a local level, employees at the group's sites and offices support their communities through volunteering and fundraising activities.

Charity partner

Premier Foods consults its employees every two years as to which charity it will partner. Cancer Research UK was announced in January 2015 as Premier Foods's corporate charity in a partnership that ran until the end of 2016. A fundraising target of £250,000 was set which, according to the group's website, had already been surpassed, with more than £300,000 raised at the time of writing (November 2016).

Past corporate charity partners include Macmillan Cancer Support, for which funds were raised amounting to £320,000.

Local support case study: Lifton site

All of Premier Foods's sites and offices are actively involved in their communities. The group website focuses on one site as an example – the site at Lifton in Devon – to show the varied ways in which its sites and offices provide support locally.

- The site works with the local primary school in Lifton 'with site visits and educational activity around communication, conduct and collaboration' as well as with a local college to 'help business students get to grips with the realities of a producing business'
- Staff at the site assisted with the renovation of the local Launceston Community Centre which acts as a venue for a range of local groups, such as for people with mental health issues, young mothers and children
- Staff fundraised and volunteered for CHICKS Children's Charity, which has a retreat close to the site

Directors with other relevant posts

Jennifer Laing: trustee of IHG Foundation.

Modern Slavery: Stronger Together

Premier Foods's strategic report for 2015/16 states: 'Early in 2016 we became a business partner of Stronger Together, a multi-stakeholder initiative of employers, labour providers, workers and their representatives focused on addressing modern day slavery and third party exploitation.'

Main locations

Premier Foods has a number of sites and offices based across England. For more information on where these are located, see www.premierfoods.co.uk/about/locations.

Community contributions

Note: The latest annual report and accounts for the group were for the financial year ended 2 April 2016; however, our figure for cash donations is based on information available from the website that refers to the 2016 Christmas period which falls outside the 2015/16 reporting year.

The annual report and accounts for 2015/16 did not declare a figure for charitable donations.

However, the Christmas charity page on the group's website (www.premierfoods.co.uk/Christmas) states: 'In addition to the funds we have raised for Cancer Research UK over the course of our two year partnership, Premier Foods will be donating £50,000 to Cancer Research UK as part of our 'Family Moments' Christmas campaign.' We have taken this figure as an indicator of the amount donated by the group.

Beneficiaries included: Cancer Research UK.

Employee-led support

Employee fundraising

In 2015/16 employees raised funds for Premier Foods's corporate charity partner through a range of activities and events including the following described in the strategic report for 2015/16: 'raft races, bake sales, dog walking days, football shirt Fridays and our Aim Higher Challenge, during which 150 colleagues spent a day cycling up to 115 miles or trekking 24 miles through the Yorkshire Dales!'

Each year, there is a company-wide charity challenge through which employees raise funds for the corporate partner charity. In September 2016 this involved cycling and trekking across the Brecon Beacons in Wales, raising £50,000.

Employees also donate goods to raise funds in Cancer Research UK shops.

Commercially led support

Cause-related marketing

In 2015 Premier Foods's brand Mr Kipling partnered with Tesco to organise a limited edition pack of Viennese Whirls. From every pack sold, 10p was given in support of Cancer Research UK's Race for Life.

Supplier Charity Benefit

Premier Foods hosts a fundraising auction which is attended by its suppliers. The proceeds from the auction are given in support of the group's corporate charity partner.

Applications

At a group level, Premier Foods lends its support to a single employee-nominated cause at any one time. A new charity partner is selected every two years. At a local level, individual Premier Food sites are actively involved with community causes in their local area.

Premier Oil PLC

Oil and gas/fuel

Correspondent: Corporate Services Team, Premier Oil PLC, 23 Lower Belgrave Street, London SW1W 0NR (tel: 020 7730 1111; email: premier@premier-oil.com; website: www.premier-oil.com)

Directors: Anne Marie Cannon; David Bamford; David Lindsell; Jane Hinkley; Joe Darby; Michel Romieu; Mike Welton, Chair; Neil Hawkings; Richard Rose, Finance Director; Robin Allan; Tony Durrant, Chief Executive Officer (women: 2; men: 9)

Year end	31/12/2015
Turnover	£876,500,000
Pre-tax profit	(£681,000,000)

Nature of business: Premier Oil PLC is an international gas and oil exploration and production company.

Company registration number: SC234781

Subsidiary undertakings include: EnCore (NNS) Ltd; Premier Oil UK Ltd; Premier Oil Exploration and Production Ltd.

Total employees: 800

Focus of giving: General charitable purposes, education, environment, animal welfare, health, ill health, heritage, housing, homelessness, small groups, local groups, overseas projects, poverty and social exclusion, safety and crime prevention, children, young people, community/social welfare, disability.

Community involvement	✓
Community contributions	✓
Company reports on anti-slavery	✓
CSR report	✓
CSR or charity committee	✓
Directors have other relevant posts	✓
AF Covenant	✓
Cash donations declared	✓
Charity partner(s)	✓
Company gives to smaller charities	✓
Employee-led support	✓
Gifts in kind	✓
Humanitarian aid: overseas	✓
Overseas giving	✓
Pro bono	✓

Charitable donations

Cash UK (latest available):	2015	£218,500
Total UK (cash and in kind):	2015	£218,500
Cash worldwide:	2015	£724,000
Total worldwide (cash and in kind):	2015	£724,000

Community involvement

According to the 2015 corporate responsibility report, the group's community activities focus on 'projects that address the impacts of our activities' in communities local to its operations. Support is given particularly to educational, health, environmental, social welfare and capacity building projects.

UK community investment
According to the 2015 corporate responsibility report, the group continued to fund the following charity partners:

- Absafe, a community health and safety charity based in Aberdeen, providing a neighbourhood watch scheme and interactive education sessions
- Horseback UK, a charity supporting those injured during military service
- GeoBus, an educational programme run by St Andrews, delivering geosciences education to schools through its outreach scheme
- Barnardo's Connect in Aberdeen, supporting young people involved in substance misuse and at risk of offending
- Archway, a charity that supports people with learning disabilities in north east Scotland

Funding was also given to a new partner, Spina Bifida Hydrocephalus Scotland, which raises awareness and provides support to families and those affected by the conditions.

The group's London office also supported The Passage, a local charity supporting people who are homeless or vulnerable.

The group also provides up to ten annual bursaries for UK-based undergraduates to study coral reef preservation as part of the Operation Wallacea research project in Indonesia.

Directors with other relevant posts
David Lindsell is a trustee of Cancer Research UK (Charity Commission no. 1089464) and Deputy Chair of Governors of the University of the Arts London.

Main locations
The group has offshore operations based around five business units: Falkland Islands; Indonesia, Pakistan; UK; Vietnam. In the UK, the group's registered office is in Edinburgh but its head office is London. There are also offices in Abu Dhabi and Brazil.

Community contributions

According to the 2015 corporate responsibility report, community investment in the UK amounted to $265,500 (around £218,500, at the time of writing). Community investment was also given in Indonesia, Norway, Pakistan and Vietnam and the worldwide total was $880,000 (around £724,000).

Beneficiaries included: Absafe ($54,000 – around £44,500); The Passage ($60,0000 or £49,500); Horseback UK ($39,000 – around £32,000); GeoBus ($13,000 – around £10,700); Archway and Barnardo's Connect Aberdeen ($7,800 each – around £6,400 each); Spina Bifida Hydrocephalus Scotland ($3,000 – around £2,500).

Note: Currency conversions were correct at the time of writing (October 2016).

Employee-led support

Employee fundraising and volunteering activities appear to focus on the company's local charity partners.

Applications

Apply in writing to the correspondent.

Pricewaterhouse-Coopers LLP

Accountants, financial services

Correspondent: David Adair, Head of Community Affairs, 1 Embankment Place, London WC2N 6RH (tel: 020 7212 7140; website: www.pwc.co.uk)

Directors: Dan Schwarzmann; Hermione Hudson; John Dwyer; Jon Andrews; Kevin Burrowes; Kevin Ellis, Chair; Laura Hinton; Marco Amitrano; Margaret Cole; Stephanie Hyde; Warwick Hunt, Chief Financial Officer (women: 4; men: 8)

Year end	30/06/2015
Turnover	£3,083,000,000

Nature of business: Provider of assurance, tax and advisory services.

Company registration number: OC303525

Subsidiary undertakings include: PricewaterhouseCoopers Services Ltd; PricewaterhouseCoopers Overseas Ltd.

Focus of giving: General charitable purposes, enterprise/training, community/social welfare.

Membership: BITC, LBG

Community involvement	✓
Community contributions	✓
Company reports on anti-slavery	✓
CSR report	✓
Community Mark	✓
Corporate charity	✓
Employee-led support	✓
Gifts in kind	✓
Humanitarian aid: overseas	✓
Matched funding	✓
Payroll giving	✓

Charitable donations

Total UK (cash and in kind):	2015	£7,400,000
Total worldwide (cash and in kind):	2015	£7,400,000

Community involvement

Disaster relief
The company's website notes there being a Disaster Emergency Committee which will launch an appeal following a natural disaster. The executive board has an authority to consider contributions to appeals on a case by case basis.

The PwC Foundation (Charity Commission no. 1144124)
This foundation was established to develop social inclusion and sustainable development in the UK.

Note that PricewaterhouseCoopers has offices all around the world and contributes to local causes in overseas operating areas. The information in this entry relates to the UK site activities.

Centre for Social Impact
PricewaterhouseCoopers runs its own Centre for Social Impact which acts as a knowledge exchange for social innovation and impact measurement. The centre is also home to the PwC Social Entrepreneurs Club which provides mentoring, masterclasses, networking events, newsletters and other support to social entrepreneurs, and has more than 250 members across the UK.

Main locations
PricewaterhouseCoopers LLP has offices throughout the UK.

Community contributions

In 2015 the value of community contributions was estimated at £7.4 million which includes cash donations, in-kind support and time.

The company contributed about £145,000 through the Matched Giving Programme in 2015.

In-kind support

Non-cash donations include staff volunteering time and expertise, gifts of furniture and tickets to PwC Pantomime shows.

Employee-led support

Employee volunteering
The company staff and partners are given an opportunity to volunteer during working hours. Over 160 people were recognised by the Blueprint Volunteering Awards and over £30,000 was given to their charities.

Payroll giving
The employees are eligible to participate in Give As You Earn scheme operated by the Charities Aid Foundation. All administration costs are covered by the company. The corporate sustainability report notes that 4.3%of staff are currently involved with annual donations of around £530,000 in 2015.

Matched funding
Through the Matched Giving Programme the company increases

employees' donations to their chosen charities. The company's website specifies that in 2015 over 850 people participated in the scheme with around £145,000 being awarded by the company to 250 UK charities and voluntary organisations.

Corporate charity

The PwC Foundation (Charity Commission no. 1144124).

Applications

Applications should generally be made in writing to the correspondent, referenced 'Community Involvement Department'.

The PwC Foundation (Charity Commission no. 1144124) has stated on its website that 'the distribution of funds donated to the foundation are decided by the foundation trustees taking into account the voting preferences of the foundation's people'.

Principality Building Society

Building society, financial services

Correspondent: Pat Ashman, Sponsorship and Events Manager, PO Box 89, Principality Buildings, Queen Street, Cardiff CF10 1UA (0292077 3318; email: pat.ashman@principality.co.uk; website: www.principality.co.uk/about-us/our-community)

Directors: David Rigney; Derek Howell; Graeme Yorston, Group Chief Executive; Julie Haines; Laurence Adams, Chair; Natalie Elphicke; Nigel Annett; Robert Jones; Sally Evans; Steve Hughes, Group Finance Director (women: 3; men: 7)

Year end	31/12/2015
Turnover	£116,200,000
Pre-tax profit	£37,700,000

Nature of business: The provision of housing finance and a range of insurance and financial services.

FSA registration number: 155998

UK employees: 1,119

Focus of giving: Sport, recreation, children, young people, community/social welfare.

Membership: BITC

Community involvement	✓
Community contributions	✓
CSR report	✓
Cash donations declared	✓
Charity of the Year	✓
Gifts in kind	✓
Sponsorship	✓

Charitable donations

Cash UK (latest available):	2015	£30,000
Total UK (cash and in kind):	2015	£30,000
Cash worldwide:	2015	£30,000
Total worldwide (cash and in kind):	2015	£30,000

Community involvement

Charity of the Year

In 2015 employees raised £90,000 for their Charity of the Year Mind Cymru through events such as bake sales, half marathons and charity dinners. In the past supported charities have included: British Heart Foundation Cymru/Wales; Cancer Research Cymru/Wales; Wales Air Ambulance; NSPCC Cymru/Wales; Breast Cancer Care Cymru/Wales; MS Society Cymru/Wales.

Kit of the Month

During the year the company held a Kit of the Month competition where sports organisations could win equipment worth up to £500.

Education and employability

The company runs education and employability initiatives with several high schools. This has included providing reading, mentoring and employability workshops as well as other support to the pupils and teachers. There is also a partnership with the University of South Wales which sees undergraduates given in five year placements at Principality as a combined work and study route to a degree.

UK locations

Branches throughout Wales.

In-kind support

Non-cash support includes staff volunteering time.

Employee-led support

Staff volunteering efforts have involved conservation work in the Brecon Beacons, improving a school tuck shop and a nature reserve, facilitating a tag rugby festival, along with supporting a school's healthy eating initiative.

Staff members choose a charity (see 'Charity of the Year') they would like to support through their fundraising.

Commercially led support

There is a branch sponsorship scheme which aims to support sport, arts and culture. For more information on sponsorships you should contact the correspondent.

Beneficiaries of sponsorships have included: the National Eisteddfod; Only Boys Aloud, Royal Welsh Show; and Wales Millennium Centre.

Exclusions

The company's website notes that it receives a high number of requests for sponsorships which are judged on an individual basis and support cannot be given for the following:

- Political or religious causes
- Projects run on behalf of charities by companies operating for profit
- Organisations/projects outside the areas where the company has branches
- Development or running costs for projects
- Individuals

Applications

Sponsorship

Apply in writing to the correspondent.

Community support

Enquiries can be made through Principality's website: www.principality.co.uk/about-us/our-community/community-request-form.

Procter & Gamble UK

Health/beauty products, healthcare, household, personal care products

Correspondent: Janette Butler, Social Responsibility Programme Manager, The Heights, Brooklands, Weybridge, Surrey KT13 0XP (tel: 01932 896000; website: www.uk.pg.com)

Directors: Alexander Buckthorp; Anthony Appleton; Vijay Sitlani (women: 0; men: 3)

Year end	30/06/2015
Pre-tax profit	£78,553,000,000

Nature of business: Procter & Gamble UK, operating in the UK and Ireland, is a wholly owned subsidiary of The Procter & Gamble Company, USA. The principal activities of the company and its subsidiaries are the manufacture and marketing of innovative consumer products, with associated research and development services.

We have used the accounts of Procter & Gamble Ltd, a UK-registered holding company, which has no employees. The company's immediate parent company is Oral-B Laboratories and its ultimate parent company is The Procter & Gamble Company, both incorporated in the US.

Company registration number: 83758

Subsidiary undertakings include: Gillette Group UK Ltd; Procter & Gamble (Enterprise Fund) Ltd; and Wella (UK) Holdings Ltd.

Brands include: Gillette; Pampers; Wella.

Focus of giving: General charitable purposes, health, ill health, overseas projects, children, young people, disasters.

Membership: BITC

Community involvement ✓
Community contributions ✓
CSR report ✓
Charity partner(s) ✓
Gifts in kind ✓
Humanitarian aid: overseas ✓
Overseas giving ✓

Community involvement

P&G Fund and P&G Grassroots Funds

The Community Foundation for Tyne and Wear and Northumberland manages the above funds on behalf of Procter & Gamble to support the company's charitable giving. The fund concentrates on two areas:

- Creating the experience of home: turning houses into homes and providing the comforts of home to the people without them or who have been displaced
- Everyday health and confidence: enabling healthy lives through everyday healthy behaviours and hygiene education that enable confidence and self-esteem

The funds are open to Tyne and Wear and Northumberland charities working in the following areas: children in care, mental health, older individuals, other vulnerable/disadvantaged people, homelessness issues, people in palliative care and similar situations. Grants tend to be under £10,000 and applications should be made through the foundation.

Save the Children

Over the last three years the company has been working with Save the Children UK and has donated a total of £390,000 to help fund its Eat, Sleep, Learn, Play! programme. The programme supports children living in poverty by providing grants to families to buy household essentials such as beds, cookers, toys and books.

Disaster Relief

Globally P&G's disaster relief programmes provide essential products to victims of natural disasters as well as cash support.

Safe Drinking Water and Vaccination Programmes

The Children's Safe Drinking Water Programme helps provide clean drinking water to children and their families in financially developing countries. Procter & Gamble work with organisations such as CARE, ChildFund and Save the Children to deliver the programme. Pampers and Unicef have also been working together to vaccinate women and children against maternal and neonatal tetanus and have so far eliminated it from 17 countries.

Main UK locations

London, Manchester, Newcastle, Reading, Seaton Delaval, Skelmersdale, Weybridge.

Community contributions

We were unable to determine a figure for Procter & Gamble UK's community contributions.

In-kind support

Procter & Gamble UK partnered with In-Kind Direct in 2002 and since then has donated an estimated £42 million worth of goods. In 2015 the company made 21 donations of stock benefitting 2,054 voluntary and community organisations. In the event of large-scale, global disasters the company has mobile relief units to provide products and services directly to those in the most highly impacted areas.

Applications

Company

More information on community support in the UK and Ireland can be obtained by contacting one of the regional co-ordinators or the correspondent.

P&G Community Fund

For more information on financial grants in Tyne and Wear and Northumberland only, contact Su Legg (email: sl@communityfoundation.org.uk, tel: 0191 222 0945). Applications should be made on the standard foundation form. For more information see: www.communityfoundation.org.uk/funds/pg-2.

Provident Financial PLC

Financial services

Correspondent: Rob Lawson, The Corporate Responsibility Manager, 1 Godwin Street, Bradford BD1 2SU (tel: 01274 351135; email: corporateresponsibility@providentfinancial.com; website: www.providentfinancial.com)

Directors: Alison Halsey; Andrew Fisher, Finance Director; Ken Mullen; Malcolm Le May; Manjit Wolstenholme, Chair; Peter Crook, Chief Executive; Rob Anderson; Stuart Sinclair (women: 2; men: 6)

Year end	31/12/2015
Turnover	£113,000,000
Pre-tax profit	£273,000,000

Nature of business: Personal credit products and services.

Company registration number: 668987

Subsidiary undertakings include: Greenwood Personal Credit; Provident Financial Management Services Ltd; Provident Investments PLC; Vanquis Bank Ltd.

Brands include: Moneybarn; Satsuma loans; Vanquis Bank.

Total employees: 3,758

Focus of giving: Local groups, financial education, community/social welfare.

Membership: BITC, LBG

Community involvement ✓
Community contributions ✓
Company reports on anti-slavery ✓
CSR report ✓
CSR or charity committee ✓
Cash donations declared ✓
Employee-led support ✓
FTSE 100 ✓
Gifts in kind ✓
Market-led giving ✓
Matched funding ✓
Payroll giving ✓

Charitable donations

Cash worldwide:	2015	£2,829,000
Total worldwide (cash and in kind):	2015	£2,869,000

Community involvement

The company's 2015 CR report notes that part of its community involvement strategy is Good Neighbourhood and The Vanquis Bank Active Community programmes.

Good Neighbour Programme

The scheme was established in 2009 as a flagship community programme and supports local projects in the UK and Ireland. The company seeks to address issues arising in the communities in which it operates, in particular to address social inclusion problems in deprived communities and through working with the money advice sector to improve financial education. In 2015 the group supported 37 projects with long-term funding of three years or more.

Vanquis Bank Active Community Programme

The programme operates through community foundations in Bradford, Chatham and London. Each community foundation invites applications from local charities which are then presented to an employee panel in each of Vanquis Bank's offices. In 2015 the programme supported 22 community projects. Vanquis Bank also supports Mencap, Friends of the Elderly and Hatua, a local education project in Kenya.

Support for the Money Advice Sector

The group has partnerships with several money advice organisations and helps them to provide better-quality advice and help individuals who are having difficulty paying their debts. Money advice providers include: Advice UK, Citizens Advice, Step Change Debt Charity, Institute of Money Advisers, Money Advice Liaison Group, Money Advice Scotland, Money Advice Trust, and National Debtline.

Main locations

UK

Community contributions

The annual report and accounts for 2015 specify that community investment totalled £3.1 million through various community initiatives, support for the money advice sector and social research. The CR report and the accounts note that the group's cash contributions amounted to £2.8 million, employee volunteering time totalled £40,500 and management costs totalled £229,000. We could not determine the amount given in cash in the UK.

Beneficiaries included: Boomerang; Byron Primary School; The Early Focus Project; Immanuel Project; Northfield Sports Association; Participate Projects; Project for the Regeneration of Druids Heath; The Royal Lyceum; Sure Start All Saints; Young People Cornwall.

In-kind support

Provident provides in-kind help in the form of employee volunteering time.

Employee-led support

Employee volunteering

Employees are encouraged volunteer in their local communities through company-led volunteering challenges and skills-based volunteering, or by volunteering outside work. During 2015 employees volunteered 2,225 hours.

Matched funding

Employees can apply for funding to match fundraising activities they undertake outside work. In 2015 Provident Financial Group provided £41,500 to support employees' fundraising.

Applications

Apply in writing to the correspondent.

Applications to the Good Neighbour Programme can be made through the programme's website: www.providentgoodneighbour.co.uk.

Prudential PLC

Financial services, insurance

Correspondent: Corporate Responsibility Team, Laurence Pountney Hill, London EC4R 0HH (tel: 020 7220 7588; email: responsibility@prudential.co.uk; website: www.prudential.co.uk)

Directors: Alice Schroeder; Ann Godbehere; Anne Richards; Anthony Nightingale; Barry Stowe; David Law; John Foley; Kai Nargolwala; Lord Turner; Mike Wells, Group Chief Executive; Nic Nicandrou, Chief Financial Officer; Paul Manduca, Chair; Penny James; Sir Howard Davies; The Hon. Philip Remmant; Tony Wilkey (women: 4; men: 12)

Year end	31/12/2015
Turnover	£41,305,000,000
Pre-tax profit	£3,321,000,000

Nature of business: Prudential PLC provides retail financial services and insurance products in Europe, the US, Asia and, recently, Africa.

Company registration number: 1397169

Subsidiary undertakings include: Prudential Annuities Ltd; The Prudential Assurance Company Ltd; Prudential Retirement Income Ltd.

Brands include: M&G; Jackson.

Total employees: 23,507

Focus of giving: Education, local groups, older people, overseas projects, disasters.

Membership: BITC, LBG

Community involvement	✓
Community contributions	✓
CSR report	✓
CSR or charity committee	✓
Cash donations declared	✓
Charity partner(s)	✓
Community Mark	✓
Employee-led support	✓
FTSE 100	✓
Gifts in kind	✓
Humanitarian aid: overseas	✓
Market-led giving	✓
Overseas giving	✓
Payroll giving	✓
Sponsorship	✓

Charitable donations

Cash worldwide:	2015	£18,800,000
Total worldwide (cash and in kind):	2015	£21,700,000

Community involvement

Community and Charity Policy

The UK Community and Charity Policy paper states:

> Our community investment activity is financed through a discretionary cash budget approved annually by the Prudential board. This is enhanced through support we also provide via the expertise of our people, and other in kind donations. We look for long-term strategic involvement with community partnerships to address local issues key to the interests of the communities we serve and to enhance our reputation as a responsible company. Many of our employees are actively involved in their local communities as volunteers and we have a volunteering policy in place to support them.

It is noted that any scheme must involve the company's employees, with priority being given to projects that will make a positive difference to retirement. The main areas of focus are:

- Education – raising levels of literacy and developing people to be the best they can be
- Employee Volunteering and personal development – encouraging our people to get involved in their local communities and at the same time developing their skills
- Making a Difference to retirement – focusing on volunteering schemes that make a difference to people's lives in retirement
- Giving to Charity – making it easy and tax efficient for employees to donate through our Payroll Giving scheme.

Education

Prudential UK and Europe is a National Champion of Business in the Community's Business Class programme. It has also partnered with three schools in London, Reading and Stirling. Since 2013, over 320 employees have helped over 3,400 children develop their interview, presentation and public speaking skills.

Disaster readiness and relief

There is a fund to support communities which have suffered from natural disasters. The website suggests that both financial and in-kind support is mainly offered in Asia, where natural catastrophes are most prone to happen.

Well-being

The Prudential RideLondon raised more than £12 million for charitable causes in 2015 with over 95,000 people taking part. Sponsorship of the event will continue until 2018.

The group also supports SportsAid by providing grants to athletes with disabilities to buy sports equipment.

Charity partner

The group has been a partner of Save the Children's Emergency Fund for a number of years and in 2016 committed to continue the partnership for another three years.

Main locations

Prudential's main offices are in London, Reading and Stirling.

Community contributions

In 2015 a total of £21.7 million was spent in community investment (including cash and in-kind support). The value of community investment is calculated using the London Benchmarking Group (LBG) standards. It is further specified that cash donations totalled £18.8 million. Around £5.8 million came from UK and EU operations broken down as follows: social welfare and environment (£3.1 million), education (£2.4 million), cultural (£227,000) and staff volunteering (£109,000). The remaining £13 million came from Jackson National Life Insurance Company, Prudential Corporation Asia and Prudential Africa.

In-kind support

A range of in-kind support is offered to organisations on a local basis. This includes employees' volunteering time and skills, and also office space, meeting rooms, computers and office furniture.

Employee-led support

Employee volunteering

Employees are encouraged to get involved in their communities through volunteering and fundraising efforts. There are also local fundraising teams organising all fundraising activities on site and donating the money to selected charities.

In 2015 employees provided a total of 51,979 volunteering hours throughout the group. Over 7,000 employees participated in Prudential's volunteering programme, the Chair's Challenge. This sees employees volunteering on projects initiated by Prudential's global charity partners, including Plan International, Help Age International and Junior Achievement. Prudential donates £150 to charity partners for each employee who registers for the programme. The charities then use the money to seed-fund charitable projects for Prudential volunteers.

Payroll giving

The company operates a payroll giving scheme to allow employees to make donations to local charities of their choice. Across the group £520,000 was donated by employees through payroll giving.

Exclusions

The UK Community and Charity Policy paper excludes the following from being eligible for support or sponsorship:

- Political parties or religious organisations
- Individuals
- Requests for sports equipment for employees taking part in local sports competitions on behalf of the organisation
- Requests for donations outside the Payroll Giving Scheme

Applications

Further information can be sought from the Corporate Responsibility Team at the address/telephone number given here.

QinetiQ Group PLC

Defence, aerospace, marine, security services, telecommunications

Correspondent: Group Head of CR and Sustainability, Cody Technology Park, Ively Road, Farnborough, Hampshire GU14 0LX (tel: 01252 392000; website: www.qinetiq.com)

Directors: Admiral Sir James Burnell-Nugent; David Mellors, Chief Financial Officer; Ian Mason; Jon Messent; Lyn Brubaker; Mark Elliott, Chair; Michael Harper; Paul Murray; Steve Wadley, Chief Executive Officer; Susan Searle (women: 2; men: 8)

Year end	31/03/2016
Turnover	£755,700,000
Pre-tax profit	£108,700,000

Nature of business: The group's principal activity is the global supply of scientific and technical solutions and services for business, defence and security.

Company registration number: 4586941

Subsidiary undertakings include: Boldon James Ltd; Optasense Ltd; Foster-Miller Inc.

Focus of giving: Education, overseas projects, science technology, children, young people.

Community involvement	✓
Community contributions	✓
Company reports on anti-slavery	✓
CSR report	✓
AF Covenant	✓
Charity partner(s)	✓
Employee-led support	✓
Gifts in kind	✓
Market-led giving	✓
Matched funding	✓
Overseas giving	✓
Payroll giving	✓
STEM-focused	✓

Community involvement

The group supports a number of charities chosen by its employees. Individual sites also help their local community projects. Note that the group receives a large number of requests for support from charities.

QinetiQ has signed the Armed Forces Corporate Covenant declaring its intentions to support the Armed Forces both through its business operations, community involvement and charitable work.

STEM programmes

The main focus of QinetiQ's community involvement is its STEM outreach programme. The group has relationships with organisations such as STEMNET, the Arkwright Scholarship Trust, Primary Engineer and the Social Mobility Foundation in the UK. The STEM ambassadors in the UK organise outreach events for schoolchildren such as the Annual Powerboat Challenge, National Women in Engineering Day and Cyber Security Challenge UK.

Main locations

The group has offices throughout the UK. Details of office locations can be found on the group's website.

Community contributions

We could not identify the amount given in charitable contributions in from the annual report and accounts for 2015/16. Cash donations have been between £100,000 and £145,000 in previous years.

Beneficiaries included: Cancer Research UK; Help for Heroes; RNLI.

In-kind support

Staff members volunteer their time and professional skills, for example through the UK Employee volunteering Scheme.

Employee-led support

Employees are encouraged to volunteer by participating in the company's programmes, supporting the three corporate charities, or helping organisations of their choice through the payroll giving scheme.

Payroll giving

A payroll giving scheme is available.

Matched funding

Employee fundraising activities are matched by the group to support the three corporate charities (Cancer Research UK, Help for Heroes and RNLI). These three organisations were voted for by employees and have formed a five-year partnership with QinetiQ.

Commercially led support

The 5% Club

An initiative has also been launched aimed at investing in the young generation and creation of apprenticeships and employment opportunities. Its current target is for 5% of UK workforce to be on apprenticeship or graduate programmes by March 2015.

Applications

Apply in writing to the correspondent. Community appeals should be addressed to the Community Liaison Officer at a local branch.

The Rank Group PLC

Gaming, leisure

Correspondent: Frances Bingham, Company Secretary, Statesman House, Stafferton Way, Maidenhead, West Berkshire SL6 1AY (tel: 01628 604000; website: www.rank.com/en/responsibility/communities.html)

Directors: Chris Bell; Clive Jennings, Finance Director; Frances Bingham, Company Secretary; Henry Birch, Chief Executive Officer; Ian Burke, Chair; Lord Kilmorey; Owen O'Donnell; Steven Esom; Susan Hooper (women: 2; men: 7)

Year end	30/06/2016
Turnover	£753,000,000
Pre-tax profit	£85,500,000

Nature of business: The Rank Group is a leisure and entertainment group with a focus on gaming. It operates casinos and bingo venues in the UK, as well as two casinos in Belgium and nine bingo venues in Spain.

Company registration number: 3140769

Subsidiary undertakings include: The Gaming Group Ltd; Grosvenor Casinos Ltd; Rank Leisure Ltd.

Brands include: Enracha; Grosvenor Casinos; Mecca.

Total employees: 10,600

Focus of giving: Health, ill health, marginalised people, poverty and social exclusion, community/social welfare.

Community involvement	✓
Community contributions	✓
Company reports on anti-slavery	✓
CSR report	✓
Directors have other relevant posts	✓
Charity partner(s)	✓
Employee-led support	✓
Gifts in kind	✓
Payroll giving	✓

Community involvement

The Rank Group website provides the following overview of the group's community involvement: 'Rank and its brands have a long history of community involvement and charitable fundraising. Our venues are often cited as 'community hubs' – particularly our Mecca bingo venues. We challenge all of our teams to consider what they can contribute to the communities that they serve. This takes the form of charitable fundraising for local and national causes, the use of our venues for community events and participation in local business and community organisations, among other activities.'

Rank Cares

In 2014 the Rank entered into partnership with the Carers Trust to create the Rank Cares programme. Through the programme, the charity benefits from the support of Mecca, Grosvenor Casino and support centre employees who take part in fundraising and volunteering activities. At the time the annual report for 2015/16 was published (August 2016), £1.25 million had been raised through the partnership and the group continues to set an annual fundraising target of £400,000.

Three dedicated Rank Cares funds have been established through the partnership, they are outlined on the website as follows:

- Essentials Fund – 'providing basic household equipment to carers who are experiencing financial hardship'
- Inspire to Be Fund – 'enabling carers to gain new skills'
- Take a Break Fund – 'giving carers time out from their caring role to relax and recharge their batteries'

Grants are considered through grant panels held approximately five times a year; the Rank Group annual report for 2015/16 further explains that '110 Rank employees have had the opportunity to sit on a panel to help decide where and to whom the money is awarded'.

In addition, a framework has been devised through the programme, which allows employees to volunteer their time, and often their skills and talents, for the Carers Trust.

The Bingo Association national charity

Mecca helped to support the chosen national charity of The Bingo Association, of which it is a member. More than £67,000 was raised for Variety, the children's charity, through merchandise sales and charity bingo games.

Directors with other relevant posts

Chris Bell: trustee of the Northern Racing College.

Susan Hooper: member of the international advisory board of LUISS Business School, Rome.

Main locations

The group has 143 venues in England, Scotland and Wales. To find your nearest Mecca or Grosvenor Casino, visit the 'Where we operate' page on the website (www.rank.com/en/about-us/where-we-operate.html).

Community contributions

The annual report and accounts for 2015/16 did not declare a figure for cash donations, nor were we able to determine the value of in-kind support given by the group.

In-kind support

Venues

Venues belonging to the group are used as venues for community events. An example of this happens at Christmas when Mecca venues collect gifts for children's hospitals and hospices in their areas.

Employee-led support

Employee volunteering

Mecca and Grosvenor Casino colleagues are actively involved in volunteering through the Rank Cares programme. Since its launch, 6,228 volunteer hours have been contributed of which 2,450 were in 2015/16. During the year, colleagues were involved in a range of activities at carers centres including pamper days, gardening and baking. We were unable to determine whether or not these hours were contributed from company or from employees' own time.

Employee fundraising

Employees fundraise for the Carers Trust and a range of other causes, including cancer charities. One particular example provided in the annual report is a pair of employees from Mecca Chester who raised more than £1,200 for the Carers Trust by carrying out a parachute jump. The duo also helped to raise awareness of the charity and its work by getting publicity in local media.

Payroll giving

One of the ways in which funds are raised is through the Pennies from Heaven payroll giving scheme, through which employees donate odd pennies from their salary. The annual report states that 20% of employees are signed up and that £17,000 has been generated. Note that the report did not specify if this figure referred to the amount raised by the group's employees for the entire time the scheme had been in place, or to the amount raised during the financial year reported (2015/16).

Applications

We would suggest that queries regarding local community support are directed to your nearest Mecca Bingo or Grosvenor Casino venue.

Rathbone Brothers PLC

Financial services

Correspondent: The Social and Environmental Committee, 1 Curzon Street, Mayfair, London W1J 5HD (tel: 020 7399 0000; email: marketing@rathbones.com; website: www.rathbones.com)

Directors: David Harrel; Jame Dean; Kathryn Matthews; Mark Nicholls, Chair; Paul Chavasse; Paul Stockton, Finance Director; Philip Howell, Chief Executive; Sarah Gentleman (women: 2; men: 6)

Year end	31/12/2015
Turnover	£229,200,000
Pre-tax profit	£70,400,000

Nature of business: The group is an independent provider of investment and wealth management services for private investors, charities and trustees. It operates in the UK and Jersey.

Company registration number: 1000403

Subsidiary undertakings include: Rathbone Investment Management Ltd; Rathbone Pension and Advisory Services Ltd; Rathbone Unit Trust Management Ltd.

Focus of giving: Education, enterprise/training, health, ill health, arts, culture, children, young people, community/social welfare.

Community involvement	✓
Community contributions	✓
Company reports on anti-slavery	✓
Payroll giving	✓
Sponsorship	✓

Charitable donations

Cash UK (latest available):	2015	£353,000
Total UK (cash and in kind):	2015	£353,000
Cash worldwide:	2015	£353,000
Total worldwide (cash and in kind):	2015	£353,000

Community involvement

The Rathbones Financial Awareness Programme

This free scheme, aimed at 16- to 24-year-olds, forms a significant part of the group's youth development initiatives. It involves investment managers delivering presentations within the company's offices and at schools around the UK on financial matters, career routes and interview techniques in order to give young people the knowledge to manage their own finances at a young age.

Partnerships

The company has ongoing partnerships with English Lacrosse and Lacrosse Scotland up until 2017.

Local communities

Regional offices are encouraged to get involved with local charity projects.

Main locations

Rathbones has 15 offices throughout the UK and Jersey. Office locations can be found on the group's website.

Community contributions

In 2015 the group made charitable donations totalling £353,000 (2014: £253,000), including an award of £140,000 to The Rathbone Brothers Foundation. Matched funding from the company totalled £152,000 (2014: £134,000).

Beneficiaries have included: Anthony Nolan Trust; Children with Cancer UK; Claire House; Rathbone Charitable Foundation; and The Oliver King Foundation.

In-kind support

Employee skills and time are donated through the educational initiatives, for example Financial Awareness Programme.

Employee-led support

Payroll giving

Employees can support charities through the Give As You Earn scheme. In 2015 employees donated £182,000 (2014: £191,000) through this scheme, administered by the Charities Aid Foundation.

Matched funding

The group will match staff donations of up to £200 per month made through Give As You Earn. In 2015 a total of £152,000 was given to increase staff donations to their chosen causes.

Commercially led support

Sponsorships

Rathbones sponsored several youth development programmes including the Chalke Valley History Festival for Schools, the dot-art art competition, the Bang Goes the Borders science festival and the attempt by University of Liverpool students to break the human-powered land speed record.

Applications

Applications to the foundation should be made in writing to the correspondent.

See the corporate foundations section for details of how to apply to the foundation.

Ravensale Ltd

Property

Correspondent: Bruce Jarvis, Trustee, The Joron Charitable Trust, 115 Wembley Commercial Centre, East Lane, North Wembley, Middlesex HA9 7UR (020 8908 4655; email: ravensale100@btconnect.com)

Directors: Bruce Jarvis; Joseph Jarvis (women: 0; men: 2)

Year end	30/06/2015

Nature of business: The principal activity of Ravensale Ltd is property development and investment, and the design and manufacture of ballpoint pen components.

The number of employees is not known.

Company registration number: 1476675

Subsidiary undertakings include: Copartnership Developments Ltd; and JGR Enterprises, Ltd (USA).

Focus of giving: General charitable purposes, education, medical research.

Community involvement	✓
Community contributions	✓
Corporate charity	✓

Charitable donations

Cash UK (latest available):	2015	£300,000
Total UK (cash and in kind):	2015	£300,000
Cash worldwide:	2015	£300,000
Total worldwide (cash and in kind):	2015	£300,000

Community involvement

The Joron Charitable Trust (Charity Commission no. 1062547)

The company directs all its charitable giving through the Joron Charitable Trust, of which the directors are trustees. The trust was established in 1997 and derives almost all of its income from Ravensale Ltd. It aims to support general charitable purposes and makes grants to registered charities in various fields where it can be demonstrated that the grants will be used effectively. Support is given to organisations throughout the UK.

Community contributions

The company's accounts for 2014/15 provided limited information, due to an exemption. The Joron Charitable Trust's accounts for 2014/15 note that it received a donation of £300,000 from Ravensale Ltd which we have taken as the company's cash donations for the year.

Corporate charity

The Joron Charitable Trust (Charity Commission no. 1062547).

Applications

Apply in writing to the correspondent.

Reckitt Benckiser Group PLC

Healthcare, household, personal care products, pharmaceuticals

Correspondent: The Corporate Communications Department, 103–105 Bath Road, Slough, Berkshire SL1 3UH (tel: 01753 217800; email: sustainability@rb.com; website: www.rb.com)

Directors: Adrian Bellamy, Chair; Adrian Hennah, Chief Financial Officer; Andre Lacroix; Chris Sinclair; Judy Sprieser; Ken Hydon; Mary Harris; Nicandro Durante; Pam Kirby; Rakesh Kapoor, Chief Executive Officer; Warren Tucker (women: 3; men: 8)

Year end	31/12/2015
Turnover	£8,874,000,000
Pre-tax profit	£2,208,000,000

Nature of business: Principal activities of the group are the manufacture and sale of household and healthcare products.

Company registration number: 527217

Subsidiary undertakings include: Reckitt Benkiser LLC; Reckitt Benkiser Pharmaceuticals Inc.; Schiff Nutrition International, Inc.

Brands include: Durex; Harpic; Dettol.

Total employees: 25,750

Focus of giving: Education, health, ill health, children, young people.

Community involvement	✓
Community contributions	✓
CSR report	✓
Cash donations declared	✓
Charity partner(s)	✓
Employee-led support	✓
FTSE 100	✓
Gifts in kind	✓
Humanitarian aid: overseas	✓

Charitable donations

Cash worldwide:	2015	£3,250,000
Total worldwide (cash and in kind):	2015	£3,250,000

Community involvement

Charity partnership

The group was Save the Children's first corporate partner in the Children's Emergency Fund (in 2007); support to the fund has continued in 2015. RB is currently working with Save the Children on the 'Save a Child Every Minute Programme' which looks to significantly reduce the number of children under five that die from diarrhoea.

Health initiatives

The group runs health and hygiene awareness programmes with its brands. For example, Dettol works with NGOs, healthcare professionals and governments to educate new mums in hygiene habits that will protect their new babies and families. So far the initiatives have reached 200 million people and RB is hoping to reach a further 200 million people by 2020.

Main locations

The group is based in Slough.

Community contributions

In 2015 RB made a donation of £6.5 million to Save the Children. This consisted of a corporate donation of £3.25 million and £3.25 million raised by staff worldwide. A figure for UK cash donations was not available.

In-kind support

The group donates products (such as, handwashing bags, soaps and liquids), educational material on health safety and hygiene, also organises health-related awareness campaigns (for example, health camps and planting of trees that naturally repel insects in India) and staff volunteering help.

Employee-led support

Employee fundraising

Employees raised £3.25 million for Save the Children in 2015 through events such as bake sales, raffles and challenges.

Applications

Apply in writing to the correspondent, referenced 'Sustainability'. The Corporate Communications and Affairs Department is concerned with charitable giving.

Redrow Group PLC

Building/construction, property

Correspondent: The Corporate Responsibility Committee, Redrow House, St David's Park, Ewloe, Flintshire CH5 3RX (tel: 01244 520044; email: groupservices@redrow.co.uk; website: www.redrowplc.co.uk)

Directors: Barbara Richmond, Group Finance Director; Debbie Hewitt; Graham Cope; John Tutte, Group Chief Executive Officer; Liz Peace; Nick Hewson; Sir Michael Lyons; Steve Morgan, Chair (women: 3; men: 5)

Year end	30/06/2015
Turnover	£1,600,000,000
Pre-tax profit	£204,000,000

Nature of business: The principal activity of the group is residential, commercial and mixed use development. Redrow PLC is a public listed company, listed on the London Stock Exchange and domiciled in the UK.

Company registration number: 2877315

Subsidiary undertakings include: The principal subsidiary company is Redrow Homes Ltd.

Focus of giving: Economic generation, education, health, ill health, arts, culture, sport, recreation, children, young people, community/social welfare.

Membership: BITC

Community involvement	✓
Community contributions	✓
CSR report	✓
CSR or charity committee	✓
Cash donations declared	✓
Charity partner(s)	✓
Corporate charity	✓
Employee-led support	✓
Gifts in kind	✓

Charitable donations

Cash UK (latest available):	2015	£800,000
Cash worldwide:	2015	£800,000

Community involvement

The majority of the group's giving is focused on the improvement of local communities. It also makes cash donations, most of which go to The Morgan Foundation (Charity Commission no. 1087056).

The group has the Redrow Foundation (Charity Commission no. 1113073) which focuses on relieving poverty and sickness and had a total expenditure of £51,000 in 2014/15.

Community contributions

In 2014/15 the group committed £128 million to 'fund the improvement of local communities'. Based on the information in previous years' reports, a large proportion of the funding was used to provide social or affordable housing, education and recreational facilities.

The annual report and accounts for 2014/15 states that a total of £800,000 was paid in charitable donations. From this £800,000 a donation of £700,000 was made to the Morgan Foundation (Charity Commission no. 1087056), a UK-registered charity of which Steve Morgan, the Chair of the group, is also a trustee.

In-kind support

Around 209 hectares of land has been provided to the Bumblebee Conservation Trust and the RSPB. Books on environmental topics have also been given to schoolchildren.

Employee-led support

The 2014/15 annual report states that 'the company and its employees are actively involved in fundraising activities for specific charities'.

Corporate charity

Redrow Foundation (Charity Commission no. 1113073).

Applications

Apply writing to the correspondent, referencing 'The Corporate Responsibility Committee'. Our research suggests that it is helpful to state how you intend to match or increase any donation you may receive in your application.

RELX Group (formerly known as Reed Elsevier)

Financial services

Correspondent: Dr Márcia Balisciano, Corporate Responsibility Director, 1–3 Strand, London WC2N 5JR (tel: 020 7166 5500; fax: 020 7166 5799; email: corporate.responsibility@relx.com; website: www.relx.com/corporateresponsibility/community)

Directors: Adrian Hennah; Anthony Habgood, Chair; Ben van der Veer; Carol Mills; Dr Wolfhart Hauser; Erik Engstrom, Chief Executive Officer; Linda Sanford; Marike van Lier Lels; Nick Luff, Chief Financial Officer; Robert MacLeod (women: 3; men: 7)

Year end	31/12/2015
Turnover	£5,971,000,000
Pre-tax profit	£1,312,000,000

Nature of business: RELX Group is a global provider of information and analytics for professional business customers in four major industries: Scientific; Technical and Medical; Risk and Business Analytics; and Legal. The group also organises exhibitions and events across 43 industry sectors.

Subsidiary undertakings include: The Medicine Publishing Company Ltd; Reed Educational and Professional Publishing Ltd; Reed Events Ltd.

Total employees: Approximately 30,000

Focus of giving: Education, enterprise/training, local groups, overseas projects, poverty and social exclusion, children, young people.

Membership: BITC, LBG

Accredited Living Wage Employer	✓
Community involvement	✓
Community contributions	✓
Company reports on anti-slavery	✓
CSR report	✓
CSR or charity committee	✓
Directors have other relevant posts	✓
Cash donations declared	✓
Charity partner(s)	✓
Company gives to smaller charities	✓
Employee-led support	✓
FTSE 100	✓
Gifts in kind	✓
Humanitarian aid: overseas	✓
Matched funding	✓
Overseas giving	✓
Pro bono	✓

Charitable donations

Cash UK (latest available):	2015	£21,500
Cash worldwide:	2015	£3,100,000
Total worldwide (cash and in kind):	2015	£6,100,000

Community involvement

RELX Group contributes to local and global communities through its RE Cares programme which, as described on the Corporate Responsibility section of the website, 'supports employee and corporate engagement that makes a positive impact on society through volunteering and giving'. Note that all amounts reported in dollars were converted into pounds sterling at the time of writing (December 2016).

RE Cares programme

This global programme is supported by a network of staff members – known as RE Cares Champions – from across the business who organise and promote community engagement. In 2015 the number of colleagues serving as RE Cares Champions rose to more than 210.

Each September, a dedicated RE Cares Month takes place, through which thousands of employees contribute time to volunteering and fundraising activities. In 2015 80% of the group's locations around the world got involved.

The dedicated CR section of the group's website explains that, through the programme, the group prioritises 'education for disadvantaged young people that furthers one or more of our unique contributions as a business, including universal, sustainable access to information'. Activities carried out through the programme 'range from reading support programmes and charity fundraising initiatives to donations of time and services'. The group's volunteering policy, 'Two Days' is also enacted through the programme.

Central donations programme

The group's central donations programme is closely tied to RE Cares's priority of promoting the education of disadvantaged young people. The CR section of the group's website describes how the allocation of funds is decided: 'The grant-giving process is employee-led; employees anywhere in the Group can nominate relevant charities for funding from a budget voted on by RE Cares Champions. Decision criteria include potential impact of a project on beneficiaries and opportunities for staff engagement, including volunteering.'

Charity partnerships

RELX Group's employee-nominated global fundraising partner from 2013 was the International Rescue Committee (IRC), with funds raised going to support the education of young people living in Sierra Leone.

The group also has a long-standing partnership of more than 20 years with Book Aid International, having donated more than 666,000 books since 2004, as well as funding to support libraries and literary activities for young people in sub-Saharan Africa.

According to the Corporate Responsibility report for 2015, LexisNexis Legal and Professional UK, which is part of RELX Group, is a founding partner of the International Law Book Facility (ILBF), and has donated more than 6,000 texts since 2005. These have been distributed to 'professional bodies, advice centres, pro bono groups, law schools and other institutions involved in access to justice'.

Directors with other relevant posts

Linda Sanford: on the boards of trustees of Rensselaer Polytechnic Institute and the New York Hall of Science.

Corporate Responsibility Forum

The group has a Corporate Responsibility Forum which, according to the Corporate Responsibility report for 2015, is 'chaired by a senior leader and involving individuals who represent all key functions and business units'. Along with the board and senior management, the CR Forum oversees and monitors responsibility objectives and the group's performance against them.

Main locations

London

Community contributions

The Corporate Responsibility report for 2015 shows that total contributions given during the year amounted to £6.1 million. The 'Community' page of the group's website breaks this figure down further, stating that the group 'donated £3.1m in cash (including through matching gifts) and £3.0m in products, services and staff time'.* We have taken this as the group's worldwide contribution.

*The website further states that these contributions had a market value of approximately £13.7 million, although – as is our usual practice – we do not take this into account when calculating the total amount for the group's contributions.

RE Cares donations

The 'Community' page on the website explains that, during 2015, RE Cares Champions donated around $400,000 (approximately £317,000) from central funds to 40 charities. We have taken this figure to be included in the totals stated above. Recipients included a project tackling the issue of violence in Colombian schools and 'the provision of legal and educational services to foster youth in Los Angeles'.

Employee Opinion Survey (EOS)

We believe that also included in the figures above is the $12,000 (approximately £9,500) given by RELX through the Employee Opinion Survey initiative to the International Rescue Committee. See 'Employee-led support' for more information.

Fit2Win

Each of the four winning teams received $1,000 for their charity/charities of choice, totalling around £3,200.

Donations in the UK

According to the website, at least £21,500 was awarded through the small grants scheme for charities working locally to the group's London head office. We have taken this as the group's UK cash donations; however, we are certain that the actual figure was higher. We were unable to determine the value of in-kind contributions in the UK.

The beneficiaries of small grants were: Futureversity and Richard House Children's Hospice (£3,300 each); Concordia, The Connection at St Martin in the Fields, KIDS, Kids Company, and School Home Support (£3,000 each).

Details of beneficiaries supported centrally by the group are available from: www.relx.com/corporateresponsibility/community/Pages/projects-we-supported-centrally.aspx

In-kind support

Staff time

Employees are able to take up to two days for volunteering purposes in company time (with their line managers' approval). In 2015 a total of 10,525 days were volunteered by employees in company time.

Gifts in-kind

RELX Group has a product donations policy which is available to download from the website. Product donations are given to registered charities in the form of hardcopy product (e.g. books and educational materials), non-hardcopy product (e.g. free access to journals and investigative solutions), and unwanted (but still useful) IT equipment and office furnishings.

It would appear that product donations are typically given through the group's partnerships with charitable organisations, such as the one it has with Book Aid International. For the redistribution of unwanted office items (IT equipment and furnishings) RELX Group works with a handful of selected partners; in the UK these are Remploy and Green Works.

Employee-led support

Employee volunteering

During the year 37% of staff were engaged with volunteering activities through the RE Cares programme. According to the 2015 key CR data included in the CR Report, this percentage reflects both those employees who used their two volunteering days helping causes that matter to them personally and those who took part with volunteering activities sponsored by the group.

Employee fundraising

In 2015 employees continued to fundraise for their nominated two-year global charity partner, the International Rescue Committee. The initial fundraising target of $100,000 (approximately £79,500) was surpassed, with $170,000 (approximately £135,000) raised to support the education of disadvantaged young people in Sierra Leone. Activities ranged from sponsored walks, runs and cycling to charity sales and dress-down days.

Fit2Win

RELX holds this annual competition which is designed to raise money for charity while promoting well-being among staff. Employees form teams to compete within four sports categories – walking, running, cycling and swimming – to win cash prizes for their chosen charities. In 2015 a total 95 teams took part in the competition.

Employee Opinion Survey (EOS)

In 2015 RELX undertook an Employee Opinion Survey, which was launched to its staff around the world. For each survey completed, RELX donated $1 to the employee-nominated charity fundraising partner, International Rescue Committee.

Matched funding

Employees of the group are supported in their fundraising efforts through a gift-matching scheme.

Applications

RE Cares programme

RELX Group's central donations programme is employee-led, with donations received by charities nominated by staff.

Aside from the group's central CSR programme, many of the group's subsidiaries have developed their own CSR initiatives.

Renishaw PLC

Instrumentation

Correspondent: Renishaw Charities Committee, New Mills, Wotton-under-Edge, Gloucestershire GL12 8JR (email: charities.committee@renishaw.com; website: www.renishaw.com/en)

Directors: Allen Roberts, Group Finance Director; Carol Chesney; Geoff McFarland; John Deer; John Jeans; Kath Durrant; Norma Tang; Sir David Grant; Sir David McMurtry, Chair and Chief Executive; William Lee (women: 7; men: 3)

Year end	30/06/2016
Turnover	£494,700,000
Pre-tax profit	£144,200,000

Nature of business: Renishaw is a scientific technology company with expertise in measurement, motion control, spectroscopy and precision machining.

Company registration number: 1106260

Subsidiary undertakings include: Renishaw International Ltd; Wotton Travel Ltd; Renishaw Software Ltd.

UK employees: 2,725

Total employees: 4,112

Focus of giving: General charitable purposes, local groups, education.

Community involvement	✓
Community contributions	✓
CSR report	✓
CSR or charity committee	✓
Employee-led support	✓
Humanitarian aid: overseas	✓
Matched funding	✓
Sponsorship	✓
STEM-focused	✓

Charitable donations

Cash UK (latest available):	2016	£100,000
Total UK (cash and in kind):	2016	£100,000
Cash worldwide:	2016	£100,000
Total worldwide (cash and in kind):	2016	£100,000

Community involvement

Renishaw's charitable work is focused through its Charities Committee and work in promoting STEM subjects to younger people.

Education

Renishaw has been involved in several initiatives to encourage more young people to keeping studying the STEM (science, technology, engineering and maths) subjects as they get older. The company has tried to target influencers such as teachers, parents and careers advisors. The company ran an event entitled 'Girl Power' at an engineering festival and also carried out a pilot project with the Design and Technology Association to tackle the skills gap of design and technology teachers.

Renishaw Charities Committee

The committee was set up to distribute funds to charitable organisations as well as support the fundraising efforts of employees. It is has a focus on assisting organisations with 30 miles of its main site that help enrich people's lives.

Beneficiaries included: animal sanctuaries; disability support groups; church restoration funds; counselling and carers support groups, primary and secondary schools.

Disasters fund

The Charities Committee also administer a fund which donates money to victims of global disasters. During the year £10,000 was donated to the Disasters and Emergency Committee to assist the victims of the Nepal earthquakes.

Main locations

The company has headquarters in Stroud and operations at sites throughout the UK. A list of offices is available on the company's website.

Community contributions

In 2015 the company made donations totalling just under £100,000 to over 200 organisations through its Charities Committee.

Commercially led support

The company has sponsored engineering teams and societies that have entered racing cars in the Global Formula Student competition.

Exclusions

According to the company's website, it will not do the following:

- Provide prizes for raffles or draws
- Provide funding for projects outside its geographical limitations
- Support charities or organisations seeking funds to redistribute to other charities
- Support political organisations and campaigns
- Purchase tables at charity fundraisers, boxes at sporting events, etc.
- Support national/international organisations (except as stated above)

Applications

Applications should be made in writing to the Renishaw Charities Committee via post or email. Applications can also be made online through the Charities Committee section of the website.

According to the company's website, beneficiary organisations should be located within 30 miles of one of Renishaw's key operating sites in:

- Gloucestershire (Wotton-under-Edge, Woodchester, Stonehouse)
- Vale of Glamorgan (Miskin)
- Yorkshire (York)
- Staffordshire (Stone)

The committee meets in January, March, May, July, September and November to discuss applications.

Rentokil Initial PLC

Business services

Correspondent: Paul Griffiths, Company Secretary, Riverbank, Meadows Business Park, Blackwater, Camberley GU17 9AB (tel: 020 7592 2700; website: www.rentokil-initial.com)

Directors: Alan Giles; Andy Ransom, Chief Executive; Angela Seymour-Jackson; Christopher Geoghegan; Daragh Fagan; Jeremy Townsend, Chief Financial Officer; John McAdam, Chair; Julie Southern; Richard Burrows (women: 2; men: 7)

Year end	31/12/2015
Turnover	£1,813,900,000
Pre-tax profit	£215,100,000

Nature of business: International company providing services to businesses, including: workwear; plants and landscaping; hygiene services; medical services; pest control; package delivery; catering; electronic security; cleaning.

Company registration number: 5393279

Subsidiary undertakings include: Dudley Industries Ltd; Knightsbridge Guarding Ltd; Modus FM Ltd; Rentokil Insurance Ltd.

Brands include: Rentokil; Initial; Ambius.

Total employees: 31,442

Focus of giving: Education, environment, health, ill health, community/social welfare, disasters.

Community involvement	✓
Community contributions	✓
CSR report	✓
Cash donations declared	✓
Employee-led support	✓
Gifts in kind	✓
Humanitarian aid: overseas	✓
Matched funding	✓

Charitable donations

Cash worldwide:	2015	£128,000

Community involvement

The company's social and community activities consist of three main areas:

Local community support

In the UK the Helping Hands scheme matches employees' fundraising and supported many local charities in 2015. There are also two educational initiatives which tour round schools in the UK. Hygiene Angels shows schoolchildren the importance of handwashing and how to do it correctly. Pestaurant educates children about the threat of pests and gives them a chance to sample edible insects. For every mile travelled by the schools team, Rentokil makes a donation to the charity Malaria No More. Internationally the company has supported Nelson Mandela Day and helped to strengthen businesses owned by black people in South Africa.

Response to natural disasters

During the floods in Chennai, India the company provided emergency support to the families of employees providing them with items such as hygiene kits, food and blankets.

Global community support

The global health initiative was launched in 2013 and gives health and safety training to children in India, Malaysia, Indonesia and South Africa.

Main locations

Rentokil has branches throughout the UK. There is a list of branches on the company's website.

Community contributions

In 2015 cash donations totalled £128,000 (2014: £77,000) including the matched donations via Helping Hands. In addition to this figure, in-kind donations and management time were also provided, although we could not determine the value for these.

UK beneficiaries of matched giving scheme: Age UK; Click Sargent; the Family Holiday Association; Macmillan; Meningitis Now; Race for Life; Royal Hospital Chelsea Pensioners; Royal Marsden; Save the Children.

In-kind support

Staff volunteering time, management support, training and professional services, also hygiene kits, food, clothing and toys to families in natural disaster affected areas.

Employee-led support

The group's Community Involvement policy paper states that one of its principles is to 'facilitate employees' involvement where possible in the cultural and educational development of their communities and adopt a permissive approach to employee's participation in community and civic affairs.'

Matched funding

A Helping Hands scheme operates to allow Rentokil Initial match any amount up to £1,000 raised by employees for charitable causes with an annual budget approved by the group board.

Employee fundraising

Employees have raised funds for Malaria No More by taking part in events such as bike rides, mountain climbs and bake sales. Over £100,000 has been raised in the last five years.

Exclusions

Generally, consideration will not be given to any charity or sponsorship-related proposal from any organisation unless a company employee or employees are involved.

Applications

Apply in writing to the correspondent.

Richer Sounds PLC

Retail – electrical

Correspondent: Teresa Chapman, PA to Julian Richer, Unit 3/4, Richer House, Gallery Court, Hankey Place, London SE1 4BB (tel: 020 7551 5343; email: teresac@richersounds.com; website: www.richersounds.com)

Directors: David Robinson; John Currier; Julian Richer (women: 0; men: 3)

Year end	02/05/2015
Turnover	£149,000,000

Nature of business: Retailer of video and audio equipment.

Company registration number: 1402643

Focus of giving: Human rights, animal welfare, poverty and social exclusion, disability.

Community involvement	✓
Community contributions	✓
Company reports on anti-slavery	✓
Corporate charity	✓

Charitable donations

Cash UK (latest available):	2015	£1,030,000
Total UK (cash and in kind):	2015	£1,030,000
Cash worldwide:	2015	£1,030,000
Total worldwide (cash and in kind):	2015	£1,030,000

Community involvement

The company is an unlisted PLC 100% owned by Julian Richer, the founder and managing director of the company. Support for charitable causes is routed through The Persula Foundation which was founded by Julian.

The Persula Foundation (Charity Commission no. 1044174)
The foundation was established in 1994 as an independent grant-making foundation. The foundation's 2014/15 annual report states that it is currently interested in supporting initiatives in the following areas:

- Social welfare
- Animal welfare
- Human rights
- Disability

Main locations
The foundation makes grants to charities throughout the UK.

Community contributions

The latest accounts of The Persula Foundation at the time of writing (October 2016) were from 2014/15. During that year the foundation had an income of £1.05 million (the donation from the company amounting for £1.03 million) and made grants totalling £1.09 million.

The foundation's beneficiaries included: Compassion in World Farming (£50,000); Acts 435 (£35,000); Prison Reform Trust (£34,000); Amnesty International (£30,500); Changing Faces (£25,000); ASB Help (£24,000); Civil Liberties Trust and World Vision (£21,000 each).

In-kind support

The company may provide staff time and expertise, office space and other facilities. The Persula Foundation also has access to many resources from the company, such as marketing, design and strategic consultation. The foundation prefers to use these resources to provide an added value aspect to its collaboration with organisations.

Commercially led support

Through the foundation the company operates Tapesense scheme supplying blind and visually impaired people with subsidised audio products and accessories, such as audio cassettes, hi-fi accessories, interconnect cables, universal remote controls, headphones, microphones and digital (DAB) radios.

Corporate charity

The Persula Foundation (Charity Commission no. 1044174).

Applications

The Persula Foundation (Charity Commission no. 1044174) considers applications for funding from a variety of charitable organisations. Applications are reviewed and the levels of grants payable are decided by the trustees.

Applications and queries regarding the Tapesense scheme should also be addressed to the correspondent.

Ridgesave Ltd

Property

Correspondent: Zelda Weiss, Secretary, 141B Upper Clapton Road, London E5 9DB (email: mail@cohenarnold.com)

Directors: E. Englander; Joseph Weiss, Chair; Zelda Weiss (women: 1; men: 3)

Year end	31/03/2015
Turnover	£2,273,000

Nature of business: Property investment and trading.

Ridgesave Ltd is a registered charity with two non-charitable operating subsidiaries: Bullion Properties Ltd and Doxit Company Ltd.

Company registration number: 1745720

Subsidiary undertakings include: Bullion Properties Ltd and Doxit Company Ltd.

Focus of giving: Education, poverty and social exclusion, religion.

Community involvement	✓
Community contributions	✓
Cash donations declared	✓

Charitable donations

Cash UK (latest available):	2015	£2,350,000
Total UK (cash and in kind):	2015	£2,350,000
Cash worldwide:	2015	£2,350,000
Total worldwide (cash and in kind):	2015	£2,350,000

Community involvement

This is a somewhat unusual entry in the context of our research into company giving. Ridgesave, although registered as a company limited by guarantee, is also a registered charity (Charity Commission no. 288020). The charity concentrates its giving to assist institutions teaching the principles of traditional Judaism, and to provide philanthropic aid to those in need.

We have decided to include the company here because it has two non-charitable operating subsidiaries – Bullion Properties Ltd (property trading) and Doxit Co. Ltd (property investment). In addition, the bulk of the charity's income is derived from other companies such as Halastar Ltd of which some of the trustees of the charity are also directors.

Main locations
The charity operates in the UK, Belgium, the USA and Israel.

Community contributions

During 2014/15 the charitable company continued its charitable activities and supported organisations engaged in areas of education, advancement of the Jewish religion, and social welfare. The income of the company was £2.3 million while grants and donations totalled over £2.35 million. The accounts did not provide a breakdown of charitable donations.

Applications

Apply in writing to the correspondent. The day-to-day management of the company's affairs is undertaken by the directors who are also trustees.

Rio Tinto PLC

Mining

Correspondent: The Community Relations Team, Legal & External Affairs, 2 Eastbourne Terrace, London W2 6LG (tel: 020 7781 2000; website: www.riotinto.com)

Directors: Ann Godbehere; Anne Lauvergeon; Christopher Lynch, Chief Financial Officer; Jan du Plessis, Chair; John Varley; Megan Clark; Michael L'Estrange; Paul Tellier; Robert Brown; Sam Walsh, Chief Executive Officer; Simon Thompson (women: 3; men: 9)

Year end	31/12/2015
Turnover	£34,829,000,000
Pre-tax profit	(£726,000,000)

Nature of business: Rio Tinto is one of the world's largest mining companies. Based in the UK, Rio Tinto has substantial worldwide interests in metals and industrial minerals with major assets in Australia, South America, Asia, Europe and Southern Africa.

Company registration number: 719885

Subsidiary undertakings include: Argyle Diamond Ltd; Alcan Alumina Ltd; Iron Ore Company of Canada Inc.

Focus of giving: Human rights, education, enterprise/training, environment, equal opportunities, health, ill health, heritage, arts, culture, overseas projects, women's issues, community/social welfare.

Community involvement	✓
Community contributions	✓
CSR report	✓
CSR or charity committee	✓
Cash donations declared	✓
FTSE 100	✓
Sponsorship	✓

Charitable donations

Total worldwide (cash and in kind):	2015	£140,700,000

Community involvement

The group's approach to working with communities aims to encompass three areas:

- Building knowledge – identifying and understanding key features of the community and assessing business impact
- Engaging – creating partnerships with government agencies, community and non-government organisations, academics and other bodies

- Developing – programmes covering educational, health or livelihood initiatives, which build long-term local skills and knowledge; and providing employment opportunities

Education partnerships
The group creates partnerships with universities and colleges, supports institutions that are important to the industries and communities in which it operates, and sponsors research activities and curriculum development. At the moment there are three global long-term partners: Imperial College London, University of Queensland and University of Western Australia.

Main locations
London

Community contributions

In 2015 the group states having spent US$184 million (over £140.7 million) in 'community contributions'. The Sustainable Development Report for 2015 further specifies that of this sum 38% went directly to community programmes, 52% were 'direct payments into benefits-receiving trusts associated with community agreements', and 10% covered management costs. During the year approximately 1,800 socio-economic programmes were supported. Programmes covered a range of activities, including: education (23.4%); recreation (16.4%); health (12.8%); environment (12.4%); business development (11.1%); other (9.9%) culture (6.9%); transport (3.2%); housing (2.3%) agriculture (1.6%); HIV (0.1%) and benefitted the group, its employees and broader community in which they operate.

Based on the above specifications we estimate that direct cash contributions to charities worldwide totalled about £73.2 million and direct support to community programmes was of £53.5 million.

The support was given in following regions: Australia and New Zealand (42.8%); North America (26%); Europe/Africa (16.8%); Asia (13%); and South America (1.3%). We could not identify the amount awarded in the UK.

Exclusions

No support is given, directly or indirectly, to any sectarian, religious or political activity. No funding is provided for building projects or general running costs, nor for advertising in charity brochures. Support is not given to individuals, animal welfare or any sporting events.

Applications

Apply in writing to the correspondent.

Rolls-Royce Holdings PLC

Engineering, industrial products/services

Correspondent: The Corporate Sustainability Team, 65 Buckingham Gate, London SW1E 6AT (tel: 020 7222 9020; website: www.rolls-royce.com)

Directors: Alan Davies; Bradley Singer; Colin Smith; David Smith, Chief Financial Officer; Dr John McAdam; Ian Davis, Chair; Irene Dorner; Jasmin Staiblin; Lee Hsien Yang; Lewis Booth; Pamela Coles; Ruth Cairnie; Sir Frank Chapman; Sir Kevin Smith; Warren East, Chief Executive (women: 4; men: 11)

Year end	31/12/2015
Turnover	£13,725,000,000
Pre-tax profit	£160,000,000

Nature of business: Rolls-Royce is a global company providing power (gas turbines and reciprocating engines) on land, sea and air.

Company registration number: 1003142

Subsidiary undertakings include: Rolls-Royce Marine India Private Ltd; Rolls-Royce Marine North America Inc.; and Rolls-Royce Singapore Pte. Ltd.

UK employees: 23,200

Total employees: 50,500

Focus of giving: Education, environment, overseas projects, arts, culture, children, young people.

Membership: BITC, LBG

Community involvement	✓
Community contributions	✓
CSR report	✓
Charity partner(s)	✓
Employee-led support	✓
FTSE 100	✓
Gifts in kind	✓
Market-led giving	✓
Overseas giving	✓
Payroll giving	✓
Sponsorship	✓
STEM-focused	✓

Charitable donations

Total worldwide (cash and in kind):	2015	£9,700,000

Community involvement

Community Investment
The website states that alongside STEM the community support is particularly focused on: education and skills; environmental activities; social investment, with the intention of making a positive contribution wherever we are in the world; and arts, culture and heritage.

STEM programmes
The group works closely with schools and universities to encourage interest and diversity in the STEM subjects. There are over 1,000 ambassadors worldwide who are involved in promoting STEM programmes and activities.

Charity partnerships
The group's co-operation includes partnership with Mercy Ships and supports the operation of Africa Mercy which is the largest non-governmental hospital ship in the world.

Main locations
The groups key locations in the UK are Bristol, Birmingham, Derby, Hucknall, Rotherham, Lincolnshire, Washington (Sunderland), East Kilbride and Inchinnan.

Community contributions

In 2015 the group's total contributions amounted to £9.7 million. This includes sponsorship, charitable contributions and over 117,000 hours of employee time. A detailed breakdown was not available.

In-kind support

According to our research, the group can offer support in-kind to local initiatives, including in-house training programmes, surplus computers, equipment and furniture, loans of engines and components, technical support, and free use of meeting rooms and premises.

Employee-led support

Employee volunteering
The group's Global Code of Conduct states that in most cases employees will be able to get support to work for voluntary organisations (for example, school communities or community groups).

Payroll giving
In the past, the group operated a Payroll Giving Scheme for UK employees, enabling them to make tax-free donations to their chosen charities. We could found no mention of the scheme in the 2015 report.

Commercially led support

Sponsorship
Rolls-Royce sponsors the UK Female Undergraduate of the Year awards with the winner receiving a paid summer internship.

Rolls Royce Science Prize
Established in 2004, the Rolls-Royce Science Prize is part of the company's commitment to promote science and engineering in schools. It rewards excellent teaching of science as well as promoting innovative and sustainable strategies for teaching science.

Exclusions

Rolls-Royce does not 'make corporate contributions or donations to political parties or to any organisations, think-tanks, academic institutions or charities closely associated to a political party or cause'.

Applications

Apply in writing to the correspondent, referenced 'Corporate Sustainability Team'.

Rothschild & Co. (record formerly titled N. M. Rothschild & Sons Ltd)

Banking

Correspondent: Community Investment Team, New Court, St Swithin's Lane, London EC4N 8AL (email: Community.Investment@Rothschild.com; website: www.rothschild.com/en/who-we-are/community-investment)

Directors: Adam Keswick; André Lévy-Lang; Angelika Gifford; Anthony de Rothschild; Arielle Malard de Rothschild; Carole Piwnica; Dr Daniel Daeniker; Éric de Rothschild, Chair; François Henrot; Jacques Richier; Lucie Maurel-Aubert; Luisa Todini; Peter Smith; Sipko Schat; Sylvain Héfès (women: 1; men: 9)

Year end	31/03/2015
Turnover	£1,379,000,000
Pre-tax profit	£366,400,000

Nature of business: Rothschild & Co. is a global financial advisory group, with offices in more than 40 countries worldwide. Rothschild & Co. is a French partnership limited by shares and is listed on Euronext in Paris.

This record previously referred to N. M. Rothschild & Sons Ltd, which is a British division of Rothschild & Co. However, as the annual report and accounts for N. M. Rothschild & Sons Ltd no longer declare charitable donations, we have instead referred to its parent firm, which reports on CSR activities from across its divisions.

Note that the firm's revenue and profit before tax were reported in Euros and were converted into GBP at the time of writing (January 2017).

Subsidiary undertakings include: N. M. Rothschild & Sons Ltd; Rothschild Private Fund Management Ltd; Rothschild Wealth Management (UK) Ltd.

Total employees: 2,800

Focus of giving: Education, enterprise/training, small groups, local groups, overseas projects, poverty and social exclusion, children, young people, community/social welfare.

Membership: BITC, LBG

Community involvement	✓
Community contributions	✓
CSR report	✓
CSR or charity committee	✓
Directors have other relevant posts	✓
Charity partner(s)	✓
Company gives to smaller charities	✓
Employee-led support	✓
Gifts in kind	✓
Matched funding	✓
Overseas giving	✓
Payroll giving	✓
Pro bono	✓
STEM-focused	✓

Charitable donations

Total UK (cash and in kind):	2015	£340,000
Total worldwide (cash and in kind):	2015	£340,000

Community involvement

The 'Community Investment at Rothschild & Co. in the UK' report (2015/16) states: 'We have merged our employee volunteering and charitable giving programmes into one CI programme, and have developed a more strategic structure to our charitable donations process.' The merger of Rothschild & Co.'s CI initiatives with its UK offices (in Birmingham, Leeds, London and Manchester), according to the report, has 'extended' its 'reach and impact'.

Through the community investment programme, the firm has the ambition of encouraging disadvantaged young people to pursue higher and further education and to follow career paths into the worlds of finance and, more generally, business, by 'raising and realising' their aspirations.

The 'Rothschild & Co. Community Investment Strategy in the UK' document, which is available to download from the website, states that Rothschild & Co. aims to achieve its 'ambition by developing six key personal capabilities (which include self-awareness, receptiveness, drive, confidence, resilience and informed) and six employability skills (which include verbal communication, written communication, teamwork, problem solving, organisational skills and numeracy), which [it believes] are crucial to a young person succeeding in education and employment'.

The strategy document further notes that the community investment programme is delivered through 'long-term and strategic partnerships with community organisations' that share the firm's values and can assist in meeting its ambition. Support is given in the form of 'unlimited' staff volunteering time (for Rothschild & Co. initiatives) and financial contributions.

Core partners

In 2016 Rothschild & Co.'s core partner organisations were: Teach First; Future First; Ashoka; The Access Project; Bow School; Regent High School; and Old Palace Primary School. According to the CSR report (contained within the annual report for 2015/16), 'Initiatives include mentoring and coaching, tutoring, work experience, and career insight events' – some of the examples provided in the Community Investment report for 2015/16 include:

- **The Rothschild & Co. Mentoring Programme (Bow School and Regent High School):** More than 470 students at the schools have benefitted from 1:2:1 mentoring from 350 Rothschild & Co. employee volunteers since the programme began. The programme targets the 'top tier of students in terms of academic potential' who 'are talented and aspirational' but have 'a lack of family experience and role models'
- **The Rothschild & Co. Bursary Trust (Bow School):** The trust increases the support provided to students at Bow School who take part in the Mentoring Programme by helping to remove financial barriers that affect their university education, enabling them to pursue an education further away from home. Bursaries of £5,000 per year were awarded to three gifted students in 2016, the trust's first year. Rothschild & Co. match funds all money raised by its staff for the trust
- **The Making it Count Project (The Access Project):** Rothschild & Co. is the 'Founding Subject Business Partner' for The Access Project's 'new model of collaboration' which sees the firm's employees volunteer as tutors for young people in schools where the charity works. The project particularly looks to provide opportunities for tutoring STEM subjects, especially maths, which many Rothschild & Co. employees have studied

Main locations

In the UK, Rothschild & Co. has offices in Birmingham, the City of London, Leeds and Manchester.

Community contributions

The Community Investment report for 2015/16 states: 'We invested £340,000 in our community programme last year.' We have taken this figure to include both cash donations and in-kind contributions; however, we were unable to determine a breakdown of distributions.

From information contained in the Community Investment report, however, we do know that the value of hours spent by staff volunteering totalled almost £220,500. The corporate social responsibility report contained within the annual report and accounts further notes that '£40,000 of the company's overall Community Investment budget is reserved for supporting its employees' personal causes'.

In 2016/17 Rothschild & Co. intended to invest £385,000 (more than 1% of pre-tax profits) into the community programme.

In-kind support

Staff time

The corporate social responsibility report notes that 'employees are entitled to unlimited volunteer leave to volunteer for a Rothschild & Co. initiative that is skills based and creates long-term change and impact'. Employees can also take an additional two days to spend volunteering for their own chosen cause. In 2015/16 a total of 3,238 hours of leave were taken for volunteering purposes.

Employee-led support

Employee volunteering

During 2015/16, 361 employees (more than 50% of London staff) volunteered on 628 occasions.

Matched funding

Funds raised by employees for The Rothschild & Co. Bursary Trust are matched on a pound for pound basis.

Payroll giving

In 2016 N. M. Rothschild & Sons achieved a Silver Payroll Giving Quality Mark.

Applications

The merger between Rothschild & Co.'s employee volunteering and charitable giving programmes has seen its charitable donations process take on a more strategic approach. According to its community investment strategy, Rothschild & Co. channels support through 'long-term and strategic partnerships with community organisations'.

Rotork PLC

Engineering, industrial products/services

Correspondent: See 'Applications', Brassmill Lane, Bath BA1 3JQ (tel: 01225 733200; website: www.rotork.com)

Directors: Gary Bullard; John Nicholas; Jonathan Davis, Finance Director; Lucinda Bell; Martin Lamb, Chair; Peter France, Chief Executive; Sally James; Stephen Jones

Year end	31/12/2015
Turnover	£546,500,000
Pre-tax profit	£101,900,000

Nature of business: The company's activities include design and manufacture of actuators and flow control equipment.

Company registration number: 578327

Subsidiary undertakings include: Rotork BV; Rotork Germany Holdings GmbH; Rotork Inc.

Focus of giving: General charitable purposes, education, overseas projects, children, young people, community/ social welfare.

Community involvement	✓
Community contributions	✓
Company reports on anti-slavery	✓
CSR report	✓
CSR or charity committee	✓
Charity partner(s)	✓
Employee-led support	✓
Humanitarian aid: overseas	✓
Overseas giving	✓

Charitable donations

Cash worldwide:	2015	£297,000
Total worldwide (cash and in kind):	2015	£297,000

Community involvement

There are local charity committees at each site providing donations to charitable causes. Local community activities throughout the group included:

- Engaged with the Right to Read programme at a primary school in Leeds
- Employees in Wolverhampton donated £250 to a local hospice
- Employees volunteered to help the clean-up effort in Malaysia following its worst floods for 30 years

Charity partnerships

The group provides ongoing support to both WaterAid and Sight Savers. The group has supported several Sight Savers projects including its trachoma and river blindness programmes in Ghana. In 2015 a WaterAid project in East Timor was supported with a donation of £60,000. The project aims to provide clean water and hygiene programmes to 12 communities.

Directors with other relevant posts

Peter France is Chair of the Bath Education Trust; and Sally James is a trustee of the Legal Education Foundation.

Main locations

The group has charity committees based in Leeds, Bath and Glasgow.

Community contributions

According to the group's 2015 CSR report, it awarded £297,000 to charities worldwide. No specific information was found on UK cash donations but in previous years the group has given between £70,000 and £90,000. In 2016 the group aims to donate 0.1% of its profit to its nominated international charity and 0.1% to charitable causes local to Rotork's operating sites.

Beneficiaries included: WaterAid (£60,000); Sightsavers (£40,000); Freedom Matters (£5,000).

In-kind support

Support is given in the form of staff volunteering time, the provision of expertise and specialist skills, food and clothing items, toys, and donations of other products.

Employee-led support

Staff fundraising efforts collected £6,600 to help WaterAid. In the USA employees donated Christmas gifts of toys and clothing to local children.

Matched funding

Our research suggests that the charity committee will normally match monies raised by employees who undertake charitable events personally.

Applications

Apply in writing to your local charity committee. The contact details are as follows:

- The Charity Committee, Rotork UK Ltd: 9 Brown Lane West, Holbeck, Leeds LS12 6BH
- The Charity Committee, Rotork UK Ltd: Brassmill Lane, Bath BA1 3JQ
- The Charity Committee, Rotork UK Ltd: 9 Queensberry Avenue, Hillington Industrial Estate, Glasgow G52 4NL

The Royal Bank of Scotland Group PLC

Financial services, insurance, banking

Correspondent: Sustainable Banking Committee, 1st Floor, House F, Gogarburn, Edinburgh EH12 1HQ (tel: 0131 556 8555; website: www.rbs.com/ community)

Directors: Aileen Taylor; Alison Davis; Baroness Noakes; Brendan Nelson; Ewen Stevenson, Chief Financial Officer; Frank Dangeard; Howard Davies, Chair; Mike Rogers; Morten Friis; Penny Hughes; Robert Gillespie; Ross McEwan, Chief Executive; Sir Sandy Crombie (women: 4; men: 9)

Year end	31/12/2015
Turnover	£16,890,000,000
Pre-tax profit	£4,405,000,000

Nature of business: RBS is a UK-based banking and financial services company. Headquartered in Edinburgh, RBS operates in the United Kingdom, Europe, the Middle East, the Americas and Asia, serving over 24 million customers worldwide.

Company registration number: SC045551

Subsidiary undertakings include: NatWest; The Royal Bank of Scotland; Ulster Bank Ltd.

Brands include: Coutts & Co.; Holt's Military Banking; Isle of Man Bank.

UK employees: 9,138

Total employees: 16,813

Focus of giving: General charitable purposes, economic generation, education, enterprise/training, groups not already known, health, ill health, non-registered charities, small groups, less popular charitable purposes, overseas projects, humanitarian help, arts, culture, poverty and social exclusion, sport, recreation, community/ social welfare, disability, disasters.

Membership: BITC, LBG

Accredited Living Wage Employer	✓
Community involvement	✓
Community contributions	✓
Company reports on anti-slavery	✓
CSR report	✓
Directors have other relevant posts	✓
Cash donations declared	✓
Charity partner(s)	✓
Company gives to smaller charities	✓
Employee-led support	✓
FTSE 100	✓
Gifts in kind	✓
Humanitarian aid: overseas	✓
Humanitarian aid: UK including food banks	✓
Matched funding	✓
Payroll giving	✓
Sponsorship	✓
Unpopular causes	✓

Charitable donations

Cash UK (latest available):	2015	£3,540,000
Total UK (cash and in kind):	2015	£3,540,000
Total worldwide (cash and in kind):	2015	£43,500,000

Community involvement

Through its charitable giving programmes, RBS seeks to help projects and causes in its communities that require support and which matter most to employees through a number of giving initiatives. Charitable and community giving and all else related to corporate social responsibility is managed by the group's Sustainable Banking Committee. The Committee also holds regular meetings with external stakeholders including universities and NGOs. In 2015 topics discussed in these meetings included financial inclusion, including debt and access to affordable credit and RBS India's sustainable development programme.

Partners

The group has a history of developing partnerships with charitable organisations. It has partnered with RNIB and the Alzheimer's Society to enable its employees to support vulnerable customers. A dementia strategy was developed with the Alzheimer's Society to deliver dementia training to frontline staff at NatWest, RBS and Ulster Bank.

The group has been in partnership with The Prince's Trust since 2009 and in 2015 decided to renew that partnership at least until 2018. The partnership involves the group making cash donations, employee volunteering.

RBS also became an official partner of Sport Relief in 2015, with employees holding a bank-wide fundraising event.

Sponsorship

According to the website, the group builds partnerships and sponsors worthy events, organisations and individuals. This kind of support must achieve goals that benefit the bank and is a commercial rather than philanthropic activity.

Skills and Opportunities Fund

RBS launched a new fund in 2015 for not-for-profit organisations with a turnover of under £10 million and state-funded education bodies in the UK and Ireland. The applicant organisation's focus must be on working with people in disadvantaged communities to help them develop skills to gain employment or start a new business. In 2015 1,800 organisations applied for funding, 180 of these went through to a public vote, and 114 won grants of up to £35,000 each.

Grants of up to £35,000 are available across the UK and Ireland. Applicant organisations must have been trading for at least two years, with the exception of schools. Projects must focus on one or more of the following themes: educations; enterprise; employability.

For further information visit www. skillsandopportunitiesfund.rbs.com

RBS Social and Community Capital

The group's charity, RBS Social and Community Capital (Charity Commission no. 1079626) provides loans to social enterprises, charities, not-for-profit organisations and social businesses, particularly for those unable to access mainstream finance. To apply for a loan, organisations must be based in the UK; be an established third sector organisation with social or environmental aims; and not eligible for mainstream funding from banks.

Brand corporate charity

The Coutts Charitable Foundation (Charity Commission no. 115784) provides a single focus for charitable disbursements. While an independent entity, it provides opportunities for staff in all locations to engage with local causes and give their time and financial support towards its objective of providing sustainable solutions to the causes and consequences of poverty in the markets in which Coutts operates. Its focus is on supporting women and girls in the UK by providing grants to a small number of organisations. Generally, it does not take unsolicited applications. For further information, visit: www. coutts.com/coutts-foundation.html. There is also a separate entry for Coutts & Co., which details information about the company.

Directors with other relevant posts

Robert Gillespie is Chair of Council at the University of Durham, Chair of the Boat Race Company Ltd and director of Social Finance Ltd.

Sandy Crombie has had a variety of cultural and community roles in the past (such as Chair of Creative Scotland and the Edinburgh World City of Literature) and is currently President of the Cockburn Association.

Main locations

The group operates in locations all across the UK and the rest of the world. Its principal offices in the UK are based in: Edinburgh; East Belfast; Jersey Channel Islands; and London. It also has a principal office in the USA.

Community contributions

According to the group's sustainability report, which used the London Benchmarking Group standard, the group made worldwide community investments totalling £43.5 million in 2015. This includes cash donations, in-kind contributions, employee time and fundraising.

In the UK, cash donations were over £3.54 million during the year. This is based on the sustainability report which notes that £1 million was donated in cash to The Prince's Trust during the year and £35,000 was donated to six Community Foundations in the north of England and Scotland following the floods in 2015. This included £10,000 to Foundation Scotland's flood recovery appeal, and five further donations of £5,000 to foundations in the north of England. A further £2.5 million was also committed to the group's Skills and Opportunities Fund, with another £2.5 million pledged to the fund in 2016. The group also made a cash donation of £5,000 and in-kind donations worth £117,500 to its corporate charity, RBS Social and Community Capital.

Corporate and employee donations were also made to Oxfam India's Tamil Nadu floods appeal.

Beneficiaries included: Beyond Food Foundation; Bubble Enterprises CIC; Co-operation Ireland; Disability Resource Centre; Foundation Scotland; Granton Youth Centre; New Direction; Oxfam India; Strood Community Project; The Prince's Trust; Women's Rape and Sexual Abuse Centre.

In-kind support

During the 2015 floods in northern England, the group offered its bank buildings as meeting points; provided food, toys and clothing; and offered payment holidays and emergency overdrafts to customers. The bank and its employees also made cash donations.

The group also offers a scheme in which customers can donate to select charities through the group's ATM machines. In 2015 the charities that customers could select to support in this way included: Barnardo's; Cancer Research UK; Macmillan; NSPCC; RNIB; Sport Relief; and The Prince's Trust. Customers could also support the Disasters and Emergency Committee (DEC) appeals for the Nepal earthquake and Ebola crisis in West Africa and the group waived international transfer fees to affected regions.

Employee-led support

Employee volunteering

There is a well-established employee volunteering and giving programme at RBS. Employees are entitled to three days of volunteering leave per year to help their local communities. In 2015 employees devoted 45,437 hours to volunteering.

Some employees volunteer for MoneySense, an RBS programme for 5- to 18-year-olds. Some employees volunteer for the group's partner The Prince's Trust by supporting young people into employment, training, education or enterprise and delivering employability workshops. Volunteer opportunities for employees are also encouraged for the group's charity, RBS Social and Community Capital.

Employee fundraising

Employees and interns at the group fundraise for charitable causes in their local communities, such as the Cumbria Flood Appeal, as well as for the group's partners, particularly The Prince's Trust and Sport Relief. In 2015 employees held a bank-wide fundraising event, a cycle ride, in aid of Sport Relief. The group also matches employees' fundraising efforts under its community cashback programme.

In 2015 a total of 10,000 employees took part in the group's payroll giving scheme.

Exclusions

According to the website, organisations and projects applying to the group's **Skills and Opportunities Fund** must not:

- Have received funding from the RBS Inspiring Enterprise programme, Large Grants programme, Skills & Opportunities Fund or the Ulster Bank Community Impact Fund in the last 12 months
- Compete with existing bank programmes
- Be a local authority or public sector body. Councils, ministerial and non-ministerial departments, agencies and public corporations are not eligible for this fund
- Be sectarian or political
- Be a university, an ex-service/veteran not-for-profit club, a trade union, fraternal, or professional society
- Seek funding for costs not directly related to the project, or for excluded activities such as personal appeals, research projects or sports teams (unless the outcomes are related to employability, enterprise or education)
- Be seeking funding for a capital-only project. Funding for capital costs must not exceed 25% of overall project costs

The group also does not generally consider **sponsorships** for the following:

- Clubs, societies or teams
- Venues
- Fundraising events
- Publications, videos, films or recordings or website development

Applications

Charitable requests should be directed to the Sustainable Banking Committee who manages RBS group's relationships with charitable organisations. The committee is chaired by Penny Hughes. Applications for sponsorship should be addressed to the Head of Sponsorship at the group's head office.

Skills and Opportunities Fund

Applicants are advised to first visit skillsandopportunitiesfund.rbs.com and check the particular funding priorities for the region in which the project is located.

RBS Social and Community Capital

To apply for a loan from the group's corporate charity visit www.business.rbs.co.uk/business/social-community-capital or contact by email: rbsscc@rbs.co.uk.

The Royal London Mutual Insurance Society Ltd

Insurance

Correspondent: Group Corporate Responsibility Manager, Royal London House, Alderley Road, Wilmslow SK9 1PF (tel: 0845 050 2020; email: corpresponse@royallondon.com; website: www.royallondon.com)

Directors: Andrew Carter; Andrew Palmer; David Weymouth; Duncan Ferguson; Ian Dilks; Jon Macdonald; Phil Loney, Group Chief Executive; Rupert Pennant-Rea, Chair; Sally Bridgeland; Tim Harris, Group Finance Director; Tracey Graham

Year end	31/12/2015
Turnover	£1,194,000,000
Pre-tax profit	£143,000,000

Nature of business: Principal activities of the group's businesses are provision of pensions, life assurance, savings and investment products, protection insurance and investment management services.

The Group comprises The Royal London Mutual Insurance Society Ltd and its subsidiaries.

Company registration number: 99064

Subsidiary undertakings include: Royal Liver Asset Managers Ltd; Royal London Asset Management Ltd; The Scottish Life Assurance Company.

UK employees: 3,000

Total employees: 3,000

Focus of giving: General charitable purposes, education, enterprise/training, environment, fundraising events, health, ill health, medical research, older people, arts, culture, sport, recreation, children, young people, disability.

Membership: BITC

Community involvement	✓
Community contributions	✓
CSR report	✓
CSR or charity committee	✓
Directors have other relevant posts	✓
Charity partner(s)	✓
Employee-led support	✓
Gifts in kind	✓
Matched funding	✓
Payroll giving	✓
Sponsorship	✓

Community involvement

The group's community involvement focuses on its partner charity. The group supports employee fundraising with matched funding, and there is also a payroll giving scheme and volunteering time for employees.

Charity partner
Since 2013, the group has been working with the charity Bloodwise. The 2015 annual report states that, since 2013, £200,000 had been raised. In 2016 the group was fundraising to support a group of families affected by blood cancer to have a holiday in Disneyland Paris.

Royal London Foundation
The foundation was launched in 2011 in honour of the group's founders Henry Ridge and Joseph Degge. The fund is administered by UK Community Foundations (Charity Commission no. 1004630). The foundation is to be relaunched in 2017 – refer to the group's website for more information.

Directors with other relevant posts
Sally Bridgeland is founder and trustee of Executive Shift (Charity Commission no. 1154850). Rupert Pennant-Rea is a trustee of Speakers Trust (Charity Commission no. 1139377). Andrew Palmer is treasurer of Cancer Research UK (Charity Commission no. 1089464) and of The Royal School of Needlework (Charity Commission no. 312774). Tracey Graham is Vice-Chair of the Nonsuch and Wallington Education Trust.

Main locations
The group has offices in the following locations: Bath; Dublin; Edinburgh; Glasgow; London; Reading; and Wilmslow.

Community contributions
No figure was given for the group's charitable contributions.

Employee-led support

Employee fundraising
Employees organise fundraising initiatives in support of the group's partner charity, Bloodwise. The group also provides matched funding. Employees can also donate to charities through the Give As You Earn scheme.

Employee volunteering
The group's Stepforward programme enables employees to volunteer in local communities. Employees are entitled to two days per year paid volunteering time.

Commercially led support

Sponsorship
The group sponsors cricket-related initiatives, including one-day international and domestic cricket, as well as grassroots cricket through the Gilbert Cup for children. The group also sponsors the PCA Benevolent Fund for current and former players in need.

It is also the sponsor of two pelican colonies, in Edinburgh Zoo and St James' Park, London, in partnership with Royal Zoological Society of Scotland and Royal Parks Foundation in London.

Applications
Apply in writing to the correspondent.

Royal Mail PLC

Miscellaneous

Correspondent: CR and Community Investment Team, 100 Victoria Embankment, London EC4Y 0HQ (tel: 0345 774 0740 (general enquiries); email: corporateresponsibility@royalmail.com; website: www.royalmailgroup.com)

Directors: Cath Keers; Les Owen; Matthew Lester, Chief Finance Officer; Moya Greene, Chief Executive Officer; Nick Horler; Orna Ni-Chionna; Paul Murray; Peter Long, Chair (women: 3; men: 5)

Year end	30/03/2015
Turnover	£9,251,000,000
Pre-tax profit	£538,000,000

Nature of business: Royal Mail PLC is the ultimate parent company of the Royal Mail Group, which operates through two core divisions UK Parcels, International and Letters (UKPIL) and GLS (operating in continental Europe and Ireland). The group's main activities include letter and parcel services, and design and manufacture of UK stamps and philatelic products.

Company registration number: 8680755

Subsidiary undertakings include: General Logistics Systems B.V.; Romec Ltd; Royal Mail Estates Ltd.

Brands include: General Logistics Systems (GLS); Parcelforce Worldwide, Royal Mail.

UK employees: 139,000

Focus of giving: General charitable purposes.

Membership: BITC, LBG

Community involvement	✓
Community contributions	✓
CSR report	✓
Cash donations declared	✓
Charity of the Year	✓
Charity partner(s)	✓
Employee-led support	✓
FTSE 100	✓
Gifts in kind	✓
Market-led giving	✓
Matched funding	✓
Payroll giving	✓

Charitable donations

Cash UK (latest available):	2015	£2,540,000
Total UK (cash and in kind):	2015	£10,370,000
Cash worldwide:	2015	£2,540,000
Total worldwide (cash and in kind):	2015	£10,370,000

Community involvement

Charity of the Year
The Royal Mail's partnership with Prostate Cancer UK ended in August 2014 having raised £2.34 million and winning the Charity Times' Corporate National Partnership Champion award. In September 2014 a new Charity of the Year partnership with the Stroke Association. It is hoped that over £2 million will be raised to fund Life After Stroke grants for up to 10,000 stroke survivors.

Partnerships
The Rowland Hill Fund (Charity Commission no. 207479)
The fund supports the welfare of current and former Royal Mail employees. The group provides around £500,000 to the group per year as well as around £60,000 of in-kind support costs.

Keep Me Posted
The group supports the Keep Me Posted campaign which looks to ensure that consumers have the choice to received paper copies of bills and do not receive financial penalties for doing so.

Articles for the Blind
The service provides free postage for blind and partially-sighted Royal Mail works with the Royal National Institute of Blind People (RNIB) and other charities for the blind to make sure the services meet their needs.

Missing People
A partnership with Missing People has been launched which utilises the group's assets in order to find vulnerable missing people.

Remploy
The group has been a partner of Remploy since 2006 and recently met the milestone of having employed over 2,000 candidates with disabilities or other disadvantages through them.

Dolly Parton's Imagination Library
The charity aims to foster a love of reading in children up to five years of age. The Royal Mail has partnered with the charity and provides free books to the children and grandchildren of employees.

Royal Mail Sports Foundation
Local sports clubs are supported through grants for equipment, trophies and training. The foundation supported 54 sports clubs and events during 2014/15.

Christmas giving
The Christmas Grants Programme makes contributions to charities that support vulnerable people over the Christmas period. During Christmas 2014 a total of £50,000 was donated to the Silver Line, Cruse Bereavement and Carers UK.

Schools

A regular magazine *Teachers Post* is published eight times a year and offers school teachers support through the provision of educational resource packs (for more details see www.teacherspost.co.uk). During 2014/15 the group also hosted a total of 212 visits to its mail centres by schools.

GSL activities

GSL is the group's European parcel delivery service. It supports local charities that address key issues in communities.

Main locations

UK

Community contributions

In 2014/15 Royal Mail gave £7.34 million directly to 'charities, good causes and disadvantaged groups'. This figure includes the mandated commitments to Articles for the Blind and BPMA totalling £4.4 million. Employees raised further £3 million for charities and good causes across the UK. Note that we deduct the figure for administration expenses from the group's overall contribution. We know that in-kind support is also provided through the GSL division in mainland Europe; however, most charitable support is focused on the UK. The CR report provides the following breakdown:

Voluntary contributions	
Cash – employee fundraising	£3.03 million
Cash – Royal Mail	£2.08 million
Time	£500,000
Administration	£260,000
In kind	£340,000
Mandated contributions	
In kind	£3.96 million
Cash	£460,000

Beneficiaries included: Abbeyfields Society; Alzheimer's Society; Barnardo's; British Postal Museum and Archive; Communications Workers Union Humanitarian Aid; County Air Ambulance Trust; Dolly Parton's Imagination Library; FareShare; Help the Hospices; Prostate Cancer UK; Remploy; Royal National Institute of Blind People (RNIB); Royal Voluntary Service (RVS); The Stroke Association; The Rowland Hill Benevolent Fund; Together for Short Live; Whizz-Kidz UK.

In-kind support

Articles for the Blind

The group's Articles for the Blind service delivered around 3.6 million items free of charge to blind and partially-sighted people across the UK.

Books

Over 9,700 free books were provided to children and grandchildren to help develop a love of reading.

Employee-led support

Employee volunteering

Staff are encouraged to volunteer and the group offers paid time off for employees supporting communities, and grants of up to £400 to cover volunteering costs. In 2014/15 the group provided over 2,000 days of paid leave and over 2,500 days of unpaid leave.

Since 2012 Royal Mail has been part of the Business in the Community Business Connectors programme which places employees in community organisations to help them connect with businesses.

Payroll giving

According to the CR Report for 2015, the payroll giving scheme began in 1989 and has helped over 1,300 charities throughout the UK. It has the Platinum Payroll Giving Quality Mark Excellence Award and a Guinness World record for the most registered charities supported through a payroll giving scheme. In 2014/15 employees raised £3 million in through payroll giving and fundraising.

Matched funding

The group will match funds raised by the staff up to £200 for each employee in a year, as part of the Community Matched Giving Scheme. A grant of up to £200 a year can also be obtained to cover the cost of fundraising activities. In 2014/15 Royal Mail provided £188,000 to match donations by employees.

The group matches donations to the Charity of the Year programme. Funds raised by employees for the Charity of the Year can be matched up to £2,500 per individual a year.

It has also extended its matched giving to retired people who can raise up to £50 that will be matched by the group, up to a limit of £100,000.

Commercially led support

Apprenticeship and employment programmes

The Ready for Work programme provides opportunities for people in long-term unemployment. In 2014/15 placements were offered to 40 people. Royal Mail also works with Remploy to support people with disabilities gain and maintain employment. Apprenticeships are also provided.

British Postal Museum and Archive (BPMA)

The Royal Mail has provided long-term funding to build a new postal museum which will educate people on British history and the history of the postal service. It will also contain the Royal Mail Archive and a dedicated learning space which can support up to 10,000 pupils per year.

Applications

Apply in writing to the correspondent. It appears that local organisations can also apply directly to their regional office for support.

RPS Group PLC

Consultancy, marine, oil and gas/fuel, water

Correspondent: The Corporate Governance Committee, Centurion Court, 85 Milton Park, Abingdon, Oxfordshire OX14 4RY (tel: 01235 438000; email: rpsmp@rpsgroup.com; website: www.rpsgroup.com/Group/About-Us/Corporate-Social-Responsibility.aspx)

Directors: Dr Alan Hearne, Chief Executive; Gary Young, Finance Director; John Bennett; Ken Lever, Chair; Louise Charlton; Nicholas Rowe; Robert Bakewell (women: 1; men: 6)

Year end	31/12/2015
Turnover	£566,972,000
Pre-tax profit	£9,855,000

Nature of business: RPS in the UK provides multi-disciplinary consultancies advising on all aspects of: built and natural environment; oil, gas and other natural resources; renewable energy; and energy infrastructure.

Company registration number: 2087786

Subsidiary undertakings include: RPS Environmental Management Ltd; The Energy Ltd; and The Environmental Consultancy Ltd.

Focus of giving: Education, environment, overseas projects.

Community involvement	✓
Community contributions	✓
Company reports on anti-slavery	✓
CSR report	✓
Cash donations declared	✓
Charity partner(s)	✓
Employee-led support	✓
Gifts in kind	✓
Overseas giving	✓

Charitable donations

Cash worldwide:	2015	£325,000
Total worldwide (cash and in kind):	2015	£325,000

Community involvement

Partnership with Tree Aid

The group is a largest corporate sponsor of TREE AID (Charity Commission no. 1135156), a UK-based development charity that focuses on planting trees as a way of reducing poverty and protecting the environment. As well as financial support, RPS also provides multidisciplinary technical support and training.

Education
RPS group also provides funding for academic bursaries and educational initiatives. In 2015 this totalled £221,000.

UK locations
Offices throughout the UK.

Community contributions

In 2015 the group 'supported a range of community and charitable initiatives with gifts in-kind and financial contributions throughout the year mostly at office level'. The annual report notes that a total of £873,000 (2014: £882,000) was awarded, which includes both the group and staff contributions and an additional £221,000 (2014: £175,000) spent on academic bursaries and educational initiatives. A further £104,000 was given to support Tree Aid's education, tree planting and woodland conservation programmes in Ghana. We were unable to separate the money donated by the company from the employee contributions nor determine the amount awarded in cash in the UK. Using the figure spent on academic bursaries and the support give to Tree Aid we estimate that the group's contributions totalled at least around £325,000.

Beneficiaries included: Tree Aid.

In-kind support

Staff volunteering time and expert advice and services.

Employee-led support

The group employees contribute to charitable causes supported by the group, through cash contributions and volunteering time.

Applications

Apply in writing to the correspondent.

RSA Insurance Group PLC

Insurance

Correspondent: Natalie Tickle, Group and UK Charity and Communities CR manager, 20 Fenchurch Street, London EC3M 3AU (020 7337 5337; email: natalie.tickle@uk.rsagroup.com; website: www.rsagroup.com)

Directors: Alastair Barbour; Enrico Cucchiani; Hugh Mitchell; Isabel Hudson; Johanna Waterous; Joseph Streppel; Kath Cates; Malcolm Le May; Martin Scicluna, Chair; Scott Egan, Group Chief Financial Officer; Stephen Hester, Group Chief Executive; Stephen Hester, Chief Executive (women: 3; men: 8)

Year end	31/12/2015
Turnover	£6,683,000,000
Pre-tax profit	£107,000

Nature of business: The group's principal activity is the transaction of personal and commercial general insurance business.

Company registration number: 2339826

Subsidiary undertakings include: Royal & Sun Alliance Reinsurance Ltd; British Aviation Insurance Company Ltd; Canadian Northern Shield Insurance Company.

Brands include: Answer; Codan; Link4; More Th>n; RSA; Trygg Hansa.

Focus of giving: Education, overseas projects, children, young people, community/social welfare, disasters.

Membership: BITC

Community involvement	✓
Community contributions	✓
CSR report	✓
Cash donations declared	✓
Employee-led support	✓
FTSE 100	✓
Gifts in kind	✓
Matched funding	✓
Overseas giving	✓

Charitable donations

Cash UK (latest available):	2015	£680,000
Total UK (cash and in kind):	2015	£680,000
Cash worldwide:	2015	£1,282,500
Total worldwide (cash and in kind):	2015	£1,350,000

Community involvement

The group's Thriving Communities scheme helps communities in three main ways. Firstly it looks to create social impact by supporting matched funding and employee volunteering. Secondly, young people are helped to develop skills needed for the workplace through the Education and Employability programme. Finally, the group work with enterprise and entrepreneurs to help them solve social issues.

Main locations
RSA works throughout the UK and has main offices in Liverpool, Birmingham, Horsham and London.

Community contributions

In 2015 the group's community contributions totalled £1.6 million. This included cash donations of £1.28 million (of which £680,000 was given in the UK) and employee fundraising totalling £223,000.

We were unable to determine the value of in-kind support given in the UK. As is our usual practice, we have not included employee fundraising in our figure for the group's total community contributions.

In-kind support

Non-cash support includes staff volunteering (7,158 hours in 2015), gifts in-kind, work experience and training schemes, business skills, expertise and use of resources (facilities and equipment).

Employee-led support

In 2015 employees of the group raised £223,000 for their chosen causes.

Matched funding
The company matches employee donations to registered charities at a capped level, set nationally.

Exclusions

The Group Charity Policy Statement notes that it is 'unable to support any organisation which supports one specific religious faith, political parties, sports (unless compelling community justification), arts (unless supporting disadvantaged groups) or individual sponsorships'. Our research indicates that requests received by circular are normally not actioned.

Applications

Generally, applications should be made in writing to the correspondent.

The group's Community and Charity Policy Statement states that:

> RSA will provide direct financial support only if one or all of the following conditions is satisfied:
>
> - The scope falls under one of the priority focus areas or regional variations
> - Actively involves RSA employees volunteering
> - Part of wider active partnership

S&U PLC

Financial services

Correspondent: Christopher Redford, Company Secretary, S&U PLC, 6 The Quadrangle, Cranmore Avenue, Solihull, Birmingham B90 4LE (tel: 012170577 77; email: info@suplc.co.uk; website: www.suplc.co.uk)

Directors: Anthony Coombs, Chair; Chris Redford; Demetrios Markou; Fiann Coombs; Graham Coombs; Graham Pedersen; Guy Thompson; Keith Smith; Tarek Khlat (men: 9)

Year end	31/01/2015
Turnover	£74,400,000
Pre-tax profit	£23,200,000

Nature of business: Founded in 1938 S&U PLC is a niche specialist finance provider in the UK.

Company registration number: 342025

Focus of giving: Health, ill health, children, young people.

Community involvement	✓
Community contributions	✓
CSR report	✓
Directors have other relevant posts	✓

Cash donations declared ✓
Charity partner(s) ✓
Employee-led support ✓

Charitable donations

Cash UK (latest available):	2015	£50,000
Total UK (cash and in kind):	2015	£50,000
Cash worldwide:	2015	£50,000
Total worldwide (cash and in kind):	2015	£50,000

Community involvement

S&U is a corporate sponsor and Anthony Coombs is the Chair of the Foundation for Conductive Education, based in Birmingham, a leading UK charity working to improve the lives of children and adults with neurological motor disorders resulting from strokes, Parkinson's disease and cerebral palsy.

Directors with other relevant posts

Anthony Coombs (Chair) is a director of a number of companies and charities including chairing the trustees of the National Institute for Conductive Education (Charity Commission no. 295873). And Tarek Khlat is a trustee of the NSPCC (Charity Commission no. 216401).

Main location

Birmingham and various locations throughout the UK.

Community contributions

According to the 2014/15 annual report, during the year the group gave over £50,000 in charitable contributions, most of it through the Keith Coombs Trust.

Previous beneficiaries have included: The National Institute for Conductive Education; Red Boots; Cure Leukaemia for Kids.

The group also makes financial contributions in the artistic and cultural fields. During the year it sponsored the Birmingham Royal Ballet and innovative new theatrical productions at The Almeida and Royal Court Theatre.

Employee-led support

Fundraising

Every year staff organise collection events for charities ranging from the British Heart Foundation, Macmillan Nurses and Marie Curie Cancer Care. In the past four years, staff have supported Healthy Hearts, walked peaks for the homeless and biked for cancer sufferers.

Applications

Apply in writing to the correspondent.

Saga PLC

Financial services, insurance, legal, leisure

Correspondent: Sarah Jenner, Trust Executive, Enbrook Park, Sandgate, Folkestone, Kent CT20 3SE (01303 774069; email: sarah.jenner@saga.co.uk; website: www.saga.co.uk/saga-charitable-foundation.aspx)

Directors: Andrew Goodsell, Chair; Gareth Williams; Jonathan Hill, Group Finance Director; Lance Batchelor, Chief Executive Officer; Orna Ni-Chionna; Pev Hooper; Phillip Green; Ray King (women: 2; men: 7)

Year end	31/01/2016
Turnover	£963,200,000
Pre-tax profit	£176,200,000

Nature of business: The group provides travel, financial, insurance, health and lifestyle products and services for people aged 50 and over.

Company registration number: 8804263

Brands include: Allied Healthcare; Claimfast; Metromail.

Focus of giving: Education, health, ill health, individuals, older people, overseas projects, children, young people, community/social welfare, disability.

Membership: BITC

Community involvement ✓
Community contributions ✓
AF Covenant ✓
Corporate charity ✓
Employee-led support ✓
Matched funding ✓
Overseas giving ✓

Charitable donations

Cash UK (latest available):	2016	£46,000
Total UK (cash and in kind):	2016	£119,000
Cash worldwide:	2016	£46,000
Total worldwide (cash and in kind):	2016	£119,000

Community involvement

Saga Charitable Trust (Charity Commission no. 291991)

The charity was founded by Saga holidays and seeks to benefit the communities in financially developing countries that the group's tours visit. The group's website invites donations to the charity and promises to cover all the UK overheads and administrative costs 'so that every penny donated goes to [its] projects overseas'.

Saga Respite for Carers Trust (Charity Commission no. 1124709)

The charity provides holidays for unpaid carers aged over 50 and pays for respite care while the carer is away.

Saga Charitable Foundation (Charity Commission no. 1147124)

The foundation was set up in 2012 as 'the principal umbrella for all of Saga's charitable activities'. However, the foundation has not had any income or expenditure since it was set up.

Main locations

Saga works throughout the UK and has headquarters in Kent.

Community contributions

As the group appears to be channelling its charitable giving through the corporate charities detailed here, we estimate the amount contributed by the group to equal the amount donated to the three charities. The latest accounts for the corporate charities available to view at the time of writing (August 2016) were for 2014/15. In that year The Saga Charitable Trust received a donation of £73,000 from the group and further £224,500 from Saga customers and staff donations; The Saga Respite for Carers Trust had a donation of £46,000 from the group. Based on these figures we estimate that the amount contributed by the group was £119,000.

Employee-led support

Employees and customers donated significant sums towards victims of the Nepal Earthquake in April 2015.

Corporate charity

The Saga Charitable Trust (Charity Commission no. 291991).

Exclusions

Our research indicates that support is not normally given for advertising in charity brochures, animal welfare, the arts, enterprise/training, fundraising events, medical research, political or religious appeals, science/technology; or sports.

Applications

The Saga Charitable Trust (Charity Commission no. 291991)

In the first instance see the website, where guidelines are available to download. Applications are accepted at any time throughout the year. Grants are decided at regular meetings by the trustees where applications are considered for various types of funding.

Funding proposals should include the following information: outline and objectives of the project; who will benefit and how; resources required and timeframe; management and sustainability of the project; how funds will be managed and accounted for; and three years of the organisation's financial accounts.

The Sage Group PLC

Computer software

Correspondent: Leigh Thompson, Sage Foundation Programme Manager, North Park, Newcastle upon Tyne NE13 9AA (tel: 0191 294 3000; fax: 0191 294 0002; website: www.sage.com)

Directors: Donald Brydon, Chair; Drummond Hall; Inna Kuznetsova; Jonathan Howell; Neil Berkett; Ruth Markland; Stephen Kelly, Chief Executive Officer; Steve Hare, Group Chief Financial Officer (women: 2; men: 6)

Year end	30/09/2015
Turnover	£1,435,500,000
Pre-tax profit	£358,500,000

Nature of business: Sage is a global technology company, providing automated business solutions to accounting, payroll and HR, and payments.

Company registration number: 2231246

Subsidiary undertakings include: Apex Software International Ltd; Computer Resources Ltd; Sky Software Ltd.

Brands include: Sage Impact; Sage Live; Sage One; Sage X3.

UK employees: 13,062

Total employees: 2,000

Focus of giving: Economic generation, poverty and social exclusion, children, young people, community/social welfare.

Membership: BITC

Accredited Living Wage Employer	✓
Community involvement	✓
Community contributions	✓
Company reports on anti-slavery	✓
CSR report	✓
CSR or charity committee	✓
Directors have other relevant posts	✓
Employee-led support	✓
FTSE 100	✓
Gifts in kind	✓
Matched funding	✓
Overseas giving	✓
Pledge 1%	✓

Community involvement

The group makes contributions to community and charitable organisations worldwide through its foundation, which is not a registered charity. Preference tends to be given to organisations that create entrepreneurship opportunities for young and disadvantaged people. In the UK, there may be some preference towards organisations in North East England as the group is very active in the community where its head office is based.

Sage Foundation

The Sage Foundation was launched in June 2015, with the aim of setting a benchmark for corporate philanthropy around the world. It is built on a '2+2+2 model', which means a donation of 2% of employee hours to charitable causes and a donation of 2% of free cash flow (about £4 to £5 million per year) to the foundation and to charities. The foundation also donates two smart technology product licences for charities or non-profit organisations. The foundation's focus is on creating social and economic opportunity in the communities in which the company operates in around the world.

The 2% of free cash flow donations is given to charities in the form of grants. The foundation also matches employees' fundraising efforts from this income source. Grants are provided to organisations that create social, economic and entrepreneurial opportunities for young people and those from disadvantaged communities.

Directors with other relevant posts

Donald Brydon was formerly Chair and is now a patron of EveryChild (Charity Commission no. 1089879).

Neil Berkett is a trustee of the NSPCC (Charity Commission no. 216401) and is Chair of the Guardian Media Group.

Main locations

The company is based in Newcastle. The foundation operates worldwide.

Community contributions

The group aims to give 2% of its free cash flow (about £4 to £5 million per year) to its foundation and to charities around the world. There were no figures available regarding cash donations made in this financial year in the UK, although the annual report noted that approximately £12,000 was donated by the company to Habitat to Humanity in the USA to match employee fundraising efforts.

In-kind support

Charities can receive a 50% discount on Sage products and all income from these sales goes directly to the Sage Foundation.

Employee-led support

Employee volunteering

The company's employees are entitled to five days per year to volunteer for charitable causes via the Sage Foundation. There are no restrictions on the charities that employees can support, although volunteering is usually focused on: young people; working with socially and economically deprived communities; and the development of entrepreneurism and social enterprise.

Applications

Applications can be made in writing to the correspondent.

To apply for a donation of a smart technology product licence, visit the Sage Foundation section of the company's website: www.sage.com/company/sage_foundation/products.

J Sainsbury PLC

Retail – supermarkets

Correspondent: Corporate Responsibility & Society Team, 33 Holborn, London EC1N 2HT (tel: 020 7695 6000; email: 20x20@sainsburys.co.uk; website: j-sainsbury.co.uk/responsibility)

Directors: Brian Cassin; David Keens; David Tyler, Chair; Jean Tomlin; John Rogers, CEO; Mary Harris; Matt Brittin; Mike Coupe, Chief Executive; Susan Rice (women: 3; men: 6)

Year end	12/03/2016
Turnover	£23,506,000,000
Pre-tax profit	£587,000,000

Nature of business: A general merchandise and clothing retailer with UK-based supermarkets, convenience stores and an online presence. Banking and financial services products are offered through the wholly owned subsidiary, Sainsbury's Bank, and the group has a number of joint ventures, including property development.

Company registration number: 185647

Total employees: 162,000

Focus of giving: Health, ill health, housing, homelessness, sport, recreation, children, young people, community/social welfare, disability.

Membership: BITC

Community involvement	✓
Community contributions	✓
Company reports on anti-slavery	✓
Charity of the Year	✓
Charity partner(s)	✓
Employee-led support	✓
FTSE 100	✓
Gifts in kind	✓
Market-led giving	✓
Payroll giving	✓
Sponsorship	✓

Charitable donations

Cash UK (latest available):	2016	£64,000
Total UK (cash and in kind):	2016	£164,000

Community involvement

Sainsbury's community involvement is supported at a local level by a 'national framework'. At a local level, charities and community groups are supported by individual Sainsbury's stores and nominated charities are supported. At a national level, through its community schemes such as Active Kids, Sainsbury's looks to make a positive contribution across the country.

Charity partners

The group's charity partners are: Carers UK; Comic Relief; The Royal British Legion.

Sainsbury Family Charitable Trusts

The Sainsbury Family Charitable Trusts is the operating office of a group of 18 grant-making charities affiliated with the Sainsbury family. Each trust is operated independently with separate boards of trustees each led by a member of the family.

Community contributions

The annual report and accounts for 2015/16 did not declare a figure for charitable donations from the group and so, we were unable to determine a total value for the cash and in-kind support given during the year. The annual report and accounts for 2015/16 state that nearly £46 million pounds was donated to charity, including more than £1 million raised for charities local to Sainsbury's stores. We were unable to determine the proportion of this contributed by the group. We know that at least £64,000 was donated through the 'Local Heroes' scheme and over £100,000 worth of gifts was donated to flooded communities near stores in the North.

Employee, customer and supplier contributions

During the year, more than £620,000 was donated to local non-profit causes through the Community Budget, which was part-funded by sales of the 'Bag for Life'.

Other customer, employee and supplier contributions included:

- £2 million raised for The Royal British Legion
- £7 million raised for Sport Relief in 2015
- £2 million raised for Save the Children's literacy campaign Read on, Get on

Active Youth

Through the programme, which is part of Sainsbury's 20x20 Sustainability Plan, the group has given itself the target of encouraging 20 million children to enjoy physical activity. Active Youth encompasses a number of sports-based initiatives and to date:

- £150 million worth of sports and cooking equipment and experiences has been donated, with the help of customers, via the Active Kids scheme since 2005
- £10 million has been pledged to Sainsbury's School Games over three years
- More than 3,100 teachers have been trained and 73,000 young people have benefitted from the £1 million Paralympic legacy programme, Active Kids for All. The programme works to include 500,000 children with disabilities in mainstream school sports

In-kind support

Gifts in kind

Surplus food fit for human consumption is donated from more than 300 local Sainsbury's stores to charities such as FoodCycle.

Employee-led support

Employee fundraising

Sainsbury's employees fundraise for various partner charities and causes. Though the Local Charity of the Year programme employees fundraise for a customer-nominated charity and also take part with national appeals such as Comic Relief. Activities have included dressing-up and running marathons.

Matched funding

Through the 'Local Heroes' scheme, employees who volunteer in their own time for their community are acknowledged and rewarded. Sainsbury donates £5 per hour spent volunteering to the employee's chosen charity or community group, up to a value of £200 per employee.

Payroll giving

Our research indicates that the Give As You Earn scheme is in operation.

Commercially led support

Customer support

Sainsbury's customers, along with employees and suppliers are involved with numerous fundraising initiatives. Examples include:

Active Kids: Customers are able to collect vouchers to donate to their local school. Schools can then use the vouchers to apply for sports and cooking equipment and related experiences to help support children to eat, exercise and live well.

Charity partners: Sainsbury's customers have helped to raise millions for charity partners including Comic Relief and The Royal British Legion through product sales (including poppies and red noses) and by taking part in fundraising initiatives.

Bag for Life: Sales of the Bag for Life part-fund the Community Budget scheme, which sees individual stores and depots manage their own budgets, which are used to support local charities and community groups.

Local charity scheme: Sainsbury's stores partner a local charity, as nominated in May or June each year by customers. From the nominations, one charity is selected and receives fundraising and volunteering support from the store for the following 12 months.

Sponsorship

Sainsbury sponsors the British Paralympic Association.

Applications

Support from J Sainsbury PLC

Charities: All requests for local sponsorship and support are managed by local Sainsbury's store, which are allocated budgets to support their local community. Contact your local store directly and, where possible, it will try to accommodate your request.

Local charity scheme: Nominations are initially made through an online nomination form. Each store then creates a shortlist of three local charities, which are then invited to present to the store. One is then selected to receive fundraising and volunteering support over the next 12 months.

Sponsorship: Sponsorship enquiries should be emailed to sponsorship.enquiries@sainsburys.co.uk.

Support from the Sainsbury Family Charitable Trusts: the trusts vary in their approach to grant-making and applications. Some have their own application forms, whereas others do not accept unsolicited proposals. More details are available from the Sainsbury Family Charitable Trusts website: www.sfct.org.uk.

Samsung Electronics (UK) Ltd

Electronics/computers

Correspondent: Corporate Citizenship Team, Samsung House, 1000 Hillswood Drive, Chertsey, Surrey KT16 0PS (tel: 01932 455000; website: www.samsung.com/uk)

Directors: Gheechan Song; Sang Ho Jo; Sung Wuk Kang

Year end	31/12/2015
Turnover	£2,688,403,000
Pre-tax profit	£72,512,000

Nature of business: Samsung Electronics (UK) Ltd's principal activities include: import and distribution of electronic and electrical goods; purchase and sale of components and capital equipment; provision of research and development services to the ultimate parent company; and import and distribution of telecommunications systems.

The accounts for 2015 state that 'all operations are UK based with the exception of two small research and development facilities in Israel and Finland and a branch office in Ireland'.

The company's ultimate holding company is Samsung Electronics Co. Ltd.

Company registration number: 3086621

Subsidiary undertakings include: Samsung Semiconductor Europe Ltd.

UK employees: 1,380

Total employees: 325,000

Focus of giving: Education, enterprise/training, environment, inner cities, arts, culture, science technology, sport, recreation, children, young people, community/social welfare.

Membership: BITC

Community involvement	✓
Community contributions	✓
CSR report	✓
Charity partner(s)	✓
Employee-led support	✓
Gifts in kind	✓
Market-led giving	✓
Pro bono	✓
Shared-value alliances	✓
Sponsorship	✓
STEM-focused	✓

Community involvement

The group's UK support focuses on STEM and digital education, particularly through its Digital Classrooms initiatives, which it delivers with schools and a range of other partners. Most of the group's support is provided through in-kind donations.

Digital Classrooms

The group works with schools to set up digital classrooms across the UK, providing technology, teacher training and support. They have also set up Digital Classrooms with their partners such as The Prince's Trust and the V&A.

Partnerships

The group works with a number of UK partners to deliver its corporate citizenship support.

The Prince's Trust

Samsung works with The Prince's Trust to establish Digital Classrooms in their centres across the UK, giving disadvantaged young people new opportunities to develop digital skills and engage with learning. It also provides kitchen equipment for the charity's Fairbridge scheme, technology for its Get Started with Digital Media programme, and sponsorship for the charity's Celebrate Success Awards.

BBC micro:bit

Samsung UK has partnered with the BBC to provide mini computers, the BBC micro:bit, to schoolchildren around the UK, introducing them to coding, with a range of projects and activities alongside.

British Museum

The group works in partnership with the British Museum to deliver the Digital Discovery Centre learning programme. The programme offers a range of activities and workshops, using digital learning to engage with the museum's collections.

The Science Museum

Samsung sponsors The Winton Gallery, opening in the Science Museum at the end of 2016, exploring how mathematicians have shaped the modern world.

Apps for Good

Samsung works in partnership with the charity Apps for Good to provide devices and training for the programme, as well as sponsoring the Apps for Good awards, which recognise the ideas of students on the programme.

Code Club

The group works with Code Club, a charity that runs volunteer-led coding sessions in schools and community centres across the UK, providing support for projects such as competitions, as well as for regional Code Club hubs at community centres around the UK.

V&A Museum

Samsung has opened a digital classroom in the V&A Museum, offering design and technology workshops for 16- to 19-year-olds, using digital technology to engage with the galleries.

Digital Academies

The group's Digital Academies provide technology-related vocational training and qualifications for young people in partnership with educational institutions. In Harborne Academy, the group trains teachers on using technology in the classroom; in Newham College, the group supports practical and vocational training for 150 students, three classrooms and a number of scholarships.

Main locations

The group operates throughout the UK and internationally. Its UK headquarters is based in Chertsey, Surrey.

Community contributions

No figures was given for the group's charitable contribution in the UK.

In-kind support

Most of the group's support for partners is provided in-kind, through donations of equipment, support, training etc.

Employee-led support

Employee fundraising

The group's employees have taken part in fundraising initiatives for The Prince's Trust, one of their partners, such as the Zero to Hero competition and the Palace to Palace cycle ride.

Commercially led support

Sponsorship and market-led giving

Much of the group's support is given through the provision of Samsung technology devices to be used for educational purposes. Many of the group's partnerships also involve sponsorship of a particular initiative – such as The Prince's Trust's Celebrate Success Awards, or the Science Museum's Winton Gallery. For more details on the programmes see 'Community involvement'.

Applications

Apply in writing to the correspondent.

Santander UK PLC

Building society, banking

Correspondent: CSR Team, 2 Triton Square, Regent's Place, London NW1 3AN (tel: 0870 607 6000; email: community@santander.co.uk; website: www.santander.co.uk/uk/about-santander-uk/csr)

Directors: Alain Dromer; Ana Botin; Annemarie Durbin; Antonio Roman, Chief Financial Officer; Baroness Shriti Vadera, Chair; Bruce Carnegie-Brown; Chris Jones; Ed Giera; Genevieve Shore; José Maria Fuster; Juan Rodriguez Inciarte; Manuel Soto; Nathan Bostock, Chief Executive; Scott Wheway (women: 4; men: 10)

Year end	31/12/2015
Turnover	£4,573,000,000
Pre-tax profit	£1,345,000,000

Nature of business: Provision of personal and corporate financial products and services.

Santander UK PLC is an autonomous unit and forms part of the Banco Santander group, which operates internationally with headquarters in Spain.

Company registration number: 2294747

Subsidiary undertakings include: Abbey National UK Investments; Alliance and Leicester Ltd; Santander Consumer (UK) PLC.

UK employees: 24,423

Focus of giving: Economic generation, education, enterprise/training, health, ill health, financial education, poverty and social exclusion, children, young people, community/social welfare.

Membership: BITC, LBG

Accredited Living Wage Employer	✓
Community involvement	✓
Community contributions	✓
CSR report	✓
CSR or charity committee	✓
Directors have other relevant posts	✓

AF Covenant	✓
Cash donations declared	✓
Charity of the Year	✓
Charity partner(s)	✓
Corporate charity	✓
Employee-led support	✓
Gifts in kind	✓
Market-led giving	✓
Matched funding	✓
Payroll giving	✓
Pro bono	✓
Sponsorship	✓

Charitable donations

Cash UK (latest available):	2015	£5,000,000
Total UK (cash and in kind):	2015	£22,000,000

Community involvement

Santander has an extensive programme of support for charitable causes, mainly focusing on education, employment, enterprise and communities, particularly through the Santander Foundation, which launched its Discovery Grants scheme in 2016. It also provides support for these causes through the Santander Universities scheme and other educational activities. Santander employees volunteer with local charities and educational initiatives, and fundraise for a nominated Charity of the Year, as well as donating to other charities through payroll giving and matched funding from the group.

In 2016 the group launched its new community investment strategy, The Discovery Project, which aims to help one million people over the next five years, with the following aims:

- Explorer – to help people learn about the world around them
- Transformer – to guide people through work-focused support and training
- Changemaker – to support community projects and fund innovations that help society

The Santander UK Foundation Ltd (Charity Commission no. 803655)

The foundation was originally set up with a donation from the then Abbey National PLC of £5 million following the sale of shares unclaimed since the company's flotation.

The foundation is the main channel of the company's corporate donations and provides grants to small, local UK-registered charities, CICs or Credit Unions helping disadvantaged people through knowledge, skills and innovation to reach new opportunities. In 2016 the foundation amalgamated its three previous grants programmes into one scheme, Discovery Grants, as part of its refreshed community investment strategy. The scheme offers grants of up to £5,000 for projects under the following three themes:

- Explorer – improving knowledge and insight
- Transformer – developing skills and experience
- Changemaker – innovative solutions to social challenges

Further detailed guidance on the funding available is provided on the foundation's website: www.santanderfoundation.org.uk.

Charity of the Year grants are also made through the foundation, as well as matched funding for employees' donations to charities of their choice.

Santander Universities

The Santander Universities programme supports universities in 20 countries through project support, mobility grants, scholarships and other grants. According to the 2015 CSR report, 80 universities in the UK received £12 million funding during the year for students' studies, internships and enterprise. Students can also take part in enterprise competitions, gain support through the Santander Universities Enterprise Portal and take part in an SME internship programme.

Santander Social Enterprise Development Award

The group provides growth funding and business support to social enterprises through this scheme, and in 2015, 101 organisations received between £5,000 and £20,000 each.

Education and employability

The group worked in partnership with the charity Career Ready to offer funding for careers support at ten schools in the UK in 2015, with employees acting as mentors and facilitating visits. The group also runs six-week summer work experience programmes for students. Santander also funds the charity PFEG, supporting its Centres of Excellence programme delivering financial education in schools, as well as delivering its own Santander MoneyWise programme, which employees volunteer to deliver.

Directors with other relevant posts

Bruce Carnegie-Brown is also a trustee of the Chartered Management Institute (Charity Commission no. 1091035), Historic Royal Palaces (Charity Commission no. 1068852) and The Shakespeare Globe Trust (Charity Commission no. 266916). Ana Botin is Vice-Chair of the World Business Council for Sustainable Development.

Main locations

Santander UK PLC operates throughout the UK. Its head office is in London. It is owned by Santander Group, which is based in Spain.

Community contributions

According to the group's 2015 CSR report, UK community investment in 2015 totalled £23 million. This included volunteering time, which totalled £957,500, as well as almost £12 million given through the Santander Universities programme. £1.3 million was given through the Santander Breakthrough programme, supporting small and medium enterprises, which we would not normally consider to be a strictly charitable activity, so we have not included this in the total charitable contributions figure.

Investment was broken down into the following categories:

Education	£12.9 million
Communities	£5.6 million
Enterprise	£3.4 million
Other	£1 million
Employment	£542,500

Santander Foundation

In 2015 Santander UK PLC donated £5 million to the Santander Foundation, in addition to services totalling £100,000. The foundation made 3,300 grants during the year, totalling £5.7 million, which were distributed in the following categories:

Note: In 2015, the foundation's previous grants schemes were still in operation, rather than the Discovery Grants scheme.

Other	£2.1 million
Health	£2 million
Education and training	£1.3 million
Financial capability	£321,000

Beneficiaries included: British Heart Foundation (£190,000); Mayor's Fund for London (£85,000); Access to Business, Headway, MS Society, Sight Cymru, Small Charities Coalition, South Gloucestershire Citizens Advice and Tees Valley Women's Centre (£10,000 each).

Employee-led support

Employee volunteering

In 2015 over 5,000 employees took part in volunteering, contributing over 31,000 hours of volunteering to 363 projects. The group's Community Days scheme allows employees to spend a day helping local charities and community groups. Employees also volunteer to deliver the group's MoneyWise financial education workshops in schools.

Charity of the Year

In 2015 employees voted to support the British Heart Foundation as the group's Charity of the Year, and organised a wide range of fundraising events and activities. A total of £1.2 million was raised during the year

Matched funding

The Santander Foundation provides matched funding for charitable donations that employees make to charities of their own choice. In 2015 matched funding totalled £2.6 million.

Commercially led support

Santander Breakthrough

Launched in 2011 Santander Breakthrough programme seeks to identify the best entrepreneurial companies in the UK and help them achieve their full potential. It is aimed at fast-growing small and medium-sized enterprises and aims to help them boost economic recovery and the creation of local employment. The group provides support with business expertise, recruitment, international opportunities, networking and finance.

Corporate charity

Santander UK Foundation Ltd (Charity Commission no. 803655).

Exclusions

Discovery Grants will not be made for the following purposes:

- General running costs
- Individuals – including trips, overseas volunteering, gap year activity, medical treatment, bursary schemes, grants for studying or research
- Fundraising activities
- Unregistered charities, not-for-profit groups, community amateur sports clubs, exempt or excepted charities
- Charities which restrict their beneficiaries to a single religious or single ethnic group
- Events, conferences or sponsorship
- Party political activity
- Start-up costs (organisations must have at least a full year of accounts)
- Funding to fill a shortfall
- Other grant-makers
- Beneficiaries outside the UK, Channel Islands or the Isle of Man
- Funding for multiple years
- Health, research and palliative care charities – these are supported through the staff fundraising scheme

Applications

The group

Any enquiries, other than those relating to the foundation, should be directed to the CSR team on: community@santander.co.uk.

The Santander UK Foundation Ltd(Charity Commission no. 803655)

Discovery Grant nominations can be made by the organisation in question, a Santander employee or a customer. Forms can be obtained from any Santander branch, and should be returned to the nomination box in the branch. You can find your nearest branch at: www.santander.co.uk/findbranch. Successful organisations should be notified by email within six weeks.

The best way to contact the foundation if you still have a question is by email to grants@santander.co.uk. The foundation can also be reached by post at: Santander Foundation, Santander, 201 Grafton Gate East, Milton Keynes MK9 1AN.

Guidelines, including frequently asked questions, can be found on the foundation's website: www.santanderfoundation.org.uk.

Schroders PLC

Financial services

Correspondent: Corporate Responsibility Manager, 31 Gresham Street, London EC2V 7QA (tel: 020 7658 6000; fax: 020 7658 6965; email: cr@schroders.com; website: www.schroders.com)

Directors: Andrew Beeson, Chair; Ashley Almanza; Bruno Schroder; Lord Howard of Penrith; Massimo Tosato; Michael Dobson, Chief Executive; Nichola Pease; Peter Harrison; Philip Mallinckrodt; Rhian Davies; Richard Keers, Chief Financial Officer; Robin Buchanan (women: 2; men: 11)

Year end	31/12/2015
Turnover	£464,100,000
Pre-tax profit	£589,000,000

Nature of business: Schroders PLC is an international asset management provider.

The group's work is divided into: wealth management; and asset management, which has two divisions: investment and distribution.

Company registration number: 3909886

Subsidiary undertakings include: Cazenove Capital Management Ltd; Schroder Administration Ltd; Schroder Unit Trusts Ltd.

Focus of giving: General charitable purposes, education, health, ill health, children, young people, community/social welfare.

Membership: BITC, LBG

Community involvement	✓
Community contributions	✓
CSR report	✓
CSR or charity committee	✓
AF Covenant	✓
Employee-led support	✓
FTSE 100	✓
Gifts in kind	✓
Matched funding	✓
Payroll giving	✓

Charitable donations

Cash UK (latest available):	2015	£538,000
Total UK (cash and in kind):	2015	£538,000
Cash worldwide:	2015	£1.3 million
Total worldwide (cash and in kind):	2015	£1.3 million

Community involvement

The charity focuses on employee-led giving, through matched funding, payroll giving and volunteering.

Main locations

The group's offices in the UK are located in: London; Chester; Edinburgh; and Oxford. The group also has offices in a number of countries worldwide.

Community contributions

In 2015 the group made charitable donations of £1.3 million around the world, most of which was through payroll giving. The company match funded donations of £538,000 (2014: £372,000) for employees in the UK.

Employee-led support

Volunteering

The group has a volunteering policy, offering employees up to 15 hours of paid volunteering leave per year, as well as donating to charities through a volunteer 'time matching' scheme for employees volunteering outside working hours.

Payroll giving

Payroll-giving schemes are operated in a number of offices. In the UK 26% of employees chose to give in this way in 2015.

Applications

Apply in writing to the correspondent.

In 2015 the board of directors discussed charitable donations at their meeting in November.

Scott Bader Company Ltd

Chemicals and plastics

Correspondent: Hayley Sutherland, Commonwealth Secretary, Wollaston Hall, Wollaston, Wellingborough, Northamptonshire NN29 7RL (tel: 01933 666755; email: enquiries@scottbader.com; website: www.scottbader.com)

Directors: Adrian de Goede; Andrew Forrester; Calvin O'Connor; Didier Mathon; Jean-Claude Pierre; Karl-Heinz Funke; Malcolm Forsyth; Peter Hartill; Steven Brown (women: 0; men: 9)

Year end	31/12/2015
Turnover	£176,217,000
Pre-tax profit	£7,171,000

Nature of business: The company is an internationally operating manufacturer and distributor of synthetic resins and chemical intermediates.

The annual report and accounts for 2015 state:

> Scott Bader Company Ltd is wholly owned as a financial and social investment by The Scott Bader Commonwealth Ltd, a company limited by guarantee and a registered charity. ... Everyone working for Scott Bader may become a member of The Commonwealth and, by this mean, become a trustee

holding, in common with other members, the shares of Scott Bader Company Ltd.

Note: The figure for UK employees includes those in the Republic of Ireland.

Company registration number: 189141

Subsidiary undertakings include: Scott Bader Community Fund Trustee Ltd; Scott Bader UK Ltd; Synthetic Resins Ltd.

Brands include: Crestabond; Crestapol; CRYSTIC Crestomer.

UK employees: 309

Total employees: 671

Focus of giving: General charitable purposes, education, enterprise/training, environment, health, ill health, small groups, local groups, humanitarian help, older people, overseas projects, poverty and social exclusion, science technology, children, young people, community/social welfare, disability, disasters.

Community involvement	✓
Community contributions	✓
CSR report	✓
CSR or charity committee	✓
Cash donations declared	✓
Charity partner(s)	✓
Company gives to smaller charities	✓
Corporate charity	✓
Employee-led support	✓
Gifts in kind	✓
Humanitarian aid: overseas	✓
Humanitarian aid: UK including food banks	✓
Matched funding	✓
Overseas giving	✓
Shared-value alliances	✓

Charitable donations

Cash UK (latest available):	2015	£321,000
Total UK (cash and in kind):	2015	£321,000
Cash worldwide:	2015	£403,000
Total worldwide (cash and in kind):	2015	£403,000

Community involvement

The group's charitable giving is mainly channelled through its charity and parent company, Scott Bader Commonwealth Ltd, which makes grants to charities worldwide. The charity receives income of equal to the group staff bonus, or 1% of salary costs – whichever is greater. The charity is also the parent company and holds the shares of Scott Bader Company Ltd in trust on behalf of its employees.

The group supports the following causes: education; environment; health; community; sustainable livelihoods; disability. Companies within the group also make donations to charities locally.

Scott Bader Commonwealth Ltd (Charity Commission no. 206391)

Within the Commonwealth, there are a number of different funds:

Central Fund

The group's members vote at the AGM to decide which projects are supported by the Central Fund. In 2015 the charities supported by the general fund were MondoChallenge Foundation and Trust for Africa's Orphans, each receiving £25,000.

An additional donation of £50,000 from the group allowed Carers Worldwide and Anza to also be supported, receiving £15,000 each. The remaining £20,000, plus a further £5,000 from the Commonwealth, was split between charities working in areas affected by the Nepal earthquake in 2015 – Mondo Challenge, Swinfen Telemedicine and Carers Worldwide each receiving £5,000, and Concern Worldwide receiving £10,000.

Local funds

Companies within the group receive funds to distribute to charities locally. Company addresses can be found on the website.

Small International Fund

Grants of between £500 and £2,000 are awarded to international projects that do not meet the criteria of either the Central Fund or local funds.

Life President's Fund

The group's Life President, Godric Bader, distributes £5,000 of funding to charities of his choice. In 2015 a total of 18 charities were supported.

Main locations

There are 16 companies within the group. The group's headquarters is based in Wellingborough, Northamptonshire. Its other companies are based in Brazil; Canada; China; Croatia; Czech Republic; Dubai; France; Germany; India; Ireland; South Africa; Spain; Sweden; USA.

Community contributions

The 2015 annual report states that during the year, a donation of £321,000 was made by the group to the Commonwealth charity, which we have taken as the group's UK contribution. An additional £82,000 was donated to various charities by companies with in the group.

In 2015 The Scott Bader Commonwealth Ltd made grants totalling around £157,000, distributed among the following causes, according to the 2015 charitable giving report:

Education/training	47%
Health	25%
Community/general	18%
Sustainable livelihoods	9%
Disability	1%

Beneficiaries included: Mondo Challenge Foundation and Trust for Africa's Orphans (£25,000 each); The Prince's Trust (£2,500); Rushden Mind (£2,000); Ro-Ro Sailing Project (£1,000); Salt of the Earth (£900); Beanstalk (£700); The Aidis Trust (£300).

In-kind support

The group offers its facilities as in-kind support for local communities. For example, the grounds of the group's head office in Wollaston, Northamptonshire hosts the Wellingborough Dog Welfare Show, and match funds the event up to £1,000, as the charity's trustees include employees of Scott Bader. The group also hosts an annual Pensioner's Tea Party at Christmas at its Wollaston site, inviting local members of the community and donating proceeds to Age UK.

Employee-led support

Employee volunteering

The group's employees are entitled to one day of paid leave for volunteering each year, which was taken up by 34% of UK employees in 2015, supporting a wide range of causes. Examples included: reading in schools; clearing a nature reserve with Wildlife Trust Cambridgeshire and Northamptonshire; helping at food banks; assisting homelessness charities in Northamptonshire; practising interview techniques with young people with special needs.

Matched funding

The group provides matched funding (up to £1,000 per employee) for employee fundraising initiatives, which is managed by the Commonwealth charity. According to the website, this totalled £20,000 in 2015, benefitting 34 charities internationally.

Corporate charity

The Scott Bader Commonwealth Ltd (Charity Commission no. 206391).

Exclusions

Local grants are not usually given for projects or large capital appeals where a significant amount of money still needs to be raised.

Applications

The Scott Bader Commonwealth Ltd

Assessment criteria are available to download from the website. Deadlines for the large project funding are available on the website. Applications for the Small International Fund are accepted all year round and are only accepted from charities that are either: registered in the UK; or already known to Scott Bader. Applications for local funds should be made to the local office – company addresses can be found on the website, and application forms can be obtained from hayley_sutherland@scottbader.com.

General enquiries regarding the group's giving or charitable policies can be addressed to the company at: enquiries@scottbader.com.

ScottishPower UK PLC

Electricity

Correspondent: The CSR & Reputation Committee in the UK, 1 Atlantic Quay, Glasgow G2 8SP (tel: 0141 248 8200; website: www.scottishpower.com)

Directors: Ignacio Sánchez Galán, Chair; Jim McDonald; José Sáinz Armada; Juan Carlos Rebollo; Keith Anderson, Chief Corporate Officer; Lord Kerr of Kinlochard; Susan Deacon; Tom Farmer

Year end	31/12/2015
Turnover	£6,590,400,000
Pre-tax profit	£512,000,000

Nature of business: In 1995 Manweb and ScottishPower merged, and combined they provide 2.5 million homes in the UK with power.

ScottishPower has been part of the Iberdrola Group since April 2007, and is one of the UK's largest energy companies employing more than eight thousand people across Generation; Transmission; Distribution and Retail sectors.

Company registration number: SC117120

Subsidiary undertakings include: Coldham Windfarm Ltd; East Anglia Offshore Wind Ltd; ScottishPower Generation Ltd; SP Manweb PLC; and SPD Finance UK PLC. A full list of subsidiary undertakings can be found in the group's accounts.

UK employees: 6,439

Total employees: 6,439

Focus of giving: Enterprise/training, environment, heritage, non-registered charities, arts, culture, science technology, community/social welfare.

Membership: BITC, LBG

Community involvement	✓
Community contributions	✓
CSR report	✓
CSR or charity committee	✓
Directors have other relevant posts	✓
AF Covenant	✓
Cash donations declared	✓
Charity partner(s)	✓
Corporate charity	✓
Employee-led support	✓
Gifts in kind	✓
Pro bono	✓
Sponsorship	✓

Charitable donations

Total UK (cash and in kind):	2015	£4,500,000
Total worldwide (cash and in kind):	2015	£4,500,000

Community involvement

Charity partnerships

In 2012 the company launched a three-year partnership with Cancer Research UK with the aim to raise £5 million. The amount has already been achieved and further funds are being raised. To show its support ScottishPower has developed its Help Beat Cancer Energy tariff, the company also distributes health information and advice to customers, and encourages employees to fundraise.

The ScottishPower Energy People Trust Fund (OSCR no. SC036980)

The trust was established in 2005 to help registered charities supporting people whose lives are affected by fuel poverty. The fund is maintained through contributions from ScottishPower and voluntary donations from independent supporters. Decisions on funding are made independently of ScottishPower. Support is given in three funding areas: income maximisation, energy efficiency and fuel debt assistance.

The ScottishPower Foundation (OSCR no. SC043862)

The foundation was established in 2013 to provide help to registered charities in areas of: education; environmental protection; the arts, heritage, culture or science; disability; ill health; prevention or relief of poverty; and community development. Similarly to the above fund, decisions to award funding are made independently of ScottishPower. As part of its education focus, the foundation runs a scholarship programme for Masters Studies.

The Iberdrola Group has its foundation (Fundación IBERDROLA); ScottishPower Foundation appears to be a UK equivalent of this.

The ScottishPower Green Energy Trust (OSCR no. SC030104)

The trust was established in 1998 as an independent charity and is funded by ScottishPower Green tariff customers who make an annual donation to the trust. It aims to support the development of new renewable sources in the UK, helping to reduce our reliance on fossil fuels and combat climate change.

Note: In response to regulatory changes, ScottishPower is not currently offering a Green Tariff and therefore the trust cannot consider any new project applications at this time. The website will be updated in due course should this situation change.

Directors with other relevant posts

Lord Kerr is also the President of St Andrews Clinics for Children, and a trustee of the Carnegie Trust for the Universities of Scotland (OSCR number SC015600). The trust has funded student fees, scholarships, bursaries and research grants. It operates across all academic disciplines to encourage wider access to higher education and further research in the Scottish universities.

Main locations

Cheshire; Merseyside; North Wales; North Shropshire; Scotland.

Community contributions

The annual report and accounts for 2015 state:

> During the year ended 31 December 2015, ScottishPower voluntarily contributed £9.2 million in community support activity of which £4.5 million was contributed to registered charitable organisations. The £9.2 million total incorporated £0.5 million in management costs, £0.1 million categorised as charitable gifts, £6.1 million categorised as community investment and £2.5 million categorised as commercial initiatives; given in cash, through staff time and in-kind donations. Included within these figures, Renewables made £3.7 million in voluntary community benefit payments to the communities neighbouring its wind farms.

We take the figure of £4.5 million contributed to registered charitable organisations to represent the company's overall figure for worldwide giving.

In-kind support

Employee volunteering time and skills.

Employee-led support

The company's employees participated in a number of volunteering and fundraising initiatives throughout the year, particularly in support of the partner charity. ScottishPower has a volunteering portal which highlights activities being delivered across the Iberdrola group, promotes local opportunities and helps employees to share their volunteering experiences. Iberdrola international volunteering day was launched in 2010 and channels the charitable spirit of employees in Spain, the US, Brazil, Mexico and the UK who join forces to complete a variety of projects across the five countries on the same day.

STEM Ambassadors

ScottishPower has STEM Ambassadors who are dedicated employee volunteers who encourage young people to study science, technology, engineering and mathematics. They work with schools throughout the communities we serve, reaching thousands of young people each year

Iberdrola International Volunteering Day

Iberdrola international volunteering day was launched in 2010 and channels the charitable spirit of employees in Spain, the US, Brazil, Mexico and the UK who join forces to complete a variety of projects across the five countries on the same day

International volunteering holidays

Iberdrola offers employees the opportunity to take part in an international volunteering project in Sao Paulo, Brazil each year. 'Sao Paulo 2.0' aims to train young people aged 12- 16 in computing and presentation skills to help them develop new skills and gain confidence to change their lives and aspire for a better future.

Matched funding

Staff fundraising efforts are matched up to a maximum of £200 per application.

Payroll giving

The company operates the Give As You Earn scheme in the UK.

Commercially led support

Sponsorships

ScottishPower has a three-year partnership with Glasgow Warriors. The three-year partnership will see Scottish Power represented through prominent back of shirt branding above the number on the Warriors home and away playing kit. The company will also work with the Warriors to develop a community youth programme in the west of Scotland.

Corporate charity

The ScottishPower Foundation (OSCR no. SC043862) and The ScottishPower Energy People Trust (OSCR no. SC036980).

Exclusions

Our research suggests that support is not generally given to appeals from individuals, expeditions, military organisations, circular appeals, advertising in charity brochures, animal welfare charities, religious appeals, local appeals not in areas of the company's presence or overseas projects.

Sponsorship for sporting events and advertisements in publications and so on, will normally only be considered commercially, in terms of potential advertising benefits.

Applications

The company: General enquiries regarding the company giving can be directed to the correspondent or for local requests – addressed to regional offices.

The charities: Applications to the foundation, the Energy People Trust Fund or the Green Energy Trust can be made online (see the company's website for links).

Email enquiries can be directed to:

- The foundation: scottishpowerfoundation@scottishpower.com
- The Green Energy Trust: greenenergytrust@scottishpower.com
- The Energy People Trust: SPEnergyPeopleTrust@ScottishPower.com

SDL PLC

Consultancy, information management and communication, Information Technology, professional support services

Correspondent: The Corporate Social Responsibility Team, Globe House, Clivemont Road, Maidenhead, Berkshire SL6 7DY (tel: 01628 410100; email: sdlfoundation@sdl.com; website: www.sdl.com)

Directors: Adolfo Hernandez, Chief Executive Officer; Alan McWalter; Chris Batterham; David Clayton, Chair; Dominic Lavelle, Chief Financial Officer; Glenn Collinson; Mandy Gradden (women: 1; men: 6)

Year end	31/12/2015
Turnover	£266,900,000
Pre-tax profit	(£25,200,000)

Nature of business: Provision of technology products and language, consulting and education services to allow companies to trade effectively in global markets.

Company registration number: 2675207

Subsidiary undertakings include: Alterian Ltd; Automated Language Processing Services Ltd; SDL Sheffield Ltd.

Total employees: 3,504

Focus of giving: General charitable purposes, economic generation, education, enterprise/training, health, ill health, housing, homelessness, large national appeals, local groups, overseas projects, women's issues, children, young people, community/social welfare.

Community involvement	✓
Community contributions	✓
CSR report	✓
Cash donations declared	✓
Charity partner(s)	✓
Corporate charity	✓
Employee-led support	✓
Gifts in kind	✓
Overseas giving	✓
Pro bono	✓

Charitable donations

Cash UK (latest available):	2015	£214,000
Total UK (cash and in kind):	2015	£214,000
Cash worldwide:	2015	£214,000
Total worldwide (cash and in kind):	2015	£214,000

Community involvement

The group's charitable giving is focused on its corporate charity, The SDL Foundation.

SDL Foundation

The foundation (Charity Commission no. 1127138) focuses on supporting sustainable projects in disadvantaged communities internationally. In 2015 the foundation celebrated its fifth anniversary, having supported 80 projects in 28 countries since 2010.

The foundation prefers to support projects where SDL employees can complement support with their own fundraising initiatives. It tends to work in partnership with charities over a number of years. For example, in the UK, the foundation renewed its support for The Prince's Trust for a further four years, and also provides support through employee volunteering. It has also worked over a number of years with St Wilfrid's in Sheffield, a day centre for people who are homeless, with employees contributing through fundraising initiatives.

Beneficiaries have included: Bead for Life; Food for The Hungry; Habitat for Humanity; Hatua Likoni; Rejoice; Santa Maria Education Fund; Seeds for Africa; St Wilfrid's; The Prince's Trust.

Main locations

The group has 55 offices worldwide. Its offices in the UK are located in Bristol; Maidenhead; and Sheffield.

Community contributions

The 2015 annual report states that during the year the group donated almost £214,000 to the SDL Foundation, which gives internationally.

Employee-led support

Employee volunteering and fundraising

The group offers employees five days of paid volunteering leave each year.

Examples of employee activities in the UK in 2015 include: staff in Maidenhead running bake sales to raise money for Comic Relief; employees in Maidenhead and Sheffield contributing to Operation Christmas Child; Mark Lancaster, CEO, undertaking a sponsored cycle in aid of the SDL Foundation, with some matched funding from the group.

Employees are particularly encouraged to engage with charitable causes that are connected to the SDL Foundation. For example, staff in the UK have volunteered with The Prince's Trust, which is supported by the foundation, delivering CV and interview workshops for young people, and employees in Sheffield have run fundraising events to support St Wilfrid's, a day centre which has also been supported by the foundation.

Corporate charity

The SDL Foundation (Charity Commission no. 1127138).

Applications

The foundation only considers causes supported by SDL employees.

SEGRO PLC

Property

Correspondent: Charity Committee, Cunard House, 15 Regent Street, London SW1Y 4LR (tel: 020 7451 9100; fax: 020 7451 9150; email: uk@SEGRO.com; website: www.segro.com)

Directors: Andy Gulliford; Baroness Ford; Christopher Fisher; David Sleath, Chief Executive Officer; Doug Webb; Justin Read, Group Finance Director; Mark Robertshaw; Martin Moore, Chair; Nigel Rich, Chair; Phil Redding (women: 1; men: 9)

Year end	31/12/2015
Turnover	£248,500,000
Pre-tax profit	£686,500,000

Nature of business: Industrial and commercial property development, construction and investment, supply of utility services and the provision of services associated with such activities.

Company registration number: 167591

Subsidiary undertakings include: Airport Property H1 Ltd; Big Box GP Ltd; Slough Trading Estate Ltd.

Total employees: 285

Focus of giving: Education, enterprise/training, environment, animal welfare, health, ill health, medical research, overseas projects, older people, arts, culture, poverty and social exclusion, sport, recreation, children, young people.

Membership: BITC

Community involvement	✓
Community contributions	✓
Company reports on anti-slavery	✓
CSR report	✓
CSR or charity committee	✓
Cash donations declared	✓
Charity partner(s)	✓
Company gives to smaller charities	✓
Employee-led support	✓
Gifts in kind	✓
Matched funding	✓
Overseas giving	✓
Pro bono	✓

Charitable donations

Cash worldwide:	2015	£213,000
Total worldwide (cash and in kind):	2015	£887,000

Community involvement

In 2015 SEGRO set out a new 'Responsible SEGRO' framework, which focuses on the following areas: Our People; Our Community; Our Stakeholders; Our Environment. Goals will be set in each of these areas. During 2015, the company also began a new approach to charitable giving, based around a Central Charity Committee, open to all employees, with four sub-committees for each of the company's Business Units.

Partnerships

The company has a long-standing relationship with the charity LandAid, which aims to improve the lives of children and young people in disadvantaged circumstances. In 2015 employees raised £92,000 for the charity. Andy Gulliford, Chief Financial Officer, is on LandAid's fundraising committee.

SEGRO also helped to establish Slough Aspire, a community interest company which provides activities and resources for training and developing local residents, business and students in Slough, where the company began.

Employment and skills programme

SEGRO works through partnerships with customer organisations to offer training and employment opportunities to local residents. In 2016 SEGRO will make it a compulsory requirement of its construction contractors to offer apprenticeships or work experience placements to local residents.

London Community Fund

This fund of £60,000 is used to fund community projects in the areas of London in which the company operates. So far, the fund has supported 13 projects in Brent, Ealing, Hounslow, Hillingdon, Enfield and Barking and Dagenham.

Directors with other relevant posts

Christopher Fisher is Chair of Trustees of The Imperial War Museum Development Trust (Charity Commission no. 1146784).

Main locations

In the UK, the group has offices in London and Slough. There are also offices in the Czech Republic; France; Germany; Italy; Luxembourg; Poland; Spain; and the Netherlands.

Community contributions

In 2015 the company's charitable contributions totalled £887,000, of which £213,000 was in grants to organisations, £54,000 in employee fundraising and £620,000 in kind. It was unclear how much of this was given in the UK.

In-kind support

Volunteering

SEGRO employees volunteered a total of 103 days for local charities.

Employee-led support

Employee fundraising

In 2015 employees raised a total of £54,000. £92,000 was raised for LandAid.

Beneficiaries included: LandAid (£92,000); SHOC (£20,000).

Applications

Apply in writing to the correspondent. Decisions are made by the Central Charity Committee or its sub-committees within each of the company's four Business Units.

Serco Group PLC

Business services

Correspondent: Mike Clasper, Chair of Corporate Responsibility Committee, Serco House, 16 Bartley Wood Business Park, Bartley Way, Hook, Hampshire RG27 9UY (tel: 01256 745900; fax: 01256 744113; email: corporateresponsibility@serco.com; website: www.serco.com)

Directors: Angie Risley; Angus Cockburn, Group Chief Financial Officer; Edward Casey Jr; Malcolm Wyman; Mike Clasper; Rachel Lomax; Ralph Crosby Jr; Rupert Soames, Group Chief Executive Officer; Sir Roy Gardner, Chair; Tamara Ingram (women: 3; men: 7)

Year end	31/12/2015
Turnover	£3,177,000,000
Pre-tax profit	(£69,400,000)

Nature of business: The provision of a range of facilities management and systems engineering services.

Company registration number: 2048608

Subsidiary undertakings include: AWE Management Ltd; Braintree Clinical Services Ltd; Serco SAS.

Total employees: 105,999

Focus of giving: Education, health, ill health, medical research, sport, recreation, children, young people, community/social welfare, disasters.

Membership: BITC

Community involvement	✓
Community contributions	✓
Company reports on anti-slavery	✓
CSR report	✓
CSR or charity committee	✓
AF Covenant	✓
Employee-led support	✓
Humanitarian aid: overseas	✓

Community involvement

The group has a Corporate Responsibility Committee, but most community activities are organised locally, within each division. In 2016 the group is rolling out a new set of values – 'Trust, Care, Innovation and Pride' – which will be at the core of its corporate responsibility strategy.

Serco Foundation

The group has a corporate charity, the Serco Foundation (Charity Commission no. 1150338), which aims to offer business services knowledge and access to Serco employees and resources to help charities. In 2015 the charity entered into a collaborative project to help develop implementation of a child immunisation strategy in India.

Directors with other relevant posts

Tamara Ingram, one of the directors, is also a trustee of Save the Children UK (Charity Commission no. 213890) and of The Royal Drawing School (Charity Commission no. 1101538).

Main locations

In the UK, the group has offices in Hampshire and London. It operates globally with offices in Australia, Belgium and the USA.

Community contributions

No figure was given for charitable contributions.

Employee-led support

Volunteering

Employees are encouraged to volunteer with local projects, and the group also awards Serco Pulse Awards to employees who have made an outstanding contribution.

Applications

Serco Group PLC

Apply in writing to the correspondent to the relevant local division.

The Corporate Responsibility Committee met four times during 2015; however, most community activities are organised locally within each division.

Serco Foundation

Applications to the foundation should be sent to: Sarah Woodall, Serco Group PLC, Serco House, 16 Bartley Wood Business Park, Bartley Way, Hook RG27 9UY.

Severfield PLC

Engineering

Correspondent: See 'Applications', Severs House, Dalton Airfield Industrial Estate, Dalton, Thirsk, North Yorkshire YO7 3JN (tel: 01845 577896; website: www.severfield.com)

Directors: Alan Dunsmore, Finance Director; Alun Griffiths; Chris Holt; Derek Randall; Ian Cochrane; Ian Lawson, Chief Executive Officer; John Dodds, Chair; Kevin Whiteman; Tony Osbaldison (women: 0; men: 9)

Year end	31/03/2016
Turnover	£201,500,000
Pre-tax profit	£8,300,000

Nature of business: Structural steel.

Subsidiary undertakings include: Severfield (UK) Ltd; Severfield (Design and Build) Ltd; Severfield (NI) Ltd.

Total employees: 1,200

Focus of giving: Older people, children, young people, disability.

Community involvement	✓
Community contributions	✓
CSR report	✓
Charity partner(s)	✓
Employee-led support	✓
Matched funding	✓
STEM-focused	✓

Community involvement

Severfield Foundation

The foundation was registered with the Charity Commission in January 2016. The aim of the foundation is to raise money for and provide assistance to charities in the UK, mainly through the activities of its employees and companies. Each year one major charity partner will be supported as well as local charities that have been chosen by employees in each office. All funds raised will be split between the partner charity and the local charities. The foundation's charity partner for 2016/17 is Prostate Cancer UK.

Main locations

Dalton; Lostock; Chepstow; Sherburn; Enniskillen; Mumbai.

Community contributions

A figure for cash donations or community contributions was not available.

Recent beneficiaries have included: Bolton Hospice; British Heart Foundation; Cancer Research UK; St Catherine's Hospice (Scarborough); Macmillan Cancer Support; Northern Ireland Chest, Heart and Stroke Baby Hearts Appeal.

Employee-led support

Employee volunteering

Employees attend events such as careers fairs and school fairs to promote the study of STEM subjects. Employees also act as mentors to students studying STEM subjects and also act as STEM ambassadors assisting teachers in the classroom.

Applications

Contact your local office.

Severn Trent PLC

Waste management, water

Correspondent: Corporate Responsibility Team, Seven Trent Centre, PO Box 5309, Coventry CV3 9FH (tel: 024 7771 5000; email: corporate.responsibility@severntrent.co.uk; website: www.severn-trent.com)

Directors: Andrew Duff, Chair; Dominique Reiniche; Dr Angela Strank; Emma FitzGerald; Gordon Fryett; Hon. Philip Remnant; James Bowling, Chief Financial Officer; John Coghlan; Kevin Beeston; Martin Lamb; Olivia Garfield, Chief Executive (women: 4; men: 7)

Year end	31/03/2016
Turnover	£1,786,900,000
Pre-tax profit	£522,800,000

Nature of business: The group's principal activities are the supply of water and sewerage services, waste management and the provision of environmental services in the UK and internationally.

Company registration number: 2366619

Total employees: 7,861

Focus of giving: Education, environment, fundraising events, financial education, humanitarian help, poverty and social exclusion, children, young people, community/social welfare.

Community involvement	✓
Community contributions	✓
CSR report	✓
CSR or charity committee	✓
Directors have other relevant posts	✓
AF Covenant	✓
Cash donations declared	✓
Charity partner(s)	✓
Corporate charity	✓
Employee-led support	✓
FTSE 100	✓
Gifts in kind	✓
Humanitarian aid: overseas	✓
Humanitarian aid: UK including food banks	✓
Matched funding	✓
Shared-value alliances	✓

Charitable donations

Cash UK (latest available):	2016	£87,000
Total UK (cash and in kind):	2016	£87,000
Cash worldwide:	2016	£87,000
Total worldwide (cash and in kind):	2016	£87,000

Community involvement

The group mainly supports charities aligned to its aims of promoting responsible use and sustainability of water, but it also supports employee initiatives, nominated charities and partnerships.

Charity partners

The group has a long-term partnership with the charity WaterAid and in 2015/16 employees voted to also support Make-A-Wish Foundation.

Severn Trent Trust Fund

The group's corporate charity, the Severn Trent Water Charitable Trust Fund (Charity Commission no. 1108278) provides support to those living in poverty or with debt who are struggling to pay their water charges. Individual customers are provided with assistance to meet water charges – and in 2015/16 over 24,000 customers were assisted. Grants are also made to organisations in areas served by Severn Trent that provide money advice or debt counselling to those in poverty. Small, one-off grants are available, as well as larger revenue grants for longer-term projects.

Beneficiaries included: Birmingham Citizens Advice/GBAS; Direct Help and Advice – Derby; The Haven – Wolverhampton.

Environmental partners

The group works with a number of environmental charities and other organisations to deliver its environmental objectives – including Wye and Usk Foundation, Trent Rivers Trust and Nottinghamshire Wildlife Trust.

Directors with other relevant posts

Andrew Duff is a trustee of Macmillan Cancer Support (Charity Commission no. 261017) and Earth Trust (Charity Commission no. 1095057). Hon. Philip Remnant is a trustee of St Paul's Cathedral Foundation (Charity Commission no. 1082711) and Goodenough College (Charity Commission no. 312894). Emma FitzGerald is a trustee of Windsor Leadership Trust (Charity Commission no. 1048589). Dr Angela Strank is a board governor of the University of Manchester.

Main locations

The group operates in the Midlands and mid-Wales. It also has operations in Ireland, Italy, and the US.

Community contributions

According to the 2015/16 annual report, donations to charitable organisations during the year totalled almost £87,000.

In-kind support

The company provides assistance with water charges for customers in need through the Severn Trent Trust Fund.

Employee-led support

Employee fundraising and volunteering

All employees are entitled to two paid days of volunteering leave per year, and the group particularly encourages volunteering around the goals of water efficiency and healthier rivers.

The group has also established employee community panels, to lead the group's approach to volunteering. The group also provides matched funding for charities nominated by employees. National fundraising events are also supported, and local teams select causes to fundraise for, volunteer with, or to use for team-building activities.

In 2016 the company launched an initiative called Love Our Network, which focuses on volunteering, education and network vigilance.

According to the website, the group's Water Champions employee volunteering initiative encourages children to think differently about water, and employees can volunteer to help create water-efficient gardens in primary schools in the region served by Severn Trent Water.

Corporate charity

The Severn Trent Water Charitable Trust Fund (Charity Commission no. 1108278).

Exclusions

The group does not make donations for political purposes.

Applications

Group corporate responsibility

The website states that enquiries about the group's corporate responsibility activities should be directed to the CR team at: corporate.responsibility@severntrent.co.uk.

Severn Trent Trust Fund

To apply for an organisation grant from the Severn Trent Trust Fund, email office@sttf.org.uk or call 0121 321 1324 to discuss criteria and funding opportunities. More information is provided on the charity's website: www.sttf.org.uk.

Shaftesbury PLC

Property

Correspondent: Penny Thomas, Company Secretary, 22 Ganton Street, Carnaby, London, W1f 7FD (tel: 020 7333 8118; email: penny.thomas@shaftesbury.co.uk; website: www.shaftesbury.co.uk)

Directors: Brian Bickell, Chief Executive; Christopher Ward, Finance Director; Dermot Mathias; Hilary Riva; Jill Little; Jonathan Lane, Chair; Oliver Marriott; Sally Walden; Simon Quayle; Tom Welton (women: 3; men: 6)

Year end	30/09/2015
Turnover	£98,700,000
Pre-tax profit	£467,300,000

Nature of business: Property investors and developers. Shaftesbury owns a portfolio properties in London's West End (Carnaby, Charlotte Street, Chinatown, Covent Garden, Soho).

Company registration number: 1999238

Subsidiary undertakings include: Carnaby Estate Holdings Ltd; Covent Garden Property Investments Ltd; Shaftesbury Charlotte Street Ltd.

UK employees: 25

Total employees: 25

Focus of giving: Education, enterprise/training, fundraising events, housing, homelessness, small groups, local groups, less popular charitable purposes, arts, culture, poverty and social exclusion, children, young people, community/social welfare.

Membership: LBG

Community involvement	✓
Community contributions	✓
CSR report	✓
Directors have other relevant posts	✓
Charity partner(s)	✓
Company gives to smaller charities	✓
Gifts in kind	✓
Sponsorship	✓
Unpopular causes	✓

Charitable donations

Total UK (cash and in kind):	2015	£515,000
Total worldwide (cash and in kind):	2015	£515,000

Community involvement

The company owns properties in the West End of London and focuses its community involvement activities on this area, supporting schools and charities for purposes including arts, sustainability and community.

Arts

The company sponsors the English National Opera's community choir, which is open to those living or working in the local community.

Scholarships

The company funds scholarships at the London College of Fashion. As part of its partnership with the House of St Barnabas, the company also sponsored three participants in the charity's Employment Academy.

Partnerships

Each 'village' owned by the company has a nominated charity that the company will fundraise for, publicise and promote. During the year of 2014/15, the company worked with four charity partners: The Connection at St Martin-in-the-Fields; Trekstock; The House of St Barnabas; and London Chinese Community Centre.

The company has also worked for many years with Soho Parish Primary School, offering fundraising support, and is also a partner for Pride in London.

Other charities that the company worked with during the year include: Environmental Justice Foundation; Zoological Society of London; Seven Dials Trust; Chinese Information and Advice Centre; The Westminster Tea Dance (sponsorship); LandAid; Westminster Tree Trust; Soho Create.

Sustainable Restaurant Association

The company works in partnership with the Sustainable Restaurant Association, providing subsidised membership to new tenants. The association helps restaurants and cafes to become more sustainable, through advice and certification.

Directors with other relevant posts
Jonathan Lane is a trustee of The Royal Theatrical Support Trust (Charity Commission no. 254671) and The Tennis Foundation (Charity Commission no. 298175). Sally Walden is a trustee of The Community Foundation for Wiltshire and Swindon (Charity Commission no. 1123126) and The Fidelity UK Foundation (Charity Commission no. 327899). Christopher Ward is a trustee of Westway Trust (Charity Commission no. 1123127).

Main locations
The group operates in the West End of London.

Community contributions

The 2014/15 annual report states that the company's overall contribution during the year was £515,000. An additional £272,000 was given to the local council in s106 planning contributions.

Beneficiaries included: London Chinese Cultural Centre; The Connection at St Martin-in-the-Fields; The House of St Barnabas; Trekstock.

In-kind support

The company provides accommodation on flexible terms to charities including Stage One, Trekstok and Central London Law Centre, as well as letting charities and communities use the company's vacant spaces for events.

Applications

The website states that CSR queries should be addressed to the Company Secretary, Penny Thomas: penny.thomas@shaftesbury.co.uk.

Shawbrook Group PLC

Banking

Correspondent: Charity Committee, Lutea House, Warley Hill Business Park, The Drive, Great Warley, Brentwood, Essex CM13 3BE (email: companysecretary@shawbrook.co.uk; website: www.shawbrook.co.uk)

Directors: David Gagle; Graham Alcock; Iain Cornish, Chair; Lindsey McMurray; Paul Lawrence; Robin Ashton; Roger Lovering; Sally-Ann Hibberd; Stephen Johnson; Steve Pateman, Chief Executive Officer; Tom Wood, Chief Financial Officer (women: 2; men: 9)

Year end	31/12/2015
Turnover	£246,000,000
Pre-tax profit	£70,100,000

Nature of business: Shawbrook is a specialist UK lending and savings bank founded in 2011 to serve the needs of SMEs, trusts and charities in the UK with a range of lending and saving products.

Company registration number: 7240248

Subsidiary undertakings include: Link Loans Ltd; Shawbrook Bank Ltd; Shawbrook Buildings and Protection Ltd.

UK employees: 606

Total employees: 606

Focus of giving: General charitable purposes, general appeals, animal welfare, health, ill health, small groups, local groups, older people, children, young people, disability.

Community involvement	✓
Community contributions	✓
CSR report	✓
CSR or charity committee	✓
Directors have other relevant posts	✓
Cash donations declared	✓
Company gives to smaller charities	✓
Employee-led support	✓
Humanitarian aid: overseas	✓
Sponsorship	✓

Charitable donations

Cash UK (latest available):	2015	£87,000
Total UK (cash and in kind):	2015	£87,000
Cash worldwide:	2015	£87,000
Total worldwide (cash and in kind):	2015	£87,000

Community involvement

Shawbrook supports a variety of local charitable organisations, which are nominated for support by the company's employees and reviewed every quarter by the company's Charity Committee.

In 2015 the company supported 15 UK charities with financial donations, and a further 14 charities were supported through employee fundraising efforts. Two of the supported charities were national organisations, Contact the Elderly and Future First, which were supported by the company at a local level.

Sponsorship
In addition to making corporate donations to Future First in 2015, the company also sponsored the launch of the charity's online UK e-mentoring platform.

Directors with other relevant posts
Sally-Ann Hibberd sits on the Governing Body of Loughborough University

Company locations
The company has offices based in the following areas: Birmingham; Brentwood; Croydon; Dorking; Glasgow; Leeds; London; Manchester; West Malling; Wisbech.

Community contributions

In 2015 the group made charitable donations totalling £87,000 (2014: £56,000).

Beneficiaries included: Ali's Dream; CATS Foundation; Contact the Elderly; Cystic Fibrosis; DEC Nepal; Dogs for the Disabled; Erb's Palsy Group; Future First; Havens Hospice; Helen Rollason Cancer; Kingsway Pre-School; Little Havens Hospice; Macmillan; National Deaf Children's Society; Romford Drum and Trumpet Corp; SAM Funds; Save the Children; Scope; The Doxa Project; The Hospice of St Francis; The Mayhew Animal Home; Wear it Pink.

Applications

Applications can be made in writing to the Charity Committee.

Shell (UK Ltd)

Oil and gas/fuel

Correspondent: Head of Shell UK Social Investment, Shell Centre, York Road, London SE1 7NA (tel: 020 7934 1234; website: www.shell.co.uk)

Directors: David Moss; Joanne Wilson; Jonathan Kohn; Michael Coates; Nigel Hobson; Paul Goodfellow; Sinead Lynch (women: 2; men: 5)

Year end	31/12/2015
Turnover	£4,600,000,000
Pre-tax profit	£412,000,000

Nature of business: Shell is a global group of energy and petrochemicals companies. Its activities in the UK correspond to those of the group and include exploration, production and sale of oil and natural gas and marketing of petroleum products. Shell's activities also include: generating electricity (including wind power); providing oil products for industrial uses; producing petrochemicals used for plastics, coatings and detergents; and developing technology for hydrogen vehicles.

Shell UK Ltd forms part of the Shell Group controlled by Royal Dutch Shell PLC.

Company registration number: 140141

Subsidiary undertakings include: Enterprise Oil Ltd; Shell UK North Atlantic Ltd; Shell Wind Energy Ltd.

UK employees: 2,294

Focus of giving: Economic generation, education, enterprise/training, environment, fundraising events, health, ill health, heritage, individuals, overseas projects, older people, arts, culture, science technology, children, young people, community/social welfare, disability, disasters.

Membership: BITC

Community involvement ✓
Community contributions ✓
CSR report ✓
CSR or charity committee ✓
AF Covenant ✓
Charity partner(s) ✓
Employee-led support ✓
FTSE 100 ✓
Gifts in kind ✓
Humanitarian aid: overseas ✓
Matched funding ✓
Overseas giving ✓
Sponsorship ✓
STEM-focused ✓

Community involvement

Shell UK supports sustainable energy and enterprise, STEM education and community initiatives. Support is offered internationally through the Shell Foundation, through grants for local community projects near its sites in the UK, educational programmes and employee volunteering.

The Shell Group also has various worldwide initiatives, detailed examples of which can be found on the website or the global Sustainability Report.

Grants for community projects

The group's website states that in the UK, the group's sites work with local charities and projects to support local communities. In Aberdeen, Bacton, Mossmorron and St Fergus, the group offers grants for community projects or events.

Shell Foundation

The group has a corporate charity, the Shell Foundation (Charity Commission no. 1080999). The foundation's website states that it focuses on entrepreneurial solutions to global development challenges – particularly on the following issues: sustainable job creation; access to energy; sustainable mobility; new technology and innovation. The foundation was established with a $250 million (around £203 million) endowment from Shell Group and is registered in the UK but operates internationally, particularly in Africa, South America and Asia.

The Shell Centenary Scholarship Fund (Charity Commission no. 1071178)

The fund provides money for Shell Centenary Scholarships to support educational development and provide opportunities for graduate students from overseas to study in the UK. It provides at least 65 full-cost scholarships (to cover tuition, accommodation, maintenance costs and return airfare) to international students on one year taught postgraduate courses at seven universities in the UK (Cambridge, Durham, Edinburgh, Imperial College London, Oxford and University College London) and also a number universities in the Netherlands.

Partnerships

Shell works in partnership with charitable organisations in many of the countries it operates in. For example, the group has a partnership with Mercy Corps, an international charity that provides humanitarian relief in areas affected by disaster.

STEM education

Various initiatives are undertaken in support of science education:

- Shell Education Service – SES delivers fun, interactive, investigative science workshops to thousands of children and teachers in primary schools across the UK every year. SES is a partnership between Shell and Sphere Science Ltd
- Girls in Energy – this programme promotes STEM career opportunities to young women
- Your Life – Shell is part of the Your Life campaign, which aims to challenge stereotypes associated with STEM subjects and encourage young people, particularly women, to take them up at school
- QEPrize for engineering – the group is a founding donor of the Queen Elizabeth Prize for Engineering
- Geobus – an educational outreach programme focusing on Earth Science, in partnership with The University of St Andrews, NERC and other organisations and businesses
- SCDI Engineers and Science Clubs – designed to give primary and secondary school students in Scotland the chance to engage in fun, hands-on STEM activities
- Researchers in Schools – Shell is part of the programme run by the government and Researchers in Schools which aims to get more PhD graduates to train as maths and physics teachers
- Bright Ideas Challenge – the group runs a STEM-focused competition on the topic of future energy solutions for cities, offering prizes of up to £50,000 for schools
- Tomorrow's Engineers – Shell has invested more than £1 million in the national programme run by EngineeringUK. It seeks to give every 11- to 14-year-old a first-hand engineering experience with local employers, and helps students connect what they learn in the classroom with the world around them and the opportunities of a career in engineering. The priority of the project is to increase the number of girls studying STEM subjects and going into engineering

Enterprise and energy

The group has two programmes which aims to support entrepreneurs with ideas for low carbon innovation or addressing future resources needs.

Shell LiveWire offers start-up grants for entrepreneurs aged 16 to 30 with ideas to address sustainable living challenges. Shell Springboard offers funding and support for low-carbon business ideas.

Main locations

Shell operates throughout the UK and globally. The group has operations or offices in Aberdeen; Fife; London; Manchester; Norfolk; Peterhead; Warwickshire.

Community contributions

According to the foundation's 2015 accounts, Shell Group donated $6 million (around £4.9 million) to the Shell Foundation in 2015.

The group's global sustainability report states that 'estimated voluntary and social investment (equity share)' in 2015 totalled $122 million (around £100 million) and 'estimated social investment spend (equity share) in lower-income countries' was $43 million (around £35 million). No further breakdown was given.

Employee-led support

Employee volunteering

The group provides Employee Action Grants to Shell UK employees and pensioners who volunteer for at least 20 hours a year with a UK-based charity or community group.

Commercially led support

Sponsorship

The group works in partnership with Scottish Sports Futures, sponsoring Twilight Basketball, which provides free sports, arts and business activities for young people in Scotland.

Exclusions

Shell is unable to support individuals or third parties (for example, Cash for Kids, Help for Heroes, etc.). Community grants are not given outside the company's operation area.

Applications

The group

An application form for the UK Community Grants and sponsorship application form are available online at www.shell.co.uk/sustainability/society/working-with-communities.

Other enquiries about local support should be directed at the community relations teams at Shell plants or offices.

Shell does not award grants outside neighbourhoods surrounding Shell plants and offices, but if you have an enquiry not appropriate for local sites, you should address it to the UK Social

Investment Department at the company's address.

Note: Unsolicited applications for community grants outside the communities in which Shell operates (Aberdeen, Bacton, Mossmorron and St Fergus) are not supported.

The foundation

The principal contact person for the foundation is Sam Parker (email: shell-foundation@shell.com) at the company's address.

Shire Pharmaceuticals Group

Pharmaceuticals

Correspondent: Responsibility Team, Hampshire International Business Park, Chineham, Basingstoke, Hampshire RG24 8EP (tel: 01256 894000; email: responsibility@shire.com; website: www.shire.com)

Directors: Amanda Miller; Jonathan Webb

Year end	31/12/2015
Turnover	£211,800,000
Pre-tax profit	(£14,970,000)

Nature of business: The company is a provider of speciality biopharmaceutical products. Shire Pharmaceuticals Group is a wholly owned subsidiary within the Shire PLC group.

The company's immediate parent company is Shire Biopharmaceuticals Holdings and the ultimate parent company and controlling party is Shire PLC, incorporated in Jersey.

Company registration number: 2883758

Subsidiary undertakings include: Ryder Laboratories Ltd; Shire Pharmaceuticals Development Ltd; Viropharma Ltd.

UK employees: 3,329

Total employees: 5,548

Focus of giving: Education, fundraising events, health, ill health, medical research, local groups, older people, overseas projects, children, young people, community/social welfare, disability, disasters.

Community involvement	✓
Community contributions	✓
CSR report	✓
CSR or charity committee	✓
Charity partner(s)	✓
Employee-led support	✓
FTSE 100	✓
Gifts in kind	✓
Humanitarian aid: overseas	✓
Matched funding	✓
Payroll giving	✓
Pro bono	✓
Shared-value alliances	✓
Sponsorship	✓
STEM-focused	✓

Community involvement

The group's global website states that it has a particular focus on improving the health and well-being of disadvantaged children and supporting children to engage with STEM education in under-resourced areas.

It delivers its community giving programme through corporate donations (both cash and in kind) and volunteer opportunities for employees. It also supports fundraising campaigns which focus on disaster relief, or local community organisations, charities and schools in the areas where it operates. For example, in 2015, the group donated $4,000 (around £3,500) to Sebastian's Action Trust.

The group also works with patient advocacy groups and other health-related organisations.

Main locations

The group has offices in 50 countries worldwide. In the UK, its offices are in Basingstoke and Staines-upon-Thames.

Community contributions

We were not able to find a recent breakdown of the group's charitable contributions in the UK.

In-kind support

The group donates surplus equipment and office supplies to charities and local schools. The group is part of a global initiative, the Partnership for Quality Medical Donations, which aims to improve healthcare in under-resourced areas and communities that have been affected by disaster.

Employee-led support

Employee volunteering and fundraising

All employees are entitled to one working day of volunteering for a charitable organisation each year. In 2016 the group held its second annual Global Day of Service, 6,500 employees volunteered over 25,000 hours to support community initiatives.

The Shire UK website provides examples of volunteering initiatives, which include: assisting with Basingstoke's Alzheimer's Society Christmas Lunch; distributing Christmas gifts to elderly local residents; taking part in national charity events such as Macmillan Coffee Morning appeal, Comic Relief and Jeans for Genes day, supported by matched funding from the company.

Matched funding and payroll giving

Where possible, the group provides matched funding for employee contributions to its fundraising campaigns for issues such as disaster relief or for employee-led fundraising initiatives. The group's UK website states that there is also a payroll giving scheme.

Exclusions

No support is given for political appeals.

Applications

Apply in writing to the correspondent.

The 2015 responsibility report states that the group is planning to provide a centralised inquiry mechanism on its website for charitable requests and queries. Refer to the group's website (www.shire.com) for updates.

Shoe Zone Ltd

Retail – clothing and footwear

Correspondent: The Trustees, The Shoe Zone Trust, Haramead Business Centre, Humberstone Road, Leicester LE1 2LH (tel: 0116 222 3000/0116 222 3007; website: www.shoezone.com)

Directors: Anthony Smith, Chair; Charles Smith; Charlie Caminada; Jeremy Sharman; Jonathan Fearn, Finance Director; Nick Davis, Chief Executive Officer (men: 6)

Year end	31/10/2015
Turnover	£166,800,000
Pre-tax profit	£10,100,000

Nature of business: The company is a footwear retailer in the UK and Ireland. It is a wholly owned subsidiary of Shoe Zone Group Ltd.

Company registration number: 148038

Subsidiary undertakings include: Shoe Zone Retail Ltd; Walkright Ltd; Zone Group Ltd.

UK employees: 3,721

Total employees: 3,721

Focus of giving: Education, fundraising events, health, ill health, overseas projects, poverty and social exclusion, children, young people, community/social welfare, disability.

Community involvement	✓
Community contributions	✓
CSR report	✓
Directors have other relevant posts	✓
Charity partner(s)	✓
Corporate charity	✓
Employee-led support	✓
Overseas giving	✓

Community involvement

According to the website, the group has previously supported a range of charities, locally and nationally. Support appears to be mainly given through the group's corporate charity, which supports causes such as children, education and relief of poverty, as well as through employee-led fundraising.

The Shoe Zone Trust (Charity Commission no. 1112972)
The group's corporate charity, The Shoe Zone Trust, makes grants to charities for the support of causes including: children and young people under the age of 18, particularly in Leicestershire and Rutland; the relief of hardship and poverty; education; charities operating in the Philippines and other countries. In 2015 grants totalled £80,000.

Beneficiaries included: Shepherd of the Hills – Philippines (£54,500); Ministries without Borders (£15,800); 500miles (£5,000); James 1v27 Foundation and Rotary Club of Kibworth and Fleckney (£2,000 each).

Directors with other relevant posts

Anthony Smith is a trustee of Uppingham School (Charity Commission no. 1147280) and The Shoe Zone Trust (Charity Commission no. 1112972). Nick Davies is a trustee of Open Heaven Church (Charity Commission no. 1138763), Fusion UK (Charity Commission no. 1073572) and Pioneer Trust (Charity Commission no. 1118766). Jeremy Sharman is a trustee of a number of charities, including James 1v27 Foundation (Charity Commission no. 1112730), Desborough Cornerstone Trust (Charity Commission no. 1155716) and Dolphin School Trust (Charity Commission no. 1145113). Charles Smith is a trustee of The Shoe Zone Trust (Charity Commission no. 1112972) and other charities including Ministries Without Borders International (Charity Commission no. 1095446).

Main locations

The group's head office is based in Leicester. It has stores throughout the UK.

Community contributions

According to the 2015 accounts for The Shoe Zone Trust (Charity Commission no. 1112972), the company did not make a grant to the trust during the year. However, the company usually donates £100,000 to the trust annually.

The trust did receive £24,000 from the company in 2015 through carrier bag sale donations, following the introduction of the mandatory 5p charge for single-use plastic carrier bags.

Employee-led support

Employee fundraising

The 2015 annual report states that, during the year, employees raised £200,000 for the group's chosen charity, BBC Children in Need.

Corporate charity

The Shoe Zone Trust (Charity Commission no. 1112972).

Applications

The Shoe Zone Trust

Applications should be made in writing to the correspondent.

Shop Direct Ltd (record formerly for Shop Direct Holdings Ltd)

Business services, financial services, property, retail – clothing and footwear, retail – department and variety stores

Correspondent: Corporate Affairs & CSR Manager, Skyways House, Speke Road, Speke, Liverpool L70 1AB (tel: 0844 292 1000; website: www.shopdirect.com/corporate-responsibility-page/chary-community)

Directors: Aidan Barclay; Alex Baldock, Group Chief Executive; David Kershaw; Howard Barclay; Michael Seal; Philip Peters; Stuart Winton (women: 0; men: 7)

Year end	30/06/2016
Turnover	£1,861,100,000
Pre-tax profit	£105,600,000

Nature of business: The principal activities of the group are online and home shopping retail and financial services, customer relationship management solutions and property management.

This record previously contained financial information taken from the annual report and accounts of Shop Direct Holdings Ltd. As Shop Direct Holdings Ltd no longer declares charitable donations from the group in its annual report and accounts, we have instead focused on the CSR reporting of its subsidiary company Shop Direct Ltd.

The latest CSR report for Shop Direct available at the time of writing (November 2016) was 'Communication on Progress: CSR Report 2015'; however, the latest financial information was for the 2015/16 financial year.

Company registration number: 4730752

Subsidiary undertakings include: Littlewoods Clearance Ltd; Littlewoods Ltd; Source Direct International Ltd (Hong Kong).

Brands include: Ladybird; Littlewoods.com; Very.co.uk.

UK employees: 3,846

Total employees: 3,846

Focus of giving: General charitable purposes, health, ill health, science technology.

Community involvement	✓
Community contributions	✓
Company reports on anti-slavery	✓
CSR report	✓
Directors have other relevant posts	✓
Charity of the Year	✓
Charity partner(s)	✓
Employee-led support	✓
Gifts in kind	✓
Matched funding	✓
Payroll giving	✓
Pro bono	✓

Community involvement

Shop Direct's 'Communication on Progress: CSR Report 2015' explains that, in October 2015, the group's charity strategy had a 'reboot'. The group now focuses all of its support behind one annual charity project, as voted for by employees. The report explains that this must be 'a project that is in line with our purpose and enables us to bring our digital expertise to bear for the benefit of our local communities'. During the 2015, Shop Direct also developed a digital 'charity hub' to support colleagues' charitable involvement, both for the chosen charity partner and charities of their choice.

Charity partners

In October 2015, Shop Direct colleagues chose Alder Hey Children's Hospital in Liverpool as its charity partner, with an aim of raising £200,000 to develop, as described on the website, a 'groundbreaking' and 'world-first' digital hospital app for children who are patients at the hospital. The hospital has also benefitted from pro bono expertise in the development of the app, which will:

- Allow children to take a virtual tour of the hospital and the room they will be staying in before they are admitted
- Provide games that can be played by children before, during or after their hospital visit
- Allow children to collect virtual badges, which can be awarded following the completion of a treatment
- Provide information on the hospital, including FAQs, a hospital map and contact details, for example

A press release from October 2016, which is available from both the Shop Direct and Alder Hey websites, states that Shop Direct colleagues managed to exceed their target, raising £210,000 for the hospital in 12 months.

In November 2016, Claire House was announced as Shop Direct's latest charity partner and a fundraising target of £400,000 was set to assist with the development of a 'world class digital hospice in Liverpool'.

Shop Direct also has a cycle scheme partnership with Bike2Work.

Directors with other relevant posts
Aidan and Howard Barclay are trustees of The Barclay Foundation (Charity Commission no. 803696).

Main UK locations
Merseyside (Liverpool and Bootle); Greater Manchester (Bolton, Manchester and Oldham); Wrexham; Dublin.

Community contributions

The annual report and accounts for 2015/16 did not declare a figure for charitable donations.

In-kind support

Pro bono
Shop Direct colleagues' skills and expertise are put to use through its chosen charity partnership. Its first chosen charity, Alder Hey, has been provided with pro bono digital expertise to assist with the development of its app.

Gifts in-kind
Shop Direct donates all sample clothing to its charity partner so that it can be sold in order to raise funds.

Digital charity hub
To better facilitate its colleagues' charitable fundraising activities, Shop Direct developed a digital charity hub, the abilities of which are set out in the CSR Report 2015:

- The Helping Hand matched funding portal and payroll giving facility are available online 'with an approval time of two weeks'
- 'Branded Just Giving fundraising portals are available that link directly to matched funding'
- The digital portal also links to an 'internal recognition scheme' enabling 'more structured reporting on progress'

Employee-led support

Employee volunteering
Shop Direct's website explains that colleagues are 'given opportunities to volunteer their time and expertise to charities and community groups'.

Employee fundraising
Colleagues can fundraise for a range of causes, either the Shop Direct chosen charity or a charity of their own choosing.

Payroll giving
Colleagues are able to donate to charities through payroll giving. Shop Direct earned a Gold Standard for its efforts in this area.

Matched funding
Through the Helping Hand online portal, colleagues can have their fundraising matched up to a value of £200 per activity.

Commercially led support

Charity ball
Shop Direct fundraises through a themed charity ball held on a biennial basis.

Exclusions

Shop Direct does not support any charities which have religious or political connections.

Applications

The CSR Report 2015 explains the group's policy as follows: 'Shop Direct supports an annual charity based on a business-wide colleague vote. Our colleagues choose from three options to support a digitally focused project that will deliver maximum impact in the communities we live and work via a variety of colleague fundraising activities.'

Siemens PLC

Electronics/computers, transport and communications

Correspondent: Corporate Citizenship Manager, Sir William Siemens Square, Frimley, Camberley, Surrey GU16 8QD (tel: 01276 696000; email: info.cc.uk@siemens.com; website: www.siemens.co.uk)

Directors: Juergen Maier, Chief Executive; Maria Ferraro, Chief Financial Officer; Simone Davina (women: 2; men: 1)

Year end	31/12/2015
Turnover	£67,613,000,000

Nature of business: Siemen's principal activities in the UK cover manufacture and sale of products in the areas of: electricity generation and distribution, transportation systems, industrial and building automation, metallurgical engineering and healthcare equipment and services. The company also provides IT and other business infrastructure services.

The company is a subsidiary of the Siemens Group AG.

Siemens PLC does not have a board of directors in the same way as most UK companies, but instead has a Supervisory Board comprised of shareholders and employee representatives.

Company registration number: 727817

Subsidiary undertakings include: A full list of subsidiary undertakings can be found within the parent company's (Siemens AG) consolidated accounts.

UK employees: 14,000

Total employees: 348,000

Focus of giving: Education, environment, local groups, arts, culture, overseas projects, poverty and social exclusion, science technology, children, young people, community/social welfare, disasters.

Membership: BITC, LBG

Community involvement	✓
Community contributions	✓
CSR report	✓
CSR or charity committee	✓
Cash donations declared	✓
Community Mark	✓
Employee-led support	✓
Gifts in kind	✓
Humanitarian aid: overseas	✓
Overseas giving	✓
Pro bono	✓
Sponsorship	✓
STEM-focused	✓

Charitable donations

Total UK (cash and in kind):	2015	£3,000,000
Total worldwide (cash and in kind):	2015	£23,700,000

Community involvement

Charitable activities are organised at a local level, to enable response to local needs, but activities are focused on the following three areas:

- Education – particularly in STEM subjects
- Social – sustainable improvements in quality of life, and humanitarian relief
- Environment – environmental protection and education

The group may also support arts and culture initiatives.

Education programmes
The group's UK education programme, the Curiosity Project, aims to encourage young people to engage with STEM subjects, particularly engineering. The website provides educational resources for schools, in partnership with the qualification body OCR, and employee volunteers also run activities in schools. There are also work experience opportunities and placements for young people.

Education partnerships and sponsorships
The group works with a range of partners, including a number of charities, to support its educational focus. It sponsors science festivals across the UK each year, such as the Cheltenham Science Festival and the Big Bang Science Fair, as well as sponsoring the Manchester Museum of Science and Industry. The group works in partnership with The Royal Photographic Society on the International Images for Science exhibition, and works with the charity Greenpower Education Trust to support its annual engineering challenge. It also works with The Prince's Teaching Institute, sponsoring its maths and science streams, and in 2016, began a

partnership with Teach First to support its STEM teachers.

Corporate charities

The group has corporate charities in: Argentina; Brazil; Columbia; Denmark; France; Germany; United States. The charities, which are part of the Global Alliance of Siemens Foundations, support sustainable social development projects and educational initiatives.

Main locations

The group has offices worldwide. In the UK, its head office is in Frimley, Surrey, but it also has offices in a number of locations across England, Scotland and Wales – a full list can be found on the Siemens UK website.

Community contributions

The 2016 Business to Society UK report states that the group donates £3 million a year, including cash, volunteering time and in-kind support.

According to the 2015 sustainability report, the group's donations worldwide totalled €26.6 million (around £23.7 million). Donations within Europe, Commonwealth of Independent States, Africa and Middle East totalled €14.8 million (around £13.2 million), of which €11.5 million (around £10.2 million) was in Germany.

The following breakdown of donations was provided:

Europe, CIS, Africa, Middle East	€14.8 million (around £13.2 million)
Americas	€9.3 million (around £8.3 million)
Asia, Australia	€2.5 million (around £2.2 million)

Education and science	€16.1 million (around £14.4 million)
Social	€6.2 million (around £5.5 million)
Arts and culture	€4.2 million (around £3.7 million)
Environment	€100,000 (around £89,000)

Note: Currency conversions taken at the time of writing (October 2016).

Employee-led support

Employee volunteering

According to the Corporate Citizenship Volunteering policy on the group's website, employees can volunteer with charitable organisations for projects relating to: education; children and young people; assisting people who are disadvantaged; local employability; protecting or improving the environment. Employees can volunteer as a team or individually, usually over one or two days, and volunteering opportunities are available through an online volunteering tool. Many employees volunteer to deliver science-related educational activities with partner schools, while others volunteer with local Wildlife Trusts and others fundraise for mental health charities. The group is aiming to get 40% of UK employees volunteering.

Payroll giving

The group's 2016 Business to Society UK report states that 10% of employees donate to charities through payroll giving.

Exclusions

The group cannot provide sponsorship for sports activities. The group does not provide volunteer support for the following causes: individuals; for-profit organisations or those without charitable status or purposes; religious causes; political organisations or organisations that are involved in lobbying; organisations whose remit is limited by religion, race, sex, age or national origin; any other projects which conflict with Siemen's values.

Applications

The group has stated that it has long-standing relationships with a number of charity partners and rarely takes on any new charity partners, apart from small-scale local relationships.

SIG PLC

Building materials, distribution

Correspondent: Samantha Parker, Group Communications Executive, 3 Sheldon Square, Paddington, London W2 6HY (tel: 020 3204 5418; fax: 0114 285 6385; email: groupcommunications@sigplc.com; website: www.sigplc.co.uk)

Directors: Andrea Abt; Chris Geoghegan; Doug Robertson, Finance Director; Janet Ashdown; Jonathan Nicholls; Leslie Van de Walle, Chair; Mel Ewell; Stuart Mitchell, Chief Executive (women: 2; men: 6)

Year end	31/12/2015
Turnover	£2,567,000,000
Pre-tax profit	£51,300,000

Nature of business: The principal activity of the group is the supply of specialist products to construction and related markets in the UK, Ireland and Mainland Europe. The main products distributed are Insulation and Energy Management, Exteriors and Interiors.

Company registration number: 998314

Subsidiary undertakings include: Drainex Ltd; SIG Trading Ltd; Hamar B.V.

Focus of giving: Education, enterprise/training, children, young people, community/social welfare.

Membership: BITC

Community involvement	✓
Community contributions	✓
Company reports on anti-slavery	✓
CSR report	✓
Cash donations declared	✓
Charity partner(s)	✓
Employee-led support	✓
Gifts in kind	✓
Humanitarian aid: overseas	✓
Matched funding	✓
Payroll giving	✓
Sponsorship	✓

Charitable donations

Cash worldwide:	2015	£99,000
Total worldwide (cash and in kind):	2015	£99,000

Community involvement

The group mainly focuses on organisations and projects which enhance its engagement in the community, assist in managing the sustainability of the local environment, educate young people and assist disadvantaged groups.

Partners

Through Business in the Community, the group has partnered with Fir Vale School in Sheffield, providing volunteer support for activities including improving students' business skills. In Poland, employees worked with the Topacz Kids City Project in 2015, which educates children at risk of social exclusion.

Donations

As well as providing matched funding for employee fundraising, the group also makes direct donations. In 2015 the group donated £1 or 1 euro for every completed response to its employee engagement survey, which raised £6,200 for the Syrian refugee appeals run by the British Red Cross and Unicef, to which the group added an additional £10,000.

Directors with other relevant posts

One of the directors, Janet Ashdown, is the Chair of Trustees of the charity Hope in Tottenham (Charity Commission no. 1155484).

Main locations

The group has 312 branches in the UK. There are also businesses in Austria; Belgium; France; Germany; Ireland; Luxembourg; Poland; the Netherlands.

Community contributions

Donations by the group in 2015, including both matched funding and direct donations, totalled over £99,000. It was not clear how much of this was given in the UK.

Employee-led support

Employee fundraising

The group offers support to employees undertaking their own fundraising efforts, particularly through its matched funding scheme, which matches up to £500 for employees' charitable efforts.

Employees in the UK can also donate through payroll giving.

Exclusions

The group has a policy not to support political parties.

Applications

Apply in writing to the correspondent. Activities may also be organised by local divisions of the group.

Simmons & Simmons LLP

Legal

Correspondent: Corporate Responsibility Team, CityPoint, 1 Ropemaker Street, London EC2Y 9SS (tel: 020 7825 3814; fax: 020 7628 2070; email: corporate.responsibility@simmons-simmons.com; website: www.simmons-simmons.com)

Directors: Alyson Lockett; Caroline Hunter-Yeats; Colin Passmore, Senior Partner; David McLaughlin, Finance Director; David Staiano; Fiona Loughrey; Jeremy Hoyland, Managing Partner; Leo Verhoeff; Michael Woodford; Patrick Wallace; Peter Meyer; Rodger Hughes

Year end	30/04/2015
Turnover	£288,971,000
Pre-tax profit	£87,603,000

Nature of business: Simmons & Simmons LLP is a limited liability partnership providing legal services and international tax advice.

Company registration number: OC352713

Subsidiary undertakings include: Beaufield Ltd; SimmLaw Services Ltd; Simmons & Simmons East Asia LLP; and Simmons & Simmons CIS LLP. A full list of subsidiaries can be found in the firm's accounts.

Total employees: 1,900

Focus of giving: Human rights, education, environment, equal opportunities, health, ill health, local groups, overseas projects, arts, culture, poverty and social exclusion, women's issues, children, young people, community/social welfare, disability.

Community involvement	✓
Community contributions	✓
Company reports on anti-slavery	✓
CSR report	✓
CSR or charity committee	✓
Charity partner(s)	✓
Corporate charity	✓
Employee-led support	✓
Gifts in kind	✓
Overseas giving	✓
Pro bono	✓
Sponsorship	✓

Charitable donations

Cash UK (latest available):	2015	£120,000
Total UK (cash and in kind):	2015	£120,000
Cash worldwide:	2015	£120,000
Total worldwide (cash and in kind):	2015	£120,000

Community involvement

The Simmons & Simmons Charitable Foundation

The group's corporate charity, The Simmons & Simmons Charitable Foundation (Charity Commission no. 1129643) provides grants mainly to smaller charities local to the group's offices that support social inclusion and where the group's employees can get involved. The group also funds pro bono work, makes certain international donations (usually relating to the charitable work of the group's branches outside the UK) and occasionally donates to other charities outside these categories.

Young Talent programme

The group works with partner school Frederick Bremer School in Walthamstow, London, on a Young Talent programme aiming to raise aspirations of young people, encourage them to consider the legal profession, and providing work experience, mentoring, internships, skills sessions and other activities. The group's foundation also provides two bursaries to assist students going to university.

Other partnerships

The group takes part in the Big Issue Foundation's Big Issue Vendor Development programme, providing a placement for a Big Issue vendor. The group's foundation has also provided funding to expand the programme, and the group has provided pro bono legal and operational advice.

The group also works with partner primary schools in Bristol and London to support reading initiatives.

Diversity

The group places a strong focus on diversity, and supports charities that share this focus. For example, in 2015, a team based in London worked with the charity Specialisterne, which supports adults with autism into employment.

Main locations

There are 21 offices worldwide. The group's offices in the UK are located in Bristol and London.

Community contributions

No figure was given for the group's charitable contributions for 2014/15. However, £120,000 was donated by the group to The Simmons & Simmons Charitable Foundation during the year.

The Simmons & Simmons Charitable Foundation

The foundation made grants totalling almost £200,000 during 2014/15, which were distributed in the following categories:

Social inclusion	£81,000
International	£42,500
Other charities	£38,000
Pro bono	£38,000

Beneficiaries included: PSL Foundation (£37,500); Battersea Legal Advice Centre (£28,000); YMCA Ltd (£25,000); Debate Mate (£15,000); Spitalfields Music and Working Families (£10,000 each); Churches Housing Aid Society and Envision (£5,000 each)

In-kind support

Pro bono

The 2015/16 corporate responsibility report states that the group prefers to offer pro bono support to charities which share its commitment to diversity, as well as medical and disability-related charities. Examples of charities supported include: Alzheimer's Society; Future First; London's Air Ambulance; NSPCC; RNIB; Women for Women International.

In 2015 the group launched its Access to Justice programme, which supports low income individuals to access legal support, specialising in disability benefit appeals. More than 30 lawyers took part in training from the charity Pro Bono Community, and the group takes referrals from a number of charitable organisations, such as Disability Rights UK, Brixton Advice Centre and The Zacchaeus 2000 Trust. The group also offers pro bono support to prisoners through the Prisoner's Advice Service.

Pro bono support is also offered to a range of arts organisations, such as English National Ballet and the Frieze Art Fair, and to environmental charities the Legal Response Initiative and PURE Leapfrog.

The 2015/16 corporate responsibility report states that pro bono work in the UK totalled '34 hours per fee earner', and internationally, the company gave 14,000 hours of pro bono support.

Employee-led support

Employee volunteering

The group's employees take part in a range of voluntary activities with different charities, projects and initiatives. For example, employees in Bristol volunteer with young people from disadvantaged backgrounds, supporting the Community Apprentice scheme with the charity Envision, and employees in London also volunteer through the Lawyers in Schools initiative. The group's foundation tends to support charities where employees can get involved with volunteering.

Corporate charity

The Simmons & Simmons Charitable Foundation (Charity Commission no. 1129643).

Applications

Application forms for the foundation are available from the group's website.

Other queries regarding the group's charitable activities can be directed to the correspondent.

Slaughter and May (Trust Ltd)

Legal

Correspondent: Corporate Responsibility Manager, One Bunhill Row, London EC1Y 8YY (tel: 020 7600 1200 or 020 7090 3433 (Charitable Trust); email: corporateresponsibility@slaughterandmay.com; website: www.slaughterandmay.com)

Directors: David Wittmann; Dominic Robertson; John Nevin; Mark Bennett; Matthew Tobin; Nicholas Gray; Rebecca Cousin; Richard Clark; Robert Sumroy; Robin Ogle; Sara Luder (women: 2; men: 9)

Year end	30/04/2015

Nature of business: Slaughter and May is a law firm, regulated by the Solicitors Regulation Authority. We have used the information of the non-charitable Slaughter and May Trust Ltd company for the main company details. All the shares in the company are beneficially owned by the partners of Slaughter and May.

Company registration number: 335458

Total employees: 1,183

Focus of giving: Education, enterprise/training, environment, inner cities, local groups, older people, poverty and social exclusion, children, young people, community/social welfare.

Community involvement	✓
Community contributions	✓
Company reports on anti-slavery	✓
CSR report	✓
CSR or charity committee	✓
Charity partner(s)	✓
Employee-led support	✓
Gifts in kind	✓
Matched funding	✓
Payroll giving	✓
Pro bono	✓
Sponsorship	✓

Charitable donations

Cash UK (latest available):	2015	£75,000
Total UK (cash and in kind):	2015	£75,000
Cash worldwide:	2015	£75,000
Total worldwide (cash and in kind):	2015	£75,000

Community involvement

The firm supports causes including education and training; children and young people; community, through donations, partnerships, pro bono work and employee-led fundraising and volunteering.

National charity partnerships

The firm has two national charity partners – the National Literacy Trust and Action for Kids – which it supports through funding, pro bono advice and in-kind support. The firm funds the National Literacy Trust's annual literacy survey and provides placements for young people with disabilities through Action for Kids.

Local charity partnerships

At a local level, the firm works with St Luke's Community Centre in Islington to deliver projects for the local community, such as Firm Futures, where employees volunteer as business mentors for local unemployed people wanting to set up their own businesses, and PC Pals, supporting older people using the Internet.

The firm works in partnership with Macquarie and the Cripplegate Foundation to deliver the CoRe (Community Resourcing) programme, which supports charities in Islington. Teams of employee volunteers are matched with local charities and provide strategic support over a six month period.

The Slaughter and May Charitable Trust (Charity Commission no. 1082765)

The firm's charitable donations are made through the corporate charity, including matched funding for staff fundraising initiatives. The trust's annual report for 2014/15 states that it is reliant on its key donors, the partners of Slaughter and May, with all administrative and other office support being provided by the firm.

Education and work experience

The firm works with a number of schools and colleges located near to its offices, particularly those with high levels of disadvantage. Its Primary Partners scheme provides volunteers for local primary schools for reading and gardening, as well as sponsoring London Symphony Orchestra's outreach activities and programmes with the National Literacy Trust and the Primary School Football League. The firm also provides funding for Teach First teachers in Islington.

The firm is a founding member of PRIME, an initiative to promote access to work experience in the legal sector. It has developed a programme called the Legal Social Mobility Partnership, which provides two weeks of intensive work experience, a third week visiting different teams and a day focused on resilience and achievement, as well as career advice to follow up. The scheme is delivered in London, Manchester, Leeds and Birmingham, and during 2016 a total of 210 students took part.

Main locations

The firm's UK office is located in Islington, London. There are also offices in Beijing, Brussels, and Hong Kong.

Community contributions

No figure was given in the 2014/15 annual report and accounts for the group's overall charitable contribution during the year.

Most of the firm's contributions are channelled through The Slaughter and May Charitable Trust. The trust's accounts for 2014/15 state that the trust received donations from Partners of the firm totalling £301,000 and an advance from Slaughter and May of £75,000 was outstanding at the year end, all of which was pending receipt of the tax recoverable from HMRC. The trust made grants totalling £465,500 during the year.

Beneficiaries included: The Access Project (£56,500); Action for Kids (£30,000); Carers Trust (£20,000); Moreland School (£10,500); The BIG Alliance (£10,000); SANE (£7,300); Advocates for International Development (£5,000).

In-kind support

Pro bono

The firm provides pro bono legal support to both individuals and charities through the following initiatives:

- Law Centre volunteering – every week the firm provides a team of volunteer advisers to staff an evening advice clinic at Islington Law Centre and an additional team of qualified litigators serve as Honorary Legal Advisers at the RCJ Advice Bureau
- Charity clients – the firm uses its legal expertise to support its charity partners

The firm also has 'pro bono champions' in each of its divisions, and receives referrals of charities and community groups locally and globally from a number of organisations including LawWorks and TrustLaw. The group also provides a 'Legal Toolkit for Charities', available online, designed to answer common questions for charity professionals, and delivers masterclasses to go alongside this.

Employee-led support

Employee fundraising

The firm has an employee charity committee, which allows staff to vote for charities to support, and organise fundraising activities. Employees also take part in London Legal Walk to raise money for London Legal Support, volunteer to collect money for The Royal British Legion Poppy Appeal, and donate funds through payroll giving.

Matched funding

The firm provides matched funding of £500 to employees who fundraise for charities and schools through its Funds for Fundraisers scheme.

Employee volunteering

The firm's employees volunteer through a range of initiatives with its charity partners, such as helping with the Job Club at St Luke's Community Centre in Islington, or offering support with reading for children at local primary schools.

Applications

The firm

Although the firm is proactive in supporting charitable groups, the website states that unfortunately it is unable to accept unsolicited funding applications from schools, charities or individuals.

The Slaughter and May Charitable Trust

The trust's 2014/15 annual report states that it 'makes annual grants at its discretion to a small number of specific charitable causes and does not generally accept unsolicited funding applications'.

DS Smith Holdings PLC

Print/paper/packaging

Correspondent: Rachel Stevens, Trustee, DS Smith Charitable Foundation, 7th Floor, 350 Euston Road, Regent's Place, London NW1 3AX (tel: 020 7756 1800; email: charitablefoundation@dssmith.com; website: www.dssmith.com)

Directors: Adrian Marsh, Group Finance Director; Chris Britton; Gareth Davis, Chair; Ian Griffiths; Jonathan Nicholls; Kathleen O'Donovan; Louise Smalley; Miles Roberts, Group Chief Executive (women: 2; men: 6)

Year end	30/04/2016
Turnover	£4,066,000,000
Pre-tax profit	£201,000,000

Nature of business: Production of corrugated and plastic packaging, primarily from recycled waste, and the distribution of office products.

Company registration number: 1377658

Subsidiary undertakings include: DS Smith Corrugated Packaging Ltd; DS Smith Plastics Ltd; St Regis Paper Company Ltd.

Total employees: 26,000

Focus of giving: Education, enterprise/training, environment, fundraising events, health, ill health, local groups, armed forces, overseas projects, poverty and social exclusion, science technology, sport, recreation, children, young people, community/social welfare, disasters.

Community involvement	✓
Community contributions	✓
Company reports on anti-slavery	✓
CSR report	✓
Charity partner(s)	✓
Corporate charity	✓
Employee-led support	✓
Gifts in kind	✓
Humanitarian aid: overseas	✓
Pro bono	✓
Sponsorship	✓

Community involvement

Most of the group's charitable activities in the UK are co-ordinated through its corporate charity, the DS Smith Charitable Foundation. However, individual businesses within the group also run their own initiatives, and there are also group-wide partnerships.

DS Smith Charitable Foundation

The foundation (Charity Commission no. 1142817) primarily supports charities working for the conservation or improvement of the environment, as well as those providing education or training opportunities. The foundation provides a mix of smaller grants (£1,000 or less), larger grants and multi-year partnerships with a small number of charities selected by the trustees. In 2015/16 the foundation made grants totalling over £300,000 to charities. Examples of grant-making activities during the year included: providing a £5,000 scholarship for former members of the armed forces taking a degree a the University of Durham; a donation towards the International Red Cross's humanitarian work in Syria; and supporting the work of Trees for Life in Scotland.

Beneficiaries included: Edinburgh International Science Festival; Trees for Life; International Red Cross; Unicef.

Sponsorship

DS Smith is the primary sponsor of the Keep Britain Tidy Green Flag Award Scheme. This sponsorship involves a pledge to volunteer and fundraise for the scheme across all the group's sites in the UK. Sites at which the group has a factory are matched up with a local green space used by employees and the local community, and the organisation contributes to improving this space for the benefit of local communities – for example, in 2015 employees in Kettering joined the community for a local clean up day. A number of DS Smith sites are also working towards Green Flag accreditation.

The group is also a sponsor of the Museum of Brands, Packaging and Advertising in London, supported by the DS Smith Charitable Foundation, and will deliver education sessions and programmes for children and students at the museum.

Other partnerships

The group is also working with the charity Heart Research UK towards getting Healthy Heart Mark accreditation for its packaging sites. So far, 29 sites have achieved bronze awards and 15 have achieved silver awards. As well as engaging in healthy lifestyle activities for the award, employees have also taken part in active fundraising challenges for the charity.

The group is one of the founding members of the Nestle Alliance for YOUth, which aims to address the problem of youth unemployment. Activities under this initiative included hosting a Girls' Day at one of the company's sites in Germany, aiming to introduce students to careers that they might not otherwise consider.

Main locations

The group has sites across England, Scotland and Wales. The head office is in London.

Community contributions

No figure was given for the group's total charitable contribution.

Employee-led support

Employee volunteering

Employees volunteer as part of the group's sponsorship of the Green Flag Award Scheme. Examples during the year included employees from Kemsley Mill volunteering to tidy up a local area popular with walkers and employees in London cleaning a local children's park.

Employee fundraising

As well as making donations through its charitable foundation, the group also supports employee fundraising efforts for a wide range of causes.

Corporate charity

The DS Smith Charitable Foundation (Charity Commission no. 1142817).

Applications

DS Smith Charitable Foundation

The website states that the foundation primarily seeks ideas for new partnerships from employees, but also accepts applications. Applications should be made using the form on the website, and are only considered from charities supporting education and training or the environment. A combination of smaller and larger grants are made every year and the foundation particularly welcomes opportunities to develop multi-year partnerships with a small number of charities.

WH Smith PLC

Retail – miscellaneous

Correspondent: Anthony Lawrence, Group Human Resources Director, Greenbridge Road, Swindon, Wiltshire SN3 3RX (tel: 01793 616161; website: www.whsmithplc.co.uk)

Directors: Annemarie Durbin; Drummond Hall; Henry Staunton, Chair; Robert Moorhead, Chief Financial Officer; Stephen Clarke, Group Chief Executive; Suzanne Baxter (women: 2; men: 4)

Year end	31/08/2015
Turnover	£1,178,000,000
Pre-tax profit	£121,000,000

Nature of business: The group is a retailer in convenience, books, news and stationery.

Company registration number: 5202036

Subsidiary undertakings include: WH Smith Hospitals Holdings Ltd; Card Market Ltd; funkypigeon.com Ltd.

Total employees: 14,000

Focus of giving: Economic generation, education, environment, fundraising events, health, ill health, inner cities, large national appeals, local groups, armed forces, arts, culture, children, young people, community/social welfare.

Membership: BITC

Community involvement	✓
Community contributions	✓
Company reports on anti-slavery	✓
CSR report	✓
Directors have other relevant posts	✓
Armed forces personnel	✓
Cash donations declared	✓
Charity partner(s)	✓
Corporate charity	✓
Employee-led support	✓
Gifts in kind	✓
Market-led giving	✓
Matched funding	✓
Pro bono	✓
Sponsorship	✓

Charitable donations

Cash UK (latest available):	2015	£885,000
Total UK (cash and in kind):	2015	£1,100,000
Cash worldwide:	2015	£885,000
Total worldwide (cash and in kind):	2015	£1,100,000

Community involvement

The company focuses particularly on communities and 'championing literacy'.

Community engagement

The group has stores in 25 towns where it has identified that regeneration of the high street is an issue, and particularly encourages employees in these stores to engage with their local community.

Literacy

Encouraging literacy and reading is the primary focus of the company's charitable work. Much of this is achieved through a partnership with the National Literacy Trust. Since 2005, this partnership has enabled play schemes, school activities and family reading programmes. The 2015 corporate responsibility report states that the company is currently supporting the National Literacy Trust's Young Readers Programme, encouraging peer reading. As part of this three-year project, schools are partnered with a local WH Smith store, where they can take part in activities such as writing book reviews to be displayed in store, and can choose their own books.

World Book Day

WH Smith continues to take a leading role in the overall organisation of the UK's World Book Day initiative, designated by UNESCO and celebrated internationally. The event involves collaboration between a group of interested parties such as booksellers and publishers and is sponsored by National Book Tokens. Many WH Smith stores celebrate the day with events and activities and welcomes local schools to participate.

WH Smith Group Charitable Trust

The group has a corporate charity, the WH Smith Group Charitable Trust (Charity Commission no. 1013782) which raises and distributes funds to charitable organisations in which members of staff are involved, and also supports projects to promote literacy. It also actively supports employees who volunteer for or raise funds for charitable organisations or schools in their local community. Support for schools is also available through: grants to employees who are on a PTA or board of governors; schools being nominated by staff members; and a monthly prize draw into which any school is eligible to enter.

The trust runs an annual schools giveaway event, in which WH Smith stores can receive a share of £27,000 in WH Smith vouchers to donate to local schools. In 2015 this involved children and teachers writing book reviews to be displayed in stores.

From 2016, the trust is offering community grants of up to £500 to charities, voluntary groups and schools from the proceeds of the plastic bag charges. Grants are awarded every six months, in March and September.

Directors with other relevant posts

Suzanne Baxter is Chair of the Business in the Community South West Strategic Advisory Board.

Main locations

The group has operations throughout the UK, as well as international units in China; Middle East; Australia; South-East Asia; India; and Europe. It has offices in London and Swindon.

Community contributions

The group's 2014/15 CR report provides the following helpful breakdown of charitable giving:

Cash donated	£885,000
Gifts in-kind	£172,000
Management costs	£64,000
Staff time donated	£40,000

We take the figure of £1.1 million (excluding management costs) to represent the group's total community contributions. It would appear that charitable giving is mainly concentrated in the UK.

In-kind support

As part of its work with the National Literacy Trust, WH Smith has funded 22 libraries in participating schools.

WH Smith's stores based in hospitals have provided in-kind donations of products such as books, stationery and craft materials to hospitals in the UK.

Employee-led support

Employee fundraising efforts often focus on raising funds for the WH Smith Charitable Charitable Trust and the CR report notes that in 2015 examples included various sports and adventure challenges, and support through the trust's shop in the group's head office.

Other initiatives included 'The Big Readcycle', where customers and employees were encouraged to donate used books at collection points, to be sold in Marie Curie shops to raise money for the charity.

Employee fundraising and volunteering is matched by the WH Smith Charitable Trust; in 2014/15 a total of 55 grants were made totalling almost £40,000.

Each year the group gives WH Smith Community Awards to recognise the contribution of employees to their local communities, and celebrate the efforts of particular store teams.

Commercially led support

The group has partnerships with a number of charities to allow customers to donate to charities through specific products. Examples include a long-standing partnership with Children in

Need, for the sale of Christmas cards and calendars, as well as pin badges and Christmas cards for a number of other charities.

Carrier bags

Following the introduction of a mandatory plastic bag levy in 2015, the group donated money raised from both the compulsory plastic bag charge and from the sale of reusable bags, to the Woodland Trust, for its schools tree planting scheme. In addition, the group has now introduced a community grants scheme, run by the WH Smith Group Charitable Trust (see 'Community Involvement'). Funds raised from the group's Travel business will instead go to Shelter.

Profits from the group's recycling scheme for inkjet cartridges go to Lord Taverners, a charity which supports young people through sport.

Corporate charity

The WH Smith Group Charitable Trust (Charity Commission no. 1013782).

Applications

The website states that queries about Corporate Responsibility should be sent by email at corporate.responsibility@whsmith.co.uk or by telephone: 01793 616161.

Applications for community grants from the WH Smith Charitable Trust can be made via a form online at: blog.whsmith.co.uk/community-grants-application.

Smiths Group PLC

Aerospace, engineering, information management and communication

Correspondent: The Corporate Responsibility Team, 4th Floor, 11–12 St James's Square, London, England SW1Y 4LB (tel: 020 7004 1600; fax: 020 7004 1644; email: cr@smiths.com; website: www.smiths.com)

Directors: Anne Quinn; Bill Seeger; Bruno Angelici; Chris O'Shea, Finance Director; David Challen; Philip Bowman, Chief Executive; Sir George Buckley, Chair; Sir Kevin Tebbit; Tanya Fratto (women: 2; men: 7)

Year end	31/07/2015
Turnover	£2,897,000,000
Pre-tax profit	£325,000,000

Nature of business: The group has five divisions which are involved in the medical; industrial; energy; aerospace; communication; engineered components; and threat and contraband detection markets. Its customers include governments, hospitals, petrochemical companies, equipment manufacturers and service providers in other sectors.

Company registration number: 137013

Subsidiary undertakings include: Smiths Heimann Ltd; TI Interest Ltd; George Maclellan Holdings Ltd.

Brands include: There are five divisions: John Crane; Smiths Medical; Smiths Detection; Smiths Interconnect; and Flex-Tek.

Focus of giving: Education, environment, health, ill health, medical research, non-registered charities, small groups, community/social welfare.

Community involvement	✓
Community contributions	✓
CSR report	✓
AF Covenant	✓
Charity partner(s)	✓
Company gives to smaller charities	✓
Employee-led support	✓
FTSE 100	✓
Gifts in kind	✓
Shared-value alliances	✓
STEM-focused	✓

Charitable donations

Cash worldwide:	2015	£154,000
Total worldwide (cash and in kind):	2015	£154,000

Community involvement

Smiths Group Corporate Charitable Donations Fund

The website states that most community involvement activities are organised at a divisional level, focusing on projects local to the group's operational facilities or connected to the industries in which the group works.

However, there is also a central budget for supporting charitable causes, the Smiths Group Corporate Charitable Donations Fund. To be eligible for a grant, organisations must demonstrate how a donation will improve the well-being of people through education, health, welfare or environmental activities. Applications are open to small charitable organisations that work in the community close to the group's head office in London, or have connections to the industries in which the group operates. Grants are generally under £1,000.

Main locations

The group's UK operations are based in London.

Community contributions

In 2014/15 the group made charitable donations totalling £154,000, in addition to employee fundraising activities. It was unclear how much of this was in the UK.

In-kind support

The 2014/15 corporate responsibility report provides some examples of in-kind support offered by the group. One of the divisions within the group, Smiths Medical, donates medical devices which cannot be sold due to limited shelf life to World Vision. The charity then distributes the products to medical staff in areas of need to use the products within their remaining shelf life.

Employee-led support

Employee fundraising and volunteering

The 2014/15 corporate responsibility report provides a number of examples of charitable initiatives undertaken by the group's employees. For example, employees in Manchester volunteered as STEM ambassadors, acting as mentors to local students and encouraging them to consider STEM-related careers.

Exclusions

The group will not fund:

- Individuals for sponsorship for fundraising activities
- Initiatives involving people engaging in dangerous activities, such as bungee jumping or parachuting
- Political organisations and campaigns
- Any initiative that does not meet the specified funding criteria

Applications

For grants from the Corporate Charitable Donations Fund, organisations that meet the eligibility criteria outlined by the group should complete an application form, which can be downloaded from the website, and send it to cr@smiths.com. Applications sent via post will not be considered. Applications are reviewed twice a year.

For applications to a local division, apply in writing to the relevant division, details of which can be found on the group's website.

Sodexo Ltd

Catering services, food services

Correspondent: Corporate Responsibility Team, One Southampton Row, London WC1B 5HA (tel: 020 7404 0110; email: CorporateResponsibility.UK@sodexo.com; website: uk.sodexo.com)

Directors: Chris John; Christopher Bray; David Bailey; Ian Spence; Janine McDowell; Laurent Arnaudo, Chief Finance Officer; Mark Seastron; Phil Hooper; Sean Haley, Chair; Simon Scrivens; Stuart Carter; Tony Leach (women: 1; men: 11)

Year end	31/08/2015
Turnover	£1,157,638,000
Pre-tax profit	£47,913,000

Nature of business: The company provides catering, facilities, vending, health and fitness support and management services to clients in commercial, industrial, educational, healthcare and other establishments.

Sodexo Ltd operates in the UK and Ireland as a wholly owned subsidiary of Sodexo Holdings Ltd. The company's ultimate parent company is Sodexo S.A., a French company.

Note: the figure of UK employees includes Ireland.

Company registration number: 842846

Subsidiary undertakings include: Prestige Ticketing Ltd; Sodexo Defence Services Ltd; Sodexo Education Services Ltd.

UK employees: 34,000

Total employees: 420,000

Focus of giving: Education, enterprise/training, environment, equal opportunities, health, ill health, housing, homelessness, individuals, less popular charitable purposes, armed forces, humanitarian help, poverty and social exclusion, safety and crime prevention, sport, recreation, children, young people, community/social welfare.

Membership: BITC

Community involvement	✓
Community contributions	✓
CSR report	✓
CSR or charity committee	✓
Directors have other relevant posts	✓
AF Covenant	✓
Armed forces personnel	✓
Cash donations declared	✓
Charity partner(s)	✓
Corporate charity	✓
Employee-led support	✓
Gifts in kind	✓
Humanitarian aid: UK including food banks	✓
Market-led giving	✓
Matched funding	✓
Payroll giving	✓
Pro bono	✓

Charitable donations

Total UK (cash and in kind):	2015	£58,000
Total worldwide (cash and in kind):	2015	£58,000

Community involvement

Much of the group's charitable support is focused on its corporate foundation, which focuses on tackle hunger and malnutrition, healthy lifestyles and training for life skills. The group works with partner charities, as well as smaller organisations, and provides support through funding, in-kind support and volunteers.

The group's Better Tomorrow Plan focuses on the following areas: nutrition, health and well-being; local communities; sustainable supply chain; environmental management.

Sodexo Stop Hunger Foundation

The group's main priority for its charitable work hunger and malnutrition in the UK and Ireland. The group's corporate charity, the Sodexo Stop Hunger Foundation (Charity Commission no. 1110266) focuses on this. The foundation's aims are: to tackle hunger and malnutrition; to promote healthy lifestyles; to encourage training in life skills, such as cooking. The foundation makes grants to a range of charities to support these aims, including the group's partner charities, FareShare and The Outward Bound Trust. In 2014/15 the foundation made grants to 13 organisations totalling £243,500.

Beneficiaries included: Outward Bound Trust (£135,500); Centrepoint (£24,000); Body and Soul (£8,900); Scouts Association (£8,000); Osmondthorpe Resource Centre (£3,500); Aberlour Child Care Trust (£3,400); Brendoncare (£2,900).

The Community Foundation for Ireland manages Sodexo's Stop Hunger work in Ireland. The Stop Hunger initiative is also supported by the group's operations worldwide.

Employment

The group is part of Movement to Work, a partnership of employers aiming to support disadvantaged young people into employment. During 2015, Sodexo provided 50 placements through this initiative. In partnership with Nuffield Health Woking Hospital, the group also supports Surrey County Council's EmployAbility scheme, helping people with disabilities to find employment, hosting seven placements over the last three years.

The group also supports employability in the prisons where it works. For example, in HMP Peterborough, the JailBirds project gives women the opportunity to make greeting cards and gifts to sell to the local community, while in HMP Northumberland, Sodexo partnered with Ocado and charity Hubbub on a project where prisoners used old corporate uniforms to make aprons and tote bags for charity.

Directors with other relevant posts

Phil Hooper is Chair of Trustees of the Sodexo Stop Hunger Foundation.

Main location

The group's UK operations are based at head office in London.

Community contributions

In 2014/15 the Sodexo Stop Hunger Foundation received £58,000 in income from Sodexo Ltd, including employee volunteer time and administration costs, and £442,500 raised by Sodexo employees. The foundation made grants totalling £243,500 during the year.

In-kind support

As well as grants and volunteer support, the group also provides in-kind support to FareShare. For example, when the charity opened its Wirral distribution centre, the group donated 120 pairs of safety boots.

Employee-led support

Employee volunteering

Employees are entitled to a day's paid leave each year for volunteering, and are encouraged to volunteer with the group's partners, Outward Bound Trust and FareShare. In 2014/15 employees volunteered a total of 94 days.

Employee fundraising

The majority of employee fundraising initiatives focus on the Sodexo Stop Hunger Foundation; during the 2014/15, £442,500 was raised by employees for the foundation. The group holds an annual fundraising Stop Hunger Day, which raised £40,000 in 2014/15.

The group has a network of employees acting as charity champions, co-ordinating fundraising in their business. In 2014/15 charity champions helped the group to raise £209,000 for charities. Awards are made annually for exceptional contributions of charity champions.

Payroll giving

Sodexo match funds 50p for every £1 given to the Sodexo Stop Hunger Foundation through the group's payroll giving scheme.

Commercially led support

Market-led giving

The group uses cause-related products to raise money for the Stop Hunger initiative. For example, 5% from the sales of Aspretto coffee are donated to Stop Hunger, which raised £8,500 in 2014/15.

Corporate charity

Sodexo Stop Hunger Foundation (Charity Commission no. 1110266).

Applications

The group

Enquiries should be sent to the Corporate Responsibility team.

The foundation

Enquiries relating to the Sodexo Stop Hunger Foundation should be made to Edwina Hughes (email: stophunger@sodexo.com) at the group's address. Application forms for the STOP Hunger initiative are also available online.

Note: In addition to supporting FareShare and a number of smaller charities that meet the STOP Hunger objectives, the trustees receive from time to time requests from employees to support a local cause. Such requests are usually met by Sodexo outside the Sodexo Foundation.

Sony Europe Ltd

Electronics/computers

Correspondent: The CSR Committee, UK Technology Centre, Pencoed, Bridgend CF35 5HZ (tel: 01656 860666; email: CSRPCD@eu.sony.com; website: www.sonypencoed.co.uk/community)

Directors: Atsushi Kobayashi; Ricky Lodema; Shigeru Kumekawa (women: 0; men: 3)

Year end	31/03/2016
Turnover	£3,835,000,000

Nature of business: The company is the distributor of Sony-branded products. These are mainly electronic goods, such as video and audio system, computer systems and media peripheral and semiconductor products, for the domestic, leisure, business and professional markets throughout Europe. Broadcast camera and digital cinema equipment is also distributed.

Company registration number: 2422874

Focus of giving: Local groups, education.

Community involvement	✓
Community contributions	✓
Company reports on anti-slavery	✓
CSR report	✓
CSR or charity committee	✓
Charity partner(s)	✓
STEM-focused	✓

Community involvement

Charity partnership

In 2014 Sony UK Technology Centre announced a partnership with The Children's Ward at the Princess of Wales Hospital in Bridgend and organised a range of activities fundraising for the cause.

Educational programmes

Sony hosts regular visits from schools, colleges and universities. Sony supports several of the programmes run by The Engineering Education Scheme Wales (EESW) which encourage young people to choose a career in one of the STEM subjects. The Sony UK Technology Environmental Centre is also used by schoolchildren for environmental field trips.

Main locations

Bridgend

Community contributions

We were unable to determine the company's community contributions for 2015/16. According to its website, 38 organisations were supported in 2015.

In-kind support

Sony supports local organisations, usually with products to help with fundraising and/or raffles.

Exclusions

According to the company's website, the following are not considered for support:

- Promotion of religious ideas
- Sexist or racist groups
- Political groups, private or secret societies
- Profit making bodies

Applications

Organisations should be located within 30 miles of Sony's UK Technology Centre in Bridgend. Application forms for support in the form of products to help with fundraising/raffles can be requested via the website: www.sonypencoed.co.uk/community-support.

School Visits

Contact Jenny Reeves – Jenny.Reeves@sony.com.

The Southern Co-operative Ltd

Retail – miscellaneous, retail – supermarkets

Correspondent: Silena Dominy, Company Secretary, 1000 Lakeside, Western Road, Portsmouth, Hampshire PO6 3FE (tel: 023 9222 2500; fax: 023 9222 2650; email: community@southerncoops.co.uk; website: www.thesouthernco-operative.co.uk)

Directors: Amber Vincent-Prior; Andrew Cast; Elizabeth Rogers; Gareth Lewis; John Harrington; Kate Hibbert; Kelly Emmence; Mike Hastilow, Chair; Neil Blanchard; Silena Dominy, Company Secretary (women: 5; men: 5)

Year end	30/01/2016
Turnover	£366,786,000
Pre-tax profit	£2,352,000

Nature of business: Independent consumer co-operative society. It operates over 250 community stores and funeral homes across 11 counties in southern England. In addition to that the co-operative operates a home shopping business supplying aids to daily living and a portfolio of rental properties.

Company registration number: IP01591R

UK employees: 3,500+

Focus of giving: General charitable purposes, economic generation, education, enterprise/training, environment, health, ill health, non-registered charities, small groups, local groups, humanitarian help, arts, culture, poverty and social exclusion, community/social welfare, disability.

Membership: BITC, LBG

Community involvement	✓
Community contributions	✓
CSR report	✓
Directors have other relevant posts	✓
Charity partner(s)	✓
Company gives to smaller charities	✓
Employee-led support	✓
Gifts in kind	✓
Humanitarian aid: UK including food banks	✓
Market-led giving	✓
Sponsorship	✓
Unregistered charities/NFP	✓

Community involvement

In 2015 The Southern Co-operative Ltd (TSC) undertook a review of its approach to community investment, consulting with employees, members and community partners. The co-operative focuses on supporting local communities and has launched a new community programme, Love Your Neighbourhood (see the 'Commercially led' section for further information). Funding and other support is given for general charitable purposes, with some preference for: education; health; economic development; environment; arts and culture; social welfare; and emergency relief.

Charity partnerships

Previously, TSC's employees and customers selected a charity partner to support for two-years. After the 2015 community investment review the co-operative has now developed a local partnership approach that is managed by local stores/funeral homes, rather than centrally, through its Love Your Neighbourhood programme. Partnerships in 2015/16 included:

Whizz-Kidz

TSC partnered with this charity that helps children with disabilities for two years. The partnership ended in 2016 and raised £257,000 in 2015/16 through employee fundraising events and members' donations through the Share the Profits scheme.

Wildlife Trusts

TSC has partnered with Hampshire and Isle of Wight Wildlife Trust for a number of years and has worked closely with the trust to develop a long-term conservation plan for Clayton Wood, TSC's natural burial ground site. The charity has helped the co-operative with restoring the site to create better habitats for wildlife. TSC also sponsored a film for the trust's Make a Wild Change Happen campaign, which aims to increase the amount of time children spend outdoors.

Dorset Wildlife Trust's Urbanlink project to create an urban living landscape across South East Dorset and Sussex Wildlife Trust's Forest Rangers project were also supported.

Support for community environmental education projects
TSC supports environmental education projects, particularly those focused towards children and young people. The following projects have been supported:

- EYE (Eco, Young and Engaged), which brings schoolchildren from West Sussex together for annual eco summits
- Tuppenny Barn, which is building a sustainable education centre to host organic food workshops for local children and other courses and events
- Youth Moves, in Bristol, is a project to engage children in growing vegetables and carry out various community events including those linked to their forest schools programme

Bereavement Centre
Through the centre's support and education service people can find: educational study days and bereavement workshops; local support, friendship and social groups; one-to-one bereavement support; memorial services held throughout the year; and major bereavement seminars and conferences. The centre is open to everyone. For further information visit www.bereavementsupportgroups.co.uk

Business in the Community
The co-operative has partnered with Portchester Community School through Business in the Community's Business Class programme. This has involved employees volunteering as mentors to Year 11 pupils and delivering workshops on employability skills.

Sponsorship
TSC sponsors and judges the Campaign to Protect Rural England (CPRE) Hampshire's annual Countryside Awards.

The co-operative is also the main sponsor of the Create and Cook competition, an annual competition for 12- to 14-year-olds across Hampshire, Isle of Wight and Sussex focusing on local food. It is run by Fit2Cook Education, whom TSC has worked with for a number of years.

Directors with other relevant posts
Mike Hastilow is a Group Scout Leader and Chair of Governors of a secondary school. He is also Deputy Launch Authority for the Royal National Lifeboat Institution (Charity Commission no. 209603) and TSC's designated beekeeper, delivering tours of the hives on Bee Island.

Andrew Cast is the Director for Holding Hands 4 Equality, an organisation that campaigns to normalise holding of hands in public for all people, particularly the LGBT+ community. He also writes for EILE magazine in support of LGBT equal rights.

Neil Blanchard is Deputy Bursar at Churcher's College, an independent school.

John Harrington is involved in a number of co-operative organisations and is an executive of and magazine editor for the National Federation of Progressive Co-operators. He also spent ten years as Vice Chair of Hermitage Housing Association.

Main locations
TSC has various stores and funeral homes across the south of England, including West and South Outer London. There is also a store in Gwent, South East Wales.

Community contributions

According to the annual review for 2015/16, a total of £955,000 was contributed to local communities through fundraising events, campaigns and donations. This includes: £670,000 invested in local communities; £257,000 raised for TSC's charity partner, Whizz-Kidz; and £170,000 invested in challenging shop crime in Sussex. No further breakdown was available regarding cash donations; employee fundraising efforts; gifts in-kind contributions; and so forth.

Employee-led support

Employee volunteering
TSC actively encourages colleagues working at all levels of the business to volunteer in work time and as a result, this has contributed to over 2,700 hours of volunteering during 2015/16. An example of employee volunteering efforts during the year included litter picks as part of the Big Co-op Clean, organised by Co-operatives UK.

Employee fundraising
Employees and customers actively fundraise for their local charity partners.

Commercially led support

Love Your Neighbourhood
This is a new programme launched by TSC in 2016 with its activities funded by the proceeds of the carrier bag charge. It focuses on four community themes: to create greener, safer, healthier and more inclusive communities; and features the following:

- In-kind product donations
- Local fundraising (giving out cash donations of between £50 to £1,000)
- Regional partnerships
- Employee volunteering
- Offering food bank collection points and housing community defibrillators on a local request basis

Support is focused on local charitable or not-for-profit organisations in areas where the co-operative operates. Local branches of national charities are welcome to apply if there is a TSC store in the locality.

Retail crime reduction
TSC is developing a co-operative approach with the police and local businesses in Sussex to address the issue of low-level retail crime, particularly in more remote communities. In 2015/16 TSC invested £170,000 in the initiative.

ProxyWatch
TSC has been involved in an initiative with Portsmouth City Council delivering a 24-hour hotline for members of the public and shop staff to report incidences of proxy-purchasing and raising awareness of the issue among retailers.

One community campaign
In 2015 TSC launched this campaign in association with the Fairtrade Foundation. Its aim is to raise awareness of farmers and workers representing Fairtrade producers' groups and to encourage customers to purchase more Fairtrade products.

Education and training
TSC has programmes of work experience placements for young people at schools and colleagues. The Learning and Development Team also organises initiatives to enhance the skills of young job seekers in local communities and works with schools and charitable organisations to improve the range of work experience places on offer.

Exclusions

Applications for local funding or partnerships through the Love Your Neighbourhood programme will not be considered for the following:

- Non-constituted, profit-making organisations or groups with less than three members on their committee or board
- Individuals
- Loan or debt repayments
- Costs already incurred prior to application
- If more than a quarter of the total funds will be used on advertising, promotion or marketing of events or services
- Projects that are generally the responsibility of statutory authorities, unless it has a wider community benefit
- Funding for grant-making organisations or third-party fundraisers
- General fundraising appeals

- Religious purposes
- Lobbying, political or fraternal activities
- Shares into businesses, whether community or co-operatively run
- Organisations that discriminate against a person or a group on the basis of age, political affiliation, race, national origin, ethnicity, gender, disability, sexual orientation or religious belief

Applications

Application forms for the Love Your Neighbourhood programme, such as applying for goods in kind, local partnerships or cash donations, can be downloaded from the website and handed in to your local store. Any queries regarding these community-based initiatives or eligibility requirements can be emailed to: community@southerncoops.co.uk.

Spar (UK) Ltd

Retail – supermarkets

Correspondent: Phillip Marchant, Company Secretary & Charitable Fund Administrator, Mezzanine Floor, Hygeia Building, 66–68 College Road, Harrow, Middlesex HA3 1BE (tel: 020 8426 3700; email: customer.relations@spar.co.uk; website: www.spar.co.uk)

Directors: Christopher Lewis; Deborah Robinson; Jacqueline Mackenzie; Mark Keeley; Phillip Marchant (women: 2; men: 3)

Year end	25/04/2015
Turnover	£67,250,000
Pre-tax profit	£413,000

Nature of business: The entity is a voluntary, independently owned trading group operating stores under the SPAR banner throughout the UK.

The group's accounts state: 'Spar (UK) Ltd is the Central Office of the Spar retail organisation owned 100% by Spar Food Distributors Ltd whose shareholders are five regional distribution companies.'

The companies are: A. F. Blakemore and Son Ltd; Appleby Westward Group Ltd; C. J. Lang and Son Ltd; Henderson Wholesale Ltd; and James Hall and Company (Holdings) Ltd.

Company registration number: 634226

Subsidiary undertakings include: Buying International Group BV; BV Intergroup Trading (IGT) (Netherlands); SPAR International BV.

Focus of giving: Health, ill health, individuals, children, young people, disasters.

Community involvement	✓
Community contributions	✓
Charity partner(s)	✓
Corporate charity	✓
Employee-led support	✓
Gifts in kind	✓
Humanitarian aid: overseas	✓
Market-led giving	✓

Community involvement

Support is given through the group's corporate charity, The Spar Charitable Fund, as well as to its partner charity, NSPCC.

Spar Charitable Fund (Charity Commission no. 236252)

The group's corporate charity, the Spar Charitable Fund, works with the Spar Benevolent Fund to support employees in need, as well as supporting charitable organisations in the retail industry. It also makes donations to the group's charity partner, NSPCC, and other charities supported by the group. In 2014/15 the fund made grants to six charities (including the SPAR Benevolent Fund) totalling £105,000.

Charity partnership

The group has supported NSPCC as its partner charity for ten years, mainly through employee fundraising.

Main locations

The group operates across the UK.

Community contributions

No figure was given for the group's charitable contribution in the 2014/15 annual report and accounts.

In 2014/15 the Spar Charitable Fund had a total income of £102,000, of which £47,000 came from the group's Benevolent Fund, £31,000 was in investment income, £16,800 was raised at the group's annual convention, and £7,500 was in funds raised for NSPCC.

Employee-led support

Employee volunteering

Employees volunteer to support the group's partner charity, NSPCC, and its Schools Service programmes, visiting primary schools to raise awareness of abuse.

Employee fundraising

Employees organise fundraising activities to raise money for the group's partner charity, NSPCC, and by 2016 had raised a total of £5 million.

Commercially led support

Market-led giving

Donations from the sales of certain ranges of sandwiches sold at SPAR stores raise money for the group's partner charity, NSPCC.

Corporate charity

Spar Charitable Fund (Charity Commission no. 236252).

Exclusions

Support is not given for political or religious causes.

Applications

The group: enquiries regarding local initiatives should be addressed to the local store manager.

Spar Charitable Fund: queries should be directed to Phillip Marchant (email: philip.marchant@spar.co.uk), trustee of the fund, at the group's address.

Spirax-Sarco Engineering PLC

Engineering, industrial products/services

Correspondent: Sustainability Team, Charlton House, Cirencester Road, Cheltenham, Gloucestershire GL53 8ER (tel: 01242 521361; fax: 01242 581470; email: info@spiraxsarcoengineering.com; website: www.spiraxsarcoengineering.com)

Directors: Andy Robson; Bill Whiteley, Chair; Clive Watson; David Meredith, Finance Director; Jamie Pike; Jay Whalen; Krishnamurthy Rajagopal; Neil Daws; Nicholas Anderson, Group Chief Executive; Trudy Schoolenberg (women: 1; men: 9)

Year end	31/12/2015
Turnover	£6,667,000,000
Pre-tax profit	£151,000,000

Nature of business: The supply of engineered solutions for the efficient design, maintenance and operation of industrial and commercial steam systems.

Company registration number: 596337

Subsidiary undertakings include: Spirax-Sarco Ltd; Watson-Marlow Ltd; BioPure Technology Ltd.

Total employees: 4,800

Focus of giving: Education, enterprise/training, health, ill health, medical research, children, young people, community/social welfare, disability, disasters.

Community involvement	✓
Community contributions	✓
Company reports on anti-slavery	✓
CSR report	✓
Cash donations declared	✓
Employee-led support	✓
Gifts in kind	✓
Humanitarian aid: overseas	✓
Shared-value alliances	✓
Sponsorship	✓
STEM-focused	✓

Charitable donations

Cash UK (latest available):	2015	£141,000
Total UK (cash and in kind):	2015	£141,000
Cash worldwide:	2015	£199,000
Total worldwide (cash and in kind):	2015	£199,000

Community involvement

The group focuses much of its community involvement on education, particularly science and engineering. For example, the company sponsored the Cheltenham Science Festival.

Companies within the group also support local charitable causes through making donations, employee fundraising and volunteering.

Corporate charity

Most of the group's donations are made through its charitable trust (The Spirax-Sarco Group Charitable Trust which is not currently registered) which supports organisations in the following areas: education; social welfare; disability; healthcare; arts; environment; disaster relief.

Main locations

In the UK, the group is based in Cheltenham, Cornwall and Hampshire. It also has operations in 57 countries worldwide.

Community contributions

In 2015 The Spirax Sarco Group Charitable Trust made 41 grants totalling £141,000 and ranging from £200 to £18,000. A further £58,000 was donated to charitable causes by companies within the group.

Applications

Apply in writing to the correspondent – donations are made by the regional divisions or by The Spirax-Sarco Group Charitable Trust.

For contact details for the regional divisions, refer to the group's website.

Sportech PLC

Gaming

Correspondent: Richard Boardley, Director of Corporate Affairs, 101 Wigmore Street, London W1U 1QU (tel: 020 7268 2400; email: cr@sportechplc.com; website: www.sportechplc.com)

Directors: Cliff Baty, Chief Financial Officer; David McKeith; Ian Penrose, Chief Executive; Mickey Kalifa; Peter Williams; Rich Roberts; Roger Withers, Chair (women: 0; men: 7)

Year end	31/12/2015
Turnover	£100,200,000
Pre-tax profit	£13,200,000

Nature of business: The principal activities of the group are sports betting entertainment and provision of wagering technology solutions.

Company registration number: SC69140

Subsidiary undertakings include: Sportech Gaming Ltd; The Football Pools Ltd; UK Lottery Management Ltd.

Brands include: Bump 50:50; The Football Pools.

Total employees: 749

Focus of giving: Health, ill health, local groups, arts, culture, sport, recreation, children, young people, community/social welfare, disability.

Community involvement	✓
Community contributions	✓
CSR report	✓
Directors have other relevant posts	✓
Charity partner(s)	✓
Gifts in kind	✓

Community involvement

The group's website states that it donates to sports, arts and community good causes, particularly grassroots projects.

Football Pools

The group raises money to support community projects through its Football Pools business. A map of projects supported by the proceeds can be found on the website. In 2013 the group entered into a two-year partnership to support the charity StreetGames with a new football programme, StreetGames Football Pools Fives, which aims to engage disadvantaged young people in UK communities.

GamCare

The group donates to and promotes the activities of the charity, which supports people suffering from gambling addictions.

Directors with other relevant posts

Ian Penrose is a trustee of the National Football Museum (Charity Commission no. 1050792). Peter Williams is a trustee of the Design Council (Charity Commission no. 272099) and the ASOS Foundation (Charity Commission no. 1153946). David McKeith is Chair of Trustees of the Hallé Orchestra (Charity Commission no. 223882) and a trustee of The Hallé Endowment Trust (Charity Commission no. 286145) and The Manchester Concert Hall Ltd (Charity Commission no. 1040342).

Main locations

The group's UK offices are in London (head office) and Liverpool. There are also two offices in the USA.

Community contributions

The 2015 annual report states that the group generates £500,000 each year 'for charitable use through its management and operation of society lotteries within its Football Pools business activities'. No specific figure was given for how much was raised during the year; however, there are examples of projects supported on the website. The group also donates to GamCare, a charity which promotes responsible gambling.

Applications

Any enquiries should be made in writing to the correspondent.

Sports Direct International PLC

Retail – clothing and footwear

Correspondent: Cameron Olsen, Company Secretary, Unit A, Brook Park East, Shirebrook, Derbyshire NG20 8RY (tel: 0344 245 9200; email: investor.relations@sportsdirect.com; website: www.sports-direct-international.com)

Directors: Claire Jenkins; Dave Singleton; Dr Keith Hellawell, Chair; Matt Pearson, Chief Financial Officer; Mike Ashley; Simon Bentley (women: 1; men: 5)

Year end	24/04/2016
Turnover	£2,900,000,000
Pre-tax profit	£361,800,000

Nature of business: Sports retailer.

Company registration number: 6035106

Subsidiary undertakings include: Dunlop Slazenger International Ltd; Everlast Sports International Inc. Corp; The Flannels Group Ltd.

Brands include: Slazenger; Karrimor; Firetrap.

Total employees: 18,280

Focus of giving: Housing, homelessness, medical research, sport, recreation, children, young people.

Community involvement	✓
Community contributions	✓
Company reports on anti-slavery	✓
Cash donations declared	✓
Employee-led support	✓
Gifts in kind	✓
Market-led giving	✓
Pro bono	✓
Shared-value alliances	✓
Sponsorship	✓

Charitable donations

Cash UK (latest available):	2016	£5,000
Total UK (cash and in kind):	2016	£5,000
Cash worldwide:	2016	£5,000
Total worldwide (cash and in kind):	2016	£5,000

Community involvement

The company's community engagement focuses on participation in sport, particularly through provision of in-kind equipment and facilities.

The annual report for 2015/16 states that, at its Shirebrook campus, the company is engaged with the Shirebrook Forward NG20 Working Group aiming to encourage involvement in community initiatives and a range of services.

Directors with other relevant posts
Dave Singleton, is Chair of Trustees of Bolton Lads and Girls Club and of Bolton Community Leisure Trust, as well as a trustee of Bolton Wanderers Community Trust. Simon Bentley is Chair of Trustees of Yad Vashem UK Foundation, as well as a trustee of the Jewish Memorial Council and of Saving Faces, the Facial Surgery Research Foundation.

Main locations
The group operates across the UK and Europe.

Community contributions

According to the 2015/16 annual report, cash donations to charities totalled £5,000. Further donations of sporting equipment were made by the group and its brands; however, we could not determine the value of these contributions.

Beneficiaries included: Salvation Army; The Breast Cancer Research Foundation; The Jerry Colangelo Prostate Cancer Event; Comic Relief; Dr Theodore A Atlas Foundation.

In-kind support

Most of the group's support for charitable causes is through in-kind donations. For example, in 2015/16 the group provided sporting equipment to organisations in the Shirebrook area, near the Sports Direct campus, including Shirebrook Academy, Shirebrook Town Council and Willow Tree Family Farm. The group also provided logistical support to local schools supporting the Operation Christmas Child Appeal.

The group's individual brands also provide in-kind support. For example, Karrimor provided jackets for comedian Jo Brand's sponsored walk for Comic Relief, while in the USA, Everlast provides sponsorship to The Breast Cancer Research Foundation, which totalled $61,000 in 2015/16 (around £47,000 at the time of writing – October 2016).

Further examples of support in 2015/16 are outlined in the annual report.

Applications

Apply in writing to the correspondent.

SSE PLC

Electricity

Correspondent: Sustainability Team, Inveralmond House, 200 Dunkeld Road, Perth, Perthshire PH1 3AQ (tel: 01738 456000; email: sustainability@sse.com; website: sse.com/beingresponsible/responsiblecommunitymember)

Directors: Alistair Phillips-Davies; Crawford Gillies; Dame Susan Bruce; Gregor Alexander, Finance Director; Helen Mahy; Jeremy Beeton; Katie Bickerstaffe; Peter Lynas; Richard Gillingwater, Chair (women: 3; men: 6)

Year end	31/03/2016
Turnover	£28,781,000,000
Pre-tax profit	£593,300,000

Nature of business: SSE produces, distributes and supplies electricity and gas and provides other energy-related services.

Company registration number: SC117119

Subsidiary undertakings include: Airtricity UK Windfarm Holidings Ltd; Keadby Generation Ltd; SSE Energy Solutions Ltd.

UK employees: 21,118

Total employees: 21,118

Focus of giving: Education, environment, sport, recreation, community/social welfare.

Community involvement	✓
Community contributions	✓
Company reports on anti-slavery	✓
CSR report	✓
CSR or charity committee	✓
Charity partner(s)	✓
Company gives to smaller charities	✓
Employee-led support	✓
FTSE 100	✓
Gifts in kind	✓
Matched funding	✓
Pro bono	✓
Shared-value alliances	✓
Sponsorship	✓
STEM-focused	✓

Charitable donations

Cash UK (latest available):	2016	£4,524,000
Total UK (cash and in kind):	2016	£4,879,000
Cash worldwide:	2016	£4,524,000
Total worldwide (cash and in kind):	2016	£4,879,000

Community involvement

The company supports the community in a variety of ways, including: community funds and sustainable development funds in every community where it has a wind farm; an employee volunteering programme, which allows charities to request support; a Resilient Communities Fund which helps communities prepare for extreme weather events.

Community investment funds
In every community where SSE builds a new wind farm, it also sets up a Community Investment Fund. According to the guide available on the website, there are now 25 community funds and for each one, £5,000 is set aside for every megawatt of 'installed capacity' from the wind farm, every year, for up to 25 years. 50% of the funding is ring-fenced as a 'local fund' for communities in the most immediate area surrounding the wind farm, and the other half as a 'regional fund', for larger, strategic projects benefitting the community in the wider local authority area of the wind farm. A local fund is run by a small panel of local community members, who decide which charitable projects to support. SSE provides support with tasks such as grants management, assessing projects and publicising the fund.

The regional funds are intended to support larger, innovative initiatives which meet one or more of the following criteria: skills development and training (particularly in rural Scotland); built or natural environmental improvements; and community renewable projects. A central panel assesses applications.

Beneficiaries included: Crossing Borders (£24,000); Aberfeldy Gaelic Choir (£3,500); Isle of Cumbrae Community Initiative (£3,000); Douglas Park Nursery (£1,500); Hopscotch Theatre (£250).

Sustainable Development Fund
In addition to the community funds, SSE provides grants through its Sustainable Development Fund within any local authority area in which an SSE wind farm was constructed after 1 January 2012. Applications must meet at least one of the following objectives: creating opportunities; empowering communities; sustainable places. Further preference is given to projects that show: value for money; community involvement; financial sustainability; contribution to the local economy. Further information about each of the objectives is provided on the company's website, along with a full list of beneficiaries.

Beneficiaries included: Inverness Kart Raceway (£150,000); Gordonbush Apprenticeship Scheme (£72,000); Abriachan Forest Trust (£21,000); Lochaber Action on Disability (£18,000); Dornoch and District Community Association (£5,000); Melvich Village Hall Association (£2,800).

Resilient Communities Fund
The sustainability report states that in 2015, SSE launched a £1.3 million two-year Resilient Communities Fund to offer support for communities to prepare for extreme weather events. Almost £500,000 was awarded during the first year.

Living Wage Friendly Funder
As well as being an accredited Living Wage Employer, during the year SSE became part of the new Living Wage Friendly Funders scheme, which aims to ensure that all employment posts funded through the company's community funds are paid the living wage, as set annually by the Living Wage Foundation.

Youth employment
Since 2008 SSE has invested over £1 million in the Barnardo's Works programme, giving young unemployed people from disadvantaged backgrounds a six-month work placement.

Education
SSE works with schools to promote careers in engineering, including a £100,000 partnership with the charity Teach First, aiming to support teachers to encourage young women to consider a career in STEM.

Sponsorship
According to the 2015/16 annual report, SSE is targeting its sponsorship activities on women's sport, including through Sports Aid and the SSE Women's FA Cup.

Other partnerships
In 2015 SSE worked in partnership with Stirling University's Dementia Services Development Centre to launch a book to help those living with dementia and their carers, with tips on heating and lighting. SSE employees also had a day of training with the centre to raise awareness of dementia.

Fuel poverty
As well as offering a £140 rebate to particularly vulnerable groups under the government-mandated scheme, and through its Priority Assistance Fund, the company also works in partnership with National Energy Action, Citizens Advice and the Home Heat Helpline. In total, SSE provided assistance totalling £48.6 million to around 325,000 customers at risk of fuel poverty in 2015/16.

Directors with other relevant posts
Susan Bruce is Chair of Trustees of both the Royal National Scottish Orchestra and of Young Scot Enterprise (OSCR no. SC029757).

Main locations
The group operates across the UK and Ireland.

Community contributions

The 2015/16 sustainability report gives a full breakdown of the group's charitable contributions during the year.

Grants totalling almost £4 million were made by SSE's 25 community investment funds. A full breakdown of all the projects supported is provided in the community benefit report, available on the SSE website.

An additional £500,000 was awarded through the Resilient Communities Fund.

Beneficiaries included: Caringorms Skills Project (£57,000); Williestruther Loch Walk (£30,000); Leadhills Silver Band (£23,000); The Bike Station (£20,000); Lochaber Action on Disability (£18,000); North Coast Leisure Centre (£15,000); Food Train (£11,500); ALIenergy (£9,200); Allt Beag Market Garden (£6,900); The Young Carers East Sutherland (£4,300); Helmsdale Dementia Activity Programme (£5,000); Bananas Playgroup (£2,800).

Employee volunteering totalled a value of £355,000.

The group also provided £67,000 in matched funding for employee fundraising initiatives.

In-kind support

The company's employee volunteering programme, Be the Difference, provides each employee one day a year to spend volunteering at a community project of their choice. In 2015/16 employees volunteered 3,422 days for 564 projects. Charities can request volunteer support using the form available on the website. In 2016 the company has launched a new online system to encourage employees to sign up for volunteering projects.

Employee-led support

Matched funding
According to the sustainability report, the company offers matched funding of up to £250 to support employees' fundraising efforts. According to the 2015/16 sustainability report, SSE gave £67,000 in matched funding during the year.

Exclusions

According to the website, grants from the company's local community funds cannot be awarded: for political or religious causes; to subsidise the cost of energy consumption; for purposes 'adverse to SSE's interests'; to replace statutory funding; or to individuals.

Grants from the Sustainable Development Fund are not awarded to individuals or to groups without a constitution.

For further details on exclusions applicable to any of the company's funds, refer to the website.

Applications

Application forms for each of the local community investment funds, as well as the Sustainable Development Fund, are available on the SSE's website, along with guidance, deadlines and appropriate contact details for each fund. The group can offer support to community groups with writing an application and it also holds funding surgeries.

To apply for volunteer support from employees through the Be the Difference scheme, download a volunteer request form from the SSE's website and send via email (volunteering@sse.com) or post (SSE, Be the Difference, Corporate Affairs, 55 Vastern Road, Reading RG1 8BU).

To apply for the Resilient Communities Fund, visit www.ssepd.co.uk/resiliencefund where applications can be downloaded, along with guidance notes and deadlines. For more information, contact Lindsay Dougan, the Community Funds Manager on 0141 224 7729 or lindsay.dougan@sse.com

Sustainability team contact email: sustainability@sse.com.

SSP Group PLC

Catering services, food services, retail – restaurants/fast food

Correspondent: Russell Chaplin, Head of Tax & Trustee of SSP Foundation, 169 Euston Road, London NW1 2AE (tel: 020 7543 3300/020 3714 5265; email: ssp.foundation@ssp-intl.com; website: www.foodtravelexperts.com)

Directors: Denis Hennequin; Ian Dyson; John Barton; Jonathan Davies, Chief Financial Officer; Kate Swann, Chief Executive Officer; Per Utnegaard; Vagn Sørensen, Chair (women: 1; men: 6)

Year end	30/09/2015
Turnover	£1,832,900,000
Pre-tax profit	£76,800,000

Nature of business: SSP is an operator of food and beverage outlets in travel locations, such as railway stations and airports, in 29 countries across the world.

Company registration number: 5735966

Subsidiary undertakings include: Millie's Cookies Ltd; Rail Gourmet Group Ltd; RG Onboard Services (Ireland) Ltd.

Brands include: Burger King; M&S Simply Food; Yo! Sushi.

Total employees: 29,354

Focus of giving: Enterprise/training, health, ill health, children, young people.

Community involvement	✓
Community contributions	✓
Company reports on anti-slavery	✓
CSR report	✓
Charity partner(s)	✓
Corporate charity	✓
Employee-led support	✓
Gifts in kind	✓
Matched funding	✓

Community involvement

The SSP Group establishes partnerships with a variety of local charities across the world located in areas where the company operates. It provides gifts in kind, hosts events in its units and provides fundraising support. Employees and customers also fundraise for these charities.

The group now focuses its UK fundraising activity through its newly established corporate charity, the SSP Foundation.

SSP Foundation

The SSP Foundation (Charity Commission no. 1163717) was established in September 2015 with the following objectives:

1. To work with partner charities on projects to promote healthy eating
   - There will be particular focus on organisations working with young people. For example, in 2015 the company partnered with the Children's Food Trust funding pilot Lets Get Cooking Clubs in 10 Further Education colleges in the Greater London area
2. To support colleague-nominated charities in the communities where SSP operates
   - Employees who are involved with a local charity, either by fundraising or volunteering, can apply to the foundation to have their fundraising efforts or value of their time matched. Support will be available to a wide range of local community causes across the UK

Main locations

The group's head office is based in London and it also operates in 20 airports and 115 rail stations throughout the UK and Ireland. Some of the locations in which it operates include: Dublin Airport; Heathrow Airport; Liverpool Street Station; London City Airport; Manchester Airport; and Stansted Airport.

The group also operates in various travel hubs in: Africa; Asia Pacific; Canada; Continental Europe; Middle East; and the USA.

Community contributions

No details were available regarding the group's charitable contributions made worldwide or in the UK. As the SSP Foundation was only established in 2015, the annual report and accounts were unavailable at the time of writing (December 2016) so we do not have details of how much the group donated to the charity.

Employee-led support

Employee fundraising

In the UK the group has been working in partnership with Cancer Research UK since 2013, with money being raised by employees and customers.

Commercially led support

The group works with organisations such as The Prince's Trust and King's Cross Partnership to bring young people from disadvantaged communities into the workplace with pre-employment training, work experience and permanent jobs.

Corporate charity

SSP Foundation (Charity Commission no. 1163717).

Applications

Applications should be directed to the group's corporate charity, the SSP Foundation, by writing to the correspondent.

St James's Place PLC

Financial services

Correspondent: CSR Manager, St James's Place House, 1 Tetbury Road, Cirencester, Gloucestershire GL7 1FP (tel: 01285 640302 or 08000138 137; email: csr@sjp.co.uk; website: www1.sjp.co.uk)

Directors: Andrew Croft, Chief Financial Officer; Baroness Wheatcroft; David Bellamy, Chief Executive Officer; David Lamb; Iain Cornish; Ian Gascoigne; Roger Yates; Sarah Bates, Chair; Simon Jeffreys (women: 2; men: 7)

Year end	31/12/2015
Turnover	£3,112,900,000
Pre-tax profit	£174,100,000

Nature of business: St James's Place PLC is a financial services group involved in the provision of wealth management services.

Company registration number: 3183415

Subsidiary undertakings include: St James's Place Allshare Income Unit Trust; St James's Place Ethical Unit Trust; St James's Place Fare East Unit Trust.

UK employees: 1,362

Total employees: 1,362

Focus of giving: Health, ill health, marginalised people, poverty and social exclusion, sport, recreation, children, young people, disability, disasters.

Membership: BITC

Accredited Living Wage Employer	✓
Community involvement	✓
Community contributions	✓
CSR or charity committee	✓
Cash donations declared	✓
Charity partner(s)	✓
Corporate charity	✓
Employee-led support	✓
FTSE 100	✓
Gifts in kind	✓
Humanitarian aid: overseas	✓
Matched funding	✓
Payroll giving	✓
Pro bono	✓
Sponsorship	✓

Charitable donations

Cash UK (latest available):	2015	£3,949,000
Total UK (cash and in kind):	2015	£3,949,000
Cash worldwide:	2015	£3,949,000
Total worldwide (cash and in kind):	2015	£3,949,000

Community involvement

St James's Place Foundation

The group's corporate charity, the St James's Place Foundation (Charity Commission no. 1144606) makes grants to registered charities under the following three themes: 'cherishing children'; 'combating cancer'; 'supporting hospices'. The foundation makes many small, one-off grants, as well as a few larger, multi-year grants for specific purposes or salaries. The website states that 80% of the funds go towards supporting charities in the UK, and 20% to charities abroad. Further information about the foundation, what is supported and how to apply can be found on its website (www.sjpfoundation.co.uk). In 2015 £7 million was raised for the foundation, including fundraising by employees, partners, supplier and others, and matched funding from the group.

Grants

As well as giving through the St James's Place Foundation, local offices also support local charitable causes through grants. For example, the annual report describes how in Cirencester, the group has supported The Churn Project, through a grant for core costs as well as employee volunteering. The project works to improve the well-being of people in the local community.

Education and employment for young people

The group works with Cirencester college to provide internships, as well as four academy programmes, in partnership with the charity Career Ready, to provide experience, skills and mentoring for students in particular areas of career development. A number of students have subsequently joined the group's apprenticeship scheme.

The group also works in partnership with the charities Young Gloucestershire and Active Communities Network on projects to develop the skills and employability of disadvantaged young people. A number of employees volunteer to support these initiatives.

During 2015 the group also developed financial education classes for schools, with employees supporting the delivery of the classes. Financial education sessions were also delivered for vulnerable young people with the charities OPENhouse and Young Gloucestershire.

The annual report states that financial education activities will be a priority in

2016, with the aim of expanding provision across the UK.

Directors with other relevant posts

Five of the group's directors, Sarah Bates, David Bellamy, Andrew Croft, David Lamb and Ian Gascoigne, are trustees of the St James's Place Foundation. Baroness Wheatcroft, is a trustee and Deputy Chair of the British Museum (Charity Commission no. 1086080).

Main locations

The group has offices in: Aberdeen; Belfast; Bristol; Cirencester; Edinburgh; Essex; Glasgow; Leeds; Liverpool; London; Manchester; Newbury; Newcastle; Nottingham; Solent; Solihull; Westerham.

Community contributions

During 2015, the group provided matched funding for the £3.5 million raised by partners, suppliers and other for the St James's Place Foundation, bring the total to around £7 million.

Local offices of the group made 258 grants totalling £449,000 during 2014/15.

Beneficiaries of local office grants included: Support Dogs (£2,500); Charlie's Beach Hut Fund (£2,000).

In 2015 a total of £7 million was raised for the foundation, including fundraising by employees, partners, suppliers and others, and matched funding from the group. The foundation supported 600 projects during the year.

Beneficiaries of the St James's Place Foundation included: Smile Support and Care (£1.2 million); Panathlon Challenge (£255,000); Philippine Community Fund (£93,600); Roald Dahl's Marvellous Children's Charity (£84,500); The Art Room (£77,000); EdUKaid (£37,000).

In-kind support

The 2015 annual report states that during the year, the group has been working with Involve Gloucestershire to look for opportunities for employees to provide support to local charities through their professional expertise.

Employee-led support

Volunteering

In 2015 the group supported 86 employees with grants of up to £1,000 to volunteer, amounting to 13,500 hours of volunteering. The annual report states that the group is hoping to roll out this initiatives to all its offices in the UK in 2016.

During the year, the group also began 'community support team challenges', where a group of employees work on charity or community activities together, for causes such as local charities or conservation projects.

Employee fundraising

Over 85% of employees and partners give to the St James's Place Foundation on a monthly basis, and many contribute to other fundraising events and activities through the year. Examples in 2015, including matched funding from the company, were a skydive raising £10,000 for Teenage Cancer Trust, and a triathlon and duathlon raising almost £93,000 for Hope and Homes for Children. Partners and employees also raised £25,000 for Save the Children's work with refugees, and £40,000 for charities in Nepal following the earthquake in 2015.

Commercially led support

Sponsorship

The group sponsors the Loughborough University Swimming Programme, running until at least the 2016 Rio Olympics. Support includes various support to swimmers, scholarships, specialist sessions, subsidised accommodation and so on.

Corporate charity

St James's Place Foundation (Charity Commission no. 1144606).

Exclusions

For exclusions from any of the St James's Place Foundation's priority areas, refer to the website.

Applications

St James's Place Foundation: applicants who believe that they fit the criteria are welcome to apply at any time via the foundation's website. The application procedure for all of the programmes can take between four and six months.

Further details can be found on the website or by calling the foundation on 01285 878037 or emailing sjp.foundation@sjp.co.uk.

Enquiries about general giving by the group should be directed to the correspondent.

St Modwen Properties PLC

Property

Correspondent: Steve Burke, Group Construction Director – CSR Steering Group, Park Point, 17 High Street, Longbridge, Birmingham B31 2UQ (tel: 0121 222 9400; fax: 0121 222 9401; email: info@stmodwen.co.uk; website: www.stmodwen.co.uk)

Directors: Bill Oliver, Chief Executive; Bill Shannon, Chair; Ian Bull; Kay Chaldecott; Lesley James; Richard Mully; Rob Hudson, Group Finance Director; Simon Clarke; Steve Burke (women: 2; men: 7)

Year end	30/11/2015
Turnover	£287,500,000
Pre-tax profit	£235,200,000

Nature of business: Residential and commercial property development. The group specialises in urban regeneration and brownfield land renewal.

Company registration number: 349201

Subsidiary undertakings include: Boughton Holdings; Festival Waters Ltd; St Modwen Investments Ltd.

UK employees: 345

Total employees: 345

Focus of giving: Economic generation, education, enterprise/training, environment, health, ill health, inner cities, local groups, older people, arts, culture, poverty and social exclusion, safety and crime prevention, sport, recreation, children, young people, community/social welfare, disability.

Membership: BITC

Community involvement	✓
Community contributions	✓
CSR report	✓
CSR or charity committee	✓
Directors have other relevant posts	✓
Charity partner(s)	✓
Company gives to smaller charities	✓
Employee-led support	✓
Gifts in kind	✓
Pro bono	✓
Sponsorship	✓

Community involvement

Much of the group's CSR strategy focuses on supporting and working with charities and organisations in the communities in which it operates. Support is given through in-kind provision as well as funding, and often through working with local communities on collaborative projects.

Community engagement

The group works with the communities in which it has development sites, engaging with local charities, community groups and schools, to support the community and to improve the local environment. Examples from 2015/16 include:

- Working with the Longridge Public Art Project to produce events, exhibitions and activities with the local community
- Sponsoring a local children's football team
- Funding equipment for Myton Hospice
- Sponsoring a glow-in-the-dark skate park in Everton
- Creating an 'Edible Avenue' gardening project in South London
- Taking part in Business in the Community's Give and Gain Day in

Kirkby, including a recycling class, an art project and gardening

Education

The group visits a number of schools each year with an education programme about safety around construction sites and careers in the construction industry. The group also ran a national schools photography competition, in partnership with The Princes Foundation for Building Communities and the architecture firm Farrells, to celebrate the group's 30th anniversary.

Charitable giving

The group generally prefers to support charities local to its development sites, rather than focusing on national charities. Support is given through in-kind donations, such as volunteer time or equipment, as well as funding.

Environmental partnerships

The group works with local communities to improve the environment around its development sites, and this often involves partnerships with charitable organisations. For example, In Branston Lea Woods in Staffordshire, the group worked with The Woodland Trust, the National Forest Company and Staffordshire Wildlife Trust on a tree planting project, which also involved engagement with local schools, community groups and volunteers.

Directors with other relevant posts

Simon Clarke is a trustee of the charity Racing Welfare (Charity Commission no. 1084042) and Chair of Trustees of the charity Racing Homes (Charity Commission no. 1122961). Leslie James was previously a trustee and is now a Vice-President of the charity I CAN (Charity Commission no. 210031). Rob Hudson is a member of the Board of Governors for the English National School of Ballet. Bill Shannon is on the council of the University of Southampton.

Main locations

The group has operations across England and South Wales.

Community contributions

No figure for total contributions was provided in the 2014/15 annual report or the July 2016 CSR report (the latest available at the time of writing – October 2016).

Employee-led support

Employee fundraising and volunteering

Examples of employee fundraising and volunteering initiatives during the year include: a sponsored 'Colour Blast Run' in aid of Shakespeare's Hospice in Stratford-upon-Avon; collecting Easter eggs for Birmingham Children's Hospital and Acorns Children's Hospice; and delivering health and safety sessions in primary schools.

Applications

Apply in writing to the correspondent.

Stagecoach Group PLC

Transport and communications

Correspondent: Steven Stewart, Director of Communications, 10 Dunkeld Road, Perth, Perthshire PH1 5TW (tel: 01738 442111; fax: 01738 443076; email: charity@stagecoachgroup.com; website: www.stagecoachgroup.com)

Directors: Ann Gloag; Garry Watts; Gregor Alexander; James Bilefield; Karen Thomson; Martin Griffiths, Chief Executive; Ray O'Toole; Ross Paterson, Finance Director; Sir Brian Souter, Chair; Sir Ewan Brown; Will Whitehorn (women: 2; men: 9)

Year end	30/04/2016
Turnover	£387,100,000
Pre-tax profit	£104,400,000

Nature of business: Principal activity of the group is the provision of public transport services in the UK and North America.

Company registration number: SC100764

Subsidiary undertakings include: American Tour Connection Inc.; Glenvale Transport Ltd; Megabus.com (UK) Ltd

Total employees: 21,000

Focus of giving: Education, enterprise/ training, health, ill health, large national appeals, local groups, overseas projects, children, young people, community/ social welfare, disasters.

Community involvement	✓
Community contributions	✓
Directors have other relevant posts	✓
AF Covenant	✓
Charity of the Year	✓
Charity partner(s)	✓
Employee-led support	✓
Gifts in kind	✓
Humanitarian aid: overseas	✓
Pro bono	✓
Sponsorship	✓

Community involvement

The group supports a wide range of causes and events, particularly children and young people and education, but also health, road safety and various community initiatives. A big part of its CSR focus is on environment and sustainability. Assistance is also given to bus and rail industry charities and events. Support is given through the Stagecoach Group Community Fund.

Donations

Charities can apply for a donation from the Stagecoach Community Fund. Individual companies within the group also support charitable causes within their local area, through donations and employee fundraising events, as well as through education on transport safety for young people. For example, according to the Stagecoach website, the South West Trains-Network Rail Alliance has a Charitable Board which considers requests and donates around £20,000 in total each year. East Midlands trains supports selected charities through collections at train stations and awareness-raising activities and events.

Companies in the USA and Canada also support a number of charitable causes locally through fundraising and volunteering.

Charity of the Year and partnerships

Many of the local companies within the Stagecoach group support a Charity of the Year. For more information, refer to the websites of the individual companies.

For example, during 2015/16 the group's Megabus brand worked with the ArbeiterKind.de, a German charity that supports equal access to education. South West Trains supported Autism Wessex; Big World Impact; On Course Foundation; and Southbank Sinfonia.

Directors with other relevant posts

James Bilefield is also a trustee of Teach First (Charity Commission no. 1098294). Ann Gloag is a trustee of Mercy Ships (Charity Commission no. 1053055).

Main locations

The group has operations across the UK, Canada, Europe and the US.

Community contributions

According to the 2015/16 annual report, the group donated £900,000 to charities during the year. It was unclear how much of this consisted of in-kind or cash donations, or came from the company or from employee fundraising.

Beneficiaries included: Mary's Meals (£70,000).

In-kind support

The group provides in-kind support in a number of ways, including a national agreement with the charity Guide Dogs for the Blind, providing free travel to dog trainers, as well as providing free travel for on-duty police officers. The group offers vehicles for use in emergency services exercises. The group also offers internships and mentoring to support young people's education and career development.

Employee-led support

Stagecoach employees help good causes through taking part in a number of local or national fundraising events (such as

Children in Need or Comic Relief). The group also has a partnership with charity Transaid, through which Stagecoach drivers offer their road safety expertise in sub-Saharan Africa.

Applications

Applications for Stagecoach Group Community Fund can be downloaded from the group's website. Once completed, they should be emailed to: charity@stagecoachgroup.com.

Other enquiries should be directed to the correspondent.

Standard Chartered PLC

Financial services, banking

Correspondent: The Corporate Affairs Manager, 1 Basinghall Avenue, London EC2V 5DD (tel: 020 7885 8888; email: our.sustainability@sc.com; website: www.standardchartered.com/uk)

Directors: Ajay Kanwal; Andy Halford, Group Chief Financial Officer; Anna Marrs; Ben Hung; Bill Winters, Group Chief Executive; David Fein; Doris Honold; Dr Michael Gorriz; Karen Fawcett; Mark Dowie; Mark Smith; Mike Rees; Pam Walkden; Sir John Pearce; Sunil Kaushal; Tracy Clarke (women: 5; men: 10)

Year end	31/12/2015
Turnover	£15,300,000
Pre-tax profit	(£1,523,000,000)

Nature of business: The group's principal activity is the provision of banking and other financial services.

Company registration number: 966425

Subsidiary undertakings include: Marina Ilex Shipping Ltd; Standard Chartered Bank Botswana Ltd; Standard Chartered Holdings Ltd.

Total employees: 84,000

Focus of giving: Health, disability.

Membership: LBG

Community involvement	✓
Community contributions	✓
CSR report	✓
CSR or charity committee	✓
Cash donations declared	✓
Charity partner(s)	✓
Employee-led support	✓
FTSE 100	✓
Gifts in kind	✓
Humanitarian aid: overseas	✓
Overseas giving	✓
Pro bono	✓

Charitable donations

Cash worldwide:	2015	£18,600,000
Total worldwide (cash and in kind):	2015	£38,000,000

Community involvement

According to the website, the group's charitable activities are organised into a number of community programmes.

Seeing is Believing

Seeing is Believing is a partnership set up between Standard Chartered and the International Agency for the Prevention of Blindness in 2003. The group has committed to raising $100 million for the charity Seeing is Believing between 2003 and 2020. By the end of 2015, the group had raised $86.3 million, including matched funding from the bank. The initiative aims to prevent and treat avoidable blindness and provide eye care in countries in Asia, Africa and the Middle East where there is a lack of quality, affordable eye care. Since it started in 2003, there have been 98 projects in 28 countries. More information is given at www.seeingisbelieving.org.

Goal

Goal is an education programme set up by Standard Chartered aimed at girls aged 12 to 18 in disadvantaged urban communities across the world, often those who are educationally disadvantaged and living on a low income. The programme's curriculum was developed in partnership with the Population Council and focuses on four key areas: communication; health and hygiene; rights; and financial literacy. The programme is delivered by organisations locally across the world, and in 2015 reached 25 countries.

Positive Living

This project aims to educate and raise awareness about HIV, through workshops and training for employees, as well as a partnership with MTV Staying Alive Foundation to support project helping people affected by HIV and AIDS.

Emergency response

The group supports emergency relief following disasters and in 2015 provided $750,000, focusing on the earthquake in Nepal.

Financial education

The group provides financial education programmes in low- and middle-income countries, which are delivered voluntarily by Standard Chartered employees. This includes a course for young people, which reached 103,000 young people in 24 countries in 2015, and a course for entrepreneurs, particularly small and micro businesses, which, according to the website, 'reached 1,200 entrepreneurs in 11 markets, 71 per cent of whom were women'.

Main locations

The group operates globally in 67 countries. In the UK, the group is based in London.

Community contributions

The 2015 annual report states that total community investment by the group amounted to $50.1 million (around £38 million), of which cash contributions totalled $24.5 million (around £18.6 million), employee time totalled $20 million (around £15.2 million), gifts in-kind totalled $100,000 (around £76,000) and management costs totalled $5.5 million (around £4.2 million).

With staff and other contributions added, the group reported that it reached $60.3 million in total. It was not specified how much of this was given in the UK or any other country.

$86.3 million was raised for the company's Seeing is Believing initiative and $750,000 was contributed to emergency relief appeals, focusing on the earthquake in Nepal.

Note: Currency conversions taken at the time of writing (August 2016).

Employee-led support

Volunteering

All employees are offered three days of paid volunteering each year and in 2015, 57% of employees volunteered for a totalled more than 77,900 days. The group also encouraged employees to volunteer to support the United Nations' Sustainable Development Goals.

Applications

Apply in writing to the Corporate Affairs Manager of the country where the project is taking place.

Standard Life

Insurance, banking

Correspondent: Sustainability Team, Standard Life House, 30 Lothian Road, Edinburgh EH1 2DH (tel: 0131 225 2552; email: sustainability@standardardlife.com; website: www.standardlife.com)

Directors: Colin Clark; Crawford Gillies; Isabel Hudson; Keith Skeoch, Chief Executive; Kevin Parry; Luke Savage, Chief Financial Officer; Lynne Peacock; Martin Pike; Melanie Gee; Noel Harwerth; Paul Matthews; Pierre Danon; Sir Gerry Grimston, Chair (women: 4; men: 9)

Year end	31/12/2015
Turnover	£8,892,000,000
Pre-tax profit	£549,000,000

Nature of business: Life assurance, pensions, health insurance, investment management and banking.

Company registration number: SC286832

Subsidiary undertakings include: Gallions Reach Shopping Park Ltd Partnership; Standard Life Investments Ethical Corporate Bond Fund; Threesixty Services LLP.

Total employees: 6,129

Focus of giving: Education, enterprise/ training, environment, equal opportunities, fundraising events, health, ill health, heritage, housing, homelessness, local groups, financial education, older people, poverty and social exclusion, children, young people, disasters.

Membership: LBG

Accredited Living Wage Employer	✓
Community involvement	✓
Community contributions	✓
Company reports on anti-slavery	✓
CSR report	✓
Directors have other relevant posts	✓
AF Covenant	✓
Charity partner(s)	✓
Corporate charity	✓
Employee-led support	✓
FTSE 100	✓
Gifts in kind	✓
Humanitarian aid: overseas	✓
Matched funding	✓
Payroll giving	✓
Pro bono	✓
Sponsorship	✓

Community involvement

Standard Life Charitable Trust

The group established this trust (OSCR no. SC040877) from the sale of shares in the Unclaimed Assets Trust, set up in 2006 to hold unclaimed shares at the demutualisation of the group. The 2015 sustainability report states that the trust funds 'charitable programmes that enable people to make lasting improvements in their lives', with particular focus on employment and financial capability. In 2015 the trust provided £720,000 grants. Between 2013 and 2016, the trust provided grants amounting to £4.2 million.

Beneficiaries were: The Prince's Trust (£400,000); Tomorrow's People (£205,000); The Royal British Legion (£53,600).

Standard Life Foundation

The Standard Life Charitable Trust came to an end in July 2016; the group's 2013–16 Community Impact report states that in 2016, the money raised from the sale of the unclaimed shares will be used to establish the Standard Life Foundation (OSCR no. SC040877), which will fund further charitable and community activities. Refer to the website for the latest information.

Charity partners – Standard Life Charity Fund

Employees vote on the charity partners that the group supports. In 2015 the group asked employees to choose from charities supporting employability; the charities chosen in the UK were Scope and Capability Scotland. These charities received donations from the payroll giving scheme and the monthly SLOTTO game, as well as from a Christmas raffle, which amounted to £330,500 in total. Funds are distributed by the Standard Life Charity Fund (OSCR no. SC030702) and in 2015, grants amounted to £266,000.

Beneficiaries were: Scope (£240,500); CARE International (£9,000); Cancer Research UK and Marie Curie Hospice Edinburgh (£8,200 each).

In 2016 the chosen partner in the UK is Place2Be.

Employment and young people

The group works with the Edinburgh Guarantee Scheme to provide six-month work experience opportunities to young people, paid at the Living Wage rate. 12-month employment opportunities are also offered through the Investment 2020 Trainee Programme, and through the group's apprenticeship scheme.

Standard Life works in partnership with the charity Career Ready, offering mentoring and placements for young people in their last two years of school. The group also sponsors the BIMA Digital Day, taking part in events in schools across the UK to promote careers in the digital sector.

Financial education

Standard Life sponsors Good Money Week, which is a UK-wide campaign to raise awareness of responsible, ethical finances and encourage people to make ethical choices with finance.

Inspiration awards

The group holds an annual awards ceremony to recognise the contributions of employees to their local communities in five categories: fundraising; community champion; diversity and inclusion; personal inspiration; and inspiration in business.

Living Wage

As well as being an accredited Living Wage Employer, Standard Life, through the charitable trust, is also the first private sector company to become a Living Wage Friendly Funder, which means that any posts in charities funded by a grant from the company will be paid the UK Living Wage.

Directors with other relevant posts

Kevin Parry is deputy Chair of the Royal National Children's Foundation (Charity Commission no. 1167491). Luke Savage is a member of the governing body of Queen Mary University of London.

Main locations

In the UK, the group is based in Edinburgh. There are also offices in Austria; China; Germany; Hong Kong; India; and Ireland.

Community contributions

The website states that the group's total charitable contribution in 2015 was over £1.9 million. This includes volunteering time, matched funding, the Standard Life Charitable Trust, Standard Life Charity Fund, in-kind donations of equipment and services and employability scheme funding.

Grants made from the Standard Life Charitable Trust/Foundation totalled £720,000 and grants from the Standard Life Charity Fund totalled £266,000.

In-kind support

The group offers in-kind support such as printing, surplus furniture and IT equipment to charities.

Secondments

Every year the group provides secondment opportunities that employees can apply for, offering their skills to local community or charitable organisations. In 2015 organisations included The Prince's Trust, Edinburgh World Heritage, The Yard, The Big Issue and Capability Scotland.

Employee-led support

Employee volunteering

Employees are entitled to three days of paid volunteering leave per year, and in 2015, the group's employees volunteered for 661 days. The group's website states that employees can engage in a wide range of activities – whether short-term opportunities, long-term commitments, team challenges, or providing targeted support and expertise to help solve a particular problem. The website also states that members of the leadership from Standard Life are often willing to offer management or trustee support to charities.

Matched funding

The group provides matched funding through its Raise and Match scheme, offering between £100 and £250 per year for each employee. The group also matched employee donations to Unicef's Syria appeal in 2015, raising £20,000, and also matched the fundraising efforts of Andy Murray, the tennis player sponsored by the group, raising £27,000 for Unicef.

Payroll giving

Through the group's Give As You Earn scheme, over £145,000 was donated to the group's charity partners in 2015.

Corporate charity

Standard Life Foundation (OSCR no. SC040877).

Exclusions

The group will not support the following: religious causes (except when not promoting a religion or making religious distinctions, but carrying out charitable work with vulnerable groups or individuals); political causes; charities that make distinctions with respect to race, gender or sexual orientation; animal charities; buildings, heritage and culture; professional sports; non-charitable arts; universities, colleges and fee-paying schools.

Applications

Charities should contact sustainability@standardlife.com to enquire about support.

For up-to-date information on the Standard Life Foundation, refer to the website.

Stobart Group

Logistics, professional support services

Correspondent: CSR Committee, Solway Business Centre, Kingstown, Carlisle, Cumbria CA6 4BY (email: charity@stobartgroup.com; website: www.stobartgroup.co.uk)

Directors: Andrew Tinkler, Chief Executive Officer; Andrew Wood; Ben Whawell, Chief Financial Officer; Iain Ferguson, Chair; John Coombs; John Garbutt; Richard Butcher (women: 0; men: 7)

Year end	28/02/2016
Turnover	£116,600,000
Pre-tax profit	£9,300,000

Nature of business: Stobart Group is an infrastructure development and support services business 'operating in the biomass energy, railway maintenance and aviation sectors as well as having investments in a national property and logistics portfolio'.

There are four main areas: Stobart Energy; Stobart Rail; Stobart Aviation; and Stobart Investments.

The group is a Guernsey-registered company but its head office is located in Carlisle.

UK employees: 964

Focus of giving: Education, health, ill health, humanitarian help, children, young people, community/social welfare, disasters.

Community involvement	✓
Community contributions	✓
CSR report	✓
CSR or charity committee	✓
Directors have other relevant posts	✓
Charity partner(s)	✓
Employee-led support	✓
Gifts in kind	✓
Humanitarian aid: UK including food banks	✓
Payroll giving	✓
Sponsorship	✓

Community involvement

The group's CSR policy states that businesses within the group and employees are encouraged to support local initiatives in their communities. The group also makes donations annually to a chosen charity. At the time of writing (December 2016), the group's website stated that its charitable donations policy was under review and that updates would be posted on the website.

Education

The group works in partnership with educational institutions to support career opportunities for young people. Stobart Rail works with Brathay Trust, supporting the charity's World of Work challenge day, providing students with experience and careers advice opportunities. London Southend worked with Essex College in 2015, providing a work experience programme for 25 students, six of whom were later employed at the airport.

Santa Flights

London Southend Airport, along with other partners, runs an annual Santa Flight event, which in 2015 raised £6,000 for three charities, and provided 169 children and families with a Christmas experience.

Directors with other relevant posts

John Garbutt is a trustee of a number of charities, including Asthma UK (Charity Commission no. 802364), The International Students Trust (Charity Commission no. 294448) and Corporation of London Benevolent Association (Charity Commission no. 206643).

UK locations

The group is based in Warrington.

Community contributions

No figure was given for the group's annual charitable contributions.

In-kind support

In 2015 the group supported relief efforts in Cumbria following Storm Desmond, setting up a Survival Reception Centre to provide clothing, food and shelter for people who were affected, donating diesel for volunteers operating machines to dredge the flooding and deploying staff to assist with clean-up efforts.

Employee-led support

Employee fundraising and volunteering

There is a group-wide employee donation scheme through which employees can make a £50 donation per annum to a charitable cause of their choice.

In 2015 employees in London Southend Airport raised £500 for a youth organisation in Carlisle following flooding, and employees of Stobart Rail raised a further £300 for the relief efforts.

The group also has a 'Get Involved' scheme, which has been running since 2014 and encourages employees to engage with local communities and charitable activities.

Commercially led support

Sponsorship

The group has a long-standing relationship with The Professional Jockeys Association and provides sponsorship for the association's career-ending insurance scheme for jockeys, as well as sponsoring The Lesters awards run by the association.

The group also provides sponsorship to maintain a horse at Carlisle Riding for the Disabled Association.

Applications

Charitable donations and sponsorship

At the time of writing (December 2016), the group's website stated that its policy for charitable donations and sponsorship was under review and that updates would be posted on the website. Enquiries should be directed to charity@stobartgroup.com.

Other CSR enquiries

Queries relating to CSR issues such as the environment or employee engagement should be directed to csr@stobartgroup.com, after reading the group's CSR policy, which is available to download online: www.stobartgroup.co.uk/stobart-group/responsibility.

STV Group PLC

Media

Correspondent: Jane E. A. Tames, Secretary, Pacific Quay, Glasgow G51 1PQ (tel: 0141 300 3000; email: jane.tames@stv.tv; website: www.stvplc.tv)

Directors: Anne Marie Cannon; Baroness Ford of Cunninghame, Chair; Christian Woolfenden; David Shearer; George Wyatt, Chief Financial Officer; Ian Steele; Michael Jackson; Rob Woodward, Chief Executive (women: 2; men: 6)

Year end	31/12/2015
Turnover	£116,500,000
Pre-tax profit	£9,800,000

Nature of business: STV Group PLC is a Scottish media company.

Company registration number: SC042391

Subsidiary undertakings include: Ginger Television Productions Ltd; STV Central Ltd; STV North Ltd; and STV Productions Ltd.

UK employees: 496

Total employees: 496

Focus of giving: Education, enterprise/training, poverty and social exclusion, children, young people, community/social welfare.

Community involvement	✓
Community contributions	✓
Directors have other relevant posts	✓
Charity partner(s)	✓
Employee-led support	✓
Matched funding	✓

Community involvement

STV Appeal Charity (OSCR no. SC042429)

The group's major initiative is the STV Appeal, mainly funded by individual donations from STV viewers and fundraising from corporate partners. In 2015 the charity raised £2.9 million with all overheads being met by STV and the Hunter Foundation. Some of the executive directors are trustees of the charity. For more details see 'In-kind support' section in this entry.

Charity partnership

The STV Appeal has been a charity partner of the freshnlo Pedal for Scotland (Glasgow to Edinburgh) cycle ride since 2013.

Education

Over 380 work experience opportunities were provided in 2015 through partnerships with City TV, Glasgow Caledonian University and Edinburgh Napier University.

Directors with other relevant posts

David Shearer is a non-executive director of The Glasgow School of Art.

Baroness Ford of Cunninghame is Chair of the STV Children's Appeal.

Rob Woodward and George Wyatt are both trustees of the STV Children's Appeal.

Main locations

STV is based in Glasgow but support is given throughout Scotland.

Community contributions

During 2015 the STV Appeal raised a total of £2.9 million. While running the initiative will involve substantial expenses for the group, the £2.9 million was collected through viewers' or staff contributions and donations from corporate partners, rather than from STV itself. Unfortunately, we were unable to determine the cash contributions or community support costs spent by the group.

In-kind support

STV Appeal 2015

The appeal was launched in 2011 in partnership with The Hunter Foundation and aims to address child poverty in Scotland. It is funded through individual donations from STV viewers and fundraising from corporate partners. The group's employees take part through fundraising and volunteering. In 2013 the charity raised £2.9 million with all overheads being met by STV and the foundation. The Scottish Government provided matched funding for the first £1 million raised, an arrangement which has been in place since the appeal started.

The money raised goes towards the provision of food and clothing, opportunities for training and employability, and practical, social and emotional support.

Employee-led support

The group's employees contribute their time and fundraising efforts to the STV Appeal and in 2015 raised £50,000 which was matched by the group.

Applications

STV Appeal Charity (OSCR no. SC042429)

Applications to the charity are not accepted. Instead, it works with charity experts to identify projects during the year.

SuperGroup PLC

Retail – clothing and footwear

Correspondent: Corporate Responsibility Team, Unit 60, The Runnings, Cheltenham, Gloucestershire GL51 9NW (tel: 01242 578376; email: investor.relations@supergroup.co.uk; website: www.supergroup.co.uk)

Directors: Beatrice Lafon; Euan Sutherland, Chief Executive Officer; Julian Dunkerton; Keith Edelman; Minnow Powell; Nick Wharton, Chief Financial Officer; Penny Hughes; Peter Bamford, Chair; Steve Sunnucks (women: 2; men: 7)

Year end	30/04/2016
Turnover	£597,500,000
Pre-tax profit	£55,400,000

Nature of business: SuperGroup is a British international clothing business, with sales in 51 countries.

Company registration number: 7063562

Subsidiary undertakings include: Superdry Retail LLC; C-Retail Ltd; SuperGroup Internet Ltd.

Total employees: 4,500

Focus of giving: Education, enterprise/training, poverty and social exclusion, children, young people, community/social welfare.

Community involvement	✓
Community contributions	✓
Company reports on anti-slavery	✓
CSR report	✓
Charity partner(s)	✓
Employee-led support	✓
Gifts in kind	✓
Matched funding	✓
Pro bono	✓
Sponsorship	✓

Charitable donations

Total worldwide (cash and in kind):	2016	£200,000

Community involvement

The group's charity and community support programme, Superdry360, supports charitable projects in the local, national and international communities in which the group operates.

Education and training

The group's Superdry School Days provide local schools with opportunities for work experience, shadowing and career discussions with employees. The group provides work experience opportunities to at least two students per month.

The group also has a partnership with the University of Gloucestershire, providing placements, materials, projects and support to undergraduates on Fashion, Graphic Design and Photography courses.

The group also sponsors and provides work placements for The Prince's Trust Get into Retail scheme, giving work experience and training to young people on the programme.

Other partnerships

In 2015/16 the group worked as a partner in Project Everyone, which aims to support and raise awareness about the UN Global Goals for Sustainable Development.

Other sponsorships

For a second year, the group continued its sponsorship of the Rush Skate Park in Gloucestershire.

Main locations

The group's head office is based in Cheltenham, but it has retail operations across the UK and worldwide.

Community contributions

In 2015/16 Superdry360, the group's charitable programme supporting local, national and international charities, raised or donated around £200,000. It was not clear how much of this was in the UK, or whether it included in-kind support.

Employee-led support

Matched funding

The group provides matched funding for employee fundraising initiatives internationally. In 2015/16 this totalled £4,100.

Applications

Apply in writing to the correspondent.

SVG Capital PLC

Financial services

Correspondent: Stuart Ballard, Company Secretary, Kean House, 6 Kean Street, London WC2B 4AS (tel: 020 3457 0000; fax: 020 3457 0009; email: investorrelations@svgcapital.com; website: www.svgcapital.com)

Directors: Andrew Sykes, Chair; David Robins; Helen Mahy; Lynn Fordham, Chief Executive; Simon Bax; Stephen Duckett (women: 2; men: 4)

Year end	31/01/2016
Turnover	£33,490,000
Pre-tax profit	£91,861,000

Nature of business: Private equity investment.

Company registration number: 3066856

Subsidiary undertakings include: SVGC Managers Ltd; SVGC Equity Partners LLP.

UK employees: 20

Total employees: 20

Focus of giving: General charitable purposes, enterprise/training, children, young people, community/social welfare.

Community involvement	✓
Community contributions	✓
Cash donations declared	✓
Employee-led support	✓
Gifts in kind	✓
Matched funding	✓

Charitable donations

Cash UK (latest available):	2016	£105,000
Total UK (cash and in kind):	2016	£105,000
Cash worldwide:	2016	£105,000
Total worldwide (cash and in kind):	2016	£105,000

Community involvement

The website states that the group makes donations to charities, as well as giving employees time out of work to volunteer and providing matched funding for employee charitable fundraising efforts.

Main locations

The group is based in London.

Community contributions

In 2015/16 the group donated £105,000 in total to two charities.

Beneficiaries were: School for Social Entrepreneurs and Outward Bound Trust.

Employee-led support

The group gives employees time off for volunteering and provides matched funding.

Applications

Apply in writing to the correspondent.

John Swire & Sons Ltd

Marine, aviation, property

Correspondent: The Administrator, The Swire Charitable Trust, Swire House, 59 Buckingham Gate, London SW1E 6AJ (tel: 020 7834 7717; email: Sarah.Irving@jssldn.co.uk; website: www.swire.com/en/sustainability)

Directors: Barnaby Swire; Gordon McCallum; James Edward Hughes-Hallet; James Wyndham Hughes-Hallet; John Swire; Lydia Dunn; Merlin Swire; Nicholas Fenwick; Samuel Swire; William Wemyss (women: 1; men: 9)

Year end	31/12/2015
Turnover	£6,936,000,000
Pre-tax profit	£579,000,000

Nature of business: Principal activities: marine including ship-owning and operating, aviation (via Cathay Pacific Airways), cold storage and road transport, industrial and trading activities, plantations and property. The company owns a stake in the tea trader, James Finlay.

Company registration number: 133143

Focus of giving: General charitable purposes, education, health, ill health, medical research.

Community involvement	✓
Community contributions	✓
Corporate charity	✓

Charitable donations

Cash UK (latest available):	2015	£1,950,000
Total UK (cash and in kind):	2015	£1,950,000
Cash worldwide:	2015	£1,950,000
Total worldwide (cash and in kind):	2015	£1,950,000

Community involvement

John Swire & Sons Ltd appears to direct its charitable contributions through several charities connected to the company. These include: **John Swire (1989) Charitable Trust** (Charity Commission no. 802142), the **Swire Educational Trust** (Charity Commission no. 328366) and the **Swire Charitable Trust** (Charity Commission no. 270726).

Main locations

The trusts give throughout the UK.

Community contributions

Although there are several trusts with connections to the company – John Swire (1989) Charitable Trust (whose income was wholly derived from investments), the Swire Educational Trust and the Swire Charitable Trust – it is the latter that receives almost all of its income from the company and it is to this that we refer.

In 2014/15 The Swire Charitable Trust received a donation of £1.95 million from John Swire & Sons Ltd.

Corporate charity

The John Swire (1989) Charitable Trust (Charity Commission no. 802142), The Swire Charitable Trust (Charity Commission no. 270726).

Applications

Apply in writing to the correspondent.

TalkTalk Group

Telecommunications

Correspondent: CSR Team, 11 Evesham Street, London W11 4AR (tel: 020 3417 1000; email: info@talktalkgroup.com; website: www.talktalkgroup.com)

Directors: Baroness Dido Harding, Chief Executive; Brent Hoberman; Charles Bligh; Iain Torrens, Chief Finance Officer; Ian West; James Powell; John Allwood; John Gildersleeve; Sir Charles Dunstone, Chair; Sir Howard Stringer; Tristia Harrison (women: 2; men: 9)

Year end	31/03/2015
Turnover	£1,795,000,000
Pre-tax profit	£32,000,000

Nature of business: Telecommunications.

Company registration number: 7105891

Subsidiary undertakings include: TalkTalk Group Ltd; TalkTalk Communications Ltd; CPW Network Services Ltd.

UK employees: 2,099

Total employees: 2,099

Focus of giving: Education, enterprise/training, poverty and social exclusion, safety and crime prevention, children, young people, community/social welfare.

Community involvement	✓
Community contributions	✓
AF Covenant	✓
Cash donations declared	✓
Charity partner(s)	✓
Employee-led support	✓
Gifts in kind	✓
Market-led giving	✓
Matched funding	✓
Pro bono	✓
Shared-value alliances	✓

Sponsorship ✓
STEM-focused ✓

Charitable donations

Cash UK (latest available):	2015	£365,000
Total UK (cash and in kind):	2015	£365,000
Cash worldwide:	2015	£365,000
Total worldwide (cash and in kind):	2015	£365,000

Community involvement

Digital inclusion

The website states that the group focuses its CSR on three areas: digital skills; digital safety; and cyber security.

The group works with Tinder Foundation (Charity Commission no. 1165209), which supports those who are digitally and social excluded to benefit from digital technology, improving their digital skills and quality of life. The company offers employee support and reduced broadband rates for learners at the foundation's online centres.

During the year, the group has supported a pathfinder scheme in the North West, a charity which the company helped to set up.

Internet Matters

TalkTalk is a partner, along with BT, Sky, Virgin Media, BBC and Google, in Internet Matters, a not-for-profit company aiming to improve the digital safety of children. Internet Matters offers online advice, articles and resources for parents and schools.

TalkTalk Digital Heroes Awards and Foundation

The group holds an annual awards ceremony, the TalkTalk Digital Heroes Awards, which recognises individuals who use digital technology in a way that has a social impact – in areas such as education, healthy living, volunteering and fundraising.

To take this initiative further, the group founded the TalkTalk Digital Heroes Foundation, established under Charities Aid Foundation (Charity Commission no. 268369), aiming to improve digital skills and inclusion.

In 2014/15 the foundation supported Apps for Good (Charity Commission no. 113656), which supports young people to create apps to solve problems that matter to them. As part of its commitment, TalkTalk provides funds to four schools near its head office in London to run the Apps for Good course, supported by employee volunteers.

The foundation also supported Code Club during the year, which supports volunteer-run coding classes in primary schools.

Partnerships

During the year, the group continued to support Ambitious about Autism, with which it has had a long-term partnership. £360,000 was raised for the charity at the TalkTalk Digital Heroes Auction event, with employee fundraising in addition. The group has raised £10 million for the charity over ten years.

Directors with other relevant posts

Baroness Dido Harding, Chief Executive, is a trustee of the charity Go ON UK (Charity Commission no. 1146972). Charles Bligh is a trustee of the National Children's Orchestra of Great Britain (Charity Commission no. 803026). Tristia Harrison is also a trustee of both Comic Relief (Charity Commission no. 326568) and Ambitious about Autism (Charity Commission no. 1063184) Sir Charles Dunstone, the group's Chair, was until 2015 Chair of Trustees of The Prince's Trust (Charity Commission no. 1079675).

Main locations

The group operates across the UK.

Community contributions

In 2014/15 both the group and its employees raised £725,000 in total for registered charities; £365,000 of this was direct cash donations from the group.

Employee-led support

Employee fundraising and volunteering

The group has a scheme called Give Something Back, which allows employees paid time out of work to volunteer and fundraise for charitable causes.

Many TalkTalk employees are trained as Digital Champions, volunteering at the Tinder Foundation's online centres near to TalkTalk offices, helping learners to improve their digital skills. Employees also volunteer with the charity Apps for Good and Code Club.

Charities supported by employee fundraising included Cancer Research UK and Children in Need.

Commercially led support

In 2014/15 the company ran three market-led giving initiatives. For every call made to the group's UK directory enquiries number, a donation was made to Ambitious about Autism. The group also encouraged customers to return old routers, which were recycled and a donation of £1 was given to charity for each one. For every customer that added a Global Minutes Boost to their phone plan, the group donated to the charity Cool Earth, which protects rainforests by engaging with indigenous communities.

Applications

Apply in writing to the correspondent.

Direct queries about the work of the TalkTalk Digital Heroes Foundation to TalkTalkDigitalHeroesAwards@ talktalkplc.com.

Tata Steel Europe Ltd

Manufacturing, metals

Correspondent: Nia Singleton, 30 Millbank, London SW1P 4WY (tel: 020 7717 4444; email: nia.singleton@ tatasteel.com; website: www. tatasteeleurope.com)

Directors: Andrew Robb, Chief Executive Officer; Bimlendra Jha; Dr Hans Fischer; Ishaat Hussain; Jacques Schraven; Koushik Chatterjee; N. K. Misra; T. V. Narendran (women: 0; men: 8)

Year end	31/03/2016
Turnover	£8,762,000,000
Pre-tax profit	(£1,005,000,000)

Nature of business: Tata Steel is involved in the manufacture and sale of steel products.

The company is a wholly owned subsidiary of Tata Steel Global Holdings Pte Ltd, an unlisted company based in Singapore. The ultimate parent company is Tata Steel Ltd, incorporated in India.

Company registration number: 5957565

Subsidiary undertakings include: Corus Group Ltd; Tata Steel UK Ltd; and Bore Steel Ltd.

Focus of giving: Education, environment, health, ill health, sport, recreation, children, young people.

Community involvement ✓
Community contributions ✓
Company reports on anti-slavery ✓
CSR report ✓
CSR or charity committee ✓
Employee-led support ✓
Sponsorship ✓

Community involvement

Community partnership programme

The main focus of the programme is 'Future Generations' which is supported through the themes of education; environment; and health and well-being. Donations are made to charitable organisations in the communities in which Tata Steel operates.

Education

Tata Steel proactively supports learning and education with programmes in the UK and Netherlands, particularly in the areas of science and technology. For example, in Wales the company runs interactive sessions with primary and secondary schools and offers advice on careers and skills development. More than 2,600 schoolchildren benefit from Tata Steel's education and learning initiatives annually. An additional 1,600 youngsters attend the Crucial Crew learning day supported by Tata Steel.

UK Steel Enterprise
UK Steel Enterprise is a subsidiary of Tata Steel. It aims to 'help the economic regeneration of communities affected by changes in the steel industry' by supporting small and medium-sized businesses with finance and business premises.

Main locations
Tata Steel has locations throughout the UK, details of which can be found on the Tata Steel Europe's website.

Community contributions

The annual report and accounts for 2015/16 did not declare a figure for charitable donations.

Employee-led support

The company's employees volunteer their time and expert skills. Our research suggests that individual fundraising activities are also encouraged.

Commercially led support

Tata Steel sponsors the Kids of Steel triathlon series which it launched in partnership with the British Triathlon Federation in 2007. The aim of the series is to encourage kids to adopt a healthier lifestyle.

Exclusions

The website notes that: 'Tata Steel is not able to offer support to commercial or profit-making organisations. The company is not able to offer donations to individuals, or to cover participation fees, expeditions or trips performed by individuals in the context of fundraising.'

Applications

Applications can be made through the company's website: www.tatasteeleurope.com/en/sustainability/communities.

Applications are assessed by a panel of representatives from Tata Steel and the communities in which it operates.

Tate & Lyle PLC

Food manufacture, sugar refiners

Correspondent: Community Relations Manager, 1 Kingsway, London WC2B 6AT (tel: 020 7257 2100; website: www.tateandlyle.com)

Directors: Anne Minto; Douglas Hurt; Dr Ajai Puri; Javed Ahmed, Chief Executive; Lars Frederiksen; Liz Airey; Nick Hampton, Chief Financial Officer; Paul Forman; Sir Peter Gershon, Chair; Sybella Stanley; William Camp (women: 3; men: 8)

Year end	31/03/2016
Turnover	£2,355,000,000
Pre-tax profit	£126,000,000

Nature of business: The group is a global provider of ingredients and solutions for the food, beverage and other industries. The company's UK sugar refinery is in London.

Company registration number: 76535

Subsidiary undertakings include: Tate & Lyle Export Holdings Ltd; Hahntech International Ltd; Tate & Lyle Japan KK.

Brands include: Tate & Lyle; Splenda; Avenacare.

Total employees: 4,326

Focus of giving: Education, environment, health, ill health, heritage, housing, homelessness, local groups, humanitarian help, arts, culture, poverty and social exclusion, children, young people, community/social welfare.

Community involvement	✓
Community contributions	✓
Company reports on anti-slavery	✓
CSR report	✓
CSR or charity committee	✓
Directors have other relevant posts	✓
Cash donations declared	✓
Charity partner(s)	✓
Company gives to smaller charities	✓
Employee-led support	✓
Gifts in kind	✓
Humanitarian aid: overseas	✓
Humanitarian aid: UK including food banks	✓
STEM-focused	✓

Charitable donations

Total worldwide (cash and in kind):	2016	£529,000

Community involvement

The group's community involvement strategy focuses on the following three areas: well-being; education (particularly STEM); and the environment.

Local initiatives
Businesses within the group support local community initiatives near to facilities and operating areas, and this local support is led by employees. Examples globally include support for food banks, children's centres, hospices, STEM initiatives, road safety events, and improvements to parks and conservation areas.

Partnerships
As well as supporting local projects, the group also works with partners globally. For example, for the last four years, in the UK the group has supported the homelessness charity Crisis. In Vietnam and America, bursaries and scholarships have been provided in partnership with universities. The group has also worked for the last four years in partnership with the charity Earthwatch.

Under its welfare objective, during 2015/16, the group in the UK supported the charity Crisis for the fourth year. Other examples of support include for a food bank network in America, hospices, healthcare and child community care.

Directors with other relevant posts
Sir Peter Gershon is also a trustee of The Sutton Trust (Charity Commission no. 1146244). Anne Minto is a trustee of the University of Aberdeen Development Trust (OSCR no. SC002938).

Main locations
The group has operations worldwide; its head office is based in London.

Community contributions

Total contributions during 2015/16 were £529,000. This was distributed in the following areas: education (36%); well-being (36%); environment (26%); other (2%).

Applications

There is a contact form on the group's website for Community Relations UK enquiries: www.tateandlyle.com/contactus.

Taylor Wimpey PLC

Building/construction

Correspondent: Charity Committee, Gate House, Turnpike Road, High Wycombe, Buckinghamshire HP12 3NR (tel: 01494 558323; fax: 01494 885663; email: tayweb.info@taylorwimpey.com; website: www.taylorwimpey.co.uk)

Directors: Baroness Ford of Cunninghame; Humphrey Singer; James Jordan; Kate Barker; Kevin Beeston, Chair; Mike Hussey; Pete Redfern, Chief Executive; Rob Rowley; Ryan Mangold, Group Finance Director (women: 2; men: 7)

Year end	31/12/2015
Turnover	£3,139,800,000
Pre-tax profit	£603,800,000

Nature of business: The group is a residential developer operating at a local level from 24 regional businesses across the UK with further operations undertaken in Spain.

Taylor Wimpey was formed through the merger of George Wimpey and Taylor Woodrow on 3 July 2007. Both businesses have a history dating 80 years or more with George Wimpey dating back to the 1880's and Taylor Woodrow to the 1920's.

Company registration number: 296805

Subsidiary undertakings include: Laing Homes Ltd; Admiral Homes Ltd; McLean Homes Ltd.

UK employees: 4,177

Total employees: 4,260

Focus of giving: Education, enterprise/training, housing, homelessness, small groups, local groups, armed forces, sport, recreation, children, young people, community/social welfare.

Community involvement	✓
Community contributions	✓
Company reports on anti-slavery	✓
CSR report	✓
CSR or charity committee	✓
Armed forces personnel	✓
Charity of the Year	✓
Charity partner(s)	✓
Company gives to smaller charities	✓
Employee-led support	✓
FTSE 100	✓
Gifts in kind	✓
Pro bono	✓
Shared-value alliances	✓
Sponsorship	✓

Community involvement

The group supports local, regional and smaller national charities, particularly those local to its development sites, as well as smaller community groups in local areas. It also works with a network of homelessness charities, and supports an annually selected national charity with employee fundraising.

Charitable giving

According to the 2015 sustainability report, during the year, the Charity Committee, which includes employee representatives from different areas across the group, developed a new Charity and Community Support Policy. This policy, along with the Donations Policy, states that the group will focus its charitable giving on the following three areas:

- Projects which promote aspiration and education in disadvantaged areas
- Intervening and improving homeless situations for seriously economically disadvantaged groups in the UK
- Local projects that have a direct link with our regional businesses and developments

The policy states that support will mainly focus on local or regional charities, or smaller national charities, and contributions will not be limited to financial support alone, but will involve encouraging employees to volunteer with selected causes, contributing to employees' development.

Support during 2015 included continued work with Centrepoint, a charity partner, and six regional homelessness charities across the UK. Regional divisions in the group also supported local initiatives through 'community chest' grants, as well as in-kind support.

Charity of the Year

According to the donations policy, the group also donates to an annually selected national charity which is chosen by employees, and is not restricted to the above criteria, and for which an employee fundraising challenge is set. This year, the chosen charity was the Youth Adventure Trust.

Community involvement

At sites where the group will be working over a long time period, it may set up Community Development Trusts, to support long-term activities, or may fund community development workers. It also provides sponsorship to community events, local clubs and other community initiatives. For example, the sustainability report describes the community development work at the group's Augusta Park development in Andover, where there are play areas, creative activities, newsletters and a new community centre.

Community engagement and planning

Much of the group's engagement with communities is focused on the planning and development of proposals for new housing. Each new development has a community engagement plan, involving consultation and communication with the local community to shape planning and find solutions to problems. Part of this engagement includes visiting local schools to present information about the dangers to children of construction sites and interactive activities around construction, design and the environment.

Employment and education

During 2015, the group took part in the Change 100 scheme, run by the charity Leonard Cheshire Disability, which provides placements and mentoring to university students and recent graduates who have disabilities. The group also worked with Career Transition Partnership and ForceSelect to provide opportunities for ex-armed forces personnel. There were also 98 apprentices hired during the year, and Taylor Whimpey also worked with educational organisations such as schools, colleges and higher education institutions to improve skills and promote careers in the construction industry, including a long-term partnership with Buckinghamshire University Technical College.

The group is also investing £185,000 over three years in the 'Be the Best You Can Be! London' scheme, which focuses on education and skills for disadvantaged children in London.

Directors with other relevant posts

Pete Redfern, Chief Executive, is also a trustee of the charity Crisis (Charity Commission no. 1082947), as well as being a patron of the construction industry charity CRASH (Charity Commission no. 1054107). Mike Hussey is a trustee of the Royal College of Surgeons of England (Charity Commission no. 212808). Baroness Ford of Cunninghame is the President of Epilepsy Action (Charity Commission no. 234343).

Main locations

The group has 24 regional businesses across the UK, divided into North, Central and South West, London and South East divisions, with a head office in High Wycombe.

Community contributions

The 2015 sustainability report states that during the year, the group donated and fundraised £746,000 for registered charities and an additional £112,000 for 'organisations such as scout groups and other local community causes'. It was unclear how much was from the group and how much was from employee fundraising.

In-kind support

Regional divisions in the company often provide in-kind support, such as materials and volunteer hours, to local projects.

Employee-led support

Examples of employee fundraising in 2015 included 51 teams taking part in a Peak District Challenge, raising over £188,000 for the Youth Adventure Trust. Many employees also volunteer with local projects. Employees on the Taylor Wimpey graduate scheme also took part in a problem-solving challenge with the charity Centrepoint, as well as participating in a fundraising Sleep Out for the charity. Employees also represented the company in the 2015 Parliamentary Tug of War, which the group sponsored, raising money for Macmillan Cancer Support.

Exclusions

Support is generally not given to: larger national charities; 'major events that are able to attract large corporate donors or elicit a national response'; political causes.

The group prefers to select causes where employees can be directly involved, rather than simply providing financial assistance.

The Donations Policy and Charity and Community Support Policy are both available to view on the website.

Applications

The website states that the Charity Committee should be contacted with requests for donations or sponsorship. National requests should be sent to the committee via email tayweb.info@

taylorwimpey.com. Regional requests should be sent to the relevant local office; for contact details, refer to the website: www.taylorwimpey.co.uk/get-in-touch/office-locations.

Telegraph Media Group Ltd

Media

Correspondent: See 'Applications', 111 Buckingham Palace Road, London SW1W 0DT (website: www.telegraph.co.uk)

Directors: Aidan Barclay, Chair; Finbarr Ronayne, Chief Financial Officer; Howard Barclay; Lorraine Twohill; Michael Seal; Murdoch MacLennan, Chief Executive Officer; Philip Peters; Rigel Mowatt (women: 1; men: 7)

Year end	03/01/2016
Turnover	£320,100,000
Pre-tax profit	£48,100,000

Nature of business: The company is a multi-platform publisher of national newspapers (The Daily Telegraph, The Sunday Telegraph and The Telegraph).

The company's immediate parent company is Press Acquisitions Ltd (PAL), ultimately controlled by Sir David and Sir Frederick Barclay's Family Settlements.

Company registration number: 451593

Subsidiary undertakings include: The Evening Post Ltd (dormant); The Sunday Telegraph Ltd (dormant); Telegraph Events Ltd.

UK employees: 1,137

Total employees: 1,137

Focus of giving: General charitable purposes, health, ill health, overseas projects.

Community involvement	✓
Community contributions	✓
Directors have other relevant posts	✓
Cash donations declared	✓
Charity partner(s)	✓
Corporate charity	✓
Employee-led support	✓
Gifts in kind	✓

Charitable donations

Cash UK (latest available):	2016	£3,014,000
Total UK (cash and in kind):	2016	£3,014,000
Cash worldwide:	2016	£3,014,000
Total worldwide (cash and in kind):	2016	£3,014,000

Community involvement

The company directs its charitable donations through **The Barclay Foundation** (Charity Commission no. 803696), of which two company directors are trustees. Some support is given to charities associated with the newspapers and their employees.

Main locations

The foundation makes grants throughout the UK.

Community contributions

In 2015/16 the company made charitable donations of £3.01 million, of which £13,800 was given principally to charities associated with its newspapers and employees. The remaining £3 million was donated to The Barclay Foundation, which in turn donated £1 million to the Great Ormond Street Hospital Children's Charity and £2 million to The Defence and National Rehabilitation Centre Charity.

Beneficiaries included: The Barclay Foundation.

In-kind support

Telegraph Christmas Appeal

Every year the company selects three charities from dozens of applications for readers of its newspapers to support. In 2015 the appeal raised money for CARE International UK, Horatio's Garden and Rethink Mental Illness. We have classed this as in-kind support as the company provides its chosen charities with a fundraising platform.

Corporate charity

The Barclay Foundation (Charity Commission no. 803696).

Applications

The company's charitable donations are directed through The Barclay Foundation, where two of its directors are trustees, and to charities associated with its newspapers and employees.

Tesco PLC

Retail – supermarkets

Correspondent: Group Corporate Responsibility Team, Tesco Stores Ltd, Tesco House, Shire Park, Kestrel Way, Welwyn Garden City AL7 1GA (tel: 01992 632222 (main switchboard); email: cr.enquiries@uk.tesco.com; website: www.tescoplc.com)

Directors: Alan Stewart, Chief Financial Officer; Alison Platt; Byron Grote; Dave Lewis, Group Chief Executive; Deanna Oppenheimer; John Allan, Chair; Lindsey Pownall; Mark Armour; Mikael Olsson; Richard Cousins; Simon Patterson (women: 3; men: 8)

Year end	27/02/2016
Turnover	£54,433,000,000
Pre-tax profit	£162,000,000

Nature of business: The principal activity of the group is retailing and associated activities in the UK and around the world, including China, the Czech Republic, Hungary, the Republic of Ireland, India, Japan, Malaysia, Poland, Slovakia, South Korea, Thailand and Turkey. The group also provides retail banking and insurance services through its subsidiary, Tesco Bank, mobile services through Tesco Mobile, and petrol station services.

Company registration number: 445790

Subsidiary undertakings include: Giraffe Cafe Ltd; Harris and Hoole Ltd; Tesco Mobile Communications Ltd; Tesco Bengaluru Private Ltd.

UK employees: 335,061

Total employees: 482,152

Focus of giving: Education, environment, fundraising events, health, ill health, medical research, small groups, local groups, overseas projects, humanitarian help, poverty and social exclusion, sport, recreation, children, young people, community/social welfare, disability, disasters.

Membership: BITC

Community involvement	✓
Community contributions	✓
CSR or charity committee	✓
Directors have other relevant posts	✓
AF Covenant	✓
Armed forces personnel	✓
Charity partner(s)	✓
Company gives to smaller charities	✓
Employee-led support	✓
FTSE 100	✓
Gifts in kind	✓
Humanitarian aid: overseas	✓
Humanitarian aid: UK including food banks	✓
Market-led giving	✓
Matched funding	✓
Overseas giving	✓
Shared-value alliances	✓
Sponsorship	✓

Charitable donations

Total worldwide (cash and in kind):	2016	£34,000,000

Community involvement

The group supports causes including health, children and young people, poverty, social welfare and the environment, through financial and in-kind support. The group works with a number of charity partners on different initiatives, and its Community Champions co-ordinate local charitable and community activities. Further examples of the group's charitable activities, in the UK and internationally, can be found on the Tesco PLC website.

Community Champions

Tesco Community Champions are employees who are responsible for engagement with their local community. They are responsible for co-ordinating activities such as getting involved in local community events and communicating charitable activities. Community Champions work with local charities to organise in-store activities, including donations, bag packing and store collections. Each store has a budget for community donations, which can be used to respond to requests from local charities.

The store collections scheme allows charities to collect money or food at the front of Tesco stores. (www.tasteattesco.com/Charity.aspx).

Bags of Help
In October 2015 it became mandatory for retailers in England to charge customers a minimum of 5p for a plastic carrier bag, and the profits must be donated to charity. Tesco distributes these funds through its Bags of Help scheme, a grants programme administered by the charity Groundwork UK. Grants are available for community groups and charities in England, Scotland and Wales for projects that create or improve green spaces in communities. The applications are filtered down to three local projects in each region, which customers then vote for. All three projects receive funding of between £1,000 and £5,000. Customers can also nominate a project, which the company will try and match up with an appropriate organisation. Further information can be found on the website: www.groundwork.org.uk/Sites/tescocommunityscheme.

National Charity partnerships
In January 2015, Tesco formed national partnerships with Diabetes UK and the British Heart Foundation, aiming to raise £30 million for the charities over three years. Half of the money raised will fund a joint project aiming to encourage healthy living, and the other half will be split between the two charities. Fundraising initiatives include a 'Big Collection' in stores, a employee fundraising activities and 'challenge events' for both charities. Further information is given at tescocharitypartnership.org.uk.

Partnership with Red Cross
The group has worked with British Red Cross since 2007, supporting the charity through both financial and in-kind donations, bucket collections and employee fundraising. Tesco also works with the Red Cross in other countries. The group is a member of the Disaster Relief Alliance through its partnership with the Red Cross, which aims to provide preventative support before emergencies occur.

Eat Happy Project
Tesco works with schools, community groups and parents to promote healthy eating for children through its Eat Happy project. This includes, among other activities, Let's Cook, a course of cooking clubs for children run in partnership with the Children's Food Trust.

Tesco Charity Trust
The group previously had a corporate charity, the Tesco Charity Trust (Charity Commission no. 297126); however, the annual report for 2014/15 states that the trustees agreed in July 2015 that the trust would be collapsed and the funds transferred under the remit of Tesco Stores Ltd, in order to 'enable us to link all our community giving to our company strategy and to concentrate on maximising communication to customers and colleagues'. It is stated that the group will 'continue to support charitable activities on a local, national and international basis and to support Tesco colleagues with their charitable activities by providing them with a discretionary 20% top up on their fundraising for their chosen charity'.

Directors with other relevant posts
Simon Patterson is a trustee of the Natural History Museum in London. Dave Lewis is Chair of Champions 12.3, a UN coalition which is working to achieve progress on the Sustainable Development Goal Target 12.3, seeking to reduce food waste. Mikael Olsson is a board member of Global Child Forum, a Swedish non-profit organisation working to advance children's rights.

Main locations
The group's head office is based in Welwyn Garden City, but the group has operations throughout the UK, as well as in China; Czech Republic; Hungary; India; Ireland; Malaysia; Poland; Slovakia; Thailand; and Turkey.

Community contributions

According to the website, the total amount donated to charitable causes during 2015/16 was £34 million. We were unable to determine how much was given in cash donations or in the UK. The amount raised by employees and customers was £23.1 million.

In-kind support

As part of its partnership with the British Red Cross, Tesco provides in-kind support for emergency response teams, allowing them to request goods from any store in the UK including, for example, for emergency relief appeals, donating items such as food, toiletries and bottled water. The website states that this agreement was used five times for crisis support in 2015.

Food donations
Tesco donates surplus food to local charitable organisations, through a programme called Community Food Connection, run in partnership with the charity FareShare.

Other donations are provided at a local level. For example, in 2016, the company also donated food worth £20,000 to local mosques during Ramadan to help those in need, and £15,000 worth of food to the United Synagogues Passover Appeal for families in need in London.

Employee-led support

Tesco offers a 20% top-up to any employee fundraising for charities.

Commercially led support

The group works in partnership with the Trussell Trust and FareShare through its Neighbourhood Food Collection scheme, providing collection points in Tesco stores for customers to donate food items, which are then distributed to local charities serving those in need – such as food banks, children's breakfast clubs and homelessness charities.

Applications

To request support from a local store, charities should contact their local Community Champion. A list of contact details can be found on the website: www.tescoplc.com/tesco-and-society/supporting-local-communities.

Applications for donations of surplus food from Tesco should be made through FareShare FoodCloud – charities can register their interest here: www.fareshare.org.uk/fareshare-foodcloud.

To request permission to do a store collection, register online through the Taste At Tesco website – www.tasteattesco.com/charity-registration.aspx.

For any other enquiries, contact the Group Corporate Responsibility Team for requests about donations and charity support on charity.enquiries@uk.tesco.com, or for any other queries, on cr.enquiries@uk.tesco.com.

Thales UK Ltd

Defence, aerospace, engineering, manufacturing, transport and communications

Correspondent: Ethics & Corporate Responsibility Department, 2 Dashwood Lang Road, The Bourne Business Park, Addlestone, Surrey KT15 2NX (tel: 01932 824800; email: ethics.cr@thalesgroup.com; website: www.thalesgroup.co.uk)

Directors: Alexander Beatty; Denis Plantier; Edwin Awang; Ewen McCrorie; Gareth Williams; Kathryn Jenkins; Paul Gosling; Philip Naybour; Shaun Jones; Stephen McCann; Stuart Boulton; Suzanne Stratton; Victor Chavez; William Wilby; Yokini Pathmanathan

Year end	31/12/2015
Turnover	£943,851,000
Pre-tax profit	£57,222,000

Nature of business: The company is involved in the fields of aerospace, defence, security and transportation. Its activities involve design, manufacture and sale of defence electronic products, encompassing electronic warfare, radar, displays, defence radio and command information systems.

The company's immediate parent company is Thales Holdings UK PLC and the ultimate parent company is Thales SA, incorporated in France.

Company registration number: 868273

Subsidiary undertakings include: nCipher Ltd; Thales Optronics Holding Ltd; Thales Properties Ltd.

UK employees: 5,121

Total employees: 62,000

Focus of giving: Education, environment, health, ill health, overseas projects, science technology, children, young people, community/social welfare, disasters.

Membership: BITC

Community involvement	✓
Community contributions	✓
CSR report	✓
CSR or charity committee	✓
AF Covenant	✓
Charity partner(s)	✓
Corporate charity	✓
Employee-led support	✓
Gifts in kind	✓
Payroll giving	✓
Sponsorship	✓
STEM-focused	✓

Charitable donations

Cash UK (latest available):	2015	£175,000
Total UK (cash and in kind):	2015	£175,000
Cash worldwide:	2015	£175,000
Total worldwide (cash and in kind):	2015	£175,000

Community involvement

The group's 2015 corporate responsibility report states that its community involvement focuses on: education, particularly STEM subjects; and humanitarian action, particularly 'natural and environmental risk protection and disaster preparedness'. Thales sites tend to support local organisations. The Thales Foundation supports projects nominated by employees globally, while the Thales Charitable Trust supports a range of charities in the UK, particularly child health and education programmes.

The Thales Charitable Trust (Charity Commission no. 1000162)

In the UK, the group's corporate charity is The Thales Charitable Trust. The trust makes grants to a range of charitable organisations for purposes such as education, youth, technology, health/medical causes and other charitable purposes. In 2015 four main charities were supported (Arkwright Scholars; Combat Stress; Railway Children; Unicef) and donations were also made to 43 other organisations.

Thales Foundation

The group also has corporate charities in other countries – the main one being the Thales Foundation in France, which supports projects proposed by employees in any country. The call for projects is held annually in September and projects are centred on the group's two areas of focus: education and prevention of humanitarian crises or natural disasters. In 2015/16 a total of 13 employee projects were selected to be supported by the foundation out of 73 proposals. The foundation also funds 'pilot programmes' which centre on social innovation; collective intelligence; and international replicability. In 2016 three projects were supported.

Education

The group works in partnership with schools and other organisations to encourage engagement with STEM subjects. In the UK, Thales Research and Technology has links with universities in Bristol, Cambridge and Southampton.

Main locations

In the UK, the group's main locations are: Basingstoke; Belfast; Crawley; Cheadle Heath; Glasgow; Leicester; London; Reading; Templecombe; Wells. The group has operations in 56 countries and is based in France.

Community contributions

The Thales Charitable Trust had an income of £175,000 in 2015, which was donated by the group. The foundation made grants to 47 organisations totalling £149,000 in 2015.

Employee-led support

Employee volunteering

The group supports projects locally with which employees can get involved. The Thales Foundation supports projects proposed by employees has a network of employee ambassadors which promote its activities and lead employee involvement in the foundation's community projects.

Commercially led support

Sponsorship

In the UK, Thales is a sponsor of the Big Bang Science Fair and also sponsors the London Transport Museum.

Corporate charity

The Thales Charitable Trust (Charity Commission no. 1000162).

Applications

The Thales Charitable Trust

Enquiries should be addressed to Mike Seabrook, the trust's secretary (email: mike.seabrook@thalesgroup.com). The trustees meet on a quarterly basis.

The group

Apply in writing to the correspondent.

the7stars UK Ltd

Media

Correspondent: Alexandra Taliodoros, Foundation Director, c/o Simon Durham, the7stars Foundation, Floor 6–8, Melbourne House, 46 Aldwych, London WC2B 4LL (tel: 07940 959817; email: alexandra@the7starsfoundation.co.uk; website: www.the7starsfoundation.co.uk)

Directors: Gareth Jones; Jenny Biggam; Mark Jarvis (women: 1; men: 2)

Year end	31/03/2016
Turnover	£209,460,000
Pre-tax profit	£1,600,000

Nature of business: The7stars is an independent media agency.

Company registration number: 5387218

UK employees: 117

Total employees: 117

Focus of giving: Health, ill health, housing, homelessness, small groups, marginalised people, less popular charitable purposes, children, young people, community/social welfare.

Community involvement	✓
Community contributions	✓
Directors have other relevant posts	✓
Company gives to smaller charities	✓
Corporate charity	✓
Employee-led support	✓
Unpopular causes	✓

Community involvement

the7stars UK Ltd established the7stars foundation (Charity Commission no. 1168240) in July 2016 as a vehicle for its charitable involvement. At the time of writing (October 2016), the trustees – who include two of the agency's co-founders, Jenny Biggam and Mark Jarvis – were in the process of approving internal giving policies and the foundation's website was being set up. The information in this entry was provided to us by the Foundation Director.

The company's motivation for establishing the foundation was described as follows: 'We collectively feel that as a group we could do more for the community. There is an amplifying effect of pooling together a fund and focusing on causes we all believe in.'

Through the foundation, the company aims to support 'the most challenged under 16 year olds in the United Kingdom, assisting forgotten young people lacking opportunity, to achieve their potential'. In order to achieve this, the company has set itself three goals:

- To donate a minimum of 5% of our profit to good causes each year
- To support at least one charity in each of the pillars*...each year
- To become an active initiative that enables our staff to be involved on a voluntary basis

*These pillars – homelessness, addiction, abuse and child carers – make up the themes of the foundation's grants programme.

Main locations

The foundation works throughout the UK.

Community contributions

The annual report and accounts for 2015/16 did not declare a figure for charitable contributions during the year. Furthermore, due to it being a newly registered charity, the foundation's annual report and accounts were not yet due at the Charity Commission. However, the Foundation Director did specify to us that the projected 2016/17 grants figure for the7stars foundation was between £50,000 and £100,000.

Corporate charity

the7stars foundation (Charity Commission no. 1168240).

Applications

Applicants are directed to the7stars foundation's website, where application forms are available to download. Completed forms can be returned to the Foundation Director by email. The Foundation Director can be contacted with any questions about your application, the application form or the application process.

Thomas Cook Group PLC

Leisure

Correspondent: Group Sustainability Team, 3rd Floor, South Building, 200 Aldersgate, London EC1A 4HD (tel: 020 7557 6400; email: Group.communications@thomascook.com; website: www.thomascookgroup.com)

Directors: Annet Aris; Carl Symon; Dawn Airey; Emre Berkin; Frank Meysman, Chair; Harriet Green; Martine Verluyten; Michael Healey, Group Chief Financial Officer; Peter Fankhauser, Group Chief Executive Officer; Warren Tucker (women: 3; men: 5)

Year end	30/09/2015
Turnover	£7,834,000,000
Pre-tax profit	£50,000,000

Nature of business: Thomas Cook Group is a global leisure travel provider. The group also offers airline and online accommodation booking services.

Company registration number: 742748

Subsidiary undertakings include: Airtours Holidays Transport Ltd; Condor Flugdienst GmbH; Sunwing Hotels Hellas SA.

Brands include: Casa Cook Hotels; Sunprime Hotels; The Co-operative Travel.

Total employees: 3,089

Focus of giving: Education, environment, animal welfare, health, ill health, local groups, safety and crime prevention, children, young people, community/social welfare, disasters.

Membership: BITC

Community involvement	✓
Community contributions	✓
CSR report	✓
CSR or charity committee	✓
Directors have other relevant posts	✓
Charity partner(s)	✓
Company gives to smaller charities	✓
Corporate charity	✓
Employee-led support	✓
Gifts in kind	✓
Humanitarian aid: overseas	✓
Payroll giving	✓
Pro bono	✓
Sponsorship	✓

Community involvement

Much of the group's support is channelled through its corporate charity, The Thomas Cook Children's Charity, which provides support for projects benefitting children, particularly focusing on improving education, and improving facilities for well-being and healthcare. Projects in communities local to the group's offices or destinations are also supported.

The Thomas Cook Children's Charity

Most of the group's charitable giving is co-ordinated through The Thomas Cook Children's Charity (Charity Commission no. 1091673), which supports projects benefitting children, particularly focusing on improving education, and improving facilities for well-being and healthcare. The charity also supports disaster relief efforts. Charity partners are nominated by customers and employees each year. In 2015 the charity supported 25 projects through its Community Grants Programme, with grants totalling £225,000.

Beneficiaries of grants from The Thomas Cook Children's Charity included: Ashfield Home Safety Project; Daisy Chain; Cloughside College; Over the Wall.

Safer Tourism Foundation

In 2015, with a pledge to underwrite the first £1 million raised, the group established the Safer Tourism Foundation (Charity Commission no. 1168944) which aims to minimise risks that tourists face when going on holiday, particularly risks associated with carbon monoxide. The foundation was set up following the deaths of two young children on holiday and will fund research into carbon monoxide as well as campaigning for change in European and UK legislation.

Sustainable Tourism Partnerships

The group works with a number of different partners, including charities, to deliver sustainable tourism, such as: Enable Holidays; The Born Free Foundation; The Travel Foundation.

2020 targets

The group's sustainability targets for 2020 include: supporting at least one sustainable community project in each of the group's main destination regions; and conducting at least three local community projects around Head Office locations.

Main locations

The group operates throughout the UK and Ireland but has its head office in London. It also operates in Europe.

Community contributions

No figure was provided for the group's charitable contributions in the 2014/15 annual report and accounts.

In-kind support

During 2015, the group made in-kind donations to support Syrian refugees in Greece, donating emergency supplies such as sleeping bags, toiletries, nappies, blankets and other essential items, as well as allowing customers to bring their own contributions on board flights, up to an additional 20kg each, which are then distributed to charities working in the destination.

The group also gave in-kind support to one of the Thomas Cook Children's Charity initiatives, Flight of Dreams 2015, providing flights from Manchester, Stansted and Glasgow for a group of children, who were nominated by Cash for Kids to meet Santa, from various schools, charities and other organisations.

Employee-led support

Staff contribute to The Thomas Cook Children's Charity through payroll giving and other fundraising initiatives. Examples of employee-led support during the year include the Retail Monopoly Challenge, where 40 employees in the retail team took part in a fundraising challenge, walking the route of the monopoly board in London, raising over £36,500 for the Thomas Cook Children's Charity.

Commercially led support

Customers are encouraged to support The Thomas Cook Children's Charity by donating unwanted coins in stores and on return flights to the UK, or by adding a £2 donation when booking a holiday.

In 2015 the group also collected gifts in Thomas Cook stores which were donated to local children at Christmas.

Corporate charity

The Thomas Cook Children's Charity (Charity Commission no. 1091673).

Applications

Apply in writing to the correspondent.

There is no open applications process for The Thomas Cook Children's Charity; charity partners are nominated each year by customers and employees. If you wish to nominate a charity for support, contact Aoife McDonogh, Charitable Relations Manager by email: thomascook.childrenscharity@thomascook.com.

Thomson Reuters (Reuters Ltd)

Media

Correspondent: The Corporate Responsibility Team, The Thomson Reuters Building, 30 South Colonnade, Canary Wharf, London E14 5EP (tel: 020 7542 7015 (general enquiries) or 020 7542 4148 (foundation); email: foundation@thomsonreuters.com; website: www.thomsonreuters.com)

Directors: David Mitchley; Giray Erol; Justin Scott; Peter Thorn; Timothy Knowland (women: 0; men: 5)

Year end	31/12/2015
Turnover	£1,364,000,000

Nature of business: The company 'supplies the global business community and news media with a wide range of products, including real-time financial data, information management systems, access to numeric and textual databases, news and news pictures'. The majority of operations are located in the UK but also in Continental Europe, Africa, Asia and Latin America.

Company registration number: 145516

Subsidiary undertakings include: Blaxmill Ltd; Lipper Ltd.

Focus of giving: Human rights, education, enterprise/training, equal opportunities, less popular charitable purposes, overseas projects, sport, recreation, women's issues, community/social welfare.

Community involvement	✓
Community contributions	✓
Company reports on anti-slavery	✓
CSR report	✓
Gifts in kind	✓

Charitable donations

Cash UK (latest available):	2015	£4,140,000
Total UK (cash and in kind):	2015	£4,140,000
Cash worldwide:	2015	£4,140,000
Total worldwide (cash and in kind):	2015	£4,140,000

Community involvement

Thomson Reuters Foundation (Charity Commission no. 1082139)

The foundation was established in 2000 to 'promote socio-economic progress and the rule of law worldwide. It acts as an impact multiplier, leveraging the skids, expertise and values of the Thomson Reuters enterprise to run programmes that inform, connect and ultimately empower people around the world.'

There are four main programmes:

Trustlaw – the foundation's pro bono legal programme which connects legal firms and NGOs around the world.

World's Under-reported Stories – the foundation covers stories such as human rights, human trafficking and women's rights that are often overlooked by the mainstream media.

Media Development and Training – the foundation promotes the high standards in journalism globally.

Trust Women – the foundation takes action to put the rule of law behind women's rights and to fight modern day slavery.

Save the Children – International Financing Review (IFR) Awards

The awards part of the Thomson Reuters Awards for Excellence. Over £24 million has been raised for Save The Children since the awards started 21 years ago.

Main UK locations

London and West Yorkshire.

Community contributions

In 2015 the foundation received £4.14 million from Thomson Reuters.

In-kind support

In kind help is given to the Thomson Reuters Foundation, including office space, communications, computer equipment, also marketing services, licences, staff time and trainers, lending of tools, an advertising platform and legal collateral.

Employee-led support

Community Champion Awards

The annual Community Champion Awards programme celebrates the personal volunteering commitments of employees. Winners receive a substantial donation for the cause of their choice.

Matched funding

Employees' charitable donations to registered charities are matched up to US $1,000 (approximately £600 at the time of writing – January 2017) a year. Worldwide, charities received over $1.9 million through the matching gifts programme.

Payroll giving

In 2014 a new My Giving system was launched on the My Community platform. The system incorporates US-based Employee Giving Campaign, along with schemes in the UK and India.

Volunteering

Staff are encouraged to volunteer and are offered two days a year with pay if volunteering for a registered charity. In 2015 employees logged 118,500 volunteering hours.

Dollars for Doers

This programme, open to all regular employees, makes a donation of US $500 (about £312) to a charity for every 20 hours volunteered (both inside and outside working hours) by a staff member, and US $1,000 (about £624) for 40 volunteering hours (the figures have been converted and are applicable at the time of writing – January 2017). In 2015 grants totalling $442,000 were made to organisations through this scheme.

Applications

Thomson Reuters Foundation does not consider unsolicited requests for support.

Other enquiries relating to the company should be directed to the CSR Team.

Daniel Thwaites PLC

Brewers/distillers

Correspondent: Susan Woodward, Company Secretary, Penny Street, Star Brewery, Blackburn, Lancashire BB1 6HL (tel: 01254 686868; website: www.thwaites.co.uk)

Directors: Ann Yerburgh, Chair; John Barnes; Kevin Wood, Group Finance Director; N. Mackenzie; Oscar Yerburgh; Richard Bailey, Chief Executive Officer (women: 1; men: 5)

Year end	31/03/2016
Turnover	£84,600,000
Pre-tax profit	£11,500,000

Nature of business: The principal activities of Daniel Thwaites PLC are the brewing and canning of beer, the distribution of wines and spirits and the operation of hotels and public houses.

Company registration number: 51702

Focus of giving: Health, ill health, children, young people, community/social welfare, disability.

Community involvement	✓
Community contributions	✓
CSR report	✓
Cash donations declared	✓
Charity partner(s)	✓

Charitable donations

Cash UK (latest available):	2016	£25,000
Total UK (cash and in kind):	2016	£25,000
Cash worldwide:	2016	£25,000
Total worldwide (cash and in kind):	2016	£25,000

Community involvement

During the year the company continued to support the development of Blackburn Youth Zone, a facility for young people in the Blackburn area to meet and develop their sporting and social skills in a safe and supportive environment. The company's 2016 chosen local charity is St Catherine's Hospice.

The company encourages its pubs to become the centre of their communities and supports their work in sponsoring local events. In partnership with British Waterways the company has adopted a stretch of the Leeds to Liverpool Canal to maintain its cleanliness.

We have no information on this company's community and charitable initiatives, apart from the cash donations declared in its annual report (Blackburn Youth Zone), and the existence of The Daniel Thwaites Charitable Trust (Charity Commission no. 1038097) which has previously benefitted from the company's annual charitable donation.

Main location

Blackburn (head office) and various locations throughout the UK.

Community contributions

In 2015/16 the company gave £25,000 in one charitable donation awarded to Blackburn Youth Zone. The Youth Zone's principle activity is the provision of a purpose built, world class 21st century facility for sport and recreation in Blackburn for young people ages eight to eighteen years old. We take this figure as the company's overall contribution.

Employee-led support

In 2015/16, through raffles, auctions and other fundraising activities, Daniel Thwaites pubs raised money for a range of charitable causes.

Exclusions

Political donations are not made.

Applications

Apply in writing to the correspondent.

Time Inc. (UK) Ltd (formerly IPC Media Ltd)

Media

Correspondent: Jane Mortimore, Corporate Responsibility Manager, Blue Fin Building, 110 Southwark Street, London SE1 0SU (020 3148 5404; email: jane.mortimore@timeinc.com; website: www.timeincuk.com/about/responsibility)

Directors: Adrian Hughes; Andrea Davies; Fiona Dent; Lesley Swarbrick; Marcus Rich, Chief Executive Officer; Michel Koch; Neil Robinson; Oswin Grady; Paul Cheal; Robbie Macdonald; Samuel Finlay; Stephen May, Finance Director; Susana D'Emic (women: 4; men: 9)

Year end	31/12/2014
Turnover	£279,578,000
Pre-tax profit	£22,792,000

Nature of business: Time Inc. UK specialises in the publication of print and digital magazine content.

Company registration number: 53626

Brands include: Look; Marie Claire UK; TV Times.

Focus of giving: General charitable purposes, education, health, ill health, older people, children, young people, community/social welfare.

Community involvement	✓
Community contributions	✓
CSR report	✓
Charity partner(s)	✓
Employee-led support	✓
Gifts in kind	✓
Payroll giving	✓
Pro bono	✓

Community involvement

Time Inc. (UK) Ltd looks to support communities in the areas surrounding its offices, with priority given to causes supported by its employees and brands.

The company's website describes how it does this:

- 'Building relationships with local schools in order to invest in our local talent pool, increase employability and career aspirations'
- 'Supporting local community organisations or charities with our skills and expertise'
- 'Having a nomination and voting process for selecting our two-year charity partnership, open to all employees'
- 'Offering brand support to charities, often on a long-standing basis.'

Charity partnerships

The charity nominated and voted for by Time Inc. UK employees as the company's partner for 2015/16 was The Silver Line, a charity providing a free 24-hour helpline for older people. The company's website explains that The Silver Line was supported with employees' fundraising and volunteering activities and benefitted from their media skills and expertise.

Other charitable support

Support for charitable causes is also leveraged through the company's brands. One example of this is the long-standing relationship between woman&home and Breast Cancer Care. Support in the form of financial or in-kind donations is given on an ad hoc basis to charities whose work is aligned to the company's key corporate responsibility priorities.

Educational initiatives

In collaboration with A New Direction, Time Inc. UK is working to deliver a programme for young people in inner London, based around employment in the media industry. The company's website states: 'We want to create networks, give support and offer opportunities to local students to find out more about working in this dynamic sector, and in the process help towards increasing workforce diversity in communications and publishing.'

As a way of achieving this, Time Inc. UK has partnered St Saviour's and St Olave's School, a secondary school in Southwark, to run the programme which, according to the website, includes 'a series of interventions, including career talks, learning experiences, employability workshops, mentoring and multi-media projects that will give the students a better understanding of the career opportunities in media today and increase their ability to compete in the media job market'.

The company's website states that it also accommodates requests it receives from school and university students, to provide them with opportunities to find out more about Time Inc. UK and the media industry, as well as to meet with 'editors, designers and other senior employees to find out more about careers in the media'.

Main locations

The company has offices in London, Birmingham and Farnborough.

Community contributions

The accounts for 2014 did not declare a figure for charitable donations.

At the time of writing (November 2016), the company's overview at the Companies House stated that the accounts for the year ending 31 December 2015 were overdue. We have taken the financial information in this record from the accounts for the year ending 31 December 2014 which were the most recent available.

In-kind support

Staff time

Employees can request up to two days' paid time per year for volunteering purposes.

Pro bono

Staff are encouraged to contribute their skills and expertise to local causes and partner charities, as well as through the company's own educational initiatives.

Employee-led support

Employee volunteering

According to the company's website, staff are offered opportunities to contribute to their communities through 'skilled' volunteering, which uses their media skills and expertise, 'more general' activities, such as primary school reading activities, or taking part in a team challenge. Employees are also able to source their own volunteering opportunities.

Employee fundraising

Employees take part with various fundraising activities, including for the company's chosen charity partner. Examples of fundraising challenges mentioned on the website include charity runs, walks and skydives. A team of employees throughout the company's offices act as 'charity champions' who organise fundraising events and activities.

Payroll giving

Employees are able to donate to charities through a payroll giving scheme. In 2016 the company was awarded a Payroll Giving Bronze Award by Charities Aid Foundation.

Applications

Apply in writing to the correspondent.

TJX UK (formerly TK Maxx)

Retail – clothing and footwear

Correspondent: The Marketing Department, 50 Clarendon Road, Watford, Hertfordshire WD17 1TX (tel: 01923 473000 (main switchboard); website: www.tkmaxx.com/page/community)

Directors: David Averill; John Klinger; Mary Reynolds (women: 1; men: 2)

Year end	30/01/2016
Turnover	£2,434,000,000
Pre-tax profit	£142,300,000

Nature of business: The main activity of TJX UK is the retail of brand-name merchandise through TK Maxx and HomeSense stores, as well as the TKMaxx.com website.

TJX UK's immediate parent company is TJX Europe Ltd and its ultimate parent company and controlling party is The TJX Companies, Inc., incorporated in Delaware, USA.

Company registration number: 3094828

Subsidiary undertakings include: TJX Europe Buying Ltd; TJX Ireland; TJX Europe Buying Group Ltd.

Brands include: HomeSense; TK Maxx.

Total employees: 17,736

Focus of giving: Environment, fundraising events, health, ill health, small groups, local groups, children, young people, community/social welfare.

Community involvement	✓
Community contributions	✓
CSR report	✓
Charity partner(s)	✓
Company gives to smaller charities	✓
Employee-led support	✓
Market-led giving	✓

Community involvement

Much of TJX's UK community involvement comes in the form of customer and employee fundraising initiatives for a handful of national charity partners. Smaller charities close to the hearts of employees and customers are supported through the Community Fund.

The Community Fund

The TK Maxx website states: 'Our Community Fund helps us support smaller charities that matter to our employees and customers – either through personal experiences or due to the support they deliver in local communities.'

Charity partners

TK Maxx supports Action for Children, Cancer Research UK, and The Woodland Trust, and HomeSense has a charity partnership with The Prince's Trust. Both TK Maxx and HomeSense have supported Comic Relief and Sport Relief.

Main locations

There are TK Maxx stores nationwide and HomeSense stores in England, Scotland and Wales. See the store search facility for details of TK Maxx and HomeSense locations (www.tkmaxx.com/store-locator/page/storelocator).

Community contributions

TJX UK's annual report for 2015/16 states:

> During the period the Company supported five major charities by raising funds for Cancer Research UK, Comic Relief, The Woodland Trust, The Prince's Trust and Action for Children. All charity initiatives within the business were directed towards these organisations. Smaller charities that are important to Company employees and customers were supported through the Company's Community Fund. This financial period, administration of the programme, Company donations and fundraising activities came to the value of £7.9 m (2015: £4.1 m).

We were unable to determine the proportion of this figure attributed to the company.

Previous beneficiaries of The Community Fund have included: The Brain Research Trust; Bury Hospice; CHICKS; Julia's House Children's Hospice.

Commercially led support

Christmas Sock Day

TK Maxx celebrated Christmas Sock Day on 6 December to help raise funds for its partner charity Cancer Research UK. Official Christmas Socks were sold at TK Maxx stores with a proportion of the proceeds from the sale of each pack donated to the charity. Children's designs were priced from £2.99 and adults' from £4.99, with at least 99p donated from children's sales and £2 from adults'. The socks were sold alongside other 'sockingfillers' including chocolate lollipops and Christmas cards.

People were encouraged to take a photo of themselves wearing their Christmas socks and show their support for the event on social media using the hashtag #socksie. For each #socksie photo uploaded on Twitter, Facebook or Instagram, TK Maxx donated £1 to Cancer Research UK.

The Sport Relief apron

Limited-edition aprons created by the designer Orla Kiely were sold at TK Maxx and HomeSense stores, as well as online, to raise funds for Sport Relief 2016. The apron, which featured on The Great Sport Relief Bake Off, was available for £12.99, with £5.25 from the sale of each product donated to Sport Relief, which benefits some of the most disadvantaged people in the UK and around the world.

Comic Relief t-shirts

In aid of Comic Relief, TK Maxx stores sell specially designed T-shirts from which all net profits are donated. According to the website, 'the t-shirts are wholly manufactured in Africa, with 100% of the cotton sourced from Fair Trade certified organic cotton co-operatives in Mali. This ensures good quality, pesticide and GM free cotton and a fair price for the farmers.'

Bags for life and carrier bag sales

As part of TK Maxx's support for Cancer Research UK, the charity has received donations from the profits generated by sales of bags for life.

The Woodland Trust receives all money raised from sales of carrier bags in Welsh stores.

Clothes collections

The public can donate unwanted items of clothing at TK Maxx stores which host permanent donation points. The clothing is then sold by Cancer Research UK, with each bag generating as much as £25.

Applications

In reference to the major charities supported by TJX UK, the annual report 2015/16 states: 'All charity initiatives within the business were directed towards these organisations.' Support from The Community Fund is given to charities which are important to TJX employees and customers.

For more information regarding the global community involvement activities of The TJX Companies, Inc., see the 'Communities' section of the website (www.tjx.com/corporate/communities.html).

Town Centre Securities PLC

Property

Correspondent: The Company Secretary, Town Centre House, The Merrion Centre, Leeds LS2 8LY (tel: 0113 222 1234; website: tcs-plc.co.uk)

Directors: Ben Ziff; Duncan Syers, Finance Director; Edward Ziff, Chair and Chief Executive; Ian Marcus; John Nettleton; Michael Ziff; Paul Huberman; Richard Lewis (women: 0; men: 8)

Year end	30/06/2015
Pre-tax profit	£6,500,000

Nature of business: Property development.

Company registration number: 623364

Subsidiary undertakings include: Citipark PLC; Dundonald Property Investments Ltd; Town Centre Car Parks Ltd.

UK employees: 125

Total employees: 125

Focus of giving: Heritage, children, young people, community/social welfare.

Community involvement	✓
Community contributions	✓
CSR report	✓
Directors have other relevant posts	✓
Cash donations declared	✓
Employee-led support	✓
Sponsorship	✓

Charitable donations

Cash UK (latest available):	2015	£99,000
Total UK (cash and in kind):	2015	£99,000
Cash worldwide:	2015	£99,000
Total worldwide (cash and in kind):	2015	£99,000

Community involvement

Directors with other relevant posts

Edward Ziff is a trustee of the Leeds Teaching Hospital Charitable Foundation and Michael Ziff is a trustee and director of the Hepworth art gallery, Wakefield.

Main locations

Leeds and London.

Community contributions

In 2014/15 the group made charitable contributions totalling £99,000.

Beneficiaries included: Candlelighters; Leeds Jewish Welfare Board; Lion Heart; The Prince's Regeneration Trust; Variety, the Children's Charity.

Employee-led support

Employee fundraising

During the year employees took part in challenges such as The Great Yorkshire Bike Ride, the Great North Run and the Yorkshire Three Peaks Walk to raise money for charities.

Commercially led support

Sponsorship

Sponsorship was provided to West of Scotland Rugby Club.

Applications

Direct requests to the correspondent.

Toyota Motor Manufacturing (UK) Ltd

Motors and accessories

Correspondent: Julie Langley, Corporate Planning & External Affairs, Burnaston, Derbyshire, East Midlands DE1 9TA (tel: 01332 283611; website: www.toyotauk.com)

Year end	31/03/2016
Turnover	£2,588,849,911
Pre-tax profit	£64,615,425

Nature of business: The principal activity of the company is car and engine manufacture. The company operates in Burnaston, Derbyshire and Deeside, North Wales.

Company registration number: 2352348

Brands include: Auris; Auris Hybrid; Avensis; Aygo; Corolla; Urban Cruiser; Yaris.

Focus of giving: Education, environment, health, ill health, local groups, children, young people.

Membership: BITC

Community involvement	✓
Community contributions	✓
Company reports on anti-slavery	✓
Cash donations declared	✓
Charity partner(s)	✓
Corporate charity	✓
Employee-led support	✓
Gifts in kind	✓
Sponsorship	✓

Charitable donations

Total UK (cash and in kind):	2016	£1,100,000
Total worldwide (cash and in kind):	2016	£1,100,000

Community involvement

Toyota Manufacturing UK Charitable Trust (Charity Commission no. 1124678)

The trust was established in 2008 to support community organisations near its plants in Burston and Deeside. Giving is focused in four main areas: environment, children, education and health. Toyota employees that are connected to a charity can apply for grants of up to £5,000 through the Members Grant Scheme. Local charities can also apply directly for an end of year award.

Charity of the Year

Toyota always has at least one nominated charity that is supported for a period of three years. The nominated charity in 2015 and 2016 was Macmillan Cancer Support.

Lucy Prince Community Grant Award

The award was initiated to commemorate an employee who passed away. The annual award provides an annual one-off grant of £5,000 to an organisation who aims to support and bring about improvements in family life in the Derbyshire area.

Derbyshire Wildlife Trust

The company is a corporate member of the trust and works together on a number of projects.

Toyota Fund for Europe

The Toyota Fund for Europe operates throughout Europe and supports projects that operate across a number of different European countries. The fund supports projects in the areas of the environment, road safety and technical education.

Main locations

Deeside and Burnaston, Derbyshire.

Community contributions

In 2015/16 the company made charitable donations totalling £1.1 million (€1.26 million). This comprised £10,500 (€12,000) donated to charities involved in environmental conservation and £1.09 million to local charities.

In-kind support

Local charitable events are regularly supported through the donation of raffle prizes. Occasionally local schools and colleges are provided parts and components to be used as training aids.

Ex-trial vehicles are also donated to support local schools and colleges as well as the emergency services. Set criteria are in place. In 2015 a total of 62 vehicles were donated, 37 of which were to Derbyshire and Cheshire Fire and Rescue Services who are able to use the vehicles to provide training for fire crews in road traffic collision techniques.

Employee-led support

Employee involvement in the community is encouraged and, where suitable, financial support is given. The company is a member of Business in the Community and participates in its Give and Gain programme, a nationwide day of volunteering.

Staff members get involved in fundraising opportunities to support the corporate charity. Activities include mountain climbing, cycling, Christmas jumper day and so on.

Commercially led support

Sponsorship

Since 1992 the company has been a corporate sponsor of Derby County Football Club.

Public visit programme

Toyota runs a public visit programme that allows members of the public, customers and businesses to visit its plants and learn about their operations. Application forms for public visits scheme at the Burnaston site have to be made online, using the 'Register Your Interest' section. Further details on public visits at the Deeside site can be directed to Martin Fry (tel: 01244282498; email: martin.fry@toyotauk.com).

Corporate charity

Toyota Manufacturing UK Charitable Trust (Charity Commission no. 1124678).

Applications

The company

Apply in writing to the correspondent.

Corporate charity

Toyota employees can apply for the members grant scheme on the website: www.toyotauk.com/the-toyota-charitable-trust/member-grants.html.

Local charities can also apply for grants via the website: www.toyotauk.com/the-toyota-charitable-trust/working-with-charities.html.

Travis Perkins PLC

Building materials, building/ construction

Correspondent: CSR Team, Lodge Way House, Harlestone Road, Northampton NN5 7UG (tel: 01604 752424; fax: 01604 758718; email: communications@travisperkins.co.uk; website: www.travisperkinsplc.co.uk)

Directors: Christopher Rogers; Coline McConville; John Carter, Chief Executive; John Rogers; Pete Redfern; Robert Walker, Chair; Ruth Anderson; Tony Buffin, Chief Financial Officer (women: 2; men: 6)

Year end	31/12/2015
Turnover	£5,942,000,000
Pre-tax profit	£224,000,000

Nature of business: Travis Perkins group is involved in marketing and distribution of timber, building and plumbing materials and the hiring of tools to the building trade and industry generally.

Company registration number: 824821

Subsidiary undertakings include: City Plumbing Supplies Holdings Ltd; Primaflow Ltd; Toolstation Ltd.

Brands include: Benchmarx; Wickes; Solfex.

UK employees: 28,000

Total employees: 28,000

Focus of giving: Fundraising events, health, ill health, medical research, older people, children, young people, community/social welfare, disability.

Community involvement	✓
Community contributions	✓
Company reports on anti-slavery	✓
Directors have other relevant posts	✓
Charity partner(s)	✓
Employee-led support	✓
FTSE 100	✓
Payroll giving	✓
Sponsorship	✓

Community involvement

Charitable activities are generally organised by each of the businesses within the group. Each one has a partnership with a different national charity selected by employees. Most recently health and disability causes have been supported.

Partnerships

The website states that teams in each of the businesses within the group choose a charity to support for at least three years. The chosen charities must support 'children and/or adults, affected by poverty, disability or disease in the UK'. Current partnerships are listed on the website.

The 2015 annual report highlights the examples of Keyline, which raised over £1 million for the charity Prostate Cancer UK, and Wickes, which has reached £5 million over its eight-year partnership with the charity Bloodwise.

Sponsorship

The group sponsors a number of sports events or teams, including the Golf Masters and British Military Fitness. As a result of sponsorship of the Americas Cup World Series in 2015, the group supported the charities Andrew Simpson Sailing Foundation and 1851 trust in a joint project bringing together 1,000 disadvantaged children to try out sailing.

Employment and training

The group provides opportunities for The Duke of Edinburgh scheme, apprenticeships and trainee schemes.

Directors with other relevant posts

Ruth Anderson is a trustee of the charity The Duke of Edinburgh's Award (Charity Commission no. 1072490). Pete Redfern is a trustee of the charity Crisis (Charity Commission no. 1082947).

Main locations

The group has operations throughout the UK; its head office is in Northampton.

Community contributions

The annual report states that the group's fundraising activities totalled £1.5 million altogether. It was not specified how much of this was from the group and how much was from employee fundraising.

Beneficiaries of partnerships included: Whizz-Kidz; Mind; Pancreatic Cancer UK; Alzheimer's Society; Macmillan Cancer Support; Parkinson's UK.

Employee-led support

Employee fundraising activities include a colleague lottery, as well as payroll giving and other employee-led initiatives. Fundraising and volunteering activities are generally organised by each business individually. For example, Wickes stores work with the project Volunteer it Yourself to offer support to local communities near to Wickes stores.

Applications

The website states that charities or community groups looking for support should contact one of the group's businesses (details are listed on the website).

It is further stressed: 'Please note that we receive hundreds of applications for help and assistance and while we do our best to support as many as we can, it is not always possible.'

To discuss volunteer support from a local Wickes store, email info@teamviy.com.

Trinity Mirror PLC

Media

Correspondent: The Company Secretary, One Canada Square, Canary Wharf, London E14 5AP (tel: 020 7293 3000; fax: 020 7510 3405; website: www.trinitymirror.com/our-values)

Directors: David Grigson, Chair; Dr David Kelly; Helen Stevenson; Lee Ginsberg; Olivia Streatfeild; Simon Fox, Chief Executive Officer; Steve Hatch; Vijay Vaghela, Group Finance Director (women: 2; men: 6)

Year end	27/12/2015
Turnover	£592,700,000
Pre-tax profit	£67,200,000

Nature of business: The main activity of the group is the publication of newspapers, websites and digital products as well as provision of printing services in the UK.

Company registration number: 82548

Subsidiary undertakings include: London and Westminster Newspapers Ltd; Midland Independent Weekly Newspapers Ltd; North Eastern Evening Gazette Ltd.

Brands include: Liverpool Echo; The Daily Mirror; The Manchester Evening News.

UK employees: 4,452

Total employees: 4,452

Focus of giving: Advertising in charity brochures, health, ill health, housing, homelessness, medical research, armed forces, older people, children, young people, community/social welfare, disability.

Community involvement	✓
Community contributions	✓
CSR report	✓
Directors have other relevant posts	✓
Armed forces personnel	✓
Charity partner(s)	✓
Company gives to smaller charities	✓
Gifts in kind	✓

Community involvement

The Corporate Social Responsibility Report explains that 'Trinity Mirror supports communities across the UK through its editorial work, raising awareness, publicising charities, running campaigns and organising fundraising appeals across all of its national and regional titles'.

The report continues: 'Trinity Mirror makes direct cash donations to various charities connected with or associated with the newspaper, printing or advertising industries and to charities operating in the communities immediately surrounding the Group's offices and sites'. Each of the group's regional newspaper companies has 'a small budget' from which they can make donations to local charities working in their community. Donations are most likely to be awarded to 'smaller community-based charities where a modest donation will make a big impact'.

Awards ceremonies

The group runs a number of award events, both nationally and at regional level.

The most widely known awards event is the Daily Mirror's Pride of Britain Awards, which has celebrated the nation's 'unsung heroes' since 1999 and is televised on ITV. At a national level, the group also runs the Pride of Sport and Animal Heroes Awards. At a regional level, the Sunday Mail Great Scot Awards has been honouring the achievements of ordinary Scottish people for more than 25 years and, as an extension of the 'Pride of...' series of awards, the group's regional news outlets also organise awards ceremonies.

Campaigns

Trinity Mirror's regional and national titles are involved with a range of issue-based campaigns. In 2015 examples included a campaign to encourage organ donor registration, co-ordinating donations for starter packs for young people facing homelessness and partnering with Teach First to promote recruitment into teaching.

Partnership with The Media Trust

In 2015 the group partnered The Media Trust to provide 60 young community journalists with experience the newsrooms of its regional titles.

Directors with other relevant posts

David Grigson: director/trustee of the Dolma Development Fund.

Vijay Vaghela: independent member of the Audit Committee of The Football Association.

Helen Stevenson: on Strategic Advisory Board of Henley Business School.

Community contributions

The annual report and accounts for 2014/15 did not include a figure for charitable donations.

In-kind support

Office facilities are available for the use by charitable organisations as well as used computer equipment, furniture, books and so on. Staff volunteering time and expert skills are also offered.

Commercially led support

Wish Campaign

The 'Community' section of the Trinity Mirror website states that the Wish Campaign was first created by the Teesside Gazette (owned by Trinity Mirror's subsidiary company the Gazette Media Company Ltd) and now runs across a number of newspapers within England, Scotland and Wales. The Gazette Live website (www.gazettelive.co.uk/all-about/evening-gazette-wish) explains that 'Our Wish campaign gives not-for-profit organisations in the local area the chance to receive a share of £25,000. Whether groups are looking for new equipment, trips away or cash for their centre, we can help make it happen'. Local not-for-profit groups can register for the initiative, which involves collecting tokens printed in issues of The Gazette – the more tokens a group collects, the bigger the group's share of the award will be. We would suggest contacting your local Trinity Mirror regional title to find out if it partakes with the campaign.

Exclusions

Support is not generally given for local appeals not in areas of the company's presence. Political donations are not normally made.

Applications

Previous research indicates that local enquiries should be addressed to the editor or manager of the newspaper/ print site based in your community. Prior agreement of the relevant managing director will be required before a donation can be made.

For support from the group, apply in writing to the correspondent.

UBM

Business services

Correspondent: Charity Committee, 240 Blackfriars Road, London SE1 8BF (tel: 020 7921 5000; website: www.ubm.com)

Directors: Alan Gillespie; Dame Helen Alexander, Chair; Greg Lock; John McConnell; Marina Wyatt, Chief Financial Officer; Mary McDowell; Pradeep Kar; Terry Neill; Tim Cobbold, Chief Executive Officer; Trynka Shineman (women: 4; men: 6)

Year end	31/12/2015
Turnover	£769,900,000
Pre-tax profit	£119,600,000

Nature of business: UBM is a global business-to-business events organiser. It operates in 20 countries across the world, and is divided into three businesses: UBM Americas, UBM Asia and UBM EMEA.

Subsidiary undertakings include: PR Newswire Association LLC; UBM Canon UK Ltd; Advanstar Communications Inc.

Total employees: 5,136

Focus of giving: Housing, homelessness, local groups, children, young people, community/social welfare, disasters.

Accredited Living Wage Employer	✓
Community involvement	✓
Community contributions	✓
CSR report	✓
CSR or charity committee	✓
Directors have other relevant posts	✓
Cash donations declared	✓
Charity partner(s)	✓
Employee-led support	✓
Humanitarian aid: overseas	✓
Market-led giving	✓
Matched funding	✓
Pro bono	✓
Shared-value alliances	✓
Sponsorship	✓

Charitable donations

Cash worldwide:	2015	£250,000
Total worldwide (cash and in kind):	2015	£829,000

Community involvement

In 2015 the company reviewed its community engagement strategy following consultation with employees, to fit in with its new 'Events First' company strategy, and decided to focus on a mix of funding and volunteering activities, as well as improving reporting. Support generally focuses on communities local to either the company's offices or the company's events.

Directors with other relevant posts

Dame Helen Alexander is also the Chancellor of the University of Southampton. Alan Gillespie is Chair of the Economic and Social Research Council.

Main locations

The group has operations worldwide. Within the UK, the group has offices in Cheshire, Kent, Manchester and London.

Community contributions

During 2015, the company made cash donations of almost £250,000, including matched funding for employees' fundraising activities, and donated a further £579,000 through in-kind support. It was not specified how much of this was in the UK.

In-kind support

Examples of in-kind support during 2015 include running an Academic Scholarship Programme, providing complimentary student passes to the Black Hat USA global security information event, as well as an additional 27 scholarships through the company's Future Female Leaders programme.

Employee-led support

Employee volunteering

The company has a policy allowing all employees in the US, Europe and Asia to take up to four days a year to volunteer with charities. In 2015 8% of employees used their volunteering allowance.

In 2015 the company also sponsored a group of UBM employees to attend One Young World, a conference bringing together young leaders internationally to discuss world issues and inspire social change.

Matched funding

The company provides matched funding of up to £500 per employee per year for employee-led charitable fundraising. The company's Charity Committee occasionally authorises an increase on this allowance – for example, this was increased to £20,000 for fundraising efforts following the earthquake in Nepal in 2015.

Commercially led support

Event charity partnerships

The company has developed event-specific charity partnerships for over 30 of its events so far, allowing customers to engage in charitable activity related to their particular industry. Employees volunteer to raise awareness and deliver these partnerships. For example, the Technology for Marketing event in London was partnered with the Media Trust, which resulted in over 100 attendees signing up to volunteer their expertise through Media Trust to help charities.

Applications

Apply in writing to the correspondent. Most activities are organised by individual businesses within the group – for contact details, refer to the website.

UDG Healthcare PLC

Healthcare

Correspondent: CSR Team, UDG Healthcare, 20 Riverwalk, Citywest Business Campus, Citywest, Dublin 24, Ireland (tel: 0353 1 468 9000; email: company.secretary@udghealthcare.com; website: www.udghealthcare.com)

Directors: Alan Ralph; Brendan McAtamney; Chris Brinsmead; Chris Corbin; Gerard Van Odijk; Liam Fitzgerald, Chief Executive; Linda Wilding; Lisa Ricciardi; Peter Gray, Chair; Philip Toomey (women: 2; men: 8)

Year end	30/09/2015
Turnover	£919,274,000
Pre-tax profit	£55,814,000

Nature of business: UDG provides healthcare services across three division: Ashfield Commercial and Medical Services; Sharp Packaging Services; Aquilant Specialist Healthcare Services. The group operates in 19 countries, including the US, the UK, Ireland and Germany.

Company registration number: 8445432

Subsidiary undertakings include: Aquilant Pharmaceuticals Ltd; Ashfield Healthcare (Ireland) Ltd; Sharp Clinical Services (UK) Ltd.

Total employees: 8,000

Focus of giving: General charitable purposes, children, young people.

Community involvement	✓
Community contributions	✓
CSR report	✓
CSR or charity committee	✓
Directors have other relevant posts	✓
Charity partner(s)	✓
Employee-led support	✓
Matched funding	✓

Community involvement

The group focuses charitable activities on a particular theme for a three-year period, as well as supporting employee-led initiatives. Individual businesses within the group may also organise activities.

Children's charities

Employees voted in 2012 for the group to focus on supporting children's charities for three years, which ended in 2015. A new theme is set to be selected in 2016. In total, €200,000 (around £170,000 at the time of writing – September 2016) was raised over the three years. Beneficiaries included Barnardo's in Ireland and United Way in the US.

Ashfield Cares

Ashfield, one of the group's businesses (known as UDG in the UK), launched a new international initiative in 2016 called Ashfield Cares. This will involve supporting charities through donations and employee volunteering, with particular focus on: healthcare; community development; education.

Directors with other relevant posts

Chris Brinsmead is a member of the council of Imperial College London.

Main locations

The group has operations in: Argentina; Austria; Belgium; Brazil; Canada; Denmark; Finland; Germany; Ireland; Italy; Japan; Norway; Portugal; Spain; Sweden; the Netherlands; Turkey; UK; and the US. The group's head office is in Dublin.

Community contributions

No figure was given for total contributions in the annual report in accounts; however, the 2014/15 report does state that over €50,000 (around £42,500) was donated in 2015 to children's charities, and over around €40,000 (around £34,000) was donated in support of employee fundraising initiatives. It was unclear how much of this came from the company or from employees, and how much was given in the UK.

Employee-led support

In 2015 the group decided to support individual employee fundraising initiatives; employees can submit initiatives to the CSR committee, which decides which causes to support.

Applications

Apply in writing to the correspondent.

UIA (Insurance) Ltd

Insurance

Correspondent: Jackie White, Foundation Administrator, Kings Court, London Road, Stevenage, Hertfordshire SG1 2TP (tel: 01438 761761 (main switchboard); fax: 01438 761762; website: www.uia.co.uk)

Directors: Ben Terrett, Finance Director; Bob Abberley; Chris McElligott; Eithne McManus; Eleanor Smith; Jon Craven, Chief Executive Officer; Lucia McKeever; Marion Saunders; Peter Dodd; Tony Woodley (women: 4; men: 6)

Year end	31/12/2015
Turnover	£23,029,000

Nature of business: UIA is a mutual insurance company primarily serving members of selected trade unions and other not-for-profit organisations, but also offering services to general public.

Company registration number: 3400457

Subsidiary undertakings include: UIA (Call Centres) Ltd; UIA Lottery Management Services Ltd; UIA (Trustees) Ltd; and Uniservice Ltd.

Focus of giving: Human rights, equal opportunities, health, ill health, housing, homelessness, small groups, marginalised people, less popular charitable purposes, older people, overseas projects, poverty and social exclusion, sport, recreation, women's issues, children, young people, community/social welfare, disability, disasters.

Community contributions	✓
Company gives to smaller charities	✓
Corporate charity	✓
Humanitarian aid: overseas	✓
Sponsorship	✓

Charitable donations

Cash UK (latest available):	2015	£73,000
Total UK (cash and in kind):	2015	£73,000
Cash worldwide:	2015	£73,000
Total worldwide (cash and in kind):	2015	£73,000

Community involvement

The UIA Charitable Foundation

According the company's website: 'The UIA Charitable Foundation is not accepting new applications for funding at this time.'

The UIA Charitable Foundation (Charity Commission no. 1079982) is a grant-making body established to provide financial support to formally constituted voluntary organisations and small registered charities that help people in need. It is funded entirely by donations from UIA (Insurance) Ltd, a mutual insurance company, that is a provider of insurances to members of UNISON, Unite and other trade unions.

The aim of the foundation is to support projects under two main categories:

- The Community Support Programme
- The World Programme

According to the website, the company is 'interested in working with charities who can demonstrate a strategy for change over a specific timeframe, supported through the achievement of project objectives that can be monitored and evaluated'. Furthermore, it 'will consider projects that empower individuals and communities to improve their lives and the prospects of the community'.

Main location

Stevenage

Community contributions

According to the charitable foundation's 2014/15 annual report, during the year the foundation received an income of £73,000 in donations from UIA and made grants amounting to £57,000. We have no figure for the company's overall charitable giving.

Beneficiaries of the foundation included: Helping Rwanda (£15,000); Tracks Autism (£5,000); Garment Workers Initiative (£5,000); GMB – Belize Project (£1,500).

Revenue: We used the figure defined as 'Gross premiums written' as the company's annual turnover.

Corporate charity

UIA Charitable Foundation (Charity Commission no. 1079982).

Exclusions

The foundation's website states that it will not fund the following:

- Work which it believes to be publicly funded
- Retrospective projects
- Organisations that have an annual turnover in excess of £500,000, unless the organisation is acting as a conduit for a partner that fulfils the criteria and may find it difficult to obtain access to funding through independent channels
- Organisations whose combined grant-related support costs and governance costs are greater than 10% of their turnover

Applications

The UIA Charitable Foundation

According to the company's website at the time of writing (October 2016):

> The UIA Charitable Foundation is not accepting new applications for funding at this time.
>
> The UIA Charitable Foundation has recently changed the way it seeks applications for funding. Applications are now sought only by proactive engagement with our key partners, our members and our staff. We are therefore unable to accept unsolicited applications.
>
> If your enquiry relates to anything other than an application, please write to us at: UIA Charitable Foundation, Kings Court, London Road, Stevenage, Herts SG1 2TP, or telephone 01438 761761 and ask to speak to the charity administrator.

UK Asset Resolution

Acquisitions

Correspondent: UKAR Press Office, Croft Road, Crossflatts, Bingley, West Yorkshire BD16 2UA (tel: 01274 555555/ 07909 213772; website: www.ukar.co.uk)

Directors: Brendan McDonagh; David Lunn; Ian Hares, Chief Executive Officer; John Tattersall, Chair; Keith Morgan; Michael Buckley; Sue Langley (women: 1; men: 6)

Year end	31/03/2016
Pre-tax profit	£1,175,800,000

Nature of business: UKAR has been established to facilitate the orderly management of the closed mortgage books of both Bradford & Bingley and Northern Rock Asset Management (NRAM) to maximise value for taxpayers.

The Executive team of UKAR manages both organisations focusing on this common objective, while ensuring that both companies continue to treat customers fairly, deliver consistently high levels of service and support those customers who are facing financial difficulty.

In addition, from 8 October 2013, UKAR Corporate Services (UKARcs) became responsible for the day to day administration of the Government's Help To Buy Mortgage Guarantee Scheme on behalf of HM Treasury. On 1 December 2015 UKARcs also became responsible for the administration of the Government's Help to Buy ISA Scheme on behalf of HM Treasury.

Company registration number: 7301961

Subsidiary undertakings include: Bradford & Bingley PLC; NRAM PLC; UKAR Corporate Services Ltd.

UK employees: 1,912

Focus of giving: General charitable purposes, health, ill health, children, young people.

Membership: BITC

Community involvement	✓
Community contributions	✓
Company reports on anti-slavery	✓
CSR report	✓
Directors have other relevant posts	✓
Cash donations declared	✓
Charity of the Year	✓
Employee-led support	✓
Gifts in kind	✓
Matched funding	✓
Payroll giving	✓

Charitable donations

Cash UK (latest available):	2016	£74,000
Total UK (cash and in kind):	2016	£74,000
Cash worldwide:	2016	£74,000
Total worldwide (cash and in kind):	2016	£74,000

Community involvement

UKAR's community investment approach focuses on using the skills of the business to support education in its communities; building the skills of its employees through community engagement; and supporting employees with their own community and charity initiatives.

Charity of the Year

The company supports a local charity, selected by employees, at each major site where it operates each year. In 2015/16 the charities supported were Yorkshire Air Ambulance in Crossflatts and Children North East in Doxford.

In 2016/17 the Charity of the Year selected by employees was Martin House Children's Hospice.

In previous years, support has been given to: Daft as a Brush Cancer Patient Care; Heart Research UK; and Mind.

Directors with other relevant posts

John Tattersall is Chair of The Oxford Diocesan Board of Finance and Retail Charity Bonds PLC and director of South East Institute for Theological Education and Diocesan Trustees (Oxford) Ltd. He is also Chair of the Court of the Royal Foundation of St Katharine, and a non-stipendiary priest in the Church of England.

Michael Buckley is an Adjunct Professor at the Department of Economics at NUI University College, Cork.

Brendan McDonagh serves on the advisory board of the business school of Trinity College Dublin.

Main locations

UKAR has offices in Crossflatts, West Yorkshire; and Doxford, Sunderland.

Community contributions

In 2015/16 the company matched both employee fundraising efforts totalling £34,000 and payroll giving totalling £40,000, bringing total corporate cash donations to the total of £74,000.

Beneficiaries included: Children in Need; Children North East; Sport Relief; Yorkshire Air Ambulance.

In-kind support

During 2015/16 employees made clothing donations to Martin House Children's Hospice. The company states in its annual report that this donation was worth £12,500.

Employee-led support

Employee fundraising

Employees fundraise for local and national charities and the company's charities of the year. Employees' fundraising efforts are matched by the company up to £250 per employee. The company also matches employee donations made through the payroll giving scheme. In 2015/16 employees raised £14,500 for Yorkshire Air Ambulance and £8,600 for Children North East.

Employee volunteering

Employees are given the opportunity to volunteer in their local communities for various charities. One such charity is Young Enterprise, which works with schools to inspire young people with the confidence, ability and ambition to succeed in a challenging and changing economy.

Applications

The company's website states that any enquiries regarding UKAR's Corporate Social Responsibility programme, which includes community support, should be made to the company's press team by phone or by using the online enquiry form on the website.

Ultra Electronics Holdings PLC

Defence, electronics/computers, security services, transport and communications

Correspondent: Corporate Responsibility Team, 417 Bridport Road, Greenford, Middlesex UB6 8UA (tel: 020 8813 4321; fax: 020 8813 4322; email: information@ultra-electronics.com; website: www.ultra-electronics.com)

Directors: Douglas Caster, Chair; John Hirst; Mark Anderson; Martin Broadhurst; Mary Waldner; Rakesh Sharma, Chief Executive; Sir Robert Walmsley (women: 1; men: 6)

Year end	31/12/2015
Turnover	£726,286,000
Pre-tax profit	£34,761,000

Nature of business: Ultra Electronics is an international defence, security, transport and energy company.

Company registration number: 2830397

Subsidiary undertakings include: Forensic Technology Inc.; Ultra Electronics Canada Inc.; Ultra Electronic Airport Systems Inc.

Total employees: 4,843

Focus of giving: Education, individuals, science technology.

Community involvement	✓
Community contributions	✓
Directors have other relevant posts	✓
AF Covenant	✓
Charity partner(s)	✓
Employee-led support	✓
Gifts in kind	✓
Matched funding	✓
Pro bono	✓
Shared-value alliances	✓
Sponsorship	✓
STEM-focused	✓

Community involvement

The group mainly supports STEM through engagement with schools and other education providers. Each of the businesses within the group has its own charitable budget and organises its own community activities.

Community engagement

The group's community activities are primarily focused on encouraging engagement with STEM. Each individual business within the group has its own charitable budget which can be used to engage in local communities.

The group's website and annual report state that many of its businesses have established relationships with local schools and higher education institutions to offer opportunities around STEM education. Examples include helping with school events, work placements, practice interviews, careers events, training programmes and visits to the company as part of AS level courses.

The group also participates in national initiatives to encourage participation in STEM, including offering Arkwright scholarships, which support students studying STEM subjects in their final years of school. In 2015 the group provided scholarships, as well as support and mentoring, to eight students.

Examples include Ultra Forensic Technology running a 'CSI for a day' scheme with local schools.

Directors with other relevant posts

Martin Broadhurst is also a trustee of the Royal Aeronautical Society (Charity Commission no. 313708). John Hirst is a trustee of Epilepsy Research UK (Charity Commission no. 1100394) and SUDEP Action (Charity Commission no. 1050459).

Main locations
The group has operations in the UK, Australia, the US and Canada. Operations in the UK are based in: Cheltenham; Dorset; High Wycombe; London; Manchester; Staffordshire.

Community contributions

No figure was given for the company's total community contributions in the 2015 annual report and accounts.

Employee-led support

The annual report states that the group encourages employees to volunteer and fundraise for local community initiatives, although it appears that this is organised at a local level by each business.

Examples outlined in the 2015 annual report include one business, Sonar Systems, which is supporting a local Code Club, set up by the charity of the same name, teaching programming to children aged 9 to 11. Another business, Ultra CIS, has established a policy allowing employees paid volunteering time and providing matched funding for events.

Applications

Community engagement is generally organised by each business in the group independently. Contact the relevant business for more information.

Unilever UK

Food manufacture, household

Correspondent: Sustainability Team, Unilever House, Springfield Drive, Leatherhead KT22 7GR (tel: 01372 945000; website: www.unilever.co.uk)

Directors: Ann Fudge; Chief Executive Officer; Feike Sijbesma; Graeme Pitkethly, Chief Financial Officer; Hixonia Nyasulu; John Rishton; Judith Hartmann; Laura Cha; Mary Ma; Michael Treschow, Chair; Nils Andersen; Prof. Louise Fresco; Vittorio Colao (women: 7; men: 7)

Year end	31/12/2015
Turnover	£39,944,000,000
Pre-tax profit	£5,414,000,000

Nature of business: Unilever is one of the world's leading suppliers of fast-moving consumer goods in foods, household and personal care products.

Unilever UK is based in a number of sites around the UK. The head office is in Walton-on-Thames, and it is from here that UK Community Involvement is managed.

Company registration number: 41424

Subsidiary undertakings include: Lipton Industries Inc.; Unilver Trading LLC; Unilver Australia Ltd.

Brands include: Dove; Domestos; Ben and Jerry's.

Total employees: 169,000

Focus of giving: Education, enterprise/training, environment, equal opportunities, health, ill health, heritage, less popular charitable purposes, humanitarian help, arts, culture, overseas projects, poverty and social exclusion, women's issues, children, young people, community/social welfare.

Membership: BITC

Community involvement	✓
Community contributions	✓
CSR report	✓
CSR or charity committee	✓
Directors have other relevant posts	✓
Charity partner(s)	✓
FTSE 100	✓
Gifts in kind	✓
Humanitarian aid: overseas	✓
Humanitarian aid: UK including food banks	✓
Overseas giving	✓
Pro bono	✓
Sponsorship	✓
Unpopular causes	✓

Community involvement

Unilever has a group-wide sustainability strategy, but activities such as employee volunteering, charitable donations and sponsorship are co-ordinated by local companies.

Examples of UK initiatives
The Lynx brand partnered with the charity CALM to raise awareness of male suicide, through their #BiggerIssues campaign.

The Dove Self Esteem project delivers sessions and workshops in schools, as well as providing online resources, aiming to improve the self-esteem of young people. Unilever employees volunteer to deliver these workshops on Dove Day, an annual event.

The group has a long-term relationship with Oxfam, supporting its UK Poverty programme, providing emergency food through food banks and supporting other opportunities.

The group also supports the Mayor of London's Team London's Young Ambassadors Programme, by providing brightFuture grants for schools to run social action projects.

Youth Employment
The company has expanded its apprenticeships scheme, as well as initiatives such as Feeding Ireland's Future, a campaign to raise awareness of careers in the food and grocery industries. It also offers placements to NEET young people through the Movement to Work programme. The Wall's ice cream brand relaunched its I am Wall's programme aimed at reducing youth unemployment, by providing training and opportunities for young people to become micro-entrepreneurs as ice cream vendors. In the UK, this programme has trained over 100 people.

Unilever Sustainable Living Plan
Unilever has an extensive Sustainable Living strategy, encompassing many different initiatives, partnerships and projects throughout the world. This entry discusses a few of these initiatives; for further information, refer to the Unilever website.

The group's sustainable living plan focuses on the following areas:

Improving health and well-being

- Health and hygiene
- Nutrition

Enhancing livelihoods

- Fairness in the workplace
- Opportunities for women
- Inclusive business

Reducing environmental impact

- Greenhouse gases
- Water
- Waste

The group has set targets to be achieved by 2020 in each of these areas.

UN Sustainable Development Goals
Unilever has engaged with the UN on the new Sustainable Development Goals, adopted in 2015, and has formed a partnership with the organisations Global Citizen and Project Everyone, to raise awareness about the SDGs and engage young people.

Climate change, sustainability and nutrition
Unilever is working with organisations including the World Economic Forum and the World Business Council for Sustainable Development to encourage businesses to take more action to prevent climate change. It is also working to encourage sustainable agriculture and nutrition through partnerships such as the Enhanced Livelihoods Investment Initiative, and with the Global Alliance for Improved Nutrition.

The group has a partnership with the Global Food bank Network, through which surplus food products can be redirected to those in need. Unilever employees are also encouraged to volunteer in food banks as part of this project, including with the Trussell Trust in the UK.

Health and hygiene
Examples of the group's international work in this area includes the Lifebuoy handwashing programme, which

received funding from the Department for International Development and the Children's Investment Fund Foundation, and focuses on improving child mortality rates in India through handwashing practices. Other partnerships include the Transform project, aiming to support social enterprises to work towards the SDGs, and working with Unicef to help improve access to toilets.

Women

Unilever has established a number of global partnerships to improve women's training, employment and livelihoods. Examples include supporting the UN HeForShe campaign.

brightFuture

Unilver also has an online platform called brightFuture, which aims to inspire people to get involved in social action and sustainable behaviours: brightfuture.unilever.com.

Directors with other relevant posts

Paul Polman, Chief Executive, is Chair of the World Business Council for Sustainable Development, on the board of the UN Global Compact, is President of the Kilimanjaro Blind Trust, and has received a number of different awards for contribution to responsible business, including WWF's Duke of Edinburgh Gold Conservation Medal and UN Environment Programme's Champion of the Earth Award. Ann Fudge is a trustee of the Rockefeller Foundation and Chair of the US Programs Advisory Panel of the Gates Foundation.

Main locations

The group has operations worldwide. In the UK, Unilever has its head office in London, research facilities in Port Sunlight (Wirral), Colworth (Bedfordshire) and Leeds, and manufacturing and distribution centres across the UK.

Employee-led support

Many of Unilever's partnerships and programmes involve employee volunteering – examples in the UK include volunteering for the Dove Self Esteem campaign, helping food banks, and handing out 'goodie bags' at the Pride in London parade.

Applications

The website states that donations and sponsorship decisions are made by local companies, and so any charity wishing to enquire about this should contact their local company using the contact form on the website: www.unilever.co.uk/contact.

Unipart Group of Companies Ltd

Acquisitions, instrumentation, motors and accessories, professional support services

Correspondent: Director of Corporate Affairs, Unipart House, Garsington Road, Cowley, Oxford OX4 2PG (tel: 01865 778966; website: www.unipart.co.uk)

Directors: Anthony Mourgue, Group Finance Director; Bryan Jackson; Frank Burns; Fred Vinton; John Clayton; John Neill, Chair and Group Chief Executive; Steve Johnson

Year end	31/12/2015
Turnover	£722,500,000
Pre-tax profit	£27,500,000

Nature of business: Unipart Group provides manufacturing, logistics and consultancy services in a range of markets including railway industry, automotive technology, retail and consumer industries.

Note: 'Unipart Group sold control of Unipart Automotive in 2011 and exercised no control over its operations since then.'

Company registration number: 1994997

Subsidiary undertakings include: E W (Holdings) Ltd; Gresty Road 2005 Ltd; Kautex Unipart Ltd; Serck Services (Bahrain) EC; and Van Wezel GmbH. For a full list of subsidiary undertakings see the accounts.

Focus of giving: Economic generation, education, environment, health, ill health, heritage, armed forces, overseas projects, arts, culture, poverty and social exclusion, sport, recreation, children, young people, community/social welfare.

Membership: BITC

Community involvement	✓
Community contributions	✓
CSR report	✓
CSR or charity committee	✓
Armed forces personnel	✓
Cash donations declared	✓
Gifts in kind	✓
Humanitarian aid: overseas	✓
Overseas giving	✓
Sponsorship	✓
STEM-focused	✓

Charitable donations

Cash UK (latest available):	2015	£58,000
Total UK (cash and in kind):	2015	£302,000
Cash worldwide:	2015	£58,000
Total worldwide (cash and in kind):	2015	£302,000

Community involvement

The group's community investment targets include:

- Investing 1% of pre-tax profit in community activities through cash donations, staff time, and gifts in-kind
- Having divisional cash donations level at £15,000 per division
- Making above 75% of community investment in areas of education, employability, health and economic development
- Having at least one community partner per site

Partnerships in India

Unipart's community strategy and partnership approach is not limited to the UK but applies across the global sites. In India three major sites – in Pune, Sanand and Bangalore – have all identified local schools to partner with.

Main location

Main UK location – Oxford (Global headquarters).

Unipart also has various locations worldwide.

Community contributions

According to the group's CSR Report for 2015, total community investment including employee-led fundraising totalled £380,000. The report says that:

> Over 75% of investment has been in form of time, reinforcing [the group's] belief that community activity and volunteering enhance employee engagement, and the value [it] can add through donating time and skills has more long-term value to [its] community partners than cash.

The support was given as follows:

Employee time	£231,000
Employee fundraising	£77,500
Company donations	£58,000
Gifts in-kind	£13,500
Total	**£380,000**

As is our usual practice, we have not included employee fundraising in the figure for total contributions.

Health and employability causes received most support.

Employee-led support

Volunteering

The group has partnerships in India, according to the 2015 CSR report:

> Our 3 major sites located in Pune, Sanand and Bangalore have all identified local schools to partner with – building employee engagement and reinforcing our values by providing opportunities for colleagues to volunteer and participate in activities to improve the facilities and learning environment available for local children.

According to the 2015 CSR report, over 60% of community investment has been in the form of time and the group has seen as 45% improvement in employee volunteering and community activity since 2010.

Exclusions

Unipart states in the online document Conducting Business The Unipart Way that it will not support 'an activity whose purpose is to benefit a political or morally corrupt cause'.

Applications

Apply in writing to the correspondent. Local sites can be approached directly.

Unite Group PLC

Property

Correspondent: Ali Hastings, Corporate Responsibility Manager, The Core, 40 St Thomas Street, Bristol BS1 6JX (tel: 0117 302 7000; email: info@unite-students.com; website: www.unite-group.co.uk)

Directors: Andrew Jones; Elizabeth McMeikan; Joe Lister, Chief Financial Officer; Manjit Wolstenholme; Mark Allan, Chief Executive Officer; Phil White, Chair; Prof. Sir Tim Wilson; Richard Simpson; Richard Smith (women: 2; men: 7)

Year end	31/12/2015
Turnover	£208,800,000
Pre-tax profit	£388,400,000

Nature of business: The group is involved in developing and co-managing student accommodation.

Company registration number: 3199160

Subsidiary undertakings include: LDC (St Pancras Way) Unit Trust; Leadmill Road Student Accommodation Ltd Partnership; Unite Finance One PLC.

UK employees: 1,250

Total employees: 1,250

Focus of giving: Education, enterprise/training, equal opportunities, health, ill health, housing, homelessness, individuals, marginalised people, humanitarian help, children, young people, community/social welfare, disability.

Membership: BITC

Accredited Living Wage Employer	✓
Community involvement	✓
Community contributions	✓
Company reports on anti-slavery	✓
CSR report	✓
CSR or charity committee	✓
Directors have other relevant posts	✓
Charity of the Year	✓
Charity partner(s)	✓
Corporate charity	✓
Employee-led support	✓
Gifts in kind	✓
Humanitarian aid: UK including food banks	✓
Matched funding	✓
Pro bono	✓
Shared-value alliances	✓

Charitable donations

Cash UK (latest available):	2015	£1,250,000
Total UK (cash and in kind):	2015	£1,315,000
Cash worldwide:	2015	£1,250,000
Total worldwide (cash and in kind):	2015	£1,315,000

Community involvement

The group works with charity partners, charities of the year, offers volunteer and in-kind support and also offers support through its corporate charity, The Unite Foundation.

The Unite Foundation

The company's corporate charity, The Unite Foundation (Charity Commission/OSCR no. 1147344/SC043324) focuses on social mobility and educational inequality. It works to enable those from disadvantaged backgrounds to access higher education, to encourage students to engage with their local communities and to help young people develop skills and access employment. Its main area of activity is providing scholarships, including free accommodation, to undergraduate students from disadvantaged backgrounds, particularly those who have been in care or who have a difficult home background. The foundation currently works in partnership with ten universities to deliver this scheme and the company's 2015 annual report states that during the 2015/16 academic year, around 125 scholarships were provided. More information can be found on the foundation's website: www.unitefoundation.co.uk.

Partnerships

The company supports three charities (in addition to its work through the Unite Foundation), selected because of their shared purposes with the company: IntoUniversity; Enactus and LandAid.

Charity of the Year

During 2015 the company launched a new Charity of the Year scheme, with Sport Relief selected as a national Charity of the Year and 22 further 'City Charities of the Year' selected by local teams.

Directors with other relevant posts

Mark Allan is also a trustee of Anchor Trust (Charity Commission no. 1052183). Prof. Sir Tim Wilson was previously Vice-Chancellor of the University of Hertfordshire, was on the board of the Higher Education Funding Council for England (HEFCE) and a trustee of The Council for Industry and Higher Education (CIHE) (Charity Commission no. 1066956). Joe Lister is also a trustee of The Unite Foundation (Charity Commission no. 1147344).

Main locations

The group has accommodation across the UK, in major university cities. The head office is in London.

Community contributions

The 2015 Responsible Business Review states that the total amount donated from the company to its three partner charities, as well as to the Unite Foundation, was £1.25 million. In addition, it is reported that in-kind and cash donations totalled £171,000, including donations of products from customers and employees to Cancer Research UK which totalled £106,000.

Employee-led support

Employee volunteering and fundraising

Employees are entitled to a day of paid volunteering with a local charitable cause; in 2015, around 20% of employees volunteered for a total of 34 charities. The annual report states that this amounted to around £35,000 worth of in-kind support through volunteering.

The company also provides matched funding for employees' fundraising initiatives.

Employee and customer-led in-kind support

Each of the company's properties has a collection point for a local food bank, where customers and employees can donate items.

The company also has a national partnership with Cancer Research UK, allowing employees and customers to donate unwanted goods for the charity at collection points in the company's properties.

Corporate charity

The UNITE Foundation (Charity Commission no. 1147344).

Applications

Apply in writing to the Corporate Responsibility Manager.

To apply to the Unite Foundation, or to get more information about the foundation, contact: info@unitefoundation.co.uk or call 0117 302 7073.

United Utilities Group PLC

Electricity, oil and gas/fuel, water

Correspondent: Julia (Ksiezyk) Hellyer, Corporate Responsibility Manager, Haweswater House, Lingley Mere Business Park, Lingey Green Avenue, Great Sankey, Warrington WA5 3LP (tel: 01925 237000; fax: 0845 070 2058; email:

sustainability@uuplc.co.uk; website: www.unitedutilities.com)

Directors: Alison Goligher; Brian May; Dr John McAdam, Chair; Mark Clare; Russ Houlden, Chief Financial Officer; Sara Weller; Stephen Carter; Steve Mogford, Chief Executive Officer (women: 2; men: 6)

Year end	31/03/2016
Turnover	£1,730,000,000
Pre-tax profit	£353,500,000

Nature of business: United Utilities Group PLC is the intermediate holding company of the UK's largest listed water business. The group owns and manages the regulated water and wastewater network in the North West of England, through its subsidiary United Utilities Water PLC (UUW), which constitutes the vast majority of the group's assets and profit. The group also applies its utility skills to manage and operate other utility infrastructure.

Company registration number: 6559020

Subsidiary undertakings include: North West Water International Ltd; United Utilities International Ltd; YCL Transport Ltd.

UK employees: 5,682

Total employees: 5,682

Focus of giving: Education, enterprise/training, environment, non-registered charities, small groups, older people, poverty and social exclusion, children, young people, community/social welfare.

Membership: BITC, LBG

Community involvement	✓
Community contributions	✓
Company reports on anti-slavery	✓
CSR report	✓
CSR or charity committee	✓
Directors have other relevant posts	✓
Charity of the Year	✓
Charity partner(s)	✓
Company gives to smaller charities	✓
Corporate charity	✓
Employee-led support	✓
FTSE 100	✓
Gifts in kind	✓
Matched funding	✓
STEM-focused	✓
Unregistered charities/NFP	✓

Charitable donations

Cash UK (latest available):	2016	£1,600,000
Total UK (cash and in kind):	2016	£1,600,000
Cash worldwide:	2016	£1,600,000
Total worldwide (cash and in kind):	2016	£1,600,000

Community involvement

The group makes community contributions locally, particularly in areas in which it is delivering long-running and disruptive engineering work. Contributions include cash donations, employee volunteering, in-kind support and schemes such as providing debt advisory services. Support has been given for social and environmental issues that relate to the group's business objectives. This includes promoting social and economic well-being, increasing youth employment, and educational initiatives. The group also helps its customers who are struggling financially.

United Utilities Trust Fund (Charity Commission no. 1108296)

This grant-making trust was established in 2005 to help people out of poverty and debt and is funded partly by United Utilities and partly by contribution from customers through their water bills. The group's website states it invests £5 million per year into the trust.

As with similar trusts established by other utility companies, it primarily assists customers who are unable to pay their water bills. According to the trust's website, it is also able to make grants to organisations to support debt and money advice work. The trust has previously supported organisations such as: Advocacy Wirral; Blackpool Citizens Advice; Gaddum Centre; Manchester Refugee Support Network; and Wythenshawe Law Centre.

Community Fund

The group's Community Fund offers grants between £500 and £1,000 to voluntary organisations and charities in selected communities where United Utilities is carrying out engineering work. The availability of grants are advertised locally and on the group's website. Projects must be able to demonstrate how they:

- Address a community issue
- Provide long-term community benefit
- Are innovative in their approach

Examples of previous beneficiaries include: church groups; hospices; Morris dancing troupes; and sports clubs.

Partnerships

The group has long-standing partnerships with several organisations, including: BeachCare; Groundwork; and RSPB. Employees volunteer for these partners on dedicated volunteering days for different teams within the business.

The group partners with Groundwork in its community investment programme and has jointly developed a Social Impact Assessment to assess the social impact of the group's investments in local projects where it operates.

In Cumbria, the group has been helping first responder groups, such as Grange and District Community First Responders, to purchase defibrillators.

Charity of the Year

A charity partner is chosen with the help of employees and is supported through employee fundraising efforts which are increased by the group's matched funding. The group has been supporting the same charity partner, North West Air Ambulance, since 2011. Employee fundraising efforts and the matched funding scheme provided a total of £250,000 'to date' (as stated on the website).

Rivington Heritage Trust (Charity Commission no. 1064700)

The trust was set up by United Utilities to preserve and take care of Rivington Terraced Gardens. The charity's 2014/15 annual report notes that several United Utilities employees are trustees, with other members including Chorley Borough Councils, Lancashire County Council and several independent trustees. In 2014/15 United Utilities donated £54,000 to the charity. For further information on the charity visit www.rivingtonheritagetrust.co.uk

Education

In order to contribute to educational causes United Utilities:

- Runs an educational programme tailored at primary and secondary schoolchildren, which includes: water efficiency workshops; online resources; protecting and enhancing beaches and bathing waters; and career advice (for STEM subjects)
- Partners with the Warrington-based Future Tech Studio college (part of the partnership will see work experience opportunities for the students)
- Works with UTV Media to run an annual schools campaign allowing students the chance to create a radio ad

Recreation

The group owns and manages over 55,000 hectares of land around its reservoirs in Cheshire; Cumbria; Greater Manchester; Lancashire; and the Peak District. It has initiated the following activities to encourage and develop public access:

- Produced an interactive map
- Resurfaced bridleways and footpaths and maintained public access infrastructure
- Runs an ongoing campaign to educate people of the dangers of swimming in reservoirs

Directors with other relevant posts

Stephen Carter is a governor of the Royal Shakespeare Company.

Sara Weller is a board member of the Higher Education Funding Council for England and a council member at Cambridge University.

Main locations

The group has a head office based in Lingley Mere, Warrington and another main office in Whitehaven, Cumbria. It also has 575 wastewater treatment works and 96 water treatment works located in various North West locations from Crewe to Carlisle.

Community contributions

According to the website, the group made community contributions in the UK totalling £1.83 million in 2015/16 as measured by the LGB method. This includes employee time, cash and in-kind donations. The group's corporate responsibility department provided us with the following information, breaking down the group's community contributions:

Cash	£1.6 million
Management costs	£182,000
Time	£60,000
In-kind	£0

As is our usual practice we have not included management costs in our figure for the group's total contributions.

Beneficiaries included: Age UK Rochdale; Beachcare; Future Teach Studio; Grange and District Community First Responders; Groundwork UK; North West Air Ambulance; Rivington Heritage Trust; Royal Society for the Protection of Birds (RSPB); UTV Media.

Employee-led support

Employee volunteering

The group's employees are allowed three days to volunteer in the local community. According to the website, in 2015/16 over 500 employees gave 3,000 hours of voluntary work within business time (which is calculated as the equivalent to a £60,000 investment). Activities included: delivering talks and workshops in schools to encourage study and careers in STEM subjects (science, technology, engineering and maths) and participating in various environmental projects (such as tree planting, beach cleaning and scrub clearance). During special volunteering days staff members volunteer for the group's partners.

Commercially led support

Help for customers

The group has a number of schemes to support customers in disadvantaged communities/circumstances:

Help to Pay

The group has partnered with Age UK Rochdale to raise awareness of its new social tariff Help to Pay. This scheme caps water bills for low income pensioners.

The Arrears Allowance Scheme

The scheme allows customers to clear their water bill debts more quickly by receiving matched funding from the group – £1 contribution for every £1 paid (for the first six months), and afterwards £2 for every £1 paid, until the arrears are cleared.

WaterSure

This financial support scheme is designed for customers with water meters who receive benefits and have either a family member with a medical condition that requires the use of large amounts of water or have three children or more.

The Support Tariff

This means-tested tariff promoted in conjunction with debt advice agencies in the region is currently on a trial basis and is only available to people in East Lancashire, Flyde Coast and certain Liverpool postcodes who are in receipt of a means-tested benefit, in arrears and live in rented accommodation.

Corporate charity

United Utilities Trust Fund (Charity Commission no. 1108296).

Exclusions

According to the website, the following projects are ineligible for the Community Fund:

- Grant and loan schemes (for example local credit unions, community loan funds etc.)
- Projects to promote a specific religious group (applications from religious or faith groups are welcome if they can demonstrate a benefit to the wider community)
- Core activities of statutory services (for example libraries or essential health services.) Statutory service providers seeking funding for special projects or initiatives outside of their core service provision are welcome
- Party political activity (including fundraising, campaigning or any other activity associated with any political party)
- Individual sponsorship

In addition, awards from the fund are not made for recurrent expenditure, running costs, salaries, and the purchase of land or buildings.

Applications

The group: The group have informed us they are not looking for any new community partners or charities to support at the present time. They have advised that organisations seeking further information about this should be directed to the 'community investment' tab under 'corporate responsibility' on the group's website.

Applications are normally made by writing to the Corporate Responsibility (CR) Manager or Committee, which is chaired by Stephen Carter. The CR Committee is comprised of senior leaders across the group.

The United Utilities Trust Fund: Grant opportunities for organisations are advertised on the trust's website. Enquiries regarding future funding rounds can be addressed to Gay Hammett at Auriga Services Ltd on 0121 321 1324 to by email: info@aurigaservices.co.uk

Enquiries regarding the trust can be addressed to the Secretary (tel: 0845 179 1791; email: contact@uutf.org.uk) at Emmanuel Court, 12–14 Mill Street, Sutton Coldfield B72 1TJ. For more details see www.uutf.org.uk/Grants.htm.

Unum Ltd

Insurance

Correspondent: Susan Sanderson, CSR Manager, Milton Court, Dorking, Surrey RH4 3LZ (tel: 01306 887766; email: susan.sanderson@unum.co.uk; website: www.unum.co.uk)

Directors: Cheryl Black; Clifton Melvin; David Stewart; Malcolm McCaig; Peter O'Donnell, Chief Executive Officer; Rick McKenney, Chair; Steve Harry (women: 1; men: 6)

Year end	31/12/2015
Turnover	£66,700,000
Pre-tax profit	£83,300,000

Nature of business: The company provides income protection insurance products, including income protection, life insurance and critical illness cover. Its immediate parent company is Unum European Holding Company Ltd (UEHCL), through UEHCL's ownership of the Company's class A share capital. Unum Group, incorporated in the USA, is the ultimate parent company and controlling party.

Unum Ltd is a member of the Unum Group of Companies.

Company registration number: 983768

Subsidiary undertakings include: Claims Services International Ltd

Focus of giving: Education, environment, health, ill health, heritage, local appeals not in area of the company's presence, local groups, humanitarian help, older people, arts, culture, playgroups, poverty and social exclusion, children, young people, community/social welfare, disability.

Community involvement	✓
Community contributions	✓
CSR report	✓
CSR or charity committee	✓
Charity partner(s)	✓
Company gives to smaller charities	✓
Employee-led support	✓
Gifts in kind	✓
Humanitarian aid: UK including food banks	✓
Matched funding	✓

Payroll giving ✓
Pro bono ✓

Charitable donations

Cash UK (latest available):	2015	£117,000
Total UK (cash and in kind):	2015	£117,000
Cash worldwide:	2015	£117,000
Total worldwide (cash and in kind):	2015	£117,000

Community involvement

The group has a grants scheme for charities working in the areas of education; health and well-being; and arts, culture and sport. It also supports charities through partnership work, and employees nominate national and regional charities to fundraise for. Employees can also volunteer for two working days each year, as well as donate through the payroll giving scheme, for which the group provides matched funding.

Grants for charities

The group's charitable donations scheme provides grants of up to £10,000 to registered charities working in the following areas: education; health and well-being (including disability); arts, culture and sport. There is some consideration given to organisations with which employees are involved.

Partner charities

The group's employees choose four charities to support under the charity partnerships programmes – one national charity and three regional charities for each of the group's offices. In 2016 and 2017, the chosen partner charities are: The Guide Dogs for the Blind Association; St Michael's Hospice (North Hampshire); Children's Hospice South West; and Rainbow Trust.

The group also has a long-term partnership with Maggie's, a charity offering support to cancer patients. The partnership focuses on supporting people who have had cancer to return to work, conducting research and producing a toolkit for employers and employees. The group also makes donations to the charity.

In 2016 the group also worked in partnership with the Mental Health Foundation and Oxford Economics to produce a report on mental health in the workplace.

Education and employability

As well as supporting education charities and schools through donations and employee volunteering, the group also offers work experience positions for students and attends school career fairs.

Main locations

The group's UK head office is based in Dorking, Surrey. The other two main offices are in Basingstoke and Bristol, and there are also regional sales offices in Birmingham, Glasgow and London.

Community contributions

In 2015 the group donated £117,000 to charities through its grants programme.

£72,000 was given to the group's national and local charity partners during the year, which appears to be raised through employee-led fundraising.

In-kind support

Pro bono

The 2016 CSR report states that the group is looking to do more pro bono work, and has previously helped charities with strategy development, marketing and campaigns.

Employee-led support

Employee volunteering and fundraising

The group has a number of Charity and Community Champions who organise volunteering opportunities and charity events, as well as sitting on the Charitable Donations Committee, helping to decide which causes to support.

Employees are entitled to up to two working days per year to volunteer for a local charity or community project. In 2016 employees volunteered almost 4,000 hours in total for a range of different projects and community partners, as well as offering unpaid professional support with areas such as accounting, social media and marketing. Examples in 2015 included employees mentoring year 9 pupils at a school in Basingstoke, offering advice on subject choices, finances and working effectively; mentoring students from disadvantaged backgrounds through IntoUniversity.

The group's employees fundraise for its chosen national and regional charity partners, organising events to fundraise. In 2016 fundraising initiatives included bake sales, sports days and charity auctions organised by employees. There is also an annual food drive in which employees donate food and toiletries to charities and community projects.

Payroll giving and matched funding

There is a payroll giving scheme and the group also provides matched funding for employee donations that fall under any of the three focus areas that the group supports.

Exclusions

The group does not provides support for: administration, staff or other general running costs; organisations that have a political or religious affiliation; medical research.

Grants are only awarded to registered charities supporting at least one of the specified areas of focus (education; health and well-being; arts, culture and sport).

Applications

Charitable donations

Application forms for the group's charitable grants scheme are available on the website, along with guidance about what should be included. Applications are considered four times a year by the charitable donations committee and only one application per organisation will be considered in a 12 month period. Some preference is also given to organisations with which Unum employees are involved.

Other requests

The group's CSR team can be contacted for any other queries.

The 2016 corporate responsibility report also states the following: 'In 2017, we hope to start funding more community support for people with health problems to reach their potential in education and at work. If you have an idea about a project you would like us to support, then please get in touch.'

Victrex PLC

Chemicals and plastics

Correspondent: Staff Committee (Charity Donations), Victrex Technology Centre, Hillhouse International, Thornton Cleveleys, Lancashire FY5 4QD (tel: 01253 897700; email: ir@victrex.com; website: www.victrex.com)

Directors: Andrew Dougal; David Hummel, Chief Executive; Jane Toogood; Larry Pentz, Chair; Louisa Burdett, Group Finance Director; Martin Court; Pamela Kirby; Patrick De Smedt; Tim Cooper (women: 3; men: 6)

Year end	30/09/2015
Turnover	£263,500,000
Pre-tax profit	£106,400,000

Nature of business: Victrex PLC, a leading global manufacturer of high performance polymers, comprises two divisions: Victrex Polymer Solutions that focuses on transport, industrial and the electronics markets and Invibio Biomaterial Solutions that focuses on providing specialist solutions for medical device manufacturers.

Company registration number: 2793780

Subsidiary undertakings include: Invibio Ltd; Kleiss Gears Inc.; Victrex USA Holdings Ltd.

Focus of giving: Education, local groups, science technology, children, young people, community/social welfare.

Membership: BITC

Community involvement ✓
Community contributions ✓
CSR report ✓

CSR or charity committee	✓
Cash donations declared	✓
Charity partner(s)	✓
Employee-led support	✓
Gifts in kind	✓
Pro bono	✓
Sponsorship	✓
STEM-focused	✓

Charitable donations

Cash UK (latest available):	2015	£141,000
Total UK (cash and in kind):	2015	£141,000
Cash worldwide:	2015	£141,000
Total worldwide (cash and in kind):	2015	£141,000

Community involvement

The group has set sustainability goals to be achieved by 2023 in three areas: sustainable solutions; resource efficiency; social responsibility.

Education

The group's social responsibility goals focus on the promotion of STEM subjects in education, inspiring young people through education activities. One of the group's interim goals, which was achieved, was to have a joint project running with the Catalyst Science Education centre in Runcorn; the group has established a 'Polymer Zone' exhibition in the museum in 2014.

The group has a partnership with Fleetwood High School, which is located near to the head office, through Business in the Community's Business Class scheme.

Main locations

The group has operations in the UK and internationally. Its head office is based in Thornton Cleveleys, Lancashire.

Community contributions

In 2015 the group made charitable donations of £141,000 in the UK.

Employee-led support

Company charitable donations

Charitable donations from the company in the UK are co-ordinated by the Staff Committee, and are awarded mainly to local charities nominated by employees, but also occasionally to national or overseas charities with which employees are involved.

Volunteering

One of the group's interim sustainability targets was to have established an employee network to support STEM activities in the UK by the end of 2015, and globally by the end of 2016. In 2015 this included training 11 STEM&SIP (Science Industry Partnership) ambassadors, who can represent the company at events such as careers fairs and science days, as well as providing support such as mentoring to students.

The 2015 sustainability report states that during the year, 100 employees spent 564 hours in total volunteering in local communities.

Applications

Apply in writing to the correspondent.

Virgin Money PLC

Financial services, banking

Correspondent: Culture & Community Team, Jubilee House, Gosforth, Newcastle upon Tyne NE3 4PL (email: community@virginmoney.com; website: uk.virginmoney.com)

Directors: Colin Keogh; Geeta Gopalan; Glen Moreno, Chair; Gordon McCallum; Jayne-Anne Gadhia, Chief Executive; Marilyn Spearing; Norman McLuskie; Patrick McCall (women: 3; men: 8)

Year end	09/12/2016
Turnover	£521,900,000
Pre-tax profit	£168,300,000

Nature of business: Virgin Money PLC is a bank and financial services company owned by the Virgin Group and based in the UK.

Company registration number: 6952311

Subsidiary undertakings include: Northern Rock Ltd; Virgin Card Ltd; Virgin Money Giving Ltd.

UK employees: 3,058

Total employees: 3,058

Focus of giving: Economic generation, education, enterprise/training, fundraising events, housing, homelessness, medical research, financial education, poverty and social exclusion, children, young people, community/social welfare.

Membership: BITC

Community involvement	✓
Community contributions	✓
Company reports on anti-slavery	✓
CSR report	✓
CSR or charity committee	✓
Directors have other relevant posts	✓
Charity of the Year	✓
Charity partner(s)	✓
Corporate charity	✓
Employee-led support	✓
Gifts in kind	✓
Market-led giving	✓
Matched funding	✓
Sponsorship	✓

Charitable donations

Total UK (cash and in kind):	2016	£985,000
Total worldwide (cash and in kind):	2016	£985,000

Community involvement

According to the 2015 annual report, Virgin Money's community programme covers four areas: fundraising; education, employability and enterprise; supporting local communities; supporting employee engagement in local communities. Support is given through the Virgin Money Foundation to projects in the North East. The group also sponsors the London Marathon and has an online donation platform, Virgin Money Giving.

Virgin Money Foundation (Charity Commission no. 1161290)

Established in 2015, the Virgin Money Foundation supports disadvantaged communities, initially in the North East, with a view to expansion. Funding is given for youth education and employment, homelessness support, social enterprise and feasibility studies for large capital projects. In 2015 the first round of grants was made to 26 organisations, totalling £1 million. A further £1 million per year has been committed by the government for four years (including 2015), which is matched by Virgin Money. The group also covers the foundation's running costs.

Charity of the Year

The group's Charity of the Year for 2016/17 is the Heads Together campaign, a coalition of mental health charities, which will be the official charity for the 2017 Virgin Money London Marathon. In for 2016, the Charity of the Year was NSPCC.

Education

Make £5 Grow and Fiver Challenge

The group runs an annual competition with primary schools across the UK to encourage enterprise and related skills, by providing pupils aged 9–11 with a loan of £5 each to start small business initiatives. Further information can be found at: make-5-grow.co.uk. Similarly, the group also supports the Fiver Challenge, run by the charity Young Enterprise. In 2015 over 245 schools participated in the Make £5 Grow scheme and 500 schools took part in the Fiver Challenge.

LifeSavers

Through the LifeSavers scheme, the group supports financial education in primary schools and the establishment of savings clubs with local credit unions, encouraging children to save small, regular amounts of money.

Virgin Money Giving

Virgin Money Giving is an online platform created by Virgin Money to enable online fundraising and donations. The website is not-for-profit, with running costs covered by a start-up fee and 2% of donations from each charity. All donations and Gift Aid are passed to each charity. In 2015 donations made through Virgin Money Giving, including Gift Aid, totalled £92.5 million.

Directors with other relevant posts
Jayne-Anne Gadhia is Chair of Business in the Community Scotland (OSCR no. SC007195). Geeta Gopalan is Vice-Chair of the England Committee of the Big Lottery Fund.

Main locations
The group has four main offices in the UK: Edinburgh, London, Newcastle and Norwich. It also has stores across the UK.

Community contributions

The 2015 accounts for the Virgin Money Foundation state that, during the year, the foundation received donations from Virgin Money totalling £985,000, including in-kind services (staff, office space and other support). As we were unable to find any other figures, we have taken this figure as the group's total charitable contributions for the year. The group has committed to make an annual donation of £1 million to the foundation for the subsequent three years 2016–18.

In-kind support

The group offers use of its Virgin Money Lounges free of charge to community groups and charities for running events.

Employee-led support

Employee volunteering and fundraising
Employees of Virgin Money are entitled to a number of days paid volunteering leave each year and in 2015 employees volunteered a total of over 1,300 days. Examples include taking part in fundraising initiatives, volunteering with local charities or in charity appeal call centres, and acting as ambassadors for the Make £5 Grow scheme in schools. Through the Virgin Money London Marathon, employees raised more than £3.7 million for the official charity partner for 2015, Cancer Research UK.

Commercially led support

Sponsorship
The group sponsors the Virgin Money London Marathon and provides the official fundraising site for the marathon, Virgin Money Giving (www.virginmoneygiving.com). In 2016 the marathon raised £59.4 million for charities. The official Charity of the Year for 2016 was NSPCC, which raised more than £2 million through the event.

Virgin Money also sponsors events on the Edinburgh Festival Fringe (Virgin Money Fringe on the Royal Mile and the Virgin Money Fringe on the Mound), as well as the Fireworks Concert which concludes the Edinburgh International Festival.

Corporate charity

The Virgin Money Foundation (Charity Commission no. 1161290).

Applications

The group
Queries can be sent by email: community@virginmoney.com or in writing: Culture and Community Team, Virgin Money, Discovery House, Whiting Road, Norwich NR4 6EJ.

Virgin Money Foundation
Refer to the website for information on the foundation's grants schemes and what is currently available: www.virginmoneyfoundation.org.uk.

Vodafone Group PLC

Telecommunications

Correspondent: Jane Frapwell, Corporate Communications Manager, Vodafone House, The Connection, Newbury, Berkshire RG14 2FN (tel: 01635 693693/0333 304 2685; email: jane.frapwell@vodafone.com; website: www.vodafone.com)

Directors: Dame Clara Furse; David Nish; Dr Mathias Dopfner; Gerard Kleisterlee, Chair; Nick Land; Nick Read, Chief Financial Officer; Philip Yea; Renee James; Samuel Jonah; Sir Crispin Davis; Valerie Gooding; Vittorio Colao, Chief Executive (women: 3; men: 9)

Year end	31/03/2016
Turnover	£42,227,000,000
Pre-tax profit	£1,095,000,000

Nature of business: The group is a mobile telecommunications provider operating worldwide.

Company registration number: 1833679

Subsidiary undertakings include: Jaguar Communications Ltd; Quickcomm UK Ltd; Vodafone Finance Ltd.

Total employees: 107,667

Focus of giving: Education, enterprise/training, environment, health, ill health, heritage, local groups, armed forces, overseas projects, older people, poverty and social exclusion, science technology, women's issues, children, young people, community/social welfare, disasters.

Community involvement	✓
Community contributions	✓
Company reports on anti-slavery	✓
CSR report	✓
Directors have other relevant posts	✓
AF Covenant	✓
Charity partner(s)	✓
Corporate charity	✓
Employee-led support	✓
FTSE 100	✓
Gifts in kind	✓
Humanitarian aid: overseas	✓
Matched funding	✓
Overseas giving	✓
Payroll giving	✓
Pro bono	✓
Sponsorship	✓

Community involvement

Much of the group's charitable activities are channelled through its corporate charity, the Vodafone Foundation, although there are also initiatives supported through employees and local stores. Quarterly updates of UK charitable activities are provided in the sustainability newsletters on the Vodafone Media Centre website (mediacentre.vodafone.co.uk).

Vodafone Foundation
The group's corporate charity, the Vodafone Foundation supports a wide range of causes. The group has 28 local foundations across the globe. The UK-registered Vodafone Foundation (Charity Commission no. 1089625) encompasses both UK and wider activities. Initiatives include the JustTextGiving platform, and TecSOS, which are both detailed below.

JustTextGiving
Vodafone developed JustTextGiving, a text donation service for charities to raise money through text donations. The company invested £5 million in the creation of the platform, and maintains the running costs. The platform is used by over 20,000 charities, as well as to support ITV's Text Santa appeal. The company also challenges employees to raise £100 in text donations and matches the funds raised, as well as giving an award for the JustTextGiving fundraiser of the year.

TecSOS
Funded by the Vodafone Foundation, the group has developed the TecSOS phone, which is designed to help those at risk of domestic violence. The phone allows the caller to contact the police with the touch of one button, which can be used covertly, and calls are treated with priority by the police, who can see the caller's location.

Other partnerships
Other partnerships between Vodafone UK and charitable organisations include working with the Scout Association to develop their Digital Manifesto, as well as providing support through employee volunteering, supported by the Vodafone Foundation.

Community Connections
According to Vodafone UK's 2016 spring sustainability report, every month five local Vodafone stores, of which there are over 500 in the UK, can invite local charities and voluntary organisations to apply for a £1,000 award, through the Community Connections scheme.

Global transformation goals
At a global level, the group's sustainability activities focus on three goals:

- Women's empowerment
- Energy innovation
- Youth skills and jobs

The group runs a variety of projects and initiatives internationally to achieve these goals. Examples include:

- Funding for girls to attend school in India
- Providing mobile banking services for women entrepreneurs in low and middle income countries
- Supporting the UN's HeForShe campaign
- Supporting the Paris Pledge for Action on climate change
- Working with Enactus to support social entrepreneurs in Egypt
- Providing mentoring, apprenticeships and internships, as well as bursaries for STEM education

Further details of the group's international activities can be found in the 2016 sustainability report, available on the website.

Directors with other relevant posts
Sir Crispin Davis is a member of the council of the University of Oxford. Valerie Gooding is a trustee of English National Ballet (Charity Commission no. 214005) and of the Royal Botanic Gardens, Kew. Philip Yea is a trustee of The Francis Crick Institute (Charity Commission no. 1140062). Nick Land is Chair of Trustees of the Vodafone Foundation.

Main locations
The group operates in 26 countries worldwide, as well as the UK.

Community contributions

No figure was provided for the group's charitable contributions.

Employee-led support

Employee volunteering
Vodafone UK gives employees 24 hours of paid volunteering leave every year, which can be taken either as individuals or in teams.

Supported by the Vodafone Foundation, employees also volunteer as 'Vodafone Business Buddies' through the Take a Chance programme run with Education Business Partnership West Berkshire, mentoring and coaching students, to develop their skills and experience and to provide an insight into how the business works. There is also an Enterprise and Skills Day at Newbury Racecourse, where students take part in challenges with Vodafone employees.

Many employees also volunteer to take calls in the company's call centres for the ITV Text Santa appeal.

Employee fundraising
Vodafone UK provides matched funding of up to £350 for employee fundraising initiatives, and also runs a payroll giving scheme.

The group also ran the Vodafone Big Bold Challenge in 2015, encouraging employees to take part in a series of challenges to raise money for charities.

Corporate charity

The Vodafone Foundation (Charity Commission no. 1089625).

Exclusions

No political donations are made.

Applications

The group
Apply in writing to the correspondent.

The foundation
Further details can be found on The Vodafone Foundation's website (www.vodafonefoundation.org). Alternatively, you can email groupfoundation@vodafone.co.uk.

Waitrose Ltd

Retail – supermarkets

Correspondent: See 'Applications', Doncastle Road, Southern Industrial Area, Bracknell, Berkshire RG12 8YA (tel: 01344 424680; website: www.waitrose.com/home/about_waitrose/our_company/coporate_social_responsibility.html)

Directors: Andrew Mayfield; John Lewis; Loraine Woodhouse, Finance Director; Mark Williamson; Nigel Keen; Rob Collins, Managing Director; Tom Athron (women: 1; men: 6)

Year end	30/01/2016
Turnover	£6,338,500,000
Pre-tax profit	£66,600,000

Nature of business: Waitrose Ltd operates supermarkets and convenience stores, Leckford Farm, online sales and business to business contracts. The company is a wholly owned subsidiary of John Lewis PLC, within the John Lewis Partnership.

Company registration number: 99405

Subsidiary undertakings include: Admiral Park Retail Management Ltd; Waitrose (Guernsey) Ltd; Waitrose (Jersey) Ltd.

UK employees: 58,970

Total employees: 58,970

Focus of giving: Economic generation, education, environment, health, ill health, housing, homelessness, small groups, local groups, humanitarian help, older people, overseas projects, poverty and social exclusion, children, young people, community/social welfare.

Membership: BITC

Community involvement	✓
Community contributions	✓
CSR report	✓
CSR or charity committee	✓
Cash donations declared	✓
Charity partner(s)	✓
Company gives to smaller charities	✓
Employee-led support	✓
Gifts in kind	✓
Humanitarian aid: overseas	✓
Humanitarian aid: UK including food banks	✓
Market-led giving	✓
Overseas giving	✓
Payroll giving	✓
Sponsorship	✓

Community involvement

As part of the John Lewis Partnership, Waitrose's community involvement is reported on alongside that of John Lewis, the department store operator. The 'Our Communities' section of the partnership's website explains: 'Contributing to the wellbeing of our communities was written into our Constitution by our founder. It remains a priority for us today.'

John Lewis Partnership encourages decision-making to be made at a local level by partners at individual Waitrose (and John Lewis) stores, who are supported to invest skills, time, resources and expertise into the communities in which they live and work. The partnership's website describes how it also manages community programmes centrally, which support its 'brand activity and motivate Partners and others to get involved'.

The partnership's community investment programmes have been created around three themes: Empowerment and Livelihoods; Health and Wellness; and Environment.

Empowerment and Livelihoods
The John Lewis Partnership's website states:

> We operate in a number of communities – both nationally and globally. What many of these communities have in common is that they can struggle with limited access to education, a skills gap and high levels of unemployment. They are also home to our Partners, customers, and suppliers.
>
> We run numerous projects and initiatives to help empower and enhance the wellbeing of the people in these communities. Projects involve education, supporting enterprise and employability, and promoting sustainable livelihoods.

Waitrose/partnership initiatives under this theme include:

- The Waitrose Foundation:
- British Red Cross: John Lewis Partnership has donated almost £1 million to the British Red Cross over the past 15 years. Recent relief efforts have included the response to

flooding in the UK. In 2016 the partnership joined the organisation's Disaster Relief Alliance
- The Golden Jubilee Trust: the partnership's flagship volunteering programme (see 'Corporate charities')

Health and Wellness

The partnership's website explains:

> A growing number of health concerns in our society threaten the wellbeing of our communities. As a grocery retailer, we have a role to play in helping to tackle growing problems associated with poor diet and lifestyle, such as obesity and diabetes. At the same time social issues such as an ageing population impact Partners, customers and local communities.
>
> We invest in a number of educational initiatives and awareness raising campaigns to support the health and wellness of our communities.

Waitrose initiatives under this theme include:

- The Grow and Sell initiative (see 'In-kind support' for more information)
- 'Tackling Isolation': In 2015 Waitrose continued with its efforts to combat isolation by making a donation in support of Crisis at Christmas. As part of the campaign, Waitrose also collaborated with John Lewis (following the success of its 'Man on the Moon' Christmas advert) to support Christmas events, such as Christmas lunches at local branches of Age UK
- Supporting food banks (see 'In-kind support' for more information)

Environment

The partnership's website states: 'From sourcing products, to operating our estate and supporting the health and wellbeing of our local communities, The Partnership recognises the importance of protecting the natural environment.'

Waitrose/partnership initiatives under this theme include:

- John Spedan Lewis Trust for the Advancement of Natural Sciences (see 'Corporate charities')
- Waitrose Duchy Organic (see 'Commercially led support')
- The Woodland Trust (see 'Charity partners')

Corporate charities

The John Lewis Partnership has a number of associated charities. Those with some relation to Waitrose include:

- **The John Lewis Partnership Golden Jubilee Trust** (Charity Commission no. 1079195): This trust provides UK-registered charities with the opportunity to benefit from the skills of the partnership's staff. Secondments organised through the trust can range from one week to six months in length and can be either full or part-time depending on what the job will involve
- **The John Spedan Lewis Trust for the Advancement of Natural Sciences** (Charity Commission no. 313335): This is a small trust which takes its name from the founder of the John Lewis Partnership and is inspired by his interest in natural history. The trust is based at the Leckford Estate (otherwise known as the Waitrose Farm), and its development is outlined on the partnership's website: 'In 1972, several small areas of Leckford farm were adopted as Nature Reserves. Over the years, visiting experts have monitored and recorded the many plant, insect and animal species that live there. The Trust also supports volunteers during conservation projects on its reserves and runs a programme of annual lectures.'

Charity partners

Waitrose works with a number of national charities including The Woodland Trust and The Prince's Countryside Fund (see 'Commercially led support' for more information).

Main locations

For details of your nearest Waitrose branch, see the 'Branch finder' tool on the website (www.waitrose.com).

Community contributions

We could not determine the amount donated solely by Waitrose Ltd. The annual report and accounts do not seem to specify the figure and John Lewis Partnership Sustainability Review for 2016 gives the information relating to *the whole of the partnership*, which was as follows:

Cash	£10.13 million
In-kind	£760,000
Time	£688,000

A further £650,500 was expended in management costs.

Beneficiaries have included:

Crisis at Christmas: Waitrose made a donation of £20,000 to Crisis at Christmas as part of the partnership's drive to combat loneliness. The donation covered the cost of vehicle hire to and from Crisis shelters.

The MK Soup Run: received a donation of almost £900 from its local Waitrose store as part of the Community Matters scheme.

St John's Church in Hythe: the church's hall hosts a weekly lunch club for older people in the area and was one of the three monthly causes supported through the Community Matters scheme by Waitrose Dibden.

In-kind support

Employee time

The Community Matters volunteering scheme was launched in May 2012 and involves each Waitrose store setting aside an annual budget which can be invested in volunteering. Local causes can then 'bid' for 'Partner time'. The website also explains that Waitrose stores can also facilitate customer volunteering by advertising vacancies where causes are supported under 'Community Matters'.

See the 'Community involvement' section for information on the volunteering scheme operated by The John Lewis Partnership Golden Jubilee Trust.

Food banks

Waitrose works with The Trussell Trust and, since 2014, 190 of its branches have hosted permanent food donation collection points, helping to support more than 150 Trussell Trust food banks. The website notes that 'Between February and December 2015, donations amounted to the equivalent of over 900,000 meals for individuals and families struggling to make ends meet'. Waitrose also hosts in-store volunteer-run collections on a regular basis.

Grow and Sell

This initiative, which was developed in conjunction with the Leckford Estate and the Seed Pantry, sees local Waitrose branches engage with schools in their communities to encourage children between the ages of 7 and 11 to eat well. The initiative involves children learning about food and where it comes from, as well as the environment and seasonality. It also provides them with the opportunity to grow their own food using Grow and Sell kits provided by Waitrose which contain seeds, equipment and instructions on how to grow. A Grow and Sell app has also been created for schools to download. The website notes that almost 250,000 schoolchildren have been involved with the scheme and 8,000 kits have been delivered.

Employee-led support

Give As You Earn

Partners can contribute to their chosen registered charities through a Give As You Earn scheme set up with Sharing is Caring (CAF).

Employee volunteering

One example of how Waitrose partners volunteer their time in their local communities is detailed on the website: partners at a store in Suffolk pay a monthly visit to The Bridge Project to teach its members – adults with learning disabilities – how to cook. Waitrose supports the partners' involvement by providing a van and driver to enable meals to be delivered to vulnerable adults who cannot cook for themselves. The website further notes that some of the project's members now work in the cafe of the Sudbury store.

Commercially led support

The Waitrose Foundation

The Waitrose website explains that the foundation, which was launched in 2005, is a partnership between Waitrose, its suppliers and the growers who 'produce, pick and pack' fresh produce in Ghana, Kenya and South Africa. When a product is sold, the foundation receives a percentage of the profit from each stage of the supply chain. This money is then put directly into the farming community, which decides how the money is allocated to educational, social and healthcare projects in the local area. These products can be identified in store by the foundation's logo printed on their packaging.

Community matters

The company facilitates fundraising opportunities in support of good causes whereby shoppers can receive tokens at the end of their shop. Customers can then put the tokens in the box of the cause they'd most like to support. The more tokens a cause gets, the larger the donation it receives. Each month every Waitrose branch donates £1,000 (£500 in convenience shops), split between three local good causes chosen by customers.

Customers who do their shopping through Waitrose.com can take part in an online version of the scheme through which £25,000 is shared between three national charities. At the time of writing (December 2016) national causes currently being supported were Crohn's and Colitis UK, Plantlife and The Trussell Trust.

Waitrose Duchy Organic

Waitrose's flagship organic brand is the result of a partnership with Duchy Originals, a company set up by The Prince of Wales. Since 2015, the company's products have been sold and distributed by Waitrose under the Waitrose Duchy Organic brand, with proceeds donated to The Prince of Wales's Charitable Foundation. The range now has more than 300 different products which, as Waitrose's website describes, are sold under the shared principles of 'Good Food, Good Farming, Good Causes'.

The Prince's Countryside Fund

Waitrose and the Waitrose Duchy Organic brand are corporate partners of the fund which works to support agriculture and rural communities in the UK. Waitrose has supported the fund by promoting its National Countryside Week campaign and by selling a range of more than 200 UK-grown food and drinks products carrying The Prince's Countryside Fund logo.

The Woodland Trust

Through a partnership with the trust, the activity of Waitrose's home delivery vehicles is linked to the planting of trees – the website notes that Waitrose is the first UK grocer to do this. Each delivery from Waitrose.com helps to plant new trees.

Carrier bags

Waitrose's plans for the proceeds from carrier bag sales are outlined on its website which explains: 'Every penny raised from the sale of carrier bags at Waitrose branches in England will go into a new community and environmental fund – with no deduction for costs. For the first year we'll be joining with a number of other supermarkets to give the money in this fund to a new world centre of excellence which is being created at University College London, for the care, treatment and prevention of Alzheimer's.'

Exclusions

The partnership does not give funding to/for: individuals; religious, ethnic or political groups; or third-party fundraising.

Applications

Donations

If you feel your organisation has a cause that Waitrose could support, get in touch with your local Waitrose's champion for community giving. The website notes 'As we are contacted by so many organisations throughout the year, we cannot always give you a swift reply, but we will get back to you as soon as possible if we can help.'

Community Matters Online

UK-registered national charities that would life to be considered for the Community Matters Online scheme should post their applications on headed paper to: Waitrose Community Matters Team, Waitrose Ltd, Doncastle Road, Bracknell, Berkshire RG12 8YA. Applications should include a brief outline of the work your charity does along with details of any current projects that you are seeking funding for. They should be no longer than one side of A4. The Community Matters Team will only contact successful applicants or those from whom they require further details.

Music Matters

The partnership runs this scheme each year to support music in local communities. Applications are invited from all varieties of local music groups. Applications for the scheme run between February and March each year. To apply, contact your local Waitrose shop.

The John Lewis Partnership Golden Jubilee Trust

The 'Information for charities' document, which is published on the partnership's website and dates from 2013/14, sets out some of the 'routes' to making an application; they include:

- Partners applying to work with a charity which is known to them, maybe they volunteer there already
- The Partner's branch, through working in the local community, knowing of charities which would benefit from a Partner's specific skills or practical help
- Charities letting us know of their need. If appropriate, we advertise the role on our internal web site in the hope of finding a suitable Partner to apply for the task requested

For more information about the trust, visit the John Lewis Partnership website (www.johnlewispartnership.co.uk) or contact the GJT Trust Manager by email (Golden_Jubilee_Trust_Enquiries@johnlewis.co.uk) or by post (Golden Jubilee Trust Manager, Partnership House, London SW1E 5NN).

The John Spedan Lewis Trust for the Advancement of Natural Sciences

The John Lewis Partnership website states 'For enquiries, contact the Secretary at the following address: JSLTANS, The Secretary, c/o Estate Office, Leckford Estate, Stockbridge, Hampshire SO20 6JF'.

Warburtons Ltd

Food manufacture

Correspondent: Nichola Atkinson, Community and Communications Co-ordinator, Back o'th' Bank House, Hereford Street, Bolton, Lancashire BL1 8JB (tel: 01204 556600; email: nicola.atkinson@warburtons.co.uk; website: www.warburtons.co.uk)

Directors: Angela Megson; Brett Warburton; Jonathan Warburton, Chair; Nigel Dunlop; Ross Warburton

Year end	26/09/2015
Turnover	£551,467,000
Pre-tax profit	£38,715,000

Nature of business: Warburtons is a family-owned bakery producer and distributer. The ultimate parent company of Warburtons Ltd is Warburtons 1876 Ltd.

Company registration number: 178711

Subsidiary undertakings include: Alliedtropic Ltd; Burneys Ltd; RBJ Foods Ltd; Warburton Asset Management Ltd.

Focus of giving: Education, enterprise/training, health, ill health, financial education, poverty and social exclusion, community/social welfare.

Membership: BITC

Community involvement	✓
Community contributions	✓
CSR report	✓
CSR or charity committee	✓
Cash donations declared	✓
Charity partner(s)	✓
Employee-led support	✓
Gifts in kind	✓
Matched funding	✓
Payroll giving	✓

Charitable donations

Cash UK (latest available):	2015	£301,500
Total UK (cash and in kind):	2015	£301,500
Cash worldwide:	2015	£301,500
Total worldwide (cash and in kind):	2015	£301,500

Community involvement

National Charity

The national charity partner for Warburton's is Cancer Research UK. Employees have undertaken a range of activities and initiatives to raise funds.

The bakery sites can provide support to local communities through the donation of its products. These donations support local community activities.

The website notes:

> You can apply for product donation support by completing the form below. We will contact you should your application be successful. Please bear in mind that we will need at least **3 weeks prior notice** to the date of your event.
>
> Please note – As much as we would like to, we cannot support all donation requests.

Financial giving programme

The group's financial giving programme aims, according to the website, to support 'projects, activities and organisations that have charitable aims and will be of direct benefit to families'. The areas of focus are, broadly: health; financial stability; worklessness; health education; aspiration; and employability and skills. The areas of focus are outlined in more detail in the financial giving policy on the website, along with the group's priorities and other useful information.

Grants are given in two categories. Community grants of up to £250 are provided to organisations in England, Scotland or Wales and should be used for a specific purpose, such as purchasing equipment for a project. Project grants of between £1,000 and £10,000 are awarded to organisations within 15 miles of a bakery or depot site and are not open to application – the group takes a proactive approach to identify suitable organisations. Further information on the group's grants schemes is provided on the website.

Main location

Various locations throughout the UK.

Community contributions

The 2014/15 supporting the community report states that 183 organisations were awarded a total of £45,500 through community grants and 34 projects were awarded £256,000 through paid grants. We take the total of £301,500 as Warburton's total charitable giving.

In-kind support

School Visits

The National School Visitor Programme has been running for over 20 years. It enables the company's 'school visitors' to pay annual visits to primary schools to introduce pupils to bread-making, food and healthy eating. Children are also provided an educational booklet to complete and necessary tools and ingredients. In 2014/15 there were 575 visits.

Donations

Warburton's also donate products to support local communities; from giving regularly to breakfast clubs and food banks, to individual donations that support charity activities or fundraising events.

Skills exchange

The company has a skills exchange programme, which aims to benefit the local community by giving people the opportunity to share skills. This can be in many different ways from tours around the bakery to mentoring schoolchildren and helping with CV writing.

Employee-led support

Payroll giving

A payroll giving scheme operates to enable monthly deductions from salaries in support of charitable causes. During 2014/15 a total of 850 staff members donated to charity.

Matched funding

The company matches employee fundraising efforts. In 2014/15 the company gave over £36,000 through matched funding.

Exclusions

According to the financial giving policy, financial support cannot be given for:

- political parties
- animal causes
- anything outside of England, Wales or Scotland
- organisations that discriminate by race, creed, gender, sexual orientation, age, religion or national origin
- individuals (in contrast to groups, teams or communities)
- individuals or organisations seeking educational bursaries (assistance to individuals for school research projects, travel costs or college and university fees)
- organisations which are not charitable and do not operate on a not-for-profit basis
- applications that solely seek support for salaries (however [the company] will consider funding a proportion of a salary or sessional worker fees where these are directly linked to project delivery)
- part funding
- activities with a negative impact on the environment
- organisations with which association can be potentially harmful to the Warburtons business
- third party fundraising (e.g. sponsoring an individual to complete a challenge)
- sponsorship, advertising and promotion alone, which primarily generate commercial returns
- raffle prizes, but please note it is possible to provide a donation for a raffle prize or a cause, but [Warburtons] cannot provide goods [itself]
- requests that solely seek to purchase something (except Community Grants) (e.g. the buying of a building or other significant purchase)

Note: The company's giving policy also states:

> In limited cases, the Community and CR Manager can authorise support for Bakery Hub projects outside of the 15-mile radius with agreement with the Chair of the Community Investment Committee. Such projects will require benefits for both the community and the business as a result of making this exception.

Applications

Financial giving programme

Applications for Community Grants can be made online directly by the applicant organisation or by a Warburtons employee if they are actively involved in the organisation. Applications are reviewed by whichever of the group's sites is closest to the organisation geographically (there is a postcode checker on the website). Applications are reviewed on a quarterly basis and deadlines are posted online. Decisions are made within six weeks of a deadline and charities will subsequently be informed of the outcome.

Project Grants are not open for application.

Product donations

There is a form on the website for organisations to request product donations. Applications should be submitted at least three weeks in advance of an event.

Wates Group Ltd

Building/construction

Correspondent: Group Sustainability Team, Wates House, Station Approach, Leatherhead, Surrey KT22 7SW (tel: 01372 861000 (main switchboard); website: www.wates.co.uk)

Directors: Andrew Davies, Chief Executive; Andrew Wates; Charles Wates; David Allen, Chief Financial Officer; David Barclay; Deena Mattar; James Wates, Chair; Jonathan Wates; Timothy Wates (women: 1; men: 8)

Year end	31/12/2015
Turnover	£1,270,000,000
Pre-tax profit	£30,300,000

Nature of business: The Wates Group is a provider of construction services and residential development. It has been wholly owned by the Wates family since its inception in 1897.

Company registration number: 1824828

Subsidiary undertakings include: Needspace? Ltd; and Wates Developments Ltd.

Focus of giving: Education, enterprise/ training, environment, local groups, children, young people, community/ social welfare.

Membership: BITC

Community involvement	✓
Community contributions	✓
Company reports on anti-slavery	✓
CSR report	✓
Cash donations declared	✓
Charity partner(s)	✓
Community Mark	✓
Corporate charity	✓
Employee-led support	✓
Matched funding	✓
Payroll giving	✓
Sponsorship	✓

Charitable donations

Cash UK (latest available):	2015	£1,000,000
Total UK (cash and in kind):	2015	£1,000,000
Cash worldwide:	2015	£1,000,000
Total worldwide (cash and in kind):	2015	£1,000,000

Community involvement

Charity partnerships

The Wates Group currently has a partnership with The Prince's Trust. A grant of £15,000 was provided to fund the trust's Get Into Construction programme.

The Wates Family Enterprise Trust (Charity Commission no. 1126007)

The trust was set up in 2008 by the Wates family with the aim 'to empower initiatives that make a real difference to society'. In 2015 a total of £1.06 million was given to local community projects.

The Wates Foundation (Charity Commission no. 247941)

The Wates Group also runs an independent grant-making family trust supporting the charitable and voluntary sector. It has been established in 1966 and since then has made grants totalling over £100 million. The charity's objectives mirror the group's values with family being at the heart of their grant-making aims. Its interests are categorised into five themes: building family values; community health; life transitions; safer communities; and strengthening the voluntary sector. The foundation has a new proactive grant-making strategy in which members of the Wates family seek out charities to support. Unsolicited applications will automatically be rejected.

Main locations

The group has offices throughout the UK. The foundation makes grants to UK organisations.

Community contributions

In 2015 Wates donated £1 million to its corporate foundation, the Wates Family Enterprise Trust. Wates Giving is the trust's giving programme which provides employee matched funding and Community Day grants as well as running its own grants programme.

The trust's annual report and accounts for 2015 state: 'The trust's income arises from a formal agreement with the Wates Group in accordance with the wishes of the Wates Family owners and shareholders of the Wates businesses.'

Employee-led support

Community Day

The annual Community Day brings together employees, customers and supply chain partners to carry out a wide range of projects. In 2015 a total of 2,000 employees donated over 4,700 hours during the day to tackle 70 community projects across the UK. In addition to the time volunteered, Wates Giving donated £30,000 to a range of local community projects.

Matched funding

During the year 107 awards were made to match funds for employees' own fundraising including sponsored climbs, runs and raffles. Wates Giving provided £32,000 of matched funding which brought the total raised by employees during the year to £124,000.

Payroll giving

There is a Give As You Earn scheme which allows regular salary deductions to support good causes. In 2015 Give As You Earn donations totalled £16,500.

Employee Community Involvement

During the year Wates Giving made donations of £47,500 to support employees who work in their community in roles such as trustees, sports coaches and fundraisers.

Corporate charity

Wates Family Enterprise Trust (Charity Commission no. 1126007) and The Wates Foundation (Charity Commission no. 247941).

Applications

The Company

Apply in writing to the correspondent or the Group Sustainability Team.

The Wates Family Enterprise Trust

The following was taken from the trust's website: 'All the proposals for Wates Giving awards come from Wates employees or the Wates Family. As a result we are unable to accept direct requests for funding.'

The Wates Foundation

The following was taken from the foundation's website:

> The Trustees of the Wates Foundation have endorsed a new pro-active grant making strategy until March 2018. Wates Family members seek out charities to support, often from within their local community. Applications are by invitation only. Unsolicited applications will be automatically rejected.

The Weir Group PLC

Engineering

Correspondent: See 'Applications', 1 West Regent Street, Glasgow, Scotland G2 1RW (tel: 0141 637 7111; email: philanthropy@mail.weir; website: www.weir.co.uk)

Directors: Alan Ferguson; Charles Berry, Chair; Dean Jenkins; John Mogford; Jon Stanton, Finance Director; Keith Cochrane, Chief Executive; Mary Jo Jacobi; Melanie Gee; Prof. Sir Jim McDonald; Richard Menell (women: 2; men: 8)

Year end	01/01/2016
Turnover	£1,917,700,000
Pre-tax profit	(£199,800,000)

Nature of business: Principal activities: engineering services and specialist engineering products.

Company registration number: SC002934

Subsidiary undertakings include: Linastex Ltd; American Hydro Corporation; Weir Floway, Inc.

Total employees: 14,000

Focus of giving: Education, enterprise/ training, health, ill health, heritage, arts, culture, overseas projects, science technology, community/social welfare.

Membership: BITC

Community involvement	✓
Community contributions	✓

Company reports on anti-slavery ✓
CSR report ✓
Directors have other relevant posts ✓
AF Covenant ✓
Charity partner(s) ✓
Employee-led support ✓
Gifts in kind ✓
Humanitarian aid: overseas ✓
Matched funding ✓
Overseas giving ✓
Pro bono ✓
Shared-value alliances ✓
Sponsorship ✓
STEM-focused ✓

Charitable donations

Total worldwide (cash and in kind):	2016	£478,000

Community involvement

Community activities, including both financial donations and volunteering support, are mainly organised by each individual business within the group. The group has a particular focus on supporting health, education and community causes in the areas where it works.

STEM education

There is a particular focus on STEM education; the group is a founding member of the Institute of Primary and Secondary Engineers, and provides work placements, internships and other opportunities. The group also supports Arkwright Scholarships, recruiting scholars to undertake placements with the group.

Examples of STEM-related activities in 2015 include support for Primary Engineer, a charity which encourages young people to engage with STEM education, and assistance with a project to improve facilities for a school in Todmorden.

Companies within the group internationally also partnered with educational institutions in their area of operation to offer opportunities such as student placements.

Health

The group has a focus on supporting health in the communities in which it operates, as well as for its employees. Examples of support in 2015 include a partnership in India with a charity to offer training for nurses and sponsorship for Orkidstudio, a humanitarian design organisation to improve health facilities in Zambia.

The group has a three-year partnership with AMAR International Charitable Foundation (Charity Commission no. 1047432), working to improve health, education and training in Basra, Iraq, where the company has operations. In 2015 the group supported a community health education project and two education and training centres through this partnership.

Directors with other relevant posts

Keith Cochrane is Chair of the Selection Group for CSCLeaders, a leadership programme across Commonwealth countries. Melanie Gee was previously a trustee of Fauna and Flora International (Charity Commission no. 1011102). Prof. Sir Jim McDonald is a trustee of Glasgow Science Centre Charitable Trust (OSCR no. SC025818)

The group states that it will be reviewing its policies in 2016 to ensure that they address this issue and will also develop a training programme to raise awareness of the Modern Slavery Act and the group's responsibilities.

Main locations

The group has operations worldwide. In the UK, it has operations or offices in Aberdeen; Alloa; Barton on Humber; Bedford; Cardiff; Derby; East Kilbride; Glasgow; Hampshire; Teesside; Todmorden.

Community contributions

The 2015 annual report states that during the year, that group donated almost £478,000 to charitable causes. This figure includes both financial donations as well as in-kind support, such as products, use of company's facilities and employee volunteer time. Charitable support was given for the following causes: Community (57%); Education (31%); Health (12%).

Beneficiaries included: AMAR International Charitable Foundation (£150,000); Primary Engineer (£20,000).

In-kind support

Examples of in-kind support during the year included providing medical supplies in countries affected by the Ebola outbreak. The group also offers matched contributions for some in-kind initiatives led by employees; in California, for example, employees collected and donated toys to a local charity for Christmas, with contributions matched by the company.

Employee-led support

Examples of employee involvement in 2015 included working with the charity WildHearts on their Micro-Tyco programme, where teams of employees competed to raise money which is used to created micro-loans for entrepreneurs in disadvantaged countries, raising over £600 in total. 180 employees in the Netherlands took part in an athletic fundraising event, the Venloop, which was sponsored by Weir Minerals Netherlands, while employees in India volunteered to offer education around road safety, health and hygiene.

In Scotland, three members of the group's legal team took part in the Citizenship Foundation's Lawyers in Schools programme, volunteering in a local school.

Applications

The website states that charitable requests should be emailed to: philanthropy@mail.weir.

Wessex Water Services Ltd

Water

Correspondent: See 'Applications', Claverton Down Road, Claverton Down, Bath BA2 7WW (tel: 01225 526000; fax: 01225 528000; email: sustainability@wessexwater.co.uk; website: www.wessexwater.co.uk)

Directors: Andy Pymer, Managing Director; Colin Skellett, Chief Executive Officer; David Barclay; Fiona Reynolds; Francis Yeoh, Chair; Gillian Camm; Hann Yeoh; Hong Yeoh; Huw Davies; James Rider, Chief Operating Officer; Kathleen Chew; Mark Watts, Director of Finance and Treasurer; Mark Yeoh; Richard Keys (women: 3; men: 11)

Year end	31/03/2016
Turnover	£520,800,000
Pre-tax profit	£164,200,000

Nature of business: Wessex Water Services Ltd is a regional water and sewage treatment business serving the South West of England. The ultimate parent company of Wessex Water Services Ltd is YTL Corporation Berhad (is incorporated in Malaysia).

Company registration number: 2366648

Subsidiary undertakings include: Wessex Water Services Finance PLC.

UK employees: 2,144

Focus of giving: Education, environment, non-registered charities, marginalised people, financial education, older people, overseas projects, children, young people, community/social welfare.

Community involvement ✓
Community contributions ✓
Company reports on anti-slavery ✓
CSR report ✓
Directors have other relevant posts ✓
Cash donations declared ✓
Charity partner(s) ✓
Company gives to smaller charities ✓
Employee-led support ✓
Gifts in kind ✓
Overseas giving ✓
STEM-focused ✓
Unregistered charities/NFP ✓

Charitable donations

Cash UK (latest available):	2016	£438,500
Total UK (cash and in kind):	2016	£438,500
Cash worldwide:	2016	£438,500
Total worldwide (cash and in kind):	2016	£438,500

Community involvement

The company focuses most of its charitable support within the region where it operates and contributes to environmental and educational projects. The company also works closely with NGOs working elsewhere in the world, such as WaterAid, which focus on increasing access to adequate clean water or sanitation.

Watermark awards

The scheme has been run for over 25 years to support organisations with their environmental projects based within the Wessex Water region. It is organised by the Conservation Foundation (Charity Commission no. 284656) and applications are reviewed by a panel of experts chaired by one of the foundation's co-founders, TV presenter David Bellamy.

Grants of up to £1,500 are available to schools, parish councils, youth groups and community organisations. A special project receives the Wessex Watermark gold award worth £2,500, which is awarded every quarter.

In 2015/16 grants were awarded to organisations such as Backwell Access Group to increase public access for wheelchair users around a local nature reserve; Dulverton Middle School for a waste and food thermos composter; and Greater Bedminster Front Garden in Bristol to promote sustainable gardening.

Grid community awards

Environmental projects located in an area affected by the company's water supply grid programme could be eligible for the grid community awards scheme. The water supply grid programme is due to be completed in 2018 and comprises of 50 schemes across Dorset, Somerset and Wiltshire.

BAP (biodiversity action plan) Partners Programme

This programme began in 1998 and funds projects that will conserve and enhance biodiversity in the region where the company operates. Partnerships and grants are made to wildlife conservation organisations. The programme generally funds projects that focus on: habitat creation; species or survey work; restoration work; or more strategic work to enhance biodiversity, water quality or promoting wider conservation.

From 2015 to 2020 the company is supporting the following four projects: Avon Wildlife Trust; Cranborne Chase Area of Outstanding Natural Beauty; Dorset Wiltshire Trust; Wiltshire Wildlife Trust.

Small grants scheme

The Partners Programme is offering grants of between £2,500 and £5,000 every six months until October 2019. The grants are aimed at short-term, small scale practical projects that, according to the website:

> Address catchment, ecosystems and science and research issues, such as habitat creation and restoration, ancillary conservation works (eg, fencing, support services for grazing), land management actions to improve water quality, provision of land management advice, dissemination and communication of information, or to meet immediate research or monitoring needs.

WaterAid

Since its creation Wessex Water has supported the international water and sanitation charity by organising fundraising events, corporate support and raising money and awareness through customers and staff. In 2015/16 numerous fundraising events were held in aid of the charity, including a biennial race night and the annual employee WaterAid lottery.

In 2008 an ongoing campaign, Wessex for West Africa, began with contractors, consultants and suppliers helping to raise money over a one year period by fundraising within their organisations. In 2015/16 the company hosted four business breakfasts to promote WaterAid's work and increase fundraising.

Education

The company offers a free education service to schools and colleges in the region in which it operates. This includes visits to primary and secondary schools to deliver a range of services including school assemblies to classroom learning. The company's school education services also include:

- Primary and secondary education packs, videos and other teaching resources
- Tailor-made lessons (that can tie-in with a variety of subjects including: geography, science, business studies, history and IT)
- Regional education centres
- Site visits

The company helps secondary schools achieve their Eco-schools Green Flag Award. For further information on this initiative, visit www.eco-schools.org.uk

Directors with other relevant posts

Gillian Camm is Vice-President of the Quartet Community Foundation (Charity Commission no. 1080418) and is a trustee of the following charities: Colston's Hospital Trust (Charity Commission no. 311737); The Charles Dixon Pension Fund (Charity Commission no. 202153); The Colston Girls' School Bursary Fund (Charity Commission no. 249186); The Cote Charity (Charity Commission no. 257237); The Merchant Venturers' Charities Investment Pool (Charity Commission no. 1053459); The Merchant Venturers' Charity (Charity Commission no. 264302); The Society of Merchant Venturers (Charity Commission no. 202152); and W. H. Blandy Trust (Charity Commission no. 202154). She is also Chair of the Board of Governors of the University of the West of England.

Fiona Reynolds is a trustee of The Green Alliance Trust (Charity Commission no. 1045395) and The Master Fellows and Scholars of Emmanuel College in the University of Cambridge (Charity Commission no. 1137456). She is also on the executive board of the BBC and was formerly the Director-General of the National Trust from 2001 to 2012.

Huw Davies is a trustee of the children's communication charity ICAN (Charity Commission no. 210031) and Chair of Business in the Community South-East Advisory Board.

David Barclay is Deputy Chair of the British Library.

Main locations

The company operates in various locations across the South West of England, including: Avon; Dorset; Gloucestershire; Hampshire; Somerset; and Wiltshire.

Community contributions

In 2015/16 the company donated £438,500 (2014/15: £450,000) to UK charities, of which £318,000 (2014/15: £325,000) was donated to local debt advice agencies to help provide debt and financial advice to customers who are struggling to pay their water bills.

Beneficiaries of the BAP Partners Programme included: Bristol Avon Rivers Trust; Dorset Extended Riverfly Monitoring Group; Somerset Wildlife Trust; South Gloucestershire Biodiversity Action Group.

Employee-led support

Speaker Service

The volunteer speaker service gives staff the opportunity to meet groups to tell them more about Wessex Water. The speaker also arranges group visits to the company's water and sewage treatment works. According to the website, several hundred community groups request talks every year. To book a talk, email: info@wessexwater.co.uk

Commercially led support

Money Matters awards scheme
Under this scheme organisations which run community-based projects to improve financial literacy and money management skills among young people and vulnerable customers can apply for a grant of up to £10,000 towards specific projects. This scheme is part of the 'tap' programme (see below).

In 2015/16 four projects were supported, working with the following beneficiaries: offenders due to leave prison; older people; secondary schoolchildren; and those under 30 years old, including young families and people with mental health issues.

Tailored assistance programme – tap
The company works with debt advisers and other community-based organisations to support vulnerable customers to afford their ongoing water bills and repay their debt.

Catchment partnerships
The company works in partnership with organisations and individuals across the region where it operates in order to protect and restore the water environment. It is part of the Catchment Based Approach: www.catchmentbasedapproach.org.

Priority Services
The programme is designed for customers with special needs, including those who are older, have mental health needs and/or have disabilities. A register of such customers is held for the company to identify and respond to their requirements. Help includes: a text telephone service for people with impaired hearing; Braille or audio bills; a doorstep security password system; and advance warning of interruptions to water supply.

Exclusions

Support is not generally given to private companies, individuals or government organisations.

Applications

Applications for the **Watermark awards** can be directed to the company on 01225 526327 or by contacting the Libby Symon at the Conservation Foundation on 020 7591 3111 or by email info@conservationfoundation.co.uk. More information can be found on the website: www.conservationfoundation.co.uk.

To enquire about your environmental project's eligibility for the **Grid Community Awards** scheme, email: gridtrunkmain@wessexwater.co.uk.

Applications for the **BAP Partners Programme** small grants scheme can be made using the application form on the company's website. The scheme is open to applications from 1 to 30 April and 1 to 31 October each year until 2019. For further information contact Dave Jones, Environment and Catchment Strategy Team:

- Address: Wessex Water, Claverton Down, Bath BA2 7WW
- Email: env.info@wessexwater.co.uk
- Telephone: 01225 526183

Grants for the **Money Matters** awards scheme are awarded in January and July each year. Applications can be made using the form available on the company's website. For further information contact Kate Pennock, Grants Approval Panel: Wessex Water, Claverton Down, Bath BA2 7WW or email kate.pennock@wessexwater.co.uk.

Schools can apply for an education service site or school visit using the company's online form, available under the 'Community' section of the website.

All other enquiries can be directed at the company's head office. Board member, Gillian Camm, is Chair of the Customer and Communities panel and CSR committee.

J. D. Wetherspoon PLC

Leisure, retail – restaurants/fast food

Correspondent: Company Secretary, Wetherspoon House, Central Park, Reeds Crescent, Watford WD24 4QL (tel: 01923 477777; website: www.jdwetherspoon.com)

Directors: Ben Whitley, Finance Director; Debra van Gene; Elizabeth McMeikan; John Hutson, Chief Executive Officer; Nigel Connor; Sir Richard Beckett; Su Cacioppo; Tim Martin, Chair (women: 3; men: 5)

Year end	24/07/2016
Turnover	£1,595,000,000
Pre-tax profit	£66,049,000

Nature of business: The development and management of public houses.

Company registration number: 1709784

Focus of giving: Health, ill health, local groups, children, young people, community/social welfare.

Community involvement	✓
Community contributions	✓
Charity partner(s)	✓
Employee-led support	✓
Market-led giving	✓

Community involvement

Partnerships
JD Wetherspoon employees and customers raise funds and awareness for CLIC Sargent, the children's cancer charity. Local pubs may also support local charities, at the discretion of the manager.

Main locations
Watford (head office). There is a pub finder facility on the company's website.

Community contributions

There was no evidence of corporate charitable contributions having been made during the 2015/16 financial year. However, the company continues to work in partnership with CLIC Sargent and states in its annual report that in 2015/16 customers and employees raised around £1.6 million, bringing the total raised to over £12.6 million.

Applications

The website states that the CLIC Sargent is the group's nominated charity, to which all of its fundraising efforts are committed. However, some pubs support a local charity, and the website states that charities should contact the manager of a local pub directly to enquire about support.

Whitbread PLC

Hotels, leisure, retail – restaurants/fast food

Correspondent: The Corporate Responsibility Team, Whitbread Court, Houghton Hall Business Park, Porz Avenue, Dunstable LU5 5XE (tel: 01582 424200; website: www.whitbread.co.uk)

Directors: Alison Brittain, Chief Executive; Chris Kennedy; Louise Smalley; Nicholas Cadbury, Finance Director; Richard Baker, Chair; Simon Melliss; Sir Ian Cheshire; Stephen Williams; Susan Martin; Wendy Becker (women: 4; men: 6)

Year end	03/03/2016
Turnover	£2,922,000,000
Pre-tax profit	£495,000,000

Nature of business: The group's principal activities are the operation of hotels, restaurants and coffee shops.

Company registration number: 29423

Subsidiary undertakings include: Coffee Nation Ltd; Coffeheaven International Ltd; Costa Ltd.

Brands include: Beefeater Grill; Brewers Fayre; Costa; Hub; Premier Inn; Table Table; Taybarns and Whitbread.

Focus of giving: Enterprise/training, community/social welfare.

Membership: BITC

Community involvement	✓
Community contributions	✓
Company reports on anti-slavery	✓
CSR report	✓
Cash donations declared	✓
Charity partner(s)	✓
Employee-led support	✓
FTSE 100	✓
Gifts in kind	✓

Market-led giving ✓
Matched funding ✓
Payroll giving ✓

Charitable donations

Cash UK (latest available):	2016	£283,000
Total UK (cash and in kind):	2016	£283,000
Cash worldwide:	2016	£283,000
Total worldwide (cash and in kind):	2016	£283,000

Community involvement

The Costa Foundation (Charity Commission no. 1147400)

The foundation was established in 2007 (registered independently in 2012) and its aims are to relieve poverty, advance education and the health and environment of coffee-growing communities around the world. In 2015/16 over £2 million was raised for the foundation and it now supports 72 communities across nine countries.

Great Ormond Street Hospital Children's Charity

Since 2012 Whitbread Hotels and Restaurants has chosen the charity as a long–term charity partner with the aim of helping children suffering from rare, complex and life–threatening conditions. In 2015/16 around £2 million was raised for the charity. Whitbread hopes to raise a total of £7.5 million by 2017 to pay for the construction of a new building that will allow the hospital treat up to 20% more children.

Main locations

UK

Community contributions

The Corporate Responsibility Report for 2015/16 states that: in support of the Great Ormond Street Hospital Raise & Match scheme brought in £60,500 and a further £22,500 through Give and Match. The Costa Community Programme donated around £200,000 to local community activities.

We take the figure of £283,000 (comprising matched funding and Costa Community Programme donations) to represent the group's charitable giving, as no other figures could be found. Around £4 million was donated to Great Ormond Street Hospital Children's Charity and the Costa Foundation but this was mainly contributed by customers, employees and suppliers as opposed to the company itself and the value of in-kind support and other costs to the group could not be determined.

Beneficiaries included: Great Ormond Street Hospital Children's Charity; and The Costa Foundation.

In-kind support

Costa Community Programme

Store teams are encouraged to support and get involved with local community projects. This support includes fundraising, giving local community groups access to stores for meetings employees giving their time within work hours to volunteer.

Work inclusion

Managers from Costa have worked closely with prisons in Milton Keynes and Aylesbury to train prisoners in coffee-making and to give them other skills that will help their employability when released from prison. In 2014/15 Costa gave 60 hours of training in three prisons helping more than 30 prisoners.

Costa for schools

During the year a new website created by teachers has been launched to provide UK secondary school teachers with the resources to support the delivery of certain parts of the national curriculum in geography. Team members are also encouraged to volunteer at local schools to help children with their reading skills.

Employee-led support

Payroll giving

The Give and Match is Whitbread's payroll giving scheme allowing employees donated to their chosen charity. During the year £270,000 was donated to charity by team members with £22,500 donated by Whitbread.

Matched funding

The Raise and Match scheme supports staff members fundraising in their own personal time for charities and good causes based in the UK. During the year £110,000 was raised by employees with £60,500 matched by Whitbread.

Commercially led support

WISE (Whitbread Investing in Skills and Employment)

WISE began in 2012 and was created to engage, educate and employ young people who are often from disadvantaged backgrounds. It offers the following schemes:

Apprenticeships

The programme was introduced in 2010. In 2015/16 a total of 207 apprenticeships were awarded with a further 1,029 in progress.

Work Experience

Aimed at 11- to 18-year-olds the scheme seeks to introduce hospitality industry as a career choice. In 2015/16 there were 2,101 placements completed.

Work Placements

In partnership with Prince's Trust individuals between 17–24 years old are referred to undertake a work placement with Costa or Premier Inn. In 2015/16 there were 1,433 placements completed.

Applications

Apply in writing to the correspondent.

Wilko Retail Ltd (formerly Wilkinson Hardware Stores Ltd)

Household, retail – DIY/ furniture

Correspondent: The Charity Department, J. K. House, Roebuck Way, Manton Wood, Worksop, Nottinghamshire S80 3EG (tel: 0800 032 9329; email: charity@wilko.com; website: www.wilko.com)

Directors: Aidan Connolly, Chief Financial Officer; Catherine Fox; Francois Adams; Ian Ayling; John Jackson; Lisa Wilkinson, Family Director and Chair; Mark Hale; Robin Lassiter; Sean Toal, Chief Operating Officer (women: 2; men: 7)

Year end	01/02/2016
Turnover	£1,464,475,000
Pre-tax profit	£25,955,000

Nature of business: Principal activity of the Wilko group is high street retailing of products for family and home.

The accounts note that 'the company is wholly controlled by the Wilkinson family via direct interests and through trusts in which they jointly or individually have interests'.

Company registration number: 365335

Subsidiary undertakings include: Wilkinson Asia Ltd; Wilkinson Hardware Stores (Leicester) Ltd; Wilkinson Property Ltd; Wilkinson Retail Ltd; and W'Innovate Ltd. A full list of subsidiary undertakings is available from the company's accounts.

Focus of giving: General charitable purposes, education, general appeals, animal welfare, health, ill health, large national appeals, armed forces, women's issues, children, young people, community/social welfare, disability.

Membership: BITC

Community involvement ✓
Community contributions ✓
Armed forces personnel ✓
Cash donations declared ✓
Charity partner(s) ✓
Employee-led support ✓
Gifts in kind ✓
Sponsorship ✓

Charitable donations

Cash UK (latest available):	2016	£76,200
Total UK (cash and in kind):	2016	£76,200
Cash worldwide:	2016	£76,200
Total worldwide (cash and in kind):	2016	£76,200

Community involvement

The company and its employees make charitable and community contributions in the areas in which it operates. Support is also given to national appeals.

Many charities selected for support are nominated by the company's employees. The website notes that in 2016 35 local charities were supported nationwide. Preference appears to be given to causes related to: health and disability; animals; children; and domestic violence.

Helping Hands
Wilko donates £300 to each of its stores to distribute to local charities and community causes. Support is given to various organisations, including: local schools, playgroups and nurseries; parent or family groups; groups for people with disabilities; clubs for young people; older people's groups; luncheon clubs; community and tenants' associations; appeals from the local police, fire service and local councils; and so on.

In 2015/16 a total of 19 stores near to Bristol pooled their Helping Hands budget together to pay for over 250 older people to have a day at the cinema.

Main locations
The company has outlets throughout the UK. Company headquarters are in Worksop, Nottinghamshire.

Community contributions

According to the annual report, in 2015/16 Wilko made charitable and community cash donations of £76,200 as part of its Helping Hands fund.

In-kind support

As part of the Helping Hands initiative, the company's various stores donate Wilko gift cards or products to community groups.

Employee-led support

Employee fundraising
Employees nominate charities regionally to be supported for 12 months with fundraising activities and events. In 2015/16 employees nominated 25 local charities and collectively raised over £1 million.

In 2016/17 the charities nominated for support are: Alzheimer's Society; Cancer Research UK; Canine Partners; Children's Hospice Association Scotland; East Anglia's Children's Hospices; Guide Dogs for the Blind; Gwent Wildlife Trust; Macmillan Cancer Support; Marie Curie; Refuge; Sheffield Children's Hospital; and The Children's Air Ambulance.

Employees are also involved in fundraising for national charity campaigns. Each year support is given to: BBC Children in Need; Comic Relief; and The Royal British Legion.

Employee volunteering
Wilko employees are entitled to one day per year to volunteer in their local communities.

Commercially led support

Carrier bag charge
The company donates the 5p carrier bag charge to charities across England, Wales in Scotland. In 2015/16 this amounted to £133,500. Out of this amount, 20% each was donated to: In Kind Direct; The Prince's Trust; The Woodland Trust; and WRAP. The remaining 20% was donated to the stores' regional charities.

Exclusions

No support is given for local appeals not in areas of the company's presence.

The Helping Hands scheme cannot support the following:

- Expeditions
- Political parties
- Private or fee-paying schools
- Branches of national charities
- Profitable organisations
- Third-party private fundraising groups

Applications

Applications for small donations through the **Helping Hands** scheme should be directed to your local Wilko store. The application forms can be picked up from the store or downloaded from the website. Once completed they should be returned to the store.

Any other enquiries can be made in writing to the correspondent at the company's address.

Willmott Dixon Holdings Ltd

Building/construction, property, services

Correspondent: Alison Symmers, Head of the Willmott Dixon Foundation, Spirella 2, Icknield Way, Letchworth Garden City, Hertfordshire SG6 4GY (tel: 01462 671852; fax: 01462 681852; email: alison.symmers@willmottdixon.co.uk; website: www.willmottdixon.co.uk/how-we-do-it/the-willmott-dixon-foundation)

Directors: Andrew Telfer; Chris Durkin; Christopher Sheridan; Colin Enticknap, Group Chair; Jonathan Porritt; Paul Smith; Philip Wainwright, Group Finance Director; Rick Willmott, Group Chief Executive (women: 0; men: 8)

Year end	31/12/2015
Turnover	£1,326,318,000
Pre-tax profit	£12,632,000

Nature of business: Willmott Dixon specialises in construction, residential development and property support services.

Company registration number: 198032

Subsidiary undertakings include: Willmott Dixon Construction Ltd; Willmott Dixon Energy Services Ltd; Willmott Dixon Interiors Ltd.

UK employees: 3,302

Total employees: 3,302

Focus of giving: General charitable purposes, economic generation, education, enterprise/training, housing, homelessness, small groups, local groups, less popular charitable purposes, armed forces, humanitarian help, overseas projects, poverty and social exclusion, children, young people, community/social welfare.

Membership: BITC, LBG

Community involvement	✓
Community contributions	✓
Company reports on anti-slavery	✓
CSR report	✓
Directors have other relevant posts	✓
Armed forces personnel	✓
Cash donations declared	✓
Charity partner(s)	✓
Community Mark	✓
Company gives to smaller charities	✓
Corporate charity	✓
Employee-led support	✓
Gifts in kind	✓
Humanitarian aid: UK including food banks	✓
Matched funding	✓
Overseas giving	✓
Pro bono	✓
Sponsorship	✓
Unpopular causes	✓

Charitable donations

Cash UK (latest available):	2015	£154,000
Total UK (cash and in kind):	2015	£2,506,000
Cash worldwide:	2015	£154,000
Total worldwide (cash and in kind):	2015	£2,506,000

Community involvement

Willmott Dixon's Social Value Policy Statement explains that community investment 'is an integral part of its business and what it does – the company has been doing this as one of its core values since it was formed in 1852'. This heritage is reflected in the company's community investment strategy, which is carried out through The Willmott Dixon Foundation (Charity Commission no. 326530).

The Willmott Dixon Foundation
The company's Social Value Policy Statement describes the foundation as the vehicle through which the company delivers its social value strategy and how, through this approach, focus is placed on 'social issues that are a natural fit with its business'. The foundation looks to add 'maximum value...where activities are a natural fit with the organisation' – through this, three focus themes have been identified:

- Youth unemployment and inspiring young people
- Social exclusion
- Community transformation

Unfortunately, it isn't possible to detail all of the work carried out by the foundation under these themes during the year. However, we've picked out some examples below and would direct anybody who'd like to find out more to the 'Willmott Dixon Foundation Annual Review 2015' which is available in PDF format from the website. The following information was obtained from the review:

Youth unemployment and inspiring young people

Many of the initiatives or 'interventions' under this theme are aimed at 'reducing the risk of young people becoming NEET – that is, not in education, employment or training'. The foundation's annual review explains:

> From helping school children to read, to upgrading facilities where children can meet and play, to providing work experience placements and apprenticeships for disadvantaged young people, all parts of our business have found opportunities over the last year to make such interventions.

Examples include:

- Grand Designs, Rotherham – 40 disadvantaged and vulnerable young people were given the opportunity to take part in The Grand Designs Summer School which allowed them to 'try new challenges and meet potential employers'
- Mexborough Children's Centre, Doncaster – a team of employees from Galatia, which is a business venture between Willmott Dixon and Acis, volunteered their weekend and evenings to help replace fencing at the centre, a facility providing support for local children from 'troubled backgrounds'. They were supported in their task with materials donated by suppliers
- 'A life in law?' – Willmott Dixon's Group Company Secretary, Wendy McWilliams, and her team worked with 19 local students to provide them with an insight into their roles and the career opportunities law presents. Activities included a mock employment tribunal, a day spent with the group's insurance brokers and a tour of Lloyds of London

During the year, 549 work experience opportunities were provided, including eight for young offenders and 46 for young people from disadvantaged backgrounds.

Social exclusion

The foundation's annual review states that Willmott Dixon challenges its businesses to work harder to identify excluded groups. The review further explains:

> Setting up the right sorts of programmes, providing the right support and keeping motivation going when there are challenges and failures requires dedication from individuals and teams...Activities have ranged from improving facilities and services for excluded groups; offering work experience placements for people from a wide range of backgrounds, including those with disabilities, long-term unemployed or homeless people; and working with charities and organisations to add to the work they do.

Examples include:

- 'Volunteering to be homeless' – a group of volunteers from Willmott Dixon's housebuilding services in the Midlands and North raised more than £2,000 for St Basils, a charity supporting young people who are homeless, by sleeping rough. Other activities volunteers have been involved with for the charity include carrying out repairs and maintenance work and providing careers support and advice
- Highcroft Community Centre, Erdington – Willmott Dixon Partnerships in Birmingham and suppliers contributed £76,000 of time and materials to help create an autism-friendly community centre. Staff from Willmott Dixon contributed almost 2,000 hours of their own time to the project and organised events to fundraise more than £3,000 towards equipment
- The Royal Marines Charity – a construction team building Somerset County Council's offices contacted the charity to offer work experience placements for beneficiaries

Community transformation

In addition to employing local companies in its supply chain, Willmott Dixon also seeks to add social value to the communities where it works through a number other activities. The annual review explains:

> These have ranged from the modest, such as clearing litter from streets, to the mammoth: major makeovers involving supply chain donations of materials and time – hundreds of work hours. ...
>
> Our approach towards such community projects is changing too – in selecting where teams will spend their time, energy and resources, the total impact of activities is being considered in much greater detail. This often means tracking down and working with the right organisation or group, which allows the skills and services our people offer to deliver maximum social value.

Examples during the year included:

- Brentford Lock – employees from the group's Prime Place and be:here companies worked together to remove 30 bags of rubbish and other large items from the lock, helping to make it a more pleasant place to be
- Foundry Wood – a team in Leamington worked to clear and create safe visitor access to a new workshop in the community wood

Another case study contained in this section of the foundation's annual review provides a great example of a company showing a commitment to transparency in its CSR reporting: As part of the refurbishment of a ten storey, 386 bedroom student accommodation building in Middlesbrough, Willmott Dixon transported all of the unwanted furniture and items – from beds to fridges to vacuum cleaners, most of which were in good condition – to a British Heart Foundation shop 0.4 kilometres away. This helped to raise more than £13,800 for BHF, provided cheap furniture for local residents and saved Willmott Dixon £7,000 in skip costs. As the annual review admits, it was 'A win-win all round!'

Partnerships

Willmott Dixon builds partnerships with other organisations, which allows the community work it carries out to have a greater impact. Partners include businesses in the group's supply chain, charities and other bodies. Partners include the Construction Youth Trust and Turn Around to Work (a programme for young offenders). At a local level, branches of Willmott Dixon form relationships with local organisations and charities, including food banks. Examples of partners at local level include Street League, London Youth, The Prince's Trust and food banks. Furthermore, the group often gets involved with charities or programmes its clients are working with, one such example being the Welsh government's LIFT programme for people who are long-term unemployed.

Directors with other relevant posts

Colin Enticknap: trustee of The Willmott Dixon Foundation.

Rick Willmott: Chair of The Willmott Dixon Foundation.

Jonathon Porritt: co-founder of Forum for the Future, President of The Conservation Volunteers, trustee of the Ashden Awards for Sustainable Energy, director of the online sustainable innovation platform, Collectively, and Chancellor of Keele University.

Main UK locations
Willmott Dixon has a number of offices in England and Wales. A map showing specific locations is available from www.willmottdixon.co.uk/contact.

Community contributions

The Willmott Dixon Foundation Annual Review 2015 shows that the company contributed just over £2.5 million through community investment during the year. These contributions were broken down according to London Benchmarking Group standards as follows:

Staff time	£2.08 million
Gifts in-kind	£276,000
Cash donations	£154,000

A further £806,000 was raised in leveraged funds, although, as is our usual practice, we have not included this amount in the company's total contributions for the year:

Supply chain – gifts in-kind	£420,000
Employee fundraising	£335,000
Supply chain – time	£50,000
Supply chain – cash donations	£1,000

The foundation review also provided a breakdown showing the purposes for which the contributions outlined above (both those given directly by the company and those leveraged from third parties) were redistributed:

Youth unemployment and inspiring young people	£1.33 million
Community transformation	£1.25 million
Other charities	£427,000
Social exclusion	£307,000
Other	£1,000

In-kind support

Staff time
During 2015, 83% of the company's community investment was in the form of staff time.

Employee-led support

The Willmott Dixon Foundation's annual review dedicates a section to celebrating the achievements of employees in their community involvement and provides case studies of employees' fundraising and volunteering activities.

Employee fundraising
Employees helped to raise £335,000 for charitable causes through 402 fundraising events. Examples include: Rick Willmott, the Group Chief Executive, and a group of divisional chief executives, COOs and MDs, who raised £37,000 for the Stoke Mandeville Trust by taking part in the Cyclotour du Leman; a team from Construction Cobham who hiked and cycled to raise more than £93,000 for Chestnut Tree House Hospice; and the team from Construction Wales and West who raised more than £600 for Ronald McDonald House Charities by holding a baton relay around their site.

Employee volunteering
During the year, 54% of employees took part in community projects and more than 6,900 hours of time were invested. Examples of employee volunteers, described in the foundation's annual review as 'unsung heroes', are: an Assistant Build Manager who channelled his own experiences into creating a programme for schoolchildren based around careers in construction; a build manager who spends two hours a week working on a Young Enterprise scheme at a local school for children with behavioural difficulties; and a Senior Project Surveyor who volunteers with the social enterprise and charity SATRO to promote STEM subjects to young people by assisting at around 30 events in schools each year.

Matched funding
The foundation added £8,500 to employees' fundraising efforts during the year.

Commercially led support

Sponsorship
The Willmott Dixon Foundation's annual review states that the group has sponsored the Greater Manchester Special Constabulary's annual awards 'for the past five years'. One of the group's employees is a chief officer with the force.

Corporate charity

The Willmott Dixon Foundation (Charity Commission no. 326530).

Exclusions

General and unsolicited appeals are not normally considered. Grants are not generally given for local appeals not in areas of the company's presence.

Applications

More information about the foundation's work is available from the correspondent.

Workspace Group PLC

Property

Correspondent: Elin Haf Davies, Group CSR Consultant, Chester House, Kennington Park Business Centre, London SW9 6DE (tel: 0845 527 3451; email: elin.davies@workspace.co.uk; website: www.workspace.co.uk)

Directors: Chris Girling; Damon Russell; Daniel Kitchen, Chair; Graham Clemett, Chief Financial Officer; Jamie Hopkins, Chief Executive Officer; Maria Moloney; Stephen Hubbard (women: 1; men: 6)

Year end	31/03/2016
Turnover	£101,200,000
Pre-tax profit	£391,300,000

Nature of business: The group lets office, industrial and other work space to small and medium-sized enterprises.

Company registration number: 2041612

Subsidiary undertakings include: Glebe Three Ltd; LI Property Services Ltd; Workspace Management Ltd.

UK employees: 214

Total employees: 214

Focus of giving: Economic generation, education, enterprise/training, inner cities, financial education, humanitarian help, poverty and social exclusion, children, young people, community/social welfare.

Membership: BITC

Community involvement	✓
Community contributions	✓
CSR report	✓
CSR or charity committee	✓
Directors have other relevant posts	✓
Cash donations declared	✓
Charity partner(s)	✓
Employee-led support	✓
Gifts in kind	✓
Humanitarian aid: UK including food banks	✓
Market-led giving	✓
Pro bono	✓

Charitable donations

Cash UK (latest available):	2016	£35,000
Total UK (cash and in kind):	2016	£92,000
Cash worldwide:	2016	£35,000
Total worldwide (cash and in kind):	2016	£92,000

Community involvement

The group supports partner charities, opportunities for young people in London, as well as community projects in the areas local to its operations.

Partnerships
The group works in partnership with FareShare and provides employee volunteering and customer donations. The 2015/16 annual report states that the group aims to increase the number of volunteers and food collections in the next year.

The group has a long-term partnership with the charity XLP, which works with disadvantaged young people. The group provides support through volunteering, placements for young people and access to apprenticeships, as well as connecting XLP with some of the group's supplier businesses.

In 2015/16 the group has also worked with MyBnk and XLP on 'Business Battle', an enterprise education project working with young people with behavioural problems or low motivation. The group has committed to fund at least three more programmes in 2016/17.

The group has also formed a partnership with Rainmaker Foundation to further develop its CSR strategy and charitable giving.

InspireSME week

The group works in partnership with the Greater London Authority and Business in the Community to provide an annual week-long event called InspireSME. The initiative offers young people from schools in London the opportunity to gain work experience and mentoring with businesses, and to develop a business idea and compete for support to take their project forward. In 2016 71 students from 19 schools undertook placements with 59 of the group's customer businesses.

Directors with other relevant posts

Jamie Hopkins is a member of the Corporate Board of Great Ormond Street Hospital Children's Charity (Charity Commission no. 1160024). Maria Moloney is a trustee of Friends of the Northern Ireland Cancer Centre in Belfast (Charity Commission no. NIC101345).

Main locations

The company operates in London.

Community contributions

The 2015/16 annual report states that during the year, charitable donations from the group totalled £35,000, and a further £57,000 of in-kind support was provided through lettings to charities. Donations from fundraising events held for employees and customers during the year totalled £16,000.

In-kind support

The group provides in-kind support through lettings to charities.

Employee-led support

Employee volunteering and fundraising

During the year, the group's employees carried out 29 days of volunteering. Staff are also given time to develop community projects, with support from a charities budget. The 2015/16 annual report states that in the next year, the group aims to increase the number of volunteering days.

Examples of employee fundraising and volunteering include: a climbing expedition to raise money for XLP, a charity working with disadvantaged young people; and 17 employees volunteering with FareShare to collect, sort and distribute food.

Applications

Contact the group's CSR consultant, Elin Haf Davies elin.davies@workspace.co.uk.

Worldpay Ltd

Business services, financial services, Information Technology

Correspondent: Derek Woodward, Group Company Secretary, The Walbrook Building, 25 Walbrook, London EC4N 8AF (tel: 0371 384 2030; email: Derek.Woodward@worldpay.com; website: www.worldpay.com/uk)

Directors: Deanna Oppenheimer; James Brocklebank; John Allan; Martin Scicluna; Philip Jansen, Chief Executive Officer; Rick Medlock, Chief Financial Officer; Robin Marshall; Ron Kalifa; Sir Michael Rake, Chair (women: 1; men: 8)

Year end	31/12/2015
Turnover	£981,700,000
Pre-tax profit	£19,100,000

Nature of business: The company provides electronic payment processing technology.

Company registration number: 3424752

Subsidiary undertakings include: Cardsave Community Ltd; Ship Midco Ltd; Worldpay (UK) Ltd.

Total employees: 5,000

Focus of giving: Fundraising events, large national appeals, medical research, children, young people.

Membership: BITC

Community involvement	✓
Community contributions	✓
Directors have other relevant posts	✓
Charity partner(s)	✓
Employee-led support	✓
FTSE 100	✓
Gifts in kind	✓
Matched funding	✓
Pro bono	✓
Sponsorship	✓

Community involvement

Partnerships

The group has supported Great Ormond Street Hospital Children's Charity since 2014, through employee fundraising and matched funding from the group. By the end of 2015, the group had raised £160,000 altogether.

Directors with other relevant posts

Philip Jansen is a trustee of Wellbeing of Women (Charity Commission no. 239281) and of the Peter Jansen Charitable Trust (Charity Commission no. 328035).

Main locations

In the UK, the group has offices in London; Cambridge; Manchester; Gateshead; and Harrogate. It also has offices in India; Canada; the Netherlands; the US; Singapore; Japan; China; Brazil; Mexico; Argentina; and Sweden.

Community contributions

No figure was given for the group's total charitable contributions. However, around £100,000 was raised during the year for Great Ormond Street Hospital Children's Charity through employee fundraising and matched funding from the group.

In-kind support

The group offers its technology and infrastructure for charity partnerships. For example, according to the 2015 annual report, the group supports Comic Relief as a 'platinum sponsor', processing donations (of which there were over 100,000 in 2015) free of charge. The group reports that in 2016 it will also offer call centres and employee volunteers to support the annual appeal nights. In 2015 the group also supported Cancer Research UK's Stand Up To Cancer event, processing around 14,000 donations free of charge.

Employee-led support

The 2015 annual report states that employees across the group internationally support charities through fundraising and volunteering. The group offers matched funding for employee fundraising efforts.

Applications

Apply in writing to the correspondent.

WPP PLC

Advertising/marketing, information management and communication

Correspondent: Vanessa Edwards, Head of Sustainability, 27 Farm Street, London W1J 5RJ (tel: 020 7408 2204; fax: 020 7493 6819; email: vanessa.edwards@wpp.com; website: www.wpp.com)

Directors: Charlene Begley; Daniela Riccardi; Hugo Shong; Jacques Aigrain; Nicole Seligman; Paul Richardson, Finance Director; Roberto Quarta, Chair; Ruigang Li; Sally Susman; Sir John Hood; Sir Martin Sorrell, Chief Executive; Sol Trujillo; Timothy Shriver (women: 4; men: 9)

Year end	31/12/2015
Turnover	£18,693,200,000
Pre-tax profit	£2,280,100,000

Nature of business: WPP Group is an international group of companies providing a wide range of communications, management, advertising and public relations services.

Company registration number: 111714

Subsidiary undertakings include: Maxus; MediaCom; Oglivy and Mather Advertising.

UK employees: 17,000

Total employees: 128,000

Focus of giving: Human rights, education, enterprise/training, environment, health, ill health, local groups, humanitarian help, arts, culture, overseas projects, poverty and social exclusion, children, young people, community/social welfare, disability.

Membership: BITC

Community involvement	✓
Community contributions	✓
Company reports on anti-slavery	✓
CSR report	✓
CSR or charity committee	✓
Directors have other relevant posts	✓
AF Covenant	✓
Cash donations declared	✓
Charity partner(s)	✓
Employee-led support	✓
FTSE 100	✓
Gifts in kind	✓
Humanitarian aid: overseas	✓
Humanitarian aid: UK including food banks	✓
Overseas giving	✓
Pro bono	✓
Sponsorship	✓

Charitable donations

Cash worldwide:	2015	£5,900,000
Total worldwide (cash and in kind):	2015	£19,400,000

Community involvement

The group and its businesses support various causes, particularly human rights, health, local communities, education, arts, environment and children and young people, through donations as well as pro bono services and media space.

Education

Many companies in the group work in partnership with schools and educational institutions to encourage development of marketing and communications industry-related skills. For example, Oglivy and Mather works with the Bishop Challoner Federation of Schools in Tower Hamlets, London, to offer mentoring opportunities and work experience placements. The group also works with Inspiring the Future (Charity Commission no. 1130760) to develop careers advice for young people, and 200 employees have volunteered in schools to offer support with careers information and employability skills.

International

All the businesses within the group are encouraged to support charitable causes through donations and pro bono work. In India, the group has established WPP India CSR Foundation, which makes grants to organisations supporting children, particularly through education, and will also work in partnership with charities to deliver projects.

Directors with other relevant posts

Timothy Shriver is Chair of Special Olympics. Sally Susman is on the board of directors of the International Rescue Committee and is a trustee of the US Library of Congress. Sir Martin Sorrell is Chair of Trustees of The JMCMRJ Sorrell Foundation (Charity Commission no. 1118913) and a trustee of The Thrombosis Research Trust (Charity Commission no. 275275).

Main locations

The group operates in 112 countries and has over 4,000 offices, with more than 200 in the UK. Details of where each of its businesses and their offices are located can be found on the WPP website.

Community contributions

According to the 2015 sustainability report, the group's cash charitable donations (worldwide) totalled £5.9 million during the year. The group also gave £13.5 million in direct pro bono support. This brings the group's total worldwide charitable contributions to £19.4 million (equivalent to 1.3% of pre-tax profit). The causes supported were broken down as follows:

Cause	Pro bono support	Cash donations
Local community	36%	41%
Health	37%	23%
Education	13%	23%
Human rights	4%	8%
Arts	5%	4%
Environment	5%	1%

Beneficiaries included: Action for Children; Chai Cancer Care; Farms for City Children; Jewish Blind and Disabled; Listening Books; National Portrait Gallery; Royal Star and Garter Homes; The Food Chain; Tower Hamlets Mission; Wellbeing of Women; Wheelchair Rugby.

The group also negotiated free media space worth £24.4 million for pro bono clients during the year.

In-kind support

Pro bono work

The group offers extensive pro bono support in areas such as communications, media, advertising, public relations and research, to charitable organisations supporting a range of causes such as health, education, human rights and arts. This support amounted to the value of £13.5 million in 2015 (worldwide). The group also negotiated free media space for pro bono clients, which was worth £24.4 million in 2015.

Beneficiaries of pro bono support have included: Age UK; British Stammering Organisation; Care International; Operation Smile; Plan UK; Pride in London; StreetSmart; Start Network; The Prince's Trust; Tusk Trust; Unicef; UNHCR.

Employee-led support

Employee volunteering and fundraising

Employees at businesses in the group worldwide offer time to charities and communities through fundraising and volunteering. Examples of employee-led support in the UK in 2015 included: employees in London taking part in a Sleep Out for Centrepoint, the homelessness charity, raising £51,000; 500 employees in London taking over a stadium to cook 5,000 meals which were distributed by FareShare to organisations for vulnerable people, such as homeless shelters and children's breakfast clubs.

Applications

Apply in writing to the correspondent. Many charitable and pro bono activities are organised by individual businesses within the group; for contact details of each of the businesses in the group, refer to the WPP website: www.wpp.com/wpp/companies.

Xerox (UK) Ltd

Print/paper/packaging

Correspondent: Cheryl Walsh, The Xerox (UK) Trust, Bridge House, Oxford Road, Uxbridge UB8 1HS (tel: 01895 251133/01895 251133; website: www.xerox.com)

Directors: Andrew Morrison; Donna Marley; Julie Hesselgrove Ward; Mary O'Driscoll; Oliver Dehon (women: 3; men: 2)

Year end	31/12/2015
Turnover	£287,000,000
Pre-tax profit	£33,600,000

Nature of business: The principal activity of the group is marketing and financing of xerographic and electronic printing equipment, document managing systems and ancillary supplies in the UK.

The ultimate parent company of Xerox (UK) Ltd is Xerox Corporation, incorporated in the USA.

Company registration number: 330754

Subsidiary undertakings include: Bessemer Trust Ltd; Xerox Finance Ltd.

UK employees: 1,827

Focus of giving: General charitable purposes, economic generation, education, enterprise/training, animal welfare, health, ill health, older people, arts, culture, poverty and social exclusion, science technology, sport, recreation, children, young people, community/social welfare, disability.

Community involvement	✓
Community contributions	✓

CSR report ✓
Charity partner(s) ✓
Corporate charity ✓
Employee-led support ✓
Gifts in kind ✓
Pro bono ✓

Community involvement

The company's giving is channelled through its associated charitable trust, Xerox (UK) Trust, which supports a range of causes including education; health and well-being; and children and young people. It is also a patron of The Prince's Trust, which is supported through employee-led initiatives.

The Xerox (UK) Trust (Charity Commission no. 284698)

The group's corporate charity, The Xerox (UK) Trust, makes grants to a wide range of causes, including education; health and well-being; children and young people. The trust receives income from investments as well as through donations from the group where necessary. The trust also receives support from the group's staff, as well as group office space.

Charity partners

The group is a patron supporter of The Prince's Trust, providing support through employee-led fundraising activities. The group has also previously provided in-kind support, donating printing equipment for the charity's office.

Globally, the group also has a number of charitable programmes, as well as an American corporate charity, The Xerox Foundation, supporting STEM education; local communities; employee volunteering; and other charitable initiatives.

Main locations

The group's UK headquarters is based in Uxbridge.

Community contributions

The company's 2015 accounts state that no charitable donations were made during the year. In previous years, the company has made donations to the Xerox (UK) Trust, but the 2015 accounts state that 'the directors deemed there to be sufficient funds for charitable purposes in respect of the year ended 31 December 2015'.

Employee-led support

Employee fundraising

The company's employees participate in fundraising events to support The Prince's Trust, of which the company is a patron. Examples in 2015 include sponsored marathons; taking part in the trust's Million Makers competition; and participating in the trust's Palace to Palace Cycle Ride.

Employee volunteering

Globally, the group has a Community Involvement programme, through which employees volunteer to support charitable causes, such as promoting STEM activities in schools, providing pro bono support to charities or volunteering with community initiatives.

Corporate charity

The Xerox (UK) Trust (Charity Commission no. 284698).

Applications

The Xerox (UK) Trust

The contact person for trust-related enquiries is Cheryl Walsh at the company's address.

The group

Other queries can be directed to: ehs-europe@xerox.com.

Yattendon Group PLC (formerly Yattendon Investment Trust)

Agriculture, leisure, media, print/paper/packaging, property

Correspondent: Catherine Fleming, Trustee of the The Iliffe Family Charitable Trust, Barn Close, Burnt Hill, Yattendon, Newbury, Berkshire RG18 0UX (tel: 01635 203929; email: ifct@yattendon.co.uk; website: www.yattendongroup.co.uk)

Directors: David Fordham; Edward Iliffe, Group Chief Executive; Francois Austin; Lord Iliffe, Chair; Michael Spencer; Stephen Sadler, Group Finance Director (women: 0; men: 6)

Year end	31/03/2016
Turnover	£50,800,000
Pre-tax profit	£10,400,000

Nature of business: Yattendon Group PLC is a private company owned by the Iliffe family, which operates in the UK, Europe and Canada through its subsidiaries. Principal business activities include marina operations, farming, printing and property management. Previously the group operated a publishing business, which was sold in 2013 (Yattendon group has retained its state of the art printing press in Cambridge).

Company registration number: 288238

Subsidiary undertakings include: Iliffe News and Media Ltd; Media Holdings Unlimited; MDL Marinas Group Ltd.

Total employees: 358

Focus of giving: Education, environment, animal welfare, health, ill health, heritage, medical research, older people, arts, culture, religion, children, young people, community/social welfare, disability.

Community contributions ✓
Corporate charity ✓

Community involvement

The group gives through its corporate charity; two of the directors are the trustees of the trust.

The Iliffe Family Charitable Trust (Charity Commission no. 273437)

The trust was established in 1977 to support charitable organisations in the UK or elsewhere in the world. In practice, the majority of donations are made to UK-registered charities in the areas of: education; health and disability; welfare; religion; conservation and heritage; children and young people; and older people.

Both Lord Iliffe and Edward Iliffe are trustees of the charity.

Main locations

The group operates in the UK, Europe and Canada. In the UK it operates 19 marinas in Southern England and 9,000 acres of land in West Berkshire. It also has a printing operation based in Cambridge.

Community contributions

The group did not declare its charitable donations in its annual report and accounts for 2015/16.

The 2015/16 annual report and accounts for The Iliffe Family Charitable Trust were not available at the time of writing (October 2016). The 2014/15 annual report notes that the trust made grants totalling £75,000. It appears that the company made no donations to the trust in 2014/15.

Beneficiaries of the trust have previously included: Afghan Connection; Berkshire Community Foundation; Countryside Learning Scotland; Game and Wildlife Conservancy Trust; Leukaemia and Lymphoma Research; RNLI; Watermill Theatre; Yattendon and Frilsham Christian Stewardship.

Corporate charity

The Iliffe Family Charitable Trust (Charity Commission no. 273437).

Exclusions

No grants are given to individuals and rarely to non-registered charities. Political donations do not seem to be made.

Applications

Applications to the trust can be made in writing to the correspondent at the company's address. Catherine Fleming is both a trustee of the charity and the group's Company Secretary. It is noted in the charity's 2014/15 annual report that 'in order to reduce costs the trustees regret that they do not always reply to unsuccessful applicants for grants'.

Yorkshire Building Society

Building society, financial services

Correspondent: Pauline Giroux, Corporate Responsibility Manager, Yorkshire House, Yorkshire Drive, Bradford BD5 8LJ (tel: 01274 472512; website: www.ybs.co.uk)

Directors: Alison Hutchinson; Andy Caton; Chris Pilling, Chief Executive; Dame Kate Barker; David Paige; Gordon Ireland; Guy Parsons; John Heaps, Chair; Mark Pain, Vice Chair; Mike Regnier; Robin Churchouse, Finance Director; Stephen White (women: 2; men: 10)

Year end	31/12/2015
Turnover	£548,000,000
Pre-tax profit	£173,000,000

Nature of business: The Building Society provides financial services, including mortgages, insurance products and financial advice. Yorkshire Building Society is part of a bigger group that includes Barnsley Building Society, Chelsea Building Society and Norwich and Peterborough Building Society.

FSA registration number: 106085

Subsidiary undertakings include: Accord Mortgages Ltd; BCS Loans and Mortgage Ltd; Tombac No. 1 PLC.

UK employees: 4,576

Focus of giving: General charitable purposes, fundraising events, general appeals, animal welfare, health, ill health, housing, homelessness, non-registered charities, small groups, local groups, humanitarian help, older people, poverty and social exclusion, children, young people, community/social welfare, disability.

Community involvement	✓
Community contributions	✓
CSR report	✓
CSR or charity committee	✓
Directors have other relevant posts	✓
Charity partner(s)	✓
Company gives to smaller charities	✓
Corporate charity	✓
Employee-led support	✓
Humanitarian aid: UK including food banks	✓
Market-led giving	✓
Payroll giving	✓
Unregistered charities/NFP	✓

Charitable donations

Cash UK (latest available):	2015	£68,500
Total UK (cash and in kind):	2015	£2,430,000
Cash worldwide:	2015	£69,500
Total worldwide (cash and in kind):	2015	£2,430,000

Community involvement

The group focuses its charitable and community contributions through its charitable foundation, fundraising activities, and by encouraging employee volunteering. Support is given for general charitable purposes, with some preference for causes relating to: older people; health and disability; community welfare; and animal welfare.

Yorkshire Building Society Charitable Foundation (Charity Commission no. 1069082)

The foundation supports registered charities providing help to vulnerable individuals, particularly: older people; people suffering hardship such as isolation; children or adults with disabilities, including learning disabilities; people who are seriously or terminally ill; and animal welfare. It is run by five trustees, three of whom are independent of the society. Assistance can be given in the areas where the society's members and staff reside.

The foundation prefers to make small donations to a variety of different causes. Charitable organisations or projects that are recommended to the foundation by YBS customers and employees can be considered for a grant of up to £2,000. Other charitable causes can apply for a grant generally up to £500. In 2015 the average grant was £260 and 89% of grants were given to charitable causes recommended by the group's customers and employees.

In 2015 the charity made a £25,000 donation to the Community Flood Appeals in Bradford, Calderdale, Cumbria, Leeds and York.

The foundation receives funding from the group annually. The group also provides administrative support. The majority of the charity's funding, however, comes primarily from the Small Change Big Difference (SCBD) scheme which the society includes as an optional term in most of its savings and mortgage products [see 'Commercially led support'].

Marie Curie Hour of Need Campaign (2014–16)

The campaign aims to raise £500,000 by December 2016. The 2015 annual report notes that throughout the campaign employees, members and the general public will be involved in a variety of fundraising activities and events. Employees will also be volunteering their time and experience to Marie Curie. The annual report states that the fundraising target has already been exceeded and the target has now increased to £1 million.

Community Involvement

The group provides support to local initiatives and causes that can be nominated by customers at their local branches. The website states: 'We hold collections for goods, such as food bank items, clothing or toys, Christmas presents and Easter Eggs to support local causes. If you would like to nominate your cause, get in touch with your local branch.'

Directors with other relevant posts

Alison Hutchinson is Chief Executive Officer of The Pennies Foundation (Charity Commission no. 1122489) and a trustee of The Charities Aid Foundation (Charity Commission no. 268369).

John Heaps is a trustee of the Garden Bridge Trust (Charity Commission no. 1155246).

Andy Caton is a trustee of the Yorkshire Building Society Charitable Foundation (Charity Commission no. 1069082).

Dame Kate Barker has a background in housing and is the author of major government reviews on housing supply and planning.

Chris Pilling is a non-executive director of The Department of Health.

Main locations

The building society is headquartered in Bradford and has branches throughout the UK.

Community contributions

The annual report notes that the group contributed the equivalent of £2.43 million to society through its corporate responsibility activities in 2015. This may well include contributions made by employees (including volunteering time), customers and direct corporate donations. The group donated £68,500 to its charitable foundation during the year, but no other figures were available regarding any other corporate cash donations to charitable causes.

The group's charitable foundation donated £393,000 (2014: £455,000) in 1,500 grants during the year.

Employee-led support

Employee volunteering

All employees are entitled to 31 hours of paid leave to take part in voluntary or charitable activities annually. In 2015 35% of employees volunteered, contributing over 11,800 (2014: 10,000) hours in the community. This included 2,900 hours of volunteering time to Marie Curie. Examples of volunteering activity have included mentoring and befriending; financial literacy sessions;

employability workshops; redecorating community centres; and holding trustee positions.

The group launched volunteering programmes in 2015 with a number of partners in order to provide new volunteering opportunities for its employees. Partners included: Be a Trustee; Silverline; and SGOSS (Governors for Schools).

Commercially led support

Small Change Big Difference
The group's customers can choose to take part in the Small Change Big Difference scheme, whereby the annual pence interest on savings and mortgage accounts is donated to the group's Charitable Foundation. A maximum of 99p per account per year is donated to the foundation. The average donation is less than 50p per year.

Affinity accounts
The group offers affinity accounts to enable its customers to pay a percentage of their savings balance to a charity or local club. In 2015 the most successful accounts were Yorkshire Air Ambulance and Marie Curie. The Marie Curie Savings bond was released in November 2015 and sold out in less than two weeks.

Corporate charity

Yorkshire Building Society Charitable Foundation (Charity Commission no. 1069082).

Exclusions

The foundation's guidelines provide the following examples where support will not be given:

- Applications for general ongoing funding, running costs, research, sponsorship, payment of salaries or expenses
- Contributions towards large funding, fundraising events or marketing appeals
- Office equipment for a charity's own use such as telephones, security systems and computers
- Donations to be given to an individual
- Causes serving only a specific sector of the community selected on the basis of ethnic, racial, political, sexual or religious grounds/advancement
- Travel, expeditions or educational expenses to fund activities outside the UK
- Support of activities in, or equipment for mainstream schools, sports clubs, scouts/guides groups, local/ government funded bodies (unless for special needs groups). Scouts/guides groups in areas of deprivation may be considered on an individual basis

Applications

The foundation: Applications to the foundation can only be made online. The society's members and staff can also nominate a cause to be supported by the foundation. Bev Cox, Community Manager, is responsible for the management of the foundation and can be contacted by email (charitablefoundation@ybs.co.uk) or at the group's head office (telephone: 01274 472877).

Local causes: Nominations for local initiatives to be supported are received from members of the society or through the society's branches or head office departments. Members can just speak to one of the team who can give more information about how the process works. This helps ensure support is given to local charities and good causes in areas important to members and staff.

All other community and corporate social responsibility enquiries can be directed to the Corporate Responsibility Manager, at the group's head office.

ZPG Ltd

Computer software, Information Technology, property

Correspondent: Ned Staple, Company Secretary, The Cooperage, 5 Copper Row, London, England SE1 2LH (website: www.zpg.co.uk)

Directors: Alex Chesterman, Chief Executive Officer; David Dutton; Duncan Tatton-Brown; Grenville Turner; Mike Evans, Chair; Robin Klein; Sherry Coutu; Stephen Daintith; Stephen Morana, Chief Financial Officer; Vin Murria (women: 2; men: 8)

Year end	31/12/2015
Turnover	£107,556,000
Pre-tax profit	£33,583,000

Nature of business: The group runs property and price comparison websites Zoopla, uSwitch and PrimeLocation, as well as supplying software and workflow solutions to the property industry.

Company registration number: 6074771

Subsidiary undertakings include: uSwitch Digital Ltd; uSwitch Communications Ltd; Ulysses Enterprises Ltd.

Brands include: PrimeLocation; uSwitch; Zoopla.

UK employees: 438

Total employees: 438

Focus of giving: Education, enterprise/ training, marginalised people, poverty and social exclusion, safety and crime prevention, children, young people, community/social welfare.

Community involvement	✓
Community contributions	✓
CSR report	✓
Directors have other relevant posts	✓
Charity partner(s)	✓
Employee-led support	✓
Gifts in kind	✓
Matched funding	✓
Payroll giving	✓

Charitable donations

Total UK (cash and in kind):	2015	£53,000
Total worldwide (cash and in kind):	2015	£53,000

Community involvement

Partnerships
The website states that the group is a supporter of The Prince's Trust and of Only Connect.

Directors with other relevant posts
Sherry Coutu is a trustee of Founders4Schools (Charity Commission no. 1162197) and is one of the founders of SVC2UK (Silicon Valley Comes to the UK), a not-for-profit series of events to bring together entrepreneurs, students and investors to discuss ways to use technology to change the world. Grenville Turner is a trustee of the English National Ballet (214005).

Main locations
The group's head office is based in Southwark, London.

Community contributions

The group's charitable contributions totalled £53,000 in 2014/15.

Employee-led support

Matched funding and payroll giving
The group has a payroll giving scheme, and provides matched funding of up to £100 per employee for individual fundraising activities.

Employee volunteering
Employees are entitled to one day of paid volunteering each year.

Applications

Apply in writing to the correspondent.

Zurich Insurance Group (record previously for Zurich Financial Services (UKISA) Ltd)

Insurance, life assurance

Correspondent: Corporate Responsibility Team, The Zurich Centre, 3000 Parkway, Whiteley, Fareham, Hampshire PO15 7JZ (website: www.zurich.co.uk/en/about-us/corporate-responsibility)

Directors: Christoph Franz; Dame Alison Carnwath; David Nish; Fred Kindle; Jeffrey Hayman; Joan Amble; Kishore Mahbubani; Monica Mächler; Susan Bies; Tom de Swaan, Chair (women: 4; men: 6)

Year end	31/12/2015
Turnover	£49,755,000,000
Pre-tax profit	£2,745,000,000

Nature of business: Zurich is an insurance company headquartered in Zurich, Switzerland which, according to its website, has about 55,000 employees working in over 170 countries. The group's UK branch provides a range of personal, business, public sector, and charity and community insurance products.

Note that the figures for turnover and pre-tax profit were reported in USD and we have converted them into GBP at the time of writing (January 2017).

Subsidiary undertakings include: Zurich Assurance Ltd; Zurich Financial Services (UKISA) Ltd; Zurich Holdings (UK) Ltd.

Total employees: 55,000

Focus of giving: General charitable purposes, education, health, ill health, housing, homelessness, small groups, local groups, older people, overseas projects, poverty and social exclusion, children, young people, community/social welfare, disability.

Membership: BITC, LBG

Community involvement	✓
Community contributions	✓
CSR report	✓
CSR or charity committee	✓
AF Covenant	✓
Charity partner(s)	✓
Community Mark	✓
Company gives to smaller charities	✓
Corporate charity	✓
Employee-led support	✓
Gifts in kind	✓
Humanitarian aid: overseas	✓
Matched funding	✓
Overseas giving	✓
Payroll giving	✓
Pro bono	✓
Sponsorship	✓

Charitable donations

Cash UK (latest available):	2015	£2,500,000
Total UK (cash and in kind):	2015	£2,500,000
Cash worldwide:	2015	£18,500,000
Total worldwide (cash and in kind):	2015	£18,500,000

Community involvement

A significant proportion of Zurich's UK community involvement is channelled through the Zurich Community Trust (Charity Commission no. 266983).

Zurich Community Trust (ZCT)

Established in 1973 as a vehicle for Zurich's community involvement, the trust uses donations from Zurich's UK businesses and employees to work towards its aim of improving the quality of life for disadvantaged people in the UK and overseas. The trust also acts as a 'broker' for Zurich employees' community volunteering activities, including for those during the annual team volunteering 'Challenge' event. The trust channels its support through three main programmes:

Social transformation programmes

According to the trust's website, these, usually long-term (five or more years), charity partnerships 'focus on key social issues that are often overlooked and where [the trust] can have the biggest impact'. The website also notes: 'The Community Trust team select an issue to support only after lengthy research, and particularly look for innovative projects which are sustainable and could be replicated elsewhere. Often this means that we fund core costs such as staff salaries.' Examples of projects supported through this fund include:

- Breaking the Cycle in partnership with the trust's charity partner Addaction
- A Call in Time, helping Age UK to tackle isolation among older people
- Young People's Mental Health, focusing on early intervention with mental health issues among young people
- India programme, which combines core funding with skills-sharing from Zurich employees to develop the capacity of selected NGOs working in Southern India

Zurich Cares programmes

These programmes are made possible by contributions of money, time and skills from Zurich employees. Funds raised for Zurich Cares by employees are doubled by the trust using the annual donation it receives from the company. In addition to the volunteering aspect of the initiative, it also involves three main grants schemes:

- National partners: Zurich employees nominate three national organisations to become partner charities and to receive an equal share of an £150,000 grant pot each year for a period of four to six years (£50,000 per year, per nominated charity). The current national charity partners are: Alzheimer's Society; CLIC Sargent; and Mind
- Local grants programme: Smaller grants, usually from a pot of around £600,000, are allocated to charities and community organisations working in the areas surrounding Zurich's UK offices. Funding is allocated by Zurich Cares charity committees made up of employees
- Overseas grants programme: Each year around 16 UK-based charities working overseas are supported with funding from a budget of £75,000

The Zurich Cares PDF, which is available to download from the website, explains that other grants programmes include:

- Nominated and small grants programmes: Employees 'can fundraise for or nominate charities which are important to them to receive a grant'
- Regional grants programme: Similar to the local grants programme but 'aimed at homeworkers and the staff at some of the smaller Zurich locations around the UK', grants are made from a budget of £40,000

Openwork Foundation

According to the trust's annual report for 2015, 'This fund within the overall charity is funded by self-employed financial advisors and employees of Openwork. The objective of the Openwork Foundation is to improve the quality of life for disadvantaged children under a theme of 'Cares 4 Kids''. Openwork is a UK financial advice company. In addition to its national charity partnership with Carers Trust, other charities working with disadvantaged children are supported through a regional grants programme. There is also a small discretionary fund for which a broader range of charities can be recommended by Openwork advisors or employees. More information is available from Openwork's website (www.openwork.uk.com/charity).

Global community initiatives

Globally, Zurich's CSR activities include flood resilience projects comprising flood research, community-based programs and risk expertise and working in partnership with the International Federation of Red Cross and Red Crescent Societies (IFRC), Practical Action (a UK-based international NGO) and two research institutes.

There is also global Z Zurich Foundation which, according to the UK website, 'expresses [the company's] commitment to community involvement at the Zurich Group level'. Its aim is to help individuals and communities manage risk, and focuses its contributions on three areas: sustainable disaster management; social and economic empowerment; insurance-relevant research and education.

Global Community Week

Zurich offices across the globe take part in a Global Community Week, which is an annual event during which employees focus on using their time and skills to benefit their communities. More than 31,000 business hours were volunteered during 2015's Global Community Week by more than 31% of Zurich's global workforce. Financial and time contributions from employees are matched by the company which, in 2015, raised $1.5 million (approximately £1.2 million, of which around £500,000 was contributed by employees and the remainder by Zurich).

Women in Finance Charter

In addition to the UK branch of Zurich Insurance being a signatory of the Armed Forces Covenant, a news item on Zurich's UK website dated 21 October 2016 states that Zurich has also signed the UK Government's Women in Finance Charter.

Main UK locations

Zurich has offices located throughout the UK. For details of specific locations see the website (www.zurich.co.uk/en/about-us/our-offices).

Zurich Community Trust's website explains:

> Most of our funds that are open to apply to are designated in areas around our main office locations in Gloucestershire, Fareham and Farnborough in Hampshire, London and Wiltshire. There are smaller budgets for Birmingham, Bristol, Cardiff, Glasgow, Manchester and Leeds.

Community contributions

UK contributions

Unfortunately, the most recent LBG breakdown of Zurich's UK community investment, as seen on the UK website, appears to note contributions given in 2014.

The 2015 annual report for Zurich Community Trust (UK) Ltd states that it received a donation of £2.5 million from Zurich businesses in the UK during the year. We have taken this as the company's UK cash donation. We were unable to determine the total value of in-kind contributions made by Zurich in the UK.

Worldwide contributions

Zurich Insurance Group's 'Corporate responsibility highlights 2015' report states that, during the year, 'Zurich made total cash contributions of USD 22.6 million' (approximately £18.5 million). We were unable to determine the total value of the in-kind support (namely in the form of employee volunteer time) contributed by Zurich globally.

In-kind support

Employee time

Members of staff are provided with business time (according information for new employees on the website, one day per year) to facilitate their involvement with volunteering and fundraising activities.

Pro bono

Zurich employees are encouraged to share their knowledge and skills through programmes involving national and local partners managed by the Zurich Community Trust. Opportunities include:

Skillshare projects

The purpose of these projects is to allow employees to use their skills to make an important contribution to a community organisation in a short space of time. They are usually one-off projects and can cover a wide range of areas (from marketing to business and strategic planning, social media training, etc.) and range in length from 2 hours to 20, either in one go or over a period of a few months. ZCT's website notes that 'in 2015 a total of 190 skillshares were either started, completed or ongoing'.

Business to charity mentoring

The trust's website explains 'Zurich already runs a successful in-house mentoring scheme, and now Zurich Community Trust is starting to develop external mentoring between a staff member and the CEO or senior manager of a local or national charity'. Mentors and mentees currently meet three or four times each year, with support also given via telephone, email or Skype.

Employee-led support

Employee and retiree volunteering

Zurich Community Trust runs a number of programme with which employees can get involved; according to the website, these include: 'Team challenges; Skillshares; becoming a Charity co-ordinator or Ambassador for the Trust; lunchtime volunteering; undertaking an assignment in India; being a Call in Time telephone befriender for older people and participating in Zurich's annual Global Community Week.'

Zurich Cares

ZCT's annual report for 2015 notes that, in addition to company time, 'a great deal of employee personal time' is 'leveraged' through the Zurich Cares programme. Furthermore, the Zurich Cares PDF published in 2016 explains: 'Approximately 35% of Zurich's employees in the UK take part in Zurich Community Trust brokered volunteering each year. In 2015 our 26th year of Challenge, Zurich employees completed a total of 312 challenges and took part in nearly 6,000 days of volunteering.'

The Evolving programme

In 2014 the trust launched this programme with the aim of encouraging former Zurich employees to contribute their time and skills for the good of the community. According to the trust's annual report for 2015, there were 'seven new volunteers in active volunteering with 12 more in the immediate pipeline'.

Employee fundraising

ZCT's website notes that in 2015 Zurich employees raised £550,000 for Zurich Cares. Efforts included a team from Zurich UK Life Finance and Investments which took on the Tough Mudder challenge, raising more than £4,000. Other fundraising opportunities for employees include marathons, abseiling and triathlons.

Payroll giving

More than 22% of Zurich's UK employees are enrolled in the payroll giving scheme, helping to earn Zurich a Platinum Quality Mark Award. Contributions help to support the work of the Zurich Community Trust.

Zurich retirees can also support the trust through tax payments on their pensions.

Matched funding

The Zurich Cares initiative is half funded by employees and is matched by the Zurich Community Trust using the annual donation it receives from Zurich UK businesses. The trust's website explains that every payroll giving donation received is matched 100%.

'Round Pound' scheme

Zurich employees can contribute odd pennies from their monthly wage packets to Zurich Cares.

Zurich Cares lottery

Employees can take part in a monthly lottery, the proceeds from which are contributed to the Zurich Cares initiative.

Trusteeship and school governorship grants

Members of staff who volunteer as trustees or school governors are given the opportunity to apply for an annual grant of £200 for their charity or school.

Commercially led support

Sponsorship

Zurich sponsors sports events, and golf in particular, and (in Switzerland) cultural initiatives. In the UK, the company sponsors the British Masters golf tournament.

According to the website, Zurich also works with industry knowledge think tanks and risk management institutions, and has a long-term partnership with the World Economic Forum. In the UK, the company is working with the University of Oxford's Smith School of Enterprise and Environment to construct a programme based around thought leadership with a focus on the Income Protection Gap.

More information on Zurich's sponsorship initiatives is available from the website (www.zurich.com/en/about-us/sponsorship).

Support for the voluntary sector Insurance and risk management guides
Zurich worked with the Guardian to produce free risk guides aimed specifically at the voluntary sector, and has also published other helpful insurance information guides for charities and community groups. Examples include 'Planning for and dealing with major incidents' which contains guidance to help organisations prepare for a crisis and minimise the impact should the worst happen, minimising the impact on beneficiaries. The guides are available on the Zurich website (www.zurich.co.uk/en/charity-insurance/get-help/support-and-resources).

My Community Starter
This free information resource is available online and helps people who want to get involved in organising smaller, straightforward community activities to help people understand and overcome potential barriers to volunteering in the local community. The website will help the public to understand some of the legal, health and safety, planning issues and insurance considerations of whatever they are involved in. See the website for more information (www.zurich.co.uk/en/charity-insurance/my-community-starter).

Corporate charity

Zurich Community Trust (UK) Ltd (Charity Commission no. 266983).

Exclusions

According to its website, ZCT does not fund the following:

- Applications by an individual for any purpose or on behalf of an individual e.g. personal medical equipment, expeditions, exchanges or study tours
- Medical research
- Statutory organisations including mainstream schools and hospitals – unless exclusively for a special needs group
- Animal welfare charities
- Conservation or environmental projects – unless involving disadvantaged people
- Political organisations or those supporting military action
- Organisations that promote religious beliefs
- Sports clubs, village halls, playgroups and mother and toddler groups – unless for special needs groups
- Scouts, Girl Guides, Cadets and other similar organisations – unless specifically supporting disadvantaged children
- Fundraising events including appeals or events for national charities
- Advertising or sponsorship connected with charitable activities

Applications

Zurich Community Trust
In the first instance see the trust's website (www.zurich.co.uk/zurichcommunitytrust) where full information of the trust's work, including its grants programmes and eligibility criteria, can be found. Queries can be sent to the Zurich Community Trust team by email (zct@zct.org.uk).

Other CR queries
General enquiries regarding Zurich's Corporate Responsibility Programme can be directed to the Corporate Responsibility team by email (CRZurichUK@uk.zurich.com).

Football clubs

This section of the guide contains a chapter detailing some of the community activities of the football clubs competing in the 2016/17 season of the Premier League. Football clubs occupy a unique space in the corporate world as many have their origins embedded in their local communities. We hope that the information contained in this section will help to shine a light on the work clubs are carrying out in their communities at a time when football is more high profile and lucrative than ever.

Arsenal Holdings PLC

Football

Correspondent: See 'Applications', Highbury House, 75 Drayton Park, London N5 1BU (tel: 020 7619 5003; website: www.arsenal.com/community)

Directors: Enos Kroenke; Ivan Gazidis; John Keswick; Josh Kroenke; Kenneth Friar; Lord Harris of Peckham (women: 0; men: 6)

Year end	31/05/2016
Turnover	£354,000,000
Pre-tax profit	£2,900,000

Nature of business: Arsenal Holdings PLC is the ultimate parent company of Arsenal FC, a football team competing in the Premier League.

Company registration number: 4250459

Focus of giving: Education, enterprise/ training, equal opportunities, health, ill health, poverty and social exclusion, sport, recreation, children, young people, disability.

Community involvement	✓
Community contributions	✓
Company reports on anti-slavery	✓
Charity partner(s)	✓
Corporate charity	✓
Employee-led support	✓

Community involvement

Arsenal in the Community was set-up in 1985 and today it delivers sport, social and education programmes to over 5,000 individuals each week.

Arsenal in the Community

Sport

Arsenal in The Community runs football programmes for women's football, people with disabilities, young people and walking football. There also programmes for other sports including hockey and bowls.

Education and training

Arsenal use the club's name to improve numeracy and literacy in young people and later on to further education and employment. Programmes include an adult learning centre, reading programmes and an employability scheme.

Social inclusion

The Positive Futures programme runs on ten estates in Islington. It includes youth engagement football sessions that offer additional activities such as trips, workshops, homework clubs and volunteer placements. Other programmes include working with local pupil referral units and a partnership with Freedom from Torture which helps provide job opportunities and training for victims of torture.

Healthy living

Arsenal in the Community is working with Jamie Oliver to provide cooking classes to the local community.

The Arsenal Hub

Over 1,000 people access the hub every week for sports and educational activities.

The Arsenal Foundation (Charity Commission no. 1145668)

The foundation makes grants throughout the UK with a preference for Islington, Camden, Hackney, Barnet, Walthamstow and Hertsmere. According to the foundation's website, the following are priority areas:

- Education (including academic, social, physical education and skills training)
- Sports capable of improving health
- Medical
- Sickness and the relief of suffering
- Disability
- Poverty
- Individual misfortune

Main locations

Islington; Camden; Hackney; Barnet; Walthamstow; Hertsmere.

Community contributions

The club's community contributions were not stated in its annual report.

Corporate charity

The Arsenal Foundation (Charity Commission no. 1145668).

Applications

The Arsenal Foundation

See the entry for The Arsenal Foundation on page 342.

AFC Bournemouth Ltd

Football

Correspondent: See 'Applications', Vitality Stadium, Dean Court, Bournemouth BH7 7AF (website: www.afcb.co.uk/community)

Directors: Igor Tikhturov; Jay Coppoletta; Jeffrey Mostyn; Matt Hulsizer; Mikhail Ponomarev; Neill Blake; Nicholas Rothwell; Oleg Tikhturov; Rico Seitz (women: 0; men: 9)

Year end	31/07/2015
Turnover	£12,900,000
Pre-tax profit	(£38,300,000)

Nature of business: AFC Bournemouth is a football team competing in the English Premier League.

Company registration number: 6632170

Focus of giving: Health and well-being.

Community involvement	✓
Community contributions	✓

Community involvement

AFC Bournemouth Community Sports Trust (Charity Commission no. 1122693)

Coaching Programmes

The trust delivers sports sessions to more than 30 schools across Dorset and Hampshire. The trust also runs soccer schools during the holidays and weekly coaching sessions across the region.

Schools programmes
Projects in schools include: Bug Busters which covers illness prevention; Respect which covers respectful and disrespectful behaviour in everyday life; and Connect With Care which covers the safe use of the Internet.

Kicks
A variety of sessions are held to encourage young people aged 14+ to engage in sport and gain qualifications.

Europartner
Europartner is a football coaching programme for German exchange students visiting Bournemouth during the summer.

Apprenticeships
The trust runs Activity Leadership Apprenticeships which include working 30 hours within the community department.

Main locations
Dorset

Community contributions

Charitable contributions were not declared in the club's annual accounts.

Applications

Enquiries can be made to: Andrew Battison, Community Operations Co-ordinator, tel: 01202726359, email: andrew.battison@afcb.co.uk; or Steve Cuss, Head of Community, tel: 01202726342, email: steve.cuss@afcb.co.uk.

Burnley FC Holdings Ltd

Football

Correspondent: The Community Team, Turf Moor, Harry Potts Way, Burnley, Lancashire BB10 4BX (tel: 01282 704716; email: community@burnleyfc.com; website: www.burnleyfccommunity.org)

Directors: Barry Kilby; Brendan Flood; Brian Nelson; Clive Holt; John Banaszkiewicz; Mike Garlick, Chair; Terence Crabb (women: 0; men: 7)

Year end	30/06/2015
Turnover	£78,800,000

Nature of business: Burnley FC Holdings Ltd is the ultimate parent company of Burnley FC, a football team competing in the Premier League.

Company registration number: 8335231

Subsidiary undertakings include: The Burnley Football and Athletic Club Ltd; Turf Moor Properties Ltd; Longside Properties Ltd.

Focus of giving: Education, enterprise/training, health, ill health, poverty and social exclusion, sport, recreation.

Community involvement	✓
Community contributions	✓
CSR report	✓
Gifts in kind	✓

Charitable donations

Total UK (cash and in kind):	2015	£92,000
Total worldwide (cash and in kind):	2015	£92,000

Community involvement

Burnley FC in the Community (Charity Commission no. 1155856)
Burnley FC in the Community delivers 35 community projects across East Lancashire including disability sport, employability courses, provision for senior citizens and young people in the most deprived local areas.

Sport
Burnley in the Community run several schemes to help schoolchildren, young people and people with disabilities become more involved with sport. An example of one such schemes is the Danny Ings Disability Sports Project. The project aims to engage and empower members of the community through sport. The project also includes the creation of Burnley Disability Football Club.

Education
UCFB Burnley is collaboration between Burnley in the Community and Nelson and Colne College. The partnership offers education opportunities to students including BTEC provision, apprenticeships, adult learning courses and employability workshops.

Inclusion
The club runs the The Duke of Edinburgh Award, The National Citizen Service and Premier League Kicks. All of these programmes help promote inclusion and help build skills for work and life.

Health
Schemes include healthy eating programmes, weight management, health checks and a veterans programme. The club also lets several local community groups use their cafe for meetings.

Brierfield Mill
Once completed the mill will be a state-of-the-art community leisure facility. It will include sports facilities, education suites, dance studios and a soft play area.

Charity partners
In January 2017 the club announced a new partnership with Pendleside Hospice. The two organisations have teamed up to raise funds for the local community.

Main locations
Burnley in The Community works throughout East Lancashire.

Community contributions

The club did not declare its charitable contributions for the year. However, in 2014/15 Burnley in the Community received £92,000 from The Burnley Football and Athletic Company Ltd. The 2014/15 annual report states that: 'During the year the company made recharges of salaries totalling £36,172 to BFC. During the year BFC provided goods and services to the company totalling £55,942 and office space to the company at no charge.'

Applications

Burnley FC in the Community
Enquiries can be made to the correspondent.

Brierfield Mill
Contact M. Hagreaves on m.hargreaves@burnleyfc.com or call 01282 704716.

Chelsea FC PLC

Football

Correspondent: Chelsea Foundation (tel: 01932 596193; website: www.chelseafc.com/the-club/foundation.html)

Directors: Bruce Buck; Eugene Tenenbaum; Marina Granovskaia (women: 1; men: 2)

Year end	30/06/2016
Turnover	£314,200,000
Pre-tax profit	(£22,753,000)

Nature of business: Chelsea FC PLC is the ultimate parent company of Chelsea FC, a football team competing in the Premier League.

Company registration number: 2536231

Focus of giving: Education, enterprise/training, overseas projects, children, young people.

Community involvement	✓
Community contributions	✓
Cash donations declared	✓
Charity partner(s)	✓

Charitable donations

Cash worldwide:	2016	£3,140,000

Community involvement

The Chelsea Foundation
The foundation was formed in 2010 and brings together the Football in the Community and the Education department along with the club's other charitable and community activities, including environment and anti-discrimination projects.

Education
The education department works closely with local schools, colleges and the local community to develop initiatives that help participants reach their learning goals. There is a wide range of initiatives for primary and secondary schoolchildren on topics including

diversity, reading and goal setting. There are also projects to improve people's employability and to help them develop business plans. The club run a BTEC in sport, traineeships and accountancy awards.

Community

The foundation runs several programmes to improve social inclusion within the local community. The Premier League Kicks programme promotes universal sports engagement within disadvantaged areas and with at risk individuals. The Unlocking Potential initiative targets vulnerable young people in an effort to reduce offending and re-offending rates.

Partnership with Plan International

Plan International is one of the oldest and largest children's charities in the world. Plan and Chelsea will work together to work with young people across the world to teach them about equality, respect and tolerance.

Soccer schools

Chelsea run over 200 soccer schools in the local area for children aged between four and thirteen years old.

Football development

The foundation has a disability inclusion programme that allows people with disabilities to take part in coaching sessions and matches in a safe and enjoyable environment. The foundation also works to spread the game and the ethos of the foundation internationally.

Main locations

London; Surrey; Sussex; Hampshire.

Community contributions

In 2015/16 Chelsea FC PLC made charitable donations totalling £3.14 million.

In-kind support

Chelsea does accept requests for signed merchandise from registered charities. However, the club states that due to high demand it is not possible to meet all requests.

Applications

Charity requests

Applications must be sent in writing to:

Charity Requests, The Foundation, Cobham Training Ground, 64 Stoke Road, Stoke D'Abernon KT11 3PT.

CPFC Ltd (Crystal Palace Football Club)

Football

Correspondent: Crystal Palace Foundation, Selhurst Park Stadium, Holmesdale Road, London, Greater London SE25 6PU (tel: 020 8768 6047/ 020 8768 6047; email: info@cpfcfoundation.org; website: www.cpfc.co.uk/club/cpfcfoundation)

Directors: David Blitzer; Joshua Harris; Philip Alexander, Chief Executive; Steve Parish, Chair (women: 0; men: 4)

Year end	30/06/2015
Turnover	£102,400,000
Pre-tax profit	£7,900,000

Nature of business: Crystal Palace FC is a football club competing in the Premier League.

Company registration number: 7270793

UK employees: 187

Total employees: 187

Focus of giving: Education, enterprise/ training, fundraising events, health, ill health, local groups, humanitarian help, overseas projects, poverty and social exclusion, safety and crime prevention, sport, recreation, children, young people, community/social welfare, disability.

Community involvement	✓
Community contributions	✓
Charity partner(s)	✓
Gifts in kind	✓
Humanitarian aid: UK including food banks	✓

Charitable donations

Total UK (cash and in kind):	2015	£22,000

Community involvement

Crystal Palace FC Foundation (Charity Commission no. 1125878)

The club's charity, the Crystal Palace FC Foundation, has the following aims, according to its website:

- Growing the game/sporting provision for all
- Supporting children's development
- Raising aspirations and broadening the horizons of young people
- Routes into education, training and employment
- Promoting health and well-being

The foundation's work is focused on the boroughs of Bromley, Croydon, Lambeth and Sutton, with additional satellite sites outside London. It works with partners including local council, schools, voluntary sector and community organisations to deliver its projects, which fall into the categories of community; disability; health; and young people. Examples of projects include:

- The Eagles Fitter Fans programme, which focuses on men's health and well-being
- Powerchair football team
- Croydon Eagles mental health football team, in partnership with Mind in Croydon
- Weekend clubs for children and young people who are blind and partially sighted in partnership with the Royal London Society for the Blind
- Aspire II, a project working in partnership with local housing associations and businesses to support disengaged young people into employment

In-kind support

The foundation can provide donations of merchandise for local registered charities or community groups that work within the boroughs of London in which the foundation works and support the following causes: young people; cultural relations; sporting activity or health; and education or literacy.

Main locations

Bromley; Croydon; Lambeth; Sutton.

Community contributions

No figure was given in the club's 2014/15 accounts for its charitable contributions.

The 2014/15 accounts for the Crystal Palace FC Foundation state that in-kind donations from the club during the year totalled £22,000 and were comprised of kits, estimated at £10,200, and office space and rent, estimated at £12,000.

Exclusions

The foundation is unlikely to support requests which are:

- Outside of the foundation's main locations
- From non-registered charities
- For animal charities
- Short notice
- Unlikely to raise significant funds for a charity
- Fundraising for individuals

Requests from individuals fundraising for a charity may be considered if supported by a headed letter from the charity, stating authorisation for the individual to fundraise for them, and including a contact name and telephone number.

Applications

In-kind support

There is an online form for charities to request in-kind donations of signed merchandise for fundraising purposes, which can be downloaded at: www.cpfc.co.uk/club/faqs.

The website states that although the club aims to help as many causes as possible, it is not able to grant every request due to the high volume it receives.

The foundation's website states that there is a preference for local registered charities or community groups which work within the London area, and support the following causes: young people; cultural relations; sporting activity or health; education or literacy.

Everton Football Club Company Ltd

Football

Correspondent: Everton in the Community, Goodison Park, Goodison Road, Liverpool L4 4EL (tel: 0151 530 5253/0151 530 5253; email: community@evertonfc.com; website: www.evertonfc.com/community)

Directors: Alexander Ryazantsev; Bill Kenwright, Chair; Denise Barrett-Baxendale; Jon Woods; Keith Harris; Robert Elstone, Chief Executive (women: 1; men: 5)

Year end	31/05/2015
Turnover	£125,600,000
Pre-tax profit	(£242,000)

Nature of business: Everton FC is a football club competing in the Premier League.

Company registration number: 36624

Subsidiary undertakings include: Everton Investments Ltd; Goodison Park Stadium Ltd; The Everton Ladies Football Club Ltd.

UK employees: 315 (+445 temporary staff on match-days)

Focus of giving: Education, enterprise/training, fundraising events, health, ill health, housing, homelessness, small groups, local groups, armed forces, humanitarian help, poverty and social exclusion, safety and crime prevention, sport, recreation, children, young people, community/social welfare, disability.

Accredited Living Wage Employer	✓
Community involvement	✓
Community contributions	✓
CSR report	✓
Directors have other relevant posts	✓
Armed forces personnel	✓
Cash donations declared	✓
Charity partner(s)	✓
Company gives to smaller charities	✓
Gifts in kind	✓
Humanitarian aid: UK including food banks	✓
Market-led giving	✓
Pro bono	✓

Charitable donations

Total UK (cash and in kind):	2015	£161,000

Community involvement

Everton in the Community (Charity Commission no. 1099366)

The club's charity, Everton in the Community, delivers a wide range of projects directly in the local community, working in partnership with other organisations such as schools, charities and public services. In 2016 it also opened a new Community Hub facility.

Health and well-being

The charity works in partnership with a range of health organisations and partners to deliver projects aimed at improving the health and quality of life of some of the most 'hard-to-reach' groups in the local community.

Young people

The charity runs a number of youth engagement projects aiming to promote community cohesion, positive life choices, personal development and education. The charity works with partners such as The Prince's Trust and National Citizen Service, delivering projects working with young people who are disadvantaged, such as young people who have offended, looked after children and young adults who are unemployed.

Sports

There are a range of sports projects run by Everton in the Community Projects include: a number of schools programmes; development programmes for people with disabilities; activities with the local children's hospital; sports for young women with mental health problems; football training with local people who have experienced homelessness.

Employment and education

The charity works in partnership with organisations such as government bodies, training and employment providers and the local NHS trust to provide opportunities for education, training and employment.

In-kind donations

According to the website, Everton in the Community provides support to help over 1,500 other charities per year. Examples of support may include signed memorabilia or official merchandise to be used for fundraising purposes, or volunteering from players in the club's first team to help raise awareness. There is an online form for charities to request support.

The club also supports Tickets for Troops, an initiative to provide free tickets to sports, music and cultural events to members and ex-members of the armed forces and their families.

Other initiatives

The club's Blue Crimbo Campaign involves outreach to people in need in the local community, such as players visiting the local Alder Hey Children's Hospital; under-23 players volunteering with a local homeless charity; and outreach activities to older people in the community.

In 2015 the club also opened Everton Free School, which focuses on provision for young people who do not currently attend school or are at risk of exclusion.

The club also has links with charities associated with Chernobyl.

Directors with other relevant posts

Denise Barrett-Baxendale is Chief Executive and a trustee of Everton in the Community (Charity Commission no. 1099366); she is also a member of the board of Sport England and a fellow of the RSA.

Main locations

Organisations within a 30-mile radius of Goodison Park.

Community contributions

The club's 2014/15 annual report states that it 'incurred net operating costs of £161,000' on behalf of Everton in the Community during the year.

Exclusions

Support can only be provided to charities within a 30-mile radius of Goodison Park.

Applications

In-kind donations

Donations such as official merchandise, signed memorabilia or support from first team players are made by the club through its charity, Everton in the Community. There is an online form for charities to request support: www.evertonfc.com/community/fundraising/the-projects/everton-giving

Other queries

There is a contact form on the website for other queries: www.evertonfc.com/functional/contact-us-form.

Hull City Tigers Ltd

Football

Correspondent: Tigers Trust, KC Stadium, West Park, Hull HU3 6HU (tel: 01482 504600/01482 358371; email: office@tigerstrust.co.uk; website: tigerstrust.co.uk)

Directors: Assem Allam, Chair; Ehab Allam (women: 0; men: 2)

Year end	30/06/2016
Turnover	£41,900,000
Pre-tax profit	(£20,600,000)

Nature of business: Hull City AFC is a football club competing in the Premier League.

Company registration number: 4032392

UK employees: 206

Total employees: 206

Focus of giving: Education, enterprise/training, health, ill health, poverty and social exclusion, sport, recreation, community/social welfare, disability.

Community involvement	✓
Community contributions	✓

Directors have other relevant posts	✓
Charity partner(s)	✓
Gifts in kind	✓
Sponsorship	✓

Community involvement

Tigers Trust (Charity Commission no. 1092287)

The club's charity, Tigers Sport and Education Trust, largely focuses on football and sports projects in the categories of juniors; youth; adults; education; and disability. The trust works with partners such as The Prince's Trust, Premier League, National Citizen Service and local schools to deliver its programmes.

In 2016 the club announced that it has committed a further two years of official charity partnerships with the Tigers Trust, until 2017/18.

In-kind initiatives

According to the website, some of the club's players provide support through visiting local schools, hospitals, etc. in the community.

The club has also offered in-kind support to charities. For example, in 2016, an official match ball was auctioned to raise money for The Royal British Legion, and shirts with the logo of the Tigers Trust were donated for fundraising purposes. In 2015, the club offered its mascots for a calendar in support a Male Cancer Awareness campaign.

Directors with other relevant posts

Assem Allam is a trustee of Hull and East Yorkshire Medical Research Centre (Charity Commission no. 1095652) and The British Egyptian Society (Charity Commission no. 1134721).

Main locations

Kingston upon Hull

Community contributions

No figure was given for the club's total charitable contributions during the year.

It is not clear from the Tiger Trust's accounts whether the trust receives any income from the club. The 2014/15 accounts state the following: 'The value of voluntary help given by the trustees and other workers, together with support from Hull City Football Club, is not included in the financial statements.'

Applications

Apply in writing to the correspondent. The website states that queries about 'Soccer Schools, Birthday Parties, Education Initiatives' should be directed to the Tigers Trust.

Leicester City Football Club Ltd

Football

Correspondent: LCFC Foxes Foundation, 0116 229 4737, King Power Stadium, Filbert Way, Leicester, Leicestershire LE2 7FL (tel: 0344 815 5000; email: lcfcfoxesfoundation@lcfc.co.uk; website: www.lcfc.com)

Directors: Aiyawatt Srivaddhanaprabha; Apichet Srivaddhanaprabha; Shilai Liu; Supornthip Choungrangsee; Susan Whelan; Vichai Srivaddhanaprabha, Chair (women: 3; men: 3)

Year end	31/05/2015
Turnover	£104,400,000
Pre-tax profit	£26,400,000

Nature of business: Leicester City FC is a football club competing in the Premier League.

Company registration number: 4593477

UK employees: 207 (+495 casual staff on match days)

Focus of giving: General charitable purposes, education, health, ill health, medical research, local groups, older people, sport, recreation, children, young people, community/social welfare, disability.

Community involvement	✓
Community contributions	✓
Cash donations declared	✓
Charity partner(s)	✓
Employee-led support	✓
Gifts in kind	✓

Charitable donations

Cash UK (latest available):	2015	£346,000
Total UK (cash and in kind):	2015	£346,000
Cash worldwide:	2015	£346,000
Total worldwide (cash and in kind):	2015	£346,000

Community involvement

LCFC Foxes Foundation Ltd (Charity Commission no. 1144791)

The club's foundation supports a number of chosen partner charities in the local area each season. The charities are supported by the foundation through fundraising activities organised by the club, its employees and fans. Examples of fundraising initiatives include an annual fun run; sponsored food and drink sales; auction of signed shirts.

Partner charities in 2015/16 were: Place2Be; Spark Arts For Children; Royal Voluntary Service; Leicester Hospitals Charity Children's Appeal; Warning Zone; Once, We Were Soldiers.

Leicester City Community Trust (Leicester City Football Club Trust Ltd – Charity Commission no. 1126526)

The Leicester City Community Trust is the club's charity that delivers its activities in the community, in the areas of education; health; social inclusion; and sports participation, with a focus on football projects. Examples of the trust's initiatives include: soccer schools and coaching courses; community cohesion projects, such as the Police Youth Integration Project, working with local police to support young people at risk of offending, with mentoring, football activities and employability skills workshops; post-16 education courses.

Charity policy

The club states on its website that its policy is to support charities in the East Midlands.

For non-registered charities in the area, the club can offer a donation of a stadium tour voucher to be used for fundraising purposes for a chosen charity.

Registered charities in the local area are supported by the LCFC Foxes Foundation.

Main locations

East Midlands

Community contributions

The 2014/15 accounts for the club state that it made charitable donations totalling £346,000 during the year.

The 2014/15 accounts for the LCFC Foxes Foundation state the following:

> During the year Leicester City Football Club Ltd collected income of £95,429 and paid expenses of £19,247 on behalf of the charity. They remitted £15,000 to the charity during the year. In addition they also provided administration services to the charity which are not being recharged to the charity.

The 2014/15 accounts for the Leicester City Football Club Trust Ltd state the following:

> During the period Leicester City Football Club Ltd collected income of £82,802 and paid expenses of £334,890 on behalf of the Trust. During this period £300,747 was repaid by the Trust. At 30 June 2015 £30,925 was due to Leicester City Football Club Ltd by the Trust.

Applications

Charitable donations

Applications should be made in writing on letter-headed paper to the following address:

LCFC Help – Charity Request, Leicester City Football Stadium, King Power Stadium, Filbert Way, Leicester LE2 7FL.

The website states that any correspondence addressed to directors or the Chief Executive will also be directed to LCFC Help.

LCFC Foxes Foundation

To be considered as a charity supported by the LCFC Foxes Foundation, contact Nayan Ramanandi: nayan.ramanandi@lcfc.co.uk.

The Liverpool Football Club and Athletic Grounds Ltd

Football

Correspondent: Liverpool FC Foundation, Anfield Road, Liverpool, Merseyside L4 0TH (tel: 0151 432 5689/ 0151 432 5689; email: lfcfoundation@liverpoolfc.com; website: www.liverpoolfc.com)

Directors: Andrew Hughes; Ian Ayre, Chief Executive; John Henry; Kenneth Dalglish; Michael Egan; Michael Gordon; Thomas Werner, Chair (women: 0; men: 7)

Year end	31/05/2015
Turnover	£298,000,000
Pre-tax profit	£60,000,000

Nature of business: Liverpool FC is a football club competing in the Premier League.

Company registration number: 35668

UK employees: 636 (+1,368 part-time employees + 67 part-time scouts and coaches)

Focus of giving: Education, enterprise/ training, health, ill health, local groups, overseas projects, humanitarian help, older people, poverty and social exclusion, safety and crime prevention, sport, recreation, children, young people, community/social welfare, disability.

Community involvement	✓
Community contributions	✓
Company reports on anti-slavery	✓
CSR report	✓
Directors have other relevant posts	✓
Charity partner(s)	✓
Gifts in kind	✓
Humanitarian aid: UK including food banks	✓

Charitable donations

Total UK (cash and in kind):	2015	£410,500

Community involvement

Liverpool FC Foundation (Charity Commission no. 1096572)

The club's charity, The Liverpool FC Foundation, focuses on four areas: sporting participation; improving life chances; inspiring social action; and supporting other charities.

The foundation runs a range projects focusing on: football and sports development; military veterans; men's health; international; education. It works with partners including schools, charities, NHS and other local organisations to deliver its initiatives.

Examples of projects include: Barracks to Boot Room, a programme of coaching and football tournaments to support ex-Armed Forces personnel in the transition to civilian life; summer holiday camps, providing football skills and games for children and young people; and disability awareness football activities delivered in schools.

Further information on the foundation and its programmes can be found on the website: foundation.liverpoolfc.com.

In-kind support

The club does not give cash donations to charities upon request, but can provide items for fundraising purposes, through the Liverpool FC Foundation. Items such as signed photographs, tickets for stadium and museum tours and other official merchandise may be provided to charities locally, nationally and internationally.

In 2015 the club also hosted an All-Star Charity Match, which raised money for the foundation as well as for a number of local charities.

Directors with other relevant posts

Kenneth Dalglish is a trustee of The Marina Dalglish Appeal (Charity Commission no. 1111193). Thomas Werner and Ian Ayre are both trustees of the Liverpool FC Foundation (Charity Commission no. 1096572).

Main location

The foundation operates within the City of Liverpool.

Community contributions

No figure was given for the club's total charitable contributions.

The 2014/15 accounts for the Liverpool FC Foundation state that the club covered operating costs of £410,500 through in-kind and support for the foundation during the year.

Exclusions

The club does not provide cash donations or sponsorship to charities.

Applications

Requests for in-kind support

The club can donate items to charity to be used for fundraising purposes, such as in raffles or auctions.

Requests should be submitted in writing, six to eight weeks in advance, to the following address: Liverpool FC Foundation, Anfield Sports and Community Centre, Breckside Park, Lower Breck Road, Liverpool L6 0AG.

The website states that the club receives a large number of requests and so is not able to satisfy every request.

Manchester City Football Club Ltd

Football

Correspondent: City in the Community, Etihad Stadium, Etihad Campus, Manchester M11 3FF (tel: 0161 438 7712/0161 438 7712; email: citc@mcfc.co.uk; website: www.mancity.com/fans-and-community/community)

Directors: Alberto Galassi; John MacBeath; Khaldoon Al Mubarak, Chair; Martin Edelman; Mohamed Al Mazrouei; Simon Pearce (women: 0; men: 6)

Year end	31/05/2015
Turnover	£351,800,000
Pre-tax profit	£10,400,000

Nature of business: Manchester City FC is a football club competing in the Premier League.

Company registration number: 40946

Subsidiary undertakings include: Manchester City Investments Ltd

Total employees: 320

Focus of giving: Education, enterprise/ training, equal opportunities, health, ill health, local groups, overseas projects, poverty and social exclusion, safety and crime prevention, sport, recreation, children, young people, community/ social welfare, disability.

Community involvement	✓
Community contributions	✓
CSR report	✓
Cash donations declared	✓
Charity partner(s)	✓
Gifts in kind	✓
Overseas giving	✓

Charitable donations

Total worldwide (cash and in kind):	2015	£2,000,000

Community involvement

City in the Community (Manchester City F.C. City in the Community Foundation – Charity Commission no. 1139229)

The club's charity, City in the Community, focuses on the following areas, according to the website:

- Education: 'using football to promote increased educational access, engagement, attainment and progression for young people aged 11–24'
- Health: 'using football to promote improved health and wellbeing through increased physical activity and a healthier diet'

- Inclusion: 'using football to improve community integration and combat negative stereotypes'

The charity runs a number of projects to deliver these aims, in partnership with organisations such as charities, local educational institutions and local council. Examples of projects include: City Pathways, a sport and vocational course for young people; City Cooks, a healthy eating programme for families; and One City Disability, a series of lessons in schools to raise awareness and understanding of disabilities.

The club provides in-kind support to the charity such as the use of facilities and promotion in match-day programmes, as well as other support and administration costs, and also organises fundraising events for the charity.

In-kind support
The club provides in-kind support in the form of signed merchandise, tickets to matches and stadium tours upon request. Priority is given to charities in the East Manchester area. The club also supports local charities through bucket collections on match days.

International projects
Through City in the Community, the club also supports international projects through the Cityzens Giving Programme, which supports young leaders in 12 cities internationally, such as Cape Town, Kolkata and Sao Paulo, to deliver football projects with a community purpose. Fans can vote to select which projects are supported. The Young Leaders programme provides training and support for 120 young people in Manchester and internationally to deliver community football projects tackling social issues.

Main locations
East Manchester

Community contributions

The club's 2014/15 accounts state that UK charitable donations during the year totalled £2 million, which includes £1.9 million supporting Premier League youth and community development expenditure.

Exclusions

The club does not provide monetary donations or sponsorship to charities upon request.

Applications

In-kind support
Requests for in-kind donations such as signed merchandise, stadium tours and match tickets can be made using the form on the club's website: www.mancity.com/fans-and-community/community/charity-support/donations. The website states that, due to the large number of requests, it is not able to grant every request.

Partnerships with City in the Community
The website states that organisations interested in working as a partner with City in the Community should contact michael.geary@cityfootball.com.

Manchester United PLC

Football

Correspondent: John Shiels, Chief Executive, Manchester United Foundation, Old Trafford, Manchester M16 0RA (0161 868 8600; email: enquiries@mufoundation.org; website: csr.manutd.com/community.html)

Directors: Avram Glazer, Executive Co-Chair; Bryan Glazer; Cliff Baty, Chief Financial Officer; Darcie Glazer Kassewitz; Edward Glazer; Edward Woodward, Executive Vice-Chair; Jamieson Reigle; Joel Glazer, Executive Co-Chair; John Hooks; Kevin Glazer; Manu Sawhney; Richard Arnold; Robert Leitão (women: 1; men: 12)

Year end	30/06/2016
Turnover	£515,345,000
Pre-tax profit	£48,833,000

Nature of business: Manchester United PLC is the ultimate parent company of Manchester United FC, a football team competing in the Premier League.

Subsidiary undertakings include: Manchester United Ltd; Manchester United Football Club Ltd; MUTV Ltd.

Total employees: 799

Focus of giving: Education, health, ill health, small groups, local groups, overseas projects, sport, recreation, children, young people, community/social welfare.

Community involvement	✓
Community contributions	✓
Company reports on anti-slavery	✓
Directors have other relevant posts	✓
Charity partner(s)	✓
Company gives to smaller charities	✓
Gifts in kind	✓

Community involvement

Manchester United carries out a CSR programme through the Manchester United Foundation (Charity Commission no. 1118310).

Manchester United Foundation
The Manchester United Foundation was established in 2006 as the charitable arm of Manchester United. According to its website, the foundation 'uses football to engage and inspire young people to build a better life for themselves and unite the communities in which they live'. The website further explains 'Dedicated staff deliver football coaching, educational programmes and personal development, providing young people with opportunities to change their lives for the better'. To facilitate its work, the foundation creates and develops strategic partnerships with local, regional and national organisations working in the areas of health, education and social justice.

The trustees' report for 2014/15 explains that 'the Charity is supported by Manchester United Ltd (MU), in that the Charity has a licence to use Manchester United Football Club's (MUFC) brand, and also certain rights to use the club's ground at Old Trafford'. Income is mainly generated from a range of fundraising activities, including the Red Heart United legends match, which takes place every two years, and a match-day lottery.

The foundation's activities fall within the following general areas: football; education, health, community cohesion; and charity. Examples of activities outlined on the foundation's website include:

Partner schools programme
The foundation partners more than 20 secondary schools across Greater Manchester through this programme which sees full-time Community Development Officers placed in targeted areas to help develop relationships within local communities.

Project work
The foundation delivers a variety of education programmes to young people in its local area. The website explains that these range 'from educating youngsters about the inner workings of a football club to improving confidence, life skills and employability'.

Charity
The foundation supports charities in a number of ways, including:

- Fundraising for and raising awareness of the club's charity partners
- Managing requests from charities, schools and grassroots sports clubs for signed items
- Working with charities that make the wishes of seriously ill children and adults come true

More information on the foundation's activities is available from the website (www.mufoundation.org).

Charity partner
Since 1999, the club has been a partner of Unicef and, in this time, has helped to raise more than £4 million for children around the world.

Directors with other relevant posts
Richard Arnold: Chair of the Manchester United Foundation.

Robert Leitão: Chair of The Pennies Foundation.

Bryan Glazer: on board of directors of the Glazer Children's Museum.

Darcie Glazer Kassewitz: Co-President of the Glazer Family Foundation.

Main locations
Greater Manchester

Community contributions

The annual report and accounts did not declare a figure for charitable donations.

The most recent annual report and accounts for the Manchester United Foundation were from the 2014/15 financial year. The financial review for the year states:

> The most significant source of funding in the year was the biennial Red Heart United legends match with turnover of £1,198,836 (2014: Nil). All other turnover is analysed in note 2 to note 5. In addition the Trustees are grateful to Manchester United Ltd for Gift in Kind for the hire of stadium for Red Heart United game, human resources, information technology, finance and payroll, legal and maintenance services, together with a discretionary staff bonus, equating to an estimated monetary value of £507, 150 (2014: £251,463). The significant increase in Gift in Kind during the year is due to the hire of the stadium for the Red Heart United game in June 2015.

Applications

Charitable requests for signed shirts, football, pennants and photographs are managed by the foundation. There is an online request form available on the foundation's website.

Information about future 'Dream Days' can be requested from the foundation by email (enquiries@mufoundation.org). Applicants must be aged seven years or older.

Middlesbrough Football and Athletic Company (1986) Ltd

Football

Correspondent: MFC Foundation, Riverside Stadium, Middlesbrough TS3 6RS (01642 757674; email: enquiries@mfcfoundation.co.uk; website: www.mfcfoundation.co.uk)

Directors: Keith Lamb; Steve Gibson, Chair (women: 0; men: 4)

Year end	30/06/2015
Turnover	£20,504,000
Pre-tax profit	(£9,000,000)

Nature of business: The company operates Middlesbrough Football Club, a professional club competing in the English Premier League.

Company registration number: 1947851

UK employees: 175

Total employees: 175

Focus of giving: Education, enterprise/ training, health, ill health, housing, homelessness, small groups, local groups, marginalised people, poverty and social exclusion, sport, recreation, community/ social welfare.

Community involvement	✓
Community contributions	✓
Directors have other relevant posts	✓
Charity partner(s)	✓
Company gives to smaller charities	✓
Gifts in kind	✓

Charitable donations

Cash UK (latest available):	2015	£7,300
Total UK (cash and in kind):	2015	£242,500
Cash worldwide:	2015	£7,300
Total worldwide (cash and in kind):	2015	£242,500

Community involvement

Middlesbrough Football Club's community involvement is mainly carried out through the registered charity, Middlesbrough Football Club Foundation (MFC Foundation – Charity Commission no. 1059418). The club also donates gifts in-kind in the form of match tickets, hospitality and signed items to charities, schools and youth teams in its community, and assists with the fundraising efforts of local charitable causes.

Middlesbrough Football Club Foundation (MFC Foundation)
According to its website, the foundation was established as the 'independent charitable arm' of Middlesbrough FC. The charity started out in 1996 as Middlesbrough Football Club in the Community before it was relaunched as the MFC Foundation in 2013.

The foundation looks to engage with the most disadvantaged communities in Teesside through a range of programmes and initiatives falling within four key themes: education; health; social inclusion; and sport participation. Its programmes and initiatives are delivered to children, young people and adults in a range of settings, including the club's Riverside Stadium, the foundation's Herlingshaw Centre, in schools and in other community spaces. Individuals can are given opportunities to gain accreditations through the foundation's programmes.

Examples of the foundation's programmes include: a school sports programme; The Big Boro Check, a men's health programme delivered through partnership with Community Learning; and The Homeless Football Project which uses football to help change the lives of people affected by homelessness.

Charity partners
In partnership with the MFC Foundation, the football club works with nominated charity partners who are given in-kind support (in the form of fundraising opportunities and publicity assistance) over the course of a season.

The club's nominated charity partners for the 2016/17 season were: Guide Dogs: Teesside Group; Remembering Rebecca; and The James Campbell Trust.

Directors with other relevant posts
Steve Gibson, Chair of the football club, is a patron of the Middlesbrough Football Club Foundation. The club's Chief Executive, Neil Bausor, is a trustee of the foundation.

Main UK locations
The club supports communities in Teesside.

Community contributions

The annual report for Middlesbrough Football and Athletic Company (1986) Ltd states that charitable donations made in the year amounted to £25,500. It is also explained that 'The Company provides match tickets, hospitality and autographed memorabilia for numerous charitable organisations, schools and youth teams in the local community'. We were unable to determine whether the figure stated consisted entirely of cash or in-kind donations, or a mixture of both.

The MFC Foundation's 2014/15 annual report and accounts note that it received £7,300 in donations from Middlesbrough Football Club. The club also contributed gifts in-kind worth £218,000 in the form of staff time and donated facilities to the foundation.

Beneficiaries: Middlesbrough Football Club Foundation.

Applications

Details of how and when to apply to become a Middlesbrough Football Club charity partner are usually announced on the club's website around May. Refer to the website for updates.

St Mary's Football Group Ltd (Southampton Football Club)

Football

Correspondent: Greg Baker, Head of Saints Foundation & Community Partnerships, St Mary's Stadium, Britannia Road, Southampton SO14 5FP (0845 688 9370; email: foundation@saintsfc.co.uk; website: saintsfoundation.co.uk)

Directors: Gareth Rogers, Chief Executive; Katharina Liebherr; Ralph Krueger, Chair (women: 1; men: 2)

Year end	30/06/2015
Turnover	£113,735,000
Pre-tax profit	£14,878,000

Nature of business: St Mary's Football Group Ltd is the ultimate parent company of Southampton Football Club, a football club competing in the English Premier League.

Company registration number: 6951765

Subsidiary undertakings include: Southampton Football Club Ltd; St Mary's Stadium Ltd; St Mary's Training Ground Ltd.

Total employees: 302

Focus of giving: Education, enterprise/training, health, ill health, small groups, local groups, marginalised people, older people, sport, recreation, children, young people, community/social welfare, disability.

Community involvement	✓
Community contributions	✓
Company reports on anti-slavery	✓
Charity partner(s)	✓
Company gives to smaller charities	✓
Gifts in kind	✓

Community involvement

Southampton's community involvement is channelled through the Saints Foundation (Charity Commission no. 1090916).

Saints Foundation (SFC)

This independent charity was initially registered in 2002 under the name Saints in the Community. According to its website, it works to 'inspire, support and deliver positive change and equality of opportunity for young people and vulnerable adults across Southampton and the surrounding areas'. The website further notes that the foundation invests more than £1.5 million into its community programmes each year, enabled by the income it receives from grants, sponsorships, coaching services, businesses and individuals. SFC's work is carried out within six key areas: youth inclusion; lifelong learning; health and well-being; education; schools and enterprise; and football and sports development.

In addition to delivering programmes, the foundation – on behalf of Southampton Football Club – provides in-kind support to charities in Southampton and its surrounding areas (Hampshire) in the form of bucket collections, a charity partners scheme, and donations of signed pennants. These forms of support are outlined below:

Bucket collections

Charities can benefit from bucket collections held at St Mary's Stadium on pre-arranged match days. The five charities chosen for the 2016/17 season were: Families First, Southampton; The Hannah Chamberlain Foundation; Southampton City Mission; Southampton Doing it for the Kids; and Southampton Women's Aid.

'Charities of Choice' – charity partners

On behalf of the football club, the foundation selects five charities to receive 'exclusive support' each season. The charities chosen for the 2016/17 season were: Andover and District Mencap; Marie Curie (Chandlers Ford Branch); One Community Young Carers; Yellow Door (formerly Southampton Rape Crisis); and YMCA Fairthorne Group.

General charitable requests

Charities can apply to receive a signed pennant for a fundraising event.

Main locations

Southampton and its surrounding areas.

Community contributions

The club's annual report and accounts for 2014/15 did not declare a figure for charitable donations. At the time of writing (January 2017), the Saints Foundation's annual report and accounts for 2014/15 were not yet available to view at the Charity Commission.

Exclusions

Note:

- The club/foundation does not give financial support of any kind
- Requests from organisations located outside Hampshire cannot be considered
- Requests must be made directly by a charity – those submitted by third parties raising funds on a charity's behalf cannot be considered
- Signed shirts and balls are not given.

Applications

The football club channels its support through the Saints Foundation. See the foundation's website for information on how to apply for support.

Stoke City Football Club Ltd

Football

Correspondent: Adrian Hurst, Head of Community, bet365 Stadium, Stanley Matthews Way, Stoke-on-Trent ST4 4EG (website: www.stokecityfc.com/community)

Directors: Peter Coates, Chair; Richard Smith; Tony Scholes, Chief Executive Officer (women: 0; men: 3)

Year end	31/05/2016
Turnover	£104,169,000
Pre-tax profit	£2,055,000

Nature of business: Stoke City Football Club is a professional football club competing in the English Premier League.

Company registration number: 99885

Total employees: 290+

Focus of giving: Sport, recreation.

Community involvement	✓
Community contributions	✓
Directors have other relevant posts	✓
Gifts in kind	✓

Community involvement

Stoke City FC's charity and community work is carried out by Stoke City Community Trust (Charity Commission no. 1104006). The club also provides in-kind support in the form of signed items, tickets and hospitality.

Stoke City Community Trust

This 'self-funding and financially independent' charity was founded in 1989 and first registered in March 2004 under the name Stoke City Football in the Community. The trust's web page explains how it 'engages with people in many varied ways to stimulate an environment in which they can realise their potential and subsequently accomplish more in whatever walk of life they choose for personal and professional development'.

Stoke City Community Trust works in communities within its catchment areas (Stoke-on-Trent, Newcastle-under-Lyme, Staffordshire Moorlands, Stafford, South Staffordshire, and parts of North West Shropshire), using sport, and particularly football, to connect with people of 'all ages, abilities and social backgrounds'. Its programmes fall within the following focus areas: sports participation; education and lifelong learning; and health and well-being.

Stoke City Community Fund

This fund, which provides grants for small, community-based projects in Staffordshire and South Cheshire, is administered by the Stoke City Community Trust. Grants of between

£100 and £1,000 are awarded to local groups, projects, community groups, self-help organisations, youth groups and charities whose work benefits their local communities. As the fund's funding criteria information describes, support can be given with 'anything from equipment to event costs, help towards rent or fixtures, sport or computer equipment'.

Monthly charity draw

The club holds a monthly draw into which individuals and charities can enter to win a charity donation. According to the Stoke City website, each month the following prizes are available:

- A personalised signed shirt from a member of the first team squad
- A personalised signed ball from a member of the first team squad
- Ten pairs of tickets to a nominated fixture
- Two pairs of hospitality tickets to a nominated fixture
- A behind the scenes ground tour of the bet365 Stadium for up to six people

Directors with other relevant posts

Tony Scholes, the football club's Chief Executive, is a trustee of Stoke City Community Trust.

Main locations

Stoke-on-Trent

Community contributions

The annual report and accounts for 2015/16 did not declare a figure for charitable donations.

Exclusions

The funding criteria for the Stoke City Community Fund state that grants cannot be awarded for:

- Groups other than community, self-help and voluntary groups
- Social enterprises (including CICs, IPS or Credit Unions except for non-core activity)
- Grant or loan schemes
- Political campaigning
- Cadets
- Statutory bodies
- A private profit making organisation/ commercial organisation
- Any project that has already started
- The sole benefit of any individual
- Specific religious worship
- Projects administered by a third party
- Projects that could be reasonably expected to secure finance by other means
- Non-charitable purposes (Groups do not have to be a charity to apply; however, the project funded must have a charitable purpose, i.e. benefit the wider community)

Applications

Stoke City Community Fund

An application form with funding criteria is available to download from the club's website (www.stokecityfc.com/community/fund). The Community Fund panel sits once a month and successful applicants are notified within two months of their application being submitted. A helpful list of FAQs included with the fund's downloadable application form informs that groups requiring further clarification regarding the eligibility of their project items can contact the club via email at communityfund@stokecityfc.com. It is also noted that, as the fund has limited funds, successful applicants do not always receive the entire amount applied for.

Monthly charity draw

There is an online application form available via the website (www.stokecityfc.com/community/charity). Applications must be made using the online form at least 24 hours before the last Friday of each month. Due to the volume of applications received, only winners are notified. Unsuccessful applications are not carried forward into future draws, however unsuccessful applicants may re-apply. The website further notes: 'All prizes relating to a fixture are valid for one game only and are subject to availability. Terms and conditions apply.'

Stoke City Community Trust

Queries can be directed to the trust by telephone (01782 592252), email (community@stokecityfc.com) or post (see the postal address above).

Sunderland Ltd

Football

Correspondent: Foundation of Light, The Sunderland Stadium of Light, Sunderland SR5 1SU (tel: 0191 551 5191/ 0191 551 5191; email: info@foundationoflight.co.uk; website: www.foundationoflight.co.uk)

Directors: Angela Lowes, Finance Director; Ellis Short, Chair; Martin Bain, Chief Executive; Per Magnus Andersson (women: 1; men: 3)

Year end	31/07/2015
Turnover	£101,000,000
Pre-tax profit	(£25,400,000)

Nature of business: Sunderland AFC is a football club competing in the Premier League.

Company registration number: 3189630

Subsidiary undertakings include: SAFC.COM PLC; Sunderland Association Football Club Ladies Ltd; The Sunderland Association Football Club Ltd.

UK employees: 287 (+ 781 part-time including match day staff)

Focus of giving: Education, enterprise/ training, fundraising events, health, ill health, local groups, humanitarian help, poverty and social exclusion, sport, recreation, community/social welfare, disability.

Community involvement	✓
Community contributions	✓
Charity partner(s)	✓
Employee-led support	✓
Gifts in kind	✓
Humanitarian aid: UK including food banks	✓

Charitable donations

Total UK (cash and in kind):	2015	£620,000

Community involvement

Foundation of Light (Charity Commission no. 1089333)

The club's charity, Foundation of Light, supports the local community by running projects focusing on education; careers and training; youth and sports clubs; football coaching; and fitness and health. It works with schools, charities and other partner organisations to deliver its programmes.

Further information about the foundation and its projects can be found on the website: www.foundationoflight.co.uk

The foundation's subsidiary, Beacon of Light Ltd, was established in 2014, and the Beacon of Light free school is due to open in 2018.

The foundation receives in-kind support from the club, which includes the running costs of the Centre of Light premises, staff time, as well as tickets and auction prizes.

In-kind donations

The club can provide in-kind support through donations of signed memorabilia to registered charities upon request.

Other initiatives

In 2016 the club partnered with the charity Centrepoint to support food bank collections over the Christmas period, and the Foundation of Light also supported the Salvation Army's campaign to collect gifts for local families in need.

Main locations

Durham; South Tyneside; Sunderland.

Community contributions

No figure was given for the club's total charitable contributions.

The 2014/15 accounts for the Foundation of Light report that the club gave in-kind support totalling £620,000 to the foundation during the year. The foundation also received £154,500 from the club 'by way of a percentage of cashback ticket sales, player fines and general donations'.

Exclusions

The club does not offer financial support to charities upon request – only in-kind donations of signed memorabilia. Requests are not accepted from third parties on behalf of registered charities.

Applications

In-kind support

The website states that requests for in-kind donations to charities should be sent in writing to: Supporter Liaison Officer, Sunderland AFC, Stadium of Light, Sunderland SR5 1SU. Applications must be on paper with the charity's official letterhead and should include: the name and registered charity number of the charity; the nature of the event in question; full contact details.

Requests are not accepted by email. The website states that the club is not able to provide a donation to all requests due to the high volume of applications it receives. The club aims to respond to all requests within four to six weeks.

Swansea City Football 2002 Ltd

Football

Correspondent: Community Trust, The Liberty Stadium, Swansea, Landore SA1 2 FA, Wales (tel: 01792 556520/ 01792 556520; fax: 01792 616606; email: info@scfccommunitytrust.co.uk; website: www.swanscommercial.co.uk/ community-trust)

Directors: Bobby Hernreich; Huw Jenkins; Jason Levien; Martin Morgan; Romie Chaudhari; Stephen Kaplan; Stuart McDonald (women: 0; men: 7)

Year end	31/07/2015
Turnover	£103,928,360
Pre-tax profit	£1,676,000

Nature of business: Swansea City Football 2002 Ltd is the ultimate parent company of Swansea FC, a football club playing in the Premier League.

Company registration number: 4305508

Subsidiary undertakings include: Swansea City Football Club Ltd; Swansea City Association Football Club Ltd.

UK employees: 307

Total employees: 307

Focus of giving: Education, enterprise/ training, health, ill health, small groups, local groups, sport, recreation, children, young people, disability.

Community involvement ✓
Cash donations declared ✓

Charitable donations

Cash worldwide:	2015	£47,000

Community involvement

The club has a registered charity – Swansea City AFC Community Trust (Charity Commission no. 1126933) – through which support is given to local communities in South West Wales in the areas of education, sports and health projects aimed at improving the lifestyles of local people and neighbourhoods. In 2013/14 the trust also launched SwansAid – a small grants scheme aimed at charities and community organisations. During the 2015/16 season awards from SwansAid included support to Plasmart PTA, Bikeability Wales, Clydach Cricket Club as well as sports kit awards to Milford United FC and Coedffranc AFC U8. The schemes priorities include children and young people and individuals of all ages with disabilities.

The club's charity is involved in partnership with other organisations. For instance, with the City and Council of Swansea it is running of the Healthy Together programme funded by the Premier League and Professional Footballers Association. The programme seeks to help families with children aged 7 to 11 lead healthier lifestyles. The trust has also been working in partnership with The Prince's Trust to deliver vocational courses. It is also involved in delivering sports courses, camps and club activities. The trust's annual report and accounts for 2015 state that its 'core activities include after school clubs, holiday and half-term courses and summer school camps'.

The trust also participates in Premier League's initiatives, such as Kicks (aimed at young people who may be disadvantaged, at risk of offending or struggling to establish an educational and/or vocational path) and Premier League 4 Sport (which seeks to involve children and young people into sporting activities).

Community contributions

The company's accounts for the 14-month period ending 31 July 2015 state that during that time a total of £47,000 was given in charitable donations.

Exclusions

Groups excluded from applying to SwansAid are: faith and political groups; those outside the counties of Swansea, Neath Port Talbot, Pembrokeshire, Carmarthenshire and Ceredigion; individuals. Staff costs are not supported.

Applications

As the club delivers its community support through the associated trust, applicants are advised to contact the charity at the contact details given. Application forms to SwansAid are also available on the website at www. swanscommercial.co.uk/community-swans-aid.

Tottenham Hotspur Ltd

Football

Correspondent: See 'Applications', Bill Nichols Way, 748 High Road, Tottenham, London N17 0AP (tel: 020 8365 5138/020 8365 5138; email: foundation@tottenhamhotspur.com; website: www.tottenhamhotspur.com/ the-club/charities)

Directors: Daniel Levy; Donna-Maria Cullen; Kevan Watts; Matthew Collecott; Rebecca Caplehorn; Ron Robson (women: 2; men: 4)

Year end	30/06/2015
Turnover	£196,377,000
Pre-tax profit	£12,053,000

Nature of business: Tottenham Hotspur Ltd is the ultimate parent company of Tottenham Hotspur FC, a football team competing in the Premier League.

Company registration number: 1706358

Subsidiary undertakings include: Tottenham Hotspur Football and Athletic Co. Ltd; Paxton Road Ltd; Tottenham Hotspur Academy (Enfield) Ltd.

UK employees: 399

Total employees: 399

Focus of giving: Education, enterprise/ training, health, ill health, small groups, local groups, overseas projects, sport, recreation, children, young people, disability.

Community involvement ✓
Community contributions ✓
Gifts in kind ✓
Humanitarian aid: overseas ✓

Charitable donations

Cash worldwide:	2015	£49,000

Community involvement

Tottenham Hotspur Foundation

The club has a registered associated charity – Tottenham Hotspur Foundation (Charity Commission no. 1113725). Through the foundation, support is given to initiatives mainly in North London which aim to build community cohesion, improve achievement, promote healthy lifestyles and support people with disabilities. The foundation works in partnership with other agencies to deliver programmes and free activities. There are community development, health and well-being, and employability and skills teams as well as a number of educational initiatives. Full details of projects the foundation runs are given on the website. The foundation delivers charitable activities on behalf of the club but operates independently (notably two of the trustees are also directors of the company). In-kind gifts (such as spare kits or equipment) provided by the club are used by the foundation in its projects.

The foundation also participates in Premier League's initiative Premier League 4 Sport, which seeks to involve children and young people into sporting activities.

Charity partnership
There is an external charity adopted by the club (currently Noah's Ark Children's Hospital).

Spurs Wishes
This initiative was set up in 2011 and exists separately within the foundation. It brings together the club's staff, management and players to assist terminally ill fans by giving them a memorable experience.

After the above three areas of support, the club prioritises supporting local charities close to its stadium and training centre.

Main locations
The foundation mainly works in North London.

Community contributions

According to the company's annual report and accounts for 2014/15, the group made cash donations totalling £49,000 'to international, UK-based and local charities during the year'. The accounts also note that 'the group continues to make contributions with a value in to its in excess of £0.5m per annum' to the foundation and also 'continues to underwrite the ongoing good works of the charity'. In-kind gifts of club memorabilia are given to local charities, especially in the Haringey and Enfield districts and nearby areas.

In the year of its incorporation, the foundation received a donation of £4.5 million from the club. The money is used to fund the foundation's activities and for the designated Enfield Section 106 project (which is scheduled to last until 2020).

Exclusions

The club's website notes that national charitable initiatives, for example disaster appeals, Sport Relief or Children in Need, are responded to centrally by the club so individual applications for such causes are not accepted. Sponsorship is not available and the club only works with its nominated charities regarding promotional matters.

Applications

Eligible applicants (see the club's guidance available on the website) are invited to complete an online application form. Note that all requests must be in writing and have to provide at least three weeks' notice before the event for which support is asked.

Appeals to Spurs Wishes should be addressed to spurs.wishes@tottenhamhotspur.com.

The Watford Association Football Club Ltd

Football

Correspondent: Charities Department, Charities Department, Watford FC, Vicarage Road Stadium, Watford WD18 0ER (tel: 01923 496362/01923 496362; email: community@watfordfc.com; website: www.watfordfccsetrust.com)

Directors: David Fransen; Scott Duxbury; Stuart Timperley (women: 0; men: 3)

Year end	30/06/2015
Turnover	£18,393,000
Pre-tax profit	(£4,783,000)

Nature of business: Watford Association Football Club is a football team competing in the English Premier League.

Company registration number: 104194

UK employees: 180

Total employees: 180

Focus of giving: Education, equal opportunities, fundraising events, health, ill health, small groups, local groups, sport, recreation, children, young people.

Community involvement	✓
Community contributions	✓
Cash donations declared	✓

Charitable donations

Cash worldwide:	2015	£127,000

Community involvement

The club has an associated registered charity Watford FC's Community Sports and Education Trust (Charity Commission no. 1102239). The trust works in partnership with other organisations and individuals and delivers its programmes in Hertfordshire and surrounding areas as well as the boroughs of Harrow and Hillingdon. The website notes that even though the trust 'may traditionally be seen as purely a football provider, this is certainly no longer the case'. The trust's current five key themes are: sports participation, social inclusion, health, education and community facilities. It focuses on promoting the welfare of children and young people and vulnerable adults. The trust is self-financing and only has a secured loan from the company totalling £669,000.

The club also participates in Premier League's initiative Kicks, which is aimed at young people who may be disadvantaged, at risk of offending or struggling to establish an educational and/or vocational path.

Main location
The trust works in Hertfordshire and the boroughs of Harrow and Hillingdon.

Community contributions

The company's accounts for 2014/15 state that a total of £127,000 was given in charitable donations during the year.

Exclusions

Requests for support from the club are not accepted via email.

Applications

The club's website notes that donation requests to the club are not accepted via email. You should write your request on a headed paper, provide full details of the event you are seeking support for and, if appropriate, include a letter of authorization from the charity the event would benefit (giving their registered charity number). Appeals should be addressed to the Charities Department.

The club's charity can be reached at the same address and any request or queries to the trust may also be directed at the Trust Administrator, Anne-Marie Burn (email: annemarie.burn@watfordfc.com).

West Bromwich Albion Holdings Ltd

Football

Correspondent: Development Manager, The Albion Foundation, Ford Street, Smethwick B67 7QY (tel: 0871 271 9840/0871 271 9840; email: info@albionfoundation.co.uk; website: thealbionfoundation.co.uk)

Director: Pi Yue Li (women: 0; men: 1)

Year end	30/06/2015
Turnover	£96,269,000
Pre-tax profit	£7,623,000

Nature of business: West Bromwich Albion Holdings Ltd is the ultimate parent company of West Bromwich Albion FC, a football team competing in the Premier League.

Company registration number: 8528749

Subsidiary undertakings include: West Bromwich Albion Group Ltd; West Bromwich Albion Football Club Ltd; WBA Football Development Ltd.

UK employees: 161

Total employees: 161

Focus of giving: Equal opportunities, inner cities, small groups, local groups, marginalised people, overseas projects, poverty and social exclusion, sport, recreation, children, young people, disability.

Community involvement	✓
Overseas giving	✓

Community involvement

The club has an associated registered charity – the Albion Foundation (Charity Commission no. 1081948). According to the foundation's website, its aim is to work in partnership with the club 'to provide sporting and educational opportunities to the most disadvantaged members of the local community', which mainly refers to West Bromwich and the surrounding areas. The foundation's main areas of focus are:

- Education and inclusion (the foundation is 'an alternative education provider commissioned by local schools to work with pupils on the verge of or excluded from mainstream provision')
- Disability sports (opportunities for people with disabilities and learning difficulties delivered in partnership with special schools and other organisations)
- Sporting opportunities (while main attention is on football other sporting activities are also included)

Some work is now also undertaken overseas in India, Sweden, Kenya and Nigeria.

The foundation also participates in Premier League's initiatives, such as Kicks (aimed at young people who may be disadvantaged, at risk of offending or struggling to establish an educational and/or vocational path) and Premier League 4 Sport (which seeks to involve children and young people into sporting activities).

Main locations

The foundation works in Birmingham, Dudley, Sandwell and Worcestershire.

Community contributions

The 2015 accounts of the company did not declare charitable donations.

'Related party disclosures' in the annual report and accounts of the foundation note that three of the trustees are also employees of West Bromwich Albion Football Club and during the year the foundation received £17,800 (of which £15,800 remains outstanding).

Applications

You can get in touch with the Albion Foundation via post, email, phone or using an online enquiry form. There are separate development managers responsible for each area of focus – disability, sports or education. Contact details of the managers as well as details of other members of each of the teams are shown on the website, at 'Meet The Team' section.

WH Holding Ltd (West Ham United)

Football

Correspondent: Lubna Alam, Administrator, 60A Albatross Close, Off Woolwich Manor Way, London E6 5NX (tel: 020 7473 7720/020 7473 7720; email: lalam@westhamunited.co.uk; website: www.whufc.com/club-foundation/foundation)

Directors: Andy Mollett; Angus Kinnear; Daniel Harris; Daniel Svanstrom; David Gold; David Sullivan; Karren Brady; Tara Warren (women: 2; men: 6)

Year end	31/05/2015
Turnover	£120,747,000
Pre-tax profit	£2,998,000

Nature of business: The principal activity of the company is acting as a holding company and the principal activity of the group is that of a football club.

Company registration number: 5993863

Subsidiary undertakings include: West Ham United Football Club Ltd; West Ham United Hospitality Ltd; Thames Iron Works and Shipbuilding Company Ltd.

UK employees: 591

Total employees: 591

Focus of giving: Education, equal opportunities, health, ill health, inner cities, local groups, marginalised people, poverty and social exclusion, safety and crime prevention, sport, recreation, children, young people.

Community involvement	✓
Community contributions	✓
Charity partner(s)	✓

Community involvement

Charity partnership

The club has two principal charity partners: Moore Family Foundation, established in memory of Bobby Moore and providing 'life-changing opportunities for some 18,000 Year 6 students in Newham, Tower Hamlets, Barking and Dagenham, Thurrock, Brentwood and Basildon'; and DT38 Foundation, which was set up in memory of the club's academy starlet Dylan Tombides and exists to offer 'testicular cancer support and awareness through education and opportunity'. The club's official charity partners include Richard House Children's Hospice, Blesma and the Bobby Moore Fund for Cancer Research UK.

West Ham United Foundation

The club also has an associated registered charity (Charity Commission no. 1114458). Its mission, stated on the website, is 'to promote health and wellbeing through community participation in sports, tackle exclusion and poverty and advance the education of children and young people'. The foundation's main areas of focus are: education, health and crime. It works in partnership with local authorities to deliver initiatives and with schools to develop access to football activities. Support is given throughout London (particularly areas local to the club) and Essex; however, the future plans of the foundation involve expansion to other UK locations. Priorities for support will include promoting health benefits sport can offer, breaking down barriers to sport, encouraging access to professional sport and, overall, using sporting activities to inspire and motivate social change.

The foundation also participates in Premier League's initiatives, such as Kicks (aimed at young people who may be disadvantaged, at risk of offending or struggling to establish an educational and/or vocational path) and Premier League 4 Sport (which seeks to involve children and young people into sporting activities).

Main locations

London and Essex.

Community contributions

The company's accounts for 2014/15 state:

> The work of the West Ham Foundation continues to carry out in fulfilling the West Ham ethos of giving back, after 25 years of being involved in the local community, reminds us of our responsibilities outside of football...Working with our partners during the last financial year we have invested over £1.3 million in our local communities.

The accounts did not provide a further breakdown of the £1.3 million figure.

The foundation's annual report and accounts explain the relationship between the charity and the club as follows:

> [The foundation] delivers all community sports and charitable activities on behalf of West Ham United Football Club Ltd...The terms of the relationship between [the foundation] and the football club are codified in a Service Level Agreement. This agreement enshrines the practices already being observed in terms of the provision of services by the football club to [the foundation] at no cost to [the foundation]. A separate licence agreement grants [the foundation] a right of occupancy, on a rent free basis, of its premises.

During the year 'a number of other goods and services were supplied to [the foundation] by West Ham United Football Club Ltd on a complimentary basis'.

Applications

The club delivers its charitable activities through an associated charity. Interested parties may get in touch with the foundation via post, email (foundation@westhamunited.co.uk) or phone.

Corporate charities

This edition of the guide provides a section containing information on 132 corporate charities (compared to 114 in the tenth edition), all of which have a close association with the company to which they are linked. Typically, the corporate charities rely on their companies for a substantial part of their income.

Each entry provides an overview of charitable activities as well as details on grant-making such as the number of grants made, the total value of those grants, the beneficiaries and beneficial areas. This information can provide a useful starting point for any organisation considering applying to a corporate charity for funding.

Aberdeen Asset Management Charitable Foundation

Education, disadvantaged young people, social welfare, communities

£856,000 (2014/15)

Beneficial area

UK and overseas where the company has a presence.

Correspondent: The Trustees of Aberdeen Asset Management Charitable Foundation, 10 Queen's Terrace, Aberdeen AB10 1YG (tel: 01224 631999; email: foundation.uk@aberdeen-asset.com; website: www.aberdeen-asset.com/aam.nsf/foundation/home)

OSCR number: SC042597

General information

Registered in 2011, this is the charitable foundation of Aberdeen Asset Management PLC, a global investment management group, managing assets for both institutional and retail clients from some 37 offices in 25 countries. The foundation looks to work in partnership with smaller charities across the globe and, since 2012, has supported more than 400 charities. It is explained on the foundation's web page that it seeks to give funds where they 'can be seen to have a meaningful and measurable impact'. Employees of Aberdeen Asset Management are also encouraged to contribute their time and skills in support of the foundation's charitable projects.

Core focuses

The foundation's two core focuses – emerging markets and local communities – reflect the business' desire to give back to areas which are a key strategic focus and to build on its pattern of giving to communities in which employees of Aberdeen Asset Management live and work. The focuses are described on the website as follows:

> *Emerging Markets*
>
> The Foundation seeks to develop partnerships with charities tackling the educational needs of disadvantaged young people in emerging market countries.
>
> The Foundation will invest in a different emerging market each year typically over a three year period and partner with charities that deliver real change on the ground through long-term investments. As part of the partnerships, a group of Aberdeen employees are able to volunteer at each of the projects.
>
> *Local Communities*
>
> As a business we value the communities in which we operate and invest, recognising the benefits we gain from them as well as the potential impact we can have. The Foundation therefore allocates a proportion of its funding to the local communities in with Aberdeen employees live and work.
>
> Through regional charity committees, employees are empowered to develop their local approach to charitable giving, supporting causes that are relevant to their community and the local team. More information on employee engagement is given on the website.

The 2014/15 annual report explains that:

> Each year a global budget is approved by the Board of Aberdeen Asset Management PLC. This is divided between the emerging markets and the local communities' allocation. From the local communities' allocation, the budget is further split between the offices. with headcount used as the basis. Regional committees are responsible for this division of budget by office. Each individual office has the discretion to choose the projects it wishes to support in line with the overall strategy of supporting local communities.

Financial information

In 2014/15 the foundation had assets of £1.76 million and an income of £2.03 million. Donations were made amounting to £856,000, of which £189,000 was given as part of long-term support of ABC (Action for Brazil's Children) Trust, SeeBeyondBorders and AfriKids. The remaining £667,000 was distributed in local community donations from individual offices.

Exclusions

The foundation does not support political causes, parties, or organisations or charities with a religious focus.

Applications

Application forms are available – along with full criteria and terms and conditions – from the website. Completed forms should be returned to the foundation by email (foundation.uk@aberdeen-asset.com), and be accompanied by a PDF copy of your latest annual review. Successful applicants will be notified within three months of their application being submitted. The foundation notes that, due to the volume of applications it receives, it cannot respond to all unsuccessful applicants. Recipients of grants will be required to complete an annual impact assessment form.

The Accenture Foundation

Economic development and employment, education and training

£1.8 million (2014/15)

Beneficial area

UK and overseas.

Correspondent: Anthony Richardson, Administrator, 1 Plantation Place, 30 Fenchurch Street, London EC3M 3BD (tel: 020 7844 4000; fax: 020 7844 4444; email: corporatecitizenship@accenture.com; website: www.accenture.com)

CC number: 1057696

General information

Registered in 1996, this is the charitable foundation of Accenture UK Ltd, a company that provides management consulting, technology and outsourcing services with more than 305,000 employees, and offices and operations in more than 200 cities in 56 countries.

The following information is given in the foundation's annual report and accounts:

> The Accenture Foundation runs a focused programme of long-term grants funded by the sponsoring company. Through establishment of long-term strategic partnerships the foundation continues to be able to make a real difference to our chosen charities, which include:
>
> - Voluntary Services Overseas (Global and Local Giving Grant)
> - The Prince of Wales Youth Business International (Global Giving Grant)
> - Cherie Blair Foundation for Women (Global Giving Grant)
> - Onside Northwest Ltd (Local Giving Grant)
>
> In addition to awards to these charities, ad hoc grants were made to other charitable causes, via the Charities Aid Foundation, to support the sponsoring company's employee fundraising 'matching scheme' – allowing Accenture employees in the UK to apply for up to £100 of matching for funds raised for charitable causes each year.
>
> The foundation's grant making activities continued to centre on supporting charities with a focus on disadvantaged people and assisting them to break the cycle of deprivation and under achievement through upskilling and employability interventions.
>
> *Grant making policy*
>
> The trustees meet quarterly to review grant progress and to consider what grants they will make. Nominations for grants are elicited by formal means, primarily through the sponsoring company's UKI or Global Corporate Citizenship functions.
>
> Though the trustees may make some grants with no formal application, they would normally ask invited organisations to submit a formal application, applying the sponsoring company's standard application forms and criteria, saying how the funds would be used and what would be achieved. The trustees prefer to enter into long-term relationships with the main organisations to which they make grants; however, this is always subject to annual review and no guarantee of future funding is given.
>
> The Accenture Foundation trustees have agreed criteria under the theme of Skills to Succeed which covers the following areas of focus:
>
> - Employability – to equip people with critical skills for employment
> - Enterprise – to equip people with the skills required to establish and sustain enterprises
>
> In addition, the Accenture Foundation considers grants that:
>
> - Are conducive to Accenture employees' involvement (or potential for) e.g. through employee volunteering to enhance the overall impact of the grant
> - Have measurable impact in the UK or other key Accenture geographies (i.e. demonstrable impact)
> - Do not lead the supported organisation to become dependent/reliant on the Accenture Foundation or Accenture
>
> Additional robust due diligence and opportunity scoping criteria are applied by the sponsoring company's Global Giving Team as they shape global giving propositions for the consideration of the UK foundation trustees. For Local Giving proposition, the sponsoring company's UKI Corporate Citizenship Lead will apply the standard due diligence and opportunity scoping criteria before presenting Local Giving propositions to the UK foundation trustees for consideration.
>
> Potential grantees must be registered UK charities or equivalent.
>
> The foundation has a policy of not responding to any correspondence unless it relates to grants it has agreed to make or to the general management of the foundation. The trustees plan to continue with the current grant making strategy for the foreseeable future.

Financial information

In 2014/15 the foundation had assets of over £2.7 million and an income of £85,000, which included £14,000 from Accenture UK Ltd. Grants were made totalling £1.8 million.

Beneficiaries included: Cherie Blair Foundation for Women (£576,000); Voluntary Service Overseas (£560,500); The Prince of Wales Youth Business International (£528,500); Onside Northwest Ltd (£127,500).

Smaller grants and grants through the Charities Aid Foundation totalled £53,000.

Exclusions

No grants are made to political or religious organisations, or to individuals.

Applications

> Proposals are generally invited by the trustees or initiated at their request, or come via the sponsoring company's Global Giving function for which the UK foundation manages grant disbursement. Unsolicited applications are discouraged and are unlikely to be successful, even if they fall within an area in which the trustees are interested.

The Addleshaw Goddard Charitable Trust

General charitable purposes, education, legal education and the legal profession, and social welfare

£43,000 (2015/16)

Beneficial area

Greater London, Manchester and Leeds.

Correspondent: Christopher Noel, Trustee, Addleshaw Goddard LLP, 100 Barbirolli Square, Manchester M2 3AB (tel: 0161 934 6000; email: christopher.noel@addleshawgoddard.com)

CC number: 286887

General information

Registered in 1983, this is the charitable trust of Addleshaw Goddard LLP, a law firm with UK offices in London, Leeds and Manchester. The objects of the trust are as follows:

> - Promote any charitable purpose for the benefit of the communities in any city (whether in England or any other jurisdiction) in which Addleshaw Goddard LLP (or any of its successor firms) operates an office and in particular the advancement of education, the furtherance of health and the relief of poverty, distress and sickness
> - Promote any charitable object or purpose connected with the legal profession and in particular to assist the persons engaged in that profession and the wives, widows, children and other dependants of such persons being in conditions of need, hardship or distress
> - to advance legal education in all its aspects insofar as such advancement may be charitable

Financial information

In 2015/16 the trust had assets of £172,000 and an income of £63,500, of which £50,000 was received from

Addleshaw Goddard LLP. Grants were made totalling £43,000 and were broken down as follows:

Matching Addleshaw Goddard staff fundraising	£32,000
Leeds charities	£7,400
National and other charities	£3,500

A full list of beneficiaries was not provided in the accounts; however, it is stated that £7,400 was donated to Martin House Children's Hospice in Leeds.

Applications

Apply in writing to the correspondent.

The Adnams Community Trust

Education, health, social welfare, the arts, recreation, the environment, buildings/ community facilities

£82,000 (2014/15)

Beneficial area

Within a 25-mile radius of St Edmund's Church, Southwold.

Correspondent: Rebecca Abrahall, Charity Administrator, Adnams PLC, Sole Bay Brewery, East Green, Southwold, Suffolk IP18 6JW (tel: 01502 727200; email: charity@adnams.co.uk)

CC number: 1000203

General information

The Adnams Charity was founded in 1990 to mark the centenary of the Adnams brewing company and is funded mainly by the annual donation from the profits of Adnams PLC. It supports a wide variety of organisations within a 25-mile radius of Southwold.

Applications from national charities which operate within a 25-mile area of Southwold may be considered if assurances can be given that the money will be used for a specific purpose within the area.

The charity prefers to make one-off grants for specific items, normally in the range of £100 to £2,500, the trustees expecting to see the result of its donations within twelve months.

Areas of work

According to the charity's website, most grants are made in the following areas:

- Education
- Health and Social Welfare
- The Arts
- Recreation
- Buildings/Community Facilities
- The Environment/Conservation

Financial information

In 2014/15 the charity assets totalled £3,700 and it had an income of £46,500, most of which came from Adnams PLC. During the year, 96 grants were made totalling £82,000.

Beneficiaries included: Lowestoft Minibus for the Blind (£2,500); Southwold Common Trust (£2,000); Middleton Recreation Ground Trust (£1,900); Jubilee Opera and Pathways Care Farm (£1,000 each); Bungay Bowls Club and SS Stars Cheerleading Club (£650 each); Cancer Campaign in Suffolk and Create (£500 each); Walberswick Local History Group (£300).

Exclusions

Grants are not made to individuals. Awards are only made for specific purposes and are not usually made to the same organisation two years in succession.

Applications

Application forms are available on request from the Charity Administrator. Grants are considered at quarterly meetings, in January, April, July and October. Application deadlines usually fall in the previous month and are listed on the charity's website.

Allchurches Trust Ltd

Churches, Christian community, heritage, general charitable purposes

£11.7 million (2015)

Beneficial area

Worldwide with a preference for the UK.

Correspondent: Iain Hearn, Grants Administrator, Beaufort House, Brunswick Road, Gloucester GL1 1JZ (tel: 01452 873189; email: atl@allchurches.co.uk; website: www.allchurches.co.uk)

CC number: 263960

General information

Allchurches Trust Ltd was established in 1972. Its income is derived from its wholly owned subsidiary company Ecclesiastical Insurance Group. Its aims are 'to promote the Christian religion, to contribute to the funds of any charitable institutions, associations, funds or objects and to carry out any charitable purpose'.

Grants policy

Grants are considered in response to appeals from Anglican churches, churches of other denominations and the Christian community. The trust's grants policy, which is available from the website, states that the trust 'supports appeals from churches for building and restoration projects, repair of church fabric, church community initiatives, religious charities, charities preserving the UK heritage and other charitable causes'.

The trust states on its website: 'We particularly welcome applications from less well-off parishes and for projects which benefit mission and help local communities.'

Priorities

According to the annual report for 2015, which was the latest available at the time of writing (February 2017), the trust's priorities for the year to follow were:

- Begin a review of our charitable giving policies, informed by the changing expectations and priorities of our major beneficiaries, not least the Church of England
- Build the expendable Capital Endowment Fund over the three years 2015.17 to make prudent provision to ensure a sustainable flow of funds to our beneficiaries, given the potentially fluctuating nature of receipts from Ecclesiastical
- Increase the amount of charitable giving to beneficiaries
- Strengthen our links with beneficiaries
- Provide funding for a number of flagship projects

Financial information

In 2015 the trust had assets of £539.5 million and an income of £21.7 million. The trust made 1,244 grants totalling £11.7 million.

Church of England Dioceses	42	£6.2 million
Large Grants, above £3,000	221	£2.2 million
Small Grants, up to £3,000	892	£1.1 million
Special and Flagship Projects	21	£1.1 million
Church of England Cathedrals	68	£968,500

Beneficiaries included: The Representative Body of the Church in Wales (£183,000); Holy Trinity Church (£55,000); Sported Foundation, London (£40,000); The Rock Cheltenham (£30,000); Birmingham Cathedral (£22,000); City YMCA London (£20,000); Stafford Elim Christian Centre (£9,000); Compton Verney House Trust (£5,000); All Saints' Church, Alburgh and ALTERnativity, Glasgow (£1,000 each).

Exclusions

The trust is unable to support the following (apart from in exceptional circumstances):

- Charities with political association
- National charities
- Individuals
- Appeals for running costs and salaries

- More than one appeal from the same applicant within a 24-month period

Applications

Applications should be submitted online via the trust's website, where the grants policy and terms and conditions can also be found. The website advises:

> To make your application stand out from the crowd follow our tips and advice.
>
> When describing your project make sure it includes:
>
> - The work you want to do
> - Who will benefit
> - How you will achieve on-going viability
>
> Your applications will catch the attention of our Trustees if:
>
> - It has vision and illustrates enthusiastic support
> - It aims to bring improvements in areas of greatest need
> - It demonstrates financial sustainability, and how you plan to keep up the good work

The Allen & Overy Foundation

Disaster relief, access to justice, access to education, employment and training

£611,000 (2014/15)

Beneficial area

London; Northern Ireland; India; Nepal; Syria; Tanzania; Uganda.

Correspondent: The Administrator of the Allen & Overy Foundation, One Bishops Square, London E1 6AD (tel: 020 3088 0000; email: allenoveryfoundation@allenovery.com; website: www.allenovery.com/corporate-responsibility/charitable-giving/Pages/Local-charitable-giving.aspx)

Trustees: Andrew Wedderburn-Day; Annelies van der Pauw; Jane Findlayson-Brown; Jane Townsend; Mark Mansell; Philip Mansfield.

CC number: 1153738

General information

Allen & Overy is a large international law firm with its headquarters in London. Its foundation is funded by contributions from all Allen & Overy partners around the world. Around 75% of funds are allocated to support local projects with the remaining 25% being donated to international causes. The following information about the two grant programmes has been taken from the foundation's website:

> *Global Grants Programme*
>
> The Foundation is funded by contributions from all of A&O's partners worldwide and supports:
>
> - Our global charity partnership
> - Disaster relief efforts
> - Three or four charities a year through a global grants programme
>
> *Local Charitable Giving (London)*
>
> The Foundation in London is administered by the London Grants Committee, which is made up of partners within the London office and a member of the Pro Bono and Community Investment team. The London Grants Committee makes donations to charities that meet one or more of the following criteria:
>
> - Charities which work to promote access to justice in the UK
> - Charities which support and develop projects focusing on issues of education, employment and training based in or benefiting those in Tower Hamlets or Hackney
> - Charities to which Allen & Overy volunteers have made a significant contribution by participating in their activities or providing pro bono and volunteering support

Financial information

In 2014/15 the foundation held assets of £465,500 and had an income of £270,000. Grants awarded to organisations totalled £611,000.

Beneficiaries included: Amref Health Africa (£307,500); Médecins Sans Frontières (£40,000); Toynbee Hall (£20,000); Coram Children's Legal Centre and Praxis (£10,000 each); The Prince's Teaching Institute (£5,900); Street Kids International (£5,000); Mencap (£4,500); The Jeremy McMullen Memorial Fund (£2,500); The Cedar Foundation (£1,100).

Applications

The Allen & Overy Foundation (London)

Application forms are available from the correspondent. Application guidelines are on the foundation's website.

Global Grants Programme

At the time of writing (October 2016) the Global Grants Programme 2016 is closed for applications. Check the website for the latest information: www.allenovery.com/corporate-responsibility/charitable-giving.

Alliance Trust Foundation

General charitable purposes, children and young people, social welfare, communities

£27,000 (2015)

Beneficial area

Dundee, Edinburgh and City of London.

Correspondent: Surrani Kali, Secretary, Alliance Trust PLC, 8 West Marketgait, Dundee DD1 1QN (tel: 01382 321071; fax: 01382 321185; email: ATFoundation@alliancetrust.co.uk; website: www.alliancetrust.co.uk/en/about-us/alliance-trust-foundation)

Trustees: Donald McPherson; Surrani Kali; Ann McLeod; Stuart McMaster; Jack Willis; James Brown; Sinead Lennon; Alvina Menzies; Kathryn Taylor; Lindsey Congdon.

OSCR number: SC044113

General information

Registered with the Scottish Charity Regulator in 2013, this is the charitable foundation of Alliance Trust PLC, an investment, savings and wealth management company. The foundation's income derives from Alliance Trust employees' fundraising activities and match funding from the company. The following information is given by the company on the foundation's activities:

> The [foundation] was formed with the purpose of building partnerships between Alliance Trust and its local communities in Dundee, Edinburgh and London.
>
> Community engagement is more than just supporting charities and sponsoring events and the foundation aims to engage with local communities through funding specific charitable projects that will impact the local communities for the long-term.
>
> The foundation is run by a committee of Alliance Trust employees from across the business. It aims to engage staff through various initiatives such as dress down days and bakes sales to raise money for local charities, and with funds raised from larger events such as the Cateran Yomp, it donates to a select number of charities during the year.

Financial information

In 2015 the foundation had an income of £39,500, an expenditure of £41,000, and donated £27,000 to six local charities. Further information on beneficiaries is given in the foundation's 2015 annual newsletter, on the website.

Beneficiaries included: Tayside Children with Cancer and Leukaemia (£8,000); Kids Company, Ocean Youth Trust and PAMIS (£5,000 each); Fife Employment Access Trust and Home-Start Dundee (£2,000 each).

Applications

Apply in writing to the correspondent.

Anglo American Group Foundation

Community development, education and training, environment, health (particularly HIV/AIDS) and welfare, international development

£1.7 million (2015)

Beneficial area

UK (London) and overseas (priority countries include: Brazil; Chile; Colombia; Peru; China; India; Mozambique; and Zimbabwe).

Correspondent: Laura Dunne, Administrator, 20 Carlton House Terrace, London SW1Y 5AN (tel: 020 7968 8888; email: aagf@angloamerican.com; website: www.angloamericangroupfoundation.org)

Trustees: Angela Bromfield; Duncan Wanblad; Jon Samuel.

CC number: 1111719

General information

The foundation was established in 2005 by Anglo American PLC, a multinational mining company. The foundation's website states: 'Anglo American seeks to ensure that its impacts contribute to sustainable livelihoods in the communities in which it operates and the Foundation was founded on the same principles.'

The foundation receives donations from, but is independent of, the Anglo American group of companies and supports development initiatives directed at global and local; community in the areas where the company has operations, projects or representative offices, this includes: UK (London, in the City of Westminster, Southwark and Lambeth); Brazil; Chile; Colombia; Peru; China; India; Mozambique; and Zimbabwe.

Who the foundation supports

As explained on its website, the foundation 'prefers to fund specific projects or components of projects within the overall activities of an organisation that are a priority area in need of support' that 'have clearly defined objectives with quantifiable outcomes'. The main objective is to promote sustainable livelihoods.

The foundation tends to provide funding to a selected range of projects on a sustained basis rather than having a high turnover of partners, this way helping charities with long-term budget planning. Applications are welcomed from charitable organisations associated with the following areas:

- Education and training
- Environment
- HIV/AIDS and welfare
- International development
- Community development (in London)

The foundation also distributes funding by matching funds raised for charities by employees in the Anglo American London and Luxembourg offices.

Financial information

In 2015 the foundation had an income of £1.2 million and made grants totalling £1.7 million. They were distributed as follows:

Education and training	£1.3 million
Other social investments	£192,000
Health and welfare	£157,500
Employee matched funding	£34,500

Beneficiaries included: Technoserve (£676,000); Royal Academy of Engineering (£500,000); Diamond Development Initiative (£195,000); International Women's Health Coalition (£157,000); Sentebale (£148,000).

A full list of beneficiaries was not given in the accounts; however, further case studies are provided on the foundation's website.

Exclusions

The foundation only funds registered charities and does not support:

- Animal charities
- Armed forces charities
- Community Interest Companies (CICs)
- Educational fees
- Expeditions overseas
- General health charities
- Hospital trusts
- Individuals
- Music festivals and choirs
- Political or quasi-political bodies
- Religious organisations (other than community outreach)
- Trade unions

Support is not provided for projects in South Africa, where funding is handled by the Anglo American Chair's Fund.

Applications

Applications may be made in writing to the correspondent. The trustees meet quarterly.

AO Smile Foundation

General charitable purposes

£191,000 (2015)

Beneficial area

England and Wales.

Correspondent: Karen Hunter, Trustee, AO Park, 5A The Parklands, Lostock, Bolton BL6 4SD (tel: 07713 312014; email: Karen@AOSmileFoundation.org)

Trustees: John Roberts; Stephen Caunce; Karen Hunter.

CC number: 1157111

General information

Registered with the Charity Commission in March 2014, the AO Smile Foundation is the corporate charity of AO World PLC, an online retailer specialising in household appliances.

The foundation's Charity Commission record states that the objective of the foundation is to help children be the best they can be and to create opportunities for those who otherwise would be deprived of such chances.

Financial information

In 2015 the foundation had an income of £65,000 and assets of £139,000. Grants totalled £191,000. At the time of writing (October 2016) no accounts were available to view.

We have no information available regarding the beneficiaries.

Applications

Apply in writing to the correspondent.

The Apax Foundation

Social entrepreneurship, relief of poverty, education

£991,500 (2015/16)

Beneficial area

UK and overseas, with a focus on disadvantaged communities.

Correspondent: Kate Albert, Foundation Manager, Apax Partners, 33 Jermyn Street, London SW1Y 6DN (tel: 020 7872 6300; email: foundation@apax.com; website: www.apax.com/responsibility/apax-foundation)

Trustees: Sir Ronald Cohen, Chair; Peter Englander; Martin Halusa; David Marks; John Megrue; Michael Phillips; Simon Cresswell; Mitch Truwit; Shashank Singh; Rohan Haldea.

CC number: 1112845

General information

The Apax Foundation is the corporate charity for Apax Partners LLP. The foundation channels the firm's charitable giving and receives a percentage of the firm's profits and carried interest.

The following is taken from the foundation's annual report:

> The charity's objects are:
>
> - the relief of financial hardship, either generally or individually, of people living in socially and economically deprived areas in the UK and overseas through the provision of grants, goods or services
> - the advancement of education
> - to further such other purposes which are charitable in accordance with the

law of England and Wales as the trustees think fit

According to the foundation's website, its main focus is social entrepreneurship:

> Social entrepreneurship is the main focus of the Apax Foundation's charitable giving. We support a range of charities, large and small, working to help people in deprived communities to lift themselves out of poverty through enterprise. The Apax Foundation has made total cumulative donations of £3 million to charities working in this field.
>
> Social entrepreneurship was chosen as the focus for the Apax Foundation's major grant giving as it is the natural extension of what Apax does commercially and builds on the firm's history of support in that area, most notably as one of the founders of Bridges Ventures. It is also an area where some of the Foundation's Trustees have significant experience. This provides us with a steady flow of introductions to leading charities in the field, both from within the firm and from our wider network.

The foundation tends to make a small number of larger donations, and a larger number of grants of £10,000 or less.

As well as making grants, the foundation provides matched funding for Apax employees fundraising for charitable causes.

Financial information

In 2015/16 the foundation had assets of £21.6 million and an income of £3.5 million. Grants were made totalling almost £991,500 and were distributed as follows:

Social enterprise and relief of hardship	£685,500
Other charitable purposes	£202,500
Education	£403,500

Beneficiaries included: Grameen America (£310,000); Joblinge (£225,000); Mosaic – Business in the Community (£86,000); Institute for the Development of Social Investment (£50,000); Impetus – The Private Equity Foundation (£41,500); B Lab UK (£20,000); Special Olympics (£17,100); Inner City (£16,000); Pilot Light (£14,400); Crisis UK (£13,500).

Donations of £10,000 or less totalled £197,500.

Applications

Apply in writing to the correspondent. The following information is provided in the foundation's 2015/16 accounts:

> To ensure that the charity reaches out as widely as possible in fulfilment of its objectives, the Apex Foundation's grant application process is open to all charities operating in all countries. The sole restriction is that the work of those organisations must be focused in the charity's primary fields of education or the relief of poverty through the stimulation of entrepreneurship.
>
> The Apax Foundation's trustees review grant applications received from all charities which meet these criteria and grants are awarded on the basis of the trustees' evaluation of: the charity's effectiveness in achieving its aims, the number of beneficiaries reached, the sustainability of the charity's programmes, the strength and stability of its management team and internal processes, and the long-term public benefits that would flow from the deployment of a grant from the Apax Foundation.

Any further enquiries can be directed to Kate Albert, Foundation Manager: apax.foundation@apax.com.

The Arsenal Foundation Ltd

Education, sport, health, medical, disability, social welfare

£790,000 (2014/15)

Beneficial area

The foundation's area of benefit is the UK and overseas, with a particular focus on: Islington, Camden, Hackney, Barnet, Walthamstow and Hertsmere.

Correspondent: Svenja Geissmar, Trustee, Highbury House, 75 Drayton Park, London N5 1BU (email: thearsenalfoundation@arsenal.co.uk)

Trustees: Kenneth Friar; David Miles; Alan Sefton; Ivan Gazidis; Svenja Geissmar; Andrew Jolly.

CC number: 1145668

General information

The Arsenal Foundation was established in 2012 as a grant-giving organisation with the mission to help young people in North London and around the world fulfil their potential.

Guidelines

The following information was taken from the foundation's website:

> Priority is given to the following areas of need:
>
> - Education (including academic, social, physical education and skills training)
> - Sports capable of improving health
> - Medical
> - Sickness and the relief of suffering
> - Disability
> - Poverty
> - Individual misfortune
>
> The following is a non-exhaustive list of potential beneficiaries or groups of beneficiaries:
>
> - Organisations connected to Arsenal FC
> - Charity or community projects connected to Arsenal FC
> - Projects that have been developed by Arsenal FC's community team
> - Staff-initiated projects
> - Supporter-initiated projects
> - Projects where The Foundation's donation, even though relatively small, will make a difference
> - Projects where the gesture of support from a charity associated with Arsenal FC can have a greater effect than the money itself
> - Football-linked campaigns or public bodies
> - Projects where the person requesting a donation is doing something active to raise money for the cause
> - Projects where the person is playing a significant and voluntary role in raising money for the charity
> - Awards to reward success or achievement in areas of endeavour that fall within the objectives of The Foundation
> - Where funds are donated to The Foundation for a specific project or purpose and The Foundation acts as a partner and makes an additional contribution

The Gunners Fund

The aim of The Gunners Fund is to support charities in Islington, Camden and Hackney boroughs by offering smaller grants of up to £2,500 that can make a big difference to the community. The priorities and objectives of the fund are the same as those of the foundation.

Financial information

In 2014/15 the foundation held assets of £1.15 million and had an income of £857,500. Grants awarded to organisations totalled £790,000.

Beneficiaries included: Save the Children (£269,000); Teenage Cancer Trust (£100,000); Islington Giving (£50,000); Willow Foundation (£40,000); Premier League Charitable Fund (£25,000).

Grants under £60,000 totalled £306,000.

Applications

The Arsenal Foundation

Application forms are available on the foundation's website and can be returned by email or post once completed.

At the time of writing (January 2017) the foundation's website stated:

> Please note that due to the high volume of applications currently being received from international organisations, grants are currently only being considered for UK-based charities in order to ensure that The Arsenal Foundation is able to carry out effective assessment of applications and monitoring of grants made.

The Gunners Fund

Application forms can be found on the foundation's website and once completed can be returned by email to ssingh@arsenal.co.uk or via post.

The Ove Arup Foundation

The built environment – education

£146,500 (2015/16)

Beneficial area

UK and overseas.

Correspondent: John Ward, Secretary, Ove Arup & Partners, 13 Fitzroy Street, London W1T 4BQ (email: ovarfound@arup.com; website: www.ovearupfoundation.org)

Trustees: Caroline Cole; Richard Haryott; Dr Andrew Chan; Joanna Kennedy; Gregory Hodkinson; Terry Hill; Mahadev Raman.

CC number: 328138

General information

This foundation was established in 1989 in the memory of Sir Ove Arup, who was an engineer, designer and philosopher. The trustees of the foundation are appointed by the board of Arup Group Ltd. The foundation's 2015/16 annual report explains that its 'principal objective is the advancement of education of the public, directed towards the promotion, furtherance and dissemination of knowledge of matters associated with the built environment'. The foundation also has subsidiary powers to support academic research and any other charitable activity with similar purposes.

As part of its work to achieve its objective, the foundation has partnered organisations from across the sector. Partners have included The Royal Academy of Arts, The Royal Institute of British Architects and The Institution of Civil Engineers.

Grant-making

Every year, the foundation's trustees set aside a proportion of its budget to support projects that fall within the foundation's education purposes in relation to the built environment. The website explains:

> In deciding whether to agree to a request for assistance, the Foundation will first need to determine that the application is relevant to the Foundation's aims.
>
> Each initiative awarded a grant by the Foundation will be assigned a Trustee, who will liaise with the organisation or individual to offer advice and encouragement. At the end of the grant-period, the sponsored organisation is required to produce a report on how its initiative has progressed, the outcomes and how the grant aided this. The Foundation may post notice of the grant or project outcome on this website.
>
> Small, one-off donations are occasionally considered for a purpose or activity that the Foundation views as worthwhile in itself.

Financial information

In 2015/16 the foundation had assets of £3.8 million and an income of £302,000 which included a donation of £165,000 from Ove Arup Partnership Charitable Trust. Donations to 12 organisations totalled £146,500.

Beneficiaries included: The University of Edinburgh (£40,000); Chongqing University (£29,000); MADE (Muslim Action for Development and Environment) (£12,000); University College London (£10,000); Royal National Institute of Blind People (£5,000); The Anglo-Danish Society (£2,000).

Exclusions

No grants are made to individuals, including students.

Applications

There is an application form available to download from the website.

Ove Arup Partnership Charitable Trust

Education, social care, health, welfare, disaster relief, the alleviation of poverty, local community development, sustainability, the environment, technology

£466,000 (2015/16)

Beneficial area

UK

Correspondent: Stephanie Wilde, Ove Arup & Partners, 13 Fitzroy Street, London W1T 4BQ (email: stephanie.wilde@arup.com)

Trustee: Ove Arup Partnership Trust Corporation Ltd.

CC number: 1038737

General information

This trust was established by a trust deed in January 1978 and was registered with the Charity Commission in 1994. The annual report for 2015/16 explains that the trust 'is not in receipt of a regular income and relies on gifts from Arup Group Ltd'.

Income from the company is used to make charitable donations to charities. Donations are made for a wide range of purposes and particularly education, social care, health, welfare, disaster relief, poverty alleviation, local community development, sustainability, the environment and technology.

Grant-making policy

As the annual report explains, grants are made for causes and charities 'that operate in areas related to Arup's skills and business activities where these are aligned with Arup's values, as expressed in Ove Arup's 'Key Speech', of doing socially useful work and of being engaged in activities for the benefit of society at large'

When making a decision, the trustee takes into account the size and structure of the recipient organisation in relation to the size of the donation 'in order to maximise the impact and effectiveness of that donation'.

Financial information

In 2015/16 the trust had assets of £16,400 and an income of £458,000, of which £457,500 was received in the form of a donation from Arup Group Ltd. During the year, donations were made totalling £466,000.

Beneficiaries included: The Ove Arup Foundation (£165,000); RedR UK (£53,000); Young Women's Trust (£50,000); Engineers Without Borders (£29,000); Bridges to Prosperity (£20,000); Ellen MacArthur Cancer Trust (£5,000); Opera North and The Francis Crick Institute (£1,000 each); Brain Tumour Research (£600).

Applications

Apply in writing to the correspondent.

The ASDA Foundation

Sport and recreation, community development, general charitable purposes

£6.68 million (2015)

Beneficial area

England and Wales.

Correspondent: The Trustees of the ASDA Foundation, ASDA Foundation, ASDA House, Great Wilson Street, Leeds LS11 5AD (tel: 0113 243 5435; website: www.asdafoundation.org)

Trustees: Paul Rowland; John Cookman; Lorraine Jackson; Annmarie Rocks; Jane Earnshaw; Francesca Haynes; James Jefcoate; Alex Simpson; Alison Seabrook; Gerald Oppenheim; Paul Rowland; Lynne Tooms.

CC number: 1124268

General information

The ASDA Foundation is ASDA's charitable hand. It supplements the good causes that colleagues support locally, as well as a number of bigger ad hoc projects in local communities. It also manages all funds raised for national charities and monies raised in ASDA House.

The foundation's main objective is to make donations to local good causes. It funds a wide range of causes with which its colleagues are involved in, including everything from local charities and playgroups to football teams.

According to the foundation's website, 'the Foundation works in partnership with other charities tackling issues within local communities and supporting charities made a real difference to thousands of people across the UK'.

Financial information

In 2015 the foundation had assets of £8.1 million and income of £8.2 million. Grants totalled £6.68 million, with £2.08 million going to the foundation's national campaigns: Tommy's (£705,000); Tickled Pink (£500,000); Orchid (£377,000); Whizz-Kidz (£236,000); Children in Need (£136,000); British Heart Foundation (£66,000); Disasters and Jamgara (£62,000 each).

A further £4.6 million was donated to other organisations.

Beneficiaries included: Silver Line, and Social Investment Business Foundation (£250,000 each); FareShare (£142,500); Run For All (£137,000); the Trussell Trust (£80,000); Motability (£74,000); YMCA Northumberland (£20,000); Help For Heroes (£1,600); Martin House (£1,400); Alva Primary School, Cransley Hospice, Bethel Community Church, and Rotary Club of Sowerby Bridge (£1,000 each).

Exclusions

ASDA Foundation does not fund expeditions or sponsor charitable activities by people other than ASDA colleagues.

The foundation will not support political, military, religious or ethnic charities or groups.

Applications

There is an eligibility checker and 'store locator' on the website. The following statement is given there: 'If your application fits the ASDA Foundation guidelines, applying could not be simpler, please contact your local store or depot and speak to the Community Champion – to see if this is something they would like to be involved with and support.'

The Ashmore Foundation

Community and economic development, education and training, health

£505,000 to organisations (2014/15)

Beneficial area

Worldwide

Correspondent: The Trustees of the Ashmore Foundation, Ashmore Group, 5th Floor, 61 Aldwych, London WC2B 4AE (tel: 020 3077 6153; email: info@ashmorefoundation.org; website: www.ashmorefoundation.org)

CC number: 1122351

General information

Established in 2008, the Ashmore Foundation is the charity of the Ashmore Group, an emerging markets investment management company.

According to the foundation's website:

> The Foundation aims to develop long-term relationships with high impact local non-government organisations (NGOs). Our financial support enables these organisations to directly enhance human welfare, opportunities and skills, particularly for the most vulnerable: children, young people and disadvantaged communities. As well as working directly with NGOs we work alongside other international funders to identify and support local solutions to social problems.
>
> Grants are usually multi-year, prioritising high impact organisations operating in priority countries, assessed over a two stage application process. Grants range in size depending on the scale and nature of the programme and the organisation's capacity, but a typical Partnership Grant is between £20,000 and £50,000 per year over three years.

Financial information

In 2014/15 the foundation had an income of £573,000 and an expenditure of £583,000. Grants made to organisations totalled £505,000.

Beneficiaries included: Lend a Hand (£101,000); IDEP Foundation (£66,000): Pragya (£32,000); Yuva (£17,000).

Applications

The foundation does not accept unsolicited applications. They source new partners through recommendations from experts, existing partners, suggestions from Ashmore staff and detailed research by the foundation team.

Autonomous Research Charitable Trust (ARCT)

People who are disadvantaged, empowering people to improve quality of life, general charitable purposes

£266,500 (2015/16)

Beneficial area

Mainly London and overseas.

Correspondent: Martin Pollock, Trust Administrator, 150 Aldersgate Street, London EC1A 4AB (tel: 020 7334 9191; email: martin.pollock@moorestephens.com)

CC number: 1137503

General information

This trust was established in 2010 for general charitable purposes. It is the charitable trust of Autonomous Research LLP, a company that provides intelligence on banking and insurance companies. The company donates a share of its profits – around 5% – to charitable causes through this trust, as well as through its US foundation, Autonomous Research Foundation US (ARFUS).

The 2015/16 annual report states that the trust's core aims are:

- To help disadvantaged people get a step up in life
- To empower people to improve the quality of their lives
- To focus our resources upon a small number of key partner charities, both in London and abroad, where we feel we can make a difference and establish long-term relationships

It is further explained that the charity works towards these aims and objectives by:

- Providing funding to other recognised charitable institutions
- Providing mentoring, business and career advice and a variety of other hands-on roles which the Trustees believe would ultimately be a benefit to the public

Grant-making policy

The trustees' report states: the following information about the grant-making process:

> At the beginning of each year, the Trustees will consider and agree a short list of charities that are to be core partner charities for that year. Specific support will be directed to these organisations, with meetings and other feedback being sought, as well as considering other

worthy causes that fall within the criteria and aims of the trustees. Alongside the core charity partners the charity maintains discretional funds for ad hoc distributions

Unsolicited applications are accepted, but the trustees do receive a high number of grant applications which, in line with the Trustees' grant making policy, are mostly unsuccessful. The trustees prefer to support donations to charities whose work they have researched and which is in accordance with the aims and objectives of the charity for the year. Financial circumstances will be relevant only in determining the amount of an award

Financial information

In 2015/16 the trust had an income of £217,500 and a total expenditure of £280,500. Grants were made totalling £266,500 and were awarded to 29 organisations.

Beneficiaries included: Find Your Feet (£101,000); Food Cycle (£100,000); Honeypot Children's Charity (£15,000); Contact the Elderly (£10,000); Marie Curie (£5,500); Nordoff Robbins (£2,000); Plan International UK and The Leukaemia and Lymphoma Society (£1,500 each); Alec's Angels and The Prince's Trust (£1,000 each).

Applications

Applications may be made in writing to the correspondent; however, note that unsolicited applications are accepted but are unlikely to be successful; the trustees prefer to take a proactive approach to their grant-making.

The Balfour Beatty Charitable Trust

General charitable purposes, particularly children, young people and education

Around £55,000 (2015)

Beneficial area

UK

Correspondent: Paul Raby, Trustee, Company Secretarial Department, Balfour Beatty Ltd, 130 Wilton Road, London SW1V 1 LQ (tel: 07940 594673; email: bbfutures@balfourbeatty.com; website: www.bbfutures.org)

Trustees: Paul Raby; Adrian McManus.

CC number: 1127453

General information

Balfour Beatty PLC is a multinational infrastructure group with capabilities in construction services, support services and infrastructure investments. The trust was founded by the company to support its corporate and social responsibility provision and to act as a focus for employee fundraising as well as to develop into a significant grant-funder.

The website states that the trust is part of the group's Building Better Futures programme, and has donated £2 million to support over 20,000 disadvantaged young people in the UK since 2009. Building Better Futures focuses on the following three themes:

- Young people's employability and employment
- Helping the most disadvantaged young people in society
- Health, sport and wellbeing

Financial information

In 2015 the trust had an income of £19,600 and a total expenditure of £70,000. Due to the charity's low income during the year, its 2015 accounts were not required to be published on the Charity Commission's website. We estimate that the amount of grants totalled around £55,000.

Beneficiaries have included: Barnardo's; Coram; The Prince's Trust.

Applications

The trustees work together with the Balfour Beatty Community Engagement Working Group (CEWG) to identify suitable charities to support.

The Bank of Scotland Foundation

Community development and improvement, financial literacy and inclusion

£1.19 million (2015)

Beneficial area

Scotland

Correspondent: Lorraine O'Neill, Finance and Grants Manager, The Mound, Edinburgh EH1 1YZ (tel: 0131 655 2599; email: enquiries@bankofscotlandfoundation.co.uk; website: www.bankofscotlandfoundation.org)

Trustees: Philip Grant, Chair; Robin Bulloch; Sarah Deas; Sir Paul Grice.

OSCR number: SC032942

General information

The Bank of Scotland Foundation is an independent charity providing grants to local, regional and national charities across Scotland, supporting people and their local communities. The foundation receives a £2 million donation from Lloyds Banking Group each year, which is used to fund its funding programmes.

What the foundation supports

The foundation gives support in two core areas, which are described on the website as follows:

The development and improvement of local communities

Within any community, there will be a diverse collection of individuals and charities tackling local issues. Some issues will be unique to the local area, others will be replicated across the country or parts of it. We feel it is important to help individuals and groups work together to ensure a better quality of life within their community. Practical ways of making this happen may include:

- Initiatives designed to encourage the involvement in the community of those too often excluded
- Working with people on low incomes, at risk from poverty or with problems finding accommodation
- Improving the standard of local facilities

Financial literacy and financial inclusion

Making informed judgements and taking effective decisions regarding money are important skills – skills which some people can find to be beyond their grasp. Building the confidence and competence of everyone about finance is a particular priority for the Bank of Scotland Foundation. In order to achieve this, we're committed to supporting financial literacy and financial inclusion right across Scotland. We aim to help make these essential skills both easy and accessible for all.

Initiatives that we are particularly interested in supporting are:

- Promoting financial awareness and money advice
- Enhancing debt counselling services within the community
- Supporting life-skills in all age groups and sections of the community

Funding programmes

The foundation has three grants programmes through which charities registered in Scotland can apply:

- **Small Grants Programme**: Grants are made to support the development and improvement of local communities. Applications are accepted for amounts between £1,000 and £10,000 and grants are awarded for one year only
- **Medium Grants Programme**: Grants are made to support the development and improvement of local communities and financial literacy and inclusion. Applications are accepted for amounts between £10,001 and £25,000 and grants are awarded for one year only
- **Large Grants Programme**: Grants are made to support the development and improvement of local communities and financial literacy and inclusion. Applications are accepted for amounts between £50,000 and £100,000 and grants can be awarded over one or two years

The foundation also runs Lloyds Banking Group's Matched Giving Programme, through which employees of the group can apply for up to £1,000 for charities of their choice (up to £500 for fundraising activities and up to £500 for voluntary time given).

All funding programmes run by the foundation are subject to their own eligibility criteria and guidelines. Full information can be found on the website.

Financial information
In 2015 the foundation had assets of £659,500 and an income of £2.35 million. Grants totalled £1.19 million.

A total of 88 grants were made during the year, of which 79, ranging between £1,000 and £98,000, were given for the development and improvement of local communities and nine, ranging between £3,000 and £63,000, were given to causes working in the areas of money advice and financial literacy.

In addition, £808,000 was paid to more than 460 charities through the employee matched giving programme, although we have not included this figure in the overall grants total.

Beneficiaries included: Quarriers (£92,000); PEEK – Possibilities for Each and Every Kid (£78,500); Financial Fitness Resource Team (£64,000); Woodlands Community Development Trust (£17,600); Livingstone Youth Foundation (£12,600); Maggie Keswick Jencks Cancer Caring Centres Trust and National Youth Choir of Scotland (£10,000 each); Orkney Alcohol Counselling and Advisory Service (£9,800); North Glasgow Community Food Initiative (£9,500); Falkirk Community Trust (£7,500); Health in Mind (£4,400); Dundee Women's Aid (£3,300); Lasswade High School PHAB Club (£1,000).

Exclusions
The foundation does not support/fund:

- Discriminatory or political organisations
- The promotion of religion
- Animal charities or medical research
- Organisations that redistribute funding for grant-making to other organisations and/or individuals
- Individuals
- Advertising or sponsorship

Applications
Applications can be made via the online form on the foundation's website, where eligibility criteria and guidelines are also available. Appeals for small and medium grants can be made once every 12 months and for large grants can be submitted only after two years have passed from the receipt of an award. Unsuccessful organisations should wait one year before trying again. The submission deadlines for each programme vary – see the website for most up-to-date information. The foundation team can be contacted via telephone should assistance be required when making an application.

The Barclay Foundation

Medical research, young people, older people, people who have disabilities, people who are ill or disadvantaged, general charitable purposes

£17.7 million to organisations (2015)

Beneficial area
UK

Correspondent: Michael Seal, Administrator, 2nd Floor, 14 St George Street, London W1S 1FE (tel: 020 7915 0915; email: mseal@ellerman.co.uk)

Trustees: Sir David Barclay; Sir Frederick Barclay; Aidan Barclay; Howard Barclay.

CC number: 803696

General information
The foundation was established in 1989 by Sir David and Sir Frederick Barclay; who own the Telegraph Media Group Ltd, and who provide all of the funds. Note that it has no association with Barclays bank. The objects of the foundation are wide and the trustees distribute the income at their own discretion for general charitable purposes, with a focus on 'aid for the young, medical research, and aid for the sick, disabled and disadvantaged', according to the 2015 annual report.

Financial information
In 2015 the foundation had assets of £7,500 and an income of almost £17.8 million from donations. Grants were made to 15 organisations totalling £17.7 million. Grants were also made to two individuals, totalling £48,000. Grants to organisations were distributed in the following categories:

Aid for people who are sick, disadvantaged or have disabilities	2	£10 million
Historical preservation	3	£3.8 million
Aid for young people	7	£3.3 million
Medical research	2	£547,500
Aid for the environment	1	£10,000

Beneficiaries included: The Black Stork Charity (£10 million); Great Ormond Street Hospital (£3 million); Dumfries House Trust (£2.5 million); Imperial War Museum (£1.3 million); Thrombosis Research Institute (£400,000); Frederick Hugh Trust (£200,000); University of Oxford (£147,500); The Fashion and Textile Children's Trust (£62,500); Make a Wish Foundation (£48,000); Wallace Collection (£20,000); Child Bereavement UK and Prince Albert of Monaco Foundation (£10,000 each); Children in Need (£2,000); Breast Cancer Campaign and Children with Cancer UK (£1,000 each).

Applications
Applications should be in writing, clearly outlining the details of the proposed project, (for medical research, as far as possible in lay terms). The total cost and duration should be stated as well as the amount, if any, which has already been raised.

Following an initial screening, applications are selected according to their merits, suitability and funds available. Visits are usually made to projects where substantial funds are involved.

The foundation welcomes reports as to progress and requires these on the completion of a project.

BC Partners Foundation

Community development, environmental conservation, arts, education

£543,000 (2015)

Beneficial area
UK and overseas.

Correspondent: The Trustees of BC Partners Foundation, BC Partners Ltd, 40 Portman Square, London W1H 6DA (tel: 020 7009 4800; email: bcpfoundation@bcpartners.com; website: www.bcpartners.com/about-us/bcp-foundation.aspx)

Trustees: Nikos Stathopolous; Joseph Cronly; Lorna Parker; Michael Pritchard; Richard Kunzer; Cedric Dubourdieu; Francesco Loredan.

CC number: 1136956

General information
Established in 2010 for general charitable purposes, this is the foundation of private equity firm BC Partners.

The firm's website states that the foundation provides matched funding for employee fundraising initiatives and supports charities nominated by employees of BC Partners or trustees of the foundation. Employees in each office also nominate two charities each year to receive donations and volunteer support from that office.

Although it has quite general criteria, the foundation focuses support on the following areas:

- Community development including infrastructure advancements,

development aid, health care improvements
- Conservation of the environment including endeavours related to pollution reduction, natural preservation, clean technologies
- Arts and Education including support for educational, scholastic, or artistic programs

The foundation is principally funded by the firm and by employee donations.

Financial information

In 2015 the foundation had assets of £614,500 and an income of £634,000. Grants were made to organisations totalling £543,000.

The largest grant was made to the Private Equity Foundation (£103,000), of which Nikos Stathopolous is a trustee.

Beneficiaries included: Private Equity Foundation (£103,000); American School in London Foundation (£50,000); Over the Wall (£23,000); English National Opera (£15,300); Wildlife Heritage Trust (£10,000); Fine Cell Works (£5,400); Music as Therapy (£5,000); Royal Horticultural Society (£4,800); Médecins Sans Frontières (£3,300); 4th Farnham Scout Group (£2,500); Jo's Trust (£1,000); Target e.V. Rüdiger Nehberg (£100).

Applications

The foundation does not accept unsolicited applications – charities must be nominated by BC Partners employees or trustees of the foundation.

The Berkeley Charitable Foundation

General charitable purposes, education, health, social welfare, the environment, community development

£1.03 million (2015/16)

Beneficial area

England and Wales.

Correspondent: Stuart Cowen, Trustee, The Berkeley Foundation, Berkeley House, 19 Portsmouth Road, Cobham, Surrey KT11 1JG (tel: 01932 896855; email: info@berkeleyfoundation.org.uk; website: www.berkeleyfoundation.org.uk)

Trustees: Anthony Pidgley; Robert Perrins; Wendy Pritchard; Elaine Anne Driver.

CC number: 1152596

General information

The Berkeley Charitable Foundation was established in 2011 and registered with the Charity Commission in June 2013. It was set up by Anthony Pidgley, founder and chair of the Berkeley Group – a British housebuilding company based in Surrey.

This is a grant-making charity operating throughout England and Wales but with a specific focus on London and the Southeast. According to its website, the foundation has four key charitable objectives:

- Homes: Helping those facing homelessness and tackling its root causes
- Jobs: Creating jobs for young, unemployed and homeless people
- Skills: Training young and unemployed people to reach their full potential
- Care: Helping people to live with disability or life-limiting illness

The foundation also focuses on urban regeneration and sustainable development within the remit of its four key objectives.

Financial information

In 2015/16 the foundation had an income of almost £1.8 million with 1.75 million contributed in donations from the Berkeley group, Give As You Earn schemes, and company fundraising benefits. The foundation had a total expenditure of £1.8 million. Grants totalled £1.03 million.

Beneficiaries include: The Lord's Taverners (£330,000), The Challenge (HeadStart London), Job Creation subsidies (£115,000).

Grants made under £50,000 totalled £493,000.

Applications

The foundation has stated that it very rarely makes unsolicited donations; however, organisations can write to the correspondent if they believe there is a partnership that could be explored.

The Bestway Foundation

Education and training, social welfare, health, medical causes, overseas aid

£1.34 million to UK organisations (2014/15)

Beneficial area

UK and overseas.

Correspondent: Mohammed Younus Sheikh, Trustee, Bestway (Holdings) Ltd, Abbey Road, London NW10 7BW (tel: 020 8453 1234; email: zulfikaur.wajid-hasan@bestway.co.uk; website: www.bestwaygroup.co.uk/responsibility/bestway-foundation)

Trustees: Mohammed Sheikh; Abdul Bhatti; Adalat Chaudhary; Sir Anwar Pervez; Zameer Choudrey; Dawood Pervez; Rizwan Pervez; Arshad Chaudhary.

CC number: 297178

General information

Registered with the Charity Commission in 1987, the Bestway Foundation is the corporate charity of Bestway (Holdings) Ltd, an independent food wholesale group in the UK. All of the foundation's trustees are directors and shareholders of Bestway (Holdings) Ltd.

The foundation's page on the Bestway Group website states that its mission statement is as follows:

- The advancement of education for public benefit in both the UK and overseas by providing assistance through promotion of local schools; provision of scholarships to university students; supporting education initiatives and endowing universities
- The relief of sickness and the preservation of health for public benefit in both the UK and overseas by way of grants and endowments to existing hospitals, clinics, medical research establishments; and by establishing new health facilities
- The provision of financial and material support to victims of natural disasters
- To have a significant impact on poverty reduction in Pakistan through strategic investments in affordable financial and social services catering to the poor
- The development of technical skills within the local communities in which we operate through structured apprenticeship and training programmes

Donations on behalf of students are made directly to academic institutions.

Financial information

In 2014/15 the foundation had assets of £6.38 million and an income of £906,500, including a donation of £700,000 received from Bestway (Holdings) Ltd. Grants were made totalling £1.53 million. Of the total amount distributed, £1.34 million was given to UK-registered charities and £190,500 to foreign charities and individuals. A total of 18 grants were made to organisations and 40 to individuals.

Beneficiaries included: Oxford University Development Trust (£1.06 million); Action for Children (£100,000); University of Bradford (£50,000); British Pakistan Foundation (£43,000); The Duke of Edinburgh's Award (£20,000); Grocery Aid (£10,000); Children's Safety Education Foundation (£300).

Exclusions

Trips/travel abroad.

Applications

Applications may be made in writing to the correspondent, enclosing an sae. The foundation has previously noted that telephone calls are not invited.

BHP Billiton Sustainable Communities

General charitable purposes

£29 million (2014/15)

Beneficial area

UK

Correspondent: The Trustees of BHP Billiton Sustainable Communities, BHP Billiton PLC, Neathouse Place, London SW1V 1LH (tel: 020 7802 4000; email: hsec@bhpbilliton.com)

CC number: 1131066

General information

According to the 2014/15 annual report: 'The Charity aims to provide s public benefit by enabling people to improve their quality of life, contribute to the conservation of the environment and developing the community's capacity to advocate for and manage effective change.'

BHP Billiton is a large international mining company. The group gives generously worldwide in areas where it has operational sites. It no longer has this in the UK but the registered office is still in London and it is not clear if in-kind giving by staff may be available from there. The future of the UK-registered charity, BHP Billiton Sustainable Communities, is to be considered in view of the company's decision that it is more effective to contribute to its other recently in the US established corporate charity, BHP Billiton Foundation. It is thought that the UK charity will continue for only a small number of years. It is not clear if UK charities can still benefit from grants and contact should be made to the correspondent before making an application. In view of the company divesting its operating assets in the United Kingdom, contributions can no longer be made to the BHP Billiton Sustainable Communities charity from the company.

Financial information

In 2014/15 the charity had assets of \$96.5 million (£78.5 million), an income of \$310,000 (£252,000) and made grants totalling of \$35.5 million (£29 million).

Beneficiaries included: Path Window of Opportunity (\$10,500); Colombia Resilience Global Communities (\$5,000); Mozambique WaterAid (\$1,000): Engineers Without Borders (\$300).

At the time of writing (October 2016) the exchange rate had altered significantly and the figures reflect the financial amounts stated in the 2014/15 annual report.

Applications

It is not clear if UK charities can still benefit from grants and contact should be made to the correspondent before making an application.

Birmingham International Airport Community Trust Fund

Community, environment, heritage, sport, health and well-being

£74,500 (2014/15)

Beneficial area

The areas affected by the airport's operation, particularly East Birmingham and North Solihull – a full list of postcodes is provided on the website.

Correspondent: Trust Fund Administrator, Birmingham International Airport Ltd, Diamond House, Birmingham B26 3QJ (tel: 0121 767 7448; email: community@birminghamairport.co.uk; website: www.birminghamairport.co.uk)

CC number: 1071176

General information

Established in 1998, the trust aims to compensate those communities most affected by Birmingham International Airport. The airport company donates £75,000 each year to the trust, which is topped up by fines imposed on airlines for exceeding the airport's noise violation levels (this usually amounts to very modest amounts).

In 2015/16 the airport reviewed its CSR strategy and it was decided that community investment should be focused as follows:

- 30% of resources targeted for disadvantaged communities in East Birmingham
- 30% of resources directed to disadvantaged communities in North Solihull
- 40% of resources shared among other communities that are still affected by the airport's activities, but have lower levels of deprivation

A full list of postcode areas eligible for support is provided on the website.

The trust acts independently of the airport management, with nine representatives of the following bodies making up the trustees: The Airport Consultative Committee (3), Birmingham City Council (2), Birmingham International Airport (2) and Solihull Council (2).

Areas of work the trust supports are, according to the website:

- Heritage conservation
- Environment improvement, improving awareness of environmental issues, environmental education and training, encouraging and protecting wildlife
- Bringing the Community closer together through facilities for sport, recreation and other leisure time activities
- Improving health and wellbeing through the promotion of healthy lifestyles and employment opportunities

Work should benefit a substantial section of the community rather than less inclusive groups, although work with older people or people with special needs is positively encouraged.

The maximum grant made is for £3,000, and grants tend to go to community groups with low incomes; organisations with large turnovers are rarely supported. Applications from organisations showing efforts to raise funds from their own resources are favoured. Grants may be for capital or revenue projects, although the trust will not commit to recurrent or running costs, such as salaries.

Financial information

In 2014/15 the trust had assets of £11,900 and an income of £78,000. Grants were made totalling £74,500.

Beneficiaries in 2015/16 included: John Taylor Hospice – Men's Shed and Training Ship Stirling (£3,000 each); Spotlight Stage School (£2,000); Coleshill Parish Church (£1,000).

Note that the 2014/15 accounts were the latest available at the time of writing (November 2016), and a list of beneficiaries was not provided; the above beneficiaries were taken from the 2015/16 Birmingham Airport Corporate Responsibility report.

Exclusions

The trust will not support:

Branches of national or international organisations are not usually supported.

- Running costs, such as salaries or expenses
- Individuals
- Medical treatment
- Organisations with statutory responsibilities, unless the project is clearly above their obligations
- Purchase of land and buildings, or general repair and maintenance (adaptions for disability or security may be supported)
- Sports kits or uniforms
- Short-term projects, such as events or trips

- Projects which have already taken place

Applications

Applicants should first read the trust's guidelines, available to download from the website, and then use the online form to request an application pack. Grants are made twice a year, in April and October, and deadlines are posted on the website.

The Boodle & Dunthorne Charitable Trust

General charitable purposes

£110,000 (2015)

Beneficial area

UK and overseas.

Correspondent: Nicholas Wainwright, Administrator, Boodle & Dunthorne, 35 Lord Street, Liverpool L2 9SQ (tel: 0151 224 0580)

Trustees: Nicholas Wainwright; Michael Wainwright.

CC number: 1077748

General information

Established in 1999, this is the charitable trust of Boodles, a family jewellers based in North West England.

Financial information

In 2015 the trust had assets of £569,000 and an income of £210,000 which included a donation of £200,000 from Boodle & Dunthorne Ltd. Grants were made totalling £110,000.

Beneficiaries included: Shining Faces in India (£55,000); Rainbow Trust (£48,500); The Message Trust (£15,000).

Applications

Applications can be made in writing to the correspondent.

Boots Charitable Trust

Health, social care, education and training, community development, general charitable purposes

£337,000 (2014/15)

Beneficial area

Nottingham and Nottinghamshire.

Correspondent: James Kirkpatrick, Funding Support, Boots UK Ltd, 1698 Melton Road, Rearsby, Leicester LE7 4YR (tel: 07739 835909; email: julie.lawrence@boots.co.uk or james@fundingsupport.co.uk; website: www.boots-uk.com/corporate_social_responsibility/boots-charitable-trust.aspx)

Trustees: Oonagh Turnbull; Judith Lyons; Richard Burbidge; Helen Jeremiah; Lavinia Moxley; Adrian Bremner.

CC number: 1045927

General information

Registered with the Charity Commission in 1995, Boots Charitable Trust is wholly funded by Boots UK Ltd. Boots UK is part of the Retail Pharmacy International Division of Walgreens Boots Alliance, Inc. Boots became a subsidiary of the new company, Walgreens Boots Alliance, on 31 December 2014. The trust is administered by members within the Corporate Social Responsibility Team, including Julie Lawrence, Assistant CSR Manager.

The trust gives to charities and voluntary organisations that benefit Nottingham and Nottinghamshire. It is explained on the Boots website: 'Supporting the Nottinghamshire community has always been important to Boots. Jesse Boot opened the very first Boots store in the mid-19th century in Nottingham, and we continue to give to local causes that are important to our colleagues and customers.'

Areas of support

The trust considers support for a wide range of charities and voluntary organisations although its main focus is on four areas which are very close to the 'heart and heritage' of Boots. These areas are outlined on the website:

- **Health**: 'Both community healthcare such as homecare or support for sufferers of medical conditions as well as health education and prevention'
- **Lifelong learning**: 'For example literacy and numeracy projects'
- **Community development**: 'Such as supporting councils in providing voluntary services'
- **Social care**: 'Be it personal, social or community activities or schemes'

The website states that it also funds 'smaller voluntary organisations in Nottinghamshire which are too small to qualify for charitable status, but who still desperately need some financial support for their projects'.

Financial information

In 2014/15 the trust had assets of £21,000 and an income of £383,000, of which £354,000 was a donation from the company and £29,000 was donated services. It gave 59 grants totalling £337,000 during the year, of which there were 53 major grants totalling £328,000 and six minor grants (under £2,000) totalling £8,900. Grants were distributed as follows:

Health	22	£130,500
Social care	12	£74,500
Lifelong learning	14	£74,000
Community development	11	£58,000

Beneficiaries included: Treetops Hospice and Nottingham Women's Aid (£10,000 each); Ravenshead Community Transport (£9,500); Home-Start Newark (£7,000); Pintsize Theatre (£6,500); Hope Nottingham and Hothouse Theatre (£6,000 each); The National Holocaust Centre and Museum (£5,500); Jigsaw Youth Club (£5,400); Mansfield CVS (£5,000).

Note that the company also has another charity, **Boots Benevolent Fund** (Charity Commission no. 1046559), which provides financial help and support to serving and retired colleagues who are unexpectedly experiencing financial hardship.

Exclusions

According to its website, the trust does not provide funding for:

- Projects benefitting those people outside of Nottinghamshire
- Individuals
- Organisations which are NOT registered charities and have an income or expenditure of more than £5,000 per year
- Charities seeking funds to re-distribute to other charities
- Projects for which there is a legal statutory obligation or which replace statutory funding

Applications

There is an online application form on the website, alongside guidance on eligibility. Paper application forms can also be requested on: james@fundingsupport.co.uk or 07739 835909.

The trustees review applications on a bimonthly basis. Applications should be received by the 7th day of February; April; June; August; October; and December. The website explains that the application process can take between two and four months.

The Bruntwood Charity

General charitable purposes, social welfare

£63,000 (2014/15)

Beneficial area

UK, mainly the four areas where the company has a presence: Birmingham; Leeds; Liverpool; and Manchester.

Correspondent: Kathryn Graham, Trustee, Bruntwood Ltd, York House, York Street, Manchester M2 3BB

Trustees: Katharine Vokes; Sally Hill; Kathryn Graham; Jane Williams; Peter Crowther.

CC number: 1135777

General information

The charity was established in 2010 for general charitable purposes. It is the charity of Bruntwood Ltd, a company which owns and manages commercial property and offices space in Birmingham, Leeds, Manchester and Liverpool. The founder of Bruntwood is Michael Oglesby of the Oglesby Charitable Trust.

The charity focuses on fundraising for five charities; they are: Claire House Children's Hospice – Liverpool; Onside and the Factory Youth Zone – Manchester; St Gemma's Hospice – Leeds; Whizz-Kidz – Birmingham.

Financial information
In 2014/15 the charity had assets of £47,000 and an income of £100,500. There were four grants made totalling £63,000.

Beneficiaries included: Factory Youth Zone (£28,500); Onside (£20,000); Whizz-Kidz (£10,000); St Gemma's Hospice (£4,500).

Applications
The charity has stated that 'as their funds are fully committed they do not seek unsolicited requests for funding'.

Bupa UK Foundation

Health and well-being, mental health, carers

£106,000 (2015)

Beneficial area
UK

Correspondent: Tina Gwynne-Evans, Head of BUPA UK Foundation, BUPA House, 15–19 Bloomsbury Way, London WC1A 2BA (tel: 020 7656 2738; email: bupaukfoundation@bupa.com; website: www.bupaukfoundation.org)

CC number: 1162759

General information
This is the corporate charity of the healthcare group Bupa Ltd and is entirely funded by the group. It was established in 2015 to replace the group's previous charity, The Bupa Foundation.

According to the website, the foundation's purpose is 'to help people live healthier, happier lives' by funding 'practical projects to tackle critical challenges in health and social care and make a direct impact on people's health and wellbeing'.

Grants programmes
The website states that the foundation's funding programmes focus on specific themes, each with their own criteria which are released on the website as the programme is announced, along with application deadlines. Grants are made to support specific projects, rather than general core costs, but the foundation awards an additional 15% of grant funding to successful applicants for core costs. Social enterprises, CICs and for-profit organisations are also eligible to apply if they are running a charitable project

The foundation has since 2015 had two main grants programmes:

Mid-life Mental Health
This fund focuses on the mental health needs of people in middle age, focusing on the following priorities:
- Piloting new interventions and services
- Supporting people in crisis
- Breaking down barriers and taboos
- Developing skills and employment opportunities
- Creating communities for mutual support

Caring for Carers
This programme focuses on the health and well-being needs of unpaid adult carers, focusing in particular on the following priorities:
- Piloting and extending new interventions and services
- Supporting the health and well-being of carers through exercise, diet and nutrition
- Creating communities for mutual support
- Improving support for carers in the workplace

Further details of the projects funded so far in both programmes can be found on the website.

Living well
At the time of writing (February 2017), the foundation was also in the process of developing a new funding programme focusing on the theme of 'Living Well'.

Financial information
In 2015 the foundation had assets of £235,000 and an income of £460,500. Grants were made totalling £106,000, with a further £230,000 committed.

Beneficiaries were not included in the accounts, but are listed on the website.

Beneficiaries have included: Age UK Enfield; Asian Lone Women Parents Association; Bipolar UK; Carers UK; Cascade Theatre Company; Down to Earth; Men's Health Forum; Sinfonia Viva; The Dove Service; Tomorrow's People Trust.

Exclusions
The website states that the following will not be funded by the foundation:
- Work that does not fall within the scope of the Bupa UK Foundation's charitable purposes
- Work that is not clearly aligned with the stated funding priorities of a specific funding programme
- Projects delivered outside of the UK
- Long-term projects and initiatives – we expect the vast majority of projects funded to be delivered within 12 to 18 months
- Work being delivered by local authorities and housing associations
- Work which might reasonably be eligible for funding from statutory bodies
- General awareness and information campaigns
- Sponsorship of or attendance at meetings, events and conferences
- Fundraising appeals, including requests for contributions to capital or equipment costs
- Unrestricted funding for charities or other organisations
- Educational bursaries or grants for university or postgraduate education, school trips or projects, gap year or elective year projects
- Academic research, including funding for educational or research posts

Applications
Applicants should first refer to the website to see which grants programmes are currently open for application, and where specific eligibility criteria and deadlines for each can be found.

Applicants can submit an initial expression of interest online. Applicants will be notified whether they are invited to submit a more detailed application within six weeks of the closing date for Stage 1 applications. Final decisions are made by the trustees.

The Burberry Foundation

Young people

£900,000 (2015/16)

Beneficial area
UK; Brazil; Hong Kong; Japan; Korea; USA.

Correspondent: Foundation Director, Burberry Ltd, Horseferry House, Horseferry Road, London SW1P 2AW (email: enquiries@burberryfoundation.com; website: uk.burberry.com/foundation/the-foundation)

CC number: 1154468

General information
The Burberry Foundation was registered with the Charity Commission in 2013 and is the corporate charity of Burberry Group.

Grants
The foundation makes grants to charities focusing on young people, particularly focusing on innovative charities, with

the aim of building sustainable partnerships, according to the 2015/16 annual report.

The annual report states that the foundation supports organisations which help young people to:

- Gain confidence in their daily lives and develop self-esteem
- Build connections to their families, friends, partners and society at large
- Develop the ability to reach for opportunities in school, work and life

The foundation has a particular preference for projects which:

- Are managed competently through accountability, cost effectiveness, strong leadership and creativity
- Provide a significant and measurable impact
- Are located in a community where Burberry Group employees live and work
- Have the potential to offer volunteering opportunities to Burberry Group employees

Organisations which receive a grant often also receive volunteer support from Burberry employees or in-kind donations from the group. Grants are usually made to registered charities; however, other organisations may be considered if it can be demonstrated that the grant will be used wholly for charitable purposes.

Burberry Create

The foundation also runs its own initiative with young people, Burberry Create, working in partnership with charities. This is a six to eight week programme for young people, providing creative training, work experience and opportunities to build skills, confidence and aspirations.

Financial information

In 2015/16 the foundation had assets of £6.5 million and an income of £2.8 million. Grants in the UK totalled £900,000 and were made to seven organisations.

Beneficiaries in the UK were: County Durham Groundwork and Place2Be (£250,000 each); City Year UK (£200,000); IntoUniversity, National Theatre, Spear – Resurgo Trust and The Prince's Trust (£50,000 each).

The accounts also include the foundation's international activities. Grants were also made in the following countries:

- In Hong Kong, grants totalling £185,000 were made to three organisations
- In China, a grant of £150,000 was made to one organisation
- In Korea, a grant of £125,000 was made to one organisation
- In the USA, grants totalling £116,000 were made to three organisations
- In Brazil, a grant of £20,000 was made to one organisation

Applications

Apply in writing to the correspondent.

The Cadbury Foundation

Education, training and employment, sport, sustainable environment, general charitable purposes

£663,000 (2015)

Beneficial area

UK and overseas.

Correspondent: Kelly Farrell, Community Affairs Manager, Cadbury Ltd, PO BOX 12, Bourneville, Birmingham B30 2LU (tel: 0121 787 2421; email: kelly.farrell@mdlz.com)

CC number: 1050482

General information

The Cadbury Foundation was set up in 1935 in recognition of the company founders George and Richard Cadbury and their investment in the welfare of their employees and wider communities. In 2010 Kraft Foods Inc. gained control of Cadbury PLC. In 2012 Kraft Foods Inc. was split into Kraft Food Group PLC and Mondelēz which now funds the Cadbury Foundation.

The following information is given in the 2015 annual report:

> The Cadbury Foundation contributes to communities near the Company's operations so that where possible donations can be backed up with employee volunteering work and gifts in kind. Grants are made by the Trustees whose current focus is on the four pillars:
>
> - Skill Development – giving an awareness of the world of work and enhancing the ability of young people and disadvantaged adults to gain and sustain employment
> - Olympic and Paralympic Legacy – to build stronger, healthier communities through sport
> - Source Projects – supporting the development of sustainable cocoa growing communities where Mondelēz International sources its cocoa and coffee beans
> - Employee Passions – some funds are reserved for employee-related grants and cash match where Company volunteers can either have their fundraising efforts matched, or where they can bid for a grant to support the work of a chosen charity
>
> Typical grants range from £10,000 to £30,000; with flagship charities which are strongly aligned with the Foundation's themes receiving larger donations of up to £100,000. Increasingly grants are made for specific projects to achieve identified objectives on an agreed timescale. This allows for proper evaluation and can be the basis for effective partnership over a number of years. All objectives and activities are reviewed on an ongoing basis and charity partners are asked to submit progress reports prior to each trustee meeting (tri-annual).
>
> In considering projects for support, the Foundation considers value-for-money in terms of attaining maximum community benefit. The Foundation is guided in making its selections for grant-giving by the demonstration of factors such as genuine community need, benefit for 'at risk' client groups or areas of social deprivation and those who will obtain the maximum community benefit from an association with the charity.
>
> The Foundation also works with major community partners to develop clear objectives and assess outcomes. Outcome measurements might include: number of people reached by the project, improvement in performance levels, evaluation rating by recipients, impact of the charity's involvement and community partner efficiency.

Financial information

In 2015 the foundation had assets of £121,000 and an income of £650,000 which included 600,000 from Mondelēz UK Holdings and Services Ltd. Grants to 33 organisations totalled £663,000.

Beneficiaries included: Taste of Work (£100,000); British Paralympic Association (£99,000); Grocery Aid (£75,000); Ready For Work (25,000); Birmingham Settlement (£10,000); Aspire 2, Irish Grocers Benevolent Fund, and Launchpad (£5,000 each); Special Needs Adventure Playground and Cocoa Life Source Project (£3,000 each).

Applications

The foundation actively seeks out projects to support and, therefore, cannot accept any unsolicited requests for funding. The 2015 annual report explains as follows:

> The Trustees' approach is to actively seek projects to support and therefore do not accept unsolicited applications for funding on an ad hoc basis. It is partly the elimination of 'token' grants in response to applications that has enabled the Foundation to provide more substantial support – and 'really make a difference' – in its chosen areas of activity.

The Cadogan Charity

General charitable purposes, in particular, social welfare, medical research, service charities, animal welfare, education and conservation and the environment

£1.98 million (2015/16)

Beneficial area

Worldwide. In practice, UK with a preference for London and Scotland.

Correspondent: Paul Loutit, Secretary, The Cadogan Group, 10 Duke of York Square, London SW3 4LY (tel: 020 7730 4567; email: paul.loutit@cadogan.co.uk)

Trustees: Rt. Hon. The Earl Cadogan; Countess Cadogan; Viscount Chelsea; Lady Anna Thomson; The Hon. William Cadogan.

CC number: 247773

General information

The trust was established in 1966 for general charitable purposes and operates two funds namely, the general fund and the rectors' fund. The rectors' fund was created with a gift from Cadogan Holdings Company in 1985 to pay an annual amount to one or any of the rectors of Holy Trinity Church – Sloane Street, St Luke's Church and Chelsea Old Church. The general fund provides support for registered charities in a wide range of areas (see below).

Financial information

In 2015/16 the trust had assets of £66.6 million and an income of almost £3 million. The trust made 84 grants totalling £1.98 million which were categorised as follows:

Social welfare in the community	38	£1.4 million
Medical research	25	£287,500
Military charities	7	£209,500
Education	6	£47,000
Animal welfare	5	£42,000
Conservation and the environment	3	£25,000

Beneficiaries included: Natural History Museum (£600,000); Historic Royal Palaces (£250,000); St Mary's Birnam (£15,000); Alzheimer's Research UK (£50,000); European Squirrel Initiative, Gurkha Welfare Trust and Parkinson's UK (£5,000 each); Addaction Family (£2,000); Family Holiday Association (£1,000).

Exclusions

No grants are provided to individuals.

Applications

Apply in writing to the correspondent.

Canary Wharf Contractors Fund

Communities, social welfare and education, with a focus on people engaged in the construction industry

£215,000 (2014/15)

Beneficial area

UK, with a preference for East London.

Correspondent: Alan Ruddy, Ruddy Joinery Ltd, Enterprise Way, Flitwick, Bedford MK45 5BS (tel: 01525 716603)

Trustees: Cormac Maccrann; James Ward.

CC number: 1097007

General information

Registered with the Charity Commission in 2003, this is a corporate charity of Canary Wharf Group PLC. The fund supports those working in the construction industry, as well as community organisations in East London.

According to the 2014/15 accounts, the objects of the fund are as follows:

- The relief of poverty generally but with special regard to persons and their dependent families who have been or are employed in the building and engineering trades and professions
- The relief of sickness and distress of persons, who by reason of their work in or association with the building and engineering trades, have become partially or totally incapacitated through injury or illness
- To support the bereaved families of persons working in the building and engineering trades or who have retired but had previously worked in the building or engineering trades
- To foster and promote high educational and training standards in the fields of building, engineering and architecture

Financial information

In 2014/15 the fund had assets of £119,500 and an income of £358,000. Grants were made to 25 organisations totalling £215,000.

Beneficiaries included: Barts Charity (£55,000); WheelPower (£44,000); Chickenshed (£20,500); Lighthouse – The Construction Industry Charity (£20,000); Advocacy for All and West Ham Ltd Community Sports Trust (£5,000 each); Bethnal Green Sharks (£1,500); Docklands Sailing Centre and WHC Social Club (£1,000 each); Tee2Green Academy (£600).

Applications

Apply in writing to the correspondent. The 2014/15 annual report states: 'Applicants are invited to submit a summary of their proposals in a specific format.' The trustees meet at least quarterly to assess applications.

The Costain Charitable Foundation

General charitable purposes, with a particular focus on health

Beneficial area

UK

Correspondent: Catherine Warbrick, Corporate Responsibility Director and Trustee, Costain House, Vanwall Business Park, Maidenhead, Berkshire SL6 4UB (tel: 07824 303378; email: costainfoundation@costain.com; website: www.costain.com/our-culture/the-costain-charitable-foundation)

Trustees: Alison Wood; Geoffrey Hunt; Catherine Warbrick; Tracey Wood.

CC number: 1159056

General information

This charity was set up by the Costain Group, an engineering solutions provider based in the UK, to celebrate its 150th anniversary in 2015.

The group ran the 150 Challenge in 2015, which aimed to raise £1 million during the year for charities. Employees raised over £600,000 and Costain Group PLC donated a further £500,000.

The website provides details of how to apply to be one of the foundation's charity partners, and states that it has a preference 'to only support charities and other non-profit organisations that have long-term goals and objectives'.

It would appear that a select group of beneficiaries are to be chosen each year. In 2015 funds raised were to be split equally between four major national charities, these being: the British Heart Foundation; Macmillan Cancer Support; The Prince's Trust; and Samaritans. The website states that in 2017, the foundation is supporting Cancer Research UK.

Financial information

In 2015 the foundation had assets of £1 million and an income of £1.1 million. Expenditure during the year totalled £4,600 but a figure was not provided for the grants made. At the time of writing (February 2017), the website states that £1.1 million was raised for the four chosen charities in total.

Beneficiaries were: British Heart Foundation; Macmillan Cancer Support; Samaritans; The Prince's Trust.

Exclusions

The website states that the foundation will only support charities or non-profit organisations which satisfy the following:

- [Are] not involved in the abuse of human rights
- Do not have employment policies or practices that discriminate on grounds of race, creed, sexual orientation, religion, gender, disability or age
- Do not discriminate unfairly in the allocation of their support according to race, creed, sexual orientation, religion, gender, disability or age
- Are not directly involved in gambling, recreational or illegal drugs, tobacco, armaments or alcohol (with the exception of those charities and organisations specifically dedicated to tackling addiction or drug abuse)
- Do not cause harm to animals for the purposes of either sport or entertainment
- Do not have, as their main purpose, the dissemination of political or religious information and do not otherwise use their charitable work to encourage support for political or religious causes
- Do not have activities which involve significant damage to the environment
- Fully disclose all relevant corporate and personal conflicts of interest

Applications

The Costain 150 Challenge website states the following: 'The application window for sponsorship from the Costain Charitable Foundation in 2018 opens on 03 July 2017 and will close on 15 September 2017. Applications before or after this date will not be considered.'

The website states that applications should be sent in writing, including: the organisation's aims, most recent income, expenditure and current financial position; and an outline of the project for which funding is required (why it is needed, who will benefit, etc.). No supporting material (such as annual reports, accounts, DVDs or brochures) should be sent with an application. Applicants will be notified within eight weeks if they have been shortlisted; otherwise, applicants must assume they have not been successful.

We would suggest that interested parties refer to the website for current information.

Coutts Charitable Foundation

Women and girls

£855,000 (2015/16)

Beneficial area

UK and communities where Coutts has a presence overseas.

Correspondent: Kay Boland, Administrator, Coutts & Co., 440 Strand, London WC2R 0QS (tel: 020 7957 2822; email: coutts.foundation@coutts.com; website: www.coutts.com/coutts-foundation.html)

Trustees: Sir Christopher Geidt; Dr Linda Yueh; Lord Waldegrave of North Hill; Leslie Gent; Michael Morley; Ali Hammad; Alison Rose; Thomas Kenrick; Peter Flavel; Camilla Stowell.

CC number: 1150784

General information

Coutts & Co. is a private bank and wealth manager. It is one of the world's oldest banks (founded 1692) and is wholly owned by the Royal Bank of Scotland Group. Headquartered in London, Coutts is the wealth division of the Royal Bank of Scotland Group, with clients from over 40 offices in financial centres in the UK, Switzerland, the Middle East and Asia.

Areas of work

Coutts Charitable Foundation was established in February 2013 and registered with the Charity Commission in the same month. The following information is taken from the Coutts website:

> The mission of the Coutts Foundation is to support sustainable approaches to tackle the causes and consequences of poverty, focusing on the communities where Coutts has a presence. This mission builds on the legacy of Angela Burdett-Coutts, the grand-daughter of Thomas Coutts, who was a progressive 19th-century philanthropist concerned with breaking cycles of poverty and providing basic human needs. At this time the core focus of the Foundation is supporting women and girls in the UK.
>
> The Coutts Foundation makes significant commitments to a small number of organisations that reflect its mission. At this time the core focus of the foundation is supporting women and girls in the UK.

Financial information

In 2015/16 the foundation had assets of £2.9 million and an income of almost £1.6 million. Grants were made to 11 organisations totalling £855,000.

Beneficiaries included: Citizens UK (£150,000); Southall Black Sisters Trust (£120,000); Working Chance (£105,000); Safe Lives Ltd and The Fairlight Trust Anawim (£90,000 each); End Violence Against Women Coalition and Women For Refugee Women (£75,000 each); Women Centre Calderdale and Kirklees (£30,000); Sentebale (£20,000); City Gateway (£10,000).

Applications

The following information is provided on the foundation's website:

> The Coutts Foundation adopts a proactive approach to its philanthropy and in its identification of organisations to support. It is especially interested in organisations that are developing innovative solutions and/or those whose successful work has the potential to be scaled up.
>
> At this stage, the Foundation does not accept unsolicited proposals for funding. However, if you wish to bring information about your organisation or programmes that fit with our funding priorities to our attention, please complete the information submission form and either email it to us or post it to:
>
> Kay Boland, Coutts Foundation, 440 Strand, London WC2R 0QS
>
> The Coutts Foundation will be in touch if we would like to learn more about your organisation.

The information submission form is available to download on the foundation's website.

Coventry Building Society Charitable Foundation

General charitable purposes, social welfare, community causes, disadvantaged and vulnerable individuals, mental health, disability, young people, older individuals

£60,000 (2015)

Beneficial area

Midlands

Correspondent: Alison Readman, Secretary, Coventry Building Society, Oak Tree Court, Binley Business Park, Binley, Coventry CV3 2UN (tel: 024 7643 5231; website: www.coventrybuildingsociety.co.uk/your-society/community.aspx#tabs-3)

Trustees: Darin Landon; Thomas Crane.

CC number: 1072244

General information

The foundation was launched in 1998 and is entirely funded by the Coventry Building Society; however, it is a separate entity managed by a board of trustees who determine the policies and decide on the grants to be made. The grant-making is administered by Heart of England Community Foundation.

The following information is taken from the funder's website and the annual report:

The foundation supports a wide range of causes based, or active, in the Midlands, with a preference for smaller local charities (charities with an annual income in excess of £250,000 are not supported). It makes donations only to registered charities that are based or active within the region covered by Coventry Building Society's branch network. Awards are generally small –

only in exceptional circumstances up to £3,000 may be awarded.

Priority is given to 'groups or activities aimed at improving the quality of life and opportunity among groups who are disadvantaged or deprived, the consequence of which may lead to social exclusion'.

The funder's website indicates that applications that focus on the following are welcome:

- Young people, particularly those who are disadvantaged
- Vulnerable groups, such as the frail older people, individuals with physical disability, people with learning difficulties or those with a mental illness
- Small neighbourhood groups in areas that are experiencing the greatest disadvantage
- Supporting communities and voluntary organisations through assisting them in the achievement of social and community development

Financial information

In 2015 the foundation had assets of £5,200 and an income of £60,000. A total of 14 grants were made totalling £60,000.

Beneficiaries were: Heart of England Community Foundation (£20,500); Birmingham and Black Country Community Foundation and Gloucestershire Community Foundation (£8,000 each); Oxfordshire Community Foundation (£6,000); Swindon and Wiltshire Community Foundation (£5,000); Quartet Community Foundation (£4,000); Leicestershire and Rutland Community Foundation and Northamptonshire Community Foundation (£1,500 each); Milton Keynes Community Foundation, Nottinghamshire Community Foundation, Somerset Community Foundation, South Yorkshire Community Foundation, Staffordshire Community Foundation and Wales Community Foundation (£1,000 each).

Exclusions

Grants are not made outside the Midlands area. The funder's website indicates that the following are not eligible for support:

- Large charities which enjoy national coverage
- Charities with no base within the branch area
- Charities with an annual donated income in excess of £250,000
- Charities with assets over £500,000
- Projects requiring ongoing commitment
- Large capital projects
- Maintenance or building works for buildings, gardens or playgrounds
- Major fundraising
- Projects which are normally the responsibility of other organisations such as NHS and local authorities
- Sponsorship of individuals
- Requests from individuals
- Replacing funds which were the responsibility of another body
- Educational institutions, unless for the relief of disadvantage
- Promotion of religious, political or military causes
- Sporting clubs or organisations, unless for the relief of disadvantage
- Medical research or equipment
- More than one donation to the same organisation in a year – further applications will be considered after a period of three years
- Animal welfare

Applications

Applications can be made online through the community foundation for your area. In order to do this, choose the area closest to where your charity operates from the table at the bottom of the foundation's website and click on the relevant link. This will take you to the relevant community foundation's website. There you will be able to find out more about your local community foundation and all of the information that you need to apply for a grant.

The foundation asks: 'If you have any queries about the application process please contact your local Community Foundation directly.'

The grants panel from each Community Foundation meet on a bimonthly or quarterly basis to consider applications. All applications are acknowledged.

Credit Suisse EMEA Foundation

Education and training, young people

£1.5 million (2015)

Beneficial area

Countries where Credit Suisse has offices, in Europe, the Middle East and Africa.

Correspondent: Kate Butchart, Credit Suisse, 1 Cabot Square, London E14 4QJ (email: emea.corporatecitizenship@credit-suisse.com)

Trustees: Stefano Toffolo; Patrick Flaherty; Michelle Mendelsson; Nicholas Wilcock; Markus Lammer; Colin Hely-Hutchinson; Ian Dembinski; Mark Ellis; Marisa Drew; Marc Pereira-Mendoza.

CC number: 1122472

General information

The foundation was established by Credit Suisse and channels the group's corporate citizenship activities in Europe, the Middle East and Africa.

According to the 2015 accounts, the foundation supports 'innovative organisations providing opportunities to youth through education' and 'projects and organisations that aim to improve the educational attainment, employability and aspirations of young disadvantaged people'.

Grants are usually made to registered charities (although other charitable organisations may be considered occasionally). The foundation looks to provide funding for two to five years if possible and 'follow on funding' may be offered to charities which meet the foundation's priorities effectively. Grants may be given for specific projects or for core costs and salaries.

The foundation also makes grants for the Credit Suisse group's Charity of the Year programme, and occasionally for other charities nominated by employees.

Financial information

In 2015 the foundation had assets of £1.1 million and an income of £1.7 million, most of which came from Credit Suisse AG, with a small amount from investments. Grants were made to eight organisations totalling £1.5 million.

Beneficiaries included: Fight for Peace (£333,000); Scope (£299,000); LEAP South Africa (£220,000); ThinkForward UK (£200,000); Rock Your Company (£194,500); Polish Children and Youth Foundation (£164,000); Orphan Opportunity Fund – Step Up (£39,500); Disasters Emergency Committee – Nepal Earthquake Appeal (£10,000).

Exclusions

According to the foundation's 2015 accounts, grants will not be made for the following purposes:

- To directly replace or subsidise statutory funding or for activities that are the responsibility of statutory bodies
- Administration and costs not directly associated with the application
- Individuals
- Promotion of religious or political causes
- Holidays
- Retrospective funding
- General appeals
- Animal welfare
- Festivals, sports and leisure activities

Applications

Apply in writing to the correspondent.

The Peter Cruddas Foundation

Children and young people

£453,000 (2015/16)

Beneficial area

UK, with a particular interest in London.

Correspondent: Stephen Cox, Administrator, 133 Houndsditch, London EC3A 7BX (tel: 020 3003 8360; fax: 020 3003 8580; email: s.cox@petercruddasfoundation.org.uk; website: www.petercruddasfoundation.org.uk)

Trustees: Lord David Young, Chair; Peter Cruddas; Martin Paisner.

CC number: 1117323

General information

Established in December 2006, this is the charitable foundation of Peter Cruddas, founder of City financial trading group CMC Markets, who has pledged to donate at least £100 million to good causes during his lifetime. Since December 2006 in excess of £13 million has already been donated and/or committed to numerous charitable causes.

The foundation provides the following information in the 2015/16 accounts about its funding priorities:

> The Foundation gives priority to programmes calculated to help disadvantaged young people to pursue their education (including vocational) and more generally develop their potential whether through sport or recreation, voluntary programmes or otherwise. Preference will be given to the support of projects undertaken by charitable organizations for the benefit of such people.
>
> The Foundation adopts a Priority Funding Programme scheme for unsolicited applications and it is available for review on the Foundation's web site. The programmes are subject to Trustee review at any time.
>
> In addition to financial funding, The Foundation has provided mentoring support to many organisations through The Foundation Administrator's experience in the Third Sector.
>
> The Foundation will also be continuing to research and develop where its grants have most impact on beneficiaries, especially at grass roots level, in support of smaller charities with clear aims and objectives in line with the criteria described above.

The foundation's priority funding streams are listed on its website as:

- Pathways/support for young disadvantaged or disengaged young people in the age range 14 to 30 into education, training or employment
- Work experience/skills projects for young people aged 16 to 30
- Youth work in London; particularly evening work for disadvantaged young people aged 16 to 30

Financial information

In 2015/16 the foundation had assets of £11,000 and an income of £522,700 from donations from CMC Markets UK PLC and Peter Cruddas. There were 38 grants made totalling £453,000.

Beneficiaries included: Royal Opera House Foundation (207,500 in five grants); Great Ormond Street Hospital Children's Charity (£34,500 in two grants); Harris Manchester College (£20,000); Bootstrap Company (£10,000); Ignite Trust, Renaissance Foundation, The Royal Aero Club Trust, Woolf Institute (£5,000 each); Bounce Back Foundation (£2,500); Nikki's Wishes (2,000).

Exclusions

The following are excluded: capital projects; CICs; and social enterprises.

Applications

Application forms are available to download from the foundation's website: www.petercruddasfoundation.org.uk/how_to_apply.htm.

The foundation provides guidance on how to complete the application form, also available on the website. Application forms must be sent by email, postal applications are only accepted in exceptional circumstances.

The De La Rue Charitable Trust

Social welfare, international development, education, communities, disasters and humanitarian aid

£70,000 (2015/16)

Beneficial area

Internationally, within given categories.

Correspondent: Trust Administrator, De La Rue House, Jays Close, Basingstoke, Hampshire RG22 4BS (tel: 01256 605000; email: appeals.secretary@uk.delarue.com; website: www.delarue.com)

Trustees: Bill Taylor; Ed Peppiatt; Amanda Wiltshire; Sarah Gilbert; Francis Carne.

CC number: 274052

General information

The trust is the corporate charity of De La Rue PLC and was established by the group in 1977.

The trust makes grants to registered charities, generally under the following criteria, as stated on the website:

> - Well-researched causes in under-developed countries, preferably through UK charities to secure both financial control and tax relief
> - Educational charities which promote relevant skills and international understanding, particularly for the benefit of disadvantaged and underprivileged students
> - Disaster funds
> - Local charities or community projects, particularly if employees are involved
> - Charities for the benefit, directly or indirectly, of employees or ex-employees

Financial information

In 2015/16 the trust had assets of £33,500 and an income of £61,000. Grants were made to organisations totalling £70,000.

Beneficiaries included: AfriKids; Cameo Aid; Cecily's Fund; Concern Universal – Bangladesh; DEC – Nepal; Disability Africa; Handicapped Children's Action Group; International Refugee Trust; Newcastle Society for the Blind; Second Chance; Their Future Today; Zambia Orphans Aid.

Exclusions

The trust does not usually support:

- Partisan political organisations
- Organisations that do not directly benefit some aspect of the community in an area where De La Rue operates
- Individuals
- Grant-makers
- National charities
- Military or religious organisations

Applications

Apply in writing to the correspondent. The website states that applications should:

> - Provide evidence of charitable status
> - Provide information about the organisation, what it does and who it seeks to help
> - Provide copies of audited accounts where possible
> - Provide an indication of the amount of donation being sought with specific details where possible of what the requested donation will be used to fund, rather than a request to go into a general fund
> - Provide, where possible, an indication of the planned timings of the project in question

The trust will get in touch if clarification is needed, or if an application has been successful. However, as it receives over 100 applications each year, it is not able to respond to every application.

Debenhams Foundation

Health, social welfare

Beneficial area

UK

Correspondent: Lisa Hunt, Debenhams PLC, 10 Brock Street, London NW1 3FG (tel: 020 3549 7891; email: lisa.hunt@debenhams.com; website: sustainability.debenhamsplc.com/debenhams-foundation)

CC number: 1147682

General information

Established in 2012 this is the charitable foundation of Debenhams Retail PLC, the department store chain. The foundation receives its income from both Debenhams Retail PLC and Debenhams Retail (Ireland) Ltd, as well as from Debenhams' customers, employees, suppliers and partners, and uses it to fund causes 'that focus on preserving and protecting health and relieving financial hardships primarily, but not exclusively, by making grants of money'.

It is described in the foundation's 2014/15 annual report that the foundation raises money:

> Through a mixture of product sales and fundraising in Debenhams stores and online, head office fundraising events (such as cake sales and cosmetic events) and supplier fundraising events such as Debenhams Foundation Ball, the Debenhams Foundation aims to primarily raise money for its key charity partners which reflect the causes that Debenhams' customers hold.

During 2014/15 Debenhams' key charity partners were BBC Children in Need, Help for Heroes, Pink Ribbon Foundation, Breakthrough Breast Cancer, Breast Cancer Campaign and Breast Cancer Now. The foundation also supports Fashion Targets Breast Cancer and charities operating in 'the Debenhams store community'.

The foundation supports some projects, which are monitored regularly, over multiple years, while other projects are funded on a one-off basis at the trustees' discretion.

Financial information

In 2014/15 the foundation had assets of £303,500 and an income of almost £1.68 million. Charitable activities amounted to £1.6 million, more than £1.4 million of which was expended in support of Debenhams' charity partners (see above). We could not determine precisely how much was expended directly in grants, but could see from the accounts that 19 charities benefitted during the year.

Other beneficiaries included: Debenhams Retirement Association (£75,000); Make a Wish Foundation (£51,500); Disasters Emergency Committee (£12,700); Cornerstone (£2,700); Hollie Gazzard Trust (£1,200); Hope for Tomorrow (£700); Beatson Cancer Charity, Michael Sobell Hospice and Rowcroft Hospice (£500 each); Look Good Feel Better (£90).

Applications

The annual report for 2014/15 explains that 'charitable fundraising is generally organised locally and colleagues in store work closely with local community charities. In addition, the trustees supported major appeals this year and have co-ordinated stores' fundraising' for Debenhams' charity partners.

The Desmond Foundation (formerly known as the RD Crusaders Foundation)

General charitable purposes, especially for the relief of poverty and sickness among children, and Jewish causes

£904,000 (2015)

Beneficial area

Worldwide

Correspondent: Allison Racher, Correspondent, Northern & Shell Media Group Ltd, The Northern & Shell Building, 10 Lower Thames Street, London EC3R 6EN (tel: 020 8612 7760; email: allison.racher@express.co.uk)

CC number: 1014352

General information

Registered with the Charity Commission in 1992, the RD Crusaders Foundation was renamed the Desmond Foundation in 2013.

The trustees of the charity are Richard Desmond, the owner of Express Newspapers and founder of Northern & Shell, Northern & Shell Services Ltd and Northern & Shell Media Group Ltd. The accounts for 2015 explain that 'RD Crusaders Ltd, a company wholly owned by [Richard] Desmond, was incorporated in December 2007 with the purpose of fundraising on behalf of the charity'.

The Northern & Shell website states:

> Northern & Shell Chairman Richard Desmond takes a personal and active interest in every charity supported and the Trust processes requests and assesses where funds should best be made available.
>
> The aim of the Richard Desmond Charitable Trust is to use donations in a focused and informed way to realize the greatest possible benefit to recipients. Its strategy is to allocate funds to a large number of smaller charities so that the money goes straight to the people who need it.
>
> In recent years the trust has focused its awards on children and young people's charities in the UK and has contributed extensively to further the wellbeing of disadvantaged sections of society, however larger charities have also benefited extensively with donations to schools, hospitals, old people's homes, carer organisations, hospices and a wide range of medical support groups.
>
> Children's charities remain the focus of the Richard Desmond Charitable Trust but consideration is given by the Trustees to worthy causes outside this area, so long as the funds awarded can make a difference.

Financial information

In 2015 the foundation had assets of £1.76 million and an income of £2.14 million. The annual report states: 'In 2015, 57 grants totalling £903,788 were made, including large donations to Canal & River Trust, Centre for Vision in the Developing World, Fight for Sight, UJIA, and World Jewish Relief.' Included in the grant total were 21 grants of less than £1,000 each, which totalled £7,600. Grants were distributed as follows:

Community	30	£700,500
Education	21	£190,000
Miscellaneous	6	£13,500

Beneficiaries include: Canal and River Trust (£237,500); World Jewish Relief (£187,500); UJIA (United Jewish Israel Appeal) (£100,000); Centre for Vision in the Developing World and Fight for Sight (£50,000 each); Sue Ryder (£40,000); Variety, the Children's Charity (£27,000); Wellbeing of Women (£15,000); Diabetes UK and The Wallace Collection (£10,000 each); Children with Cancer and Haven House Foundation (£5,000 each); Care After Combat (£1,800); Guide Dogs Saffron Walden (£1,000).

Applications

Apply in writing to the correspondent. All grant requests are considered and awards made are based on the merits of each proposal.

The Laduma Dhamecha Charitable Trust

General charitable purposes

£1.5 million (2015/16)

Beneficial area

UK and overseas.

Correspondent: Pradip Dhamecha, Trustee, The Dhamecha Group, 2 Hathaway Close, Stanmore, Middlesex HA7 3NR (tel: 020 8903 8181; email: info@dhamecha.com)

CC number: 328678

General information

The trust was founded by the Dhamecha family who founded and operate the Dhamecha cash and carry group based in Greater London. The trust supports a wide range of organisations in the UK and overseas. The aims of the trust are listed in the annual report as being:

- To provide relief of sickness by the provision of medical equipment and the establishing or improvement of facilities at hospitals
- To provide for the advancement of education and/or an educational establishment in rural areas to make children self-sufficient in the long term
- Other general charitable purposes

Financial information

In 2015/16 the trust had assets of £533,000 and an income of £594,000 mainly from donations including £451,000 from Dhamecha Foods Ltd. Grants totalled £1.5 million. Awards were made to UK organisations totalling £438,000 and to organisations and projects outside the UK totalling £1.1 million.

No further information was available on the size or number of beneficiaries during this year.

Applications

Apply in writing to the correspondent.

The Diageo Foundation

General charitable purposes, education and training, disaster relief, community development

£800,000 (2014/15)

Beneficial area

Worldwide

Correspondent: Lynne Smethurst, Head of Community Investment, Diageo PLC, Lakeside Drive, Park Royal, London NW10 7HQ (tel: 020 8978 6000; email: diageofoundation@diageo.com; website: www.diageo.com)

CC number: 1014681

General information

Diageo PLC is an international manufacturer and distributor of premium drinks. The foundation is a registered charity funded entirely by Diageo. It makes grants in support of projects or causes proposed by Diageo businesses and externally.

The following was taken from the foundation's website:

> The Foundation is a registered charity funded entirely by Diageo. The Foundation prioritises its activity in Africa, Latin America, and Asia. The Foundation's programmes focus on access to water and sanitation (WASH), skills and employability and Female empowerment.

The foundation also supports disaster relief and local charitable causes, particularly in regions where employees of Diageo are affected.

Financial information

In 2014/15 the foundation had an income of £676,500 and expenditure of £867,000. At the time of writing (June 2016), accounts for the year were not available to view on the Charity Commission's website; we estimate that the amount of grants totalled around £850,000.

Previous beneficiaries have included: Desnoes and Geddes Foundation (£266,500); Antigua and Barbuda Hospital (£48,500); Idejen (Haiti) (£12,000); Samarthanam Trust (£5,200); Sports for Special Needs (£1,500).

Applications

The website states: 'The Diageo Foundation is not accepting unsolicited applications. We are currently sourcing new investments through recommendations from experts, donors and existing partners, and through detailed research.'

The James Dyson Foundation

Science, engineering, medical research, and education

£2.4 million including organisations, bursaries and foundation awards (2015)

Beneficial area

The foundation gives worldwide but has a preference for the UK, particularly around its headquarters of Malmesbury.

Correspondent: Kevin Walker, Administrator, Dyson Group PLC, Tetbury Hill, Malmesbury, Wiltshire SN16 0RP (tel: 01666 828416; email: jamesdysonfoundation@dyson.com; website: www.jamesdysonfoundation.com)

CC number: 1099709

General information

This company foundation was set up in 2002 to promote charitable giving, especially to charities working in the fields of science, engineering, medicine and education.

The 2015 annual report states:

> The objects of the foundation, as stated in its governing document, are as follows:
>
> - To advance education and training, particularly in the fields of design and technology – this work can take a number of forms including the free provision of support resources for teachers of design and technology in schools, the running of design engineering workshops and lectures in schools and universities, as well as bursary schemes and collaborative projects
> - To support medical and scientific research
> - To support charitable and educational projects in the region in which the foundation operates

Each year, the foundation donates a number of Dyson vacuum cleaners (for raffle prizes) to charitable causes which fall within its objectives. The cost of these is included in the total grants figure. Small grants may also be made to charitable projects that share the philosophies and objectives of the foundation. The foundation also works with schools and universities, providing bursaries and educational activities and events, and runs the annual James Dyson Award, a design engineering competition for students.

Financial information

In 2015 the foundation had a total deficit of £7.5 million and an income of £5.5 million. Grants, including foundation awards and student bursaries paid to institutions, totalled £2.4 million and were distributed in three categories as follows:

Education and training	£2.3 million
Science and medical research	£106,500
Social and community welfare	£7,100

Beneficiaries included: Cambridge University (£1.4 million); Postgraduate Bursaries (£249,500); Royal College of Art (£50,000); Malmesbury School Project (£42,000); Undergraduate Bursaries (£24,000); The Blue Star Trust and The Star and Storm Foundation

(£5,000 each); Imperial College London (£200).

Applications

Organisations can apply through the 'Contact' section of the foundation's website.

The Economist Charitable Trust

General charitable purposes, education and training, economic and community development, children and young people, older people, people with disabilities

£85,000 (2015/16)

Beneficial area

UK

Correspondent: The Trustees of the Economist Charitable Trust, The Economist Group, 25 St James's Street, London SW1A 1HG (tel: 020 7576 8546; website: www.economist.com)

Trustees: Ada Simkins; Kiran Malik; Daniel Franklin; Cecelia Block; Susan Clark.

CC number: 293709

General information

The Economist Newspaper Ltd is a multinational media company specialising in international business and world affairs. Its principal activities are newspapers, magazines, conferences and market intelligence.

The Economist Charitable Trust was established in 1985 and its principal activity is the disbursement of monies received from the Economist Newspaper Ltd to various charities. 50–60% of the trust's donations go to charities in the fields of communication, education, literacy and retraining for individuals and groups who are disadvantaged in some way. Approximately 30–40% of funds are used to match donations made by employees of the Economist Group. Remaining funds are utilised to make small donations to small and local charities.

Financial information

In 2015/16 the trust had assets of £19,200 and an income of £104,000, mostly from the Economist Newspaper Ltd. There were grants made totalling £85,000. The average donation made in this year was £612. Details of the beneficiaries were not available.

Applications

The trust does not accept unsolicited applications.

EDF Energy Trust (EDFET)

Fuel poverty, money/debt advice, fuel debt prevention

£276,000 to organisations (2015)

Beneficial area

UK

Correspondent: The Trustees of EDF Energy Trust, Freepost EDF ENERGY TRUST (tel: 01733 421060; email: edfet@charisgrants.com; website: www.edfenergytrust.org.uk)

Trustees: Denise Fennell; Tim Cole; Brian Cross; Bob Richardson; Richard Sykes; David Hawkes; Vic Szewczyk; Peter Hofmann.

CC number: 1099446

General information

EDF Energy Trust, established in October 2003, makes grants to support individuals and families who are in 'need, poverty, suffering and distress who are struggling to pay their gas and/or electricity debts'. The trust's grants scheme is administered by Charis Grants Ltd.

Type of grants

Individuals and families

EDF Energy Trust's main grants programme is for individuals and families, providing grants for current domestic account holders of EDF Energy, with the aim of enabling them to stay debt-free moving forward. It is part of the 'Shared Programme of Giving', with a number of other utility providers, which allows for one application to be considered by any of the providers involved. According to the website, grants are made for the following purposes:

- To clear domestic gas and electricity debts to EDF Energy and other suppliers
- To purchase essential energy efficient white goods and cookers (known as Further Assistance Payments (FAP))
- For Bankruptcy and Debt Relief Order fees

Organisations

In addition to the individuals and families grants programme, the trust also provides grants for organisations to support its purposes. The 2015 annual report states grants are given to organisations for the following purposes:

- Provision of specialist money/debt advice and resolving energy debt problems for all clients
- Supporting EDF Energy customers to apply to the charity where appropriate
- Promoting the Charity to local organisations, developing partnerships for referrals
- Promotion of energy debt awareness and prevention

Details of current funding opportunities are posted on the trust's website. The 2015 annual report, states that the current three beneficiary organisations would receive funding until the end of 2016.

Financial information

In 2015 the trust had assets of almost £5 million and an income of £7.8 million. Grants were made to three organisations totalling £276,000. Grants were also made to 3,751 individuals and families totalling £2.7 million.

Beneficiaries included: Plymouth Citizens Advice (£106,000); Talking Money (£88,000); Thanet Citizens Advice (£82,000).

Exclusions

No grants are made to assist with: fines for criminal offences; overpayments of benefits; educational or training needs; business debts; debts to central government departments (e.g. tax and national insurance); catalogues, credit cards, personal loans and other forms of non-secured lending; medical equipment, aids and adaptations; deposits to secure accommodation; or holidays.

Applications

Grants for organisations are announced on the trust's website and in its newsletter as they come up. Alternatively, contact the trust for more information.

The easiest way to apply for grants for individuals is via the trust's online application form. Alternatively, you can print an application form to complete by hand which can be sent to the trust's freepost address or request one from the trust. Forms may also be available from some advice centres such as Citizens Advice.

The ERM Foundation

Environment, sustainable development

£30,500 (2015/16)

Beneficial area

UK and overseas.

Correspondent: Shona King, Administrator, ERM Group Holdings Ltd, Exchequer Court, 33 St Mary Axe, London EC3A 8AA (tel: 032065331; email: shona.king@erm.com; website: www.erm.com/foundation)

Trustees: Tassilo Metternich-Sandor; Robin Bidwell; John Simonson; Ian Bailey; Sabine Hoefnagel.

CC number: 1113415

General information

Registered in 2006, this is the charitable foundation of Environmental Resources Management Ltd, a global provider of environmental, health, safety, risk and social consulting services. The foundation's 2015/16 annual report states that its objectives are 'to provide human resources and/or financial assistance to projects around the world that contribute to the improvement of the earth's environment, quality of life and sustainable development', and that 'this is done through appropriate charitable, educational and technical endeavours'.

The following information was taken from the foundation's website:

> The ERM Foundation focuses on areas that align with the professional expertise and interests of ERM employees:
>
> - Low carbon development
> - Conservation and biodiversity
> - Water, sanitation and hygiene (WASH)
> - Environmental education
> - Empowering women and girls
>
> This year we have undergone a process to align our activities with the UN Sustainable Development Goals (SDGs), including a new focus on empowering women and girls.
>
> The ERM Foundation raises money from employees of ERM and other donors. ERM provides matching funds where those donations are raised by employees specifically for charitable purposes. The ERM Foundation is advised by a committee of specialists from ERM's current staff and alumni.
>
> The ERM Foundation also coordinates a variety of activities whereby ERM staff provide professional and volunteering support to environmental initiatives of benefit to local communities.
>
> A key programme of The ERM Foundation is the Low Carbon Enterprise Fund (LCEF), which supports enterprises in the developing world where entrepreneurs are seeking to build a low carbon business. The LCEF provides financial support (low interest loans and equity stakes) to these small businesses and also provides pro-bono management and technical support for a wide range of low carbon enterprises. The funds of The LCEF are designated for specific purposes therefore the income, expenditure and resources that are related to The LCEF are shown as designated.

Financial information

In 2015/16 the foundation has assets of around £950,000 ($1.2 million) and an income of £312,000 ($394,000) which included funds from the company and the value of donated services. Grants were made totalling around £30,500 with further charitable expenditure focused on support services through the LCEF.

Applications

Apply in writing to the correspondent.

Esh Foundation

Children and young people, vulnerable individuals, environmental community regeneration, education and skills development, health, community development

£87,500 (2015)

Beneficial area

North East England and Scotland.

Correspondent: Andrew Radcliffe, Secretary, Esh Holdings Ltd, Esh House, Bowburn North Industrial Estate, Bowburn, Durham DH6 5PF (tel: 07976 077621; email: enquiries@esh.uk.com; website: www.eshgroup.co.uk/added-value/community/esh-communities)

CC number: 1112040

General information

The foundation was set up in 2005. It is the charitable foundation of the Esh Group, a civil engineering, construction and house building company based in Durham. The company makes an annual grant and has committed to provide the foundation with £1 million over five years until 2017, subject to profits. The latest accounts note the following:

> Despite the continuing economic uncertainty, the directors of Esh Group were again pleased to grant £130,000 in further contributions during the year.
>
> In addition to the £130,000 from Esh Group, smaller contributions were received from local businesses and other individuals £5,567, as well as £44 in interest on cash deposits.

The 2015 accounts state that the trust supports the following areas of activity:

- Children and young people – groups and projects that help children and young people access activities and services
- Vulnerable people – groups and projects working with disadvantaged and isolated people, in particular providing increased access to services and facilities for people with disabilities, the homeless and the elderly
- Environmental community regeneration – groups and projects looking to improve local facilities for community use including refurbishment of community buildings and greening and opening up access to the local physical environment
- Education, capacity and skills development – group and community-based training and education programmes, particularly for those who have had no previous access to training opportunities, or for the longer-term unemployed
- Health – groups and community-based projects providing access to healthy eating, increased physical activity and self-help services, which aim to improve the health and well-being of local people

The trust makes grants of up to £1,000 to community groups and charities working in the communities where it operates – namely, North East England, Yorkshire, North West England and Scotland.

According to the website, in 2016/17 the trust is welcoming projects relating to the following objectives:

> - To improve the quality of life for local residents
> - To support disadvantaged or vulnerable communities
> - To increase prospects of becoming employed
> - Promoting equality by engaging minority and hard to reach groups

Financial information

In 2015 the foundation had assets of £63,500 and an income of £135,500, which included £130,000 from the company. There were 52 grants made totalling £87,500.

Beneficiaries included: Eagles Community Foundation (£20,000); SAFC Foundation (£8,000); British Transplant Games (£6,000); Butterwick Hospice and Durham County Cricket Club (£5,000); Artichoke Trust (£1,000); Bathgate Street Pastors, East Lothian Special Needs, Homelife Carlisle, Sicklinghall Village Hall, Sheffield Alcohol Support Group, The Conservation Volunteers and Whitley Bay Sea Cadets (£500 each); House of Light Post Natal Support (£400); Young Asian Voices (£300); Prescription Delivery Service (£250).

Applications

Apply in writing to the correspondent. The 2015 annual report states that trustees meet quarterly to consider all applications.

Applications can be made through the company's website: www.eshgroup.co.uk/added-value/community/esh-communities.

Refer to the website for the latest application deadlines.

Euro Charity Trust

Relief of poverty, social welfare, education, religion, health, overseas aid

£3.08 million to organisations (2015)

Beneficial area

Worldwide, mainly India and Africa (particularly Malawi).

Correspondent: Nasir Awan, Trustee, 20 Brickfield Road, Yardley, Birmingham B25 8HE (email: info@eurocharity.org.uk)

CC number: 1058460

General information

This trust, which is also known as ECT, receives the majority of its income from Euro Packaging Holdings Ltd. Euro Packaging has grown from a small paper-bag merchant into a large diversified packaging group. Paper-bag production commenced in 1984 and today the firm is the UK's largest manufacturer. It has its own facilities for polythene-bag manufacture, and also recycles both plastic and paper products.

Areas of work

The trust's objectives are:

- The relief of poverty
- The relief of older people, and people who are vulnerable (such as young children or anyone with special needs) or facing hardship
- The provision of basic necessities and amenities to those in need (for example, water, electricity and medical facilities)
- The advancement of education
- 'To assist in any purpose which would be considered to be charitable by the Charity Commissioners which the Trustees may from time to time decide that may be in need of assistance'

The three ways in which the trust works to achieve these objectives are explained in the trustees' report:

- **Grants** – 'ECT does not undertake direct project implementation; instead ECT gives grants in the form of donations primarily to non-governmental organisations (NGOs) who work to further objectives which are in line with that of ECT.' It is also described that in the long term, the trust will continue to support its work in India and projects in Africa, particularly Malawi, while also considering projects in other countries on a case-by-case basis. The trust will continue to focus on charitable work in the areas of: education; the provision of housing and accommodation for poor people; the provision of health and water facilities; and care for orphans and children who are in need
- **Educational support for deserving students** – 'ECT assists individual students in enabling them to enhance their education and to encourage students to continue the development of skills, knowledge and ability in order to further their career development which will in turn help them find a job. ECT assists with primary and secondary schooling and University education up to the end of the academic year in which a student takes G.C.S.E., A levels or a degree/ equivalent.'
- **Loans for educational and religious establishments** – 'The Trustees of ECT recognise that there is a need for religious institutions and therefore provides financial assistance establishing places of worship. In the UK and abroad, the support is usually in the form of a grant or loan.'

Financial information

In 2015 the trust had assets of £4.6 million and an income of 5.8 million. Grants were made totalling £3.1 million and included £24,500 given to individuals.

Grants were distributed as follows:

Education and sponsorship	£2.32 million
Construction of education/ training and religious establishments	£735,000
Welfare	£208,500
Medical provision	£50,000
Other activities	£1,200

Beneficiaries included: Nathani Charitable Trust (£2 million); Imdadul Muslimeen (£200,000).

Applications

Apply in writing to the correspondent.

The Fidelity UK Foundation

Support is mainly given in the fields of arts and culture, community development, education and health

£6.3 million (2015)

Beneficial area

UK with a strong preference for London, Kent and Surrey.

Correspondent: Sian Parry, Head of Foundations, Oakhill House, 130 Tonbridge Road, Hildenborough, Tonbridge, Kent TN11 9DZ (tel: 01732 777364; email: foundation@fil.com; website: www.fidelityukfoundation.org)

CC number: 327899

General information

This foundation was established in 1988 and primarily supports UK-registered charities based in areas where Fidelity Worldwide Investment has corporate offices: London; Kent and Surrey. Grant applications are also considered from registered charities based and operating in Manchester and Birmingham. See below for specific details.

Grants from the foundation are made only for charitable purposes and are designed to encourage the highest standards of management and long-term self-reliance in non-profit organisations. Taking an investment approach to grant-making, it funds organisations where it can add lasting, measurable value. The aim is to support major initiatives that charitable organisations undertake to reach new levels of achievement.

Grant programmes

The foundation's charitable giving is mainly in the areas of:

- Arts and culture – 'including the visual and performing arts, heritage, museums'
- Community development – 'including projects which help the young and/or disadvantaged achieve their potential'
- Education – 'including special educational needs'
- Health – 'including disability, chronic illness, palliative care'

The following information is provided on the foundation's website:

> ***Sector focus***
>
> Investment is typically directed to specific projects in the following categories:
>
> - **Capital improvements** such as new construction, renovations, expansions and equipment which are central to sustainability and the strategic vision of the organisation
> - High impact **information technology upgrades** which substantially increase an organisation's efficiency, effectiveness and sustainability
> - **Organisational development** projects which seek to establish a new, transformational strategic path. This can include helping charities to investigate and proceed with mergers
> - **Planning initiatives**, including those that use expert/external consultants
>
> Some international grants are made outside the UK by the FIL Foundation, which shares some administration with the Fidelity Foundation. The priorities and restrictions are similar and grants are made to established charities serving beneficiaries in Continental Europe, Australia, Japan, China, Hong Kong, Korea and Taiwan.
>
> ***Geographical focus***
>
> Grantees are typically, although not exclusively, mid-large charities operating

in locations in which Fidelity International has offices and other business interests. Although the majority of grantees are based in **London, Kent** and **Surrey**, applications are also considered from elsewhere in the UK, provided the organisation is a nationally-recognised centre of excellence with national coverage.

Scale of Organisation and Project
Grants are generally made only to organisations with an annual operating budget in excess of £250,000.

Grants are normally made towards significant, transformational projects with a total budget of £50,000 or more, and are unlikely to cover the entire cost of a project. Grants are one-off investments; they are rarely awarded for, or across, multiple years and will not normally be awarded to the same organisation in successive years.

Grant Size
The minimum grant size is normally £10,000, and the majority of awards fall in the £25,000 to £100,000 range. Grants for projects with a particularly compelling investment case including significant measurable outcomes may exceed £100,000.

Grants will not normally cover the entire cost of a project. You may wish to request a sum related to a specific budget item or grants already received from other funders.

International Grants
Grants for projects outside the UK are awarded by the FIL Foundation, a separate charitable foundation whose principal donor is also Fidelity International. The FIL Foundation and the Fidelity UK Foundation are jointly administered, and have some trustees in common. The funding priorities, application guidelines and restrictions for the FIL Foundation are similar to those for the Fidelity UK Foundation.

The FIL Foundation welcomes funding applications from established international charities serving beneficiaries in Continental Europe, Australia, Bermuda, China, Hong Kong, India, Japan, Korea, Singapore and Taiwan. Charities can either be based in these countries or headquartered elsewhere but delivering charitable services in these countries. Potential grantees should submit an initial Letter of Enquiry providing key information about both the organisation and proposed project as detailed further in the How To Apply section.

Financial information

In 2015 the foundation had assets of £194.5 million and an income of £12.2 million. During the year, 56 grants were made totalling £6.3 million.

Grants by purpose

Arts, culture and heritage	23	£2.9 million
Education	12	£1.23 million
Community Development	13	£1.1 million
Health	8	£1.1 million

Grants by type of support

Building acquisition, development, restoration	25	£2.96 million
Information technology	23	£2.09 million
Equipment	5	£808,000
Organisational/ development planning	2	£250,000
Core costs/programme costs	1	£235,000

Beneficiaries included: Action for Children (£250,000); The Public Catalogue Foundation (£100,000); King's College Hospital Charity (£75,000); Toynbee Hall (£69,000); The Royal Surrey County Hospital's Charitable Fund (£70,000); Northern Stage (£40,000); AHOY Centre (£30,000); Children's Discovery Centre (£25,000); New Horizon Youth Centre (£10,000).

Exclusions

Grants are not generally made to:

- Start-up, political or sectarian organisations
- Organisations which have been running for less than three years
- Individuals
- Private schools

Grants are not generally made for:

- Sponsorships
- Scholarships
- Corporate membership
- Advertising and promotional projects
- Exhibitions
- General running costs
- Replacement of dated IT equipment
- Grants will not normally cover costs incurred prior to application and/or the grant being awarded

Applications

According to the foundation's website:

> Our preference is to learn more about your request through an initial Letter of Enquiry of no more than three pages. This can be submitted either by post or email. However, if you require additional clarification regarding our grant-making criteria or process prior to submitting a Letter of Enquiry, you may contact us by telephone.

Your Letter of Enquiry should include the following information:

- Contact information, including contact name, title, organisation legal name, Charity Commission registration number, address, telephone number and email address
- A brief overview of your organisations mission, work and impact
- Description of your organisations financial condition, including operating revenues and expenses and unrestricted reserves
- An outline of the proposed project requiring investment, how it fits into your strategic plan, details of the anticipated outcomes and ways in which your organisation will be strengthened
- An indication of the project timeline and budget, fundraising progress and how much you wish to request

(See the website for further details on specific points of interest).

There are no deadlines for submitting grant proposals. All applications will normally receive an initial response within three months. The review process can take up to six months, which should be factored into the applicant's funding plan. The foundation may request additional information or a site visit to better familiarise itself with the organisation, its management team and the project. The foundation welcomes informal phone calls prior to the submission of a formal application.

The Sir John Fisher Foundation

General charitable purposes with a preference for the maritime, medicine, people with disabilities, education, music, the arts, community projects

£1.6 million (2015/16)

Beneficial area

UK, with a strong preference for charities in the Furness peninsula and adjacent area.

Correspondent: Dr David Jackson, James Fisher & Sons PLC, Heaning Wood, Ulverston LA12 7NZ (tel: 01229 580349; email: info@sirjohnfisherfoundation.org.uk; website: www.sirjohnfisherfoundation.org.uk)

Trustees: Diane Meacock; Daniel Tindall; Rowland Jackson; Sir David Hardy; Michael Shields; Thomas Meacock.

CC number: 277844

General information

Registered with the Charity Commission in 1979, the Sir John Fisher Foundation was established by the founders, Sir John and Lady Maria Fisher, and is closely associated with James Fisher and Sons PLC.

Areas of support

The foundation's website states that it supports charitable causes particularly in the six following categories:

- maritime
- medical and disability
- education
- music
- arts
- community projects in and around Barrow-in-Furness

Priorities

Community Projects

In the Barrow-in-Furness and surrounding area the Foundation seeks to meet the needs of the local community and in particular the vulnerable and disadvantaged.

The Trustees are likely to favour those local organisations who have sound and stable governance, and who have a strategy and considered plans for the future.

In the local area community projects involving sick, disabled, children, education, family support, maritime, arts and music will receive priority.

Other causes

Outside the Barrow-in-Furness area, a very much more limited number of community causes will be supported in Cumbria and North Lancashire.

Nationally, high quality maritime, music and art projects are considered together with limited medical research projects. Capital and revenue funding is available for up to three years. Most grants are for less than £10,000.

Financial information

In 2015/16 the foundation had assets of £103 million and an income of £1.9 million, of which £121,000 was a donation from the J. M. Fisher Settlement and £1.7 million was dividend income from James Fisher and Sons PLC. During the year there were 160 grants made: 117 locally and 43 nationally. Grants totalled £1.6 million, of which £1.1 million was given locally and £530,000 was given nationally.

Beneficiaries included: Loughborough University Development Trust (£73,000); University of Lancaster (£60,000); Lakeland Arts Trust Windermere Steamboat Museum (£40,000); The Ashton Group Theatre (£15,000); Cumbria Deaf Vision (£10,000); The Birchall Trust (£9,000); Ulverston Mind (£7,000); Trinity Sailing Foundation (£2,500); Kendal Choral Society (£1,000); Silverdale Street Activity Group (£500).

Exclusions

According to its website, the foundation will not generally fund:

- Individuals
- Sponsorship
- Expeditions
- Promotion of religion
- Places of worship
- Animal welfare
- Retrospective appeals
- Pressure groups
- Community projects outside Barrow-in-Furness and surrounding area (except occasional projects in Cumbria or North Lancashire, or if they fall within one of the other categories supported by the foundation)

Applications

The following information has been taken from the foundation's website:

Applications should be made by submitting a completed application form, together with all relevant information (set out on the application form) to the Secretary at least six weeks in advance of the Trustees' meeting. The Trustees meet at the beginning of May and the beginning of November each year. The closing date for the May meeting is the 1st March and the November meeting is the 21st September annually. Application forms should be obtained from the Secretary, whose contact details appear on the contacts page of this site. Alternatively please use the link below to download a Word document which you can fill in and submit by email or post.

You are always welcome to contact the Secretary for an informal discussion before submitting an application for funding.

Ford Britain Trust

Communities, children and young people, education, special educational needs, disability

£164,500 (2015/16)

Beneficial area

Local to the areas in close proximity to Ford Motor Company Ltd locations in the UK. These are Essex (including East London); Bridgend; Daventry; Liverpool; Manchester; Southampton. A list of eligible postcodes is provided on the website.

Correspondent: Deborah Chennells, Trust Director, Room 1/445, c/o Ford Motor Company Ltd, Eagle Way, Brentwood, Essex CM13 3BW (email: fbtrust@ford.com; website: www.ford.co.uk/fbtrust)

CC number: 269410

General information

The Ford Britain Trust serves the communities in which Ford Motor Company Ltd and its employees are located. The trust provides grants mainly to registered charities and schools that are in support of the development of young people; schools and education, with particular emphasis on special educational needs; disabilities; and community-related services.

The trust particularly encourages applications from Ford employees, but is open to all, provided that applicants meet the selection criteria.

Grants

The website states that grants are typically one-off, provided for specific capital projects or parts of a project, and fall into two categories:

- Small grants – for amounts of up to £250, available four times a year
- Large grants – for amounts of over £250 and usually up to £3,000, available twice a year

Grants can be made to registered charities, schools or PTAs, and other non-profit organisations. Support is given in the following categories:

- Local community or environment
- Young people and children
- Education and schools
- Special education needs
- People with disabilities

Grants can be given for the following purposes:

- Contributions towards capital projects, such as refurbishments
- Capital expenditure items, such as equipment or furniture
- Contributions towards purchase of new Ford vehicles (only of up to £2,000, and when two-thirds of the purchase price can be raised from other sources
- General funds (awards of up to £250)

Guidelines on applications for IT equipment, such as the maximum grant available, can be requested from the trust. The website also states: 'Applications relating to core funding, operating costs, salaries or revenue expenditure will be considered in the same way as requests for general funding and will, therefore, be eligible for small grants only.'

Financial information

In 2015/16 the trust had assets of £366,500 and an income of £159,000. 148 grants were made totalling £164,500, broken down as follows:

Youth	50	£75,000
Schools/education	41	£59,500
Community service	43	£23,500
Disability	13	£4,800
Special needs education	1	£1,800

Beneficiaries included: The Prince's Trust (£25,500); Robert Clark School (£15,000); Business in the Community (£4,000); A World for Girls, Billericay Rugby Football Club, Magram Youth Centre, One World Foundation Africa, Sutton at Hone CE Primary School and St Joseph's Hospice (£3,000 each).

Grants of less than £3,000 totalled £87,000.

Exclusions

Ford Britain Trust does not make grants for the following purposes:

- Major building works
- Sponsorship or advertising
- Research

- Overseas projects
- Travel
- Religious projects
- Political projects
- Purchase of second-hand vehicles
- Third-party fundraising initiatives (exceptions may be made for fundraising initiatives by Ford Motor Company Ltd employees and retirees)
- Fee-paying schools
- Individuals

Applications

Applications can be made in three ways:

- Download the PDF version of the form from the website to print out, complete and return by post to the correspondent
- Save the Word version of the form to your computer, complete it electronically and return it by email to fbtrust@ford.com
- Request a paper copy of the form on 01277 252551 to complete and return by post to the correspondent

Applications for large grants should include a copy of the organisation's most recent report and accounts.

Small-grant applications are considered in March, June, September and November and should be submitted by the 1st of each month. Applications for large grants are considered in March and September.

The Genesis Charitable Trust

Economic generation, enterprise, sustainable development

£748,500 (2015)

Beneficial area

Bangladesh; Botswana; Brazil; China; Colombia; Egypt; Ethiopia; Ghana; India; Indonesia; Jordan; Kazakhstan; Kenya; Lebanon; Malawi; Malaysia; Mexico; Mongolia; Morocco; Mozambique; Myanmar; Namibia; Nigeria; Pakistan; Peru; Philippines; Russia; Rwanda; Senegal; South Africa; Sri Lanka; Tanzania; Thailand; Tunisia; Turkey; Uganda; Ukraine; Vietnam; Zambia; Zimbabwe.

Correspondent: Tom Hoyle, Trust Manager, 21 Grosvenor Place, London SW1X 7HU (tel: 020 7201 7200; email: genesischaritabletrust@giml.co.uk; website: www.giml.co.uk/charitable-trust.php)

CC number: 1148643

General information

Registered with the Charity Commission in 2012, The Genesis Charitable Trust is the corporate charity of Genesis Investment Management LLP.

The trust provides grants to organisations to improve the living standards of individuals and communities in financially developing countries. In particular, according to the website, the trust has an interest in 'projects that provide sustainable, long-term income generation and self-sufficiency, especially those making a demonstrable positive impact on marginalised communities currently beyond the reach of traditional government or market-based solutions'.

The website states that the trust prioritises support for projects which generate income – in particular:

- entrepreneurial initiatives
- targeted improvement of economic opportunities
- improvements to the efficiency of markets and the ease of doing business

Grants are made only to organisations which are registered as a non-profit organisation in their country of origin, or are associated with a UK- or US-based non-profit organisation, and work to support disadvantaged communities. The trust only supports projects in specified countries (see 'Beneficial Area').

The website states that priority is given to organisations which meet the following criteria:

- have a track record in activities that accord with our income-generation priorities
- can demonstrate positive effects of their interventions
- are cost-effective in their approach
- have good governance and financial management
- engage beneficiaries and people who are local to beneficiaries in management and decision-making
- work to achieve sustainability of the social mission, by developing local capacity to increase resilience and independence

The trust's 2015 accounts state that, following the appointment of a new Trust Manager during the year, the trust is looking to 'trial different approaches to giving, including a discreet programme of light-touch small 'encouragement' grants'.

Financial information

In 2015 the trust had assets of £2.9 million and an income of £1.4 million, of which £1.1 million was donations from 'Genesis Investment Management, LLP Partners', with £280,000 in gift aid and a further £12,000 in services donated by the company, such as seconded staff and rent. The trust also had £6,000 in investment income. Grants were made to 16 organisations totalling £748,500.

Beneficiaries included: Camfed International (£238,000); Hope and Homes for Children (£127,500); Build It International (£75,000); Learning for Life (£36,000); Precious Sisters (£30,000); Mumbai Mobile Creches (£23,000); World Sight Foundation (£15,000); Renewable World (£13,000); New Life Mexico (£800).

Exclusions

The website states that funding will not be provided for:

- Activities based in countries other than those listed
- Individuals
- Political or religious activities
- Animal charities
- Building or infrastructure projects
- Retrospective appeals
- Medical research

Applications

Application forms can be downloaded from the website and should be submitted by email to GenesisCharitableTrust@giml.co.uk.

Applicants that are felt to be potentially eligible will be invited to an interview and asked to submit a detailed financial review.

The Goldman Sachs Charitable Gift Fund (UK)

Education, arts and culture, social welfare, humanitarian relief and medical causes

£2.2 million (2015/16)

Beneficial area

USA, UK, Australia and Hong Kong.

Correspondent: Jenny Evans, Executive Director, Goldman Sachs International, Peterborough Court, 133 Fleet Street, London EC4A 2BB (tel: 020 7774 1000)

CC number: 1120148

General information

This fund was established by Goldman Sachs International in 2007 as one of the vehicles for its charitable giving. The fund states that it makes grants in the USA and the UK, and well as Canada, France and Hong Kong, although in practice organisations are supported worldwide. It is also connected to Goldman Sachs Gives.

The fund's 2015/16 annual report provides information on its operational activities, a summary of which is given here:

> The objects of the fund are to promote for the public benefit the advancement of education, the relief of poverty and any

other charitable purposes in both English and American law. In furtherance of those objects the Fund focuses on supporting charities and charitable activities that built and stabilise communities, increase educational opportunities, advance health, relieve poverty, promote the arts and culture, provide humanitarian relief and any other charitable purposes.

The on-going strategy of the fund is to make grants pursuant to its objects from donated funds solicited from the Goldman Sachs Group, Inc. and its predecessors, subsidiaries, affiliates and successors, current and former employees, partners and managing directors of Goldman Sachs. The fund, including its Hong Kong branch, operates as a donor advised fund whereby the directors establish donor accounts for individual donors to make recommendations, although the ultimate decision for the distribution of funds rests solely with the directors [trustees] of the fund. Consequently, the directors consider that it is appropriate to disclose the funds as unrestricted. The directors pursue a broad strategy of ensuring proper due diligence in the assessment of grant applications with regard, among other things, to:

- proper identification of grant recipients
- establishing that grant purposes are charitable in both English and American law; and
- ensuring the legality of making grants to the recipients

The fund is the wholly owned subsidiary of...the Goldman Sachs Charitable Gift Fund, which has been recognised by the United States Internal Revenue Service as a tax-exempt organisation.

The fund has established its grant making policy to achieve its objects for the public benefit. The fund ensures that proper due diligence is undertaken to establish that proposed projects are charitable. In addition, the fund's grants are made on terms either requiring reporting or entitling the Fund to require reporting at its discretion, and in all cases restrict private benefit to donors to the fund (and those connected with them).

Financial information

At the time of writing (February 2017) all figures have been converted from $US. In 2015/16 the fund had assets of £10.6 million ($13.5 million) and an income of £2.3 million (almost $3 million). There were 87 grants made during the year totalling around £2.2 million ($2.8 million), broken down as follows:

Education	£1.8 million
Arts and culture	£151,400
Medical	£104,700
Other	£56,600
Community	£28,900
Humanitarian	£15,800

The largest donations, listed in the fund's accounts, were largely made to organisations in the USA.

Beneficiaries of the largest grants included: The Board of Trustees of the Leland Stanford Junior University (£791,000); Gilman School Inc. (£316,000); Trustees of the College of the Holy Cross (£158,000); Trustees of Tufts College (£134,500); Trustees of Dartmouth College (£79,000); Trustees of Princeton University (£79,000); Northwood Prep Educational Trust (£67,000); The American Fund for Westminster Abbey (£59,000); Cornell University (£58,000).

Applications

Apply in writing to the correspondent.

Goldman Sachs Gives (UK)

Education, health, the relief of poverty, arts and culture, humanitarian causes, general charitable purposes

£22.8 million (2014/15)

Beneficial area

Worldwide

Correspondent: Jenny Evans, Trustee, Goldman Sachs, Peterborough Court, 133 Fleet Street, London EC4A 2BB (tel: 020 7774 1000)

Trustees: Jennifer Evans; Robert Katz; Mike Housden; Peter Fahey.

CC number: 1123956

General information

The income of this charity, which was established in 2008, is principally made up of donations from affiliate and subsidiary companies in the Goldman Sachs Group, Inc. and from past and present senior employees of these companies. It is a donor-advised fund, as the charity's annual report 2014/15 explains:

The ongoing strategy of the Fund is to make grants pursuant to its objects from donated funds solicited from The Goldman Sachs Group, Inc. ('Goldman Sachs') and its predecessors, subsidiaries, affiliates and successors, current and former senior employees of Goldman Sachs. The Fund, including its Hong Kong branch, operates as a donor advised fund whereby the directors establish donor accounts for individual donors to make recommendations, although the ultimate decision for the distribution of funds rests solely with the directors of the Fund. Consequently, the directors consider that it is appropriate to disclose the funds as unrestricted. The directors pursue a broad strategy of ensuring proper due diligence in the assessment of grant applications with regard, among other things, to

- proper identification of grant recipients;
- establishing that grant purposes are charitable; and
- ensuring the legality of making grants to the recipients.

The Fund is formally recognised by HM Revenue & Customs for tax purposes within the United Kingdom.

The directors have paid due regard to the Charity Commission's guidance on public benefit, as required by the Charities Act 2011, when reviewing the objects and ongoing strategy of the Fund. In particular, the directors have considered whether grants being awarded by the Fund are for the public benefit.

The Fund has established its grant making policy to achieve its objects for the public benefit. The Fund ensures that proper due diligence is undertaken to establish that proposed projects are charitable. In addition, the Fund's grants are made on terms either requiring reporting or entitling the Fund to require reporting at its discretion, and in all cases restrict private benefit to donors to the Fund (and those connected with them).

Areas of support

The annual report 2014/15 states:

The objects of the Fund are to promote for the public benefit the advancement of education, relief of poverty and any other charitable purposes. In furtherance of those objects the Fund focuses on supporting charities and charitable activities that build and stabilise communities, increase educational opportunities, advance health, relieve poverty, promote the arts and culture, provide humanitarian relief and any other charitable purposes.

Financial information

In 2014/15 the charity had assets of £83.3 million and an income of £23.2 million, including £14.27 million from Goldman Sachs International and a further £7.6 million contributed on behalf of employees and former employees of the group. There were 476 grants made during the year totalling almost £22.8 million. Grants were given in the following categories:

Education	£12.1 million
Medical	£4.2 million
Community	£3.16 million
Humanitarian	£2.1 million
Arts and culture	£711,000
Other	£505,000

Beneficiaries included: Greenhouse Schools Project Ltd (£7.1 million); The Brain Tumour Charity (£1.6 million); University of Cape Town Trust (£1.4 million, all but £14,000 of which was provided for needs-based scholarships); Cancer Research UK (£775,000); Room to Read UK Ltd (£710,500); Opportunity International United Kingdom (£484,500).

Applications

Goldman Sachs Gives is a donor-advised fund through which Goldman Sachs and its senior employees, past and present, can recommend grants to eligible organisations.

Gowling WLG (UK) Charitable Trust

General charitable purposes, particularly health, disability, children and young people, and social welfare

£107,000 (2015/16)

Beneficial area

UK, with some preference for West Midlands.

Correspondent: Lee Nuttall, Trustee, Gowling WLG (UK) LLP, Two Snowhill, Snowhill Queensway, Birmingham B4 6WR (tel: 0121 233 1000)

Trustees: Lee Nuttall; Andrew Witts; Philip Clissitt.

CC number: 803009

General information

Registered in 1990 as the Wragge & Co. Charitable Trust, the trust was renamed in 2016 as Gowling WLG (UK) Charitable Trust, following the merger of Wragge Lawrence Graham & Co. LLP, the UK-based international law firm, and Gowling LLP, an international law firm based in Canada. The trust is the corporate charity of Gowling WLG LLP.

The trust's accounts for 2015/16 state that 'the trustees have no fixed policy on grant making and support a wide range of local and national charities ... however, they do not usually make grants to individuals or organisations which are not themselves charities'.

According to the group's website, the trust also provides matched funding for Gowling WLG employee fundraising initiatives. Assistance is given for a wide range of purposes including children and young people, the elderly, health and disability, in the West Midlands area and nationally.

Financial information

In 2015/16 the trust had assets of £39,000 and an income of £108,000, of which was wholly made from Gift Aid donations. Grants were made to 137 charitable organisations totalling £107,000.

Beneficiaries included: Birmingham Children's Hospital Charity (£13,000); Dogs for Good (£10,500); SIFA Fireside (£5,000); Teach First (£4,000); Mental Fight Club (£2,000); The Cotteridge Church, The Outward Bound Trust, and U Can Do IT (Internet Training) (£500 each); Theatre Absolute and WheelPower (£250).

Exclusions

The foundation does not make grants to individuals or to organisations which are not charities.

Applications

Apply in writing to the correspondent. The day-to-day management of the trust is carried out by Gowling WLG, including co-ordinating grant applications, which are presented to the trustees for their consideration at meetings throughout the year.

The Greggs Foundation

Social welfare, community causes, disadvantaged groups. Projects in the fields of the arts, environment, conservation, education, and health will be considered as long as they have a social-welfare focus and/or are located in areas of deprivation

£1.8 million (2015)

Beneficial area

England, Wales and Scotland, with a preference for the north east of England, (Northumberland, Tyne and Wear, Durham and Teesside), and in the regional divisions of Greggs PLC.

Correspondent: Justine Massingham, Grants Manager, Greggs House, Quorum Business Park, Newcastle Upon Tyne, Tyne and Wear NE12 8BU (tel: 0191 212 7626 or 0191 212 7813; email: greggsfoundation@greggs.co.uk; website: www.greggsfoundation.org.uk)

Trustees: Andrew Davison; Kate Welch; Fiona Nicholson; Richard Hutton; Jane Irving; Tony Rowson; Roisin Currie; Karen Wilkinson-Bell; Kate Bradley.

CC number: 296590

General information

The Greggs Foundation was registered with the Charity Commission in 1987. It is the corporate charity of Greggs PLC, whose principal activity is the retailing of sandwiches, savouries and other bakery-related products with a particular focus on takeaway food and catering. Greggs PLC donates at least 1% of its pre-tax profit annually to the foundation. In addition to cash donations, Greggs PLC also provides office accommodation and finance and administrative support via part-time secondment of qualified staff.

The latest annual report and accounts state: 'Ian Gregg (former chairman of Greggs PLC) set up the foundation as a registered charity in 1987 with the aim of giving something back to the communities where Greggs PLC trades, and where customers and employees live.'

The foundation makes grants to organisations with charitable objectives in the north east of England with the aim of improving the lives of disadvantaged people and enhancing the quality of life in local communities. Divisional Charity Committees based within the regional divisions of Greggs PLC also make grants on behalf of the trust and are located in Newcastle upon Tyne; Glasgow; Gosforth; Leeds; Manchester; Birmingham; Treforest; and Twickenham.

Grant programmes

The following information is taken from the foundation's website:

North East Core Funding

Financial support is offered to help sustain and increase the capacity of organisations that are based in and support people who live in the north east of England. Awards are of up to £45,000 (up to £15,000 per year) and aim 'to increase the capacity of the organisation to provide quality services', including support for core running costs. Priority groups are: people with disabilities; homeless people; voluntary carers; older and isolated people. Any not-for-profit organisation can apply.

Local Community Projects Fund

Small grants of up to £2,500 are made 'to help organisations based in local communities to deliver activities that they wouldn't otherwise be able to'. The programme is administered by seven regional charity committees based throughout England, Wales and Scotland. Any not-for-profit organisation can apply as long as the project supports a community interest and benefits people who: have disabilities; live in poverty; are voluntary carers; are homeless individuals; are isolated older people; or those who have other demonstrable significant need. The website states:

> We are interested in projects that improve resilience within your community of interest. This can include sessional activities/respite support, equipment for sessional activities, trips and residential breaks. We are also interested in new approaches and innovative ideas as well as sustainable approaches to supporting your community of interest.

Grants are more likely to be made to local organisations based near Greggs shops. Organisations 'with a turnover in excess of £300,000 are unlikely to be successful'.

Small Environment Grants

Funded by the 5p levy on carrier bag sales, this fund is dedicated to 'projects that improve the physical environment in a way that will improve people's lives'. Small grants of up to £2,000 are available on a one-off basis. Preference is given to projects 'which involve or benefit people who are disadvantaged'. The fund is administered in a similar way to the

Local Community Projects Fund. Any not-for-profit organisation can apply although preference is given to smaller, locally based, community-led organisations with a turnover of under £300,000. The foundation encourages schools to also apply.

Hardship Fund

Grants of up to £150 are made to individuals and families (via recognised social organisations) who live in extreme financial hardship. The grants are used to provide household goods, such as cookers, fridge freezers, clothing, beds and bedding, baby equipment and flooring.

Breakfast Clubs

The club programme was established to help primary schoolchildren to get nutritious start of their day. Through the scheme, schools in England, Wales, Scotland or Belfast are provided with fresh bread from their nearest Greggs shop, and a grant to support start-up and ongoing costs of the initiative. There are currently over 360 breakfast clubs operating.

Financial information

In 2015 the foundation had assets of almost £17.6 million and an income of £2.6 million, of which £875,000 was donated by Greggs PLC. A total of £84,000 was received in company donations from product sales, and employees also donated £57,000 to the foundation through the Give As You Earn scheme. Grants totalled £1.8 million during the year. Support was distributed as follows:

Regional Charity Committees (Local Community Projects Fund)	£516,500
Breakfast Club	£423,000
Major grants (now North East Core Funding)	£405,000
Hardship Fund	£229,000
Other grants and donations	£193,000

Beneficiaries included: Beacon Hill Arts (£40,500); Blue Sky Trust (£37,500); Toby Henderson Trust (£36,000); Hospitality and Hope (£35,000); Auckland Youth and Community Centre (£9,900); Liberty, Project for the Regeneration of Druids Heath, Riding for the Disabled Glasgow Group and The Toolbox Project (£2,000 each); Maltby Residents Association and Refugee Action York (£1,000 each).

Exclusions

The website provides lists of exclusions for each funding programme, check for further details. In general, the following are unlikely to receive funding:

- Animal charities
- Friends of associations
- Branches or federations of national charities
- Larger organisations with a greater capacity to fundraise
- Uniformed groups such as scouts, guides and sea cadets
- Sports clubs and associations
- Overseas travel
- Curricular activities that take place during the school day
- Religious promotion
- Research grants
- Repayment of loans
- Purchase of vehicles
- Equipment for hospitals/medical equipment
- Major capital projects
- Sponsorship of events or activities
- Unspecified costs
- Bankruptcy petition fees
- Holidays
- Funeral expenses
- Computer equipment

Note that organisations with a turnover in excess of £300,000 are unlikely to be successful. For the North East Core Funding programme, grants are not made to:

- Organisations with a turnover in excess of £300,000
- Organisations with more than six months of free reserves

Applications

Each grant programme has its own detailed criteria, guidelines and application process, all of which are available to view on the website.

Note that there is a waiting list for new **Breakfast Clubs**. The foundation's website states: 'We are currently experiencing unprecedented demand for the scheme and are actively fundraising to meet the need.'

Applications for **Hardship Fund** grants are only accepted via recognised social organisations, such as charities, housing associations and social services acting on behalf of a family or individual in need. Applications are assessed weekly, but at the time of writing (February 2017) the funder was oversubscribed and could only fund around half of the requests. The website indicates that the fund will prioritise the following:

- Families (over individuals)
- People who are most excluded financially
- Items that will make most difference

The website notes that **North East Core Funding** programme is 'highly competitive, with only around 1 in 5 eligible applications being successful'. The foundation discusses grants once per quarter and typically has considerably more requests for funding than it can support.

Similarly, the **Local Community Projects Fund** is 'over-subscribed and there is huge competition for the grants available'. The foundation asks not to be too disappointed if it is unable to support your project. It is unable to give tailored feedback on every application but will let you know whether it has been successful as early as possible. Applications can be made once a calendar year.

The **Small Environment Grants** programme is 'keeping the criteria very open. This means we are likely to receive a very high number of applications and an accordingly low success rate.' Applicants can expect a decision within eight weeks of the deadline date, which will be published on the website.

Halifax Foundation for Northern Ireland (previously known as Lloyds Bank Foundation for Northern Ireland)

Social and community needs, education and training

£1.27 million (2015)

Beneficial area

Northern Ireland

Correspondent: Brenda McMullan, Grants Manager, Lloyds Bank, 2nd Floor, 14 Cromac Place, Gasworks, Belfast BT7 2JB (tel: 028 9032 3000; email: grants@halifaxfoundationni.org; website: www.lloydstsbfoundationni.org)

CC number: 101763

General information

Previously known as the Lloyds Bank Foundation for Northern Ireland, the foundation was renamed in 2016, due to the strong presence in Northern Ireland of the Halifax, which is part of Lloyds Banking Group. The foundation is one of four Lloyds Banking Group charities, covering England and Wales, Scotland, Northern Ireland and the Channel Islands. The foundation is an independent grant-maker, receiving its income from shares held in the banking group.

Funding objectives

The overall aim of the foundation is to support underfunded, grassroots registered charities that enable people, especially people who are disadvantaged or who have special needs, to play an active role in their communities. There are two main areas – social and community needs, and education and training – where the foundation directs its funding.

1. Social and community needs

The foundation supports a wide range of activities and the following examples are listed on the website as a guide:

- **Community Services:** Family centres, youth clubs, older people's clubs, after schools clubs, self-help groups, childcare provision preschools and playgroups
- **Advice Services:** Homelessness, addictions, bereavement, family guidance, money advice, helplines and suicide awareness
- **People with Special Needs:** Residences, day centres, transport, carers, information, advice, and advocacy
- **Promotion of Health:** Information and advice, mental health, hospices, day care, home nursing, independent living for older people
- **Civic Responsibility:** Young people at risk, crime prevention, promotion of volunteering, victim support, mediation, rehabilitation of offenders
- **Cultural Enrichment:** Improving access and skills development in the arts and national heritage for disadvantaged people and those with special needs

2. Education and training

Through this funding area, the foundation seeks to improve educational opportunities for people of all ages who are disadvantaged or who have disabilities. According to the website, support is given in the following areas:

- **Employment:** Projects which help disadvantaged people develop their potential and secure employment
- **Life Skills:** Promotion of life skills, independent living skills for people with special needs
- **Training and Education:** Accredited, vocational or personal development training

Grant programmes

At the time of writing (October 2016) the foundation was running two grant programmes, one of which is open to applications from organisations.

Community Grant Programme

The programme continues to be the foundation's main focus through which grants are made within its funding objectives (social and community welfare, and education and training). Grants currently average between £3,000 and £4,000.

In order to be eligible to apply, organisations must have an income of less than £1 million in the previous 12 months. For registered charities which have a headquarters based outside Northern Ireland, the foundation will use the figure of the income of their Northern Ireland operation to determine their eligibility.

The reason for this income limit is explained on the website:

> The Trustees have taken this decision as there have been an increasing number of applications to the Foundation which makes the decision process more difficult. Also the Trustees are keen to ensure they stay in line with the overall aim of the Foundation, 'to support *underfunded* charities that enable people, especially disadvantaged or people with special needs, to play a fuller role in the community.' This new eligibility will stay in place for the foreseeable future.

Full guidelines for the programme are available from the website.

Matched Giving Scheme

The scheme allows employees of Lloyds Banking Group to claim up to £1,000 per year for a charity they have fundraised or volunteered for, within the scheme's eligibility criteria. The foundation matches every pound raised, or donates £8 per hour of voluntary time given, for a maximum of £500 in fundraising or time given. Full guidelines are provided on the foundation's website.

Financial information

In 2015 the foundation had assets of more than £1 million and an income of £1.1 million, all but £12,500 of which was derived from its covenant with Lloyds Banking Group. A total of 647 grants were made over three grant programmes operated during the year, amounting to £1.27 million.

Grants were distributed across the three programmes as follows:

The Community Grant Programme	368	£1.18 million
The Matched Giving Programme	277	£76,000
The Special Initiatives Programme	2	£13,000

Grants were awarded through the Community Grants Programme for the following purposes:

Community	117	32%
Children and young people	63	17%
Disability	36	10%
Health and illness support	35	10%
Arts	31	8%
Education and training	20	5%
Sports	19	5%
Older years	17	5%
Advice	14	4%
Social enterprise	9	2%
Support for men	5	1%
Support for women	5	1%

A breakdown of Community Grants according to the age of beneficiaries was also provided:

Mixed age groups	187	51%
Young people (ages 12 to 24)	63	17%
Age 50+	45	12%
Adults (ages 25 to 49)	27	7%
Infants (ages 0 to 4)	24	7%
Children (ages 5 to 11)	22	6%

Beneficiaries included: Appleby Careers Project Ltd and Gleann Amateur Boxing Club (£5,000 each); Loughside FC (£4,100); Child Brain Injury Trust (£4,000); Citizenship Foundation (£3,600); Cathedral Quarter Trust, St John's Parish Church, Strabane Community Unemployed Group and Youth Hostel Association of Northern Ireland (£3,000 each); Greenpower Education Trust (£1,500); Ballynure and District Friendship Club (£700); Ballymacward Preschool Playgroup (£500).

Exclusions

The guidelines on the foundation's website give the following information about what would generally not be funded under the Community Grant Programme:

- Non-registered charities
- Organisations which have an income of more than £1 million in the previous year's accounts
- Organisations which are insolvent
- Organisations who have over 12 months reserves would not be seen as a priority
- Individuals, including students
- Animal welfare
- The environment
- Hospitals and Medical Centres
- Schools, universities and colleges (except for projects specifically to benefit pupils with special needs)
- Sponsorship or fundraising events either for your own organisation or another
- Promotion of religion
- Endowment funds
- We are less likely to fund organisations who do not charge a nominal fee for activities
- Activities that are normally the responsibility of central or local government or some other responsible body
- Loans or business finance
- Travel or activities outside of Northern Ireland
- Capital build (except in the case of disabled access)

Applications

All applications must be made online via the foundation's website, where full guidelines, including a list of supporting documentation required, are available. The Community Grants Programme is operated on a rolling basis, meaning organisations can apply at any time. It can take at least four months for a decision to be made, and applying organisations may receive a telephone call or visit as part of the application process. A period of at least one year must be left between applications. However, those organisations that have received funding for three consecutive years must wait for at least two years before re-applying.

The foundation welcomes applicants to discuss their projects before submitting an application. This helps to ensure that a project falls within the foundation's eligibility criteria and allows applicants to have any queries they may have about the application process answered. Projects can be discussed by telephone and the foundation also runs one-to-one 'Application Information Sessions' at its office. These sessions are primarily aimed at organisations that have previously made an unsuccessful application or are applying for the first time. The next available dates are detailed on the website and can be reserved by telephoning the office.

Heathrow Community Fund (BAA Communities Trust)

Projects which benefit the local community in the following areas: young people and their education skills and employment, environmental protection, and communities

£851,500 (2015)

Beneficial area

The areas close to Heathrow Airport (Ealing, Hillingdon, Hounslow, Richmond, Runnymede, Spelthorne, Slough, South Bucks, Royal Borough of Windsor and Maidenhead).

Correspondent: Heathrow Community Fund, c/o Groundwork South, Colne Valley Park Centre, Denham Court Drive, Denham, Uxbridge, Middlesex UB9 5PG (tel: 01895 839916; email: community_fund@heathrow.com; website: www.heathrowcommunityfund.com)

CC number: 1058617

General information

BAA PLC – now known as Heathrow Airport Holdings Ltd – established this trust under the name 'BAA 21st Century Communities Trust' in 1996. The majority of the trust's funding is received from Heathrow Airport Ltd (a subsidiary of Heathrow Airport Holdings Ltd) and other companies based at Heathrow Airport, such as John Lewis, as well as from money raised by fines levied on airlines for breaching noise limits.

The trust is a grant-making charity which until recently supported communities close to the airports at Aberdeen, Glasgow, Heathrow and Southampton through local community funds. However, following the sale of the airports at Aberdeen, Glasgow and Southampton, the local community funds at each of these airports no longer fall under the governance of the trust.

The primary focus of the trust is now the Heathrow Community Fund (HCF) which works to support the communities in the areas surrounding Heathrow Airport. The fund also supports the fundraising and volunteering efforts of Heathrow staff. Heathrow Airport Ltd has committed to making an annual contribution of around £750,000 to support the trust's charitable activities, all of which contribute to the trust's vision to 'work with communities to create significant and positive social change'.

The trust carries out its grant-making with the following objectives:

- To create learning opportunities for young people and so raise their aspirations
- To break down barriers to employment through skills development
- To help protect the environment
- To support staff active in the community

Grants programmes

In support of its objectives, the Heathrow Community Fund (HCF) makes grants through five programmes.

Organisations can apply for grants through three programmes. These are:

- **Youth projects – Communities for Youth**: 'invites grant applications from organisations working on projects linked to education and economic regeneration schemes that give young people new skills and help them into employment'. Young people are generally defined as being those between the ages of 13 and 25. Grants range from £2,500 to £25,000 and are given for projects costing no more than £100,000 in total. Projects under this programme must take place in one of the following boroughs: Ealing, Hillingdon, Hounslow, Spelthorne or Slough
- **Sustainability and environmental projects – Communities for Tomorrow**: 'invites grant applications from organisations working on environmental or sustainability projects and schemes that involve recycling, tackling climate change or improving the local environment'. Grants range from £2,500 to £25,000 and are given for projects costing no more than £100,000 in total. Projects under this programme must take place in one of the following boroughs: Ealing, Hillingdon, Hounslow, Richmond, Runnymede, Slough, South Bucks, Spelthorne or Windsor and Maidenhead
- **Community projects – Communities Together**: 'invites grant applications from organisations looking for small amounts of funding to support projects that draw communities closer together – funding can support all sorts of community activities from gardening to sports or the arts'. Grants are awarded up to £2,500. Projects under this programme must take place in one of the following boroughs: Ealing, Hillingdon, Hounslow, Richmond, Runnymede, Slough, Spelthorne, South Bucks, or Windsor and Maidenhead

More information on these programmes, including full eligibility criteria and guidelines, is available from the fund's website.

There are also two funds to which employees can apply for support with their own charitable involvement:

- **Heathrow Active People Initiative (HAPI):** 'Employees of Heathrow Airport Ltd are encouraged to actively volunteer for charities and community groups working in their local communities, the Trust supports this with a grant programme awarding up to £2,500 to charities for projects involving Heathrow staff volunteering.'
- **Matched Funding**: 'Employees of Heathrow Airport Ltd are also supported in their fundraising for charity by a Matched Fund scheme in which the Trust will match funds raised.'

Financial information

In 2015 the trust had assets of £201,000 and an income of £831,000 (of which £700,000 was received from Heathrow Airport Holdings Ltd). Grants totalled £851,500 and were distributed as follows:

Inspiring Youth	-	£250,000
Communities for Tomorrow	21	£247,500
Communities for Youth	19	£240,000
Communities Together	87	£49,500
Staff match funding	54	£35,500
Midnight Marathon	-	£28,000
Heathrow Active People Initiative (HAPI)	-	£1,000

Exclusions

Applications which benefit individuals only, whether or not they meet the other criteria, will fail. No support is given for religious or political projects. Grants will not be made to nation-wide organisations unless the direct benefit will be felt locally and the other criteria are satisfied. The trust does not support general running costs or staff costs.

Note that each of the grants programmes are subject to their own eligibility criteria and restrictions.

Applications

Application forms and guidance notes for each of the grants programmes are available from the HCF website, where important dates for application submissions and decision-making are also listed. There are two application rounds: Round 1 involves the submission of an expression of interest form and Round 2, a full application.

The fund's grants programmes are managed by the charity Groundwork South – the website explains: 'Trustees and panel members live and work locally and are supported by the Trust Director and a team at Groundwork, who draw on their local knowledge and experience to help you submit a strong bid showing the full value of your work.' Decisions are made by the trustees and the Review Panel according to the priorities and criteria set for the funding programmes.

The Hiscox Foundation

General charitable purposes, particularly: education, medical science, the arts, independent living for older people, disadvantaged or vulnerable people

£228,500 (2014/15)

Beneficial area

Principally the UK.

Correspondent: c/o Peresha McKenzie, PA to the Chair, Hiscox Underwriting Ltd, 1 Great St Helen's, London EC3A 6HX (tel: 020 7448 6011)

Trustees: Alexander Foster; Robert Hiscox, Chair; Rory Barker; Andrew Nix; Amanda Brown.

CC number: 327635

General information

Registered with the Charity Commission in 1987, this foundation is the corporate charity of Hiscox PLC, a specialist insurance provider.

The foundation makes grants to organisations working in the areas of education, medical science, the arts, and independent living for people who are older, disadvantaged or vulnerable.

Financial information

In 2014/15 the foundation had assets of £6.4 million and an income of £697,000, principally from a donation from Hiscox PLC. Grants were made to 84 charities totalling £228,500.

Beneficiaries included: Richard House Children's Hospice (£25,500); Melanoma Action and Support Scotland (£25,000); Royal Academy of Arts (£10,000); Headway Essex (£2,000); Pimlico Opera and ZANE – Zimbabwe a National Emergency (£1,000 each); Walking with the Wounded (£500); Save the Rhino (£250); Syria Relief (£150).

Applications

Apply in writing to the correspondent. Our research suggests that support is mainly given to causes known by the trustees and, according to the annual report for 2015, 'priority is given to any charitable endeavour by members of staff of the Hiscox group to encourage such activity'. The trustees meet quarterly to consider applications.

The Hoover Foundation

Social welfare, health, education and training

£193,000 (2015/16)

Beneficial area

UK, but with a special interest in South Wales, Glasgow and Bolton.

Correspondent: S. Herbert, Hoover Candy Group, Pentrebach, Merthyr Tydfil, Mid Glamorgan CF48 4TU (tel: 01685 725530; email: sherbert@hoovercandy.com)

Trustees: David Lunt; Alberto Bertali; Robert Mudie; Matthew Given.

CC number: 200274

General information

The objectives of the foundation are primarily to support educational, environmental and charitable work in and around the areas of Hoover Ltd locations throughout the UK, namely South Wales, Glasgow and Bolton.

Financial information

In 2015/16 the foundation had assets of £3 million and an income of £73,000. Grants were made totalling £193,000.

Beneficiaries included: Alzheimer's Research UK, Bloodwise, and Brain Tumour Research (£25,000 each); Claire House Children's Hospice (£5,000); Bolton Brass Fund (£2,800).

Exclusions

The trustees do not make grants to individuals, including students.

Applications

Applications can be made in writing to the correspondent.

The Hudson Foundation

General charitable purpose, especially the relief of people who are older or ill

£130,500 (2014/15)

Beneficial area

Wisbech and district.

Correspondent: David Ball, Trustee, 1–3 York Row, Wisbech, Cambridgeshire PE13 1EA (tel: 01945 461456)

Trustees: David Ball; Stephen Layton; Edward Newling; Stephen Hutchinson.

CC number: 280332

General information

Registered in 1980, this foundation wholly owns Alan Hudson Ltd, a fruit and vegetable producing company, from which it receives its income. The object of the foundation is the relief of ill and/or older people, in particular the establishment and maintenance of residential accommodation and the provision of grants for other charitable purposes with a preference for the Wisbech area. The accounts state that 'whilst the trustees do make contributions to revenue expenditure of charitable organisations, they prefer to assist in the funding of capital projects for the advancement of the community of Wisbech and district'.

Financial information

In 2014/15 the foundation had assets £2.2 million and an income of £1.036 million (most of it is normally the trading income from the company). Grants were made to 14 organisations totalling £130,500.

Beneficiaries included: Cambridgeshire Lawn Tennis Association (£30,000); Wisbech Angles Theatre and Wisbech St Mary Pre-School (£20,000 each); Wisbech Swimming Club (£10,000); Wisbech Sea Cadets (£8,000); Methodist Homes for the Aged (£7,900); Wisbech Grammar School (£5,000); Wisbech C.P. School (£4,000); Wisbech Interfaith Forum (£1,500) Cambridgeshire Army Cadet Force (£1,000); Motability UK (£500).

Applications

Applications should be made in writing to the correspondent. The trustees meet quarterly.

IBM United Kingdom Trust

Education and training in ICT (Information and Communication Technology)

£1.2 million (2015)

Beneficial area

UK; Europe; Middle East; Africa.

Correspondent: Mark Wakefield, Trust Manager, IBM United Kingdom Ltd, 1PG1, 76–78 Upper Ground, London SE1 9PZ (tel: 020 7202 3608; email: wakefim@uk.ibm.com)

Trustees: Prof. Derek Bell; Anne Wolfe; Naomi Hill; Andrew Fitzgerald; Jonathan Batty.

CC number: 290462

General information

The focus areas for IBM's community investment are the strategic and innovative use of Information and

Communication Technology (ICT) in education and training and the promotion of digital inclusion, with the broad objective of raising standards of achievement. Most activity is within the compulsory education phase. The vast majority of IBM's community investment is delivered through specific programmes initiated and developed by IBM in partnership with organisations with appropriate professional expertise. The trust gives preference to organisations concerned with people disadvantaged by poverty and/or at risk of digital exclusion. Preference is given to supporting projects and organisations in areas in which the company is based and/or where there is employee involvement.

The trust's annual report gives the following information on its objects and activities:

- The advancement of education, particularly through the use and understanding of information technology
- The advancement of research, with emphasis (though not exclusively) on information technology
- Improving the condition of life for the disadvantaged or disabled through the use of information technology
- Encouraging the use and understanding of information technology in the charitable sector
- Through the provision of information technology and related services, or otherwise, supporting the relief of poverty, the health of the community and the preservation of the environment

Based on the above objects, and with consideration for public benefit, the Trust has the following aims:

- Increasing the scope, usage and understanding of information technology through education
- Providing information technology and other services to enable not for profit organisations and the disadvantaged to acquire skills
- Promoting volunteering by IBM employees
- Providing aid in the form of technology and technical support for disaster relief
- Providing support for research at universities and other educational institutes

The Trust primarily achieves its aims by supporting the development and delivery of IBM's own community programmes, where these meet the charitable objects of the Trust. The support is delivered through the provision of grants of equipment, technical support and cash. The support is provided for IBM's community involvement programmes in the United Kingdom, and across EMEA. Additionally the Trust incurs expenditure where it directs activities in its own right, which achieve the Trust's objects.

The Trust's approach to grant making falls into two key areas:

- The provision of grants that advance both the aims of the Trust and support IBM programmes
- The provision of small grants in support of charitable organisations in the communities surrounding IBM sites

In this way the Trust seeks to achieve its aims, not only through key longer term programmes, but also through support for smaller scale initiatives by providing direct contributions, and encouraging ongoing links between charitable and educational organisations and IBM.

Financial information

In 2015 the trust had assets of £4.6 million and an income of £938,000 which comprised of donations from IBM International Foundation and IBM subsidiaries. Grants were made totalling just over £1.2 million, and were distributed as follows:

Provision of IT and other services	£759,000
Increasing use of technology in education	£305,000
Support for research	£70,000
Miscellaneous	£2,000

The accounts give general information on the IBM programmes and initiatives which the trust supports. Five research grants were made to universities.

Beneficiaries included: Lagos State Universal Education Board (£64,000); Age Friendly Ireland (£31,000); Egyptian Ministry of Youth and Sports (£24,000); National College for Digital Skills (£21,000).

Exclusions

The trust does not provide core funding or contribute to appeals for/from:

- Building projects
- Religious or sectarian organisations
- Animal charities
- Individuals (including students)
- Overseas activities or expeditions
- Recreational and sports clubs
- Third parties on behalf of charities or individuals

Applications

Very few unsolicited requests are considered. If you decide to submit an appeal then it should be done by email or in writing and include a brief resumé of the aims of your organisation and details of what assistance is required. Those considering making an application are advised to telephone first for advice.

IHG Foundation (UK) Trust

Education and training, tackling modern slavery, disaster relief, environment, communities

Beneficial area

UK and overseas, including Brazil, China and the USA.

Correspondent: Kate Gibson, IHG Foundation, Broadwater Park, Denham, Buckinghamshire UB95HR (tel: 020 7655 1780; email: enquiries@ihgfoundation.org; website: www.ihgfoundation.org)

Trustees: Kate Gibson; Jennifer Laing; George Turner; Nick Watson.

CC number: 1164791

General information

The IHG Foundation (UK) Trust is the corporate charity of Intercontinental Hotels Group PLC and was registered with the Charity Commission in 2015.

According to its website, the foundation has four areas of focus:

> ***Providing skills for local people***
> Disadvantaged groups and young people often face challenges finding work. The IHG Foundation supports community groups and education providers working to equip and empower them by providing hospitality skills and helping them to secure employment.
>
> ***Supporting those impacted by disasters***
> IHG has a long tradition of providing disaster relief to communities in need. Through the IHG Foundation, we help local communities when they need it the most. When disaster strikes, the foundation works with humanitarian agencies around the world to help people get back on their feet and ensure they are better prepared for future disasters.
>
> ***Protecting our environment***
> We're mindful of the impacts the hospitality industry has on our environment, so we provide support for organisations who are looking for ways do things differently, to preserve scarce resources, and to help create a more sustainable future for everyone.
>
> ***Grassroots Community Support***
> We support the work of grassroots community organisations around the world, providing grants to help them in their work to make local communities better places to be for all.

The website reports information on a number of the organisations that have received grants so far. Examples include:

- Unseen – supporting work on modern slavery in the hospitality industry, including training and education to raise awareness, and work experience to victims of modern slavery

- British Red Cross – supporting the recovery programme following floods in Cumbria in 2015
- The Wildfowl and Wetlands Trust – towards the creation of a sustainable drainage system in London Wetland Centre

Financial information

At the time of writing (February 2017) there are no accounts yet available for the IHG Foundation on the Charity Commission website.

Beneficiaries include: British Red Cross; Care International; The Prince's Trust; The Wildfowl and Wetlands Trust; Unseen.

Applications

The website states the following: 'IHG Foundation adopts a targeted approach to grant funding focused on supporting a small number of beneficiaries. As a result, IHG Foundation does not accept speculative requests for funding.'

The Iliffe Family Charitable Trust

General charitable purposes, health and disability, medical, heritage and conservation, education

£86,000 (2015/16)

Beneficial area

Worldwide

Correspondent: Catherine Fleming, Trustee, Barn Close, Burnt Hill, Yattendon, Berkshire RG18 0UX (tel: 01635 203929; email: ifct@yattendon.co.uk)

CC number: 273437

General information

The trust was set up in 1977 by the Iliffe Family who own Yattendon Group PLC which is a private British company with interests in printing, agriculture, marinas and property. The chair of the group Lord Iliffe and Group Chief Executive Edward Iliffe are both trustees of the charity.

Grants are given to groups concerned with medical causes, disability, heritage and education. The bulk of the grants made are to charities already known to the trustees, to which funds are committed from year to year. Other donations are made for a wide range of charitable purposes in which the trust has a special interest.

Financial information

In 2015/16 the trust had assets of £1.3 million and an income of £37,500. Grants to 17 organisations totalled £86,000 and were broken down as follows:

Welfare	6	£42,500
Education	5	£36,000
Religious	2	£3,500
Conservation	1	£2,500
Medical	3	£1,700

Beneficiaries included: Newbury and District Agricultural Society (£25,000); Afghan Connection (£10,500); Jubilee Sailing Trust, RNLI, and RYS Foundation (£10,000 each); Red Squirrel Survival Trust (£2,500); Falklands Islands Memorial Chapel Trust, Macmillan Cancer Care, and West Berkshire Citizen Advice Bureau (£500 each); Northern Centre for Cancer Care (£150).

Exclusions

Grants are not made to individuals and rarely to non-registered charities.

Applications

Applications can be made in writing to the correspondent. Only successful applications will be acknowledged. Grants are considered at ad hoc meetings of the trustees, held throughout the year.

The Innocent Foundation

World hunger, sustainable agriculture, local food poverty in the UK

£781,000 (2015/16)

Beneficial area

Worldwide

Correspondent: Kate Franks, Manager, The Innocent Foundation, 342 Ladbroke Grove, London W10 5BU (tel: 020 3235 0352 or 020 7993 3311; email: hello@innocentfoundation.org; website: www.innocentfoundation.org)

CC number: 1104289

General information

The Innocent Foundation was set up by the founders of Innocent Drinks in 2004. Innocent is now majority-owned by The Coca-Cola Company but continues to give at least 10% of its profits to charity, the majority of which is received by the foundation. The trustees of the Innocent Foundation include the three founders of the company – Adam Balon, Jon Wright and Richard Reed – and its current Chief Executive, Douglas Lamont.

The foundation works with partner charities around the world 'so that they can help the world's hungry'. Its website states that all of its partners 'have the same core principles [it does] and are working to help communities on a sustainable path to a better life, a life where they won't be hungry any more'. It is further noted: 'We work with some partners supporting one-off short-term projects, but with the majority the partnership commitment is for three years'. The foundation tries to contribute more than just financial assistance; Innocent employees have travelled to support some of its partner projects by sharing their expertise.

What the foundation funds

The foundation makes grants to support four different types of project, as outlined on the website:

- Seed funding – grants of up to £30,000 per year for three years are given to help get new sustainable agriculture projects off the ground. Funding can only be given to support work in countries categorised as 'serious', 'alarming' or 'extremely alarming' on the Global Hunger Index
- Local food poverty – the foundation makes grants to charities working on projects to combat food poverty in the UK. It has already worked with the Trussell Trust, Make Lunch and the Matthew Tree Project. At the time of writing (November 2016) the criteria for funding under this category was being reviewed
- Breakthrough development – funding is given to support innovative, untested ideas to 'find new models that over time will become the gold standard to address hunger issues'
- Emergency hunger relief – the foundation helps to get food to people affected by humanitarian crises, working with Oxfam to support its emergency relief work around the world

Full information about funding from the foundation is available from the website.

Financial information

In 2015/16 the foundation had assets of almost £2.9 million and an income of £1 million, including a donation of £950,000 from Innocent Ltd. There were grants made to 16 projects totalling £781,000.

Beneficiaries included: Action Against Hunger (£326,000); Oxfam (£100,000); Kew (£40,000); Action on Disability and Development (£36,500); Find Your Feet (£30,000); Send a Cow (£20,500); Feedback Madagascar (£27,000); Make Lunch (£24,000); Trussell Trust (£21,000); Jeevika Trust (£12,000).

Exclusions

Organisations which are not UK-registered charities or which do not have UK representation (some staff based in the UK) cannot be supported.

Seed funding – the foundation will not support the following: individuals; religious or political causes; general appeals or circulars; events or conferences; and major capital costs, such as buildings or machinery. Seed funding is not given for core costs alone (but these can be included as overheads pro-rated to the project).

Local food poverty – at the time of writing (November 2016), the criteria for this type of funding was being reviewed. See the website for updates.

Applications

In the first instance, see the website for full information of the foundation's work. Applications are accepted for two types of funding: seed funding and local food poverty. At the time of writing (November 2016) detailed criteria for seed funding was available from the website. Criteria for local food poverty funding was under review but was due to be provided on the website in the near future.

The foundation's website states:

> We know that raising funds is a major focus for charities and that it can take you away from the real work. So we'd like to make the process of applying to us for funding as easy as possible which is why in the beginning we only want a very brief description of your project. We'll get in touch to find out more if we need to.

You can get in touch with the correspondent via an online form, email, phone or post, providing the following:

- Your name
- Your email address
- Your telephone number
- The name of your organisation
- Your organisation's website (if it has one)
- Your organisation's registered charity number
- Which type of funding you are applying for (seed funding or a local food poverty grant)
- In no more than 200 words, a summary of your project including how you set up the project, your long-term goal and what you would use the money for

The annual report states that each organisation must:

- Benefit a community rather than individuals
- Be a not-for-profit organisation
- Be pursuing charitable purposes
- Consider taking part in The Foundation scholarship programme which offers employees of Innocent Ltd the opportunity to volunteer with partners, using their business skills to bring benefit to the organisation. There are up to three scholarships a year

Interserve Employee Foundation Ltd

General charitable purposes, disaster relief, education/ training, social welfare

£123,000 (2015)

Beneficial area

Worldwide

Correspondent: The Trustees of Interserve Employee Foundation Ltd, Interserve PLC, Interserve house, Ruscombe park, Ruscombe, Reading RG10 9JU (tel: 0118 932 0123; email: Info.foundation@interserve.com; website: www.interserve.com/about-us/interserve-employee-foundation)

CC number: 1145338

General information

Interserve is one of the world's foremost support services and construction companies, operating in the public and private sectors in the UK and internationally. Interserve is headquartered in the UK and is listed in the FTSE 250 index.

The Interserve Employee Foundation – also known by the abbreviation IEF – works to improve the quality of life of people who are living in communities where Interserve has a presence, by encouraging and facilitating employees in the UK and overseas to be actively involved in charitable and community-based activities. The foundation's page on the Interserve website explains that this is achieved by:

- Receiving monetary donations from employees, Interserve Plc, suppliers and customers to finance employee run charitable projects
- Capturing and sharing charitable activities from across the group, inspiring employees to give back to their communities

The aim of IEF is to improve the quality of life for people in the communities where they operate, enlisting the skills, capabilities, resources and enthusiasm of their employees.

The foundation has ambassadors who work across the business to promote the foundation's aims and to encourage employees to take part in activities in their local areas. In particular, ambassadors promote the 'Give a Day of Your Time' initiative, through which employees can take up to two days leave each year in order to assist with local projects or charities in their communities.

According to the website, 'the charities and good causes supported by IEF reflect the wide scope of our operations and of the interests and concerns of our staff'. Examples listed on the website at the time of writing (February 2017) included:

- Our colleagues in the Philippines joined the Typhoon Haiyan relief effort by using their skills and equipment to set up temporary shelter for displaced people. Fundraising to help people find alternative accommodation took place across the Group raising more than £20,000 in just two weeks
- Supporting the Big Book Drop for Literacy for Life, a charity aimed at improving the life chances of disadvantaged children in the territories where we work. To date, more than 50,000 books have been collected in the UK, which have been sent to schools in the Philippines, South Africa, India and Chile
- Funding the building of a £25,000 cycle track for Pathways Primary School in Yorkshire, a school for children with special needs and which offers specialist resources for pupils with Autistic Spectrum Disorder

Financial information

In 2015 the foundation had assets of £54,000 and an income of £213,500. Grants were made totalling £123,000.

Beneficiaries included: Nepal Disaster Recovery (£26,000); Providence Row (£2,000); Oasis Playspace (£450).

Applications

The foundation supports charities nominated by Interserve employees.

John Laing Charitable Trust

Education, community regeneration, young people, homelessness, with a particular emphasis on day centres, general charitable purposes

£671,000 to organisations (2015)

Beneficial area

UK and, occasionally, countries where John Laing Group PLC operates.

Correspondent: Jenny Impey, Trust Director, 33 Bunns Lane, Mill Hill, London NW7 2DX (tel: 020 7901 3307; email: jenny.impey@laing.com; website: www.laing.com/top/corporate_responsibility/john_laing_charitable_trust.html)

CC number: 236852

General information

The trust was established in 1962 by John Laing Group PLC, an infrastructure investor and asset management company.

The trust provides an avenue for John Laing PLC and its subsidiaries to make charitable donations and provide welfare support to existing and former employees as well as helping charitable organisations. Charitable activities of the trust are split into the following fields:

- Welfare
- Charitable donations
- Staff applications
- Named funds

Areas of work

Although the trust was established with general charitable purposes, the trustees have placed priority on the following areas:

- Education
- Community regeneration, which includes causes relating to older people
- Disadvantaged young people
- Homelessness with a particular emphasis on day centres

Historically the trust has tried to match its areas of donations to sectors allied to the company's business. The trust supports charitable activity in the areas in which the company operates. This is primarily in the UK, although grants are also awarded to organisations working in Australia and the USA.

Grant-making policy

According to the website, donations normally range from £250 to £25,000, with only up to a dozen charities receiving more than £10,000. The annual report for 2015 states:

> Major grants for revenue expenditure purposes range from £7,500 to £50,000 per year. Some grants are awarded for multiple periods up to three years. ... Smaller donations between £500 and £1,500 are paid under Staff Matching, Make a Difference and Long Service Award schemes available to current employees of the Company and a number of one-off grants are also given up to a value of £5,000. Minor Grants of up to £1,000 are administered for us by selected Community Foundations granting to small charities operating locally in the following regions: Wiltshire and Swindon; Lancashire and Merseyside; Oxfordshire; and Essex.

As of May 2015, the trust no longer accepts unsolicited applications.

Financial information

In 2015 the trust had assets of £56.3 million and an income of £2 million. There were grants awarded during the year totalling £1.34 million, of which £671,000 was awarded to over 50 organisations. Grants made to individuals totalled £646,000.

Beneficiaries included: NWG Network (£79,000); Leap (£50,000); Hertfordshire Groundwork (£37,500); Young Enterprise (£30,000); Alzheimer's Research UK and Cumbria Community Foundation (£25,000 each); Church Action on Poverty (£10,000); Crossroads Children's Home (£5,000); Slinfold Mini Bus Club (£3,000); British Heart Foundation (£2,000); Wanstead Playgroup Association (£1,500); Chai Cancer Care, Diamond Centre for Disabled Riders and Sefton Carers (£1,000 each).

There are also other four charities set up by the Laing family and administered at the same address – for more information see www.laingfamilytrusts.org.uk.

Exclusions

Grants are not made to individuals or organisations whose main purpose is animal welfare.

Applications

Unsolicited applications are no longer accepted. However, the website does state: 'Minor Grants of up to £1,000 are administered for us by selected Community Foundations granting to small charities operating locally in the following regions: Wiltshire and Swindon; Lancashire and Merseyside; Oxfordshire; Essex; Leicestershire and Rutland.'

The charity takes a pro-active approach in seeking out eligible organisations for its other grant-making activities.

Johnson Wax Ltd Charitable Trust

General charitable purposes, social welfare, disadvantage, older people, children, education and training, employment, the environment, health and disability, the arts, local community needs

£217,000 (2014/15)

Beneficial area

Areas surrounding S. C. Johnson's sites; local neighbourhood in Frimley Green, Surrey.

Correspondent: Faye Gilbert, Trustee, S. C. Johnson Ltd, Frimley Green Road, Frimley, Camberley, Surrey GU16 7AJ (email: givinguk@scj.com)

Trustees: Faye Gilbert; Trevor Jessett; Tina Wadhera; Margaret Shukla; Martina Leahy.

CC number: 200332

General information

Registered with the Charity Commission in 1961, Johnson Wax Ltd Charitable Trust is the corporate charity of S. C. Johnson Ltd, a manufacturer of cleaning products for the consumer and industrial markets. The trust receives an annual donation from S. C. Johnson Ltd. Our research shows that each year about 2.5% of pre-tax profit from S. C. Johnson goes to the trust. The trustees aim to give 80% of the charity's income to local communities in the areas surrounding S. C. Johnson's sites.

The trust's annual report states that it has the following objectives:

> - To promote general charitable purposes for the benefit of the local communities surrounding the sites of SC Johnson and to provide relief from financial hardship and social or economic disadvantage and to advance the education of its residents of all ages
> - To develop the capacity and skills of those socially and economically disadvantaged members (generally but not individually) in the local community surrounding the sites of SC Johnson, in such a way that they are able to better identify and help meet their needs and to participate more fully in society
> - To advance the education of the pupils at those schools in the local communities surrounding the sites of SC Johnson by providing and assisting in the provision of facilities to the extent not provided by the local education authority
> - To relieve financial hardship, sickness and poor health, generally but not individually, of elderly people and people living or working in the local communities surrounding the sites of SC Johnson by making grants of money for providing or paying for items, services or facilities, or through the provisions of grants, goods or services
> - To promote art for the benefit of the public (generally but not individually) in the local communities surrounding the sites of SC Johnson
> - To promote for the benefit of young persons, inhabiting the local communities surrounding the sites of SC Johnson and who have need of such facilities by reason of their disablement or infirmity, the provision of facilities of recreation or other leisure time occupation, with the object of improving the condition of life of the said inhabitants
> - The promotion for the benefit of the public of urban or rural regeneration in areas of social and economic deprivation by all or any of the following means: – the protection or conservation of the environment; – the maintenance, improvement or provision of public amenities; and – the relief of unemployment
> - Such further charitable objects as the trustees in their absolute discretion think fit

Financial information

In 2014/15 the trust had assets of £236,000 and an income of £325,000.

Grants totalled £217,000, including employee-led schemes. Support was categorised as follows:

Health-related charities	£133,500
Education	£37,500
June community day	£15,200
Arts and sports	£11,600
Local community	£11,000
Samuel C Johnson award	£5,000
Employee-led schemes (match funding)	£3,000
Environment	£200

Unfortunately, a list of beneficiaries was not included in the latest accounts.

Exclusions

Individuals

Applications

Applications may be made in writing to the correspondent, specifying the amount requested and what it is needed for, details of how the grant will benefit a broad cross-section of the Frimley Green community and how a clear social need will be met within it.

The Joron Charitable Trust

General charitable purposes, education, medical research

£360,000 (2015/16)

Beneficial area

UK and overseas.

Correspondent: Bruce Jarvis, Trustee, Ravensale Ltd, 115 Wembley Commercial Centre, East Lane, North Wembley, Middlesex HA9 7UR (tel: 020 8908 4655; email: ravensale100@btconnect.com)

CC number: 1062547

General information

Established in 1997 the trust receives the majority of its funding from Ravensale Ltd. The company is owned by the Jarvis family and is involved in property investment and development as well as the manufacture of ballpoint pens. Both the company's directors Bruce Jarvis and Joseph Jarvis are also trustees of the trust.

The trust's policy is to make grants to registered charities in the fields of education, medical research and other charities who can demonstrate that the grants will be used effectively. In the 2015/16 annual report the trustees note that future plans involve continuing to support 'local, national and international charities'.

Financial information

In 2015/16 the trust had an income £852,500, mostly received in donations from Ravensale Ltd, and a total expenditure of £362,000. Grants were made to three organisations and totalled £360,000.

Beneficiaries included: The Wilderness Foundation (£250,000); Child's Dream Association (£100,000); Urology Foundation (£10,000).

Applications

Applications may be made in writing to the correspondent.

The KPMG Foundation

Children and young people in or leaving care, children and young people in disadvantaged families, refugees, young offenders, people lacking educational and employment opportunities

£956,500 (2015/16)

Beneficial area

England, Scotland and Wales.

Correspondent: Jo Clunie, Director, KPMG LLP, 15 Canada Square, Canary Wharf, London E14 5GL (tel: 020 7311 4733; email: jo.clunie@kpmgfoundation.co.uk; website: home.kpmg.com/uk/en/home/about/corporate-responsibility/kpmg-foundation.html)

CC number: 1086518

General information

According to its 2015/16 annual report, The KPMG Foundation was established in October 2000 and supports 'education and social projects for the disadvantaged and under privileged, with particular emphasis on unlocking the potential of children and young people (up to 30 years old) who, for primarily social reasons, have not fulfilled their educational potential'.

The annual report also informs that currently the foundation particularly focuses on projects which 'unlock the potential of children and young people in care and/or unlock the potential of children and young people in deprived families'. The foundation is looking for projects that:

- Focus primarily on improving access to education, training and employment
- Demonstrate that early intervention can prevent problems further downstream
- Build on a thorough understanding of the core issues facing the most disadvantaged children and how their lives could be transformed
- Utilise the Foundation's convening and collaboration power by bringing others together around an issue (funders, policy makers, academics etc.)
- Demonstrate potential to evidence success over the long-term through rigorous evaluation and quantitative metrics
- Enhance the work of the Foundation through leveraging the power of KPMG and the skills of its staff
- Focus on outcomes as opposed to focusing on what is being done
- Have the potential to be scalable; and
- Will leverage other funds and be sustainable

The trustees believe that 'the key to unlocking potential is education, training and employment and that the earlier the intervention the better'. It is the foundation's preference to support 'fewer larger projects that have the depth to potentially achieve real change' and local projects which will have national impact.

The foundation's impact report available on its website gives an extensive list and further details of projects supported in the past as well as currently assisted initiatives.

Financial information

In 2015/16 the foundation had assets of £7 million and an income of £1.9 million, including donations of £1.4 million and support costs were covered by KPMG. There were 12 grants made totalling £956,500, broken down as follows:

Children and young people in deprived families	6	£556,000
Children and young people on edge of care, in care or leaving care	4	£355,000
Young offenders and those at risk of offending	2	£42,000

Beneficiaries were: The Fostering Network (£247,000); Teach First (£150,000); Future First (£143,500); Barnardo's (£111,500); Working Chance (£91,000 in two grants); Education Endowment Foundation (£70,000 in two grants); Action For Access (£34,000); Into University (£25,000); Shaftesbury Young People (£20,000); Watts Gallery (£5,000).

Applications

According to the website, the director and advisor to the foundation 'pro-actively seeks projects to support and does not accept any unsolicited applications'. The trustees can also make referrals to the director of the foundation should they identify a programme or charity that fits with the foundation's objectives.

Ladbrokes in the Community Charitable Trust

General charitable purposes, healthcare, education/sport, community projects

£466,000 (2015)

Beneficial area

UK and Ireland (communities in which the shops and businesses of Ladbrokes Betting and Gaming Ltd or Ladbrokes eGaming Ltd operate).

Correspondent: Michael O'Kane, Trustee, Ladbrokes PLC, Imperial House, Imperial Drive, Harrow, Middlesex HA2 7JW (tel: 020 8515 5611; email: rachael.edwards@ladbrokes.co.uk; website: www.ladbrokesplc.com/corporate-responsibility/communities.aspx)

Trustees: Michael O'Kane; Susan Trill; Jan Kunicki; Lucy Capon.

CC number: 1101804

General information

Ladbrokes in the Community Charitable Trust (LCT) was established in 2003. Its funding comes not from the Ladbrokes company, but via the fundraising efforts of the head office and shop staff, customers and 'Event Days'.

The trust's record on the Charity Commission's website states that support can be given to a range of causes 'with the overriding requirement being that the causes supported operate and serve the community in which the shops and businesses of Ladbrokes Betting and Gaming Ltd or Ladbrokes e-Gaming Ltd operate'.

According to the annual report for 2015, grants are commonly given in the following categories:

- **Health**: 'Principally research/treatment, hospice services & disability support'
- **Education**: supporting people who are disadvantaged or who have disabilities
- **Community**: with a focus on projects for people who are older or homeless or social activity projects for people who are at risk

Financial information

In 2015 the trust had assets of £152,000 and an income of £481,500. Grants were made totalling £466,000 and were distributed under the following categories:

Hospices and hospitals	£441,000
Medical	£25,000

Beneficiaries included: Children with Cancer UK; Coalfields Regeneration Trust; Cancer Research UK; Marie Curie Cancer Care; Starlight Charity.

Applications

In the first instance, the support of a local shop should be secured in raising funds on behalf of a cause. The trustees meet every month 'to consider grant requests from shop and head office fundraisers and registered charities'.

The Lancashire Foundation

General charitable purposes with a particular focus on young people and people who are severely disadvantaged

£1.5 million (2015)

Beneficial area

UK, Bermuda and worldwide. Mainly international giving.

Correspondent: Donations Committee, Lancashire Insurance Company (UK), Level 29, 20 Fenchurch Street, London EC3M 3BY (tel: 020 7264 4056; website: www.lancashiregroup.com/en/responsibility/lancashire-foundation.html)

Trustees: Michael Connor; Derek Stapley; Richard Williams.

CC number: 1149184

General information

This foundation is the corporate charity of the Lancashire group of insurance companies which operates in Bermuda and London. It receives its income through an annual donation from the group. The foundation's page on the Lancashire group's website explains:

> The Foundation currently holds 330,713 shares in the Company, which were generously provided to it by the Company. The additional income from dividends payable on the shares and the benefits that arise from the increase in the share price, link the performance of the Company to the resources of the Foundation.

The Lancashire Foundation forms a core part of the group's corporate social responsibility commitments and uses its resources to support local and international communities, with a particular focus on assisting young people and people who are severely disadvantaged.

Strategy

The annual report for 2015 states:

> The Charity's strategy is to provide grants to other charities or organisations, whose work reflects the values and interests of the people and businesses within the Lancashire group of insurance companies, with an expectation that it will remain as part of the Charity's annual donations budget and will be renewed each year for a minimum term of three years, subject to an annual review at the discretion of the Charity.
>
> The Charity also invites applications for grants from members of staff of The Lancashire Group to charities or organisations with which they have a link.
>
> The Charity continues to fund its key flagship partnerships with Medecins Sans Frontieres, International Care Ministries, St Giles Trust, Tomorrow's Voices and Family Centre.

The foundation's page on the group's website explains that 'in very exceptional circumstances' additional emergency funding can be provided and that 'in certain circumstances' charities suggested by others in its market place can be supported.

Financial information

In 2015 the foundation had assets of £3.7 million and an income of £2.1 million. During the year the foundation distributed £1.5 million in grants to 52 charities.

Beneficiaries included: Médecins Sans Frontières (£326,500); International Care Ministries – Philippines (£129,000); Kiva Microloans (£113,500); The Family Centre (£99,500); Vauxhall City Farm (£53,000); Anti-Slavery International (£35,000); FareShare and Noah's Ark Children's Hospice (£20,000 each); Young Enterprise (£10,000); RP Fighting Blindness (£5,000); Victor Scott Primary School (£4,000); Pancreatic Cancer UK, St George's Hospital and War Child (£2,000 each).

Applications

The foundation principally channels its funding through key partner charities and those nominated by staff of the Lancashire group. Its page on the Lancashire group's website explains:

> Prospective charitable organisations are asked to provide a grant application form to the staff Donations Committee, which considers their funding proposals and, if agreed, provides a recommendation to the Trustees of the Foundation for their approval to release funds accordingly. Donations Committee members and other members of staff act as advocates for the charitable organisations that the Foundation supports throughout the year.

Leeds Building Society Charitable Foundation

General charitable purposes, community projects focusing on social welfare and relief in need, vulnerable people and disadvantaged individuals

£102,000 (2015)

Beneficial area

Areas where the society's branches are located.

Correspondent: Ellen Hamilton, Leeds Building Society, 105 Albion Street, Leeds, West Yorkshire LS1 5AS (tel: 0113 216 7296; email: foundation@leedsbuildingsociety.co.uk; website: www.leedsbuildingsociety.co.uk/your-society/about-us/charitable-foundation)

CC number: 1074429

General information

The foundation was established by and is closely associated with Leeds Building Society. It was registered with the Charity Commission in 1999 and supports the communities around the nationwide branches of the society.

The foundation's website states:

> Generally, we will consider applications for community based projects which aim to provide relief of suffering, hardship or poverty, or their direct consequences.
>
> Some examples of the areas in which we have made donations include:
>
> - Homeless people
> - Adults and children with physical and mental disabilities
> - Older people
> - Underprivileged families
> - Deaf, blind and partially sighted people
> - Community projects benefiting local residents
> - Victims of natural and civil disasters in the UK
> - Scout, Guide & Play groups

Financial information

In 2015 the foundation had assets of £35,000 and an income of £129,500. During the year, 124 grants were made totalling £102,000

A list of beneficiaries was not included within the annual report and accounts.

Exclusions

The foundation is unlikely to make donations for:

- The restoration or upgrading of buildings, including churches
- Environmental charities (unless there is a benefit to a disadvantaged community)
- Administration equipment such as IT equipment for a charity's own use

The foundation is unable to support:

- Projects with religious, political or military purposes
- Overseas charities or projects
- Individuals, including sponsorship of individuals
- Animal welfare projects; and
- Medical research

Church projects will be considered only where they involve community outreach and benefit (e.g. supporting the homeless, disadvantaged families).

Applications

Apply online through the foundation's website.

All applications will be acknowledged. The trustees meet quarterly in March, June, September and November. Following the meeting the foundation we will write to you and let you know whether or not your application has been successful.

If you need more information or advice contact the secretary of the charitable foundation on 0113 225 7518 or foundation@leedsbuildingsociety.co.uk. Because the foundation operates independently of the Building Society, local branch staff are unable to answer questions about the foundation.

The John Spedan Lewis Foundation

Natural sciences, particularly horticulture, ornithology, entomology, environmental education and conservation

£66,500 to organisations (2015/16)

Beneficial area

UK

Correspondent: Ruth Bone, Secretary, Partnership House, Carlisle Place, London SW1P 1BX (tel: 020 7592 6284; email: jslf@johnlewis.co.uk; website: johnspedanlewisfoundation.wordpress.com)

CC number: 240473

General information

The foundation was set up in 1964 and makes grants at the instigation of John Lewis stores' partners (employees) to commemorate the interests and life of the founder of the Partnership. It can give support in the areas of natural sciences, especially horticulture, environmental education, ornithology, entomology and conservation, and to associated educational and research projects. According to the 2015/16 annual report, 'funding is currently divided annually between a number of small and medium sized projects and a PhD research project, the latter determined by invitation only'.

The website states that grants are made to UK-registered charities which explicitly state natural history topics in their charitable purposes – such as wildlife conservation, entomology, ornithology or horticulture.

Financial information

In 2015/16 it had assets of £2.6 million and an income of £84,000, of which £19,000 was in donated services from John Lewis PLC (administration costs) and the rest from investments. Grants to 16 organisations totalled £66,500. Two awards to individuals totalled £30,000 (multi-year grants for research purposes at the Durrell Institute of Conservation and Ecology and University of Kent.

Beneficiaries included: Rare Breeds Survival Trust (£5,100); Colwall Orchard Trust (£4,400); Bumblebee Conservation Trust (£2,600); Nottinghamshire Wildlife Trust (£2,300); Children's Hospice South West, The Royal Botanic Garden Edinburgh, The Swanage Pier Trust and Trees For Cities (£2,000 each); Devon Bird Watching and Preservation Society (£1,000); Manx Wildlife Trust (£500).

Exclusions

Support will not be given for salaries or capital building costs.

Applications

Applications should be made in writing (maximum three sides of A4) and emailed to the foundation's secretary at: jslf@johnlewis.co.uk. Guidance on what should be included in the application is provided on the foundation's website. The trustees meet twice a year to consider applications from charities – deadlines are posted on the website.

Lloyd's Charities Trust

General charitable purposes

£569,000 to organisations (2015)

Beneficial area

UK, with particular interest in East London.

Correspondent: Suzanna Nagle, Secretary, Lloyd's of London, Lloyd's Building, 1 Lime Street, London EC3M 7HA (tel: 020 7327 6144; email: suzanna.nagle@lloyds.com or communityaffairs@lloyds.com; website: www.lloyds.com/lct)

CC number: 207232

General information

The charity was set up in 1953, and is the charitable arm of Lloyd's insurance market in London. There are three separate funds that are used to administer grants: the General Fund, the Lloyd's Community Programme and the Education Fund. The following information on these funds is taken from the 2015 annual report:

> *General Fund*
>
> Lloyd's Charities Trust's current funding priorities aim to maximise the impact of the Trust's charitable giving, by focusing on three key areas:
>
> - Making a great city greater: supporting London-based charities to help those who are disadvantaged and foster opportunity
> - Responding to disasters and emergencies: supporting efforts to relieve suffering and help people rebuild their lives
> - Preparing for the future: providing support to equip individuals and communities with the resources and skills they need to meet the challenges of a rapidly changing world
>
> During 2015, Lloyd's Charities Trust made donations amounting to £356,000 from its General Fund.
>
> *Lloyd's Community Programme*
>
> Lloyd's Community Programme (LCP) is a sub-fund of the Trust. LCP encourages volunteering and acts as a catalyst for the Lloyd's market to improve the lives of people in our neighbouring London communities.
>
> In meeting this objective, LCP funds organisations in the field of education, employability and sport. Through long-standing relationships with these organisations, LCP has established many volunteering opportunities for employees within the Lloyd's market.
>
> In 2015 Lloyd's Community Programme disbursed grants to its community delivery partners of over £166,958, including to Tower Hamlets Education Business Partnership who coordinate many of the education volunteer programmes.
>
> *Lloyd's Education Fund*
>
> Lloyd's Education Fund is a sub-fund of Lloyd's Charities Trust managed by the Lloyd's Community Programme Management Board. In 2015, based on recommendations from the Lloyd's Community Programme management board, income has primarily been used to support: The Lloyd's University Bursary scheme, which funds 14 low-income students from Cambridge Heath Sixth Form in Tower Hamlets to study at selective universities outside of London.

Future priorities

According to the website, the trust will be supporting the following organisations from 2016 to 2019: Build Change; Mayor's Fund for London; RedR UK; Whizz-Kidz.

Financial information

In 2015 the trust had assets of £2.9 million and an income of £535,000. There were grants made totalling £569,000, with an additional £55,000 given in bursaries.

Beneficiaries included: Ready to Respond (£100,000); Bromley By Bow Centre and The Mayor's Fund for London (£80,000 each).

Applications

The trust's website states that it will be supporting its partner charities until 2019 and are 'not accepting any new funding submissions at this time'.

Lloyd's Register Foundation

Engineering-related education, research, science and technology

£12.66 million (2014/15)

Beneficial area

Worldwide

Correspondent: Michelle Davies, Company Secretary, 71 Fenchurch Street, London EC3M 4BS (tel: 020 7709 9166; email: michelle.davies@lr.org; website: www.lrfoundation.org.uk)

CC number: 1145988

General information

Lloyd's Register Foundation was registered with the Charity Commission in 2012. It is funded by the profits of its trading arm, Lloyd's Register Group Ltd, a professional services organisation working mainly in the transportation and energy sectors.

According to the 2014/15 annual report, the foundation's mission is:

> - To secure for the benefit of the community high technical standards of design, manufacture, construction, maintenance, operation and performance for the purpose of enhancing the safety of life and property at sea and on land and in the air
> - The advancement of public education including within the transportation industries and any other engineering and technological disciplines

Grant guidelines

The foundation funds 'the advancement of engineering-related education and supports work that enhances safety of life at sea, on land and in the air', and its current funding priorities are as follows:

- Structural integrity and systems performance
- Resilience engineering
- Social and human factors
- Emergent technologies
- Supporting safety organisations
- Communication and public debate of scientific research
- University and pre-university education
- Vocational training and professional development

The foundation states that potential for impact is a key criterion in all of its grant-giving.

The 2014/15 annual report also notes the following:

> A unique feature of the Foundation is that we are able to focus on the long-term because of our governance structure and the assets we own. In many cases we work with our grants community to build long-term relationships, working together on the challenges facing modern society. This means our funding can go into tackling root problems rather than just alleviating the symptoms. It also means that our grants can be significant, both in terms of their value and duration.

In 2014 the foundation established a follow-on fund to allow 'selected research grant holders nearing the end of their grants to apply for funding to address the foundation's new strategy'. During the year, five such requests for funding were approved.

Financial information

In 2014/15 the foundation had assets of £250 million and an income of £19.5 million. There were 35 grants made totalling £12.66 million of which £9 million was committed to research and education in the field of nanotechnology. Grants were broken down as follows:

Supporting excellent scientific research	17	£11.9 million
Advancement of skills and education	12	£555,000
Promoting safety and public understanding of risk	5	£183,000
Accelerating the application of research	1	£20,000

An award of £10 million was made to the Alan Turing Institute to be paid over five years for research into the engineering applications of big data.

Beneficiaries included: University of Southampton (£3.7 million in four grants); University of Manchester (£3 million); University of Cambridge (£2.94 million in two grants); University of Western Australia (£468,000); Royal Academy of Engineering Fellowship Scheme (£430,000); University of Nottingham (£307,000 in two grants); HELMEPA Greece (£204,000); Young Engineers UK (£170,000); Foundation for Science and Technology UK (£105,000); EDT UK – Go4SET (£75,000); Big Bang 2015 – Tomorrow's

Engineers (£40,000); Carbon Disclosure Project (£20,000); Children's Radio (£10,000); Geologists' Association of London (£8,000); Global Young Scientists Summit (£3,000).

Exclusions

No funding is provided for individuals, capital works or infrastructure.

Applications

Applicants should read the guidance notes and complete a proposal form which are both available on the foundation's website. The website also details the latest calls for research funding proposals and application deadline dates. Applications for over £250,000 are considered at quarterly board meetings; all other applications are considered monthly.

Lloyds Bank Foundation for England and Wales

Social and community needs

£17.6 million (2015)

Beneficial area

England and Wales.

Correspondent: Paul Streets, Chief Executive, Pentagon House, 52–54 Southwark Street, London SE1 1UN (tel: 0370 411 1223; email: enquiries@lloydsbankfoundation.org.uk; website: www.lloydsbankfoundation.org.uk)

CC number: 327114

General information

The foundation receives the majority of its income from Lloyds Bank PLC. There is an agreement with Lloyds Bank that until 2020 the foundation will receive 0.3616% of the group's adjusted pre-tax profits/loss, averaged over three years.

Grant programmes

The foundation runs three main funding schemes, details of which have been taken from the website:

Invest

Invest provides longer term core or delivery funding for charities which meet the programme aim and are delivering clear outcomes as a result of their work. These grants are from £10,000 up to maximum of £25,000 per year for two or three years, with the opportunity for continuation funding for a further period – up to six years in total. We fund 'core' organisational costs (including running costs and salaries). By 'core costs we mean those related to the day to day running of your charity. These include salaries, rent, utilities, insurance, IT and consumables. We will only consider requests for 'core costs'; where the majority of your charity's work (over 50% of your work and expenditure) meets our criteria.

We also fund costs associated with the direct delivery of your work. These include volunteer expenses, training, travel, promotion, consumable materials, sessional workers, recruitment and salary costs linked directly to the delivery of your work.

Enable

Enable provides a great opportunity to strengthen your charity so it can deliver more effectively. It can reinvigorate the charity by funding; organisational improvements; development of areas such as leadership and governance; improved systems; demonstrating outcomes etc. These developments will put the charity in a stronger position to be able to deliver services better and attracting funding.

Enable grants are for up to £15k over two years. Grants are awarded to charities that meet the same basic criteria as the Invest programme (charities addressing issues of multiple disadvantages at points of transition) but have also identified clear development areas which will support their growth.

Enable can fund a range of activity related to the development and improvement of the capability of your organisation, for example:

- Business and service developments and plans
- Development of monitoring systems
- Investigation of mergers, partnerships, shared services, contract diversification
- Consultancy support
- Quality standards
- Development of new income streams and enterprise

Enhance

Enhance is a 'grants plus' programme, which provides non-financial support to charities. If a charity is awarded an Invest or an Enable grant, the Foundation will work with them to identify whether they would benefit from additional support to complement the grant funding.

Enhance support is **not** a condition of any grant award and if agreed will be tailored to the specific needs of the charity. Foundation Grant Managers will work with a charity to identify whether there is any additional support that would help the charity operate more effectively and/or respond to any challenges it faces.

Examples of this additional support might include:

- Help to develop or refresh the charity's strategy and supporting business plan
- Development of an outcomes or monitoring framework
- Reviews of the charity's governance arrangements
- Specific guidance on areas such as HR advice or building a digital infrastructure
- A mentor or 'critical friend' relationship with a senior executive within Lloyds Banking Group

Eligibility

The foundation's eligibility criteria, available on the website, states:

- You must be a Charity or Charitable Incorporated Organisation (CIO) registered with the Charity Commission.
- Your charity must have an income between £25,000 and £1 million.
- Your charity must work with disadvantaged people aged 17 and over. The only exception to this is support to people aged under 17 that are young parents, or looked after children and learning disabled young people moving into independent living.

Our grants fund charities that are working with people experiencing multiple disadvantage at one of the following critical points in their life – transition points.

In order to be eligible to apply, your **charity must be supporting people facing multiple disadvantage through one or more of *these transition points*.** Our grants do not support work on transition points that differ from the ones listed.

- Offending
- Children and young people leaving the care of a local authority to live independently
- People moving from community based or institutional care for mental ill health
- Unemployment
- Homelessness/vulnerably housed
- To independent living for those with a learning disability
- From dependency on alcohol, drugs, gambling
- From an abusive or exploitative relationship – domestic violence
- From trafficking or sexual exploitation
- To UK settlement – refugees and asylum seekers
- To parenthood for young parents
- Those taking on caring responsibilities
- For older people losing independence

Financial information

In 2015 the foundation had assets of £26.4 million and an income of £13.8 million. Not including matched giving, programme costs or expenditure through the Enhance programme, grants were *approved* totalling just under £18.1 million.

Grants were approved in the following categories:

Invest	230	£13.95 million
Enable	144	£1.87 million
National	11	£1.86 million
Homeshare	3	£397,000

Note that the above figures include grants totalling £476,000 that were cancelled or recovered. The total of grants payable for the year was £17.6 million.

Exclusions

According to the foundation's website, the following work cannot be funded:

- Organisations not registered with the Charity Commission
- Community Interest Companies
- Second or third tier organisations (unless there is evidence of direct services to individuals with multiple disadvantage). By 'second or 'third tier' we mean organisations whose main purpose is to support other organisations. These are also known as infrastructure or umbrella organisations. We would consider requests from these organisations only for any direct delivery of support to disadvantaged people
- Organisations whose primary purpose is to give funds to individuals or other organisations. By this we mean organisations using more than 50% of annual expenditure as grants
- Hospitals, health authorities or hospices
- Rescue services
- Nurseries, pre-schools or playgroups
- Schools, colleges or universities
- Animal charities
- Charities working outside England and Wales

Grants are not given for:

- Medical care or medical research
- On-line or telephone advice services
- Events and short-term interventions including holidays, expeditions and trips
- Activities for which a statutory body is responsible
- Capital purchases or building work. This includes IT, building work, purchase of vehicles/equipment etc
- Environmental, arts based or sports activities. However we would consider requests from charities who use these activities as part of the transition process – the final outcomes and destination must meet all other guidance – for example we may fund a food growing project for people with mental health problems
- The promotion of religion. This does not exclude organisations that may have a religious element to them as long as their charitable objectives show a wider benefit other than just religion and they are working with the identified groups through transition points – we do not fund charities where the Trustees, staff or volunteers are required to be of a particular faith unless there is a Genuine Occupational Requirement – see ACAS for further guidance on GORs
- Loan repayments
- Sponsorship or funding towards an appeal
- Work that has already taken place
- Evaluation which is not related to the funded work
- Professional qualifications such as ACCA
- Professional fundraisers or bid writers – we will invest in up skilling your staff or volunteers in fundraising skills to make your charity more sustainable
- Redundancy payments

Applications

The following information on the application procedure was taken from the foundation's website:

> **Step 1 – Check My Eligibility** – Read about our Invest and Enable grant programmes to decide which funding is right for you. Then read the guidelines below, click 'Check My Eligibility' button to find out whether we can help your charity, and complete the Eligibility Checklist.
>
> **Step 2 – Application Form** – When you've completed the Eligibility Checklist you'll be given access to our Initial Application Form which you should complete and submit online.
>
> **Step 3 – Full Application and Assessment** – If your application is eligible we will contact you after the application deadline to let you know if it will be taken forward. One of our Grant Managers will then arrange to visit you to discuss your application and if appropriate will invite you to complete the full application online. The decision on whether to award a grant will then be made by our Grants Panel. If your application is ineligible we will let you know as soon as we can.
>
> Before you can access the Initial Application form you should read the guidelines and complete an eligibility checklist which will appear on the final page. These guidelines include a breakdown of 'work we fund' and 'work we can't fund' and are designed to help you decide whether your charity is eligible for a grant or to save you time if it is not.
>
> Please check you are giving correct answers as many applications do not meet our basic eligibility criteria.

Enable grants are accepted on an ongoing basis. Applications for Invest grants are accepted at set stages each year; specific dates for application rounds can be found on the 'Funding Timetable' section of the website (www.lloydsbankfoundation.org.uk/how-to-apply/fundingtimetable).

Lloyds Bank Foundation for the Channel Islands

General charitable purposes

£630,000 (2015)

Beneficial area

The Channel Islands

Correspondent: Jo Le Poidevin, Executive Director, Sarnia House, Le Truchot, St Peter Port, Guernsey GY1 4EF (tel: 01481 706360; email: jlepoidevin@lloydsbankfoundation.org.uk; website: www.lloydsbankfoundationci.org.uk)

CC number: 327113

General information

The foundation was set up by Lloyds Bank in 1986. The foundation derives its income almost entirely from Lloyds Banking Group, but is an independent entity with policies determined by a board of trustees, which meets three times each year, agrees on strategic priorities and distributes funding. According to the foundation's website, grants are made 'to support charitable organisations which help people, especially those who are disadvantaged or disabled, to play a fuller role in communities throughout the Channel Islands'.

What the foundation funds

The trustees are keen to support charities that contribute at a grassroots level to the lives of people in their local communities. The website further explains: 'The trustees are also keen to encourage the infrastructure of the voluntary sector and encourage applications for operational costs. This includes salary costs, which may be funded over two or three years, and training and education for managers and staff.'

Areas of interest

From time to time, the trustees consider the changing social needs of communities, and identify specific areas they wish to focus on within the foundation's overall objectives. The trustees' current areas of interest are listed on the website:

- **Creating positive opportunities for people with disabilities**: 'enabling people with learning or physical disabilities to live independently'
- **Family support**: 'including the development of relationship skills for young people, and encouraging good relationships between generations'
- **Homelessness**: 'in particular helping homeless people back into mainstream society, including support after temporary or permanent accommodation has been secured'
- **Prevention of substance misuse**: 'including both education and rehabilitation'
- **The needs of carers**: 'for example, information and support services, and the provision of respite care'
- **Challenging disadvantage and discrimination**: 'promoting understanding and encouraging solutions which address disadvantage, discrimination or stigma'

Further information, including guidelines, is available from the website.

Financial information

In 2015 the foundation had assets of £1.12 million and an income of £557,500, including £535,500 under the deed of covenant from Lloyds Bank. Grants to 22 organisations totalled £630,000. This figure does not include the amount awarded through the matched giving scheme for Lloyds Bank staff (this totalled £47,500). Grants were distributed as follows:

Health, including mental health	2	£160,000
Support for children and young people	6	£150,500
Support for people with disabilities	4	£124,000
Victim support	1	£45,000
Training, employment and lifelong learning	1	£29,000
Community support	1	£26,000
Relationships, including caring	1	£25,000
Homelessness	1	£23,500
Advice and advocacy	1	£20,000
Support for older people	1	£15,000
Offenders/ex-offenders	1	£12,000

Beneficiaries included: Brighter Futures (£90,000); Families in Recovery Trust (£70,000); Guernsey Employment Trust (£29,000); Jersey Citizens Advice (£20,000); Jersey Arts Centre (£16,000); Offenders Deposit Assistance Scheme (£12,000); Caring Cooks of Jersey (£6,250).

Exclusions

According to the application guidelines, the following fall outside the funding criteria:

- Organisations which are not recognised charities
- Activities which are primarily the responsibility of the Insular Authorities in the Islands or some other responsible body
- Activities which collect funds to give to other charities, individuals or other organisations
- Animal welfare
- Corporate subscription or membership of a charity
- Endowment funds
- Environment – conserving and protecting plants and animals, geography and scenery
- Expeditions or overseas travel
- Fabric appeals for places of worship
- Fundraising events or activities
- Hospitals and Medical Centres (except for projects which are clearly additional to statutory responsibilities)
- Individuals, including students
- Loans or business finance
- Promotion of Religion
- Schools and colleges (except for projects that will benefit disabled students and are clearly additional to statutory responsibilities)
- Sponsorship or marketing appeals
- International appeals – Trustees may from time to time consider a limited number of applications from UK registered charities working abroad

Applications

Application forms, along with guidelines, are available to download from the website. Forms should be submitted together with:

- A copy of a recent bank statement
- An income tax letter of exemption
- Your organisation's latest audited accounts
- If you are applying for funding for a post(s), the job description
- If you are applying for funding over multiple years, a business plan

Applications can be returned to the foundation at any time and must be submitted by post. The foundation does not accept forms that have been emailed or faxed.

Applications are assessed on a continual basis. The trustees meet three times a year to approve grants. Deadline dates for these meetings may vary but generally fall in mid-February, mid-June and mid-October. The process of making a decision can, therefore, take up to four months. All applicants are informed of the outcome of their application.

Applicants are encouraged to discuss their project with the Executive Director before completing an application form. This will help to ensure that your project is within the criteria and that you are applying for an appropriate amount.

Lloyds TSB Foundation for Scotland

Social welfare

£2.7 million (2015)

Beneficial area

Scotland; overseas (see information for International Development Small Grants Programme).

Correspondent: Connie Williamson, Grants Manager, Riverside House, 502 Gorgie Road, Edinburgh EH11 3AF (tel: 0131 444 4020; email: enquiries@ltsbfoundationforscotland.org.uk; website: www.ltsbfoundationforscotland.org.uk)

OSCR number: SC009481

General information

The foundation is one of four Lloyds Banking Group charities, covering England and Wales, Scotland, Northern Ireland and the Channel Islands. The foundation is an independent grant-maker; its relationship with Lloyd Banking Group is outlined on the website:

> In 1985, four independent charitable trusts (Scotland, England & Wales, Northern Ireland, Channel Islands) were created by the will of an Act of Parliament when the Trustee Savings Bank Group was floated on the Stock Market.
>
> A covenant was implemented which stated that Lloyds Banking Group should distribute 1% of pre-tax profits, averaged over three years, to the foundations. Scotland receives 19.46% of this amount.
>
> Lloyds Banking Group chose to serve notice on this agreement in early 2010, and that means we are now in a nine year notice period until the covenant is terminated.

What the foundation does

The foundation works to improve the lives of disadvantaged individuals and communities with the following mission: 'To make a difference to the lives of individuals and communities in Scotland, by encouraging positive change, opportunities, fairness and growth of aspirations, which improve quality of life.' It has three strategic objectives:

- To be the best grant maker we can be through continued progressive grant making
- To reach communities traditional grant making doesn't through innovative asset-based community empowerment (our place-based programme)
- To work with other grant makers so we can all be the best we can by maximising our expertise

Foundation programmes

The following programmes are available from the foundation, as stated on the website:

Henry Duncan Awards

The foundation's main grants programme was renamed in 2010 in honour of the Rev. Henry Duncan, the founder of the first Trustee Savings Bank.

In order to be eligible to apply for a grant, charities must have an annual income of less than £500,000 and be working to deliver programmes or services which are clearly aimed at improving quality of life for people in their community who are facing disadvantage. According to the website, awards of up to £7,000 are made on a one-off basis to charities working with people 'who may typically be experiencing challenging family circumstances, disability, mental ill health, abuse or poverty'. Grants are awarded for projects addressing a wide range of issues, a list of which can be found in the guidance notes on the foundation's website.

The foundation's website explains that trustees are particularly interested in projects supporting:

- Vulnerable children and young people
- Isolated older people
- Carers
- Families in poverty
- People affected by disability or mental-health issues

Funding can be awarded for core costs, such as salaries or running costs, or project funds. The trustees will also consider applications for small capital costs such as equipment.

Partnership Drugs Initiative
The Partnership Drugs Initiative (PDI) was established in 2001 to support work carried out by the voluntary sectors with children and young people who are affected by issues associated with substance abuse. The initiative is delivered in partnership with the Scottish Government and The Robertson Trust. According to the foundation's website, the initiative specifically looks to:

- Increase the wellbeing of children and young people (0 to 25) in Scotland affected by alcohol and other drugs
- Help develop and influence both local and national policy

In 2014 the PDI adopted a new strategic direction addressing four specific areas, which are: identifying and addressing geographical gaps; identifying and addressing thematic gaps; disseminating learning; and optimising funding.

The PDI is based around building relationships between 'policy makers, local partners and projects to ensure collectively we can make a positive difference to children and young people affected by drugs and alcohol'. It is further explained that:

> PDI works closely with all potential and supported groups to help us improve our approach and understanding of what it takes to make a difference to children and young people. Support for groups is offered by sharing our learning and knowledge from other groups and partners.

The initiative targets three areas, which are outlined on the website:

- Children and young people affected by parental substance issues (alcohol and other drugs)
- Pre-teen children who are at higher risk of developing issues relating to alcohol and other drugs
- Young people in need of support due to their own alcohol or drug issue

> PDI provides funding support and will contribute up to a maximum of 50% towards the overall costs of delivering a project/service that will help improve outcomes for children and young people. You can apply for up to three years.

Full information, including how to make an initial application, is provided on the website.

Managed programmes
The foundation also administers and manages programmes on behalf of other organisations. At the time of writing (October 2016) these included:

Scottish Government International Development Small Grants Programme
The foundation distributes funding to incorporated not-for-profit organisations which have a presence in Scotland and an annual turnover of less than £150,000.

Support is given to projects that benefit one of the Scottish Government's priority countries, contribute to the achievement of the UN's Sustainable Development Goals, and alleviate poverty and encourage economic growth. The priority countries are listed on the website as Malawi, Rwanda, Tanzania, Zambia, Pakistan, Bangladesh and the Indian States of Bihar, Madhya Pradesh and Orissa.

Grants are awarded:

- Project: three years, up to £60,000
- Feasibility: one year, up to £10,000
- Capacity building: one year, up to £10,000

For more information, including guidance notes and details of the next funding round, see the website.

The Children, Young People, Families, Early Intervention and Adult Learning and Empowering Communities Fund (CYPFEIF and ALEC Fund)
The foundation is working in partnership with the Scottish Government to deliver this fund.

The core elements of the CYPFEIF aspect of the fund, which the website states 'aims to improve outcomes for children, young people and their families', are:

- Promote the GIRFEC wellbeing indicators and the implementation of UNCRC
- Delivery of prevention and early intervention activities
- Improving parenting capacity and family support

The website further explains that the ALEC element of the fund 'supports third sector organisations to deliver outcomes that improve opportunities for adult learning and building community capacity'. This fund has the following objectives:

- Prevention and early intervention through adult learning and community capacity building
- Supporting the delivery of lifelong, learner-centred adult learning as outlined in the Adult Learning in Scotland Statement of Ambition
- Using asset based approaches to work with adult learners or with communities to plan and co-design learning or capacity building opportunities

Both core funding and project funding are available through the CYPFEIF and ALEC Fund. See the website for full information.

Financial information
In 2015 the foundation had assets of £5.18 million and an income of £2.4 million. Grants were awarded totalling £2.7 million and were distributed through the following programmes:

Partnership Drugs Initiative (PDI)	£1.4 million
Henry Duncan Awards (HDA)	£908,000
International Small Grants Scheme	£367,000
Recovery Initiative Fund (RFI)	£20,000

Beneficiaries in 2015, according to the foundation's website, included: Clued Up Project (£396,000); Quarriers (£234,500); Bellshill and Mossend YMCA (£108,500); Stable Life (£34,000); Voluntary Action Orkney (£13,000); Town Break SCIO (£7,000); Reidvale Adventure Play Association Ltd (£6,00); The Well Multi-Cultural Advice Centre (£5,500); Headway Highland (£5,000); Hidden Gardens Trust and Stillbirth and Neonatal Death Society Lothians (£4,500 each); Coatbridge Citizens Advice (£3,600); Sheddocksley Baptist Church (£2,000); Relationships Scotland (£1,800); Edinburgh Chinese Elderly Support Association (£1,000); Scottish Huntington's Association – Glasgow South Branch (£700).

Exclusions
Each programme has its own criteria. Refer to the foundation's website for more information.

Applications
Application forms for all programmes, complete with comprehensive guidance notes and application deadlines, are available from the foundation. These can be requested by telephone, by email, or online through its website. Foundation staff are always willing to provide additional help.

Man Group PLC Charitable Trust

Literacy and numeracy
£357,000 (2015)

Beneficial area
UK, with some preference for London.

Correspondent: Angeline Boothroyd, Trust Secretary, Man Group PLC, Riverbank House, 2 Swan Lane, London EC4R 3AD (tel: 020 7144 1737; email: charitable.trust@man.com; website: www.man.com/GB/man-charitable-trust)

CC number: 275386

General information

This trust, which was registered in 1978, is the corporate charity of the investment management firm Man Group PLC. The trust is the vehicle for most of the company's charitable donations and operates as an independent charity.

The trust has two main aims: firstly, it looks to support organisations working to raise literacy and numeracy levels in the UK and, secondly, it looks to facilitate opportunities for Man Group employees to share their time and expertise for charitable causes. It works to achieve these aims by carrying out the following activities which are outlined on the website:

- **Providing grants** via a two stage application process, or through negotiated partnerships with selected charities
- **Tracking success** by measuring impact, carefully monitoring all grants to ensure progress against agreed objectives
- **Providing volunteering opportunities** to Man Group UK employees via the Trust's community volunteering programme, ManKind
- **Supporting Man Group UK employees** fundraising activity and charitable donations via the Trust's Sponsorship Matching and Give As You Earn

Funding criteria

The trust supports small to medium-sized charities registered in the UK whose work is focused on the promotion of literacy and/or numeracy. There is a document available to download from the website which sets out full criteria and details of how to apply. It states that, in order to be eligible, a charity must:

- Have an annual income greater than £1 million and less than £10 million
- Raise levels of literacy and/or numeracy with evidence of an increase in attainment in one or both of these areas
- Have a significant impact; changing wider policy and practice or having the potential to be mainstreamed or replicated
- Have clear and measurable outcomes and benefits and use evidence of results to improve performance
- Lead to leverage of additional funding wherever possible

The document further explains that applicants must be able to show that they are 'well run, with good governance and financial management'; and that they 'have an ambitious approach to tackling social issues'. The trustees prefer to support activities that provide assistance directly to individuals, families and communities and also those that increase the capacity of organisations and individuals.

The trustees also consider the 'interest and involvement' of employees of Man Group and seek to find out about volunteering opportunities within an applicant organisation; however, no preference is given to organisations or projects that can offer such opportunities.

Grant-making

The document from the Man Group website explains that 'the trust is currently funding one year grants of up to £50,000, but will consider longer-term support for applications that are deemed by trustees to have particular merit'. Grants are typically given to fund core costs (including salaries and overheads) and project costs.

Financial information

In 2015 the trust had assets of £1.94 million and an income of £754,500, of which £750,000 was received in the form of a donation from Man Group PLC. Not including expenditure on employee sponsorship matching (which amounted to £29,500), employee Give As You Earn matching (£25,000) or employee volunteering (£1,800), grants totalling £357,000 were made to 13 charities and were distributed by category as follows:

Literacy and numeracy	£322,000
Annual charity (Children's Cancer Recovery Project)	£25,000
Disadvantaged youth – education	£10,000

Beneficiaries included: National Literacy Trust and Tower Hamlets Education Business Partnership (£50,000 each); NSPCC (£29,000); School-Home Support (£28,000); Children's Cancer Recovery Project (£25,000); The Boxing Academy and Westside School (£12,500 each); Longford Trust (£10,000).

Exclusions

The guidelines state that:

> The trust does not as a rule support, through its grants programme or its broader giving:
>
> - Large national charities
> - Charities which use external fundraising agencies
> - Charities primarily devoted to promoting religious beliefs
> - Endowment funds
> - Requests to directly replace statutory funding
> - Individual beneficiaries
> - General media campaigns or campaigning or advocacy work to influence policy debates
> - Applicants which have been successful during the last twelve months
> - Work which has already been completed
> - Capital projects and appeals
> - Sponsorship or funding towards marketing appeals or fundraising events
> - Organisations or projects whose primary purpose is political

Furthermore, the trust will not consider charities with 'high administration costs relative to the services provided'.

Applications

In the first instance, see the trust's page on the Man Group website, where a document detailing eligibility criteria and guidelines on how to apply is available.

The document states that the trust has a two-stage application process. After reading the trust's eligibility criteria, principles and exclusions, a brief expression of interest that is no longer than one side of A4 should be sent to trustees@man.com. The expression of interest should include the following:

- A brief summary of your organisation's aims and activities, and if relevant the project for which you are applying for funding (outlining the work you hope to carry out, what the need for this is, who will benefit, when you plan to undertake it, and where it will be based)
- Details of how your organisation meets the Trust's focus
- The amount of funding requested
- How the funds will be used if granted
- Contact details

If your expression of interest is successful you will be invited to submit a stage 2 application form for consideration by the trustees who usually meet twice a year. Successful applicants will be notified by telephone or email. All unsuccessful applicants will be notified and will usually receive an outline explanation for the rejection.

The guidelines state: **'Please note that meeting all of the criteria does not guarantee you will be invited to complete a full application form or that if you are invited to do so, you will receive funding. All awards are made at the discretion of Trustees and their decision is final.'**

Manchester Airport Community Trust Fund

Environment, social welfare, community development

£119,000 (2015/16)

Beneficial area

Within a ten-mile radius of Manchester airport, concentrating on the areas most exposed to aircraft noise.

Correspondent: Tina Large, Administrator, Manchester Airport PLC, Olympic House, Manchester Airport, Manchester M90 1QX (tel: 0161 489

5281; email: trust.fund@manairport.co.uk; website: www.manchesterairport.co.uk/community/working-in-our-community/community-trust-fund)

CC number: 1071703

General information

Registered with the Charity Commission in 1998, the Manchester Airport Community Trust Fund is a corporate charity of Manchester Airports Group PLC. The trustees are employees of Manchester Airport, as well as trustees appointed by the Manchester Airport Consultative Committee from the council areas of Stockport, Manchester, Trafford, Tameside, Cheshire East and Cheshire West and Chester. The fund receives £100,000 each year from Manchester Airport Group, as well as the proceeds of fines charged for aircraft which exceed noise limits.

According to the accounts for 2015/16, the fund's aims are as follows:

- promote, enhance, improve, protect and conserve the natural and built environment by projects of tree planting, afforestation and landscaping and other works of environmental improvement and heritage conservation
- enable within those areas facilities in the interests of social welfare for recreation, sport and leisure time occupation with the object of improving the conditions of life for those living or working in or visitors to those areas
- promote and provide for the benefit of the public a better appreciation of the natural and urban environment and ways of better serving, protecting and improving the same and education and training in all matters relating to the natural, physical environment and its interaction with the economic wellbeing of the community

Grants

According to the website, grants of up to £3,000 are awarded to charitable organisations based within a ten-mile radius of Manchester Airport (a map is provided on the website) and which are 'community, socially or environmentally focused'.

To be eligible for funding, projects should:

- Improve, enhance, protect and conserve the natural and built environment; or offer heritage conservation; or promote or advance social welfare; or provide better appreciation of the natural and urban environment; or create a safe habitat for flora and fauna
- Demonstrate lasting benefit to the community
- Benefit all members of the community regardless of race, gender or religion
- Be from an established group or charity able to demonstrate clear banking or financial records, and not an individual or commercial organisation working for profit

Projects must be open to the whole community, or a large section of it, and grants are given only for 'anything which is tangible and long lasting', such as equipment.

Financial information

In 2015/16 the fund held assets of £29,000 and had an income of £129,000, of which £100,000 was a monetary donation and £17,000 an in kind donation from Manchester Airport Group PLC for administration costs. Grants to 64 charitable organisations were made totalling £119,000.

Beneficiaries included: Cheadle Golf Club, Fairey Brass Band and Scott Avenue Allotments (£3,000 each); Friends of Romiley Park (£2,800); Knutsford Musical Theatre (£2,700); Dunham Massey Village Hall (£2,100); Manchester Rugby Club (£1,900); Chorlton Central Church (£1,500); Venture Arts (£1,000); Re-Dish and Wimbourne Social Club (£500 each).

Exclusions

Grants are not awarded for:

- Maintenance or running costs (including, for example, repair work, energy costs, salaries, coach fees, uniform or kits)
- Purchase of land or buildings
- Projects which have already taken place
- Individuals

Applications

Application forms can be found on the charity's website, along with guidelines. The trustees meet four times a year, in January, April, July and October and applicants should be informed of a decision within seven to ten days of a meeting.

Successful applicants are encouraged to promote their grant through the local media, and in their own newsletters and publications.

D. G. Marshall of Cambridge Trust

Aviation, disability, health and life threatening conditions, education, hospitals and related organisations, churches, children, local community

£46,000 (2014/15)

Beneficial area

Mainly Cambridgeshire, with some grants made to UK national charities.

Correspondent: Julie Ingham, Administrator, Airport House, The Airport, Newmarket Road, Cambridgeshire CB5 8RY

CC number: 286468

General information

The trust was established in December 1982 by its corporate settlor Marshall of Cambridge Aerospace Ltd (referred to in the trust's annual report and accounts as 'the Company'), Marshall of Cambridge (Holdings) Ltd and Marshall Motor Group Ltd. The trust's annual report for 2014/15 explains that 'initially the trust capital was £100 but since then further donations have been paid into the Trust by the settlor'.

The trust's primary objectives are to support:

- People who are in need, particularly those who are employees or ex-employees of the company or any subsidiary or associated company; and their dependants
- Local charities
- Local educational institutions of a charitable nature

Grants are made to support local charities in Cambridgeshire (where Marshall is headquartered), as well as to UK national charities.

Financial information

In 2014/15 the trust had assets of £2.24 million and an income of £223,000, of which £155,000 was received from Marshall of Cambridge (Holdings) Ltd. During the year, 40 grants were made to organisations, amounting to £46,000. Grants were distributed in the following categories:

Aviation	£16,500
Disability, health and life threatening conditions	£12,700
Education	£9,600
Hospitals and related organisations	£2,500
Churches	£2,000
Children's charities	£1,600
Local community	£1,200

Beneficiaries included: Arthur Rank Hospice Charity and The National Spitfire Project (£5,000 each); Air League (£3,000); The Royal Aeronautical Society (£2,500); Age UK Cambridgeshire (£1,700); Cambridge Science Centre and Ely Cathedral Restoration Trust (£1,000 each); East Anglian Children's Hospice (£500); Institute of Economic Affairs (£350); Alzheimer's Society (£250).

Applications

The trustees will consider all applications, providing they are consistent with the objectives of the trust.

Mazars Charitable Trust

General charitable purposes

£327,500 (2015/16)

Beneficial area

UK and Ireland.

Correspondent: Bryan Rogers, Trust Administrator, 1 Cranleigh Gardens, South Croydon, Surrey CR2 9LD (tel: 020 8657 3053)

CC number: 1150459

General information

The firm Mazars LLP specialises in audit, tax and advisory services across a range of markets and sectors. This associated charitable trust was registered with the Charity Commission in January 2013 and makes grants to charitable organisations in the UK and Ireland. In 2015/16 the majority of the trust's income was received from Mazars LLP. It does not respond to unsolicited applications; however, applications can be made by a team member of Mazars LLP.

The trustees appoint a committee made up of regional representatives, which meets annually to decide on and administer national grants which are nominated by employees. Ten local offices also award smaller grants within their region.

The company has a commitment to corporate social responsibility and states on its website: 'The firm also supports the fundraising efforts of individual team members participating in sponsored events such as marathons, long distance bike rides, parachute jumps and other challenges.'

Financial information

In 2015/16 the trust had assets of £408,000 and an income of £329,500. The trust made 213 grants totalling £327,500.

Beneficiaries included: The Prince's Trust (£25,000); St Catherine's Hospice Lancashire (£16,500); Humanity First and Women For Women International (£15,000 each); ADRA UK, Ithemba Study Centre and Ripple Africa (£5,000 each); Crisis (£1,600); Motor Neurone Disease Association (£1,400); Sport Relief (£1,000).

Grants of between £45 and £1,000 to 179 charities totalled £73,000.

Exclusions

National grants are not generally repeated within three years and they are rarely given for core costs.

Applications

The trust does not respond to unsolicited applications. All nominations for grants have to be proposed by staff members of Mazars LLP and no grant applications should be submitted directly to the trust.

The Robert McAlpine Foundation

General charitable purposes, medical research, social welfare, children with disabilities, older people

£681,000 (2014/15)

Beneficial area

UK

Correspondent: Brian Arter, Sir Robert McAlpine Ltd, Eaton Court, Maylands Avenue, Hemel Hempstead, Hertfordshire HP2 7TR (tel: 01442 233444; email: b.arter@sir-robert-mcalpine.com)

CC number: 226646

General information

Sir Robert McAlpine Ltd is a family-owned UK construction and civil engineering company. Its most recent projects have included the O2 Arena, Emirates Stadium, the Eden Project and the Olympic Stadium. The Robert McAlpine Foundation was registered with the Charity Commission in 1964 and its current trustees are all members of the McAlpine family; with two serving as directors of the company.

Its 2014/15 accounts state that 'the foundation operates virtually exclusively by making identified benefit grants to carefully selected charitable organisations working in the sectors which the foundation particularly wishes to support'.

Areas of support

The foundation generally supports causes concerned with children who have disabilities, older people, medical research, social welfare and charities with an income of less than £1 million. The annual report for 2014/15 also states that: 'The policy of the trustees is to make grants to charitable institutions of amounts from £5,000 upwards in the specific categories of objectives which they support.'

Financial information

In 2014/15 the foundation had assets of £15.6 million and had an income of £928,000, which included a £500,000 donation from Sir Robert McAlpine Ltd. Grants paid during the year totalled £681.000.

A list of beneficiaries was unavailable.

Previous beneficiaries have included: Age Concern; Community Self Build Agency; DENS Action Against Homelessness; Downside Fisher Youth Club; Ewing Foundation; the Golden Oldies; Grateful Society; James Hopkins Trust; Merchants Academy Withywood; National Benevolent Fund for the Aged; National Eye Research Centre; Prostate UK; Royal Marsden NHS Trust; St Johns Youth Centre; and the Towers School and 6th Form Centre.

Applications

Applications can be made in writing to the correspondent at any time. Applications are considered annually, normally in November.

The Morgan Foundation

Children and young people, older people, health and disability, social welfare

£2.35 million (2015/16)

Beneficial area

North Wales, Merseyside, West Cheshire and North Shropshire.

Correspondent: Jane Harris, Foundation Administrator, PO Box 3517, Chester CH1 9ET (tel: 01829 782800; fax: 01829 782223; email: contact@morganfoundation.co.uk; website: www.morganfoundation.co.uk)

CC number: 1087056

General information

The foundation was established in 2001 with an endowment of over £2 million from Stephen Morgan, founder of Redrow PLC and chair of Wolverhampton Wanders FC. The following outline of the foundation's aims and objectives is given on its website:

> Our aim is to provide funding for small to medium-sized organisations who are addressing specific needs in [North Wales, Merseyside, West Cheshire and North Shropshire]. We are particularly keen to support those who have already begun to make an impact, but need a helping hand to expand their work and increase their effectiveness.
>
> We focus our help mainly on those who work directly with children and families, but we recognise that many wider issues may also affect their welfare so we are interested in any project which contributes to the quality of life of the people in our region.

Grant-making guidelines

The foundation gives the following information on its website:

> *Where we fund*
>
> The Morgan Foundation operates exclusively within the areas of North Wales, Merseyside, West Cheshire and North Shropshire. Only applications from charities, organisations and projects based in these areas will be considered
>
> *Who we fund*
>
> The Morgan Foundation specialises in supporting organisations helping children and families as well as the elderly, disabled and socially isolated. We will consider any work which has a positive effect on their welfare and quality of life, or which expands the opportunities and life choices for young people in this region.
>
> Areas of support to date have included physical and learning disability, physical and mental health, plus social challenge and deprivation.
>
> Though the majority of the recipients of our grants are registered charities, we will also consider applications from other types of organisations which are pursuing charitable causes and where aims and objectives are 'not for profit'. Whilst we recognise the need for specialist, professional care in some circumstances, preference is given to 'hands on' organisations with a high volunteer input.
>
> *What we fund*
>
> Grants may be considered for a range of purposes and could include:
>
> - Single awards for capital projects
> - Start-up and/or ongoing running costs for specific projects
> - Multi-year revenue grants for core funding
> - Standard and wheelchair accessible minibuses are offered under the Smiley Bus scheme
>
> The type, size and time period of the award is decided on the basis of the perceived 'difference' that our support will make to the organisation, to the project and to the targeted beneficiaries.
>
> It is important that you tell us in your application the full extent of the funding you really need to achieve your aims and objectives, in order for us to assess how best we can contribute.

Financial information

In 2015/16 the foundation had assets of almost £13 million and an income of £936,000, of which Redrow PLC donated £732,000. There were 93 grants made totalling almost £2.35 million.

Beneficiaries include: Newlife Foundation (£100,000); North Perk (Ykids) (£90,000); Wirral Society of the Blind (£60,000); Chester Sexual Abuse Support Services (£45,000); Liverpool Homeless Football (£22,500); Neuromuscular Centre (15,400); Wolves Aid (£10,000); Burtonwood Sewing Group (£5,000); Whitechapel (£500); Down's Syndrome Association (£100).

Exclusions

The foundation will not give grants for the following:

- Animal welfare
- Arts/heritage
- Conservation/environment
- Expeditions and overseas travel
- General fundraising appeals
- Individual and sports sponsorship
- National charities and large organisations
- Mainstream education
- Mainstream sport
- Promotion of specific religions

Note that local branches of national charities which are based within the remit area, or programmes delivered locally by organisations working on a national basis, are also not generally supported.

Applications

The foundation gives the following guidance about making an application on its website:

> First, please ensure that you are eligible under our policy:
>
> - Check that your organisation/project is based within our geographic area
> - Check that your organisation/project is not listed in our exclusions
> - Ring us for an informal chat and request an application form
>
> Before finalising or submitting an application please telephone for an informal chat to check that your proposed application falls in line with current policy. We understand that it can be daunting to pick up the phone, but we believe that an initial chat can save you and us lots of wasted time, and we will be happy to give you guidance as to what specific information we need to process your application.
>
> Once you have contacted us by phone and it has been agreed that your application is appropriate, we will ask you to send in a description of your organisation, its history, activities, volunteers, beneficiaries, achievements to date and current funding needs. Please enclose copies of most recent reports and accounts. If you have a project in mind, describe its purpose, targets, budget, and timescale.
>
> All applications will be acknowledged and we will contact you for any further information we require. All charities and projects will be visited before a grant is approved.
>
> Timing of Applications: Trustee Meetings are held regularly throughout the year and there are no specific dates for applications to be received. However, organisations should be aware that applications are considered in chronological order and it can take up to six months for the process to be completed.

The Morrisons Foundation

General charitable purposes

£1.6 million (2015/16)

Beneficial area

Areas of the company's presence in the UK.

Correspondent: David Hewitt, Communities Manager, Hilmore House, 71 Gain Lane, Bradford, West Yorkshire BD3 7DL (tel: 0845 611 4449; email: community@morrisonsplc.co.uk; website: www.morrisonsfoundation.com)

CC number: 1160224

General information

The Morrisons Foundation, registered with the Charity Commission in January 2015, was established by the supermarket chain Morrisons to make a difference to the lives of people living in the UK communities in which it has a presence.

The foundation makes charitable contributions in two ways: firstly, by match funding employee fundraising efforts; and secondly, by making grants.

Funding is given only to registered charities for particular projects which aim to improve people's lives.

Financial information

In 2015/16 the foundation had assets of £3.3 million and an income of almost £4.1 million which largely came from the sale of carrier bags in Morrisons' stores. Grants were made totalling almost £1.6 million and the foundation donated over £111,000 in the matched funding of employees' fundraising.

Beneficiaries included: W.O.T.S. Project (£16,500); Willow Wood Hospice (£10,000); Hey Smile Foundation (£9,300); MedEquip4Kids (£6,900); Carers' Support Bexley (£6,600); Couple Counselling Lothian (£5,900); Theodora Children's Charity (£5,000); Mansfield Play Forum (£4,700); The Comedy Trust

(£2,000); Deaf Children North West (£500).

Applications

An application form is available to download from the website and applicants will be notified of a decision within three months of submitting an application, even if the application is unsuccessful.

The website states that charities 'that have previously received a grant donation can submit an application after completing a post-grant report'. It is further noted: 'We don't limit the timeframe in which charities can apply for a grant following an unsuccessful application.'

The Nationwide Foundation

Community development, housing, legal assistance, and social welfare

£1.5 million (2015/16)

Beneficial area

UK

Correspondent: The Trustees of the Nationwide Foundation, Nationwide Building Society, Nationwide House, Pipers Way, Swindon SN38 2SN (tel: 01793 655113; email: enquiries@nationwidefoundation.org.uk; website: www.nationwidefoundation.org.uk)

CC number: 1065552

General information

Registered with the Charity Commission in 1997, the Nationwide Foundation is principally funded by Nationwide Building Society, which donates 1% of its pre-tax profit. Its aims and objectives are to create decent affordable housing for people in need, as well as to create conditions which increase the number of decent affordable homes.

The foundation's accounts for 2015/16 state that the trustees 'seek to fund work that addresses the root cause of social issues' and award grants to organisations based in and delivering work in the UK. Grants will be given towards the costs of refurbishment and can include a fair contribution towards organisational core costs. Funds will also be considered towards legal and other such costs associated with obtaining empty homes.

Grant-making

The foundation's annual report states that its 'vision is for everyone in the UK to have access to a decent home which they can afford' and that the trustees award grants under the following categories:

Empty properties

The focus is on 'bringing empty properties into use for people in need'.

Private rented sector

The foundation seeks to improve 'the living conditions of vulnerable tenants in the private rented sector (PRS)'. In particular this includes projects that:

- raise awareness of the need to improve the living conditions of vulnerable tenants in the PRS
- help vulnerable tenants in PRS homes to improve their living conditions on a national, regional or local scale
- increase the number of affordable, decent, PRS homes which provide more favourable living conditions to vulnerable tenants

Housing models

The aim is to support alternative housing models in order to provide more affordable homes. Funding is given in the form of grants and programme-related social investments.

The foundation may also support work that includes research, development, piloting and scaling up of alternative affordable housing models. Models may address: increasing the availability of social housing; creating new routes to affordable home ownership; or devising new ways to provide decent, affordable housing to rent or buy.

Financial information

In 2015/16 the foundation had assets of £1.23 million and an income of almost £1.67 million of which £1.57 million came from a donation from the Nationwide Building Society. In addition the society donated services to the foundation totalling £92,000, which represented the provision of office space, technology, legal and accountancy support. There were 16 grants made totalling £1.5 million all under the 'Decent Affordable Homes' grant-making strategy.

Beneficiaries included: Locality (£160,500); Canopy Housing (£160,000); YMCA Glenrothes (£159,000); Action Homeless Leicester (140,000); Grimsby Doorstep (£130,000); Generation Rent (£107,500); Community Campus 87 (£75,000); Rural Action Yorkshire (£34,000); Community Land Trust Fund (£22,000); DAH Added Value (£14,500).

Exclusions

The foundation will not consider funding for the following:

- Charities with unrestricted reserves which exceed 50% of annual expenditure, as shown in their accounts
- Charities which are in significant debt as shown in their accounts
- Promotion of religion or politics
- Charities which have been declined by the foundation within the last 12 months
- Applications which do not comply with the foundation's funding criteria/guidelines

Applications

At the time of writing (February 2017), the foundation was not accepting any new applications. However, its website stated that preparation was underway for the next stage of its Decent Affordable Homes funding strategy, the details of which will be released in early 2017. Check the foundation's website for the latest information.

The NFU Mutual Charitable Trust

Community development, education, the relief of poverty, social welfare, and research focusing on initiatives that will have a significant impact on rural communities

£224,000 (2015)

Beneficial area

UK, with a preference for rural areas.

Correspondent: James Creechan, Secretary to the Trustees, The National Farmers Union Mutual Insurance Society Ltd, Tiddington Road, Stratford-upon-Avon, Warwickshire CV37 7BJ (tel: 01789 204211; email: nfu_mutual_charitable_trust@nfumutual.co.uk; website: www.nfumutual.co.uk/company-information/charitable-trust)

CC number: 1073064

General information

Registered with the Charity Commission in 1998, the NFU Mutual Charitable Trust is the corporate charity of the National Farmers Union Mutual Insurance Society Ltd (NFU Mutual), one of the UK's leading insurers. Notable trustees include Richard Percy, Chair of NFU Mutual and Lindsay Sinclair, its Chief Executive.

The website states that:

> The objectives of The NFU Mutual Charitable Trust are to promote, facilitate and support such purposes as are exclusively charitable according to the laws of England and Wales in the areas of agriculture, rural development and

insurance in the United Kingdom and in particular.

- To advance the education of the public by means of research and dissemination of information in relation to agriculture
- To advance the education of young people within rural areas
- To relieve poverty within rural areas
- To promote the benefit and social welfare of inhabitants of rural communities by associating together with the inhabitants and local authorities, voluntary and other organisations to advance education and leisure
- To promote research into agriculture associated activities
- To advance the education of the public by means of research and dissemination of information in relation to insurance

In 2015 the Charitable Trust continued to support The NFU Mutual Charitable Trust Centenary Award. The Centenary Award gives annual bursaries of up to 75% of the course fees for selected postgraduate students in agriculture. Three bursaries were awarded in 2015.

Financial information

In 2015 the trust had assets of £246,500 and an income of £258,000. Grants totalled £224,000 and were made to 17 charitable organisations.

The annual report 2015 states: 'The grants included within expenditure on charitable activities are all paid to institutions with no grants paid to individuals.'

Beneficiaries included: Farming and Countryside Education (£60,000); The National Federation of Young Farmers (£30,000); Addington Fund (£15,000); Nuffield Farming Scholarships Trust (£11,000); Farms for City Children (£4,000); Children's County Hospital Fund (£1,000).

Applications

Apply in writing to the correspondent either via post or email. The application form is available from the trust's website.

According to the trust's website:

> Applications for funding for projects and initiatives falling within the Objects of the Trust can be made in writing to:
>
> The NFU Mutual Charitable Trust, Tiddington Road, Stratford upon Avon, Warwickshire CV37 7BJ
>
> Email: nfu_mutual_charitable_trust@nfumutual.co.uk
>
> When making an application, details should be included of:
>
> - The project, initiative or organisation for which funding is sought
> - An indication of the amount of the donation requested
> - Any business plans
> - Details of any other funding sought and or obtained
> - Any recognition which would be given to the Trust in recognition of its support
> - Confirmation of whether or not the applicant is a registered charity
>
> Following a recent strategic review, the Trustees have indicated that in future, the Trust will focus on providing funding to larger initiatives, which would have a significant impact on the rural community. The Trustees are particularly interested in initiatives in the areas of education of young people in rural areas and relief of poverty within rural areas.
>
> The Trustees meet twice a year to consider applications received. These meetings are currently held in June and November.

Oglesby Charitable Trust

General charitable purposes, particularly: arts, education, environment, social welfare, and medical aid and research

£2.26 million (2014/15)

Beneficial area

Primarily (although not exclusively) the North West.

Correspondent: The Trustees of Oglesby Charitable Trust, PO Box 336, Altrincham, Cheshire WA14 3XD (email: welcome@oglesbycharitabletrust.org.uk; website: www.oglesbycharitabletrust.co.uk)

Trustees: Jean Oglesby; Michael Oglesby; Bob Kitson; Katharine Vokes; Jane Oglesby; Chris Oglesby; Peter Renshaw.

CC number: 1026669

General information

The Oglesby Charitable Trust was established in 1992. The funding of the trust comes from annual contributions from Bruntwood Ltd, part of a group of North West-based property investment companies owned by the founding trustees.

The following information is taken from the trust's website:

> The Trust was set up to support activities in the North West of England to further the well-being of the Region and its people through a very wide range of activities which include the Arts, Education, Environment, Medical Research and tackling Social Inequality. Since its inception the principal activities of the OCT have remained focused in the North of England, although the Trustees have supported a limited number of projects outside both the North West and the UK.
>
> The Trustees take both a grassroots and a strategic approach to their giving, understanding that local approaches tend to reach those most in need, whilst broader initiatives and collaborations are sometimes necessary to drive meaningful change. The Trustees have therefore taken the decision to become focused on root causes, rather than consequences.

While grants are made primarily in the North West, the 2014/15 annual report notes that the trustees have also made grants to UK-based charities working on projects in East Africa and, through Aston University, a project in Northern India. The report also notes that there are no further plans to contribute to other overseas projects.

Eligibility

Who we help

According to the website, the trust supports primarily the following:

- Registered charities whose activities are based in the north west of England
- Organisations who can demonstrate that the funds are making a real difference, rather than being absorbed into a large anonymous pool, no matter how significant the end result may be
- Organisations that demonstrate both the highest standards of propriety and sound business sense in their activities. This does not mean high overheads but it does mean focused use of funds, directly to where they are needed
- Projects that can be ring-fenced

Types of activity

The trust supports the following:

- Artistic development, both on an individual and group level
- Educational – revenue grants, bursaries and building projects
- Environmental projects
- Tackling social inequality, especially projects in which individuals and communities can be enabled to become self-supporting
- Medical aid and research

Financial information

In 2014/15 the trust had assets of £10 million and an income of £5.68 million. There were grants made totalling £2.26 million, £1.98 million of which went to 33 organisations and £278,000 was distributed in 'other' grants. All grants were broken down in the annual report as follows:

Medical aid and research	35%
Improving the lives and welfare of the underprivileged	26%
Artistic development	19%
Education	14%
Environmental activities	6%

Beneficiaries included: Seashell Trust (£500,000); Chetham's School of Music (£250,000); Manchester Cancer Research Centre (£112,500); Community Forest Trust (£87,000); RNCM (£75,000); HOME and Whitworth Art Gallery (£50,000 each); After Adoption (£30,000); The Clink Charity (£25,000); Cheadle Hulme School (£15,000).

Exclusions

The trust does not support:

- Non-registered charities
- Activities which are for the purpose of collecting funds for redistribution to other charities
- Animal charities
- Charities mainly operating outside the UK
- Church and all building fabric materials
- Conferences
- Continuing running costs of an organisation
- Costs of employing fundraisers
- Expeditions
- General sports, unless there is a strong association with a disadvantaged group
- Holidays
- Individuals
- Loans or business finance
- Charities promoting religion
- Routine staff training
- Sponsorship and marketing appeals

Applications

Unsolicited applications are not acknowledged. The trust's website states the following:

> The Trustees are generating, through existing and new relationships, a level of giving that more than matches the Trust's income. This is despite planned growth in the future income over the next few years. The Trustees have taken the decision to develop further this proactive stance to their giving, and only give to charities that they themselves select.
>
> Please do not, therefore, make unsolicited approaches, either by email, letter or in any other form, as they will not be considered or acknowledged.

The Persimmon Charitable Foundation

General charitable purposes, including: community and economic development, sustainable development, education, work with young people, sport, health, social welfare

Beneficial area

England and Wales.

Correspondent: The Trustees of the Persimmon Charitable Foundation, Persimmon PLC, Persimmon House, Fulford, York YO19 4FE (tel: 01904 642199; website: corporate.persimmonhomes.com/corporate-responsibility)

Trustees: Gerald Francis; Jeff Fairburn; Marion Sears; Mike Killoran; Nicholas Wrigley.

CC number: 1163608

General information

The foundation was registered with the Charity Commission in September 2015, established by Persimmon PLC, a large housebuilding company.

According to the Charity Commission record, the foundation's objects are as follows:

- To promote urban regeneration in areas of economic and social deprivation through: education and training, particularly for young people and those who are unemployed; provision of public amenities; provision of public recreational facilities, particularly for those who are disadvantaged in any way
- To promote sustainable development, particularly through the conservation of the environment in residential development, and through sustainable economic growth and regeneration
- To advance young people's education, skills and participation in society
- To advance amateur sport
- To advance health and to further the prevention of, cure of, and research into, ill health and disease
- To relieve the needs of those who are disadvantaged through poverty, age, ill health, disability or other disadvantage

Financial information

At the time of writing (February 2017), there were no accounts yet available for the foundation.

Applications

Apply in writing to the correspondent. Check the Persimmon PLC website for updates.

The Personal Assurance Charitable Trust

General charitable purposes, social welfare, health

£197,000 (2015)

Beneficial area

UK

Correspondent: Sarah Mace, Trustee, Personal Group Holdings PLC, John Ormond House, 899 Silbury Boulevard, Milton Keynes MK9 3XL (email: sarah.mace@personal-group.com)

Trustees: Michael Dugdale; Philip Yates; Sarah Mace.

CC number: 1023274

General information

The Personal Assurance Charitable Trust (PACT) was registered with the Charity Commission in 1993. It is the corporate charity of Personal Group Holdings PLC, a provider of employee benefits and financial services. The trust's annual report states:

> There are no geographical or other restrictions on the type of donations that can be made. However preference will be given to recommendations made by policyholders of Personal Assurance Plc, their employers, and employees of Personal Group Holdings Plc and its subsidiary undertakings. In addition the trustees prefer to make donations that benefit the wider community rather than individual causes.

Financial information

In 2015 the trust had assets of £85,000 and an income of £100,500 of which £100,000 was received as a donation from Personal Assurance Group Holdings PLC. Grants were made totalling £197,000.

Beneficiaries included: Memusi Foundation (£120,500); Special Forces Club (£15,000); Cancer Research UK (£6,000); Alzheimer's Society (£5,900); The Outward Bound Trust (£5,000); St Francis Hospice (£3,600); Hospitality Action (£3,000); SANDS (£1,800); Latch Wales and Mind (£1,000 each).

Donations under £1,000 totalled £20,000.

Exclusions

Grants are rarely made to individuals.

Applications

Apply in writing to the correspondent.

The Persula Foundation

General charitable purposes, including: people who are homeless, people with disabilities, human rights, and animal welfare

£1.07 million (2014/15)

Beneficial area

Worldwide

Correspondent: Teresa Chapman, Secretary to the Trustees, Richer Sounds PLC, Gallery Court, Hankey Place, London SE1 4BB (tel: 020 7551 5343; email: info@persula.org)

Trustees: Hanna Oppenheim; Julian Richer; David Robinson; Rosie Richer; Robert Rosenthal; Jonathan Levy.

CC number: 1044174

General information

The Persula Foundation was established in 1994 by Richer Sounds PLC, the UK home entertainment retailer. It is an independent grant-making foundation and supports any cause which the trustees feel strongly about. The trustees include Julian Richer, founder of the company and David Robinson, the Managing Director.

Grant-making priorities
The foundation's annual report for 2014/15 states that the trustees' current funding priorities are:

- Homelessness
- People with disabilities
- Human rights
- Animal welfare

The Persula Foundation also manages four projects, including Storytelling Tour, which gave over 100 free sessions of storytelling and music to the visually impaired, older people and children and adults with disabilities. The foundation also has a Tapesense project, providing a subsidised mail-order service for blank media and popular hi-fi accessories to blind and visually impaired people. In addition, the charity has a project called ACTS 435, which is a website that allows people to give money directly to those struggling financially, and another called ASB Help.

Financial information
In 2014/15 the foundation had assets of £43,500 and an income of £1.06 million, mostly from donations from Richer Sounds PLC. There were grants made to a variety of organisations totalling £1.07 million and were broken down as follows:

Human welfare	£639,000
Animal welfare	£240,500
Human rights	£103,500
People with disabilities	£74,500
Storytelling	£11,000

Beneficiaries included: Compassion in World Farming (£50,000); ACTS435 (£35,000); Prison Reform Trust (£34,000); Amnesty International (£30,500); Changing Faces, Hope and Homes for Children and The Eden Project (£25,000 each); ASB Help (£24,000); Civil Liberties Trust (£21,000). Grants of under £20,000 were not listed in the annual report.

There were ten grants awarded of over £20,000 totalling £290,500, and the rest were for grants of under £20,000 totalling £778,000.

Exclusions
Grants are not given for buildings, individuals or core funding.

Applications
Apply in writing to the correspondent. The charity considers applications from a variety of charitable organisations.

The Petplan Charitable Trust

The welfare of dogs, cats, horses and rabbits, veterinary research and education

£607,000 (2015)

Beneficial area
UK

Correspondent: Catherine Bourg, Trust Administrator, Great West House (GW2), Great West Road, Brentford, Middlesex TW8 9EG (tel: 020 8580 8013; email: catherine.bourg@allianz.co.uk; website: www.petplantrust.org)

CC number: 1032907

General information
The trust was established in 1994 by pet insurance company Petplan Ltd which is a subsidiary company of Allianz Insurance PLC. Petplan gives its policy holders the option of making a small annual donation to the trust, which they are able to increase from the suggested £2 per year should they wish to do so. The trust aims to promote the welfare of dogs, cats, horses and rabbits by funding clinical veterinary investigation, education and welfare projects.

Grant programmes
Scientific grants
The trust awards two types of scientific grant:

- Full grants for in-depth research for up to three years
- Pump priming grants of up to £10,000 over a period of no more than one year to fund initial research which should ideally lead to further research

Support is given for clinical research that will potentially help vets in practice to treat and care for animals. Only work which involves the study of companion animals will be funded. Applications for these grants are invited from the major veterinary schools.

Welfare grants
According to the trust's terms and conditions document, the following grants are given:

- One major welfare grant of up to £20,000 towards an innovative project which will improve animal care and welfare
- Up to £40,000 to be distributed in general grants of between £5,000 and £7,500
- Up to £40,000 to be distributed for general grants of up to £5,000
- Grants to assist with vehicle purchase

General grants can include items such as neutering, kennelling and veterinary costs but not general overheads. Projects involving pet therapy have previously been supported.

Capital grants
When funds permit, grants for major projects may be awarded to veterinary schools.

Financial information
In 2015 the trust had assets of £503,500 and an income of £863,500. Grants were made totalling £607,000 and were distributed as follows:

Scientific grants	£306,500
Welfare and educational grants	£206,500
Pedigree Adoption Scheme grants	£94,000

Beneficiaries included: Royal Veterinary College (£156,500 in five grants); Brooke Hospital for Animals (£25,000); Blue Cross (£20,000); University of Bristol (£19,500); University of Northumbria (£10,000); Gables Farm Dogs and Cats Home (£6,400); Rotherham Rescue Rangers (£1,500); Border Collie Trust and Labrador Welfare (£100 each).

Exclusions
Grants are not made for individuals, non-registered charities and studies involving invasive procedures or experimental animals. The trust cannot consider applications for funding for overheads such as rent or general staff costs.

Applications
In the first instance, see the website where full information on how to apply, including funding criteria and dates of application rounds, is available.

The Prince of Wales's Charitable Foundation

Arts and culture, education and young people, conservation and heritage, environmental sustainability, community support, health and hospices, religion, emergency relief, the welfare of service personnel

£7.7 million (2015/16)

Beneficial area
UK and overseas.

Correspondent: Yvonne Abba-Opoku, The Prince of Wales's Office, Clarence House, St James's, London SW1A 1BA (email: yvonne.abbaopoku@royal.gsx.gov.uk; website: www.princeofwalescharitablefoundation.org.uk)

CC number: 1127255

General information

The Prince of Wales's Charitable Foundation was established in 1979 and has the aim of transforming lives and building sustainable communities.

The foundation's website states:

> This is achieved locally through supporting causes such as community projects, nationally through grants to charities such as Plantlife International, The Prince's Trust, Soil Association and the Rare Breeds Survival Trust and globally through the Charitable Foundation's International Sustainability Unit.

Support is principally given to charitable bodies and purposes in which the founder has a particular interest. The website states that the foundation's main areas of interest are 'built environment, responsible business and enterprise, young people and education, and global sustainability'.

Grant programmes

The foundation states that, in view of its aim of making a difference to people and their communities, it particularly welcomes small grants applications from UK-based grassroots community projects. It operates two grants programmes:

Major grants

This programme awards grants of £5,000 upwards. Unsolicited applications are not accepted.

Small grants

Grants of up to £5,000 are awarded through this programme. They average £1,500 and are awarded for a single financial year. Applications are considered from UK-registered charities that have been active for at least two years and are able to submit accounts.

Financial information

In 2014/15 the foundation had assets of £9 million and an income of £13.5 million. Grants were made totalling £7.7 million from both restricted and unrestricted funds.

Beneficiaries included: The Great Steward of Scotland Dumfries House Trust (£3.1 million); Prince's Foundation for Building Community (£1.6 million); The Soil Association (£500,000); Royal Drawing School (£439,000); Prince's Regeneration Trust (£250,000); Prince's Trust International (£150,000); Turquoise Mountain (£80,000); The Tusk Trust (£49,000); The College of Medicine and Norfolk Churches Trust (£10,000 each).

Exclusions

According to the foundation's website, grants will not be made to:

- individuals
- public bodies
- organisations that mainly distribute grants to other organisations
- organisations that are looking to deliver similar projects to any of The Prince's Charities (please visit The Prince's Charities page for further project details)
- organisations with an income of £1m or more
- organisations with political associations or interests
- cover capital expenditure with the exception of community-based, religion-related and heritage restoration projects

Applications

In the first instance, fill out the online eligibility form which will give you access to the full online application form, should you be eligible. The major grants programme is not open to unsolicited applications.

The PwC Foundation

Education, employability, healthcare

£1.26 million (2014/15)

Beneficial area

UK

Correspondent: Sean Good, PricewaterhouseCoopers LLP, 1 Embankment Place, London WC2N 6RH (tel: 07764 902846; email: sean.good@uk.pwc.com; website: www.pwc.co.uk/corporate-sustainability/the-pwc-foundation.jhtml)

CC number: 1144124

General information

The PwC Foundation was established in 2011 and is the corporate charity of PricewaterhouseCoopers LLP (PwC group), which was formed by a merger between Coopers and Lybrand and Price Waterhouse in 1998. The foundation consists of a board of trustees, all of whom are current members of PwC.

The objectives of the PwC Foundation are to promote sustainable development and social inclusion for the public benefit. The foundation is also PwC group's vehicle for providing matched funding to the charity sector.

Financial information

In 2014/15 the foundation had assets of £324,500 and an income of £1.44 million, of which £1.03 million was donated from PwC group. It made grants totalling £1.26 million, which were broken down as follows:

Education	48	£343,000
Employability	59	£299,000
Healthcare	125	£283,500
Matched giving	N/A	£228,500
Other	43	£96,000

Beneficiaries included: TeachFirst (£202,500); Wellbeing of Women (£170,000); Beyond Food Foundation (£101,500); The Shakespeare Globe Trust (£45,000); Groundworks (£40,500); LandAid Charitable Trust (£16,000); Tiny Life (£15,500); Step up to Serve (£15,000); Alzheimer Scotland and PRIME (£10,000 each).

Exclusions

The foundation will not fund political organisations, lobbying groups, animal rights groups or religious bodies.

Applications

The following was taken from the PwC Foundation's website: 'The distribution of funds donated to the foundation are decided by the foundation trustees taking into account the voting preferences of our people.'

The Rathbone Brothers Foundation

General charitable purposes

£15,500 (2015)

Beneficial area

UK

Correspondent: Joanna Gostling, 1 Curzon Street, London W1J 5FB (tel: 020 7399 0000; email: rathbonefoundation@rathbones.com)

CC number: 1150432

General information

This foundation was established in November 2012 for general charitable purposes and registered with the Charity Commission in January 2013. It is the associated charitable foundation of Rathbone Brothers PLC, a company which is one of the UK's leading providers of investment management services for private clients, charities and professional advisers.

Financial information

In 2015 the foundation had assets of £473,000 and an income of £211,000. Grants totalling £15,500 were made to five organisations.

Beneficiaries were: Jersey Autism and St Martins (£5,000 each); Central Aid Society Cambridge and Connections Bus Project Cambridge (£2,500 each); Basing Project Winchester (£700).

Applications

Apply in writing to the correspondent. According to the foundation's Charity Commission record, 'the trustees consider applications for funding when received'.

The Rugby Group Benevolent Fund Ltd

Community projects in specific geographical areas where employees and ex-employees of Rugby Group Ltd live

£229,000 to organisations (2015)

Beneficial area

Barrington (Cambridgeshire); Chinnor (Oxfordshire); Kensworth (Bedfordshire); Lewes (Sussex); Rochester (Kent); Rugby and Southam (Warwickshire); South Ferriby (North Lincolnshire); and Tilbury (Essex).

Correspondent: Daphne Murray, Secretary, Cemex House, Coldharbour Lane, Thorpe, Egham, Surrey TW20 8TD (tel: 01932 583181; email: info@rugbygroupbenevolentfund.org.uk; website: www.rugbygroupbenevolentfund.org.uk)

Trustees: Graeme Fuller; Ian Southcott; Norman Jones; Nigel Appleyard; Jim Wootten; Geoff Thomas.

CC number: 265669

General information

This fund was established in 1955 with the aim of supporting employees and former employees of Rugby Group Ltd, and their dependants. The Rugby Group is now a part of CEMEX UK, a global cement manufacturer but the fund has kept its independence and is managed by a group of employees and former employees.

Today, the fund maintains the same objectives with which it was established but has broadened its scope to include charitable causes in communities where employees, former employees and their dependants are resident. These are: Barrington (Cambridgeshire); Chinnor (Oxfordshire); Kensworth (Bedfordshire); Lewes (Sussex); Rochester (Kent); Rugby and Southam (Warwickshire); South Ferriby (North Lincolnshire); and Tilbury (Essex).

Grants are made to provide capital for specific projects.

Financial information

In 2015 the fund had assets of more than £2.5 million and an income of £61,500. Grants totalled £256,500. Of this amount, £229,000 was given in 47 grants to organisations. Grants to individuals amounted to a further £27,500.

Beneficiaries included: Thomley Activity Centre (£50,000); Napton School (£25,000); Dogs for the Disabled (£14,000); Warwickshire and Northamptonshire Air Ambulance (£13,000); Arthur Rank Hospice (£10,000); Haslingfield Lawn Tennis Club (£8,000) Saxby Parish Church (£5,000) Rugby Hospital Radio (£2,500); Beating Bowel Cancer and Marie Curie Hospice (£1,000 each).

Exclusions

Organisations operating outside the areas of benefit. Support is not normally given for day-to-day revenue costs.

Applications

At the time of writing (January 2017), the 'Applying' page on the fund's website stated that an initial expression of interest form and a full application form would soon be available. The page also gives guidelines on making an application.

The Saga Charitable Trust

Sustainable projects in the areas of education, health, training and income generation

£145,000 (2015/16)

Beneficial area

Financially developing countries visited by Saga holidaymakers.

Correspondent: Sarah Jenner, Trust Executive, Saga Group Ltd, Enbrook Park, Sandgate High Street, Sandgate, Folkestone CT20 3SE (tel: 01303 774069; email: sarah.jenner@saga.co.uk; website: www.sagacharitabletrust.org)

Trustees: Makala Thomas; James Duguid; Andrew Stringer; Paul Green.

CC number: 291991

General information

Saga PLC is a UK company which focuses on serving the needs of those aged 50 and over through insurance, travel, financial services and healthcare. The Saga Charitable Trust was registered with the Charity Commission in June 1985 and is funded by the Saga group, Saga customers and staff.

The prime objective of its charitable work is to benefit worthy community projects at destinations in financially developing countries that host Saga holidaymakers. According to the website, the trust aims to not just donate money, but to invest in sustainable projects that will empower and support local communities, provide practical help to those in need, and offer increased opportunities for disadvantaged groups to benefit from tourism.

Grant programmes

The trust focuses its charitable activities on the following areas:

Education

According to the 2015/16 annual report, the trust funds 'projects that provide access to better educational facilities and services'. Examples of projects funded in the year include a feeding programme at a primary school in Kenya; materials and equipment for a higher education project in Guatemala; and the rebuilding of a school in Nepal which was destroyed during the 2015 earthquake.

Training

In 2015 the trust funded an HIV awareness training programme in primary schools in Malawi.

Healthcare

In 2015/16 the trust funded childcare centres and a community healthcare programme in India and the installation of solar panels in a health centre in Kenya.

Income generation

An example of the type of project funded includes a women's education centre in Morocco with the aim of establishing a workers co-operative within the Berber community.

Other examples of the types of projects the trust may consider funding include: school buildings, facilities and equipment; medical equipment; vocational training programmes; and community centres. Further detailed examples of projects that the trust has supported can be found on its website.

Financial information

In 2015/16 the trust had assets of £448,000 and an income of £450,000, of which £224,500 was donations from Saga customers and staff. There were 12 grants awarded totalling £145,000.

Beneficiaries included: St Jude Childcare Centre India (£22,000); International Development Enterprises Nepal (£21,000); Haller Foundation Kenya (£20,000); EMMS International India, Friends of Seva Mandir India and Ghurka Welfare Trust Nepal (£15,000 each); Agounsane Education Centre Morocco (£12,700); Centre for Early Childhood Development South Africa (£10,000); Mikoroshoni Primary School Kenya (£6,000); Education for the Children Guatemala (£5,600); Ekari Foundation Malawi (£1,700); Rope Charitable Trust India (£1,000).

Exclusions

No grants are made to individuals.

Applications

Applications should be made in writing to the correspondent. Note that only projects sited in or close to destinations within financially developing countries currently visited by Saga holidaymakers will be considered for funding. The trust welcomes contact from organisations to discuss their proposals prior to application. Applications are accepted at any time throughout the year and application guidelines are available from the trust's website.

Funding proposals must include the following information: outline and objectives of the project; who will benefit and how; resources required and time frame; management and sustainability of the project; how funds will be managed and accounted for; and the last three years of the organisation's audited financial accounts.

Santander UK Foundation Ltd

Education, financial education, employability, social welfare, enterprise and social innovation

£5.7 million (2015)

Beneficial area

UK

Correspondent: Alan Eagle, Foundation Manager, Santander Foundation, Santander House, 201 Grafton Gate East, Milton Keynes MK9 1AN (email: grants@santander.co.uk; website: www.santanderfoundation.org.uk)

CC number: 803655

General information

The Santander UK Foundation Ltd was established in 1990 by Santander UK PLC, the UK bank, and changed its name from the Abbey National Charitable Trust in 2010. The trustees are all directors and/or employees of Santander.

The foundation is the main channel of the company's corporate donations and provides grants to UK-registered charities 'to support knowledge, skills and innovation to give disadvantaged people the confidence to discover and create a new world of opportunities'.

In 2016 as part of Santander UK PLC's CSR initiative the Discovery Project, which aims to help one million people over the next five years, the foundation amalgamated its previous three grants programmes to form one grants scheme – Discovery Grants.

Discovery Grants

The Discovery Grants scheme provides up to £5,000 to small, local registered charities, CICs and Credit Unions in the UK for projects which support one or more of the following themes:

- **Explorer – improving knowledge and insight**

  Examples include a series of Money Management workshops to help people understand how to budget and identify the affordable credit choices available to them. A Freedom Training course giving abused women knowledge of how to regain control over their lives.

- **Transformer – developing skills and experience**

  Examples include work-based training and mentors to help socially isolated people develop skills to get back into work. Sign language training for parents with hearing impaired children. Or teaching young people with autism vocational skills.

- **Changemaker – innovative solutions to social challenges**

  Examples include a new social networking program for visually impaired young people which uses specially developed braille laptops to access the internet. An inclusive cycling social enterprise which adapts bicycles to enable people with disabilities to enjoy the outdoors.

Grants are available for one year only. The foundation prefers to fund a complete project or item, which should be local in scale and may include salaries, equipment or materials.

Other grants

The foundation also supports the employee-led giving within Santander UK PLC. Donations to the group's Charity of the Year are made through the foundation, as well as matched funding for donations made by employees to charities of their choice.

Financial information

In 2015 the foundation had assets of £13.4 million and an income of £5.6 million. The foundation's income included £5 million from Santander UK PLC as well as £100,000 of services in kind from the company, and also £389,000 in investment income.

The foundation made 3,300 grants to charities amounting to a total of £5.7 million. Of this, £2.6 million was given in 2,584 grants through the staff matched donation scheme and £2.4 million was given in 640 grants under the previous programme, 'Community Plus'.

Grants in 2015 were made through the previous grants programmes, before the Discovery Grants scheme was established. Grants were distributed in the following categories:

Other	1,372	£2.1 million
Health	1,398	£2 million
Education and training	495	£1.3 million
Financial capability	35	£321,000

Beneficiaries of grants of £10,000 or more included: British Heart Foundation (£190,000); Mayor's Fund for London (£85,000); Access to Business, Headway, MS Society, Sight Cymru, Small Charities Coalition, South Gloucestershire Citizens Advice and Tees Valley Women's Centre (£10,000 each).

The British Heart Foundation received an exceptionally large grant as it was Santander UK PLC's Charity of the Year.

Exclusions

Discovery grants will not be awarded for:

- Unregistered charities, not-for-profit groups, amateur sports clubs, exempt or excepted charities
- Start-ups (must have at least a full year of accounts)
- Individuals – including trips, overseas volunteering, gap year activities, medical treatment, grants for studying or research
- Funding for multiple years
- Fundraising activities
- Shortfall funding (the foundation prefers to fund a full project or item)
- Other funders and grant-makers
- Organisations which restrict their beneficiaries to a single religious or single ethnic group
- Events, conferences or sponsorship
- Party political activity
- Beneficiaries outside the UK, Channel Islands or the Isle of Man
- Health, research and palliative care charities (these are funded through the group's employee fundraising scheme)
- General running costs

Applications

Nominations for a Discovery Grant can be made by Santander employees, customers, or by the organisations themselves. Application forms can be obtained from any Santander branch (you can find your nearest branch at: www.santander.co.uk/findbranch) and should be returned to the branch for consideration. Supporting material or annual reports are not required.

There are no deadlines – nominations are considered every month, and successful organisations should be notified within six weeks. The foundation is unable to notify unsuccessful applicants due to the volume of applications, but they are welcome to apply again at any time.

Guidelines and frequently asked questions are available to view on the foundation's website. Any further queries should be sent by email to: grants@santander.co.uk.

The Scott Bader Commonwealth Ltd

Social welfare, education and training, overseas aid, conservation, children and young people, socially excluded and disadvantaged people, women, and minority communities

£14,400 (to organisations in the UK) (2015)

Beneficial area

UK, as well as locations close to where the company operates.

Correspondent: Sue Carter, Commonwealth Secretary, Scott Bader Company Ltd, Wollaston Hall, Wollaston, Nr Wellingborough, Northants NN29 7RL (tel: 01933 666755; email: commonwealth_office@scottbader.com or hayley_sutherland@scottbader.com; website: www.scottbader.com)

Trustees: Andrew Radford; Syed Hayat; Anne Atkinson-Clark; Les Norwood; Jacquie Findlay; Karl-Heinz Funke; John Pike; Tony Clarke; Gary Coldwell.

CC number: 206391

General information

The following information comes from the company's current annual report. The Scott Bader Commonwealth Ltd was established in 1967. It is a registered charity and a company limited by guarantee, which owns the share capital of the global chemical company, Scott Bader Company Ltd and receives 1% of the annual staff salary cost of the group.

The charity is a membership organisation and everyone employed by the Scott Bader Commonwealth Ltd or any of its subsidiaries may become a member of the charity. There are around 640 people employed worldwide, of which over 500 are members of the charity.

The charity fulfils its objectives by making grants to charitable organisations around the world whose purposes are to help young or disadvantaged people, especially anyone suffering deprivation and discrimination, such as poor, homeless and vulnerable women and children or minority communities, particularly where people are affected by poverty, lack of education, malnutrition and disease.

Funds are divided into two categories:

Local Funds: funds are made available to all the companies in the Scott Bader Group for them to submit applications to the commonwealth for charities they wish to support. Each supports the work of charities associated with them or situated nearby.

Central Fund:

- £50,000 is allocated annually to support two large, community-based environmental or educational projects which can be located anywhere in the world (to the value of £25,000 each)
- £10,000 was allocated in 2013 to a Small International Fund to provide small grants of £500–£2,000 to support international projects that do not fit the local fund or large fund criteria
- £5,000 is made available for distribution to charities chosen by the Life President, Godric Bader

Financial information

In 2015 the charity had assets of £573,000 and an income of £324,000, primarily in donations from the Scott Bader Company. Grants were made totalling £158,000 of which £35,500 was given in the UK.

Beneficiaries included: Hope Project (£3,000); The Prince's Trust, Northampton (£2,500); Rushdon Mind (£2,000); Giggles Play CIC and Young Enterprise Northampton (£1,000 each); Tall Ships Youth Trust (£900); Beanstalk (£730); The Aidis Trust (£255).

Exclusions

No support can be given for: charities concerned with animals; individual sponsorships; travel and adventure schemes; arts projects; any form of advertising; medical research and equipment; sports clubs; general charitable appeals; and the construction/renovation/maintenance of buildings.

Applications

Assessment criteria are available to download from the website. Application forms are available on request by email to hayley_sutherland@scottbader.com. Deadlines for the large-project funding are available on the website. Applications for the Small International Fund are accepted all year round. Applications for local funds should be made to the local office.

The ScottishPower Energy People Trust

Fuel poverty, social welfare, energy efficiency

£1.09 million (2015)

Beneficial area

UK

Correspondent: Irene Murdoch, Environmental and Social Policy Support Assistant, ScottishPower Energy Retail Ltd, Cathcart Business Park, 44 Spean Street, Glasgow G44 4BE (tel: 0141 614 4480; email: SPEnergyPeopleTrust@ScottishPower.com; website: www.energypeopletrust.com)

Trustees: Ann Loughrey, Secretary; Norman Kerr, Chair; Douglas McLaren; Joan Fraser; Neil Hartwell; Dr Bill Sheldrick; Alan Hughes; Peter Sumby.

OSCR number: SC036980

General information

Established by ScottishPower in 2005, the trust has distributed over £14.5 million to projects run by grassroots organisations that help people who are on low incomes, live in poor housing or suffer from ill health.

Grant-making

The trust is funded primarily by donations from ScottishPower; however, funding decisions are made by the independent trustee board. The following projects are eligible for funding (taken from the trust's website).

> Registered charities can apply for funding to support projects in the following categories:
>
> - Energy Efficiency Advice – it is a condition of funding that all projects include the provision of energy efficiency advice. Energy advisors should be trained to City and Guilds standard or equivalent
> - Energy Efficiency Measures – improving home energy efficiency through draught proofing, insulating and or other practical measures
> - Income Maximisation – providing funding to front line charities who carry out benefits advice to households missing out on financial help that they are entitled to through welfare benefits and tax credits
> - Fuel Debt Assistance – providing assistance, or funding the provision by other persons of assistance, to reduce or cancel debts for household electricity or gas supply, where such assistance is provided as part of a package of measures aimed at providing customers with long-term relief from fuel poverty
>
> Or any combination of the above. Priority will be given to projects aimed at helping families with young children and young people.
>
> Please note that all projects must address fuel poverty explicitly and as the primary purpose (not just as an add on).
>
> The trust will award funding at levels appropriate to the type of project and the number of people to be helped, from small sums up to a maximum of £50,000.
>
> Projects may be funded for a maximum of one year, but the maximum amount of £50,000 applies, regardless of the timescale of the project.
>
> We provide funding on the condition that overheads or administration costs associated with a project do not exceed 12.5% of the total funding requested. However, the trustees may make an exception to this condition in special

circumstances, where a valid reason is provided.

Refer to the 'Applications' section in this entry for further information.

Financial information

In 2015 the trust had an income of £35,500 primarily in donations from ScottishPower, and a total expenditure of almost £1.13 million. Around £1.09 million was made in grants to organisations. Grants for less than £20,000 totalled £224,500.

Beneficiaries include: The Footprint Trust and Suffolk Community Foundation (£45,000 each); The Environment Centre (£44,500); Community Energy Plus (£43,000); Disability Resource Centre (£41,500); Greener Kirkcaldy (£40,500); East Ayrshire Carers Centre (£36,000); South Liverpool Homes (£31,000); The Wise Group (£30,500); The Befriending Scheme (£28,000).

Exclusions

Grants are not made to individuals or commercial organisations.

Applications

There is an online application form on the trust's website. The trustees meet to consider applications three times a year, in March, July and November. Applications should be submitted at least seven weeks prior to the date of the meeting (exact dates are available on the site). However, early applications are advised as only 30 applications will be considered at each meeting, with additional applications received being carried over to the next meeting.

The following guidelines are available on the trust's website:

> All projects must address fuel poverty explicitly. Tackling fuel poverty must be the primary purpose of the project (not just as an add on).
>
> Project applications must identify how the outcomes and outputs of a project will reduce fuel poverty and how a project will meet the trust objectives.
>
> Each application should demonstrate how many people will be helped as a direct result of the project.
>
> Please note that we will only accept one application per organisation at each trustee meeting.
>
> All applicants should create a link to their organisation's latest annual audited accounts and confirm any previous applications to the trust. This information should be updated in the **Project Controls** section of the application.
>
> Charity registration number must be included in application, if not it will be rejected.

Applicants will be notified within two weeks of the trustee meeting and unsuccessful applicants may re-apply only after six months. Successful applicants may re-apply for further funding either six months after the initial funding has expired, or on completion of the project – whichever happens first.

Grants are usually made in annual instalments with 10% of the annual total retained by the trust pending receipt of a satisfactory report on the progress or completion of the project which the trust says is to 'encourage transparency and responsible reporting'. More details on reporting requirements are available on the trust's site.

The ScottishPower Foundation

General charitable purposes including education, the environment, community development, arts, heritage, culture and science, social welfare, community development

£765,000 (2015)

Beneficial area

UK

Correspondent: María Elena Sanz Arcas, Company Secretary, 1 Atlantic Quay, Robertson Street, Glasgow G2 8SP (tel: 0800 027 0072; email: scottishpowerfoundation@scottishpower.com; website: www.scottishpower.com/pages/the_scottishpower_foundation.asp)

Trustees: Mike Thornton; Elaine Bowker; Sarah Mistry; Keith Anderson; Ann Loughrey.

OSCR number: SC043862

General information

ScottishPower is part of the Iberdrola Group, a global energy company with operations focused in the UK, US, Brazil, Mexico and Spain. The foundation was set up in 2013 in order to reinforce the company's commitment to supporting charitable work throughout Britain.

Areas of work

The following was taken from the foundation's website:

> The ScottishPower Foundation will consider applications from registered charities and non-profit organisations under the following purposes:
>
> - **the advancement of education**
> - **the advancement of environmental protection or improvement**, in particular, promotion, dissemination and support of knowledge, research and culture in their most varied forms, with a special focus on the development of and progress toward a sustainable energy model that respects the environment and biodiversity;
> - **the advancement of the arts, heritage, culture or science,** in particular; o cultural initiatives for the promotion and support of scientific, technological dissemination and environmental protection activities, encouraging, in particular, the development of studies of all kinds in the areas of energy, biodiversity and environmental impact in general; and o in the areas of restoration, development and conservation of the cultural heritage, as well as the development of projects and activities to promote and disseminate art and culture, and to technically and financially support cultural and artistic activities carried out by public and private institutions;
> - **the prevention or relief of poverty and the relief of those in need by reason of disability or other disadvantage**, in particular, the development of initiatives to support social action in the areas of cooperation and solidarity in order to actively contribute to the improvement of the quality of life of the most underprivileged groups, through initiatives for the development of infrastructure and services that provide for their full social and labour integration, as well as professional training, insertion into the work force and the generation of employment opportunities for disadvantaged persons that allows for the creation of jobs for them, and ultimately, for the integration into the labour market;
> - **the advancement of citizenship and community development.**

Grants of between £5,000 and £50,000 are available to organisations for projects meeting the above objectives.

Financial information

In 2015 the foundation had an income of £801,000, primarily in donations from ScottishPower and an expenditure of £910,000. 30 grants were made totalling £765,000.

Beneficiaries included: National Museum of Scotland (£40,000); RSPB Scotland (£32,500); National Library of Wales (£27,000); SYHA Hostelling Scotland (£25,000); The Outward Bound Trust (£22,000); Loch Lomond and The Trossachs Countryside Trust, Trees for Life and Wigtown Book Festival (£20,000 each); The Aloud Charity (£16,000); Northern Lights (£11,200); Royal Lyceum Theatre Company (£10,000).

Exclusions

The foundation's website states that it will not fund the following:

- Organisations that are not registered charities or non-profit organisations
- General appeals and circulars including contributions to endowment funds
- Local charities whose work takes place outside the United Kingdom
- Medical research

- Individuals or support organisations for travel or for expeditions, whether in the United Kingdom or abroad
- Projects which are primarily or exclusively intended to promote political or religious beliefs
- Second- or third-tier organisations (unless there is evidence of direct benefit to disadvantaged people)
- Sponsorship or funding towards a marketing appeal or fundraising activities

Applications

At the time of writing (February 2017), the foundation's website stated that funds had already been committed to projects for 2017, and the application period for 2018 funding would begin in summer 2017.

Applications should be made using the application form which will be available to download from the website, along with applications guidelines, during the next application period.

The SDL Foundation

Sustainable community and economic development, overseas aid, social welfare, education and training

£281,000 (2015)

Beneficial area

Worldwide

Correspondent: Alastair Gordon, Trustee, SDL PLC, 64 Castelnau, London SW13 9EX (email: agordon@sdl.com; website: www.sdl.com/about/corporate-citizenship/foundation)

Trustees: Mark Lancaster; Alastair Gordon; Dominic Kinnon; Michelle Wilson.

CC number: 1127138

General information

Established in 2008, this is the corporate charity of SDL PLC. The company provides interpretation and translation services, and content and software development. It is one of the largest language services companies in the world, working in over 30 countries. The global nature of the company's business is reflected in the activities and aspirations of the foundation. The foundation's trustees are all present or former employees of SDL International PLC, most notably Mark Lancaster who was until 2015 CEO and is a founder of the company.

The objects of the SDL Foundation are to promote sustainable development in order to relieve poverty and improve the lives of disadvantaged communities; and to promote sustainable means of achieving economic growth and regeneration.

The following information is taken from the company's website:

> The SDL Foundation is dedicated to supporting initiatives that provide sustainable solutions for people in need around the globe.
>
> The mission of the SDL Foundation is to work with charities and projects across the globe to support disadvantaged communities. It provides sustainable aid through financial grants, educational and vocational training to help people become self-sufficient and encourages SDL employees to get involved with their local charities and give their time and support to those who need.

Partners are often supported over a number of years.

The foundation prefers to support projects where SDL employees can complement support with their own fundraising initiatives. Employees of SLD PLC are entitled to five days of paid leave each year to support the foundation's activities.

In 2015 the foundation celebrated its fifth anniversary since it was established, having supported 80 projects in 28 countries.

Financial information

In 2015 the foundation had assets of £149,000 and an income of £180,000, £179,000 of which was received as a donation from SDL PLC. Grants awarded to organisations totalled £281,000 (this figure also includes £1,500 given to support fundraising by individual SDL employees and a refund of a grant of £6,250). More detail on the causes and projects supported during the year is given on the website and in the 2015 annual report.

Beneficiaries included: Prince's Trust – UK (£100,000); Habitat for Humanity – Romania (£55,000); Gua Africa – Sudan (£25,000); Hatua Likoni – Kenya (£20,000); Bread For Life – Uganda (£16,200); Santa Maria Education Fund – Paraguay and St Wilfrid's – UK (£15,000 each); Microloan Foundation – Malawi (£5,000); Translators Without Borders (£3,400).

Exclusions

No grants will be given to causes where trustees or SDL employees would directly benefit. The foundation will also not support political or discriminatory activities; or those appeals that are recognised as being large or well known.

Applications

Only causes supported and sponsored by SDL employees will be considered by the SDL Foundation. Contact the foundation by email for further information on how to request the support of staff and application procedures.

The foundation's accounts state:

> Donations to appropriately qualified charities and causes are approved at the quarterly meetings by the Trustees after a review and discussion of detailed proposals received from the employees of SDL and presented by the Chairman of the Trustees
>
> On occasion the Foundation may receive a request for funding from an external source supported by a Trustee or an SDL Director. In this instance the application will be subject to the same rigorous criteria as other applications and the proposing Trustee will absent themselves from the approval process.

The Severn Trent Water Charitable Trust Fund

Relief of poverty, money advice and debt counselling

£166,000 to organisations

(2015/16)

Beneficial area

The area covered by Severn Trent Water Ltd, which stretches from Wales to East Leicestershire and from the Humber estuary down to the Bristol Channel. A map is provided on the website: www.sttf.org.uk/organisations/grants-funding.

Correspondent: The Trustees of the Severn Trent Water Charitable Trust Fund, Severn Trent Trust Fund, FREEPOST RLZE – EABT – SHSA, Sutton Coldfield B72 1TJ (tel: 0121 355 7766; email: office@sttf.org.uk; website: www.sttf.org.uk)

Trustees: Elizabeth Pusey; David Vaughan; Alexandra Gribbin; Lowri Williams; Clive Mottram; Andrew Phelps; Stuart Braley.

CC number: 1108278

General information

The fund is an independent charity established by Severn Trent Water Ltd in 1997 with a donation of £2 million.

The main objects of the charity are to help people out of poverty and debt by helping needy individuals to pay their water bills, as well as making grants to organisations that provide debt and money advice. The charity aims to help individuals in immediate crisis and financial difficulty while also encouraging future financial stability.

Grants are mainly awarded to individuals or families to clear water debt or assist with water charges. Assistance may also be given with other household costs if it can be demonstrated that it will help towards future financial stability or make a significant improvement to the recipient's circumstances. The charity provides counselling and education in relation to debt, debt awareness and debt prevention.

Grants for organisations

Also provided are grants to organisations in the charity's area of benefit to support the delivery of debt advice and financial education. According to the charity's website, there are two grant schemes for organisations:

Small Grant Funding

One-off awards are provided for the purpose of developing or enhancing an organisation's activities around money or debt advice and financial literacy. The trustees are flexible about how support is provided, but it may include capital expenditure, staff training or promotional work.

Revenue Project Funding

Grants are also provided over a longer term, up to three years, for projects that meet the charity's current criteria. In 2016/17 the it has a particular preference for organisations delivering services in the rural parts of its area of benefit. The website states that current criteria and funding opportunities can be discussed by contacting the charity (see 'Applications').

Financial information

In 2015/16 the charity had assets of £1.9 million and an income of £4.8 million. Grants totalled £2.9 million of which £2.8 million was given to individuals and £166,000 to organisations that provide debt advice and other support services.

A list of organisational beneficiaries was not available.

Previous beneficiaries have included: ASHA/Worcester CASH; Birmingham Disability Resource Centre; CARES Sandwell; Castle Vale Tenants and Residents Alliance; Citizens Advice Leicester; Community Focus; Coventry Citizens Advice; EDAS (Essential Drugs and Alcohol Services); Forest of Dean Citizens Advice; IMA; Ladywood Project; Life Matters; Sherwood Forest Community Church; South Birmingham Young Homeless Project; Telford and Wrekin Citizens Advice; Wood End Advice and Information Centre.

Exclusions

Only applications from organisations within the Severn Trent Trust Fund area will be considered. A map of this area can be found on the website.

Applications

Organisations interested in applying for a grant should contact the charity on 0121 321 1324 or email at office@sttf.org.uk to discuss current funding criteria and future funding opportunities.

Application forms for individuals are provided on the website.

The Shoe Zone Trust

Education and training, social welfare, children and young people

£80,000 (2015)

Beneficial area

Preference for Leicestershire and Rutland and for certain charities operating in the Philippines and other countries.

Correspondent: Michael Smith, Trustee, Shoe Zone Retail Ltd, Haramead Business Centre, Humberstone Road, Leicester LE1 2LH (tel: 0116 222 3007; website: www.shoezone.com/ShoeZoneTrust)

Trustees: Michael Smith; Anthony Smith; Charles Smith.

CC number: 1112972

General information

Registered with the Charity Commission in 2006, The Shoe Zone Trust is the corporate charity of Shoe Zone Retail Ltd, a UK footwear retailer.

The trust's 2015 annual report states that its objective is 'to make grants and donations to other charities to relieve financial hardship and poverty and/or advance education, mainly for children and young people in Leicestershire and Rutland and for certain charities operating in the Philippines and other countries'.

Financial information

In 2015 the trust had assets of £94,500 and an income of £43,500, of which £24,000 was due to carrier bag sales donated by Shoe Zone Retail Ltd and £19,000 from other donations. Grants totalled £80,000 during the year.

Beneficiaries included: Shepherd of the Hills – Philippines (£54,500); Ministries Without Borders (£15,800); 500 Miles (£5,000); James 1v27 Foundation and Rotary Club of Kibworth and Fleckney (£2,000 each).

Donations of £250 and under totalled £550.

Applications

Apply in writing to the correspondent.

The Simmons & Simmons Charitable Foundation

Social welfare, education and training, access to justice and legal aid

£162,000 (2014/15)

Beneficial area

Worldwide, with a preference for the City of London and Tower Hamlets.

Correspondent: The Trustees of the Simmons & Simmons Charitable Foundation, Simmons & Simmons LLP, Citypoint, 1 Ropemaker Street, London EC2Y 9SS (tel: 020 7628 2020; email: corporate.responsibility@simmons-simmons.com; website: www.simmons-simmons.com)

Trustees: Richard Dyton; Fiona Loughrey; Colin Passmore; Noro-Lanto Ravisy.

CC number: 1129643

General information

The foundation was established in 2009 by the law firm Simmons & Simmons LLP. Its four trustees are Richard Dyton (CR and Pro Bono Partner), Fiona Loughrey (Partner Hong Kong), Colin Passmore (Senior Partner) and Noro-Lanto Ravisy (Partner Paris).

The following information was taken from the foundation's 2014/15 accounts:

> The foundation seeks to support smaller charitable organisations which are local to the offices of Simmons & Simmons and which seek to address social exclusion. The foundation also seeks to provide access to justice, work and opportunities to those less privileged or fortunate, for example by providing direct grants to talented individuals from low income backgrounds.

Preference is given to charities in which the firm's employees can be involved.

Financial information

In 2014/15 the foundation had assets of £175,000 and an income of £206,000. This included a donation of £120,000 from Simmons & Simmons and donated services of £13,400. Grants were made totalling almost £162,000 and were broken down as follows:

Social inclusion	£81,000
International	£42,500
Other charities	£38,000

A further £38,000 was given in pro bono support.

Beneficiaries included: Battersea Legal Advice Centre (£36,000); YMCA Ltd (£25,000); Debate Mate and The Big Issue Foundation (£15,000 each); Spitalfields Music and Working Families (£10,000 each); The Aire Centre

(£8,200); Churches Housing Aid Society and Fair Trials (£5,000 each).

Smaller grants (under £5,000) totalled £16,000.

Applications

Applications can be made on a form available to download from the company's website. Applicants must explain how they meet one of the following objectives:

- Social inclusion (increasing access to education and/or work)
- Governance (supporting the rule of law and access to justice)

They must also explain how they will provide support to communities local to where Simmons & Simmons have offices.

The Slaughter and May Charitable Trust

Legal advice, education and training, health, social welfare, children and young people and older people

£377,000 (2014/15)

Beneficial area

Mainly local to the Slaughter and May offices in Islington and close to Tower Hamlets and Hackney.

Correspondent: Kate Hursthouse, Corporate Responsibility Manager, Slaughter and May (Trust Ltd), 1 Bunhill Row, London EC1Y 8YY (tel: 020 7090 3433; email: corporateresponsibility@slaughterandmay.com; website: www.slaughterandmay.com)

Trustee: Slaughter and May Trust Ltd.

CC number: 1082765

General information

Established in 1991 and registered with the Charity Commission in 2000, this trust is the corporate charity of the legal firm Slaughter and May. The trust's annual report for 2014/15 states that it is 'reliant on its key donors, the partners of Slaughter and May with all administrative and other office support being provided by the firm'.

The trust supports a range of legal, educational, health and community projects, with a particular interest in children and young people and older people.

Financial information

In 2014/15 the trust had assets of -£125,000 and an income of £382,000, of which £337,000 was donated by the partners of Slaughter and May. Grants totalled £377,000.

Beneficiaries included: The Access Point (£57,000); Islington Law Centre (£35,000); Action for Kids (£30,500); City YMCA London (£25,000); Legal Advice Centre (£15,000); National Theatre and The Big Alliance (£10,000 each); SANE (£7,000); Advocates for International Development and RCJ Advice Bureau (£5,000).

The trust's annual report for 2014/15 states:

> The charity's intention is to distribute all donations received in the year. Any net surplus or deficit (other than the initial £10 capital sum) is due to short-term timing differences. The deficit in 2015 of £125,000 (under the initial capital sum) is comprised of grants which the charity is committed to paying but which are not payable until subsequent years (e.g. three year commitments).

Applications

The trust's 2014/15 annual report states that it 'makes annual grants at its discretion to a small number of specific charitable causes and does not generally accept unsolicited funding applications'.

The DS Smith Charitable Foundation

Education and training, conservation

£143,000 (2014/15)

Beneficial area

England and Wales.

Correspondent: Rachel Stevens, Trustee, 7th Floor, 350 Euston Road, London NW1 3AX (tel: 020 7756 1823; email: charitablefoundation@dssmith.com; website: www.dssmith.com/company/sustainability/social-responsibility/charitable-trust)

Trustees: Anne Steele; Rachel Stevens; Nicholas Feaviour; Mark Greenwood; Mark Reeve; Catriona O'Grady.

CC number: 1142817

General information

DS Smith was started by the Smith brothers in 1940. The company provides corrugated packaging in Europe and plastic packaging worldwide. It operates across 25 countries and employs around 21,500 people.

Registered in 2011, the foundation supports charities engaged in conservation of the environment and providing training or educational opportunities.

The following information was taken from the foundation's website:

> Please note that only charities in the fields of environmental improvement and of education and training, will be considered, so please ensure that any application fulfils this criteria. The charity aims to make a combination of small donations (£1,000 or less) and larger donations each year. We particularly welcome opportunities to develop multi-year partnerships with key selected charities.

Financial information

In 2014/15 the foundation had assets of £2.7 million and an income of £83,000. Grants totalling £143,000 were made to organisations.

Beneficiaries included: Keep Britain Tidy (£60,000); Unicef (£39,000); Arkwright Scholarship Trust (£20,000); IT Schools Africa (£240).

Other grants totalled £23,500.

Applications

Application forms are available from the foundation's website.

Note that the foundation's website states the following: 'The DS Smith Charitable Foundation principally seeks ideas for partnering with charities from its employees. We also accept applications for donations from third parties.'

The WH Smith Group Charitable Trust

General charitable purposes, including medical causes and education

£128,500 (2015)

Beneficial area

UK

Correspondent: The Secretary, WH Smith Ltd, Greenbridge Road, Swindon SN3 3JE (tel: 01793 616161; email: communitygrants@whsmith.co.uk; website: www.whsmithplc.co.uk/corporate_responsibility/whsmith_trust)

Trustees: Faye Sherman; Anthony Lawrence; Sarah Heath; Adrian Mansfield; Natalie Davidson; Chris Welch; Paul Green.

CC number: 1013782

General information

This trust is unusual in that although it is connected to a company, it is totally independent and controlled by the employees rather than the management. Employees of WH Smith Group have effectively established their own trust for which they raise funds, making grants to the organisations which inspired them to solicit those donations. Any surplus can be awarded at the discretion of the trustees to other charitable organisations nominated by the staff of WH Smith Group.

Two principal objectives of the trust, as listed on the website, are to:

> - support the local communities in which WH Smith staff and customers live and work

- support education and lifelong learning, helping people of any age to achieve their educational potential

Grants are made for charities nominated by employees and for projects working to promote literacy.

Community grants

Employees of WH Smith Group can nominate charities, community organisations or schools to be supported by the trust, through matched funding of up to £1,000 for individual employee fundraising efforts, or £2,000 for team fundraising. The trust also matches the value of any time volunteered by employees to support a charity or organisation.

Examples of organisations previously supported range from small groups like brownies or scouts, through to hospices, local charities, or larger national charities.

WH Smith also donates some of the funds from the compulsory plastic bag charge to the community grants scheme; the rest of the funds are donated to the Woodland Trust to support a tree-planting scheme for schools.

Reading and literacy

The trust's main work is to support the promotion of literacy and reading for pleasure among children. The trust works in partnership with WH Smith PLC to support the National Literacy Trust's Young Readers Programme. The trust is currently working with children aged six to nine in 20 schools, encouraging peer-reading and reading for pleasure, and giving children the opportunity to choose a free book.

The trust also runs a schools giveaway raffle, where WH Smith stores nominate themselves to receive a share of WH Smith vouchers to give away to local schools. In 2015 the trust asked each school to write book reviews to be displayed in their local store in exchange for the vouchers.

The trust also runs a Volunteers in Schools scheme, supporting employees to volunteer with schools as governors or with a PTA.

Financial information

In 2015 the trust had assets of £88,500 and an income of £141,000. Grants were made to organisations totalling £128,500.

Beneficiaries included: National Literacy Trust (£62,000); WH Smith Promotions Ltd – Schools Giveaway (£24,000); Macmillan Cancer Support (£3,200); Regain Sports Charity (£2,000); Cancer Research UK (£1,400); All Cannings Pre-School, Hartley Primary Academy, MS Society, Savernake Forest Scouts Group, The Arts Circus and Wiltshire Air Ambulance (£41,000 each).

Grants of less than £1,000 totalled £12,900 altogether.

Applications

Applications for a community grant can be made online: blog.whsmith.co.uk/community-grants-application.

There are two application rounds each year:

- 1 October to 31 March
- 1 April to 30 September

Grant applications are reviewed and decided by the trustees at the end of each six month period.

Any queries should be submitted to: communitygrants@whsmith.co.uk.

Sodexo Foundation

Education and training, health, community and economic development, social welfare

£246,500 (2014/15)

Beneficial area

UK and Ireland.

Correspondent: Edwina Hughes, Corporate Responsibility Manager, Sodexo, 1 Southampton Row, London WC1B 5HA (email: stophunger@sodexo.com; website: uk.sodexo.com/home/corporate-responsibility.html)

Trustees: Phil Hooper; Harbhajan Brar; Rebecca Symon; David Mulcahy; Gareth John; Margot Slattery; Neil Murray; Lee Brittain; Patrick Forbes.

CC number: 1110266

General information

Registered with the Charity Commission in June 2005, the Sodexo Foundation is the corporate charity of the food services and facilities management company, Sodexo Ltd.

Areas of work

The Sodexo Foundation's 2014/15 annual report states that the principal objectives of the foundation 'focus on either advancing the education of the general public in relation to health nutrition and wellbeing or providing relief from financial hardship and the improvement of the quality of life in socially and/or economically disadvantaged communities'.

The foundation's STOP Hunger campaign was launched in 2005. The campaign aims to promote good nutrition and healthy lifestyles, and basic life skills such as cooking. It provides a central focus for Sodexo's charitable and community interests and supports FareShare and a number of smaller charities in order to meet the STOP Hunger objectives.

The trustees receive some requests from employees to support local causes; these are usually met by Sodexo UK, not the foundation.

Financial information

In 2014/15 the foundation had assets of £155,000 and an income of £500,500, of which £58,000 was donated by Sodexo Ltd to cover the foundation's running costs. Grants totalled £246,500 and were given to 13 organisations.

Beneficiaries included: Outward Bound Trust (£135,500); Coram Life (£24,000); Centrepoint (£23,000); Community Foundation of Ireland (£13,000); Body and Soul (£8,900); Scouts Association (£8,000); Osmondthorpe Resource Centre (£3,500); Aberlour Child Care Trust (£3,400); Brendoncare (£2,900).

Applications

Application forms can be downloaded from the foundation's website. The trustees meet to consider applications quarterly.

Any queries should be sent to Edwina Hughes at: stophunger@sodexo.com.

Spar Charitable Fund

General charitable purposes, particularly children and young people

£105,000 (2014/15)

Beneficial area

UK

Correspondent: Philip Marchant, Administration Committee, Spar (UK) Ltd, Hygeia Building, 66–68 College Road, Harrow HA1 1BE (tel: 020 8426 3700; email: philip.marchant@spar.co.uk)

Trustee: The National Guild of Spar Ltd.

CC number: 236252

General information

Registered with the Charity Commission in 1970, the Spar Charitable Fund is the corporate charity of the retail chain, SPAR (UK) Ltd.

Its 2014/15 accounts state that:

> The Spar Charitable Fund with the support and assistance of the Spar Benevolent Fund seeks to provide charitable assistance to independent Spar retailers who face adverse problems and difficulties with health, bereavement and social issues. The charitable fund also supports retail industry charitable organisations.
>
> One major objective of the Spar Charitable Fund is to provide a vehicle to enable the Spar organisation through its 2,242 stores across the UK to engage with the public to raise awareness of public charitable needs and raise funding in a wide variety of ways.

The charity also makes grants to the group's partner charity, NSPCC, for which SPAR UK employees raise funds.

Financial information

In 2014/15 the charity had assets of £924,000 and an income of £102,000, of which £47,000 was a donation from the SPAR Benevolent Fund, £31,000 was generated from investments, £16,800 was raised at the SPAR UK annual convention and £7,500 was funds raised for NSPCC. Six grants were made during the year, totalling £105,000, including to NSPCC and the SPAR Benevolent Fund.

Beneficiaries included: Oxfam Ebola Crisis (£50,000); Grocery Aid (£24,500); NSPCC (£8,500); ARC Children's Centre and Northern Ireland Cancer Fund for Children (£7,500 each).

Applications

Apply in writing to the correspondent.

St James's Place Foundation

Social welfare, children and young people (up to the age of 25) who are disadvantaged, or who have mental or physical conditions, life-threatening or degenerative illnesses, young carers, oncology, hospices

£5 million (2015)

Beneficial area

UK and overseas.

Correspondent: Mark Longbottom, Foundation Manager, St James's Place PLC, St James's Place House, 1 Tetbury Road, Cirencester GL7 1FP (tel: 01285 878037; email: sjp.foundation@sjp.co.uk; website: www.sjpfoundation.co.uk)

CC number: 1144606

General information

Background

The St James's Place Foundation was originally established in 1992, when it was known as the J. Rothschild Assurance Foundation. Following a strategic review, the foundation was wound up in 2012 and re-registered with the Charity Commission with a new registered charity number. The foundation is the corporate charity of St James's Place Wealth Management, a UK wealth-management company.

Themes

The foundation's grant-making in the UK is guided by three themes. These themes change on a three-yearly basis and, at the time of writing (February 2017), were listed on the foundation's website as:

Cherishing Children

Cherishing Children is the foundation's largest theme and focuses on supporting children and young people under the age of 25 who are disadvantaged, who are young carers, or who have physical or mental health difficulties or life-threatening degenerative conditions. Grants are made for small capital items, support for staff working directly or hands on with beneficiaries, and support for projects of direct benefit to beneficiaries.

Combating Cancer

Grants are given for capital items of direct benefit to cancer patients, support towards the salary of staff working directly with cancer patients, and grants and support projects aimed at increasing the quality of life for cancer patients.

Supporting Hospices

Grants are given to hospices working with all age ranges. The foundation is currently working with Help the Hospices who will distribute funds to hospices on the foundation's behalf and, therefore, does not invite applications from hospices directly.

Grant programmes

- **Small Grants Programme:** grants of up to £10,000 are available to UK charities with an annual income of up to £750,000
- **Major Grants Programme:** at the time of writing (February 2017), this programme was closed; however, 2015 annual report states that, although the programme is not currently open to unsolicited applications, charities are invited to apply. Grants are usually for more than one year and are awarded to charities with an annual income of above £900,000
- **Major Projects:** projects are funded from the company's matched funding of money raised by partners and staff. The foundation's trustees and management committee will select a cause and then a charity working within that field will be approached by the foundation
- **Local Office Allowance:** £20,000 is available for each of the St James's Place locations. Grants of up to £2,500 can be given to any local charity

Approximately one third of funding raised by the foundation is allocated to UK charities operating overseas, particularly those 'helping children and young people to escape poverty, malnutrition and neglect'. Unsolicited applications are not accepted from charities working overseas.

Financial information

In 2015 the foundation had assets of almost £3.2 million and an income of £7.85 million. Grants to over 500 charities were made during the year totalling almost £5 million.

Beneficiaries included: Education for the Children (£200,000); Missing People (£140,000); Heel and Toe Children's Charity (£94,000); Roald Dahl's Marvellous Children's Charity (£84,500); The Art Room (£77,000); Noah's Ark Children's Hospice (£60,000); EdUKaid (£37,000); HealthProm (£7,500); SeeBeyondBorders (£2,500); Charlotte's Tandems (£400).

Exclusions

The foundation does not provide support for:

- Charities with reserves of over 50% of income
- Administrative costs
- Activities which are primarily the responsibility of statutory agencies
- Replacement of lost statutory funding
- Research
- Events
- Advertising
- Holidays
- Sponsorship
- Contributions to large capital appeals
- Single-faith charities
- Charities that are raising funds on behalf of another charity

Applications

Applicants who believe that they fit the criteria are welcome to apply at any time via the foundation's website. The application procedure for all of the programmes can take between four to six months. The following information is given on the foundation's website: 'Applications for a small grant will normally receive a visit from a representative of the foundation, who will subsequently report to the trustees. Following the trustees' decision, successful applicants will be notified.'

Consult the foundation's website for further details.

Standard Life Foundation

Social welfare and financial security

£658,500 (2015)

Beneficial area

UK and overseas (where Standard Life PLC operates).

Correspondent: Frances Horsburgh, Secretary, Group Secretariat, 30 Lothian Road, Edinburgh EH1 2DH (website: www.standardlife.com/sustainability)

OSCR number: SC040877

General information

This charity was registered with the Scottish Charity Regulator in 2009 and is funded by Standard Life PLC. Previously known as the Standard Life Charitable Trust, the foundation was renamed in 2016, and the company announced that it would receive the funds of the assets derived from the closure of its Unclaimed Asset Trust. In July 2016, these assets amounted to £42 million in cash and 13.5 million shares, and transfers were expected to begin by the end of 2016.

The foundation will focus on the issue of the 'savings gap'; the 2015 annual report states:

> Our motivation to equip people from all backgrounds to aspire to a better future, and to find ways to deliver sustainable change that builds stronger communities, remains unchanged...in the future our focus will be on providing opportunities through the transformative impact of being enabled to save.

The foundation particularly values working in partnership with charities and other organisations to deliver programmes and research. The 2013–16 Community Impact Report, on the Standard Life PLC website, states that 'the foundation will focus on public interest research and practical activities to help close the savings gap and ensure more people are financially secure over the long-term'.

Note that in 2015 the charity's focus was still on skills development and access to employment, so the information listed here reflects the charity's previous activities prior to this shift in focus. The report states that the foundation would continue to support its existing partners in 2016 – namely, SkillForce, Tomorrow's People and The Prince's Trust.

Financial information

In 2015 the foundation had assets of £1.8 million and an income of £48,400. Grants were made to three organisations totalling £658,500.

Beneficiaries were: The Prince's Trust (£400,000); Tomorrow's People (£205,000); The Royal British Legion (£53,500).

Applications

It is unclear at the time of writing (October 2016) whether the foundation will be accepting unsolicited applications; refer to the website for up-to-date information.

The John Swire (1989) Charitable Trust

General charitable purposes, especially: community and social welfare, heritage, and education and training

£1.4 million (2015)

Beneficial area

UK (with some preference for Kent) and overseas.

Correspondent: Sarah Irving, Correspondent, John Swire & Sons Ltd, Swire House, 59 Buckingham Gate, London SW1E 6AJ (tel: 020 7834 7717; email: Sarah.Irving@jssldn.co.uk)

CC number: 802142

General information

Established in 1989 by Sir John Swire of John Swire & Sons Ltd, a diversified group of global companies, the trust supports a wide range of organisations, especially in the area of arts, welfare, health, sports, education, medicine and research.

Financial information

In 2015 the trust had assets of £37 million and an income of £1.26 million. There were grants made totalling £1.4 million.

Beneficiaries included: Canterbury Cathedral Trust (£100,000); Gurkha Welfare Trust (£61,000); Action on Elder Abuse (£30,000); Innovation for Agriculture (£12,500); Musicians Benevolent Fund, National Trust, Order of St Johns for Kent, RSPB, Samaritans, Soil Association (£1,000 each).

Donations of under £1,000 totalled £18,400.

The Swire Charitable Trust

General charitable purposes, with a focus on community and social welfare, education and training, and heritage

£1.94 million (2015)

Beneficial area

Predominantly the UK.

Correspondent: Sarah Irving, Grants Manager, Swire House, 59 Buckingham Gate, London SW1E 6AJ (tel: 020 7834 7717; email: info@scts.org.uk; website: www.swirecharitabletrust.org.uk)

CC number: 270726

General information

Established in 1975, the trust's core grant-making programme offers grants to UK-registered charities working in the following areas: community and social welfare; education and training; and heritage. This programme is funded by John Swire & Sons Ltd, a diversified group of global companies. As a result of the merger of the Swire Charitable Trust and the Swire Educational Trust on 31 December 2015, the trust also operates a separate graduate and postgraduate scholarship programme for overseas students.

The following information on the trust's grant programmes and funding types is taken from the application guidelines on its website:

> *What is funded?*
>
> The Swire Charitable Trust awards grants via three funding programmes to UK registered charities working in England, Scotland, Wales and Northern Ireland. These grant-making programmes are currently open and welcoming eligible online funding requests.
>
> - Community and social welfare
> - Education and training
> - Heritage
>
> *Funding programmes*
>
> *Community and Social Welfare*
>
> We fund charities that help to foster long-term positive change in the lives of disadvantaged people and their communities, we particularly welcome funding requests from charities working with:
>
> - Young people leaving care
> - People with physical and learning disabilities
> - Homeless people
> - Ex-servicemen and women
> - Victims of slavery and human trafficking
>
> *Education and training*
>
> We fund charities that help children and adults from all backgrounds to fulfil their potential and make the most of their talents. We particularly support charities that are:
>
> - Working to narrow the attainment gap for disadvantaged and marginalised children
> - Targeting improvements in essential skills such as literacy and numeracy
> - Empowering young people not in education, employment or training (NEETs), or marginalised adults, to engage with education or training
>
> *Heritage*
>
> We fund charities working to restore neglected buildings and monuments which can contribute to community regeneration, particularly in areas of deprivation. We would especially like to hear from smaller heritage charities that

focus on providing employment or volunteering opportunities for the local community – and contributing to the regeneration of the area.

Types of funding

Grants from our core programme will aim to meet the needs identified in your application. We will fund individual projects that are aligned with our funding priorities but we also recognise that charities themselves are often best placed to allocate resources within their organisations. Therefore our grants can be awarded on a restricted or an unrestricted basis and we are willing to support core costs, capital expenditure and salaries.

There is no maximum or minimum grant size and, although we base our grants on the amount requested and the size of organisation, we may award more or less than you applied for.

Indeed the amount requested will only be used for guidance and the size of the grant will be entirely at the discretion of the trustees.

While most of our grants are for one year only, we appreciate that charities welcome security of funding. So, where a longer-term commitment can be clearly justified, we are willing to consider multi-year grants of up to three years. But these are likely to come with additional conditions, such as reporting requirements.

Financial information

In 2015 the trust had assets of £11.2 million and an income of £2.2 million. Grants to charitable organisations totalled £1.94 million.

Beneficiaries included: Air League Trust (£28,000); Combat Stress (£20,000); Cardinal Hume Centre, Marine Society and Sea Cadets, Motability and Oasis Partnership (£10,000 each); Heritage of London Trust (£7,500); Amber Foundation, Beanstalk and Living Paintings (£5,000 each).

Exclusions

The trust's application guidelines give the following information about what it is unable to consider:

- Applications received by post or email, i.e. not via its online funding request form
- Organisations that are not UK-registered charities
- Requests from charities that have applied to the trust in the last 12 months
- Individual applicants or proposals that will benefit only one person
- Activities taking place outside England, Scotland, Wales or Northern Ireland
- Work that has already taken place
- Statutory bodies or work that is primarily the responsibility of statutory authorities (e.g. residential, respite and day care, housing and provision of mainstream education through individual schools, nurseries and colleges)
- Activities of local organisations which are part of a wider network doing similar work (e.g. uniformed youth groups, YMCA, Mind, Relate, Citizens Advice, Age UK)
- Medicine-related charities, including those that provide care, support and equipment or fund research
- Animal welfare charities
- Academic research, scholarships or bursaries

Applications

The trust welcomes funding applications from UK-registered charities. Applications should be made via the online application form on the trust's website. They are considered throughout the year.

The Thales Charitable Trust

General charitable purposes, education, technology, children and young people, health, people with disabilities

£149,000 (2015)

Beneficial area

UK

Correspondent: Michael Seabrook, Trustee, Thales Corporate Services Ltd, 2 Dashwood Lang Road, Bourne Business Park, Addlestone, Surrey KT15 2NX (tel: 01932 824800; email: mike.seabrook@thalesgroup.com)

CC number: 1000162

General information

Registered in 1990 with the Charity Commission, the Thales Charitable Trust is the corporate charity of Thales Corporate Services Ltd, a major electronic systems company acting in areas such as defence, airlines security and safety, information technology and transportation.

Areas of work

The trust has general charitable purposes but principally supports charitable organisations in the fields of children and youth; technology; education and training; and the care for those with terminal illnesses. The trustees may use their discretion to meet requests from other causes from time to time.

Financial information

In 2015 the trust had assets of £71,000 and an income of £175,000 which was wholly received in donations from the Thales group. Grants totalled £149,000.

Beneficiaries included: Alzheimer's Scotland; Blind Children UK; CLIC Sargent; Julian Campbell Foundation; National Museum of Computing; Scottish Veterans Residences; Sign Health; The Railway Benefit Fund; Together for Short Lives; Young Epilepsy.

Applications

Apply in writing to the correspondent. The trust does not generally solicit requests unless for major donations.

the7stars foundation

The foundation supports the most challenged individuals under 16 year of age in the country – specifically those suffering as a result of homelessness, addiction or abuse and child carers

£50,000 to £100,000 (2016/17 – projected)

Beneficial area

UK

Correspondent: Alexandra Taliadoros, Foundation Director, c/o Simon Durham, the7stars Foundation, Floor 6–8, Melbourne House, 46 Aldwych, London WC2B 4LL (tel: 07940 959817; email: alexandra@the7starsfoundation.co.uk; website: www.the7starsfoundation.co.uk)

CC number: 1168240

General information

Registered with the Charity Commission in July 2016, the7stars foundation is the charitable foundation of the7stars UK Ltd, the UK's largest independent media agency.

At the time of writing (August 2016), the trustees – who include two of the agency's co-founders, Jenny Biggam and Mark Jarvis – were in the process of approving internal giving policies and the foundation's website was being set up; however, the following information was provided to us:

the7stars UK Ltd objective

To be a modern successful business that leads by example by doing the right thing for our clients, staff and the community, the7stars has decided to set up a foundation. the7stars foundation will support the most challenged under 16 year olds in the UK – the forgotten kids who lack the opportunity to achieve their potential. Support will be achieved through grant making to organisations delivery programmes supporting this group. We will donate a minimum of 5% of our profit each year to the Foundation.

Motivations for giving

We collectively feel that as a group we could do more for the community. There is an amplifying effect of pooling together a fund and focusing on causes we all believe in.

Our goals

- To donate a minimum of 5% of our profit to good causes each year
- To support at least one charity in each of the pillars (homelessness, addiction, abuse, child carers) each year
- To become an active initiative that enables our staff to be involved on a voluntary basis

the7stars foundation mission statement

To support the most challenged under 16 year olds in the country – specifically those suffering as a result of homelessness, addiction, abuse and child carers.

Applications

Applicants are directed to the foundation's website, where application forms are available to download. Completed forms can be returned to the Foundation Director by email. The Foundation Director can be contacted with any questions about your application, the application form or the application process.

TONI&GUY Charitable Foundation Ltd

General charitable purposes, children and young people, health, disability, social welfare

£31,000 (2014/15)

Beneficial area

Worldwide

Correspondent: Laura Gurney, Charity Events and Fundraising Co-ordinator, 58–60 Stamford Street, London SE1 9LX (email: laura.gurney@toniandguy.co.uk; website: www.toniandguyfoundation.org.uk)

CC number: 1095285

General information

The TONI&GUY Foundation was established in 2003 and is the official charity of the UK-based hairdressing and training company, TONI&GUY, which was set up by brothers Giuseppe (Toni) and Gaetano (Guy) Mascolo in 1963. Mascolo Ltd is the parent company of the TONI&GUY salons. The trustees include Toni Mascolo, co-founder/CEO of TONI&GUY, as well as company directors and franchisees.

Strength in Style

Strength in Style is the TONI&GUY Foundation's collaboration with Macmillan Cancer Support, which was set up in 2009 and looks to help those affected by cancer with a specialised training scheme for hairdressers. New staff are trained through courses which are held four times a year in London and Manchester.

Financial information

In 2014/15 the foundation had assets totalling £1,600 and an income of £85,000 from donated goods and services from Mascolo Ltd and specific fundraising activities in TONI&GUY salons. Grants awarded to organisations totalled £31,000.

Beneficiaries included: Macmillan (£16,000); Stroke Association (£15,000).

Exclusions

No grants are available for individuals.

Applications

Applications can be made in writing to the correspondent. The annual report suggests that future grants will be made to organisations that have particular relevance to TONI&GUY salons, their staff and clients; for example, The Little Princess Trust – a charity that provides wigs for children with cancer.

Toyota Manufacturing UK Charitable Trust

Children, education, environment, health

£145,000 (2015)

Beneficial area

The areas local to Toyota's two plants: Burnaston (Derbyshire) and Deeside (North Wales).

Correspondent: Jean Sayers, Toyota Motor Manufacturing (UK) Ltd, Derby DE1 9TA (tel: 01332 283609; email: charitabletrust@toyotauk.com; website: www.toyotauk.com/the-toyota-charitable-trust/charitable-trust-overview.html)

CC number: 1124678

General information

Registered in 2008, this is the charitable trust of Toyota Motor Manufacturing (UK) Ltd. Income is largely derived from company employees through fundraising activities. The trust makes donations to local organisations in the Burnaston (Derbyshire) and Deeside (North Wales) areas with a focus on the environment, children, education and health.

It is explained on the Toyota UK website that the trust also encourages employee involvement in the community and where suitable offers 'financial support for our employees who undertake fund raising activities'. Support is also given to local community organisations where employees play an active role.

Financial information

In 2015 the trust had an income of £211,000 and a total expenditure of £171,500. We estimate that over £145,000 was made in grants, but specific amounts were undeclared in the annual report. Over £11,500 was contributed through matched funding and the trust covered any seminar and volunteer costs.

Beneficiaries include: Action for Charity – Women v Cancer, Alvaston Infant and Nursery School, Comic Relief, Derbyshire, Leicestershire and Rutland Air Ambulance, Epilepsy Society, Erlas Victorian Walled Garden, Prostate Cancer UK, Sight Support Derbyshire, Welsh Air Ambulance Charitable Trust.

Applications

Applications may be made in writing to the correspondent.

UIA Charitable Foundation

Financially developing countries, human rights, social welfare, rehabilitation of offenders, homeless people, young people and older individuals, victims of domestic abuse

£57,000 (2015)

Beneficial area

Worldwide

Correspondent: Jackie White, Administrator, UIA Charitable Foundation, Kings Court, London Road, Stevenage, Hertfordshire SG1 2TP (tel: 01438 761761; fax: 01438 761762; email: charitable.foundation@uia.co.uk; website: www.uia.co.uk/About-Us/Charitable-foundation)

CC number: 1079982

General information

The UIA Charitable Foundation is a grant-making body established to provide financial support to formally constituted voluntary organisations and small registered charities that help people in need. It is funded entirely by donations from UIA (Insurance) Ltd, a mutual insurance company, that is the provider of insurances to members of

UNISON, UNITE and other trade unions.

The objectives are to support the relief of poverty, sickness, disability and suffering, the advancement of education and the promotion of other purposes that are beneficial to the community.

The foundation's aim is to support charities that help people in need to improve the quality of their lives. According to the website, the preferred areas for the provision of funding to good causes were those that deal with:

- Addressing poverty and improving human rights
- Rehabilitation of offenders
- Support for older people
- Support for young people
- Tackling homelessness
- Victims of domestic abuse

Financial information

In 2015 the foundation had an income of £73,000, all of which was a donation from UIA (Insurance) Ltd. Seven grants were made and totalled £57,000.

Beneficiaries included: Amy Marren (£20,000); Hertfordshire Community Foundation (£12,300); Banana Link, Ellesmere Port and Romanian Appeal, Iris Prize Outreach Ltd, and War on Want (£5,000 each); Tracks Autism (£4,900).

Exclusions

The foundation's website states that it will not fund the following:

- work which it believes to be publicly funded
- retrospective projects
- organisations that have an annual turnover in excess of £500,000 unless the organisation is acting as a conduit for a partner that fulfils the criteria and may find it difficult to obtain access to funding through independent channels
- organisations whose combined grant related support costs and governance costs are greater than 10% of their turnover

Applications

The foundation is not accepting new applications for funding. The website states that:

> The UIA Charitable Foundation is not accepting new applications for funding at this time. UIA and its key partners, members and staff proactively seek and nominate good causes all year round for consideration at trustee meetings. At present, trustee meetings are held twice a year in February and September. Receipt of a nomination does not guarantee that it will be considered at the next meeting. You will be informed of the decision in writing as soon as possible after the meeting.

Check the foundation's website for further information.

United Utilities Trust Fund

Money advice, debt counselling, financial literacy

£287,000 to organisations (2015/16)

Beneficial area

The area supplied by United Utilities Water PLC (predominantly the north west of England).

Correspondent: The Secretary (Auriga Services Ltd), Emmanuel Court, 12–14 Mill Street, Sutton Coldfield B72 1TJ (tel: 0845 179 1791; email: contact@uutf.org.uk; website: www.uutf.org.uk)

CC number: 1108296

General information

United Utilities Trust Fund is an independent grant-making charity established in early 2005. Grants are mainly awarded to individuals in financial hardship who have a liability to pay water charges to United Utilities Water (directly or indirectly) and who are unable to pay.

Grants are also given to organisations that can deliver money advice and financial literacy services. The trustees' annual report for 2015/16 provides the following information: 'Recognising the value of long-term help and support to individuals of professional money advice services, the Trustees adopted a policy of making grants available to organisations that provide free debt advice and debt counselling services.'

Financial information

In 2015/16 the charity had assets of £749,000 and an income of £6.2 million, almost all of which came from United Utilities. During the year the trust received 8,295 (2015: 9,322) applications and was able to provide grants and further assistance to 5,486 (2015: 6,213) individuals or families amounting to £5.26 million (2015: £5.78 million). In pursuit of charitable objectives, the trustees have paid £287,000 (2015: £163,000) to organisations towards debt advice and debt counselling during this year.

Beneficiaries included: St Helens Citizens Advice (£40,000); Centre 63 (£37,000); South Liverpool Citizens Advice (£32,500); Cheetham Hill Advice Centre and Preston and District Citizens Advice (£31,000 each); Blackpool Citizens Advice and Local Solutions (£30,000 each); North Lancashire Citizens Advice (£23,000); Age UK South Lakeland and Salford Foundation (£15,600 each); Lan Comm Finance Trust (£1,500).

Exclusions

The charity will not fund:

- Existing projects
- Charities which appear to it to have sufficient unrestricted or free reserves, or are in serious deficit
- Projects outside the geographical area
- National charities that do not have the facility to accept the funding on a regional basis
- Grant-making bodies seeking to distribute grants on UUTF's behalf
- General appeals, sponsorship and marketing appeals
- Replacement of existing programmes or statutory funding

Applications

Application forms are available from the correspondent or the charity's website. Check the website for current information.

The Virgin Money Foundation

General charitable purposes, community development, employment and enterprise, education and training, deprived communities, housing, young people

£895,500 (2015)

Beneficial area

Currently focused on the North East, to be expanded across the UK.

Correspondent: Paul Armstrong, Company Secretary, Jubilee House, Gosforth, Newcastle upon Tyne NE3 4PL (tel: 0330 123 3624; email: info@virginmoneyfoundation.org.uk; website: virginmoneyfoundation.org.uk)

CC number: 1161290

General information

The foundation was registered with the Charity Commission in April 2015. It was set up following the demise of the Northern Rock Foundation (established by the Northern Rock Bank which was purchased by the Virgin Money bank), 'to promote the sustainable regeneration of economically and socially deprived communities in the United Kingdom'.

The foundation has initially focused its work on supporting charitable projects in the North East and has had £4 million committed to it by the UK Government

(£1 million each year over the course of four years) which will be matched by Virgin Money. The foundation's work will be rolled out across the UK over time.

North East Fund

The foundation's first £1 million funding round to support communities in the North East was launched in August 2015 and followed by a second funding round in 2016. According to the foundation's website, applications were accepted that:

> Promoted long-term change in communities that need it most [through]:
>
> - Enabling homeless people or people at risk of homelessness to find a home. The Foundation is particularly interested in supporting applications from organisations working to increase the supply of good quality, affordable rented properties
> - Providing opportunities for young people to secure sustainable employment
> - Creating and supporting community and social enterprises that bring money and jobs into a deprived community

The website notes that since the fund's launch in 2015 a total of 50 community organisations have received support in the form of grants ranging from around £16,800 to £50,000. A total of £752,000 has been awarded to 18 organisations working with homeless people, a further £738,500 has been shared between 19 organisations working with young people, and 13 social enterprises have been awarded a total of £422,500.

The Ripple Fund

At the time of writing (February 2017) the foundation's website stated that this fund was due to launch shortly. The website explained that 'the fund will work with organisations seeking investment in projects that will make a real and long-term difference to areas of deprivation in the North East and across the UK'.

Financial information

In 2015 the foundation had assets of £957,000 and an income of almost £2 million. A total of 25 grants were awarded during the year, amounting to £895,500.

According to the annual report, of the grants awarded during the 2015 financial year:

- Nine were given to assist disadvantaged young people into employment
- Nine were given to support a new or existing social enterprise
- Seven were given to assist homeless people to find and keep a home

The annual report further notes: 'A further £850,000 was also designated by the Foundation to be paid to Onside Youth Zones, the charity that will build a Youth Zone in Sunderland to give young people a safe and inspiring place to go in their leisure time.' This grant will be distributed in stages depending on conditions being met.

Exclusions

At the time of writing (February 2017) the foundation did not have any open funding programmes and so information regarding eligibility was not readily available. We obtained the following information at an earlier date when the North East Fund was open and have kept it as a general guide to indicate expenditure that cannot be funded:

- Capital costs
- Anything that isn't defined as charitable by law
- Charities with more than 12 months' running costs in unrestricted reserves
- International appeals
- Sponsorship or marketing appeals
- Existing projects looking for backdated funding
- Services that central or local government would normally pay for
- Individual appeals
- Animal welfare charities
- The day-to-day costs of schools and other educational establishments
- Medical treatment or research, hospices and medical centres
- Promotion of religious, political or advocacy-based groups
- Smaller projects like overseas travel, minibuses, holidays and outings, or sports equipment
- Requests which could be funded through any other existing Virgin Group or Virgin Money scheme

Applications

Refer to the website for more information and for updates regarding open funding rounds.

The Vodafone Foundation

General charitable purposes, with a preference for technology, disadvantaged communities, humanitarian crises and disasters

£18.6 million (2015/16) worldwide. £725,000 in the UK

Beneficial area

UK and overseas (where Vodafone operates).

Correspondent: Andrew Dunnett, Foundation Director, Vodafone Group PLC, 1 Kingdom Street, London W2 6BY (email: groupfoundation@vodafone.com; website: www.vodafone.com/content/index/about/foundation.html)

CC number: 1089625

General information

The Vodafone Foundation was established in 2001. Its 2015/16 trustees' annual report states that during that year it distributed funds to:

- Charities and individual programmes selected by its 27 local Vodafone foundations
- Global programmes that fit with the foundation's grant-making strategies

The report also states that the foundation has a funding partnership with Vodafone's local foundations to provide public benefit by investing in programmes that support communities in which Vodafone has commercial roots. The trustees also allocate funds to global programmes, run in partnership with NGOs.

The following statement is taken from the 2015/16 trustees' annual report:

> The Trustees of The Vodafone Foundation continue to drive forward the Foundation's Mobile for Good programme, an initiative aimed at linking the Trust's charitable giving with Vodafone's mobile technology which in so many ways is changing the world.
>
> At the heart of our Foundation is the belief that mobile communications technologies can address some of the world's most pressing humanitarian challenges and our responsibility is to use our innovative mobile technology in mobilising social change and improving people's lives. By 2016, around 70% of our giving was allocated to Mobile for Good.

The summary report for this financial year provides the following information:

The foundation funds projects that span these major themes:

Mobile for Good

This programme connects Vodafone's giving to its technology, maximising the impact of our charitable giving by funding projects that can benefit from leveraging Vodafone's technologies and expertise to address 'some of the world's most pressing humanitarian challenges'.

Disaster relief

Through its Instant Network programme Vodafone Volunteers and technology are deployed in emergencies to provide free communications and technical support to aid 'agencies and victims and develop new technologies to support the humanitarian community. Vodafone continues to enable customers to donate to charity via our network and through The Vodafone Foundation's mobile giving programme.'

In-country Grants

There are 27 local Vodafone foundations, giving financial support to projects that benefit 'local communities in significant and timely ways'. Each of the foundations is financed by an annual contribution from The Vodafone Foundation, as well as additional funds from the local operating company. These independent 27 foundations support the communities where Vodafone customers, employees and other stakeholders live. They select charities and projects 'that fit with our overarching strategic direction and major themes, while also addressing the social issues that affect the people they are close to'.

UK programme

The trustees' annual report for 2015/16 states that The Vodafone Foundation is responsible for Vodafone UK's social investment activities. The programmes include:

JustTextGiving

The report states:

> Working with the online fundraising platform JustGiving and Vodafone UK, The Vodafone Foundation has continued to develop the JustTextGiving service. JustTextGiving enables charities in the UK, no matter how big or small, to raise money via text donations. Since its inception in May 2011, JustTextGiving has been used by more than 250,000 individual fundraisers and by 24,000 charities and has helped raise more than £37 million for charity.

TecSOS

This is a specialised handset designed for use by victims of domestic violence which connects them directly to the police wherever they are. Six European countries are using the handset with almost 11,000 UK victims benefitting. The report states that over 70% of UK police forces are using the service to support victims of domestic violence in their area.

Matched funding

The Vodafone Foundation gives financial support to UK-based Vodafone employees or teams that fundraise in their own time. This is processed through matched funding of up to £350 per employee, per event, and up to four times per year. In 2015/16 Vodafone employees raised nearly £1.8 million for their chosen causes. The Vodafone Foundation contributed £645,000 towards employee fundraising.

Financial information

In 2015/16 the foundation had assets of over £7.1 million and an income of almost £21 million. During the year, the foundation made grants worldwide totalling £18.6 million (excluding restricted activities and support costs) but which included over £725,000 in grants to local Vodafone foundations.

Beneficiaries in the UK include: Digital Scouts (£250,000); JustTextGiving (£224,000); Text Santa (£100,000); Prince's Trust (£151,500).

Applications

Contact the foundation or see the website for details of all application processes for different grant programmes. Note that the foundation's website states that the foundation receives an average of 12,000 requests per year for funding and support and that while seeking to respond to all requests for information, it normally approaches only those charitable organisations which it believes can help in the delivery of its charitable aims.

Wates Family Enterprise Trust

Education, employment and training, community projects, social enterprise, sustainability, thought leadership

£1 million (2015)

Beneficial area

UK

Correspondent: Jerry Wright, Director, Wates House, Station Approach, Leatherhead, Surrey KT22 7SW (tel: 01372 861251; email: director@watesfoundation.org.uk; website: watesgiving.org.uk)

CC number: 1126007

General information

Registered in 2008, the trust is the vehicle for the philanthropic and charitable activities of the Wates family, owners of the Wates Group.

Wates Giving

The trust's charitable grants programme is called Wates Giving. It supports the following causes:

- Education
- Employment and training
- Community building
- Social enterprise
- Sustainability
- Thought leadership

Further information and examples of causes supported in each of these categories are provided on the website.

There are three types of grant which may be made by the trust, according to the 2015 annual report:

> - **Major awards** – in support of bids originating from initiatives of the Wates Group and its business units
> - **Family awards** – in support of bids which are the initiative of the Wates family
> - **Employee awards** – in support of initiatives of employees of the Wates businesses acting in a private capacity.
>
> Employee awards may include: personal fundraising for local charitable or community causes; Give as You Earn donations through payroll; engagement with community organisations as volunteers, trustees, governors or other roles; participation in sport at national and international levels; and major sponsorship events for a Charity of the Year.

The following information was taken from the 2014 annual report:

> The purpose of Wates Family Enterprise Trust Ltd is to provide a means for the Wates family to be engaged stewards of the family business, blending wealth creation with social responsibility, to deliver impact on social need for the public benefit through an effective charitable programme – Wates Giving. Over a five to ten-year period, the objective set for the trust is to connect the family's motivation as its patrons to the resources, enthusiasm, leadership and knowledge intrinsic to its enterprises; and in doing so to create opportunities for business to play a responsible philanthropic role in the communities in which the family business and its employees live, work and build.
>
> The trust makes its awards in six areas or themes as follows:
>
> - Education
> - Employment and training
> - Community building
> - Social enterprise
> - Sustainability
> - Thought leadership
>
> Funding is allocated to bids originating from initiatives of the Wates Group and its business units, the Wates family and employees of the Wates businesses acting in a personal capacity. This includes: fundraising for local charitable and community causes; Give As You Earn donations through payroll; engagement with community organisations as volunteers, trustees, governors or similar roles; participation in sport at national and international levels; and major sponsorship events for a Charity of the Year.

Financial information

In 2015 the trust had an income of just over £1 million, almost all of which came from the Wates Group. Grants awarded to organisations totalled just over £1 million. A further £11,900 was given in four grants to individuals, for sports sponsorship. Grants to organisations were broken down as follows:

Major projects	50	£709,000
Family projects	33	£198,000
Community projects	33	£77,500
Matched funding	11	£34,000
Give As You Earn	1	£16,400
Supply chain fund	18	£13,500

Beneficiaries included: University of Westminster (£60,000); Manchester

HOME (£30,000); New Economics Foundation Consulting (£15,000); Child Bereavement UK and MS Society (£10,000 each); Surrey Care Trust (£8,600); Bunbury Cricket Club (£6,000); Institute of Social Entrepreneurs (£5,000); Community Links (£2,000); Cumberworth Junior Football Club (£300); Cloch Housing Association and Beaston Cancer Charity (£150).

Applications

All proposals come from Wates employees or the Wates family. Note that unsolicited applications are not considered.

The Wates Foundation

Social welfare, employment and education, health, community safety, building voluntary sector capacity

£397,000 (2015/16)

Beneficial area

Most of the southern half of England.

Correspondent: James Webb, Grants Officer, Wates House, Station Approach, Leatherhead, Surrey KT22 7SW (tel: 01372 861250; fax: 01372 861252; email: director@watesfoundation.org.uk; website: www.watesfoundation.org.uk)

CC number: 247941

General information

In 1966, three brothers Norman, Sir Ronald and Allan Wates of the Wates building firm (now the Wates Construction Group), amalgamated their personal charitable trusts into the single entity, The Wates Foundation. The foundation has three grant-making committees, which each usually meet once a year, and are named after their respective founder: the Allan Wates Family Committee; the Norman Wates Family Committee and the Ronald Wates Family Committee. According to the 2015/16 accounts, the foundation aims 'to improve for the public benefit the quality of life of the deprived, disadvantaged and excluded in the community in which we live'.

Grants

Grants may be paid between one and four years. The foundation awards grants under the following six themes:

- Building Social Values
- Employment and Education
- Community Health
- Safer Communities
- Life Transitions
- Strengthening the Charitable and Voluntary Sector

Financial information

In 2015/16 the foundation had assets of £16.6 million and an income of £343,000. Grants were made to organisations during the year totalling almost £397,000 and were distributed in the following categories:

Family Values	13	£120,500
Safer Communities	7	£87,000
Community Health	11	£85,000
Education and employment	7	£71,000
Strengthening voluntary sector	6	£63,000

Beneficiaries included: Butler Trust (£32,000); Mayday Trust (£30,000 in two grants); Moorfield's Eye Charity (£12,700); Cotswold Riding for the Disabled and The Parenting Project (£10,000 each); Cutteslowe Community Association (£8,000); Reading Quest (£6,000); Inside Out – HMP Wormwood Scrubs (£5,000); Art for Youth UK (£2,000); The Genesis Trust (£500).

Exclusions

Grants are not made for the following purposes:

- Work that is not charitable according to law
- Political activities
- Promotion of religion or a specific faith (although religious organisations may be awarded a grant for projects with other charitable purposes, such as education, health, community work, etc.)
- Individuals
- Statutory organisations
- Other grant-making bodies (except for partnerships)
- Major capital works. Minor capital works, such as equipment or renovations may be allowed up to a total budget of £30,000
- General appeals and fundraising

Any organisations which have received a grant already must wait a period of 24 months before a new application will be considered.

Applications are by invitation only.

Applications

Following a review of its grant-making policy in 2011, the Wates Foundation decided to take a new proactive grant-making strategy, which will be in place until March 2018, according to the foundation's website. The trustees seek out charities to support, often in their local communities, and state that: '**Applications are by invitation only. Unsolicited applications will be automatically rejected.**'

Check the foundation's website for the latest information.

The Westminster Foundation

Social welfare, with an emphasis on poverty and supporting communities

£40 million (2015)

Beneficial area

In the UK, there is a preference for: Westminster (parts of the Old Metropolitan Borough of Westminster); Cheshire West and Cheshire; North West rural Lancashire (near Forest of Bowland); and North West Sutherland. Overseas grants are awarded in areas where the Grosvenor Organisation operates.

Correspondent: Jane Sanders, Director, The Grosvenor Office, 70 Grosvenor Street, London W1K 3JP (tel: 020 7312 6157; email: westminster.foundation@grosvenor.com; website: www.westminsterfoundation.org.uk)

CC number: 267618

General information

The foundation was established in 1974 for general charitable purposes by the fifth Duke of Westminster and continues to make grants to a wide range of charitable causes. In 1987 the Grosvenor Foundation, a separately registered charity, transferred all its assets to the Westminster Foundation. The foundation continues to receive regular donations from Grosvenor Group Ltd and supports a wide range of charities through its grant-making, with a focus on the areas in which the group operates.

Grants

The foundation's grant-making currently focuses on poverty, through the Supporting Communities programme. The website states that the foundation is interested in the following two issues:

> **Supporting vulnerable groups:** projects to tackle the challenges faced by people who are isolated or alone whether they are in rural or urban areas. This might include those who are suffering because of the absence of family and social networks to turn to for help and support, such as vulnerable older people. For example, outreach and community groups, befriending schemes, help on the doorstep, nutrition, welfare advice, emergency alarms, learning new skills, access to specialist transport services and communication.
>
> **Building resilience through strengthening local voluntary organisations:** initiatives such as volunteer training to help organisations develop the skills they need to become better equipped to provide more effective

and sustainable support to vulnerable people within our communities.

Grants of up to £5,000 are available, and are made only to registered charities or organisations with exempt or excepted status, such as schools or churches.

The 2015 annual report states that the foundation also makes major grants of over £5,000; however, at the time of writing (February 2017), there was no information about major grants on the foundation's website.

The foundation provides matched funding for funds raised by employees of the Grosvenor Estate, up to £1,000 per person. It also provides subsidised office accommodation for charities in Westminster, and allows charities to use its facilities for events and fundraising purposes. There are a small number of overseas grants made through nominations from overseas companies in the Grosvenor group.

In 2015 the foundation also made an exceptionally large grant to the Black Stork Charity to support the establishment of the Defence and National Rehabilitation Centre, with a further £30 million committed in 2016.

Financial information

In 2015 the foundation had assets of almost £4 million and an income of £3.2 million, which included £2.3 million from Grosvenor Group Ltd. There were grants made totalling almost £42 million. This included awards made through: the Supporting Communities programme; the Youth Homelessness programme; discretionary grants; charity offices; overseas grants; and an exceptionally large grant of £40 million to support the establishment of the Defence and National Rehabilitation Centre (see above).

Beneficiaries of grants over £20,000 included: Ashden (£120,000); Hong Kong Cancer Fund (£85,500); The Foundation Years Trust (£75,000); Atlantic Salmon Trust (£50,000); Fine Cell Work (£56,500); Caritas Madrid (£44,500); Forgiveness Project (£35,000); Crisis UK (£32,500); Age UK Cheshire (£25,000); Small Charities Coalition (£22,000).

Exclusions

The foundation does not consider:

- General appeals or letters requesting non-specific donations
- Organisations that do not have charitable aims (e.g. commercial companies and companies limited by shares)
- Overtly political projects (including party-political and campaigning projects)
- Individuals (or organisations applying on behalf of an individual)
- Student fees/bursaries
- Projects taking place or benefiting people outside the UK
- Projects/work benefiting people outside its specific geographical criteria
- Overseas trips
- Holidays/trips
- Organisations that have applied to the foundation unsuccessfully within the previous 12 months
- Projects where the main focus is website development or maintenance
- Start up costs, organisations that do not yet have a demonstrable track record

Applications

Applicants should first refer to the website to ascertain whether they are eligible for funding from the foundation.

Applications should be made through the foundation's application form provided on the website, where full application guidelines can also be found. The Grants Review Panel meets around every eight weeks and successful applicants will be notified within two weeks. If you do not hear back in this period, you should assume that you have not been successful.

The Garfield Weston Foundation

General charitable purposes, with preference for education, the arts, health (including research), welfare, environment, young people, religion and other areas of general benefit to the community

£58.7 million (2015/16)

Beneficial area

UK

Correspondent: Philippa Charles, Director, Weston Centre, 10 Grosvenor Street, London W1K 4QY (tel: 020 7399 6565; email: gdarocha@garfieldweston.org; website: www.garfieldweston.org)

CC number: 230260

General information

The Garfield Weston Foundation was established in 1958 by Willard Garfield Weston, a Canadian businessman who moved to the UK with his family in 1932. He was the creator of Associated British Foods and the foundation was endowed with the donation of family-owned company shares. According to the foundation's 2015/16 annual report, at 5 April 2016 it owned 79.2% of Wittington Investments Ltd, the ultimate holding company of Associated British Foods PLC. Awards are regularly made in almost all fields except animal welfare. Grants are made in the general fields of arts, education, environment, health, religion, welfare, young people and community. Requests for specific activities or programmes, capital projects and core costs are considered. Applications for very large grants are also considered.

The foundation's website states:

> The foundation aims to be responsive to where need is greatest. We therefore support a wide range of charitable activity rather than having specific priorities for funding or regional bias. The foundation appreciates how challenging it is for charities to raise funds and aims to keep the process of applying uncomplicated with a one-stage application. Despite the diversity of organisations and projects the foundation funds, the common themes are charities that demonstrate quality and excellence with projects that have clear outcomes and benefits, good leadership and sensible business plans.

Regarding current priorities, at the time of writing (February 2017), the foundation's website states:

> Mindful of the challenging economic climate, the Foundation has continued to grow its donations (giving almost £55 million in the last year) and the Trustees are especially keen to see applications for core and project costs for charities delivering services directly to beneficiaries, especially in the welfare, youth and community fields, and also in regions of economic disadvantage.

In 2014/15 the foundation launched the 'Weston Charter', which sets out the foundation's commitments to its applicants and approach to grant-making. This is available on the foundation's website or in the annual report.

The foundation has two streams of activity:

- Main grants – under £100,000
- Major grants – £100,000 and above

The foundation has a helpful website which provides detailed guidance for applicants, case studies and further useful information.

Financial information

In 2015/16 the foundation had assets of £12.75 billion and an income of £62.2 million. Grants totalled £58.7 million and were broken down as follows:

Education	175	£14.3 million
Arts	152	£10.4 million
Welfare	343	£9.5 million
Health	107	£7.5 million
Community	211	£5.5 million
Youth	193	£4.4 million
Faith/places of worship	377	£4.2 million
Environment	43	£2.2 million
Other	16	£714,500

Beneficiaries include: The Courtauld Institute of Art (£3 million); Breast

Cancer Now (£500,000); National Army Museum (£150,000); Rewilding Britain (£90,000); Aylesbury Grammar School (£50,000); Bounce Back Foundation and The National Lobster Hatchery (£40,000 each); The Sobriety Project (£30,000); Derby Cathedral and London Bubble Theatre Company (£25,000 each); Mind the Gap (£10,000).

Exclusions

According to the foundation's guidelines, which can be found on its website, the foundation does not fund the areas indicated below:

- Any funding request made within 12 months of the outcome of a previous application, whether a grant was received or not
- Charities which are not registered in the UK (unless a charity holds exempt status as a church, educational establishment, hospital or housing corporation)
- Overseas projects
- Individual applicants, individual research or study, including gap year activities, study trips, fundraising expeditions and sponsorship
- Animal welfare charities
- Umbrella organisations, as organisations working with beneficiaries at a grassroots level are preferred
- One-off events such as galas or festivals, even if for fundraising purposes
- Specific salaries and positions; however, core operating costs are supported where general salary costs are recognised
- Funding commitments over several years – grants made are typically for a single year
- Organisations that cannot demonstrate significant progress with fundraising

Applications

Applications can be made using the foundation's online system or by post, downloading the application form from the website. The foundation's website states that applications are accepted at any time during the year and that there are no formal deadlines for the submission of applications. Full information on criteria and how to complete an application are given in the foundation's guidelines, available from the website or by request. The foundation asks that you do not apply both online and by post.

For major grants (over £100,000), trustees meet eight times each year, and an initial letter should be sent by post outlining the project, objectives, overall cost, current shortfall and time frames. The trust will then be in contact for further discussion. Refer to the foundation's website for more information.

The Willmott Dixon Foundation

Young people, people with disabilities

£66,500 (2014/15)

Beneficial area

UK

Correspondent: Laurence Holdcroft, Administrator, Willmott Dixon Holdings PLC, Spirella 2, Icknield Way, Letchworth Garden City, Hertfordshire SG6 4GY (tel: 01462 671852; email: laurence.holdcroft@willmottdixon.co.uk; website: www.willmottdixon.co.uk/how-we-do-it/the-willmott-dixon-foundation)

Trustees: Colin Enticknap; Richard Willmott; Andrew Telfer.

CC number: 326530

General information

Willmott Dixon Group is a privately owned construction, housing and property development business. The Willmott Dixon Foundation was set up in 1984 and is chaired by the Group Chief Executive, Rick Willmott. The current focus of the foundation is tackling social exclusion, inspiring young people and community transformation.

According to the foundation's website, the objectives of the foundation are to:

- strategically channel the skills, experience and know-how to make a positive impact in society
- make sure that the time and money we invest in communities has maximum impact
- strengthen the skills of our employees and increase engagement through participation in community activities
- build strong partnerships with customers through our focused approach to social investment
- provide transparency and public reporting of social investment and outcomes

The local businesses and sites work with their clients and the local communities to identify their needs and aspirations. At the same time the company also works at regional and national level with charity partners to develop programmes of activity to maximise the impact it can have.

Financial information

In 2014/15 the foundation had assets of £18,500 and an income of £77,000, including £52,500 from Willmott Dixon Holdings Ltd. Grants to 34 charities were made totalling £66,500.

Beneficiaries included: Chestnut Tree House (£25,000); Action for Children (£14,100); Macmillan (£5,200); St Basils (£3,400).

Other awards of less than £2,500 amounted to £18,700.

Applications

Applications can be made in writing to the correspondent. Note that the foundation tends to work with a small number of partner charities.

The Xerox (UK) Trust

Education, social welfare and general charitable purposes

£14,000 (2015)

Beneficial area

UK

Correspondent: Cheryl Walsh, Xerox UK Ltd, Bridge House, Oxford Road, Uxbridge UB8 1HS (tel: 01895 251133)

Trustees: Jeffrey Donald McMahon; Francis James Mooney; John Hopwood.

CC number: 284698

General information

Xerox is a multinational company that produces printers, photocopiers, printing presses and printing supplies. This trust supports local or medium-sized organisations working towards the advancement of equality of opportunities; particularly among people who are young, disadvantaged, terminally ill or have disabilities.

Financial information

In 2015 the trust had an income of £44,000. The annual report shows that ten grants were made totalling £14,000.

Previous beneficiaries have included: Bedford and District Cerebral Palsy Society (£6,500); B-4–8's Family Support Centre (£3,000); Wipe Your Tears (£1,000); Snaps (£800); My Life My Choice (£700); Amy and Friends, and Down Syndrome Training and Support Service Ltd (£500 each); Marches Family Network (£350); Kneelman's Way School (£300); Tower Hamlets Opportunity Group (£250).

Exclusions

No grants are made to individuals, religious or political organisations, or national bodies.

Applications

Applications can be made in writing to the correspondent. Priority is given to charities with strong links to Xerox (UK) Ltd employees.

Yorkshire and Clydesdale Bank Foundation

Health, education, community development, social welfare, sports, the environment, arts and culture, equality and diversity, animal welfare, young people, older people, people with disabilities, disadvantaged people and communities

£865,000 (2014/15)

Beneficial area

UK

Correspondent: Company Secretary, Ground Floor Mezzanine, 30 St Vincent Place, Glasgow G1 2HL (email: yorkshire.and.clydesdale.bank.foundation@cybg.com; website: www.cbonline.co.uk/about-clydesdale-bank/community)

Trustees: Douglas Campbell; Lorna Macmillan; Graeme Duncan; David Blair; Debbie Crosbie; Sandra Delamere.

OSCR number: SC039747

General information

The Yorkshire and Clydesdale Bank Foundation was established in 2008 and is registered with the Office of the Scottish Charity Regulator. It is the corporate charity of the Clydesdale Bank, a commercial bank formed in Glasgow in 1838. The bank itself has a long tradition of providing funds for the communities in which it works.

The foundation's 2014/15 annual report states that it looks to support registered charities, community and other voluntary organisations under the following categories:

- Prevention and relief of poverty
- Advancement of education
- Advancement of health
- Advancement of citizenship or community development
- Advancement of the arts, heritage, culture or science
- Advancement of public participation in sport
- Promotion of equality and diversity
- Advancement of environmental protection or improvement
- Relief of those in need by reason of age, ill health, disability, financial hardship or disadvantage
- Advancement of animal welfare
- Saving of lives

The foundation also offers grants through its Spirit of the Community Awards. The following information is taken from the foundation's website:

> The Yorkshire and Clydesdale Bank Foundation continues the tradition of supporting people and their local communities by providing funds to help registered charities, not-for-profit organisations, community and other voluntary organisations make life safer, healthier and better for all of us.
>
> The awards support projects that help people have a healthy relationship with money, help people into employment and help people improve their local environment.

Readers are advised to check the website for up-to-date opening and closing dates for applications.

Financial information

In 2014/15 the foundation had assets of £110,500 and an income of £753,500, of which it is considered that £752,000 was a donation from Clydesdale Bank. Grants made totalled £865,000 and were distributed between 358 organisations, broken down as follows:

Health	£394,500
Citizenship or Community development	£164,500
Education	£101,000
Sports	£73,000
Environmental protection or improvement	£62,000
Relief of those in need by reason of age, ill health, disability, financial hardship or other disadvantage	£55,500
Arts, heritage, culture or science	£10,500
Animal welfare	£2,500
Saving of lives	£2,000

Beneficiaries included: Help the Hospices (£389,500); Money Advice Trust (£50,000); Business in the Community (£34,000); The Chartered Institute of Bankers in Scotland (£12,000); BEAT, Visibility, Money Charity and Hebridean Whale and Dolphin Trust (£10,000 each); Charities Aid Foundation (£6,000).

Donations under £5,000 totalled £262,000.

Applications

Application forms and guidelines can be found on the foundation's website. Applicants for the Spirit of the Community Awards will be expected to demonstrate:

- The need/demand for the project and how the project will effectively respond to/meet the need
- An innovative approach to addressing the issue which should be unique in the community
- Positive and practical benefits for the wider community
- Evidence of how the project will be managed and monitored
- A practical vision for the longer term sustainability of the work of the project

Yorkshire Building Society Charitable Foundation

General charitable purposes including education and training, health, animal welfare, people with disabilities, children and young people, older people

£346,500 (2015)

Beneficial area

UK, with a preference for grant-making in the society's branch localities.

Correspondent: Mrs B. Cox, Yorkshire Building Society, Yorkshire House, Yorkshire Drive, Bradford, West Yorkshire BD5 8LJ (tel: 01274 472877; email: charitablefoundation@ybs.co.uk; website: www.ybs.co.uk/your-society/charity/charitable-foundation/apply.html)

Trustees: Christopher Parrish; Andy Caton; Christopher Faulkner; Richard Brown; Vanessa White.

CC number: 1069082

General information

Registered with the Charity Commission in 1998, the Yorkshire Building Society Charitable Foundation is the channel of giving of Yorkshire Building Society. Its purpose is to support good causes where the society's members and staff live and work, helping to demonstrate the value and support that it provides to local communities throughout the UK.

The foundation's income is acquired from Yorkshire Building Society and SCBD (Small Change Big Difference), a scheme promoted by Yorkshire Building Society under which the holders of savings or loan accounts agree to transfer an amount equivalent to the pence of interest received on savings accounts, or rounding up to the nearest pound, the pence of interest paid on a mortgage account.

The accounts for 2015 state that the foundation supports 'registered charities or good causes involving anyone who is vulnerable (particularly children, the elderly or those with physical/mental/communication disabilities)'. It is further noted that 'the Trustees also extend these priorities to registered charities working to relieve suffering in animals, and will consider other locally based charities and good causes'. The foundation has also stated that it prefers to assist with specific tangible items rather than donating to general funds or expenses.

The following list provides some examples of activities likely to fall within the foundation's main areas of focus:

- Sensory toys and equipment for children with special needs
- Items to care for isolated and/or vulnerable elderly people
- Support of specially adapted equipment to be used by people with physical/mental/communication disabilities
- Items and equipment for causes that care for the seriously ill
- Apparatus for children with special needs in schools/community groups
- Equipment for charitable sectors of the NHS
- Items or equipment to aid the recovery of, or ease the suffering of animals (animal homes/sanctuaries)
- Items or tangible social activities for Community Centres providing a benefit to many in the local community
- Provision of tangible and social interaction activities for the vulnerable and/or isolated

Financial information

In 2015 the foundation had assets of £201,500 and an income of £482,500, of which £68,500 was a donation from Yorkshire Building Society and £346,500 which was a donation from SCBD. Grants totalling £393,000 were made to 1,500 charities and good causes.

Beneficiaries included: Cumbria Community Foundation (£5,000); Allerton Cat Rescue (£2,100); Baildon Imagination Library, Bramley Elderly Action, Brine Leas School, Dove House Hospice, Hearing Dogs for Deaf People and York Toy Appeal (£2,000 each).

Donations under £2,000 totalled £316,500.

Exclusions

The foundation does not support the following:

- Contributions towards large funds
- Expenses
- Fees
- Salaries
- Administration
- Research
- Sponsorship of individuals or events
- Religious or political activities
- Mainstream schools, sports clubs, scouts/guides groups
- Local or government funded bodies
- Overseas travel, expeditions or educational expenses

Applications

Application forms should be downloaded, together with guidelines and criteria, from the society's website. The foundation is no longer able to accept paper application forms or requests for support received by letter.

Zurich Community Trust (UK) Ltd

Social welfare, community and economic development, helping disadvantaged people move from dependence to independence

£1.7 million (2015)

Beneficial area

UK and overseas, with priority given to locations where the company has offices.

Correspondent: Pam Webb, Head of Zurich Community Trust (UK) Ltd, Zurich Financial Services (UKISA) Ltd, PO Box 1288, Swindon SN1 1FL (tel: 01793 502450; email: pam.webb@zct.org.uk; website: www.zct.org.uk)

CC number: 266983

General information

Registered with the Charity Commission in 1974, the Zurich Community Trust (UK) Ltd is the corporate charity of Zurich Financial Services (UKISA) Ltd, a holding company and part of the Zurich Financial Services Group, which comprises the group's operations in the UK, Ireland and South Africa and provides insurance services.

The trust's main purpose is helping disadvantaged people move from dependence to independence by giving time, money and skills donated by Zurich and Openwork and its employees. It focuses on issues that are often overlooked and where the charity can have the biggest impact.

Grant programmes

According to the 2015 accounts, the trust fulfils its objectives through:

Long-term transformation programmes

Long-term transformation programmes focusing on particular areas of social need are delivered over a minimum of a five-year period. During 2015 this included: making core funding grants to southern Indian NGOs to build their capacity; providing core funding to Age UK and providing Zurich volunteers for a telephone befriending service; funding Addaction family workers who address parental substance misuse; developing The Children and Young People's Mental Health Coalition in partnership with the Mental Health Foundation.

In 2015 grants were made totalling £182,000 under this programme.

Zurich Cares programme

Charity partnerships through the Zurich Cares programme are currently with CLIC Sargent, Alzheimer's Society and Mind. Zurich employees are involved in the selection of these partnerships and also volunteer and donate. Donations are matched from the Zurich UK businesses. 'In addition, a wide range of local and overseas charities are supported each year through grant programmes with an emphasis on core funding and multi-year relationships.' During 2015 a total of £1 million was committed through partnerships and an extensive grant programme.

The Openwork Foundation programme

The objective of the Openwork Foundation programme is to help disadvantaged children under a theme of Cares 4 Kids through charity partnerships and grant programmes. In 2015 the foundation focused on supporting the national charity partner, the Carers Trust, in supporting a project to identify hidden young carers, provide respite for existing young carers, and prevent bullying of young carers. Other children's charities are supported through a regional grant programme, via sponsored application. 'There is also a small discretionary grant programme supporting disadvantage people, where advisors and employees of Openwork can recommend charities for support.'

In 2015 a total of £382,000 was donated for this programme, 62% of which went on regional grants; 10% went to national partners; and 1% went on the discretionary grants programme.

The trust's website has further information on the following grant programmes open to applications:

Local communities programme

Zurich Community Trust (UK) Ltd gives to local community organisations that are located close to where the company operates. Local budgets are delegated to staff committees to award local grants and usually range from between £100 to £5,000, depending on location. The following locations are eligible:

- Birmingham (within a 15-mile radius of the Zurich office) – grants of £250 to £1,000 are available
- Bristol – grants of £250 to £1,000 are available
- Brighton – grants of £1,000 to £2,000 are available
- Cardiff – grants of £1,000 to £2,500 are available
- Croydon – grants of £500 to £1,500 are available
- Cheltenham (within a 25-mile radius of the Zurich office) – grants tend to range from £1,500 to £3,000

- Fareham (within a 25-mile radius of the Zurich office) – grants of up to £3,000 are available
- Farnborough (within a 25-mile radius of the Zurich office) – grants of up to £2,000 are available
- Glasgow – grants of £250 to £1,000 are available
- Leeds (within a 15-mile radius of the Zurich office) – grants of £250 to £1,000 are available
- London – grants tend to range from £1,000 to £5,000
- Manchester – grants of £250 to £1,000 are available
- Swindon (within a 25-mile radius of the Zurich office) – grants tend to range from £1,000 to £5,000

Overseas grant programme

The trust considers applications for overseas projects provided that there is a UK partner organisation to administer the grant. The trust's annual overseas budget is £75,000 and in 2015 it made grants to 16 charities. The website states that the trust is looking for projects which show some or all of the following:

- A high degree of training and skills transfer
- Innovation
- A holistic approach to development
- Cost effective and effective solutions
- Clear objectives and outcomes which can be measured and evaluated within a reasonable timescale

Financial information

In 2015 the trust had assets of £4.85 million and an income of £4.03 million, of which £2.5 million was a donation from Zurich UK businesses. There were grants made totalling £1.7 million, broken down as follows:

Zurich cares	
Local grants	£576,000
Employee nominated grants	£272,000
National partners	£150,000
Overseas grants	£75,000
Local partners	£41,000
Transformation and trust	
India programme	£100,000
Young People's Mental Health	£37,000
Call in Time (Age UK)	£25,000
Breaking the Cycle (Addaction)	£16,000
New transformation programme	£5,000
Openwork Foundation	
Regional grants	£327,000
National partners	£50,000
Discretionary grants	£5,000

Beneficiaries of major grants only included: CLIC Sargent (£68,000); Alzheimer's Society (£59,000); Mind (£52,000); Carers Trust (£50,000); Mental Health Foundation (£37,000).

Grants of less than £30,000 to a single organisation totalled £1.4 million.

Exclusions

No grants are made for:

- Individuals
- Medical research
- Statutory organisations including mainstream schools and hospitals, unless exclusively for a special-needs group
- Animal welfare
- Conservation or environmental projects, unless involving disadvantaged people
- Political or military organisations
- Religious organisations
- Sports clubs, village halls, playgroups and mother-and-toddler groups, unless for a special-needs group
- Scouts, girl guides, cadets and other similar organisations, unless specifically supporting disadvantaged children
- Fundraising events including appeals or events for national charities
- Advertising or sponsorship connected with charitable activities

For overseas projects the trust will not fund: disaster relief or emergency work; proposals which show any racial, political or religious bias; individuals; expeditions or study exchanges; medical research; and fundraising events or appeals.

Applications

Applicants must firstly visit the trust's website and follow the links to check eligibility. Then download the guidelines and application forms. The website provides detailed contact information and deadlines for each of the local communities programme. For more information on the overseas grant programme email Sarah Barter at sarah.barter@zct.org.uk.

Note the following information on the trust's website regarding applications under the **local communities** programme: 'Due to a large increase in grant applications, we will only consider applications from organisations who have not applied for two years to the Birmingham, Bristol, Glasgow, Leeds and Manchester grant programme.'

If applying for an **overseas grant** note that the trustees hold a series of meetings from May to September each year. The deadline date for applications is usually in March; check the trust's website for further details.

The website also notes the following:

> Please note that our Social Transformation programmes supporting young people with mental health issues, vulnerable older people and our programme to break the cycle of generational drug misuse in families are fully committed, and [we] **DO NOT** accept ad hoc applications.

Business in the Community

Business in the Community (BITC) aims to make community involvement a natural part of successful business practice, and to increase the quality and extent of business activity in the community. It exists to work with companies to mobilise resources (skills, expertise, influence, products and profits) to promote social and economic regeneration.

Scottish Business in the Community and Business in the Community have merged to form a new network in Scotland called Business in the Community Scotland. Further information on the new network can be found at: www.bitc.org.uk/scotland.

Contacts

Business in the Community head office (covering London and South East)

137 Shepherdess Walk
London
N1 7RQ

Tel: 020 7566 8650
Email: information@bitc.org.uk
Web: www.bitc.org.uk

Northern Ireland

Belfast
Bridge House
Paulett Avenue
Belfast
BT5 4HD

Tel: 028 9046 0606
Email: info@bitcni.org.uk

North West
BEAM Social Enterprise Centre
Invista House
Maydown Works
Derry/Londonderry
BT47 6TH

Tel: 028 7186 1550
Email info@bitcni.org.uk

Wales

Cardiff
2nd Floor
33–35 Cathedral Road
Cardiff
CF11 9HB

England

London – head office
Business in the Community
137 Shepherdess Walk
London
N1 7RQ

Tel: 020 7566 8650

North West
Manchester
2nd Floor
Amazon House
3 Brazil Street
Manchester
M1 3PJ

Tel: 0161 233 7750

Yorkshire and Humberside
Leeds
44–60 Richardshaw Lane
Pudsey
Leeds
West Yorkshire
LS28 7UR

Tel: 0113 205 8200

Sheffield
SOAR Works Enterprise Centre
Knutton Road
Parson Cross
Sheffield
S5 9NU

Tel: 0114 213 4691

East Midlands
3rd Floor
30–34 Hounds Gate
Nottingham
NG1 7AB

Tel: 0115 924 7400

West Midlands
Birmingham
83 Bournville Lane
Birmingham
B30 2HP

Tel: 0121 451 2227

Coventry
Education Business Partnership Centre
Browns Lane
Coventry
CV5 9DR

Tel: 024 7640 1065
Email: westmidlands@bitc.org.uk

South West
Bristol
Portwall Place
Portwall Lane
Bristol
BS1 9HS

Tel: 0117 930 9380

Members (as of February 2017)

ABB Ltd
Abellio Greater Anglia
Aberdeen Asset Management
Aberdeen City Council
Accenture
Achilles
ACT Training
Addaction
Addleshaw Goddard
ADI Group
Adler and Allan Ltd
Adnams PLC
AF Blakemore and Son Ltd
Affinity Water
Alstom UK
Amazon
Amey
AmicusHorizon
Anglia Farmers Ltd
Anglian Water Group
Anglo American
Anthesis Consulting Group PLC
ANZ Bank New Zealand Ltd
Aon UK Ltd
APCO
APS Group
Aramark
Arriva Rail North Ltd (Northern)
Artex
Arup
ASDA Stores Ltd
Associated British Foods
Avis Budget Group
Aviva PLC
AWE
Axis Europe

Bank of Ireland
Barclays
Barques Design
Bayer
BBC
BEAR Scotland
Bentley Motors Ltd
Bettys and Taylors Group Ltd
Bevan Brittan LLP
Birmingham Airport
Birmingham City University
Birmingham Metropolitan College
Black Country Housing Group Ltd
Blackadders Solicitors
Bloomberg
Bluestone Resorts Ltd
BNP Paribas
Bolton at Home
Bombardier Transportation UK
Bouygues Energies and Services FM
Bouygues UK
Bowmer and Kirkland
BP
Brakes
Brewin Dolphin Holdings
British Airways
British American Tobacco
British Horseracing Authority
British Land
Britvic Soft Drinks
Broadridge Financial Solutions Ltd
Broomfield and Alexander
Brother Industries UK (Wales)
BT
Bupa
Burges Salmon

Calico Housing
Callcredit Information Group
Calor Gas Ltd
Camelot Group PLC
Campus Living Villages
Canary Wharf Group
Canon
Capgemini
Capital Law LLP
Capital One
CarbonClear
Carillion PLC
Carlson Rezidor
Carpetright
Castell Howell Foods
Castle Leisure
Casual Dining Group
CATSurveys Group
CBRE
CDL
Central England Co-operative
Centrica
Cereal Partners Worldwide
Certas Energy UK Ltd
CH2M
Chime Communications
Citi
Citrix Systems
City and Guilds Group
City Building Glasgow
City of Edinburgh Council
City of London
CityWest Homes
Clarion Housing Group
Cleone Foods
Clugston Construction
Clydesdale and Yorkshire Bank
Coca-Cola Enterprises
Colas
Columbia Threadneedle Investments
Companies House
Cook Foundation UK
Costain Group
County Durham Housing Group Ltd
CPJ Field
CrossCountry Trains
Cucumber Public Relations Ltd

DAC Beachcroft LLP
Dacrylate Paints
DAHER Aerospace Ltd
Dairy Crest Group
Dalehead Foods
Danone Nutricia Early Life Nutrition
David MacBrayne Ltd
de Poel Community
Deloitte LLP
DFS Trading Ltd
DHL
Diageo
Diamond Resorts International
Direct Line Group
DLA Piper – Yorkshire
Dolmans Solicitors
Doosan Babcock Ltd
Dovecote Park
Dundee City Council
Dunhills (Pontefract) PLC
DWF LLP
Dŵr Cymru Welsh Water

E. H. Booth and Co.
East of England Co-operative Society
Ecclesiastical Insurance Group
Eden Springs
EDF Energy
Efficiency North Ltd
Electricity North West Ltd
Elior UK
EMCOR (UK)
emh group
EMIS Group PLC
Engie (previously Cofely)
Enterprise Rent-A-Car
ERIKS UK
Esh Group
Eurovia UK Ltd
Eversheds
Experian
EY

Faccenda Foods
Farrows
FBC Manby Bowdler
Ferrovial Agroman UK and Ireland
Finance Wales PLC
Firstsource Solutions UK Ltd
Fiskars Living Business
Fletchers
FLR Spectron Ltd
Ford
Four Seasons Hotels and Resorts
Frank Roberts and Sons Ltd
Freixenet Ltd
Freshfields Bruckhaus Deringer
FRHI
Fujitsu

Galliford Try PLC
Genesis Housing Association
Gentoo Group
Gi Group Recruitment Ltd
Glasgow Caledonian University
GlaxoSmithKline
Gleeds
Glenmorangie Company
Goldman Sachs International
Google
Gowling WLG (Wragge)
Grant Thornton
Green Motion
Greenleaf Publishing
Greenredeem
GreenZone Cleaning and Support Services Ltd
Greggs
Gresham Technologies PLC
GTR (Govia Thameslink Railway)

H. Weston and Sons Ltd
Hadley Group
Hafod Housing Association
Harrods
Heathrow Airport Ltd
Heineken
Henry Boot PLC
Hermes Investment Management
Higgs and Sons Solicitors
High Speed 2 Ltd
Hilton Worldwide
Hitex International Group
Hogan Lovells International LLP
Hogg Robinson Group PLC
Home Retail Group
Honda Motor Europe
House of Fraser
HSBC Bank
Hull University Business School
Hyatt Hotels Corporation
Hypnos Contract Beds

IBM UK
Ibstock Brick
IDHL Group
IKEA
Impact Creative Recruitment Ltd
Imtech
Inprova Energy
Intellectual Property Office
InterContinental Hotels Group
Interserve PLC
Intertek Group
Intu Properties PLC
Ipswich Building Society
ISG
ISS UK
ITV

J Sainsbury
Jagex Ltd
Jaguar Land Rover
JLL
JN Bentley
John Laing
John Lewis Partnership/Waitrose
Johnson Matthey PLC
Johnstons of Elgin
Joseph Rowntree Foundation
JRP Group
JTI

KCOM
Keele University
Keepmoat
Kelda Group
Keoghs
Kier Group
Kingfisher PLC
Kingspan Group
Knight Frank

KPMG
L&Q Group
Ladbrokes Coral Group
Laing O'Rourke
Lancaster University
Land Securities
Landmarc Support Services Ltd
LeasePlan
Leeds Building Society
Leeds City College
Leeds City Council
Legal & General Group PLC
Leo Burnett
Lincolnshire Co-operative
Linklaters
Livin Housing Ltd
Lloyds Banking Group
Lloyd's of London
London Borough of Barking and Dagenham
London City Airport
Lovell
Lubrizol Ltd
Lucion Services

Magenta Living
Manchester Airport Group
Manufacturing Technology Centre
Marks and Spencer
Marriott International
Mars UK
Marsh
Marshalls
Marston Group
Matchtech Group
Maxxium UK
Mayborn Group
Mazars
McKinsey
Media Wales
Medline Industries Inc.
Meggitt
Meldrum Construction Services Ltd
Mercer Ltd
MFS
Michelin Tyre
Miituu
Mitie
Mondelēz International
Mondi Group PLC
Monmouthshire Building Society
Morgan Stanley
MotoNovo Finance
MWH Ltd

National Grid
National House-Building Council
Nationwide
NATS
Nestlé
Holdings UK
Network Rail
Newcastle Business School
Next
NFU Mutual Insurance Co.
NG Bailey
NH Hoteles
Noble Foods
Nominet
North Coast 500
North Midland Construction PLC
North Star Housing Group
Northern Gas Networks
Northern Powergrid
Northumbrian Water Group
Nottingham Trent University
Nottingham University Business School
Novacroft
Novus Property Solutions
NPTC Group of Colleges
NSG Group
NuGeneration Ltd

Oakland International
OCR – Oxford Cambridge and RSA Examinations
Office for National Statistics
OH Assist
ON5 COMPANY
One Advice Group
OneE Group
Oracle Corporation UK
Orbit Group Ltd

Paramount 21 Ltd
PD Ports
Pearson
Pennine Healthcare
Pennon Group
Perrett Laver
Pertemps Ltd
PGIM Real Estate

Phoenix Group
PIMCO Europe
Pinsent Masons LLP
PLADIS (formerly United Biscuits)
Portakabin Group
Post Office
Principality Building Society
Procter & Gamble UK
Provident Financial
Prudential UK and Europe
PwC
PZ Cussons (UK) Ltd

Quorn Foods Ltd

Rabbie's Trail Burners
Real Good Food PLC
Recycling Lives Ltd
Redrow
Reed Smith
Rehab Works
RELX Group
Remploy Ltd
RES – Group
Revo
Rhondda Housing Association
Ricardo
Ricoh UK
Robertson Group
Rolls-Royce
Rothschild & Co.
Royal Bank of Scotland
Royal London Group
Royal Mail Group
RR Donnelley
RSM

Safran Nacelles Ltd
Sage (UK) Ltd
Saint-Gobain Ltd
Samworth Brothers (Holdings)
Santander UK
School of Management Swansea University
Schroders
ScotRail
Scottish and Southern Energy
Scottish Enterprise
Scottish Qualifications Authority
Scottish Union of Supported Employment
Scottish Water
ScottishPower
SEGRO
Shakespeare Martineau LLP
Sheffield Business School
Sheffield University Management School
Shell UK
Shoosmiths
SHS Group Ltd
Siemens PLC
SiteVisibility
Skanska UK
Skipton Building Society
Sky PLC
SmartestEnergy Ltd
WH Smith Retail
Societe Generale
Society
Sodexo
Solution Sciences
Soneva
South Wales Fire and Rescue Service
Southampton Solent University
Southern Water
SPV Group
Squire Patton Boggs (UK) LLP
St James's Place
St Leger Homes of Doncaster
Standard Life
Starbucks Coffee Company
Starwood Hotels and Resorts
State Street
Steelite International PLC
Story Homes
Styles and Wood Group PLC
Symantec

Taj Hotels, Resorts and Palaces
Tata Consultancy Services
TD Direct Investing
Telefónica UK Ltd (O2)
TEN Group
Tesco
Thales Group
Thames Water
The Clancy Group PLC (Clancy Docwra Ltd)
The Community Housing Group
The Co-operative
The Crown Estate
The Go-Ahead Group
The Hongkong and Shanghai Hotels, Ltd
The Midcounties Co-operative
The Southern Co-operative Ltd
The University of Birmingham
Tideway
Timpson Ltd
Tolent Construction
Toyota Motor Manufacturing (UK)
Trivallis Ltd
TUI Travel PLC

UBS
UK Flood Barriers Ltd
UK Power Networks
Unified
Unilever
Unipart Group
Unite Students
United Utilities
University of Bradford Faculty of Management and Law
University of East London
University of Huddersfield Business School
University of Manchester
University of Portsmouth
University of South Wales
University of Warwick
University of Winchester
UPS Ltd

V12 Retail Finance
Vauxhall
Veolia
Veris Strategies
Victrex PLC
Virgin East Coast Main Line Company Ltd
Virgin Money
Virgin Trains
Vista
VocaLink
Volvo Construction Equipment

Wakefield and District Housing
Wales and West Utilities Ltd
Walgreens Boots Alliance
Walt Disney Company
Wandle Housing Association Ltd
Warburtons
Wates Group
Watts Truck and Van
Wesleyan Assurance Society
Westmorland
Wheatley Group
Whitbread
Wiggle Ltd
WildHearts
Wilko Retail Ltd
William Grant and Sons
William Jackson Food Group Ltd
Willmott Dixon
WJ Group
Wm Morrison Supermarkets PLC
Woodford Investment Management LLP
Working Links
Workspace Group
Worldpay
WPP Group
Wright, Johnston and Mackenzie LLP
WSP | Parsons Brinckerhoff
Wyndham Worldwide

XL Catlin

York St John University

Zenith Intelligent Vehicle Solutions
Zurich

Business in the Community's CommunityMark

Business in the Community (BITC) aims to make community involvement a natural part of successful business practice, and to increase the quality and extent of business activity in the community. BITC states on its website that:

> *It challenges companies to minimise their negative and maximise their positive impact on society by taking a holistic approach to community investment, which means they are good from the inside, out.*
>
> *The CommunityMark highlights how organisations are transforming their business by integrating responsible business practices and transforming the communities in which they operate, creating positive impacts for society.*
>
> *Open to companies in the UK of all sizes and sectors, this national standard has been developed by Business in the Community in consultation with the private, public and voluntary sector bodies. The CommunityMark challenges companies to minimise their negative and maximise their positive impact on society through an assessment process that recognises milestones on the way to achieving long term sustainable benefits to both business and the community.*

There are 58 companies that have achieved the CommunityMark since its launch. Of these, 34 are currently recognised as upholding this standard of excellence, and are listed here.

Barclays
Boots
Brentford
British Gas
Camelot UK Lotteries
Capgemini
Capital One
DWF LLP
East Midlands Airport
Ecclesiastical Insurance
Heineken
Hogan Lovells
Intu Properties PLC
Jaguar Land Rover
JTI
KPMG
Linklaters
London Stansted Airport
LSI Airport
Manchester Airport
Marks and Spencer
Mid-Counties Co-operative
Nationwide
Octlink
Prudential
PwC
RWE nPower
Siemens Digital Factory and Process Industries and Drives
TD Direct Investing
UBS
Wates Group
Willmott Dixon
Zurich Insurance

Institute of Corporate Responsibility and Sustainability

The Institute of Corporate Responsibility and Sustainability (ICRS) is the new institute dedicated to helping corporate responsibility and sustainability professionals to excel at all stages of their careers. ICRS's organisational membership was historically known as CRG (Corporate Responsibility Group), which was established in 1987 by a small group of senior corporate affairs professionals. In January 2015, the CRG members became a part of the ICRS brand as organisational members.

The role of the ICRS is to:

- Recognise professional achievements through assessment
- Reward accomplished professionals through granting post-nominal letters
- Support professionals through continuing professional development
- Listen to and represent the corporate responsibility and sustainability profession

Members (as of February 2017)

Patrons

Barclays
British American Tobacco
Citi
Linklaters
QinetiQ
The Crown Estate
Wates

Members

Accenture
Airbus Group
Allen & Overy
BAE Systems
Bank of America Merrill Lynch
BBC
British Airways
Centrica
Charities Aid Foundation
City and Guilds
City of London
CMS
Coca-Cola Enterprises Ltd
Deloitte
Diageo
E-on
Financial Conduct Authority
Flag
Generali
Gowling WLG
Herbert Smith Freehills
Hogan Lovells
IBM
Imperial Tobacco
ISG
John Lewis Partnership/Waitrose
KPMG
L'Oreal UK and Ireland
Land Securities
Leonard Cheshire Disability
National Grid
Nestlé
O2
Olswang
Pearson
PwC
Q&S Commercial Landscaping
Relx Group
RES
Santander
ScottishPower
Shell
Societe General
Standard Life
SustainAbility
Tata Consultancy Services
Telereal Trillium
University of Westminster
Visa
Walgreens Boots Alliance
White and Case
Woodland Trust
Zurich

London Benchmarking Group

The London Benchmarking Group (LBG) is a group of over 150 companies working together to measure Corporate Community Investment (CCI). It is a member-driven organisation where companies have been working collectively since 1994 to:

- Continue development of a global measurement standard – the LBG model
- Benchmark and share best practice
- Develop and refine measurement tools
- Improve management and implementation of CCI projects
- Better communicate CCI results to stakeholders with LBG centres

The challenge facing the founding members of the LBG was how to effectively report their community activities to demonstrate that they are indeed responsible corporate citizens. Effective reporting is best based on solid measures of performance, but in the 'soft' area of social reporting hard measures are still in their infancy.

Their solution was to devise a tool with which to manage, measure and compare their relationship with the community – the London Benchmarking Model. The model is used by hundreds of leading businesses around the world and LBG has centres in a number of key world markets including Australia, Canada, the Czech Republic, Germany and the United States. Members include multinationals such as Coca-Cola, KPMG and Deloitte, as well as major UK companies such as Marks and Spencer and BSkyB.

All members recognise that companies are expected to get involved in the community and are often judged on the amount they contribute. This involvement often goes beyond straightforward donations to charity. The LBG model provides a comprehensive and consistent set of measures for CCI professionals to determine their company's contribution to the community, including cash, time and in-kind donations, as well as management costs. The model also captures the outputs and longer-term impacts of CCI projects on society and the business itself.

Further information about the group and its benchmarking model may be found at www.lbg-online.net.

Members (as of February 2017)

3M
Abbott
AbbVie
Accenture
AkzoNobel
Allianz UK
Anglian Water
ANZ
Arab African International Bank
ARM
Astra Zeneca
Australia Post
Australian Unity
Aviva
AXA
BAE Systems
BAM Construct UK
Barclays
Berkeley Group
Bettys and Taylors of Harrogate
British Land
Britvic
BSkyB
BT
Capital One
Carlton Football Club
Centrica
Citi
Clarks
Coca-Cola Enterprises
Coca-Cola Hellenic
Coles
Cricket Australia
CSL
CUA Deutsche Bank
Datacom
David Jones
Deloitte
Deutsche Post DHL
Deutsche Telekom AG
DP World
EDP
Essendon Football Club
Experian
FirstGroup
Foxtel
Freshfields Bruckhaus Deringer
Galp Energia
GlaxoSmithKline
GMHBA
Go-Ahead
Gowling WLG
Hammerson
Hawthorn FC
Holden
Home Retail Group
HSBC
HSS Hire
ING
International Personal Finance
Intesa San Paolo

Intu Properties PLC
Investec PLC
ISS UK
Jaguar Land Rover
Japan Tobacco
Jemena
Jeronimo-Martins
JLL UK
John Lewis Partnership/Waitrose
Johnson Matthey
JT International S.A.
JTI UK
Kellogg's
Kingfisher
KPMG
Lakehouse
Land Securities
Lend Lease
Liberty Global Europe
Linklaters
L'Occitane
London City Airport
Manchester Airport Group
Marks and Spencer
Maybank
Medibank
Michelin
Mirvac Pty Ltd
Myer
National Australia Bank Ltd
National Grid
Nationwide
New Zealand Post Group Port of Milford Haven
New Zealand Rugby
Optus
Payce Consolidated Ltd
Pearson
Philip Morris International Management S.A.
Port of Tyne
Power Community
Provident Financial
Prudential
PwC
Quintain Estates and Development PLC
RBS
RELX Group
Richmond FC
Ricoh UK
Rolls-Royce
Rothschild
Royal Mail
Santander UK
Scentre Group
Schroders
ScotRail
ScottishPower
SGN
Shaftesbury
Siemens
SingTel
Skanksa
Skycity
Southern Co-operatives
St James's Place
ST Microelectronics
Standard Chartered
Standard Life
Stockland
Stora Enso Oyj
Suncorp
Swisse
Sydney Airport Corporation Ltd
Tabcorp Holdings Ltd
Target
Terna
Thames Water
The Boots Group
The Co-operative Group
Toyota Australia
Toyota Financial Services
UBS
UniCredit
United Utilities
Vicinity Centres
Wesfarmers Chemicals, Energy and Fertilisers
Wesfarmers Corporate
West Coast Eagles Football Club
Willmott Dixon
Wood Group
Woodside Energy Ltd
Zurich

Useful contacts

In this section we list national agencies which may be helpful in the context of company giving, under the general headings: employees/ professional advice; enterprise and training; education; donations; promoting good practice; media; and general company information.

Employees/ professional advice

Business in the Community

137 Shepherdess Walk
London
N1 7RQ

Tel: 020 7566 8650
Email: info@bitc.org.uk
Web: www.bitc.org.uk

Chartered Surveyors Voluntary Service

CSVS (Charity Commission no. 1043479) provides professional property advice from a chartered surveyor for those who would not otherwise be able to afford it. If you feel that the CSVS could benefit you it can be contacted through your Citizens Advice (www.citizensadvice.org.uk) and other advice agencies.

Tel: 024 7686 8555
Email: csvs@rics.org
Web: www.rics.org/csvs

LawWorks

National Pro Bono Centre
48 Chancery Lane
London
WC2A 1JF

Tel: 020 7092 3942
Email: info@lawworks.org.uk
Web: www.lawworks.org.uk

National Pro Bono Centre

48–49 Chancery Lane
London
WC2A 1JF

Tel: 020 7092 3960
Web: www.nationalprobonocentre.org.uk

ProHelp

c/o Business in the Community
137 Shepherdess Walk
London
N1 7RQ

Tel: 020 7566 8650
Web: www.bitc.org.uk

Reach Volunteering

89 Albert Embankment
London
SE1 7TP

Tel: 020 7582 6543
Web: www.reachskills.org.uk

NCVO – Volunteering

Society Building
8 All Saints Street
London
N1 9RL

Tel: 020 7713 6300
Web: www.ncvo.org.uk/ncvo-volunteering

Step on Board – NCVO

Society Building
8 All Saints Street
London
N1 9RL

Tel: 020 7713 6161
Email: steponboard@ncvo.org.uk
Web: www.ncvo.org.uk/practical-support/information/governance/step-on-board

Volunteering Matters

The Levy Centre
18–24 Lower Clapton Road
London
E5 0PD

Tel: 020 3780 5870
Web: www.volunteeringmatters.org.uk

Enterprise and training

British Chambers of Commerce

65 Petty France
London
SW1H 9EU

Tel: 020 7654 5800
Email: enquiries@britishchambers.org.uk
Web: www.britishchambers.org.uk

Common Purpose UK

Common Purpose
38 Artillery Lane
London
E1 7LS

Tel: 020 7608 8118
Email: info@commonpurpose.org.uk
Web: www.commonpurpose.org.uk

National Enterprise Network

12 Stephenson Court
Acorn House
381 Midsummer Boulevard
Milton Keynes
MK9 3HP

Tel: 01908 605130
Email: enquiries@nationalenterprisenetwork.org
Web: www.nationalenterprisenetwork.org

Education

Charity IT Association

The Worshipful Company of
Information Technologists
39A Bartholomew Close
London
EC1A 7JN

Tel: 020 7600 1992
Email: contact@charityithelp.org.uk
Web: www.charityithelp.org.uk

Confederation of British Industry (CBI)

Cannon Place
78 Cannon Street
London
EC4N 6HN

Tel: 020 7379 7400
Email: enquiries@cbi.org.uk
Web: www.cbi.org.uk

National Centre for Universities and Business

Studio 11
Tiger House
Burton Street
London
WC1H 9BY

Tel: 020 7383 7667
Email: ncub@ncub.co.uk
Web: www.ncub.co.uk

The Work Foundation

The Work Foundation
1 Northumberland Avenue
London
WC2N 5BW

Email: info@theworkfoundation.com
Web: www.theworkfoundation.com

Donations

Charities Trust

Suite 20–22
Century Building
Brunswick Business Park
Tower Street
Liverpool
L3 4BJ

Tel: 0151 286 5129
Web: www.charitiestrust.org.uk

Charity Commission

London
2nd Floor
One Drummond Gate
Victoria
London
SW1V 2QQ

Liverpool
PO Box 211
Bootle
L20 7YX

Taunton
Woodfield House
Tangier
Taunton
Somerset
TA1 4BL

Newport
Room 1.364
Government Buildings
Cardiff Road
Newport
NP10 8XG

In Kind Direct

11–15 St Mary at Hill
London
EC3R 8EE

Tel: 0300 30 20 200
Email: info@inkinddirect.org
Web: www.inkinddirect.org

ShareGift

PO Box 72253
London
SW1P 9LQ

Tel: 020 7930 3737
Email: help@sharegift.org
Web: www.sharegift.org

Promoting good practice

Business in the Community

137 Shepherdess Walk
London
N1 7RQ

Tel: 020 7566 8650
Email: info@bitc.org.uk
Web: www.bitc.org.uk

Business in the Community Scotland

Previously known as Scottish Business in the Community, the name changed after merging with Business in the Community. Contact details are the same as in the previous listing.

Charity Finance Group (CFG)

15–18 White Lion Street
London
N1 9PG

Tel: 0845 345 3192
Email: info@cfg.org.uk
Web: www.cfg.org.uk

Charities Tax Group (CTG)

Church House
Great Smith Street
London
SW1P 3AZ

Tel: 020 7222 1265
Email: info@charitytax.info
Web: www.charitytaxgroup.org.uk

Corporate Citizenship

Holborn Gate
26 Southampton Buildings
London
WC2A 1PQ

Tel: 020 7861 1616
Email: mail@corporate-citizenship.com
Web: www.corporate-citizenship.com

The Foundation for Social Improvement (FSI)

The Grayston Centre
28 Charles Square
London
N1 6HT

Tel: 020 7324 4777
Email: admin@thefsi.org
Web: www.thefsi.org

Institute of Corporate Responsibility and Sustainability

Durham House
Durham House Street
London
WC2N 6HG

Tel: 020 7839 0199
Email: info@icrs.info
Web: www.icrs.info

Directory of Social Change

London
Resource for London
352 Holloway Road
London
N7 6PA

Tel: 0845 077 7707
Email: cs@dsc.org.uk
Web: www.dsc.org.uk

Liverpool
Suite 103
1 Old Hall Street
Liverpool
L3 9HG

Email: research@dsc.org.uk

International Business Leaders Forum (IBLF)

Preiskel and Co. LLP
Fleet Place
London
EC4M 7RD

Tel: 020 7164 6892
Email: info@iblfglobal.org
Web: www.iblfglobal.org

Small Charities Coalition

Unit 9/10
83 Crampton Street
London
SE17 3BQ

Email: info@smallcharities.org.uk
Web: www.smallcharities.org.uk

The London Benchmarking Group

c/o Corporate Citizenship
5th Floor Holborn Gate
330 High Holborn
London
WC1V 7QG

Tel: 020 7861 1616
Email: lbg@corporate-citizenship.com
Web: www.lbg-online.net

Media

BBC Charity Appeals Office

BC2 A1 Broadcast Centre
201 Wood Lane
London
W12 7TP

Tel: 020 8752 7044
Email: charityappeals@bbc.co.uk
Web: www.bbc.co.uk/charityappeals

Campaign for Press and Broadcasting Freedom

2nd Floor
Vi and Garner Smith House
23 Orford Road
Walthamstow
London
E17 9NL

Tel: 07729 846 146
Email: freepress@cpbf.org.uk
Web: www.cpbf.org.uk

Channel Four Television Company

Channel 4 Enquiries
PO Box 1058
Belfast
BT1 9DU

Tel: 0345 076 0191
Web: www.channel4.com

Charity Comms

2–6 Tenter Ground
Spitalfields
London
E1 7NH

Web: www.charitycomms.org.uk

ITV Network Centre

200 Gray's Inn Road
London
WC1X 8HF

Tel: 020 7156 6000
Web: www.itv.com

Media Trust

Block A, Ugli Campus
56 Wood Lane
London
W12 7SB

Tel: 020 7871 5600
Email: info@mediatrust.org
Web: www.mediatrust.org

General company information

Companies House

Crown Way
Cardiff
CF14 3UZ

Tel: 0303 1234 500
Email: enquiries@companies-house.gov.uk
Web: www.companieshouse.gov.uk

Co-operative and Community Finance

Brunswick Court
Brunswick Square
Bristol
BS2 8PE

Tel: 0117 916 6750
Web: www.coopfinance.coop

Trades Union Congress (TUC)

Congress House
23–28 Great Russell Street
Fitzrovia
London
WC1B 3LS

Tel: 020 7636 4030
Email: info@tuc.org.uk
Web: www.tuc.org.uk

UK Regeneration

1 Stamford Brook Avenue
London
W6 0YB

Email: info@ukregeneration.org.uk
Web: www.ukregeneration.org.uk

URBED (Urbanism Environment Design)

The Building Centre
26 Store Street
London
WC1E 7BT

Tel: 0161 200 5500
Email: info@urbed.coop
Web: www.urbed.com

Young Enterprise UK

Peterley House
Peterley Road
Oxford
OX4 2TZ

Tel. 01865 776845
Email: info@y-e.org.uk
Web: www.young-enterprise.org.uk

Company activity listing

This section classifies the companies included in the guide according to their main activities. It should enable charities to target companies for specific appeals or services.

Accountants

Deloitte
KPMG LLP
Mazars LLP
PricewaterhouseCoopers LLP

Acquisitions

UK Asset Resolution
Unipart Group of Companies Ltd

Advertising/marketing

Abbott Mead Vickers – BBDO Ltd
IP Group PLC
WPP PLC

Aerospace

BAE Systems PLC
Cobham PLC
QinetiQ Group PLC
Smiths Group PLC
Thales UK Ltd

Agriculture

Carrs Group PLC
Alan Hudson Ltd
Pfizer Ltd
Yattendon Group PLC (formerly Yattendon Investment Trust)

Airport operators

Birmingham International Airport Ltd
Heathrow Airport Holdings Ltd (formerly BAA Ltd)
Manchester Airport Group PLC

Aviation

British Airways PLC
Cobham PLC
easyJet PLC
Marshall of Cambridge (Holdings) Ltd
John Swire & Sons Ltd

Banking

Barclays PLC
Bestway (Holdings) Ltd
Close Brothers Group PLC
Co-operative Group Ltd
Coutts & Co
Credit Suisse
CYBG PLC
Deutsche Bank
Goldman Sachs International
HSBC Holdings PLC
Investec PLC
Lloyds Banking Group
Rothschild & Co. (record formerly titled N.M. Rothschild & Sons Ltd)
The Royal Bank of Scotland Group PLC
Santander UK PLC
Shawbrook Group PLC
Standard Chartered PLC
Standard Life
Virgin Money PLC

Brewers/distillers

Adnams PLC
Diageo PLC
Greene King PLC
Marston's PLC
Daniel Thwaites PLC

Building materials

Aggregate Industries Ltd
Bestway (Holdings) Ltd
SIG PLC
Travis Perkins PLC

Building Society

Coventry Building Society
Leeds Building Society
Nationwide Building Society
Newcastle Building Society
Nottingham Building Society
Principality Building Society
Santander UK PLC
Yorkshire Building Society

Building/construction

Amec Foster Wheeler PLC (formerly Amec PLC)
Bellway PLC
Berkeley Group PLC
Carillion PLC
CEMEX UK Operations Ltd
Costain Group PLC
Esh Group
Galliford Try PLC
Interserve PLC
John Laing PLC
Kier Group PLC
Sir Robert McAlpine Ltd
Persimmon PLC
Redrow Group PLC
Taylor Wimpey PLC
Travis Perkins PLC
Wates Group Ltd
Willmott Dixon Holdings Ltd

Business services

Ashmore Group PLC
Autonomous Research LLP
Balfour Beatty PLC
Economist Newspaper Ltd
ERM Group Holdings Ltd
Euromoney Institutional Investors PLC
Informa PLC
IP Group PLC
Micro Focus International PLC
MITIE Group PLC
Rentokil Initial PLC
Serco Group PLC
Shop Direct Ltd (record formerly for Shop Direct Holdings Ltd)
UBM

Worldpay Ltd

Cash 'n' Carry

Bestway (Holdings) Ltd
Booker Group PLC
Dhamecha Holdings Ltd

Catering services

Sodexo Ltd
SSP Group PLC

Chemicals and plastics

3M United Kingdom PLC
Bayer PLC
Dow Corning Ltd
Fenner PLC
Pfizer Ltd
Scott Bader Company Ltd
Victrex PLC

Clothing manufacture

Burberry Group

Commodity traders

Cargill PLC

Computer software

Game Digital PLC (formerly The Game Group PLC)
Microsoft Ltd
The Sage Group PLC
ZPG Ltd

Confectionery

Cadbury

Consultancy

ERM Group Holdings Ltd
IP Group PLC
RPS Group PLC
SDL PLC

Consulting engineers

Amec Foster Wheeler PLC (formerly Amec PLC)
Arup Group Ltd

Dairy products

Dairy Crest Group PLC

Defence

BAE Systems PLC
Cobham PLC
Marshall of Cambridge (Holdings) Ltd
QinetiQ Group PLC
Thales UK Ltd
Ultra Electronics Holdings PLC

Distribution

Bunzl PLC
Cargill PLC
Electrocomponents PLC
SIG PLC
John Menzies PLC

Domestic appliances

Dyson Ltd

Drinks manufacture

A. G. Barr PLC
Britvic Soft Drinks PLC
Coca-Cola Holdings (United Kingdom) Ltd
Innocent Ltd
Nestlé UK Ltd

Electricity

Drax Group PLC
EDF Energy PLC
National Grid PLC
Northern Powergrid Holdings Company (formerly C E Electric UK Funding Company)
ScottishPower UK PLC
SSE PLC
United Utilities Group PLC

Electronics/computers

Cobham PLC
IBM United Kingdom Ltd
Motorola Solutions UK Ltd
Samsung Electronics (UK) Ltd
Siemens PLC
Sony Europe Ltd
Ultra Electronics Holdings PLC

Engineering

Amec Foster Wheeler PLC (formerly Amec PLC)
BBA Aviation PLC
Carrs Group PLC
Cobham PLC
Costain Group PLC
Dyson Ltd
Fisher (James) and Sons
GKN PLC
Goodwin PLC
IMI PLC
John Laing PLC
Laird PLC
Marshall of Cambridge (Holdings) Ltd
Sir Robert McAlpine Ltd
Meggitt PLC
Network Rail Infrastructure Ltd
Rolls–Royce Holdings PLC
Rotork PLC
Severfield PLC
Smiths Group PLC
Spirax-Sarco Engineering PLC
Thales UK Ltd
The Weir Group PLC

Financial services

3i Group PLC
Aberdeen Asset Management PLC
Alliance Trust PLC
Apax Partners LLP
Bank of Ireland UK (PLC)
BC Partners Ltd
Brewin Dolphin Holdings
Capital One (Europe) PLC
Close Brothers Group PLC
CMC Markets PLC
Experian Ltd
FIL Holdings (UK) Ltd (formerly Fidelity Investment Management Ltd)
Hargreaves Lansdown PLC
Henderson Group PLC
HSBC Holdings PLC
ICAP PLC
IG Group Holdings PLC
Impetus – The Private Equity Foundation
International Personal Finance
Investec PLC
Jupiter Fund Management PLC
Just Retirement Group PLC
Legal & General PLC
Liontrust A.M
Liverpool Victoria
Lloyds Banking Group
London Stock Exchange Group PLC
Man Group PLC
Marks and Spencer Group PLC
The Midcounties Co-operative
Morgan Stanley International Ltd
Phoenix Group Holdings
PricewaterhouseCoopers LLP
Principality Building Society
Provident Financial PLC
Rathbone Brothers PLC
RELX Group (formerly known as Reed Elsevier)
The Royal Bank of Scotland Group PLC
S&U
Saga PLC
Schroders PLC
Shop Direct Ltd (record formerly for Shop Direct Holdings Ltd)
St James's Place PLC
Standard Chartered PLC
SVG Capital PLC
Virgin Money PLC
Worldpay Ltd
Yorkshire Building Society
Prudential PLC

Food manufacture

Arla Foods Ltd
Associated British Foods PLC
Carrs Group PLC
Duchy Originals Ltd
Greggs PLC
McCain Foods (GB) Ltd
Nestlé UK Ltd
Premier Foods PLC
Tate & Lyle PLC

Unilever UK
Warburtons Ltd
Diageo PLC

Food services

Cargill PLC
Cranswick PLC
Ocado Group PLC
Sodexo Ltd
SSP Group PLC

Football club

Arsenal Holdings PLC
AFC Bournemouth Ltd
Burnley FC Holdings Ltd
Chelsea FC PLC
CPFC Ltd (Crystal Palace Football Club)
Everton Football Club Company Ltd
Hull City Tigers Ltd
Leicester City Football Club Ltd
The Liverpool Football Club and Athletic Grounds Ltd
Manchester City Football Club Ltd
Manchester United PLC
Middlesbrough Football and Athletic Company (1986) Ltd
St Mary's Football Group Ltd (Southampton Football Club)
Stoke City Football Club Ltd
Sunderland Ltd
Swansea City Football 2002 Ltd
Tottenham Hotspur Ltd
The Watford Association Football Club Ltd
West Bromwich Albion Holdings Ltd
WH Holding Ltd (West Ham United)

Furniture manufacture

Cadogan Group Ltd
Howden Joinery Group PLC

Gaming

Camelot UK Lotteries Ltd
Genting UK PLC (formerly Genting Stanley PLC)
Ladbrokes PLC
Paddy Power Betfair PLC (record formerly for Betfair Group PLC)
Playtech PLC
Sportech PLC
William Hill PLC
The Rank Group PLC

Health/beauty products

Avon Cosmetics Ltd
Lush Cosmetics Ltd
Mascolo Ltd
Procter & Gamble UK

Healthcare

Alliance Boots Holdings Ltd
Bupa Ltd
GlaxoSmithKline PLC
Pfizer Ltd
Procter & Gamble UK
Reckitt Benckiser Group PLC
UDG Healthcare PLC

Hotels

Adnams PLC
Intercontinental Hotels Group PLC
Whitbread PLC

Household

S. C. Johnson Ltd
Procter & Gamble UK
Reckitt Benckiser Group PLC
Unilever UK
P. Z. Cussons PLC
Wilko Retail Ltd (formerly Wilkinson Hardware Stores Ltd)

Industrial products/services

Ashtead Group PLC
Diploma PLC
Essentra PLC
Rolls–Royce Holdings PLC
Rotork PLC
Spirax-Sarco Engineering PLC

Information management and communication

Informa PLC
IP Group PLC
SDL PLC
Smiths Group PLC
WPP PLC

Information Technology

Aveva Group PLC
Computacenter PLC
Fujitsu Services Holdings PLC
Keysight Technologies UK Ltd (formerly Agilent Technologies UK Ltd)
SDL PLC
Worldpay Ltd
ZPG Ltd

Instrumentation

Renishaw PLC
Unipart Group of Companies Ltd

Insurance

AA PLC
Admiral Group PLC
Allianz Insurance PLC
MS Amlin PLC (formerly Amlin PLC)
Aviva PLC
Beazley PLC
Brit Ltd (record formerly Brit Insurance Holdings PLC)
Bupa Ltd
Co-operative Group Ltd
Direct Line Insurance Group PLC
Ecclesiastical Insurance Group PLC
Hastings Group Holdings PLC
Hiscox Ltd
Jardine Lloyd Thompson Group PLC
Lancashire Holdings Ltd
Liverpool Victoria
Lloyd's
Marsh Ltd
The National Farmers Union Mutual Insurance Society Ltd
Novae Group PLC
Personal Group Holdings PLC
Prudential PLC
The Royal Bank of Scotland Group PLC
The Royal London Mutual Insurance Society Ltd
RSA Insurance Group PLC
Saga PLC
Standard Life
UIA (Insurance) Ltd
Unum Ltd
Zurich Insurance Group (record previously for Zurich Financial Services (UKISA) Ltd)

Legal

Addleshaw Goddard LLP
Allen & Overy LLP
Co-operative Group Ltd
Freshfields Bruuckhaus Deringer LLP
Gowling WLG (UK) LLP (formerly knowns as Wragge Lawrence Graham & Co. LLP)
Linklaters LLP
Saga PLC
Simmons & Simmons LLP
Slaughter and May (Trust Ltd)

Leisure

Center Parcs Ltd
Enterprise Inns PLC
William Hill PLC
Ladbrokes PLC
Merlin Entertainments
The Rank Group PLC
Saga PLC
Thomas Cook Group PLC
J. D. Wetherspoon PLC
Whitbread PLC
Yattendon Group PLC (formerly Yattendon Investment Trust)

Logistics

John Menzies PLC
Stobart Group

Manufacturing

Euro Packaging UK Ltd
Morgan Advanced Materials PLC
Thales UK Ltd
Tata Steel Europe Ltd

Marine

Fisher (James) and Sons
QinetiQ Group PLC
RPS Group PLC
John Swire & Sons Ltd

Media

Bloomsbury Publishing PLC
British Sky Broadcasting Group PLC
Economist Newspaper Ltd
Guardian Media Group PLC
ITV PLC
Northern Shell & Media Group Ltd (entry formerly titled Northern & Shell Network Ltd)
STV Group PLC
Telegraph Media Group Ltd
the7stars UK Ltd
Thomsons Reuters (Reuters Ltd)
Time Inc. (UK) Ltd (formerly IPC Media Ltd)
Trinity Mirror PLC
Yattendon Group PLC (formerly Yattendon Investment Trust)

Metals

Johnson Matthey PLC
Tata Steel Europe Ltd

Mining

Anglo American PLC
The Banks Group Ltd
BHP Billiton
Rio Tinto PLC

Miscellaneous

Amey UK PLC
The Midcounties Co-operative
Moneysupermarket.com Group PLC
Royal Mail PLC

Motors and accessories

AA PLC
Ford Motor Company Ltd
Halfords Group PLC
Inchcape PLC
Jaguar Land Rover Ltd
Marshall of Cambridge (Holdings) Ltd
Michelin Tyre PLC
Toyota Motor Manufacturing (UK) Ltd
Unipart Group of Companies Ltd

Oil and gas/fuel

Amec Foster Wheeler PLC (formerly Amec PLC)
BP PLC
Cairn Energy PLC
Calor Gas Ltd
Centrica PLC
EnQuest PLC
Fisher (James) and Sons
Premier Oil PLC
RPS Group PLC
Shell (UK Ltd)
United Utilities Group PLC

Personal care products

Essentra PLC
Mascolo Ltd
Procter & Gamble UK
Reckitt Benckiser Group PLC

Pharmaceuticals

Alliance Boots Holdings Ltd
AstraZeneca
BTG PLC
Co-operative Group Ltd
P. Z. Cussons PLC
Dechra Pharmaceuticals PLC
GlaxoSmithKline PLC
Merck Sharp & Dohme Ltd
Reckitt Benckiser Group PLC
Shire Pharmaceuticals Group

Print/paper/packaging

Bunzl PLC
De La Rue PLC
Essentra PLC
DS Smith Holdings PLC
Xerox (UK) Ltd
Yattendon Group PLC (formerly Yattendon Investment Trust)

Professional support services

Capita Group PLC
Impetus – The Private Equity Foundation
PageGroup PLC
SDL PLC
Stobart Group
Uni

Property

Amec Foster Wheeler PLC (formerly Amec PLC)
The Banks Group Ltd
Berkeley Group PLC
Bestway (Holdings) Ltd
British Land Company PLC
Bruntwood Group Ltd
Cadogan Group Ltd
Canary Wharf Group PLC
Capital & Counties Properties PLC
Daejan Holdings PLC
Derwent London PLC
Enterprise Inns PLC
Grainger PLC
Great Portland Estates PLC
Grosvenor Group
Hammerson PLC
Helical bar PLC
intu Properties PLC
Kingfisher PLC
Land Securities Group PLC
LondonMetric Property PLC
Marshall of Cambridge (Holdings) Ltd
Paragon Group of Companies PLC
Ravensale Ltd
Redrow Group PLC
Ridgesave Ltd
SEGRO PLC
Shaftesbury PLC
Shop Direct Ltd (record formerly for Shop Direct Holdings Ltd)
St Modwen Properties PLC
John Swire & Sons Ltd
Town Centre Securities PLC
Unite Group PLC
Willmott Dixon Holdings Ltd
Workspace Group PLC
Yattendon Group PLC (formerly Yattendon Investment Trust)
ZPG Ltd

Quarrying

Aggregate Industries Ltd

Retail – Clothing and footwear

Ted Baker PLC
Burberry Group
Dunelm Group PLC
JD Sports Fashion PLC
Marks and Spencer Group PLC
Next PLC
Shoe Zone Ltd
Shop Direct Ltd (record formerly for Shop Direct Holdings Ltd)
Sports Direct International PLC
SuperGroup PLC
TJX UK (formerly TK Maxx)

Retail – Department and variety stores

Central England Co-operative
Co-operative Group Ltd
Debenhams PLC
Dunelm Group PLC
Fenwick Ltd
House of Fraser (UK and Ireland) Ltd
John Lewis Partnership PLC
Marks and Spencer Group PLC
Shop Direct Ltd (record formerly for Shop Direct Holdings Ltd)

Retail – DIY/furniture

DFS Furniture PLC
Howden Joinery Group PLC
Kingfisher PLC
Marks and Spencer Group PLC
Piranha Trading Ltd
Wilko Retail Ltd (formerly Wilkinson Hardware Stores Ltd)

Retail – Electrical

AO World PLC
Richer Sounds PLC

Retail – Miscellaneous

Associated British Foods PLC
Bestway (Holdings) Ltd
The Body Shop International PLC
Boodle & Dunthorne Ltd
Central England Co-operative
Dixons Carphone PLC
Halfords Group PLC
Home Retail Group PLC
Inchcape PLC
intu Properties PLC
Pets at Home LTD
WH Smith PLC
The Southern Co-operative Ltd

Retail – Restaurants/fast food

Compass Group PLC
Enterprise Inns PLC
Greggs PLC
McDonalds Restaurants Ltd
Mitchells & Butlers PLC
SSP Group PLC
J. D. Wetherspoon PLC
Whitbread PLC

Retail – Supermarkets

ASDA Stores Ltd
Central England Co-operative
Co-operative Group Ltd
Costcutter Supermarkets Group Ltd
John Lewis Partnership PLC
Marks and Spencer Group PLC
McColl's
The Midcounties Co-operative
Wm Morrison Supermarkets PLC
J Sainsbury PLC
The Southern Co-operative Ltd
Spar (UK) Ltd
Tesco PLC
Waitrose Ltd

Securities/shares

Goldman Sachs International

Security services

QinetiQ Group PLC
Ultra Electronics Holdings PLC

Services

Big Yellow Group PLC
HomeServe PLC
Interserve PLC
Mears Group
Willmott Dixon Holdings Ltd

Shipping

Cargill PLC

Sugar refiners

Tate & Lyle PLC

Telecommunications

BT Group PLC
Channel 4 Television Corporation
Dixons Carphone PLC
EE Ltd (formerly T-Mobile (UK) Ltd)
Motorola Solutions UK Ltd
QinetiQ Group PLC
TalkTalk Group
Vodafone Group PLC

Tobacco

British American Tobacco PLC
Imperial Tobacco Group PLC

Transport and communications

BBA Aviation PLC
FirstGroup PLC
G4S PLC
The Go-Ahead Group PLC
National Express Group PLC
Siemens PLC
Stagecoach Group PLC
Thales UK Ltd
Ultra Electronics Holdings PLC

Transportation

Network Rail Infrastructure Ltd

Waste management

Severn Trent PLC

Water

Anglian Water
Northumbrian Water Group Ltd (formerly Northumbrian Water Group PLC)
Pennon Group PLC
RPS Group PLC
Severn Trent PLC
United Utilities Group PLC
Wessex Water Services Ltd

Wholesale

Bestway (Holdings) Ltd
Booker Group PLC
Dhamecha Holdings Ltd

Charitable causes index

Animal welfare

Arts and culture

Children and young people

Community and social welfare

Disability

Disasters

Economic generation

Education

Enterprise and training

Environment

General charitable purposes

Health

Heritage

Housing and homelessness

Human rights

Humanitarian aid – overseas

Humanitarian aid – UK including food banks

Marginalised people

Medical research

Older people

Overseas

Poverty and social exclusion

Religion

Safety and crime prevention

Science and technology

Sport and recreation

STEM

Unpopular causes

Women's causes

Forms of giving index

Charity partner(s)/Charity of the Year

Corporate charity

Employee-led support

Gifts in kind

Company gives to non-registered charities

Company gives to smaller charities

Market-led giving

Matched funding

Payroll giving

Pro bono

Sponsorship

Alphabetical index